THE GENERA OF
FLOWERING PLANTS

THE GENERA OF FLOWERING PLANTS

(*ANGIOSPERMAE*)

BASED PRINCIPALLY ON THE

GENERA PLANTARUM

OF G. BENTHAM AND J. D. HOOKER

BY

J. HUTCHINSON, LL.D., F.R.S.

FORMERLY KEEPER OF MUSEUMS OF BOTANY
ROYAL BOTANIC GARDENS, KEW
ENGLAND

DICOTYLEDONES

VOLUME I

OXFORD

AT THE CLARENDON PRESS

1964

Oxford University Press, Amen House, London E.C.4

GLASGOW NEW YORK TORONTO MELBOURNE WELLINGTON
BOMBAY CALCUTTA MADRAS KARACHI LAHORE DACCA
CAPE TOWN SALISBURY NAIROBI IBADAN ACCRA
KUALA LUMPUR HONG KONG

PRINTED IN GREAT BRITAIN
AT THE UNIVERSITY PRESS, OXFORD
BY VIVIAN RIDLER
PRINTER TO THE UNIVERSITY

197439

PREFACE

THE principal object of this work is to provide an account of the families and genera of *Angiospermous Flowering Plants* arranged so far as possible on evolutionary and phylogenetic lines for the use of botanists throughout the world, and at the same time to re-establish the work of the de Jussieus in France, that of the de Candolles in Switzerland, and more especially Bentham and Hooker's classical *Genera Plantarum* in Britain. It seems probable that the combined work of these great botanists would still have been in more general use, at least among British botanists and in the Commonwealth, had it been revised and kept up to date. For their joint classification is no less logical from a phylogenetic point of view than that of Engler and Prantl in Germany, which largely replaced it on the continent of Europe and in America.

So far back as 1920 I became keenly interested in the phylogeny of flowering plants, largely through the work of Hallier in Germany, Bessey in America, and Arber and Parkin in Britain, and soon realized the need for a new taxonomic system. With this object in view I examined in detail all the *apocarpous families* regarded by these botanists as being the *most primitive* of living angiosperms. The first results of these studies were published in the *Kew Bulletin* (1923: 65 et seq.), and in my *Families of Flowering Plants* (vol. i, 1926; vol. ii, 1934; ed. 2, 1959).

About the same time I had commenced to write, with the help of Dr. J. M. Dalziel, M.B., the *Flora of West Tropical Africa*, and this was completed after eleven years' work, during which I gained valuable detailed knowledge of the many families of flowering plants represented in that vast region. During that period I was also fortunate to be able to make two collecting expeditions in Southern Africa in 1928 and 1930, thereby gaining valuable experience in the field, and the results were published in 1946 in my book *A Botanist in Southern Africa*.

In 1936 I was transferred from the Kew Herbarium to be Keeper of the Museums, and during the Second World War, which soon intervened, and because of my new duties, it was not possible to make much progress owing to the removal from Kew of most of the herbarium collection and library.

Since my retirement from official duties at Kew in 1948, however, I have continued with the aid of periodical grants for out-of-pocket expenses from the Royal Society of London, of which I have had the honour to be a Fellow since 1947. I am indeed most grateful to that Society, without whose aid I would not have been able to continue with the work. In 1954 a useful monetary contribution was also received from the Marsh Fund of the National Academy of Sciences, Washington, U.S.A., for which I was also very grateful. This is not, in consequence, an official Kew publication, and Kew should not in any way be held responsible for its merits or demerits, though it has been largely prepared at the unrivalled Herbarium and Library of that institution, wherein full facilities for the work have always been available.

There may be quite a number of botanists, not having access to the larger herbaria of the world, who will welcome the appearance of this new classification of the families and genera of flowering plants. It would be quite impossible, however, to satisfy all of them, especially those taxonomists who are engaged in splitting up long-established genera by raising to generic rank subgenera or sections, sometimes quite justifiably, sometimes on very slender grounds. With regard to generic concepts there is a gap as wide as the Thames at Kew Bridge between a Baillon and a Britton, the one a so-called 'lumper', the other a 'splitter', usually resulting in a fresh crop of new combinations and adding to the confusion. In the present work I have considered it preferable to steer something of a middle course between these two extremes, no doubt sometimes leaning too much to either one side or the other. I cannot hope to escape criticism in consequence.

The concept of genera varies greatly, of course, from family to family. The more homogeneous or natural a family is, the more trivial seem to be the generic characters, especially in such groups as *Fabaceae* (*Papilionaceae*), *Brassicaceae* (*Cruciferae*), *Apiaceae* (*Umbelliferae*), and *Asteraceae* (*Compositae*), in the Dicotyledons, and the *Liliaceae*, *Cyperaceae*, and *Poaceae* (*Gramineae*), in the Monocotyledons, to quote only a few examples. For instance, a tiro in botany might be excused a feeling of astonishment that taxonomists have recognized no fewer than 350 genera in *Brassicaceae* (*Cruciferae*) with its simple formula of 'Calyx 4; petals 4, free; stamens 6, tetradynamous; ovary superior, of 2 united carpels with parietal placentas, but with a great variety of fruits'. In *Asteraceae* (*Compositae*), with its universal capitulum, inferior 1-ovuled ovary and syngenesious anthers, there are over 900 genera, and in *Fabaceae* (*Papilionaceae*), with zygomorphic, polypetalous flowers, usually more or less united stamens, and a monocarpic gynoecium, about 480 genera, and again with a great variety of fruits.

In addition to the two principal works mentioned above, my background for this vast undertaking has been many years of general taxonomic work in the Kew Herbarium, including the writing and illustrating of several more popular books, besides field work in South Africa, Rhodesia, the Cameroons, Canary Islands, the Pyrenees, the British Isles, and, more recently, a fleeting voyage around the world.

During my first few years at Kew, Bentham and Hooker's conception of families and genera was regarded, willynilly, as the correct standard to be rigidly followed, and any deviation from it by members of the staff was not encouraged by those in authority. Eventually, however, that restraint at length gave way to more scientific freedom, which was soon reflected in my subsequent work and publications. But my veneration for the great work of Bentham and Hooker has remained unimpaired, though I trust it has not prejudiced my judgement in the present task.

Although I arrived in this world too late to see George Bentham (I was actually born the very year he died, in 1884), I was fortunate to meet Sir Joseph Hooker in 1906, when he visited Kew for the last time. I was detailed to procure for him from the herbarium cabinets specimens of the genus *Impatiens*, which he was still revising, although in his ninetieth year. Having provided him with the covers he required, I stood by his side hoping to be of further assistance, but was brought down to earth by being told to 'get on with your work'. Little did he or I imagine that one day the young man he so curtly dismissed would attempt to revise and bring up to date his own and Bentham's classical *Genera Plantarum*!

At the beginning of my career as a botanist I had the good fortune to be under the supervision and guidance of the late Dr. Otto Stapf, F.R.S., renowned for his work on the *Poaceae* (*Gramineae*) and other families, besides other senior members of the staff, such as Dr. N. E. Brown (*Asclepiadaceae* and Succulents), Mr. R. A. Rolfe (*Orchidaceae*), Mr. C. H. Wright (Monocotyledons and Ferns). I also collaborated with the late Dr. T. A. Sprague (General Taxonomy and later Nomenclature), whilst the late Mr. S. A. Skan, Librarian, was always most helpful with botanical literature.

Besides those former colleagues, who have all passed on, the work here presented has also benefited not a little from that of more recent members of the staff, especially, to mention only a few, that of Mr. N. Y. Sandwith in the American section, Mr. H. K. Airy-Shaw in the Malayan, and Mr. E. W. B. Milne-Redhead, Mr. J. P. M. Brenan, and Mr. J. B. Gillett in the African section, whilst last but not least, Mr. A. A. Bullock has saved me much time in dealing with knotty points of nomenclature. To all of them I am deeply grateful. In its early stages I was also indebted to Mr. H. S. Marshall, until lately Librarian, who rendered valuable assistance in compiling references to generic names and synonyms from that mine of information on such matters, Dalla Torre and Harms, *Genera Siphonogamarum ad Systema Englerianum conscripta* (1900–7), and the indispensable *Index Kewensis*.

I am again indebted to Mr. J. E. Dandy, Keeper of Botany at the British Museum (Natural History), for the account of the *Magnoliaceae*, to Dr. C. C. J. van Steenis, Director of the Rijksherbarium, Leiden, Holland, for continuing to send me advance information of researches by himself and his colleagues, and to Dr. C. R. Metcalfe for advice, when required, on anatomical matters.

J. H.

Kew, 1964

CONTENTS

ABBREVIATIONS

B.H.   G. Bentham and J. D. Hooker, *Genera Plantarum* (1862–83).

E.P.   Engler and Prantl, *Die natürlichen Pflanzenfamilien* (1887–98).

E.P.N.   Engler and Prantl, *Die natürlichen Pflanzenfamilien, Nachträge*.

E.P. ed. 2   Second edition of E.P.

Sol.   H. Solereder, *Systematic Anatomy of the Dicotyledons* (translation by L. A. Boodle and F. E. Fritsch (1908)).

M.C.   C. R. Metcalfe and R. Chalk, *Anatomy of the Dicotyledons* (1950).

Erdt.   G. Erdtman, *Pollen Morphology and Plant Taxonomy* (1952).

Knuth   Knuth, *Handbook of Flower Pollination* (translation by J. R. Ainsworth Davis (1908)).

INTRODUCTION

THE descriptions of the families and genera are based primarily on those in Bentham and Hooker's *Genera Plantarum*, often considerably abbreviated, and sometimes added to or modified from direct observation and from more recent diagnoses in large regional Floras and Revisions. The translation into English of about 11,500 descriptions has been an arduous task over a period of many years.

The descriptions of those genera established since Bentham and Hooker's work are based on the originals, also sometimes modified, reduced, or added to where necessary. Many of them include purely specific characters such as 'branches pubescent', 'leaves thin', 'leaves large', &c., and the colour of the flowers is rarely of much generic value, except in such families as *Asteraceae* (*Compositae*) and a few others.

The great taxonomic work of Engler and Prantl (with many collaborators), *Die natürlichen Pflanzenfamilien*, has always been consulted, though many of the descriptions in that work are of necessity little different from those in the British work, and often not nearly so complete. Great help has also been derived from the second edition of the same work, and from the invaluable *Pflanzenreich*, so far as published.

The families are arranged according to the author's own phylogenetic system as it appeared in the second edition of his *Families of Flowering Plants* (1959).[1] The tribes and genera of each family are also disposed so far as possible according to the general principles adopted in that work (reprinted on pp. 10–11); i.e. the apparently more primitive tribes and genera are placed first, followed by the more advanced, and ending with those which appear to be the most highly evolved (often also the most widely distributed).

For example, in the order LEGUMINALES the family *Caesalpiniaceae* is clearly the most primitive group and not far removed from the more basic stock of *Rosaceae*, whilst the *Mimosaceae* (with actinomorphic flowers), and *Fabaceae* (*Papilionaceae*) (with zygomorphic flowers) take second and third place respectively, the last mentioned being relatively the most highly evolved and more widely distributed, especially in temperate regions.

All references to and descriptions of sections of genera in Bentham and Hooker's original work have been omitted, as they are now largely out of date. Likewise references to illustrations have not been included because the *Index Londinensis* contains them up to the year 1938, and a further supplement is being prepared at Kew. However, whenever an illustration is given with the original description, it has always been quoted.

The type species or a selected (lectotype) species is indicated, and for these the *Index Genericorum*, which is being prepared on an international basis, has been consulted so far as issued.

The number of species for each genus has been ascertained from the estimate given by Dalla Torre and Harms in 1900–7 (evidently based by them on

[1] J. Hutchinson, *The Families of Flowering Plants*, Oxford, at the Clarendon Press, 1959.

the *Index Kewensis*, to which have been added those recorded in the several *Supplements* to the *Index Kewensis* published since that date. The total number of species, however, especially of large genera distributed through many regions can only be approximate, because there is usually a fair proportion of 'bad species', amounting sometimes to as much as 10 per cent. or even more. This fact is often brought to light when careful monographs of such genera are published.

It would be invidious to draw attention to any particular botanists, past or present, in this connexion, for botanists are all liable to commit similar 'crimes' to a greater or lesser extent according to the amount of taxonomic work accomplished. Throughout the history of descriptive botany, however, nearly every country wherein it has been practised has suffered at one time or another through excessive zeal in the making of species and genera, and botany would probably have suffered less if the practice of attaching the name of the author to a species or new combination had never become the fashion.

Charles Darwin held very strong views on this very point. He condemned in round terms the custom of scientists appending their names to the species they described, and he regarded this practice as having been the greatest curse to Natural History. He considered that thereby the description suffered because of the naming. He asked why naturalists should append their own names to new species, when mineralogists and chemists do not do so to new substances. He was of the opinion that no more credit was due to a man for defining a species than to a carpenter for making a box. On the other hand he admitted that he was 'foolish and rabid against species-mongers, or rather against their vanity', and that it was useful and necessary work which must be done. Writing to J. D. Hooker from Down, Kent, on 12 October 1849, he says of nomenclature:[1]

What miserable work, again, it is searching for priority of names. I have just finished two species, which possess seven generic, and twenty-four specific names. My chief comfort is, that the work must be sometime done, and I may as well do it, as any one else.

Darwin's attitude towards the subject of nomenclature was a fortunate one for the world, otherwise if he had become tied up with the subject, he might never have written the *Origin of Species*!

It is necessary to recognize that the status of a genus may change and is never rigidly determined. Thus the addition of a few species formerly unknown to botanists may change the concept of a genus, because some new characters or set of characters are introduced into it. Conversely the same thing happens if a species or group of species is taken out of a genus and described as a separate one, with the result that the residue requires a new or modified description or perhaps further segregation.

In some families there are often certain large genera defined by a *single character*. In many cases this has led to the 'dumping' into them of a considerable number of species only some of which may be said to be related to others. For example, the late Dr. H. Schindler showed very convincingly that there were several well-defined groups of species allotted to the genus

[1] *The Life and Letters of Charles Darwin*, edited by Francis Darwin, 1: 380 (1887).

Desmodium and raised or restored them accordingly to generic rank. In the preparation of this work I have examined carefully the whole of the species of this and many other genera, and where necessary treated as separate these smaller units, especially when they appear as distinct as some other genera in the same family.

During the last decade or so taxonomic botanists have sometimes been reproached for neglecting or not taking full advantage of new techniques in the science, such as anatomy, genetics, physiology, pollen-morphology, &c. A. J. Sharp, in his presidential address delivered to the American Society of Plant Taxonomists in August 1961, made some cogent remarks in their defence, from which I quote:

Traditionally, taxonomists and systematists primarily have used comparative gross morphology, and to a more limited extent ecology and geography, in pursuing their science. In addition, many of our interpretations have been opinions, and in the words of some of our censors, 'not quantitative'. Up to the present our science has been, in part, an art, intuitive and descriptive, and of necessity in part must continue to be so. We are not quite ready to communicate to our present-day colleagues, or to botanists of the future, descriptions of plants or species or even vegetation in strictly quantitative terms.

It is true that many taxonomists have of necessity a limited knowledge of paleontology, cytology, genetics, and pollen morphology, but it is equally true that those versed in these branches of botany have usually a very vague idea of taxonomy and nomenclature, and above all phylogeny. Until a super-botanist arises with a full knowledge of all branches of botany, we must still rely mainly for classification purposes on gross morphology, such as floral structure, leaf-arrangement, presence or absence of stipules, cohesion and adhesion of sepals and petals, relative number of stamens, polycarpy and syncarpy, and last but not least different kinds of inflorescences and fruit and seed structure, besides many other minor characters. It may also be said with truth that taxonomic botany built up on such characters and governed at the present day by the International Rules of Nomenclature is in a very advanced state. The crying need at the present day is for more Regional Floras and for Monographs of genera based on phylogenetic principles such as are listed on pp. 10–11 of this work.

THE PHYLOGENY OF FLOWERING PLANTS[1]

ANGIOSPERMS

One might have expected that the publication of *The Origin of Species* about the middle of last century would have had as great an effect on the minds of such distinguished botanists as G. Bentham, J. D. Hooker, and Asa Gray as it had on prominent zoologists and geologists of the same period. It is well known that Hooker, at any rate, was Darwin's confidant and helper and that 'without Hooker's aid Darwin's great work would hardly have been carried out on the botanical side'.[2] Yet it remains a fact that the classic *Genera Plantarum* of Bentham and Hooker contains no hint of the descent of plants, written as it was in the very hey-day of 'Darwinism'.

It was left, therefore, to the German botanists, Engler and Prantl (but mainly Engler), to rearrange the families of flowering plants on supposedly phylogenetic lines. In their great work, *Die natürlichen Pflanzenfamilien*, they more or less reversed the system of Jussieu+de Candolle+Bentham and Hooker, because they regarded *apetalous* plants as being *more primitive* than those *with petals*, so that their arrangement commenced with *Poaceae* (*Gramineae*) in the Monocotyledons, and with the so-called *Amentiferae* in the Dicotyledons.

Hooker[3] did not share Engler's views as expressed in his classification and writings. He considered the system to be 'neither better nor worse in the abstract than de Candolle's (so-called), and far more troublesome to apply for practical purposes'. He held to Robert Brown's view of the families' being reticulately, not lineally related.

Early in this century Engler's system, as we may more conveniently call it, was questioned by several botanists, prominent among them being Bessey,[4] in America, Hallier, in Germany, and Arber and Parkin, in Britain. It should be noted, too, that Engler's system has received little or no support from palaeontologists. Eventually, besides the attempt at a rearrangement of the families by Bessey, the present author ventured to propose a new arrangement of the flowering plants, firstly in the *Kew Bulletin*, and then in two volumes published in 1926 and 1934.[5] On the appearance of the first of these papers, a prominent American teacher of botany wrote to him:

I have for years put a good deal of thought into teaching a rather old-fashioned course on flowering plants, and I am constantly embarrassed with trying to justify to students the Engler–Prantl System, which is imposed on us by all our recent manuals which the student must use.

Over the years since that time others have written to me in the same strain. It is noteworthy that the late W. L. Jephson, in California, reverted

---

[1] Most of this chapter was written for the International Botanical Conference at Ithaca, U.S.A., in 1928, and read there on the author's behalf by the then Director of Kew, the late Sir Arthur W. Hill, during the writer's absence in South Africa.

[2] L. Huxley, *Life and Letters of Sir Joseph Dalton Hooker*, 1: 486 (1918).

[3] Ibid., 2: 22.   [4] C. E. Bessey, *Annals Missouri Bot. Gard.*, 2: 109 (1915).

[5] J. Hutchinson, *Families of Flowering Plants*, vol. i (1926), vol. ii (1934).

to a modification of the system of Bentham and Hooker in 1924 (*Economic Plants of California*).

Thus there seemed to be a need for a phylogenetic system, based principally on more modern ideas of the evolution of the flower, correlated with anatomical structure, cytology, pollen-structure, growth-form, and geographical distribution. It seemed desirable that the artificial systems, which were essentially practical and obviously framed mostly for the determination of plants and for little else, should give place to a more natural system, for the deadening effect of these systems, with their dull *floral formulas* and *floral diagrams*, was only too obvious. The consequence is that many physiologists, ecologists, and palaeontologists, even today, are still somewhat handicapped for want of a work on taxonomic botany based on an evolutionary system.

Soon after the First World War I began a detailed examination of the Angiosperms with a view to a rearrangement of the families on what I considered to be more logical lines than appeared to be used in the German system, for I was far from satisfied with that of Bessey. In my spare time[1] I examined in the great collections at Kew every species and genus of all the families which appeared to be likely to furnish evidence of phylogenetic relationships, and at the same time took note of important facts with regard to geographical distribution, regional habitat, anatomical structure, and growth-form or habit. At that time the study of cytology and pollen-structure was not far advanced.

It seemed to be quite illogical to entertain the belief that the parts of a flower were derived from leaves, a belief which has rarely been seriously challenged, and at the same time accept the apetalous so-called 'Amentiferae' as representing the most primitive groups of the Dicotyledons, as in the Engler and Prantl system. If carpels are really modified leaves, then *free carpels* (polycarpy) and *not united carpels* (syncarpy) would be the more primitive condition. There is *no polycarpy* in the 'Amentiferae'. Furthermore, we should not expect to find in the earliest flowering plants (Angiosperms) a specialized inflorescence such as the catkin. We should look rather for a solitary terminal flower composed of modified leaves such as that of a *Magnolia* or *Ranunculus*.

If we regard the least specialized type of floral structure as being the most primitive, we should begin our phylogenetic classification with either the *Magnoliaceae* or the *Ranunculaceae*, as in the de Candolle+Bentham and Hooker f. system, and as so ably advocated by Bessey, Hallier, Arber and Parkin, and others. My own task, therefore, has been to bridge the gulf between a *Magnolia* or a *Ranunculus*, on the one hand, and a *Composite* (*Asteraceae*) or *Labiate* (*Lamiaceae*) on the other, and similarly attempt to trace the general evolution of Monocotyledons from the apparently most primitive families such as *Alismataceae* to the *Marantaceae*, from the *Liliaceae* to the *Orchidaceae*, and finally from the *Liliaceae* to the *Cyperaceae* and *Poaceae* (*Gramineae*).

Engler probably regarded the Monocotyledons as the older group; at any rate they are placed first in his system. It should be noted, however, that nearly all the monocotyledonous families are very natural (homogeneous),

---

[1] At that time I was fully occupied during official hours in the Kew Herbarium in writing *The Flora of West Tropical Africa*, as already mentioned in the Preface to the present work.

the genera differing very slightly from one another. I have been led to regard all such natural families as being the most advanced and recent in the evolutionary sequence. There is clear evidence of this in the Dicotyledons. For example, everyone considers such families as the *Brassicaceae* (*Cruciferae*), the *Malvaceae*, the *Fabaceae* (*Papilionaceae*), the *Apiaceae* (*Umbelliferae*), and the *Asteraceae* (*Compositae*) to be highly advanced and therefore more recently evolved families, and they are also the most natural or homogeneous. In short, they are completely *climax* families from the stock of which no further evolution has taken place.

As to whether the Monocotyledons are monophyletic or polyphyletic in their origin I do not propose to enter into here, but some of the families, such as the *Alismataceae* and the *Butomaceae*, are so closely related morphologically to the *Ranunculaceae* as to suggest a direct origin from the same stock as that family, and to have diverged therefrom on parallel lines. It is considered that, taken as a whole, Monocotyledons are more advanced that Dicotyledons, and they are therefore placed second in this system.

In the more primitive groups of Dicotyledons there is a marked difference in growth-form. For example, all the *Magnoliaceae* are woody, all the *Ranunculaceae* are herbaceous, except some softly woody climbing *Clematis*, which is clearly a very advanced member of its own family. The floral structure in these two families is undoubtedly very similar, but this resemblance is *probably due to parallel evolution*, and not an indication of real affinity, *for one may look in vain* for relationship between any two or more of the genera in each family.

I do not for a moment suggest that we should revert to the old Herbal classification into Trees, Shrubs, and Herbs, for there are of course many familiar examples of quite natural families containing both woody and herbaceous plants; but I am convinced that in the more primitive groups, at any rate, the habit character is of primary and fundamental importance. With it there is sometimes associated a striking difference in the stomata of the leaves, in the woody groups (*Magnoliales*, for example) the guard-cells of the stoma are accompanied by special subsidiary cells parallel to the pore (known as the Rubiaceous type), these being absent from the early herbaceous groups (*Ranales, Saxifragales*, &c.).

It seems unnecessary to occupy space in the present work to discussion of the evolution of the major groups (Orders) of flowering plants. I have already published accounts in other places, especially in the second edition of my *Families of Flowering Plants*, in which I arranged the families into two main phyla, dependent on whether they are *fundamentally woody* (**Lignosae**), or *fundamentally herbaceous* (**Herbaceae**). In my first edition, although I suggested the desirability of their division into these two groups, I did not venture to rearrange the families so drastically, preferring at that early period in my studies to alternate the groups of the one type with those of the other, perhaps not very satisfactorily.

I also continued to keep separate the two divisions of the *Archichlamydeae* (*Polypetalae* and *Monochlamydeae* of Bentham and Hooker), and the *Metachlamydeae* (*Gamopetalae* of Bentham and Hooker), though I said of them (ed. 1, vol. i, p. 4) that a phylogenetic classification would be better attained if the gamopetalous character were regarded in its true light, i.e. as a general tendency, for gamopetaly is quite a common feature in many so-called polypetalous families, and that it was perhaps too early to suggest so revolutionary a change. Eventually, however, with added conviction I distributed the various groups and families of the *Metachlamydeae* amongst the *Archichlamydeae* (*British Flowering Plants*, 1948), and in the second edition of my 'Families', already quoted.

The rearrangement of the **Orders** as published in the second edition of my *Families* (1959) is shown in the following table. Included in that work is a *key to the families*, which, I believe, has proved to be quite useful to students and taxonomists the world over.

PHYLOGENETIC ARRANGEMENT OF THE ORDERS
OF FLOWERING PLANTS

This diagram, reproduced from my *Families of Flowering Plants*, is intended to provide a 'bird's-eye' view of the linear sequence of the orders of Angiosperms as arranged in the present system. On the left are the fundamentally woody groups of Dicotyledones, the LIGNOSAE, beginning with the most primitive order *Magnoliales* and ending with the *Verbenales*. It is noteworthy that *zygomorphic* flowers, apart from *Leguminales* and *Bignoniales*, are comparatively rare, whilst *apetalous* orders are mainly derived from *Rosales* and *Tiliales*. These and other important basic orders are printed in bold face type (black) and their connexions with groups higher up the scale are shown by arrows.

Such herbs as occur in these orders are clearly derived from woody ancestors (e.g. in *Fabaceae* (*Papilionaceae*)) and are not related to the herbs in the middle column, HERBACEAE. Conversely the few woody members found in the orders of the *Herbaceae* are in turn not related to any in the *Lignosae* column.

In the middle column, HERBACEAE, it is suggested that the *Ranales* are a parallel development of the *Magnoliales*, perhaps evolved from common but relatively more remote ancestors, and that the climax group at the top, the *Lamiales*, are a parallel development equivalent to but not phylogenetically related to the *Verbenales* at the head of the *Lignosae* column. The more important basic orders are also shown in bold-face type.

In the right-hand column are the Monocotyledones, the more primitive orders of which appear to be closely related to the *Ranales* and derived from less remote common herbaceous ancestors.

The groups at the foot of each column are characterized by having *free carpels, free stamens, free sepals,* and *free petals.*

The MONOCOTYLEDONES are divided into: I. **Calyciferae,** with a distinct calyx and corolla or reductions from these and ending in the Zingiberales; II. **Corolliferae,** with the whorls of the perianth more or less merged into one, beginning with the *Liliales* and ending with *Orchidales*; and finally III. **Glumiflorae,** destitute, or almost so, of a perianth and largely anemophilous, as in the group popularly known as 'Amentiferae' in the Dicotyledones.

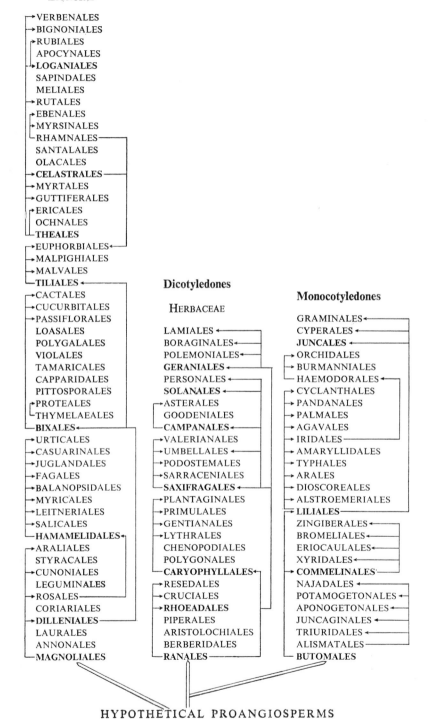

Dicotyledones

Lignosae

→VERBENALES
→BIGNONIALES
↗RUBIALES
  APOCYNALES
↳**LOGANIALES**
 SAPINDALES
 MELIALES
→RUTALES
↗EBENALES
↦MYRSINALES
↳RHAMNALES
 SANTALALES
 OLACALES
→**CELASTRALES**
→MYRTALES
→GUTTIFERALES
↗ERICALES
 OCHNALES
↳**THEALES**
→EUPHORBIALES
→MALPIGHIALES
→MALVALES
↳TILIALES
→CACTALES
→CUCURBITALES
→PASSIFLORALES
 LOASALES
 POLYGALALES
 VIOLALES
 TAMARICALES
 CAPPARIDALES
 PITTOSPORALES
↗PROTEALES
↳THYMELAEALES
↳**BIXALES**
→URTICALES
→CASUARINALES
→JUGLANDALES
→FAGALES
→BALANOPSIDALES
→MYRICALES
→LEITNERIALES
→SALICALES
↳**HAMAMELIDALES**
↗ARALIALES
 STYRACALES
→CUNONIALES
 LEGUMINALES
→ROSALES
 CORIARIALES
→**DILLENIALES**
 LAURALES
 ANNONALES
↳**MAGNOLIALES**

Dicotyledones

Herbaceae

 LAMIALES
 BORAGINALES
 POLEMONIALES
 GERANIALES
 PERSONALES
 SOLANALES
→ASTERALES
 GOODENIALES
↳**CAMPANALES**
→VALERIANALES
↳UMBELLALES
→PODOSTEMALES
→SARRACENIALES
↳**SAXIFRAGALES**
→PLANTAGINALES
→PRIMULALES
→GENTIANALES
→LYTHRALES
 CHENOPODIALES
 POLYGONALES
↳**CARYOPHYLLALES**
→RESEDALES
→CRUCIALES
→**RHOEADALES**
 PIPERALES
 ARISTOLOCHIALES
 BERBERIDALES
↳**RANALES**

Monocotyledones

 GRAMINALES
 CYPERALES
 JUNCALES
→ORCHIDALES
→BURMANNIALES
↳HAEMODORALES
→CYCLANTHALES
→PANDANALES
→PALMALES
→AGAVALES
→IRIDALES
→AMARYLLIDALES
→TYPHALES
→ARALES
→DIOSCOREALES
→ALSTROEMERIALES
⇉**LILIALES**
 ZINGIBERALES
 BROMELIALES
 ERIOCAULALES
 XYRIDALES
→**COMMELINALES**
 NAJADALES
 POTAMOGETONALES
 APONOGETONALES
 JUNCAGINALES
 TRIURIDALES
 ALISMATALES
↳ **BUTOMALES**

HYPOTHETICAL PROANGIOSPERMS

GENERAL PRINCIPLES FOLLOWED FOR THE CLASSIFICATION OF FLOWERING PLANTS IN THE PRESENT SYSTEM[1]

OTHER things being equal, it may be stated that:

1. Evolution is both (1) upwards, and (2) downwards, the latter involving degradation and degeneration; examples: (1) towards the sympetalous condition; epigyny; (2) towards the apetalous state of many flowers; unisexuality in flowering plants.
2. Evolution does not necessarily involve all organs of the plant at the same time; and one organ or set of organs may be advancing while another set is stationary or retrograding.
3. Evolution has generally been consistent, and when a particular progression or retrogression has set in, it is persisted in to the end of the phylum; examples:

Relating to the General Habit of Plants

4. In certain groups, trees and shrubs are probably more primitive than herbs; examples: *Caesalpiniaceae* and *Mimosaceae* (trees and shrubs) as compared with the derived family *Fabaceae* (*Papilionaceae*) (often herbaceous).
5. Trees and shrubs are older than climbers, the climbing habit having been acquired through special environment, overcrowding, &c.
6. Perennials are older than biennials, and from them annuals have been derived; note the very few annuals in the primitive family *Ranunculaceae* and in *Rosaceae*; the great number in the more advanced *Brassicaceae* (*Cruciferae*).
7. Aquatic Phanerogams are as a rule more recent than terrestrial (at any rate in the members of the same family or genus), and the same may be said of epiphytes, saprophytes, and parasites.

Relating to the General Structure of Flowering Plants

8. Plants with collateral vascular bundles arranged in a cylinder (Dicotyledons) are more primitive in origin than those with scattered bundles (Monocotyledons), though it does not necessarily follow that the latter have been directly derived from the former.
9. The spiral arrangement of leaves on the stem and of the floral leaves (sepals and petals) preceded that of the opposite and whorled type.
10. As a rule simple leaves precede compound leaves.

[1] See Bessey, 'Phylogenetic Taxonomy', *Annals of the Missouri Botanic Garden*, 2: 112 (1915).

Relating to the Flowers and Fruits of Plants

11. Bisexual (hermaphrodite) precede unisexual flowers, and the dioecious is probably more recent than the monoecious condition.
12. The solitary flower is more primitive than the inflorescence, the highest forms of the latter being the umbel and capitulum; examples of the latter: *Apiaceae* (*Umbelliferae*) and *Asteraceae* (*Compositae*) respectively.
13. Spirally imbricate floral parts are more primitive than whorled and valvate; examples: *Magnolia* and *Clematis*.
14. Many-parted flowers (polymerous) precede, and the type with few parts (oligomerous) follows from it, being accompanied by a progressive sterilization of reproductive parts (sporophylls); examples: *Magnolia* and *Cheiranthus* (Wallflower).
15. Petaliferous flowers precede apetalous ones, the latter being the result of reduction.
16. Free petals (polypetaly) are more primitive than connate petals (sympetaly).
17. Actinomorphic (regular) flowers are earlier than zygomorphic (irregular); examples: *Caltha* and *Delphinium*.
18. Hypogyny is the primitive structure, and from it perigyny and epigyny were derived later.
19. Free carpels (apocarpy) are more primitive and from them connate carpels resulted; sometimes, however, when the carpels have remained loosely united during evolution they may again become quite free, especially in fruit; example: *Asclepiadaceae*.
20. Many carpels (polycarpy) precede few carpels (oligocarpy); examples: *Ranunculus* and *Nigella*.
21. The endospermic seed with small embryo is primitive and the non-endospermic seed more recent; examples: *Ranunculaceae* and *Rosaceae*.
22. In primitive flowers there are many stamens, in more advanced flowers few stamens; examples: *Ranunculus* and *Cheiranthus*.
23. Separate stamens precede connate stamens; examples: *Tiliaceae* and *Malvaceae*; *Campanulaceae* and *Lobeliaceae*.
24. Aggregate fruits are more recent than single fruits, and as a rule the capsule precedes the drupe or berry.

GEOGRAPHICAL DISTRIBUTION

THE regions of the world adopted for the notes on geographical distribution in this work are largely political and are the same (with a few modifications) as those used for the arrangement of species in each genus in the Kew Herbarium. These are as follows:

EUROPE

NORTH AFRICA and ORIENT:
> *Orient.* Including Egypt, Baluchistan, Afghanistan, and Arabia.
> *North Africa.* Eastward to western frontier of Egypt.
> *Atlantic Islands.* Azores, Madeira, Canaries.

NORTHERN ASIA. Central and Northern Asia, northern Tibet and China, including Manchuria and Saghalien.

CHINA and JAPAN. Including Hainan, Formosa, Luchu Islands, Bonin Islands, Korea, and Kurile Islands.

INDIA. India, Pakistan and Kashmir, Ceylon, Burma, Andaman, Nicobar, Laccadive and Maldive Islands, southern Tibet.

MALAYA
> *Malay Peninsula* (from Singapore to 10° north).
> *Indo-China.* Thailand (Siam), Cambodia, Cochin-China, Annam, Tonquin.
> *Malay Archipelago.*
> *Philippines.*
> *New Guinea.*

AUSTRALIA. Including Tasmania and Lord Howe's Island.

NEW ZEALAND. Including Norfolk and near islands, Kermadecs, Auckland, Campbell, Chatham, Antipodes and Macquarie, and westward to Kerguelen and Marion Islands.

POLYNESIA. Including Hawaiian (Sandwich) Islands, New Caledonia and Solomon Islands.

TROPICAL AFRICA. Africa between the tropics of Cancer and Capricorn (including the Transvaal north of Zoutpansberg).

MASCARENE ISLANDS. Madagascar, Mauritius, Bourbon, Seychelles and islets, Comoro Islands.

SOUTH AFRICA. Excluding northern Transvaal north of Zoutpansberg; including Tristan da Cunha, Gough, St. Paul and Amsterdam Islands.

NORTH AMERICA. Canada, United States, Greenland, Bermudas.

CENTRAL AMERICA. Mexico, Lower California, Central American States (excluding Panama).

WEST INDIES (excluding Trinidad and Curaçao).

EAST TROPICAL SOUTH AMERICA. Brazil, Guianas, Paraguay.

WEST TROPICAL SOUTH AMERICA. Panama, Venezuela, Trinidad, Curaçao, Colombia, Ecuador, Peru, Bolivia, Galapagos, and Cocos Island.

TEMPERATE SOUTH AMERICA. Chile, Argentine, Uruguay, Juan Fernandez, Falkland Islands, South Georgia.

GENERIC REFERENCES

REFERENCE to the original description of each genus is given in every case; also to Bentham and Hooker f. *Genera Plantarum* (B.H.), to Engler and Prantl, *Nat. Pflanzenfamilien* (E.P.), to recent monographs and revisions, and to modern regional Floras in which a considerable number of the species are described. It should be understood, however, that these references are not necessarily exhaustive, and some quite important ones may have been inadvertently omitted.

For **Anatomy,** reference is usually made to Solereder, *Systematic Anatomy of the Dicotyledons* (English Translation, 1908), abbreviated Sol., and Metcalfe & Chalk's comprehensive *Anatomy of the Dicotyledons* (1950), abbreviated (M.C.). **Pollen** is not usually mentioned in the family descriptions, but reference is given to Erdtman's *Pollen Morphology and Plant Taxonomy, Angiosperms* (1952), abbreviated (Erdt.).

GEORGE BENTHAM AND
JOSEPH DALTON HOOKER

JOINT AUTHORS OF THE *GENERA PLANTARUM*

I T seems fitting that this work should be prefaced by an account of the lives of the two great Kew botanists and their respective shares in preparing their *Genera Plantarum*, upon which the present work is largely based.

GEORGE BENTHAM, F.R.S.

George Bentham was born on 22 September 1800 in the small village of Stoke, near Portsmouth, Hampshire. His father, Samuel (afterwards Sir Samuel) Bentham, was the son of a wealthy scrivener in the Minories, and the only brother of Jeremy Bentham, the publicist. He devoted himself as a youth to the study of naval architecture. At the age of 22 he went to Russia with a view to further instruction in that subject. Then he visited the Crimea and thence Siberia. Afterwards he performed distinguished service under the Empress Catherine II, and built a flotilla of gunboats.

In due course George's father returned to England and entered the service of the Admiralty, by whom he was commissioned to return to Russia to superintend the building of some ships for the British navy. He took with him his wife and family, including his son George, who thus began very early his extensive travels.

George's mother was the daughter of Dr. G. Fordyce, F.R.S., an eminent London physician. She was a woman of remarkable mind and aided her father and husband in their scientific work. George fell under the influence of his uncle Jeremy 'who imbued in him that love of methodical and logical analysis which is so conspicuous in all his nephew's writings'. 'The same inherited aptitude and contemporary influences which produced a great publicist in Jeremy, yielded, by an almost accidental deflection, a great systematic botanist in his nephew.'[1]

Bentham was one of five children (three girls), who were taught to read by words and not by syllables or letters, and the two brothers commenced learning Latin before they were five years old. While they were with their father in Russia in 1805 their education was entrusted to a talented Russian lady who could speak no English, and the boys were instructed in Latin by a Russian priest. Music, of which George later became passionately fond, was not neglected, and he became an accomplished pianist. Thus it came about that the future botanist, and joint maker of Kew, could at seven years of age converse fluently in English, French, German, and Russian, to which later he added Swedish.

[1] Quoted from Thiselton-Dyer's Eulogium, *Proc. Linn. Soc., London*, 1887–9.

After returning to England George's father lived at Hampstead, daily visiting his office at the Admiralty, but in winter he transferred to Berry Lodge, between Alverstoke and Gosport, not far from the Portsmouth dockyard. The two boys continued their education under private tutors. Thus George was never sent to school or college, which probably accounted for a shyness and reserve characteristic throughout the remainder of his life.

At the end of the Franco-Russian war Sir Samuel took his family to France and lived successively at Tours, Saumur, and Paris. In 1816 he organized a caravan tour for himself and family. The outfit consisted of a two-horse coach fitted up as a sleeping room, a one-horse spring van furnished with library and piano (!) for himself and Mrs. Bentham, and another for his daughters and their governess. From Paris they visited Orléans, Tours, Angoulême, Bordeaux, Toulouse, Montpellier, and finally Montauban. The caravan having broken down, the tour was continued by ordinary conveyances to Carcassonne, Narbonne, Nîmes, Tarascon, Marseille, Toulon, and Hyères.

From a botanical point of view the most interesting incident of this journey occurred at Angoulême. His mother had purchased a copy of de Candolle's *Flore française*. Young George, accidentally taking it up, became interested in the analytical tables for determining the affinities and names of the plants described, which fitted in with the ideas he had derived from his uncle Jeremy's works, when constructing his own geographical tables. He at once went into the yard of the house, gathered the first plant he found, and after spending the morning in studying its structure, with the aid of the *Flora*, succeeded in referring it to its order, genus, and species. This historical plant was *Salvia pratensis* DC. (*Lamiaceae*). Encouraged by his success, he pursued the study of the native flora as a diversion, naming every plant he subsequently found.

At Montauban George was entered as a student in a protestant theological college, and at home, during the holidays, occupied his time with drawing plants, learning Spanish, and music, society, and dancing, of the last of which he was passionately fond. He also devoted some time to ornithology, shooting and stuffing birds, and entomology, surely an ideal foundation for the future systematic botanist.

From Montauban George's father moved to a large estate of 2,000 acres which he had purchased, near Montpellier. He appointed George manager of the property, consisting of farms and vineyards. All his spare time was devoted to botanical excursions in the Cevennes and Pyrenees, and to making a French translation of his uncle's *Essay on Nomenclature and Classification*.

In 1823 George was sent to England to study agriculture, and he then met Sir Joseph Banks, Robert Brown, and at the Horticultural and Linnean Societies the *élite* of the naturalists of the day. During a tour in Scotland he became acquainted with Professors Graham of Edinburgh, W. J. Hooker of Glasgow, and G. A. W. Arnott, the last subsequently succeeding Hooker in Glasgow. In 1824 Arnott accompanied him on a collecting excursion in the Pyrenees which resulted in his first botanical work, *Catalogue des Plantes Indigènes des Pyrénées et du Bas Languedoc, avec des notes et observations* (Paris, 1826). At this date the estate was given up and the Bentham family returned to England for good. Bentham was then employed as secretary to his uncle Jeremy, a post not always congenial, from which he was released on his uncle's death in 1832.

For a time he studied law and was called to the Bar, but soon abandoned the practice of the profession. In 1828 his herbarium had arrived from France, and in that year he was elected a Fellow of the Linnean Society. In the next year he accepted the honorary secretaryship of the Royal Horticultural Society, a post he held until 1840. During this period many of our most popular garden plants were introduced, especially from California, through collectors sent out by the Society, Douglas, Hartweg, and others. These plants were named and many novelties among them described by Bentham. Dr. Wallich returned about this time with large collections of Himalayan, Burmese, and Indian plants, and Bentham co-operated with him in their identification and distribution to the principal herbaria of Europe. As a result of this collaboration, Bentham became interested in tropical floras, and published his *Scrophularineae Indicae* in 1835, followed in 1836 by the completion of his great work *Labiatarum genera et species*, which established him in the very forefront of taxonomic botanists.

Bentham was married in 1833, and from 1836–7 he resided with his wife in Germany, visiting the principal botanic gardens and herbaria, and especially occupied in studying the order *Leguminosae*. This resulted in his masterly *Commentationes de Leguminosarum generibus* in the Annalen des Wiener Museums (vol. 2).

For better accommodation for his library and herbarium and to devote himself exclusively to science, Bentham removed in 1842 to Pontrilas, in Herefordshire, whence he contributed the families *Ericaceae, Polemoniaceae, Scrophulariaceae, Polygonaceae*, and *Labiatae* to de Candolle's Prodromus, besides the *Botany of the Voyage of the Sulphur in the Malayan Seas and Pacific Ocean*, a quarto volume with 60 plates.

In the year 1854 Bentham was almost lost to botany. Finding the cost of keeping up his library and herbarium threatening to exceed his income, he offered these to the government, with the stipulation that they should form part of the establishment at Kew, where there was at that time no other library or herbarium than the private ones of Sir William Hooker, the Director of Kew. Bentham had decided to abandon botany, but was fortunately persuaded by his friends to reconsider the matter. In 1855, therefore, he took up residence in London, whence he went to Kew daily for five days a week, devoting the evenings to writing out the notes of his day's work.

Sir William Hooker induced Bentham to begin a series of Colonial *Floras*, the first being that of Hong Kong. This was followed by the *Flora Australiensis* in seven volumes, the first *Flora* of any continental area to be completed. It was commenced in 1861 and concluded in 1870, containing about 7,000 species, a record that has never been equalled. Bentham says that, although the *Flora Australiensis* was sometimes quoted as the joint work of himself and Baron von Mueller, the work was exclusively his own:

with the assistance, indeed, but not the co-operation of Baron von Mueller, this assistance being of precisely the same description as that which I derived from the herbarium and detailed MS. descriptions of Robert Brown, from the herbarium and notes of A. Cunningham, from the rich herbaria of Kew, from the *Flora Tasmanica* and other published works of the Hookers, as well as from the numerous instructive notes of the Hookers, of Planchon, and others who had worked in the herbarium. In the case of Baron von Mueller, however, the extreme liberality with which he gave up in my favour his own projects for a general *Flora* of Australia, and the great value for my purposes of the very numerous specimens of each species which he had collected into the Melbourne herbarium, the whole of which he unreservedly lent to me, seemed to me to demand a special recognition in the title page of the *Flora*, which has thus been misconstrued into an indication of co-operation.

Then Bentham began with the younger Hooker (J. D.) their *magnum opus*, the *Genera Plantarum*, of which Hooker later generously stated that Bentham undertook an overwhelming share of the work which might in consequence be justly regarded as on the whole the product of one botanist. Even whilst preparing that prodigious and classical work, Bentham found time to produce a *Handbook of the British Flora*, illustrated by W. H. Fitch (1858), of which there have been several subsequent editions. During this period Bentham was also President of the Linnean Society of London, a position he held with great distinction from 1863 until 1874.

Of Bentham's somewhat reluctant acceptance of Darwin's theory of the origin of species, reference should be made to J. D. Hooker's account of his life from which most of the information given here has been compiled. Bentham also equipped the University of Cambridge with an authentically named consulting herbarium. This consisted for the most part of that of Dr. C. Leman, a zealous collector, mainly by purchase, which he had disposed to leave by will to Bentham. The latter urged its being left to Cambridge, and it was finally arranged between them that the collections should be sent to Bentham for him to select from them any specimens which he might want for his own herbarium, whilst the remainder augmented by duplicates from Bentham's own herbarium should go to Cambridge. Therewith, according to Hooker, 'Bentham classified, named, had fastened down and enclosed in genus covers, a consulting herbarium of 30,000 species, a labour occupying more or less ten years of his life'. He also labelled and divided into sets for sale the great collections of Robert and Richard Schomburgk made in Brazil, and of Hartweg made in British Columbia, California, and Mexico. A still greater service to botanical science was the distribution and sale of the magnificent collection of Richard Spruce in the Amazon regions of Brazil and Peru, which were sent to him as collected, to be arranged, named, and divided into 20 to 30 sets.

Bentham's last work was the *Genera Plantarum*, of which the first part appeared in July 1862, the last part in April 1883. Bentham explained that some six- or seven-and-twenty years previously, when his botanical workshop had become firmly established in the Kew Herbarium and his connexion with Hooker, always very intimate, had become more constant, they had both felt the inconvenience of the want of a *Genera Plantarum* founded on actual observation to replace the already antiquated ones of Endlicher and Meisner, both of which, especially the latter, had been in a great measure mere compilations, and each of them had formed the project of endeavouring to supply the deficiency; but it appeared almost too vast an undertaking to be carried out by a single hand. Hooker proposed as the best chance of seeing the work brought to a successful issue, that they should join their forces. Notwithstanding his normal aversion to partnership botany, Bentham saw that here there was nothing to fear from collision, and but little from any permanent separation. He had always found that he could perfectly coincide with Hooker in his views on botany, or at any rate readily defer to them on consideration. He therefore agreed to Hooker's proposal, and plans were matured to which they adhered during the quarter of a century which the work required.

The two authors of this prodigious work divided the families between them for working up in detail, but always consulted together when any doubt or difficulty occurred. And the family characters, general observations, and subdivisions and generic arrangements prepared by each of them were almost invariably submitted to the other in manuscript for study and comment before being finally revised for press. The proofs were read through by both authors, and by their friend the Rev. M. J. Berkeley, who undertook to go over them chiefly for their latinity, in which both authors felt deficient.

The families of the first volume, containing the *Polypetalae*, were almost equally divided between them. Bentham did the first few, and Hooker worked up the *Brassicaceae* (*Cruciferae*), *Capparidaceae*, and *Resedaceae*. Bentham then did the remainder of the *Thalamiflorae*, whilst Hooker elaborated the whole of the long series of *Disciflorae* with the exception of the *Linaceae*, *Humiriaceae*, *Geraniaceae*, and *Olacaceae*. Then of the *Calyciflorae* Bentham did the *Leguminosae*, and Hooker all the remaining families except *Myrtaceae*, *Apiaceae* (*Umbelliferae*), and *Araliaceae*.

Hooker did *Rubiaceae*, and Bentham tackled *Asteraceae* (*Compositae*), a task which he accomplished with a master mind. Of the remainder of the *Gamopetalae*, Bentham began with the *Campanulaceae* and allied families, and Hooker did the *Ericales*, *Myrsinaceae*, and *Primulaceae*, and a portion of *Sapotaceae*.

Then Bentham explains that Hooker's official duties and occasional absences prevented him for a time from a continuous detailed elaboration of genera, and the remaining gamopetalous families all devolved upon Bentham. When one considers that these included such large families as *Apocynaceae*, *Asclepiadaceae*, *Boraginaceae*, *Gentianaceae*, *Solanaceae*, *Scrophulariaceae*, *Gesneriaceae*, *Bignoniaceae*, *Acanthaceae*, *Verbenaceae*, and *Lamiaceae* (*Labiatae*), one realizes the great amount of work accomplished by Bentham for the second volume.

For the third volume, containing the *Monochlamydeae* (*Apetalae*) and Monocotyledons, Bentham again did the greater portion of the first part, including the large and difficult families *Euphorbiaceae* and *Urticaceae*. The Monocotyledons appeared at first so formidable an undertaking, that, because of the uncertainty of being able to carry it through to the end, the two authors determined to commence with the most difficult families. Hooker attacked the Palms, which he found very difficult, whilst Bentham devoted more than a year each to the *Orchidaceae* and *Poaceae* (*Gramineae*). Hooker then prepared the *Araceae* and allied families, and the *Alismataceae* and allied families, the others falling to Bentham.

Thus the greatest taxonomic work ever produced in Great Britain was brought to a successful conclusion. Bentham gave a summary of the number of the families, genera, and species of flowering plants known at that date (1883). This was as follows:

	Families	Genera	Species
			(estimated)
Polypetalae . . .	82	2,610	31,874
Gamopetalae . .	45	2,619	34,556
Monochlamydeae . .	36	801	11,784
Gymnospermae . .	3	44	415
Monocotyledones . .	34	1,495	18,576
Totals . . .	200	7,569	97,205

Thirty years later an estimate of the number of genera and species was published by Thonner (*Genera of African Plants*, Engl. ed. preface dated 1913, publ. 1915):

Families	Genera	Species
Archichlamydeae (= Polypetalae +Monochlamydeae) . .	4,512	67,500
Metachlamydeae (Gamopetalae) .	3,549	50,400
Gymnospermae	50	500
Monocotyledones . . .	1,944	26,000
Totals	10,055	144,400

At the present time (early 1963) there are probably about 9,500 described genera of *Dicotyledones*, and about 2,000 genera of *Monocotyledones*.

Bower said of the *Genera Plantarum*:

The characters embodied in the diagnoses were drawn from the actual examination of specimens, which could only be derived from a reliable and rich herbarium such as that of Kew. Thus the book is not in any sense a compilation from the work of earlier writers, but it contains a redrafting of the diagnoses on the basis of personal observation. Probably into no work on Botany is there condensed so wide a field of personally recorded fact, expressed in such concise terms. The authors were both mature observers. But while Hooker was at home in the forest and the jungle, Bentham was rather a denizen of the herbarium. His education as a conveyancing barrister gave point to his naturally acute mind in the exact wording of diagnoses. The difficulty of the task of Bentham and Hooker f. was greater than that of their predecessors on account of the considerable increase in the number of recognized genera consequent on the activity of collectors the world over. Their *Genera Plantarum* was at that time a near approach to finality. Hitherto its supremacy has not been challenged. On the other hand it has formed the source from which diagnoses have been liberally borrowed.

Bentham was tall, of spare habit, with a slight stoop; his features were strongly marked, his complexion rather dark, his hair black and eyebrows bushy. In diet he was extraordinarily abstemious, taking but two meals a day. Though shy and reserved, he was a most amiable warm-hearted man, the kindest of helpmates, and the most disinterested of friends. He was the recipient of the Royal Medal of the Royal Society, of which he was a Fellow, and of the Clarke Medal of the Royal Society of New South Wales; was a Companion of St. Michael and St. George; and was elected a correspondent of many scientific societies abroad. He died at the age of 84, retaining his faculties to the last. His wife predeceased him by four years, and he had no family.

SIR JOSEPH HOOKER, F.R.S.

Joseph Dalton Hooker was born at Halesworth in Suffolk on 30 June 1817. His maternal grandfather was Dawson Turner, F.R.S., a banker of Yarmouth, and well known as an archaeologist, a naturalist, and a writer on seaweeds. His paternal grandfather was also a naturalist, who collected insects and spent much of his time in cultivating rare plants. But it was from his father that the most direct stimulus of example and of teaching came. He was Sir William Jackson Hooker, F.R.S. (1785–1865), for twenty years Regius Professor of Botany in the University of Glasgow, and afterwards, for the remainder of his life, Director of the Royal Botanic Gardens, Kew.

Joseph, the second son, accompanied his father to Glasgow in 1820. The conditions in Glasgow were most propitious for giving such a boy free scope to develop those faculties which he had inherited. Under the advantages yielded by a great port trading with all parts of the world the newly founded garden was growing in richness when the new professor arrived. In his hands it quickly became a notable centre for the reception and distribution of new and rare plants.

Besides the activities connected with the garden, where the herbarium, museum, and library grew rapidly, Sir William used to take his students for summer excursions, sometimes far up into the highlands, and Joseph and his elder brother often went with the party. The boys attended the High School of Glasgow, and when Joseph was 15 he entered the University, having as a contemporary Lord Kelvin. His medical course was completed early in 1839, when he graduated and thus became qualified for employment in the Naval Medical Service. The reading of Darwin's *Voyage of the Beagle* had increased his desire to travel, and his ambition was realized on his appointment as assistant surgeon in H.M.S. *Erebus*, under Captain Ross, on a voyage to the Antarctic.

The primary object of the voyage was a magnetic survey, with special reference to the magnetic pole, and it was completed within four years. During three successive summers the *Erebus*, accompanied by the *Terror*, entered the Antarctic ice, and the great Ice Barrier, McMurdo Sound, Mts. Erebus and Terror were added to the map of the southern hemisphere. As Ross was also an ardent naturalist, Hooker had the fullest scope given him. When sailing in icy seas Hooker's opportunities were slight, but as Bower says in his biography of Hooker: 'He interested himself in all organic life, and found fascinating problems in the floating plankton of both warm and cold oceans, as well as in depths down to four hundred fathoms. He collected, examined under the microscope, and drew all forms of life that came into his tow-nets and seines, or were brought up by dredges.'

During the southern winter, however, the expedition visited Ascension, St. Helena, the Cape, New Zealand, Tierra del Fuego, and the Falkland Islands. This gave Hooker the opportunity of collecting plants on much of the circumpolar lands of the southern hemisphere. The results were published in his first great work, the *Flora Antarctica*. His collections were considerable and were forwarded regularly to his father, together with his drawings. The expedition finally returned to Woolwich in September 1843.

His father was now Director of the Royal Gardens at Kew, and Joseph at once became an enthusiastic assistant. Whilst working up his collections he lectured in 1845 at Edinburgh University (in place of Graham in failing health). He also was temporarily employed as official botanist to the Geological Survey of Great Britain, but relinquished this in order to visit the Himalayas. He longed to see a tropical flora in a mountainous country and to compare it at different levels with that of temperate and arctic zones. He sailed from England in November 1847. First of all he made himself acquainted with the flora of the plains and hills of western Bengal, and then proceeded north into the Sikkim Himalaya. The story of this remarkable journey, including an account of the forcible detention of himself and his companion, Dr. Campbell, by the court of Sikkim, is given in his fascinating *Himalayan Journal*. He spent two years in the botanical exploration and topographical survey of Sikkim and of a number of passes leading into Thibet and Nepal.

In 1849 Hooker returned to Darjeeling, where he was joined by his old fellow student in Glasgow, Dr. Thomas Thomson. The two friends spent the year 1850 in exploring eastern Bengal, Chittagong, Silhet, and the Khasia Hills, and in 1851 they returned to England. In the Himalayas Hooker had climbed to 19,300 feet, and in these higher elevations found genera of flowering plants characteristic of temperate and cold climates.

In 1855 Hooker was appointed Assistant Director of Kew. In 1860 he visited Syria and Palestine, and in 1871 collected with Ball and Maw in the Atlas Mountains in North Africa, where he was disappointed at the absence of Alpine plants. His last great journey was in 1877, at sixty years of age, when he visited the Western States of North America with Asa Gray of Harvard. He returned with upwards of 1,000 species of dried specimens and the results were worked up into a joint report.

Bower, in his life of Hooker, sums up the results of his field work:

At one time or another Hooker touched upon every great continental area of the earth's surface. Many isolated islands had also been examined by him, especially on the Antarctic voyage. . . . Each expedition helped to suggest or to solve major problems . . . relating not only to the distribution but also to the very origin of species, Darwin saw this with unerring judgment as early as 1845. In a letter to Hooker Darwin wrote 'I know I shall live to see you the first authority in Europe on that grand subject, that almost keystone of the laws of creation, geographical distribution.' Never was a forecast more fully justified, for that position which Hooker undoubtedly had later could only have been attained through his personal experience as a traveller. Observation at first hand was the foundation on which he chiefly worked. Hooker the traveller prepared the way for Hooker the philosopher.

On his father's death in 1865 Joseph Hooker became Director of Kew. His father had transformed the garden, which until 1841 had been a mere appendix to a palace, where a more than usually extensive collection of plants was grown. He had added his private collection and library, and by his zeal, knowledge, and judgement had stamped a scientific ideal upon Kew which was worthily upheld in later years by his son Joseph.

The present sketch is more concerned with the life of Joseph Hooker as a taxonomist, ably written in a condensed form by Bower, than with the history of Kew Gardens. Bower considered his *Himalayan Journal* to rank with Darwin's *Voyage of the Beagle*, and Wallace's *Malay Archipelago*, these books 'forming a veritable trilogy of the golden age of travel in pursuit of science'.

In 1870 Hooker f., as we may now call him, published his classical *Student's Flora of the British Islands*, no doubt the result of his one time appointment as official botanist to the Geological Survey of Great Britain. Thereafter he produced a steady stream of botanical work, an exhaustive list of which is given in the Kew Bulletin for 1912: 8. The greatest of his works are his *Flora Antarctica*, the *Flora of British India*, and the *Genera Plantarum*, in addition to which he had much to do with the *Index Kewensis*, so ably compiled by Dr. Daydon Jackson, for many years secretary of the Linnean Society of London.

The *Genera Plantarum* was produced in collaboration with Mr. George Bentham. Both men had felt the great need of a work founded on actual observation, to replace the already outdated ones of Endlicher and Meisner. In view of the gigantic nature of the task they joined forces. The amount done by each is noted in the accompanying account of Bentham (see p. 19), the latter eventually doing the lion's share, owing to Hooker's numerous duties as Director of Kew.

Personally Sir Joseph Hooker (he was knighted in 1873) was of tall and rather spare build, with features striking and forcible rather than handsome, and he was somewhat unconventional in dress. He was twice married, first in 1851 to Frances, daughter of Professor Henslow of Cambridge, who earlier on had recommended Darwin as naturalist on the *Beagle*. She died in 1874, leaving him with a young family of four sons and two daughters. He married again in 1876, Hyacinth, Lady Jardine, by whom he had two sons. None of his family continued directly the botanical succession, but his elder daughter married Sir William Thiselton-Dyer, who followed Hooker as Director of Kew.

Sir Joseph outlived all his contemporaries, Darwin, Wallace, Bentham, Huxley, Lubbock, &c., many of whom were members of a social club, the X-Club, which met at intervals for dinner and discussion. He died in his ninety-fifth year on 10 December, 1911, at The Camp, Windlesham, Surrey.

CONSPECTUS OF ORDERS AND SEQUENCE OF FAMILIES[1]

ANGIOSPERMAE

DICOTYLEDONES

Division I. LIGNOSAE (see p. 6)

Order 1. MAGNOLIALES

Entirely woody group; flowers hypogynous, ⚥, rarely ♂ ♀ accompanied by reduction, acyclic to cyclic; petals usually present; stamens numerous, free or rarely connate in a mass; carpels free or reduced to 1; endosperm copious, not ruminate; embryo minute. Leaves alternate, very rarely opposite, simple, stipulate or not.—Mainly in N. Temperate Regions.

Families—Magnoliaceae, Illiciaceae, Winteraceae, Canellaceae, Schisandraceae, Himantandraceae, Lactoridaceae, Trochodendraceae, Cercidiphyllaceae.

Order 2. ANNONALES

Entirely woody group; flowers hypogynous to perigynous, ⚥; apocarpous to rarely syncarpous with parietal placentation; petaliferous with occasional gamopetaly; stamens ∞, free; endosperm constantly and markedly ruminate; embryo minute. Leaves alternate, simple, exstipulate.—Tropics and Subtropics.

Families—Annonaceae, Eupomatiaceae.

Order 3. LAURALES

Entirely woody group; flowers hypogynous to perigynous, ⚥ or ♂♀; cyclic; apocarpous to one carpel: apetalous; stamens definite, free; endosperm uniform to rarely ruminate or absent; embryo often minute. Leaves alternate or opposite, simple, exstipulate.—Mainly Tropics.

Families—Monimiaceae, Austrobaileyaceae, Trimeniaceae, Lauraceae, Gomortegaceae, Hernandiaceae, Myristicaceae.

Order 4. DILLENIALES

Trees or shrubs, rarely herbs; flowers hypogynous, ⚥, actinomorphic; calyx imbricate; petals imbricate, often crumpled in bud; stamens numerous, free; apocarpous; seeds with copious plain endosperm and small to fairly large

[1] As arranged in the author's *Families of Flowering Plants*, ed. 2, Clarendon Press, Oxford (1959).

embryo, often arillate. Leaves usually alternate with marked pinnate nervation; stipules absent or adnate to the petiole, rarely free.—Mostly Tropics and Subtropics.

Families—Dilleniaceae, Connaraceae, Crossosomataceae, Brunelliaceae.

ORDER 5. CORIARIALES

Shrubs with scaly buds; flowers hypogynous, ♀ or ♂ ♀, actinomorphic; sepals imbricate; petals persistent; stamens 10, free; apocarpous, with solitary pendulous ovule; seeds with straight embryo and thin endosperm. Leaves opposite or verticillate, simple, without stipules.—Warm-Temperate and Tropical Regions.

Family—Coriariaceae.

ORDER 6. ROSALES

Trees, shrubs, or herbs; leaves alternate or rarely opposite, simple or compound; stipules rarely absent; flowers mostly ♀, actinomorphic; petals free; stamens perigynous to epigynous, mostly free; carpels free or variously united and then ovary often inferior; seeds without endosperm.—Mainly Temperate Regions.

Families—Rosaceae, Dichapetalaceae, Calycanthaceae.

ORDER 7. LEGUMINALES

Trees, shrubs, or herbs; leaves simple to bipinnate; stipules present or absent; flowers actinomorphic to zygomorphic; petals free or some partially united; stamens numerous to few, free or variously connate, often diadelphous; carpel solitary, superior; fruit often a *legume* or indehiscent, sometimes winged; seeds without endosperm.—World-wide distribution.

Families—Caesalpiniaceae, Mimosaceae, Fabaceae (Papilionaceae).

ORDER 8. CUNONIALES

Trees or shrubs; leaves alternate, opposite or whorled, simple or compound; stipules mostly present; flowers mostly ♀, perigynous to epigynous; petals usually present, free; stamens numerous to few; carpels free or united, with parietal or axile placentation; seeds with mostly copious endosperm and small embryo.—Temperate and Subtropical Regions.

Families—Pterostemonaceae, Cunoniaceae, Philadelphaceae, Hydrangeaceae, Grossulariaceae, Oliniaceae, Greyiaceae, Escalloniaceae, Baueraceae, Crypteroniaceae.

ORDER 9. STYRACALES

Trees or shrubs, often with stellate indumentum; leaves simple, alternate; stipules absent; flowers actinomorphic; sepals valvate; petals free to united, imbricate or valvate, rarely contorted; stamens free from or adnate to the corolla-tube, few and alternate with the lobes or more numerous; anthers opening lengthwise; ovary superior to inferior, with axile placentation; seeds with copious endosperm.—Warmer Regions.

Families—Lissocarpaceae, Styracaceae, Symplocaceae.

ORDER 10. ARALIALES

Woody, or rarely reduced to herbs; leaves simple or compound; stipules present or absent; flowers mostly small and often arranged in umbels or heads; petals free or united; stamens definite, alternate with petals or corolla-lobes; ovary inferior; seeds with copious often ruminate endosperm.—World-wide distribution.

Families—Cornaceae, Alangiaceae, Garryaceae, Nyssaceae, Araliaceae, Caprifoliaceae.

ORDER 11. HAMAMELIDALES

Trees or shrubs; leaves simple, alternate, rarely opposite, mostly stipulate; flowers usually ⚥, actinomorphic, often collected into heads or pendulous catkins; petals present or absent; stamens perigynous or subepigynous; ovary semi-inferior to inferior, rarely quite superior, often bicarpellary; ovules pendulous from axile placentas; seeds with rather thin endosperm and straight embryo.—Mainly North Temperate Regions, some in Southern Africa.

Families—Tetracentraceae, Hamamelidaceae, Myrothamnaceae, Platanaceae, Stachyuraceae, Buxaceae, Daphniphyllaceae, Bruniaceae.

ORDER 12. SALICALES

Trees or shrubs; leaves alternate, stipulate; flowers dioecious, in erect or pendulous catkins; calyx absent or much reduced; petals absent; stamens 2 or more; ovary 1-locular with parietal placentas; ovules numerous, ascending; seeds covered with fine hairs; no endosperm; embryo straight.—Widely distributed.

Family—Salicaceae.

ORDER 13. LEITNERIALES

Shrubs; leaves alternate; no stipules; flowers dioecious, in erect catkin-like spikes; no calyx in the ♂ flowers, small in the ♀; stamens few; ovary superior, with 1 parietal ovule; seeds with thin endosperm and straight embryo.—N. America.

Family—Leitneriaceae.

ORDER 14. MYRICALES

Trees or shrubs, aromatic; leaves alternate, with or without stipules; flowers unisexual, in axillary spikes; no sepals or petals; stamens 2 or more; ovary 1-locular, with 1 erect basal ovule; seed without endosperm.—Widely distributed.

Family—Myricaceae.

Order 15. BALANOPSIDALES

Trees or shrubs; leaves alternate; no stipules; flowers dioecious, male in catkins, female solitary in an involucre of bracts; no sepals or petals; stamens few; ovary imperfectly 2-locular, with two parietal sub-basal placentas; seeds with some endosperm and straight embryo.—Western Pacific, NE. Australia.

Family—Balanopsidaceae.

Order 16. FAGALES

Shrubs or trees with perulate buds; leaves alternate, simple, stipulate; flowers often precocious, ♂♀, monoecious, in erect or pendulous catkin-like spikes or the female like cones; calyx much reduced or absent, the female flower often surrounded by an involucre of bracts; stamens 2 to many; ovary inferior or nude, 2-6-locular; styles free or nearly so; ovules 1–2 in each loculus, pendulous.—Mainly North Temperate Zone.

Families—Betulaceae, Fagaceae, Corylaceae.

Order 17. JUGLANDALES

Trees with hard wood; leaves alternate or rarely opposite, pinnate or trifoliolate; stipules present or absent; flowers bisexual or unisexual, spicate or paniculate; bracts often enlarged in fruit; calyx usually present; petals and disk absent; stamens numerous to few, erect in bud; ovary superior to inferior, 2-1-locular; ovules 2 or 1; fruit a drupe or nut; seeds without endosperm; cotyledons often much contorted.—Mostly Temperate Regions of N. Hemisphere.

Families—Rhoipteleaceae, Juglandaceae, Picrodendraceae.

Order 18. CASUARINALES

Trees or shrubs with jointed branches and much reduced connate leaves; flowers ♂♀, male spicate, female in heads; calyx and petals absent; stamen solitary; ovary superior, 1-locular; ovules 2, inserted above the base of the ovary; fruits in cone-like heads; seeds without endosperm.—Mascarenes, Malaya to Australia.

Family—Casuarinaceae.

Order 19. URTICALES

Trees, shrubs, or herbs, sometimes epiphytic; leaves mostly alternate and usually stipulate; flowers ♀ or ♂♀; calyx small; no petals; stamens few, erect or inflexed in bud; ovary superior, 1–2-locular; ovule solitary, erect or pendulous; seeds with or without endosperm.—Widely distributed.

Families—Ulmaceae, Cannabiaceae, Moraceae, Urticaceae, Barbeyaceae, Eucommiaceae.

Order 20. BIXALES

Trees or shrubs; flowers hypogynous to rarely perigynous, ♀ to ♂♀, actinomorphic; sepals imbricate to valvate; petals present or absent; stamens numerous to few, mostly free; ovary superior with parietal placentation, rarely axile or basal; seeds with copious endosperm and small embryo. Leaves mostly alternate and stipulate, simple.—Tropics and Mediterranean.

Families—Bixaceae, Cistaceae, Flacourtiaceae, Cochlospermaceae, Hoplestigmataceae, Achatocarpaceae, Lacistemataceae.

ORDER 21. THYMELAEALES

Mostly woody and usually apetalous; calyx often corolline; mostly monocarpellary; ovules few to solitary; seeds with or without endosperm and usually straight embryo. Leaves alternate or opposite; stipules absent or minute and glandular. Flowers often in heads surrounded by an involucre of leafy bracts.—Tropics and Subtropics, mainly, many in Southern Africa.

Families—Gonystylaceae, Aquilariaceae, Geissolomataceae, Penaeaceae, Thymelaeaceae, Nyctaginaceae.

ORDER 22. PROTEALES

Trees or shrubs, rarely subherbaceous; flowers perigynous; calyx valvate, tubular, often coloured; stamens 4, opposite the calyx-lobes; ovary 1-locular; seeds without endosperm. Leaves alternate or rarely opposite, without stipules.—Mostly S. Hemisphere, especially South Africa and Australia.

Family—Proteaceae.

ORDER 23. PITTOSPORALES

Trees, shrubs, or climbers; flowers hypogynous, mostly ⚥, actinomorphic; sepals and petals imbricate or valvate; stamens the same as or double the number of the petals, free; anthers opening lengthwise or by pores; syncarpous with parietal to axile placentation; seeds with copious endosperm and minute embryo. Leaves alternate to verticillate, simple, exstipulate.—Warmer Regions of Old World, rare in America.

Families—Pittosporaceae, Byblidaceae, Stegnospermaceae, Vivianaceae, Tremandraceae.

ORDER 24. CAPPARIDALES

Woody to herbaceous; flowers hypogynous or subperigynous, often somewhat zygomorphic; petals present or absent; stamens numerous to few, usually free; syncarpous with mostly parietal placentation; ovary often stipitate, often of two carpels; seeds without or with very little endosperm; embryo curved or variously folded. Leaves mostly alternate, simple or digitate, rarely stipulate.—Mainly Tropics.

Families—Capparidaceae, Moringaceae, Tovariaceae.

ORDER 25. TAMARICALES

Trees or shrubs; flowers hypogynous, ⚥, actinomorphic; sepals imbricate or valvate; petals free to connate; stamens mostly definite; syncarpous with parietal placentation; seeds with or without endosperm, often hairy. Leaves alternate or opposite, often very small; no stipules.—Largely confined to maritime habitats.

Families—Frankeniaceae, Tamaricaceae, Fouquieriaceae.

ORDER 26. VIOLALES

Woody to herbaceous; flowers hypogynous to perigynous, mostly zygomorphic; petals present, sometimes divided; stamens several to few, mostly free; ovary syncarpous with parietal placentation; seeds with or without endosperm; embryo straight or curved. Leaves alternate, rarely opposite, stipulate.—Tropics and Temperate Regions.

Family—Violaceae.

ORDER 27. POLYGALALES

Woody to herbaceous; flowers hypogynous to subperigynous, zygomorphic; petals present, sometimes some partially united; stamens definite, free or monadelphous, sometimes some infertile; syncarpous with axile or apical placentation; seeds with or without endosperm, pilose or with cottony hairs or winged; embryo straight. Leaves alternate, rarely opposite; stipules mostly absent.—Temperate and Tropical Regions.

Families—Polygalaceae, Krameriaceae, Trigoniaceae, Vochysiaceae.

ORDER 28. LOASALES

Woody to herbaceous; stipules absent; flowers hypogynous to epigynous, actinomorphic; petals present, contorted or valvate; stamens numerous to few, sometimes in bundles; syncarpous with parietal placentation; seeds with copious endosperm, often arillate; embryo straight. Leaves alternate, simple to much divided, exstipulate.—Mostly Tropical and Temperate America.

Families—Turneraceae, Loasaceae.

ORDER 29. PASSIFLORALES

More or less as in *Bixales*; seeds with pitted testa; corona often present; fruits often stipitate; habit often more herbaceous and frequently climbing by tendrils; stipules present or absent.—Tropics and Subtropics.

Families—Malesherbiaceae, Passifloraceae, Achariaceae.

ORDER 30. CUCURBITALES

Mostly herbaceous, often climbing by tendrils; flowers epigynous; mostly ♂ ♀; calyx-lobes imbricate or valvate; petals free or united, rarely absent; stamens numerous to few, free or united; anther-loculi straight or often flexuous; ovary inferior with parietal or axile placentation; seeds with scanty or no endosperm.—Mostly Tropics and Subtropics.

Families—Cucurbitaceae, Begoniaceae, Datiscaceae, Caricaceae.

ORDER 31. CACTALES

Succulent or woody, often very spiny; sepals, petals, and stamens mostly numerous and in several series on a tubular axis; ovary inferior, 1-locular, with parietal placentas; fruit a berry; seeds usually without endosperm and with straight or semicircular embryo.—Mostly desert regions of America.

Family—Cactaceae.

ORDER 32. TILIALES

Trees or shrubs; indumentum mostly stellate; leaves simple to compound, mostly alternate, usually stipulate; flowers hypogynous, actinomorphic, ♂ or ♂♀; calyx usually valvate; stamens free to monadelphous; anthers 2–1-locular; ovary superior, with axile placentation; seeds with copious endosperms.— Mostly Tropics (except some *Tiliaceae*).

Families—Dirachmaceae, Scytopetalaceae, Tiliaceae, Sterculiaceae, Peridiscaceae, Bombacaceae.

ORDER 33. MALVALES

More or less as in *Tiliales*, but herbaceous to softly woody, often fibrous; stamens more perfectly monadelphous and anthers 1-locular.—Temperate Regions and Tropics.

Family—Malvaceae.

ORDER 34. MALPIGHIALES

Mostly climbers with opposite leaves; flowers hypogynous, actinomorphic to subzygomorphic; calyx often bearing a pair of large glands; stamens usually definite, often connate at the base; anthers usually 2-locular, rarely 4-locellate; ovary superior, syncarpous with subapical or sub-basal placentation; ovules few; seeds usually without endosperm.—Tropics.

Families—Ixonanthaceae, Malpighiaceae, Humiriaceae, Linaceae, Irvingiaceae, Huaceae, Ledocarpaceae, Erythroxylaceae, Ctenolphonaceae, Lepidobotryaceae, Balanitaceae, Zygophyllaceae.

ORDER 35. EUPHORBIALES

Trees, shrubs, or rarely annual herbs; indumentum simple, stellate, or lepidote; leaves simple or rarely compound; stipules mostly present; flowers hypogynous, ♂ ♀, actinomorphic; calyx rarely absent, imbricate or valvate; petals rarely present; stamens very numerous to solitary, free or monadelphous; ovary superior, with axile placentation; seeds with copious endosperm. —Widely distributed, most numerous in the Tropics.

Family—Euphorbiaceae.

ORDER 36. THEALES

Trees, shrubs, or rarely woody climbers, sometimes epiphytic; leaves simple, alternate, *without stipules*; flowers hypogynous to rarely subperigynous, mostly ♀; sepals imbricate, rarely contorted; petals contorted or imbricate; stamens numerous or few, free or shortly connate; ovary superior, with axile placentation; seeds with scanty or no endosperm.—Mostly Tropics and Temperate E. Asia.

Families—Bonnetiiceae, Theaceae, Saurauiaceae, Actinidiaceae, Pellicieraceae, Pentaphylacaceae, Tetrameristaceae, Marcgraviaceae, Caryocaraceae, Medusagynaceae.

ORDER 37. OCHNALES

Mainly as in *Theales*, but leaves with stipules, intra- or extra-petiolar; calyx-lobes often enlarged and wing-like in fruit or involucrate by bracts.—Tropics.

Families—Strasburgeriaceae, Ochnaceae, Sarcolaenaceae, Sphaerosepalaceae, Dipterocarpaceae, Ancistrocladaceae.

ORDER 30. ERICALES

Shrubs, rarely herbs or trees, sometimes parasitic or epiphytic; leaves simple, sometimes scaly, alternate to rarely opposite; stipules absent; flowers ♀, rarely ♂ ♀, actinomorphic; petals united (rarely free); stamens hypogynous or epigynous, very rarely epipetalous, usually double the number of the corolla-lobes; anthers often opening by terminal pores; ovary superior to inferior, with axile placentation; seeds with copious endosperm and small embryo.—Mainly Temperate Regions, and Mountainous Regions of the Tropics.

Families—Clethraceae, Pyrolaceae, Ericaceae, Epacridaceae, Diapensiaceae, Monotropaceae, Lennoaceae, Vacciniaceae.

ORDER 39. GUTTIFERALES

Advanced hypogynous types derived from the *Theales* (p. 30), with opposite leaves as in *Myrtales* and frequently gland-dotted or resinous-lined; some herbs; stipules rare; stamens often united into separate bundles (phalanges); usually no endosperm; sepals always imbricate; flowers bisexual or unisexual.—Widely distributed.

Families—Hypericaceae, Clusiaceae, Eucryphiaceae, Quiinaceae.

ORDER 40. MYRTALES

More or less as in *Theales* (No. 36), but leaves mostly opposite and often gland-dotted; ovary inferior; calyx becoming valvate, and ovules reduced in number in the higher types; stamens show tendency to grouping in bundles as in *Hypericaceae*, sometimes dimorphous and then opening by terminal pores.—Tropics and Australia.

Families—Myrtaceae, Lecythidaceae, Rhizophoraceae, Sonneratiaceae, Punicaceae, Combretaceae, Melastomataceae.

ORDER 41. CELASTRALES

Trees, shrubs, or climbers; leaves alternate or opposite, simple, not glandular; stipules absent or very small; flowers actinomorphic, mostly ♀, often small; calyx imbricate or valvate; petals usually present, imbricate, free to partially connate; stamens definite, alternate with the petals; disk often present; ovary superior or partially immersed in the disk; ovules 1-2, erect or pendulous from the inner angles; seeds with endosperm.—Generally distributed, but mostly tropical.

Families—Pandaceae, Aquifoliaceae, Salvadoraceae, Koeberliniaceae, Cneoraceae, Cardiopteridaceae, Cyrillaceae, Icacinaceae, Empetraceae,

Aextoxicaceae, Pentadiplandraceae, Celastraceae, Corynocarpaceae, Stack-housiaceae, Goupiaceae, Hippocrateaceae, Erythropalaceae, Capusiaceae, Scyphostegiaceae.

ORDER 42. OLACALES

More or less as in *Celastrales*; petals mostly valvate, sometimes more or less connate, rarely absent; ovules pendulous from the apex of the ovary or the top of a basal placenta.—Mainly Tropics.

Families—Olacaceae, Opiliaceae, Octoknemaceae, Aptandraceae, Dipento-dontaceae, Medusandraceae.

ORDER 43. SANTALALES

Trees, shrubs, or herbs, often parasitic; leaves mostly opposite, sometimes reduced to scales; stipules absent; flowers actinomorphic; calyx valvate or open, often reduced; petals present or absent; stamens definite, opposite the calyx-lobes, or opposite the petals when latter present; disk often present; ovary inferior; placentation axile or at the top of a basal placenta; ovules few; seeds with abundant endosperm and straight embryo.—Mainly Tropics.

Families—Loranthaceae, Grubbiaceae, Santalaceae, Myzondendraceae, Balanophoraceae.

ORDER 44. RHAMNALES

Trees, shrubs, or climbers; leaves alternate or opposite, simple to compound, mostly stipulate; flowers more or less as in *Celastrales* (p. 31), but stamens opposite the petals or alternate with the sepals when petals absent; petals imbricate or valvate, rarely absent; seeds with copious or scanty endosperm, sometimes ruminate; embryo usually straight.—Tropics and Temperate Regions.

Families—Heteropyxidaceae, Elaeagnaceae, Rhamnaceae, Vitaceae.

ORDER 45. MYRSINALES

Leaves mostly gland-dotted; stipules absent; flowers small; petals united, rarely free, usually contorted or imbricate; stamens the same number as and *opposite* the corolla-lobes, usually epipetalous; anthers opening lengthwise or by apical pores; ovary superior to half-inferior, with numerous ovules on a free-basal placenta.—Mostly Tropics.

Families—Myrsinaceae, Theophrastaceae, Aegicerataceae.

ORDER 46. EBENALES

Trees or shrubs; leaves alternate, entire; stipules absent; flowers ♂ or ♂ ♀, actinomorphic; petals united, imbricate; stamens epipetalous or rarely hypo-gynous, 1–4 usually 2 times as many as the corolla-lobes; petaloid staminodes often present; anthers opening lengthwise; ovary superior; loculi 1–2 ovuled; ovules axile; seeds with copious or thin endosperm.—Mainly Tropics.

Families—Ebenaceae, Sapotaceae, Sarcospermataceae.

ORDER 47. RUTALES

Trees, shrubs, or climbers, rarely herbs; leaves often gland-dotted, simple or compound; stipules very rarely present; flowers hypogynous to slightly perigynous, mostly ☿; sepals mostly imbricate; petals contorted to valvate, free or connate near the base; disk mostly conspicuous; ovary superior, syncarpous or subapocarpous; styles free or connate; ovules 1–2; seeds with or without endosperm and straight or curved embryo.—Mainly Tropics.

Families—Rutaceae, Simaroubaceae, Burseraceae, Averrhoaceae.

ORDER 48. MELIALES

Very similar to preceding group, but stamens often completely connate into a tube with the anthers inside; leaves not gland-dotted.—Warm regions.

Family—Meliaceae.

ORDER 49. SAPINDALES

Trees or shrubs; leaves mostly compound, usually pinnate, rarely digitate, not gland-dotted; stipules rare; flowers hypogynous or slightly perigynous, often polygamous or unisexual, sometimes zygomorphic; sepals imbricate; petals mostly present; disk usually present; ovary superior, with 1–2 very rarely numerous ovules in each loculus, axile; seeds mostly without endosperm; embryo curved or crumpled.—Mainly Tropics.

Families—Melianthaceae, Sapindaceae, Podoaceae, Sabiaceae, Anacardiaceae, Aceraceae, Hippocastanaceae, Staphyleaceae, Akaniaceae, Julianaceae, Didiereaceae.

ORDER 50. LOGANIALES

Mostly trees and shrubs with opposite, simple or rarely compound leaves; stipules present or absent; sepals mostly valvate; corolla sympetalous, rarely polypetalous, lobes contorted, imbricate, or valvate; stamens epipetalous, alternate with the corolla-lobes or fewer; ovary superior, 2–4-locular; ovules mostly numerous; seeds with endosperm and straight embryo.—Tropics and Temperate Regions.

Families—Potaliaceae, Loganiaceae, Buddleiaceae, Antoniaceae, Spigeliaceae, Strychnaceae, Oleaceae.

ORDER 51. APOCYNALES

Woody or herbaceous; leaves opposite, simple, without stipules; petals united; stamens the same number as the corolla-lobes; pollen granular or glutinate; corona often present; carpels 2, often free, or becoming free in fruit; styles united above, with a common stigma, rarely free; seeds usually with endosperm and straight embryo, often winged or appendaged with long silky hairs.—Mainly Tropics.

Families—Plocospermaceae, Apocynaceae, Periplocaceae, Asclepiadaceae.

ORDER 52. RUBIALES

Trees, shrubs, or herbs; leaves opposite, stipulate, mostly entire; stipules inter- or intra-petiolar; petals united (very rarely free); stamens epipetalous (very rarely epigynous), alternate with the corolla-lobes; ovary inferior, syncarpous; placentation axile, very rarely parietal; style 1; ovules numerous to one; seeds mostly with endosperm.—Mainly Tropics.

Families—Dialypetalanthaceae, Rubiaceae.

ORDER 53. BIGNONIALES

Trees, shrubs, climbers, or herbs, sometimes with tendrils; leaves alternate or opposite, mostly compound; stipules mostly absent; flowers bisexual, calyx-lobes or segments imbricate or valvate; corolla sympetalous, mostly zygomorphic, lobes imbricate, rarely contorted; stamens 5, 4, or 2, inserted on the corolla-tube; staminodes often present; disk present; ovary superior, 4–1-locular, with axile or parietal placentas; style terminal; fruit capsular or indehiscent; seeds without or with very scanty endosperm.—Tropics and Subtropics.

Families—Cobaeaceae, Bignoniaceae, Pedaliaceae, Martyniaceae.

ORDER 54. VERBENALES

Trees, shrubs, or rarely herbs, branches often quadrangular; leaves opposite or whorled, simple or compound; stipules absent; flowers bisexual; calyx persistent; corolla actinomorphic or zygomorphic, 4–5-lobed, lobes imbricate; stamens as many as corolla-lobes or one fewer, often 4, rarely 5 or 2, inserted in corolla-tube, anthers 2-locular; ovary superior, 8–1-locular; style terminal, simple; ovules 1 or 2 in each loculus, erect, axile, or rarely pendulous; fruit a drupe or berry; seeds with scanty or no endosperm.—Tropics and Warm Temperate Regions.

Families—Ehretiaceae, Verbenaceae, Stilbeaceae, Chloanthaceae, Phrymaceae.

DIVISION II. HERBACEAE (see p. 6)

ORDER 55. RANALES

Herbaceous, often with scattered vascular bundles in the stem, or softly woody with broad medullary rays; flowers hypogynous to rarely perigynous, ♀, hemicyclic to rarely completely cyclic; petals mostly present; stamens ∞, free; apocarpous, or rarely 1 carpel; seeds with copious uniform endosperm and minute embryo. Leaves alternate or rarely opposite, very rarely stipulate, simple or much divided.—Cosmopolitan, but rare in the Tropics.

Families—Paeoniaceae, Helleboraceae, Ranunculaceae, Nymphaeaceae, Podophyllaceae, Ceratophyllaceae, Cabombaceae.

ORDER 56. BERBERIDALES

Herbaceous to shrubby or climbing; stem often with broad medullary rays; flowers hypogynous, ♂ to ♂♀, cyclic; petals present, small or rarely absent; stamens mostly definite in number, free, opposite the petals; carpels usually 1–3, free, rarely numerous; seeds with copious endosperm and small to large embryo. Leaves alternate, simple or compound, exstipulate.—Mainly N. Temperate Zone and Tropics.

Families –Sargentodoxaceae, Lardizabalaceae, Menispermaceae, Nandinaceae, Circaeasteraceae, Berberidaceae.

ORDER 57. ARISTOLOCHIALES

Softly woody with broad medullary rays, or parasitic or epiphytic herbs, flowers hypogynous to epigynous, ♂ to♂♀; no petals or rare; stamens ∞ to few; parietal or axile placentation; endosperm present or absent, with small to large embryo. Leaves (when present) alternate, simple, exstipulate.— Mostly Tropics.

Families—Aristolochiaceae, Hydnoraceae, Cytinaceae, Nepenthaceae.

ORDER 58. PIPERALES

Herbs, shrubs, or trees; herbaceous stems often with scattered bundles as in *Monocotyledons*; flowers hypogynous to epigynous; usually no calyx; petals absent; ovary superior to rarely inferior; carpels rarely free; placentation parietal to subaxile; seeds with copious endosperm and minute embryo. Leaves alternate or opposite, usually stipulate.—Mostly Tropics.

Families—Piperaceae, Saururaceae, Chloranthaceae.

ORDER 59. RHOEADALES

Herbaceous to subwoody; flowers hypogynous to rarely subperigynous, ♂, actinomorphic to zygomorphic; petals present; stamens ∞ to few, free or united in two bundles; syncarpous, with parietal placentation; seeds with copious endosperm and minute embryo. Leaves alternate or rarely subopposite, simple or much divided, exstipulate. Mainly N. Temperate Regions.

Families—Papaveraceae, Fumariaceae.

ORDER 60. CRUCIALES

Herbs, rarely somewhat woody, with watery juice; sepals 4; petals 4; stamens 6, tetradynamous (4 longer and 2 shorter); ovary of 2 united carpels with 2 parietal placentas, often divided by a false septum; seeds without endosperm. Leaves mostly alternate; stipules absent.—Cosmopolitan, rarer in the Tropics.

Family—Brassicaceae (Cruciferae).

ORDER 61. RESEDALES

More or less as in *Cruciales* but flowers mostly zygomorphic and with a variable number of stamens.—Mostly Mediterranean Region.

Family—Resedaceae.

ORDER 62. CARYOPHYLLALES

Herbaceous, becoming fleshy; flowers hypogynous to perigynous, ⚥, actinomorphic; petals usually present; stamens mostly definite; syncarpous; axile to free-central placentation; seeds with copious endosperm and curved (rarely straight) embryo. Leaves mostly opposite or verticillate, stipulate or not.— Mainly Temperate Regions.

Families—Elatinaceae, Molluginaceae, Caryophyllaceae, Aizoaceae (Ficoidaceae), Portulacaceae.

ORDER 63. POLYGONALES

Herbaceous, &c., as in *Caryophyllales*, but without petals; ovary 1-locular, 1–2-ovuled; seeds with straight or curved embryo in copious endosperm. Leaves alternate or opposite; stipules mostly present, often intrapetiolar or sheathing and membranous or scarious.—Cosmopolitan.

Families—Polygonaceae, Illecebraceae.

ORDER 64. CHENOPODIALES

More or less as in *Polygonales* but stipules absent or very small; carpels numerous to solitary, free or connate; seeds with curved embryo around the endosperm, rarely the embryo straight. Leaves alternate or opposite. Mostly dry regions.—Cosmopolitan.

Families—Barbeuiaceae, Phytolaccaceae, Gyrostemonaceae, Agdestidaceae, Petiveriaceae, Chenopodiaceae, Amaranthaceae, Cynocrambaceae, Batidaceae, Basellaceae.

ORDER 65. LYTHRALES

Herbaceous to woody, reduced forms often aquatic; flowers perigynous to epigynous, ⚥, actinomorphic; calyx tubular, lobes valvate, rarely calyx absent; petals usually present, often clawed; stamens as many or twice as many as the petals, sometimes in two distinct whorls; placentation axile; seeds usually with no endosperm. Leaves simple, usually opposite and without stipules. —Widely distributed.

Families—Lythraceae, Onagraceae, Trapaceae, Haloragidaceae, Callitrichaceae.

ORDER 66. GENTIANALES

Herbs with opposite, rarely alternate, leaves; corolla actinomorphic; stamens epipetalous, the same number as and alternate with the corolla-lobes; disk often present; ovary superior, 1-locular with parietal placentation; ovules numerous; seeds with copious endosperm and small embryo.—Temperate Regions and Subtropics mainly.

Families—Gentianaceae, Menyanthaceae.

ORDER 67. PRIMULALES

Herbs or rarely climbers; no stipules; flowers often subumbellate; petals united, imbricate, rarely absent; stamens epipetalous, the same number as and opposite the corolla-lobes; ovary superior, 1-locular, with free-basal placenta and numerous to solitary ovules; seeds with or without endosperm. —Mainly mountains of Northern Hemisphere and maritime shores.

Families—Primulaceae, Plumbaginaceae.

ORDER 68. PLANTAGINALES

More or less as in *Primulaceae*, but the stamens alternate with the corolla-lobes; flowers anemophilous.—Widely dispersed.

Family—Plantaginaceae.

ORDER 69. SAXIFRAGALES

Herbaceous; flowers actinomorphic, more or less perigynous or rarely epigynous; petals present; stamens definite, free; apocarpous to syncarpous with axile placentation; seeds with copious endosperm and small straight embryo. Leaves radical, alternate or opposite, sometimes much modified, exstipulate.—Cosmopolitan.

Families—Crassulaceae, Cephalotaceae, Saxifragaceae, Eremosynaceae, Vahliaceae, Francoaceae, Donatiaceae, Parnassiaceae, Adoxaceae.

ORDER 70. SARRACENIALES

Characters more or less as in *Saxifragales*, but adapted for entrapping insects; leaves tubular or covered with viscid glands, usually radical; stamens numerous to few; syncarpous with parietal or axile placentation.—Cosmopolitan.

Families—Droseraceae, Sarraceniaceae.

ORDER 71. PODOSTEMALES

Submerged freshwater herbs like mosses, hepatics, or algae; petals absent; stamens 1–4, free or partly connate; syncarpous with parietal or central placentation; seeds minute, without endosperm.—Tropics and Subtropics.

Families—Podostemaceae, Hydrostachyaceae.

ORDER 72. UMBELLALES

Herbs, rarely somewhat woody, with furrowed hollow stems or with wide soft pith; leaves alternate, usually much divided, sheathing at the base; no stipules; flowers in simple or compound umbels, rarely in heads; ovary inferior, 2-locular; fruit dividing into 2 mericarps; carpels mostly ribbed and often with parallel resin canals (vittae).—Mainly Temperate Regions and Mountains in the Tropics.

Family—Apiaceae (Umbelliferae).

ORDER 73. VALERIANALES

Perennial or annual herbs; leaves radical, alternate or opposite; stipules absent; flowers usually zygomorphic, sometimes unisexual, cymose to capitate or verticillate, sometimes with an involucre of bracts; calyx and sympetalous corolla epigynous; stamens usually 4, alternate with the corolla-lobes; ovary inferior, 3–1-locular, only 1 loculus fertile; ovule 1, pendulous; fruit indehiscent.—Generally distributed, but rare in America and Australasia.

Families—Valerianaceae, Dipsacaceae, Calyceraceae.

ORDER 74. CAMPANALES

Herbaceous to somewhat woody; corolla actinomorphic to zygomorphic, epigynous; stamens free from or inserted low down on the corolla; anthers free to connivent; ovary inferior or rarely superior; ovules usually numerous, axile.—Mainly Temperate Regions.

Families—Campanulaceae, Lobeliaceae.

ORDER 75. GOODENIALES

Herbs or undershrubs; leaves alternate or rarely opposite, simple, or all radical; stipules absent or scale-like; flowers bisexual, actinomorphic to zygomorphic; calyx-tube adnate to the ovary, rarely free; corolla sympetalous, 2–1-lipped, lobes imbricate or valvate; stamens 5, alternate with the lobes, or 2; filaments free or connate around the style; anthers opening lengthwise; ovary mostly inferior, 1–4-locular; stigma indusiate.—Mostly Southern Hemisphere.

Families—Goodeniaceae, Brunoniaceae, Stylidiaceae.

ORDER 76. ASTERALES

Herbaceous to woody, rarely trees; leaves alternate, opposite, or all radical; no stipules; flowers collected into heads surrounded by an involucre of bracts, rarely heads compound; outer flowers either ligulate and female (rarely sterile), the inner flowers tubular and bisexual, or all the flowers ligulate and bisexual; anthers united into a tube; filaments free, inserted on the corolla-tube; ovary inferior, 1-locular; style mostly 2-lobed; ovule 1, erect; fruit an achene, usually crowned by a pappus (modified calyx).—World-wide distribution.

Family—Asteraceae (Compositae).

ORDER 77. SOLANALES

Mostly herbs or twiners; leaves alternate; no stipules; corolla actinomorphic; stamens the same number as and alternate with the corolla-lobes; ovary superior, 1–4-locular, often 2-locular, or of almost free carpels, ovules numerous to solitary, axile; seeds with some endosperm and often curved embryo.—General distribution.

Families—Solanaceae, Convolvulaceae, Nolanaceae.

ORDER 78. PERSONALES

More or less as in preceding; leaves alternate to opposite; corolla always more or less zygomorphic; stamens fewer than the corolla-lobes, often 4 or 2;

placentation usually axile but sometimes parietal; ovules numerous.—General distribution.

Families—Scrophulariaceae, Acanthaceae, Gesneriaceae, Orobanchaceae, Lentibulariaceae, Columelliaceae.

ORDER 79. GERANIALES

Herbs or undershrubs, very rarely arborescent; flowers hypogynous, ♀, actinomorphic to zygomorphic; sepals imbricate or rarely valvate; petals present and often clawed, usually free; stamens as many to twice as many as the petals; disk-glands often present; syncarpous with axile placentation; ovules solitary to few; seeds mostly without endosperm, embryo straight. Leaves alternate or radical, rarely opposite, simple to much-divided or pinnate; stipules present or absent.—General distribution.

Families—Geraniaceae, Limnanthaceae, Oxalidaceae, Tropaeolaceae, Balsaminaceae.

ORDER 80. POLEMONIALES

Herbs or rarely shrubs or twiners; corolla sympetalous, actinomorphic; stamens epipetalous, alternate with the corolla-lobes; ovary superior, entire, with numerous or few ovules on parietal or axile placentas.—Mostly American.

Families—Polemoniaceae, Hydrophyllaceae, Cuscutaceae.

ORDER 81. BORAGINALES

More or less as in *Polemoniales*; ovary often deeply lobed with gynobasic style, bicarpellate with paired ascending ovules.—General distribution.

Family—Boraginaceae.

ORDER 82. LAMIALES

As in preceding groups but leaves mostly opposite or whorled, rarely alternate; ovary often deeply lobed with gynobasic style; ovules mostly paired; corolla often bilabiate; stamens 4 or 2.—General distribution.

Families—Myoporaceae, Selaginaceae, Globulariaceae, Lamiaceae (Labiatae).

MONOCOTYLEDONES

DIVISION I. CALYCIFERAE (see p. 8)

ORDER 83. BUTOMALES

Perennial, aquatic herbs in fresh or salt water; leaves radical or cauline, alternate to whorled; flowers showy to small and minute, bisexual or unisexual, hypogynous to epigynous; perianth 2-seriate, the outer usually green and sepal-like, the inner petaloid; stamens numerous or reduced to 3; gynoecium apocarpous or syncarpous, if the latter then inferior; ovules numerous, scattered on the walls of the carpels; seeds without endosperm.—Temperate and Tropical Regions.

Families—Butomaceae, Hydrocharitaceae.

ORDER 84. ALISMATALES

Marsh or aquatic or rarely saprophytic herbs in fresh or brackish water; rootstock a rhizome; leaves radical, alternate, opposite or clustered; flowers bracteate, medium-sized to very minute, bisexual or unisexual, hypogynous; perianth, when present, with the outer segments often calyx-like and the inner petaloid, or perianth absent; stamens numerous to solitary; gynoecium apocarpous; ovules numerous to solitary, basal or on the inner angle; seeds without endosperm.—Temperate and Tropical Regions.

Families—Alismataceae, Scheuchzeriaceae, Petrosaviaceae.

ORDER 85. TRIURIDALES

Saprophytes, with scale-like, colourless leaves; flowers very small, racemose or subcorymbose, unisexual; perianth-segments 1-seriate, valvate; stamens 6-2; anthers 2-locular; gynoecium of several free carpels; ovule solitary, basal from the inner angle of the carpels; fruit dehiscent.—Tropics.

Family—Triuridaceae.

ORDER 86. JUNCAGINALES

Marsh perennial or annual herbs; roots from a rhizome, fibrous or tuberous; leaves mostly radical, sheathing at the base; sheaths open; flowers small, bisexual, polygamous or unisexual, racemose or spicate; bracts absent; perianth 6- or 3-merous or of only 1 segment resembling a bract; stamens 6-1, on very short filaments; anthers extrorse; carpels 6-1, free or connate and superior; style various, sometimes elongated in the female flowers; ovules more or less basal; seed without endosperm.—Mostly marshy places in Temperate and cold regions.

Families—Juncaginaceae, Lilaeaceae, Posidoniaceae.

ORDER 87. APONOGETONALES

Fresh-water or marine perennials; roots from a rhizome; leaves oblong to linear, sheathing at the base; flowers small, bisexual or unisexual, spicate, spikes secund, simple or forked, free or at first enclosed in the leaf-sheath; bracts absent; perianth-segments 3-1 or absent, sometimes bract-like on the margin of the flattened axis; stamens 6 or more, or only 1; anthers 2-1-locular; gynoecium apocarpous or of one ovary; ovules several to 2; seeds without endosperm.—Widely distributed.

Families—Aponogetonaceae, Zosteraceae.

ORDER 88. POTAMOGETONALES

Fresh-water or marine perennials; roots from a rhizome; leaves alternate or opposite, sheathing at the base, sheath often ligule-like at the apex, linear to nearly orbicular; flowers small to minute, spicate, racemose, or solitary, bisexual or unisexual; bracts absent; perianth-segments 3–4 or absent; stamens 4–1; anthers 2-locular, extrorse, usually on very short filaments; gynoecium of several free carpels or of one carpel; ovule solitary, pendulous; fruit indehiscent; seeds without endosperm.—Widely distributed.

Families—Potamogetonaceae, Ruppiaceae.

ORDER 89. NAJADALES

Submerged aquatic perennials or annuals; leaves alternate or opposite, sheathing; flowers minute, unisexual, axillary; perianth of small scales or absent; stamens 3–1; anthers mostly sessile, 4–1-locular; gynoecium of 9–1 free carpels; ovule 1; fruit indehiscent; no endosperm.—Widely distributed in fresh or salt water.

Families—Zanichelliaceae, Najadaceae.

ORDER 90. COMMELINALES

Terrestrial or rarely aquatic herbs; leaves with a closed sheath or rarely not sheathing; flowers actinomorphic or zygomorphic, mostly bisexual, often showy, in cymes or panicles, rarely solitary; perianth 2-seriate, the outer green and calyx-like, the inner of three often clawed and mostly free petals; stamens 6 or 3; anthers opening lengthwise or by pores; gynoecium of united carpels, superior; style 1; ovules several to solitary, on axile or parietal placentas; fruit capsular or baccate; seeds with endosperm, often marked by a disk-like callosity.—Tropical and warm regions.

Families—Commelinaceae, Cartonemataceae, Flagellariaceae, Mayacaceae.

ORDER 91. XYRIDALES

Perennial or annual usually marsh herbs with radical linear to terete leaves, often with broad sheathing bases; sheaths open and embracing the nude flowering stem; flowers small, arranged in usually bracteate heads; perianth double and distinctly 2-seriate, the outer hyaline or glumaceous, imbricate, the inner corolline, with a short or long tube; stamens 6 or 3; anthers 2–4-locular, opening by slits or pores; gynoecium syncarpous, 1-locular or imperfectly 3-locular; ovules parietal or from the base; fruit capsular; seeds with copious endosperm.—Marshy habitats of warm regions.

Families—Xyridaceae, Rapateaceae.

ORDER 92. ERIOCAULALES

Perennials with tufted narrow leaves; flowers capitate, small, unisexual, usually monoecious; perianth scarious or membranous, segments in 2 distinct series, the inner often united; stamens free, anthers 2–1-locular; ovary superior, 3–2-locular, ovules solitary, pendulous; fruit a capsule; seeds with endosperm. Mainly Tropical Regions.

Family—Eriocaulaceae.

ORDER 93. BROMELIALES

Mostly epiphytic or on moist rocks; leaves in a dense cluster, strap-shaped, mostly spinulose-toothed; inflorescence terminal, bracts often coloured; perianth 2-seriate, outer calyx-like, imbricate, inner corolla-like; stamens 6; ovary superior to inferior, 3-locular; ovules numerous on axile placentas; fruit usually fleshy; seeds with endosperm.—American Tropics and Subtropics; one in W. Africa.

Family—Bromeliaceae.

ORDER 94. ZINGIBERALES

Herbs with rhizomes and fibrous or tuberous roots; stems often very short or formed by the imbricate bases of the sheathing petioles; leaves spirally arranged or distichous; sheath open or rarely closed; calyx and corolla in separate whorls; stamens 5–6 or reduced to 1, the remainder transformed into petaloid staminodes; ovary inferior; fruit a capsule or fleshy and indehiscent; seeds with endosperm, sometimes arillate.—Tropics and Subtropics, generally in moist or swampy forest regions.

Families—Musaceae, Strelitziaceae, Lowiaceae, Zingiberaceae, Cannaceae, Marantaceae.

DIVISION II. COROLLIFERAE (see p. 8)

ORDER 95. LILIALES

Herbs with rhizomes, corms, or bulbs; stems leafy or leaves clustered at the base or all radical, rarely reduced and the branchlets leaf-like (cladodes); flowers small to large and very showy, usually bisexual; perianth actinomorphic or slightly zygomorphic, mostly corolla-like; stamens usually 6, opposite the perianth-segments or lobes; ovary superior or semi-inferior, usually 3-locular with axile placentas; fruit a capsule or berry; seeds with copious endosperm.—Cosmopolitan.

Families—Liliaceae, Tecophilaeaceae, Trilliaceae, Pontederiaceae, Smilacaceae, Ruscaceae.

ORDER 96. ALSTROEMERIALES

Rootstock a rhizome with fibrous or tuberous roots; stems leafy, erect or climbing; leaves alternate, linear to ovate; flowers showy, in a terminal cluster or raceme; perianth-segments 6, free or partly connate, equal or sometimes one somewhat dissimilar; stamens 6, free or partly connate; ovary superior or usually inferior; 3-locular with axile placentas, or 1-locular with parietal placentas; fruit a capsule or berry; seeds with copious endosperm.—Mainly Southern Hemisphere.

Families—Alstroemeriaceae, Petermanniaceae, Philesiaceae.

ORDER 97. ARALES

Herbs, rarely climbing and woody, very rarely aquatic; leaves radical, or if cauline alternate, entire or variously divided, often hastate; flowers very small, densely arranged on a spike (spadix) usually subtended by or enclosed in a large bract (spathe), bisexual or unisexual; perianth present and small, or absent; stamens hypogynous, free or united; ovary superior; fruit usually a berry; seeds with copious endosperm.—Temperate and Tropical Regions.

Families—Araceae, Lemnaceae.

ORDER 98. TYPHALES

Aquatic or marsh herbs with rhizomes; leaves elongate-linear, sheathing at the base; flowers unisexual, anemophilous, very small or minute, crowded into clusters or dense spikes; perianth much modified and reduced; stamens 2 or more; ovary 1-locular; ovule 1, pendulous.—Generally distributed.

Families—Sparganiaceae, Typhaceae.

ORDER 99. AMARYLLIDALES

Herbs with a tunicated bulb (very rarely a rhizome); leaves radical, usually linear; flowers mostly showy, umbellate or rarely solitary on a leafless stem (scape) and subtended by an involucre of 1 or more mostly thin bracts; stamens generally 6; corona present or absent; ovary superior or inferior, mostly 3-locular with axile placentas; fruit a capsule or berry.—Temperate and Warm Temperate Regions, rarer in Tropics.

Family—Amaryllidaceae.

ORDER 100. IRIDALES

Characters as for Liliales, whence this family has been evolved (and probably independently of *Amaryllidaceae*), but ovary inferior (superior in *Isophysis*), and stamens reduced to 3; style-arms often divided, sometimes petaloid.— General distribution, numerous in South Africa and South America.

Family—Iridaceae.

ORDER 101. DIOSCOREALES

Herbs or climbers from rhizomes or tubers; stems leafy; leaves alternate or rarely opposite, mostly ovate or cordate with prominent nerves and reticulate venation, sometimes digitately lobed; flowers small, bisexual or unisexual; perianth usually white or pale-coloured, segments mostly united; stamens 6–3; ovary usually inferior, rarely superior or semi-inferior, 3-locular or rarely 1-locular; fruit a capsule, rarely indehiscent or baccate; seeds with endosperm, often winged.—Mainly Tropical and Warm Temperate Regions.

Families—Stenomeridaceae, Trichopodaceae, Roxburghiaceae, Dioscoreaceae.

ORDER 102. AGAVALES

Perennials with a thick woody caudex or rhizome; stem reaching tree form; leaves usually crowded at the base or apex of the stem, thick and fleshy or fibrous, sometimes prickly; flowers bisexual to dioecious, mostly actinomorphic, bracteate, often small and in much-branched panicles; perianth dry and glumaceous to fleshy; lobes or segments more or less alike; stamens 6; anthers 2-locular, introrse or opening at the sides; ovary superior or inferior, 3- or 1-locular, with axile or centrally attached ovules; fruit a capsule or berry; seeds with endosperm.—Numerous in Australia, and in Tropics and Subtropics, often in arid regions.

Families—Xanthorrhoeaceae, Agavaceae.

ORDER 103. PALMALES

Stem herbaceous, from almost nothing to very tall and woody, sometimes climbing and armed with hooks, often covered by the persistent leaf-bases; leaves often very large, entire or pinnately or flabellately divided and nerved; rhachis often extended at the base into a fibrous sheath; flowers small, actinomorphic, bisexual to dioecious, mostly in panicles, and often furnished with large spathe-like bracts; perianth double; stamens usually 6; ovary superior, of free or united carpels; ovule solitary in each ovary or loculus; fruit a berry or drupe; seeds with endosperm.—Tropics and Subtropics.

Family—Arecaceae (Palmae).

ORDER 104. PANDANALES

Trees or shrubs, often with aerial roots; leaves mostly spirally arranged, cauline, spinulose on the margins; flowers minute, dioecious in panicles or crowded into spadix-like inflorescences with large spathe-like bracts; ovary superior, sometimes connate into groups and in fruit forming a syncarp; fruits woody or baccate; seeds minute.—Tropics and Subtropics of Old World, especially in oceanic islands.

Family—Pandanaceae.

ORDER 105. CYCLANTHALES

Herbs of Palm-like habit; leaves often deeply bilobed; flowers small, densely crowded into a spadix which is subtended by large more or less caducous spathe-like bracts enveloping the spadix when young; flowers spirally arranged on the axis, or the different sexes in alternating whorls; fruit a fleshy syncarp; seeds with abundant endosperm and small embryo.—Tropical America and West Indies.

Family—Cyclanthaceae.

ORDER 106. HAEMODORALES

Rootstock a rhizome or rarely a corm; leaves entire or rarely lobed, often all radical, often very hairy, hairs sometimes branched; flowers bisexual, solitary to paniculate or subumbellate; perianth mostly with a distinct tube, segments or lobes in 2 or 1 series, in the latter case subvalvate; stamens numerous to 6 or rarely 3, free or in bundles; anthers 2-locular opening lengthwise; ovary superior to inferior, 3-locular with axile placentas, or

1-locular with parietal placentas; seeds usually with copious endosperm.—
Tropics and Subtropics, especially in Southern Hemisphere.

Families—Haemodoraceae, Hypoxidaceae, Velloziaceae, Apostasiaceae,
Taccaceae, Philydraceae.

ORDER 107. BURMANNIALES

Small herbs, often saprophytes, with usually reduced leaves; perianth tubular,
outer lobes valvate; stamens 6 or 3; ovary inferior, 1–3-locular; ovules and
seeds very numerous and small, the latter with scanty endosperm.—Tropics
and Subtropics.

Families—Burmanniaceae, Thismiaceae, Corsiaceae.

ORDER 108. ORCHIDALES

Terrestrial, epiphytic or saprophytic herbs; no bulbs; leaves undivided, often
fleshy; flowers zygomorphic, mostly bisexual; inflorescence never umbellate
or cymose; perianth of 6 petaloid segments in two whorls, or the outer caly-
cine and the inner petaloid; stamens 2 or 1; pollen granular or more usually
agglutinated into masses; ovary usually 1-locular with parietal placentas and
very numerous ovules, often twisted through 180° and placing the labellum
in an abaxial position; seeds minute and very numerous, without endosperm;
often drawn out at each end; embryo not differentiated.—Widely distributed.

Family—Orchidaceae.

DIVISION III. GLUMIFLORAE (see p. 8)

ORDER 109. JUNCALES

Perennial or annual herbs, rarely shrubby; leaves linear, often grass-like,
sheathing at the base, sheaths open or closed, or often the leaf-blade reduced
and the sheath embracing the stem; flowers mostly *anemophilous*, very small,
spicate or capitate or paniculate; perianth glumaceous, in 2 whorls or much
reduced or absent; stamens 6, 3, or 2–1; anthers 2- or 1-locular; ovary superior;
fruit a capsule or nut.—Cosmopolitan, many in Southern Hemisphere.

Families—Juncaceae, Thurniaceae, Centrolepidaceae, Restionaceae.

ORDER 110. CYPERALES

Perennials (or rarely annuals) with rhizomes; stems usually full of pith,
rarely hollow, mostly triquetrous; leaves narrow, grass-like, sheathing at the
base, rarely ligulate; flowers very small, bisexual or unisexual, arranged in
heads or small spikes, solitary within a glume-like bract, the latter spirally
or distichously arranged; perianth reduced to scales or bristles or absent;
stamens usually 3; anthers basifixed, 2-locular; ovary superior, 1-locular,
with 1 erect ovule; fruit nut-like, indehiscent; endosperm copious—World-
wide distribution.

Family—Cyperaceae.

ORDER 111. GRAMINALES

Annual or perennial herbs, rarely shrubs or trees; flowering stems (culms) cylindrical, jointed, usually hollow between the nodes, closed at the nodes; leaves alternate, consisting of sheath, ligule, and blade, blade parallel-nerved; flowers usually bisexual, small, consisting of stamens and gynoecium and of 2 or 3 minute scales (lodicules) representing the perianth, subsessile between two bracts (lemma and palea), the whole termed a floret; stamens 1–6, usually 3; anthers 2-locular; ovary 1-locular; ovule 1, anatropous; styles usually 2, stigmas generally plumose; fruit a caryopsis with a thin pericarp adnate to the seed, rarely a nut, berry, or utricle; endosperm starchy, embryo at the base.—World-wide distribution.

Family—Poaceae (Gramineae).

DESCRIPTION OF ORDERS, FAMILIES, TRIBES AND GENERA

DICOTYLEDONES

ORDER 1. MAGNOLIALES

Entirely woody group of families, probably representing the most ancient types of existing Dicotyledons and basic for the succeeding also predominantly woody groups beginning respectively with *Dilleniales, Rosales, Bixales, Tiliales,* and so on to the end of the woody phylum with the family *Verbenaceae,* as shown on p. 9.

Perianth present, conspicuous, never operculate; indumentum not lepidote:

 Flowers bisexual (or very rarely unisexual and then stamens free):

 Stamens free among themselves:

 Leaves stipulate, the stipules large and enclosing and protecting the young growths, but soon deciduous and leaving an annular scar around the shoot; flowers large, solitary, terminal or axillary; axis usually elongated and cone-like; stamens and carpels spirally arranged
1. Magnoliaceae

 Leaves without stipules, pellucid-punctate; flowers small or medium-sized, rarely solitary; axis short and never cone-like in fruit; carpels more or less in a single whorl:

  Sepals imbricate   2. *Illiciaceae*

  Sepals valvate   3. *Winteraceae*

 Stamens united; ovary 1-locular, with parietal placentas   4. *Canellaceae*

 Flowers unisexual; stamens partially or wholly connate into a globose mass; leaves without stipules; climbing shrubs   5. *Schisandraceae*

Perianth present, operculate; indumentum lepidote; stamens petaloid
6. Himantandraceae

Perianth absent or much reduced and bract-like; indumentum never lepidote; stamens not petaloid:

 Carpels 3; stipules large and intrapetiolar, membranous; leaves minutely pellucid-punctate; flowers polygamo-monoecious   7. *Lactoridaceae*

 Carpels more than 3; stipules absent or small; leaves not pellucid-punctate:

 Flowers bisexual or andro-dioecious, clustered or racemose-paniculate; seeds not winged   8. *Trochodendraceae*

 Flowers dioecious, solitary on short arrested branchlets; stipules adnate to the petiole; seeds winged   9. *Cercidiphyllaceae*

1. MAGNOLIACEAE

A. L. de Jussieu, Gen. Pl. 280 (1789) (*Magnoliae*)

J. E. DANDY

Trees or shrubs, glabrous or with an indumentum of simple hairs composed of one row of cells. Leaves evergreen or deciduous, alternate, simple, entire or 2–10-lobed, penninerved; stipules present, at first enclosing and protecting the young growths, later deciduous and leaving an annular scar around the node. Flowers terminal or axillary, mostly large and solitary, bisexual or very rarely unisexual, pedunculate; peduncle bearing 1 or more deciduous spathaceous bracts which leave annular scars. Perianth 2- or more-cyclic; tepals 6 or more, 3–6-merous, free, imbricate, usually subequal and fleshy but the outer whorl sometimes reduced in size or texture so as to simulate a calyx. Androecium of numerous free stamens spirally arranged; filaments short or more or less elongated; anthers linear, 2-locular, dehiscing introrsely or latrorsely or extrorsely; connective usually more or less produced into an appendage, rarely unappendaged; pollination by insects. Gynoecium sessile or stipitate; carpels numerous to few (rarely reduced to 1), spirally arranged, free or sometimes concrescent; ovules 2 or more, biseriate on the ventral suture. Fruit apocarpous or sometimes syncarpous; fruiting carpels longitudinally dehiscent along the dorsal or ventral suture, or more rarely circumscissile or indehiscent. Seeds 1 or more in each fruiting carpel, large, suspended (when carpel dehiscent) by a silky thread-like funicle, the testa externally arilloid or more rarely adherent to the endocarp; endosperm copious, oily; embryo minute. Type genus *Magnolia* Linn.

Genera 12; species about 210.

DISTRIBUTION. Temperate and tropical SE. Asia; also SE. North America and thence southward through West Indies and Cent. America to E. Brazil; represented in Europe by fossil remains; absent from Africa, Australasia, and Polynesia.

CLASSIFICATION. Benth. & Hook. f., Gen. Pl. 1: 16 (1862); Prantl, Engl., & Prantl, Nat. Pflanzenfam. 3, 2: 12 (1888); Dandy, Kew Bull. 1927; 257 (key to genera of *Magnolieae*); Dandy, Camellias and Magnolias, Rep. Conf. R. Hort. Soc. 64 (1950) (key to subgenera and sections of *Magnolia*); and in Hutch. Fam. Fl. Pl. ed. 2, 1: 123, fig. 1 (1959).

ANATOMY. Sol. 1: 27; MC. 1: 27. POLLEN. Erdt. 254.

ADDITIONAL LITERATURE. A. Gray, A short exposition of the structure of the ovule and seed-coats of *Magnolia*, Journ. Linn. Soc. 2: 106–10, figs. 1–18 (1858). R. Groppler, Vergleichende Anatomie des Holzes der Magnoliaceen, Bibl. Bot. 31: 1–51, tt. 1–4 (1894). F. M. Andrews, Karyokinesis in *Magnolia* and *Liriodendron*, Beih. Bot. Centralbl. 11: 134 (1901–2). E. W. Berry, Phylogeny of *Liriodendron*, Bot. Gaz. 34: 44 (1902). W. E. Maneval, The development of *Magnolia* and *Liriodendron*, incl. a discussion of the primitiveness of the *Magnoliaceae*, Bot. Gaz. 57: 1–31 (1914). R. A. Good, Past and present distrib. of the *Magnoliaceae*, Ann. Bot. 39: 409 (1925). J. G. Millais, Magnolias, pp. 251 (1927). J. E. Dandy & R. d'O. Good, *Magnoliaceae* Jaume, Pflanzenareale, 2: 35–38, Karte 41–43 (1929). R. Lemesle, De L'Ancienneté des caractères anatomiques des Magnoliacées, Rev. générale de Botanique, 45: 341 (1933). R. P. McLaughlin, System. anatom. of the woods of the *Magnoliales*, Tropical Woods, 34: 3 (1933). C. R. Evans, Germination behavior of *Magnolia grandiflora*, Bot. Gaz. 94: 729–54 (1933). K. K. Shaparenko, The Tulip-tree (*Liriodendron*) (introduction to an evolutionary monograph), Acta Inst. Bot. Acad. Sci. USSR, ser. 1, fasc. 4: 93–170, figs. 1–28, tt. 1–2 (1937). T. T. Earle, Origin of the seed coats in *Magnolia*, Amer. Journ. Bot. 25: 221–2, figs. 1–3 (1938). R. A. Howard, Morphology and systemat. of West Indian *Magnoliaceae*, Bull. Torr. Cl. 75: 335 (1948). J. E. Canright, Comparative morph. and relationships of the *Magnoliaceae*, Amer. Journ. Bot. 39: 484 (1952); Phytomorphology, 3: 355 (1953). M. A. Johnson, Relationship in the *Magnoliaceae* as determined by the precipitin reaction, Bull. Torr. Cl. 80: 349 (1953). J. E. Canright, Comparative morph. and relationships of *Magnoliaceae*, Journ. Arn. Arb. 36: 120 (1955).

Characters occurring in relatively few Genera. Leaves 2–10-lobed and enclosed in bud within opposite stipules in *Liriodendron*. Flowers axillary in *Elmerrillia* and *Michelia*; unisexual in *Kmeria*. Perianth 2-cyclic with only 6–7 tepals in *Kmeria* and *Michelia* spp.; heterochlamydeous (the outer whorl of tepals much reduced in size and simulating a calyx) in *Magnolia* spp. and *Michelia mannii* King. Anthers extrorse in *Liriodendron*; latrorse or sublatrorse in *Magnolia* spp. and *Michelia*. Fruit a woody loculicidal capsule in *Pachylarnax*. Fruiting carpels circumscissile in *Talauma*; samaroid (winged, deciduous, and indehiscent) in *Liriodendron*.

Economic Properties. The wood of *Liriodendron tulipifera* Linn. is one of the most valuable timber products of the E. United States; the American Indians made their canoes from it, and it has been largely used for the interior finish of houses, door panels, boat building, utensils, &c.; at one time imported into this country as Whitewood or Poplar. The wood of most other *Magnoliaceae* is light, close-grained, and easily worked, but not very durable. The Japanese used *Magnolia* wood for making swords and sheaths. The bark and flower-buds of *Magnolia officinalis* Rehd. & Wils. and other species yield a valuable drug exported from central and W. China; the bark when boiled yields an extract taken internally as a cure for coughs and colds, and as a tonic. The source of Champak in India is *Michelia champaca* Linn. An alkaloid of *Liriodendron* bark stimulates the action of the heart (Lloyd, Drugs and Med. N. Amer. 2: 1–46 (1886); Sargent, Sylva N. Amer. 1: 1–16; Rehder and Wilson, Sarg. Pl. Wils. 1). Many *Magnoliaceae* are cultivated for their ornamental qualities, *Magnolia* being one of the best-known genera of trees and shrubs in cultivation. In temperate regions the most popular species are the precocious-flowered E. Asiatic Magnolias which are remarkable for their beauty when in flower; a number of garden hybrids of these species are established in cultivation. Species of *Manglietia*, *Michelia*, and *Liriodendron* (especially *L. tulipifera* Linn.) are also grown in temperate countries. Several species of *Magnoliaceae* are widely cultivated in the tropics, notably *Magnolia grandiflora* Linn., *Michelia champaca* Linn., and *M. figo* Spreng.

Phylogeny and Morphology. As here defined the *Magnoliaceae* are a natural and homogeneous group; this the family certainly was not when, as a wider concept, it was held to include the *Winteraceae, Schisandraceae, Trochodendraceae*, &c. As noted in the introduction to this work, the *Magnoliaceae* are here regarded as one of the oldest, if not the oldest, of existing angiospermous families. This view is held as being logical following the interpretation of the derivation of the floral parts from foliage leaves.

A constant feature of the family is the deciduous stipules which leave annular scars at the nodes; they are either free from the petiole or more or less adnate to it. Another constant feature is the presence on the peduncle of one or more deciduous spathaceous bracts which leave similar annular scars. There is no doubt that these bracts consist of a petiole plus a pair of adnate stipules, and that the adnate condition is primitive. Probably the tepals have the same morphological origin as the bracts, but it is to be noted that in no case is there any transition between bracts and tepals. The stamens and carpels, like the bracts and foliage leaves, are always spirally arranged; but the tepals, at least as regards the outer whorls, are always strictly cyclic. Usually there are three or more whorls of tepals, but in *Kmeria* and some species of *Michelia* there are only two. In some species of *Magnolia* and *Michelia* the outer whorl of the perianth is much reduced in size and calyx-like; this is well seen in *Magnolia quinquepeta*.

Prolongation of the anther-connective into an appendage, often short but sometimes very long, occurs in most *Magnoliaceae* and is very marked, for example, in *Aromadendron*.

The basic type of gynoecium (sessile, with numerous free carpels) has undergone modification in some genera. In *Alcimandra* and *Michelia*, as well as in some species of *Magnolia*, the gynoecium is stipitate. Sometimes the number of carpels is much reduced, the extreme being reached in some species of *Michelia* (e.g. *M. montana*) where the flowers occasionally have only one carpel; in *Pachylarnax* there are 2–8. Concrescence of the carpels occurs in several genera. This may result in a fleshy syncarp (as in *Aromadendron*) or in a woody loculicidal capsule (*Pachylarnax*), but in *Talauma* the fruiting carpels are circumscissile, the upper portions falling away and leaving the persistent concrescent basal portions with their suspended seeds. When the fruit is apocarpous the carpels usually dehisce primarily along the dorsal suture (as in *Magnolia*), but in *Kmeria* the dehiscence is primarily along the ventral suture, while in *Liriodendron* the carpels are samaroid and do not dehisce at all. It is characteristic of all Magnoliaceous seeds (except those of *Liriodendron*) that the outer testa is fleshy and arilloid, and that when the fruiting carpels are dehiscent the seeds hang suspended on silky thread-like funicles.

Kmeria is exceptional in the family in having unisexual flowers, but is clearly a close ally of *Magnolia*, which it resembles in having terminal flowers and biovulate carpels.

Liriodendron, on the other hand, occupies an isolated position and is well worthy of tribal rank as *Liriodendreae*. The distinctive characters of its fruits and seeds have already been mentioned. In addition it has extrorse anthers, whilst the highly characteristic lobing of the leaves is well known to all botanists.

Geographical Distribution. The *Magnoliaceae* have a markedly discontinuous distribution and they once occupied a much larger area of the earth's surface, fossil remains being well marked and widely distributed. These are found in tertiary deposits in the Arctic Circle, Greenland, Europe, and the central plains of North America. The advent of the ice ages probably destroyed the greater part of the family, those now remaining occurring in SE. North America, the West Indies, Central America to E. Brazil, and in SE. Asia. The family contains no austral elements, though in Brazil and the Malay Archipelago it extends via mountain-ranges and plateaux into the southern hemisphere. Its greatest concentration of species is in SE. Asia, in the region extending from the E. Himalayas eastwards to China and southwards to Java.

The genera *Magnolia, Talauma,* and *Liriodendron* all have discontinuous distributions which more or less epitomize that of the family as a whole. *Magnolia,* the largest genus of the family, is both temperate and tropical. *Talauma,* another large genus, is essentially tropical and extends farther south than any of the others. *Liriodendron,* on the other hand, is an essentially temperate genus with only two species, one of which has a considerable range in SE. North America while the other has a more restricted range in S. China and adjacent Tongking; the two are very closely related. *Manglietia* and *Michelia,* two of the larger genera, are distributed on the mainland and islands of SE. Asia but have not been found in America. *Elmerrillia* replaces the closely allied *Michelia* in the south-eastern islands of the Malay Archipelago. *Aromadendron,* a small genus, is entirely Malayan, while farther to the north in SE. Asia occur three other small genera, *Alcimandra, Pachylarnax,* and *Kmeria.* It is noteworthy that no genus is endemic to America.

KEY TO TRIBES

Anthers introrse or latrorse; fruiting carpels longitudinally dehiscent or circumscissile, or if indehiscent then forming a syncarp, never samaroid; testa free from the endocarp, externally arilloid; leaves entire or occasionally 2-lobed at the apex   1. MAGNOLIEAE

Anthers extrorse; fruiting carpels indehiscent, samaroid (produced at the apex into a long wing-like beak), deciduous; testa adherent to the endocarp; leaves 2–10-lobed, the apex truncate or widely emarginate; stipules free from the petiole   2. LIRIODENDREAE

Tribe 1. MAGNOLIEAE

Flowers terminal:

Flowers bisexual (rarely abnormally female by tepalody of the stamens); tepals 9 or more, the outer whorl sometimes much reduced in size or texture; fruiting carpels either dorsally dehiscent, circumscissile, or indehiscent:

Fruit not capsular, the carpels usually numerous:

Fruiting carpels dehiscent, not fleshy:

Gynoecium sessile or shortly stipitate, more or less exserted from the androecium:

Carpels free, in fruit dehiscent along the dorsal suture:

Ovules 4 or more in each carpel   1. **Manglietia**

Ovules 2 in each carpel (rarely 3–4 in the lower carpels)   2. **Magnolia**

Carpels concrescent at least at the base, in fruit circumscissile and woody, the upper portions falling away either singly or in irregular masses, the lower portions persistent with the suspended seeds; stipules adnate to the petiole   3. **Talauma**

Gynoecium stipitate, not exserted from the androecium; tepals 9, subequal; carpels 2–5-ovulate, in fruit dehiscent along the dorsal suture; stipules free from the petiole   4. **Alcimandra**

Fruiting carpels indehiscent, concrescent to form a fleshy syncarp; tepals 18 or more, subequal; connective-appendage very long, subequalling or longer than the anther-loculi; ovules 2 in each carpel; stipules free from the petiole   5. **Aromadendron**

Fruit a woody loculicidal capsule composed of few (2–8) concrescent carpels; tepals 9–15, subequal; ovules about 4–8 in each carpel; stipules free from the petiole   6. **Pachylarnax**

Flowers unisexual; tepals 6–7, subequal; fruiting carpels woody, dehiscent completely along the ventral suture and partly along the dorsal suture, thus finally becoming bifid; ovules 2 in each carpel; stipules adnate to the petiole   7. **Kmeria**

Flowers axillary:

Gynoecium sessile; anthers introrse; stipules free from the petiole

     8. **Elmerrillia**

Gynoecium stipitate; anthers latrorse or sublatrorse; stipules adnate to or free from the petiole   9. **Michelia**

Tribe 2. LIRIODENDREAE

Single genus   10. **Liriodendron**

Since the above key was prepared for my *Families of Flowering Plants*, Mr. Dandy has recognized as distinct genera *Paramichelia* Hu and *Tsoongiodendron* Chun, both allied to *Michelia*; descriptions of these are given on page 56, numbered 9a and 9b respectively. J. H.

Tribe 1. MAGNOLIEAE

1. **Manglietia** Blume, Verh. Bat. Genootsch. 9: 149 (1823). *Paramanglietia* Hu & Cheng, Act. Phytotax. Sin. 1:1 (1951), 25 spp., tropical and subtropical Asia from E. Himalayas to S. China and Malay Archipelago; type *M. glauca* Blume, Malay Peninsula and Archipelago. BH. 1: 19.

Trees; stipules more or less adnate to the petiole; flowers terminal solitary, bisexual; tepals 9–13, 3-merous, subequal; anthers dehiscing introrsely, the connective produced into a short or elongated appendage; gynoecium sessile; carpels numerous, free; ovules 4 or more; fruiting carpels dehiscing along the dorsal suture; seeds 1 or more in each carpel.

2. **Magnolia**[1] Linn., Sp. Pl. 535 (1753); Gen. Pl. ed. 5: 240 (1754). *Parakmeria* Hu & Cheng, Act. Phytotax. Sin. 1:1 (1951). 80 spp., temperate from tropical Asia from E. Himalayas to China, Manchuria, Japan, Formosa, and Malay Archipelago, also SE. North America, Central America, and Greater Antilles; type *M. virginiana* Linn., E. United States. B.H. 1: 18; E.P. 3, 2: 16.

Trees or shrubs; leaves often deciduous; stipules adnate to or free from the petiole; flowers terminal, solitary, bisexual, sometimes precocious and strikingly conspicuous; tepals 9–21, 3–5-merous, subequal or more rarely the outer whorl much smaller and calyx-like; anthers dehiscing introrsely or laterally, the connective produced into an appendage or rarely unappendaged; gynoecium sessile or sometimes shortly stipitate; carpels numerous or few, free; ovules 2 (rarely 3–4 in the lower carpels); fruiting carpels dehiscing along the dorsal suture; seeds 1–2 in each carpel.

3. **Talauma** Juss., Gen. 281 (1789). *Blumia* Nees (1825) non *Blumea* DC. *Santanderia* Cespedes ex Triana & Planch. (1862), *nom. synon. Violaria* Post & O. Ktze. (1903). *Svenhedinia* Urb. (1927). 40 spp., tropical and subtropical Asia from E. Himalayas to Indo-China and Malay Archipelago, also tropical America from S. Mexico and West Indies to E. Brazil; type *T. dodecapetala* (Lam.) Urb., Lesser Antilles. B.H. 1: 18; E.P. 3, 2: 16.

Trees or shrubs; stipules adnate to the petiole; flowers terminal, solitary, bisexual; tepals 9–15, 3–4-merous, subequal; anthers dehiscing introrsely, the connective produced into a short appendage; gynoecium sessile; carpels numerous or few, concrescent at least at the base; ovules 2; fruiting carpels woody, circumscissile, the upper portions falling away either singly or in irregular masses, the lower portions persistent with the suspended seeds; seeds 1–2 in each carpel.

4. **Alcimandra** Dandy, Kew Bull. 1927: 260. 1 sp., *A. cathcartii* (Hook. f. & Thoms.) Dandy, E. Himalayas to Tongking.

Trees; stipules free from the petiole; flowers terminal, solitary, bisexual; tepals 9, 3-merous, subequal; anthers much elongated, dehiscing introrsely, the connective produced into a short linguiform appendage; gynoecium stipitate, not exserted from the androecium; carpels numerous, free; ovules 2–5; fruiting carpels dehiscing along the dorsal suture; seeds 1–4 in each carpel.

5. **Aromadendron** Blume, Bijdr. 10 (1825). 2 spp., Malaya; type *A. elegans* Blume, Java, Sumatra, Malay Peninsula; *A. nutans* Dandy, Sarawak.

Trees; stipules free from the petiole; flowers terminal, solitary, bisexual (sometimes abnormally female by tepalody of the stamens); tepals 18 or more, 3–5-merous, subequal; anthers dehiscing introrsely, the connective produced into a very long setaceous appendage subequalling or longer than the loculi; gynoecium sessile; carpels numerous, concrescent; ovules 2; fruiting carpels indehiscent, forming a fleshy syncarp; seeds 1–2 in each carpel.

6. **Pachylarnax** Dandy, Kew Bull. 1927: 260. 2 spp., Assam to Indo-China and Malay Peninsula, Sumatra; type *P. praecalva* Dandy, Penang and Annam, Sumatra; *P. pleiocarpa* Dandy, Assam.

Trees; stipules free from the petiole; flowers terminal, solitary, bisexual; tepals 9–15, 3–5-merous, subequal; anthers dehiscing introrsely, the connective produced into a short

---

[1] Synonyms of Magnolia: *Lassonia* Buchoz (1779). *Burtinia* Buc'hoz (1785), *nom. nud. Gwillimia* Rottl. ex Sims (1806), *nom. synon. Sphenocarpus* Wall. (1832), *nom. nud. Yulania* Spach (1839). *Tulipastrum* Spach (1839). *Lirianthe* Spach (1839). *Buergeria* Sieb. & Zucc. (1846). *Kobus* Nieuwl. (1914). *Micheliopsis* Keng. (1955).

appendage; gynoecium sessile; carpels few (2–8), concrescent; ovules about 4–8; fruit a woody loculicidal capsule, the carpels dehiscing along the dorsal suture and sometimes separating towards the apex; seeds up to about 6 in each carpel.

7. **Kmeria** (Pierre) Dandy, Kew Bull. 1927: 262. *Magnolia* subgen. *Kmeria* Pierre (1879). 2 spp., S. China to Indo-China; type *K. duperreana* (Pierre) Dandy, Cambodia and adjacent Thailand; *K. septentrionalis* Dandy, Kwangsi.

Trees; stipules adnate to the petiole; flowers terminal, solitary, unisexual; tepals 6–7, 3-merous, subequal; anthers dehiscing introrsely, the connective produced into a short or moderately elongated appendage; gynoecium sessile; carpels comparatively few, concrescent; ovules 2; fruiting carpels woody, separating on dehiscence, dehiscing completely along the ventral suture and partly along the dorsal suture, thus finally becoming bifid; seeds 1–2 in each carpel.

8. **Elmerrillia** Dandy, Kew Bull. 1927: 261. 7 spp., Malay Archipelago from SE. Borneo to S. Philippines and New Guinea; type *E. papuana* (Schltr.) Dandy, New Guinea.

Trees; stipules free from the petiole; flowers axillary, solitary or sometimes 2–3-nate, bisexual; tepals 9–15, 3–5-merous, subequal; anthers dehiscing introrsely, the connective produced into a short appendage; gynoecium sessile; carpels numerous, free or concrescent; ovules 2 or more; fruiting carpels either free and dehiscing along the dorsal suture, or concrescent to form a fleshy syncarp; seeds 1 or more in each carpel.

9. **Michelia** Linn., Sp. Pl. 536 (1753); Gen. Pl. ed. 5: 240 (1754). *Champaca* Adans. (1763). *Liriopsis* Spach (1839) non Reichb. *Sampacca* O. Ktze. (1891). *Paramichelia* Hu (1940). 45 spp., tropical and subtropical Asia from India to China, S. Japan, Formosa, and Malay Archipelago; type *M. champaca* Linn., India to Indo-China, widely cultivated in the tropics (especially SE. Asia) for its wood and highly fragrant flowers. B.H. 1: 19; E.P. 3, 2: 17.

Trees or shrubs; stipules adnate to or free from the petiole; flowers axillary, solitary, bisexual; tepals 6–21, 3–6-merous, subequal or rarely the outer whorl much smaller; anthers dehiscing laterally or sublaterally, the connective produced into an appendage or more rarely unappendaged; gynoecium stipitate; carpels numerous or few (occasionally only 1), free or sometimes concrescent; ovules 2 or more; fruiting carpels either free (laxly spaced) and dehiscing along the dorsal suture; seeds 1 or more in each carpel.

9a. **Paramichelia** Hu, Sunyatsenia 4: 142 (1940). 3 spp., Assam to S.W. China, Malay Peninsula, and Sumatra; type *P. baillonii* (Pierre) Hu, Assam to SW. China and Indo-China.

Trees; stipules adnate to the petiole; flowers axillary, solitary, bisexual; tepals 12–18, 4–6-merous, subequal; anthers latrorse or sublatrorse, connective produced into a short or elongated appendage; gynoecium stipitate; carpels numerous or fairly numerous, concrescent; ovules 2–6; carpels of the mature fruit indehiscent or tardily irregularly dehiscent, forming a fleshy syncarp, midribs often woody, hooked, and persistent.

9b. **Tsoongiodendron** Chun, Act. Phytotax. Sin. 8: 281 (1963). 1 sp., *T. odorum* Chun, S. China, N. Indo-China.

Tree; stipules adnate to the petiole; flowers axillary, solitary, bisexual; tepals 9, 3-merous, subequal; anthers latrorse or sublatrorse, connective produced into a short appendage; gynoecium stipitate; carpels fairly numerous, concrescent; ovules numerous; fruit large, with woody mature carpels with circumscissile dehiscence, terminal parts deciduous in an irregular mass, basal parts persistent with pendulous seeds.

Both these additional genera differ from *Michelia* in the concrescent carpels forming a syncarpous fruit. They differ from each other in the form of the fruit and in the number and arrangement of the tepals.—J. E. DANDY.

Tribe 2. LIRIODENDREAE

10. **Liriodendron** Linn., Sp. Pl. 535 (1753); Gen. Pl. ed. 5: 239 (1754). *Tulipifera* Mill. (1754). 2 spp., SE. Asia and SE. North America; type *L. tulipifera* Linn., S. Ontario and E. United States; *L. chinense* (Hemsl.) Sarg., S. China and Tongking. B.H. 1: 19; E.P. 3, 2: 17.

Trees; leaves deciduous; stipules free from the petiole; leaf-lamina 2–10- (usually 4–6-) lobed, the apex truncate or widely emarginate; flowers terminal, solitary, bisexual; tepals 9–17, 3-merous, subequal; anthers dehiscing extrorsely, the connective produced into a short appendage; gynoecium sessile; carpels very numerous, free, the lowermost sterile; ovules 2; fruiting carpels woody, samaroid (produced at the apex into a long wing-like beak), indehiscent, deciduous; seeds 1–2 in each carpel.

2. ILLICIACEAE

Hu, Bull. Chin. Bot. Soc. 1: 86 (1935)

Shrubs or small trees. Leaves alternate, simple, sometimes clustered or sub-verticillate, entire, pinnately nerved; stipules absent. Flowers bisexual, solitary, axillary or supra-axillary, rarely lateral and below the leaves or on the trunk; pedicels bracteate. Sepals and petals numerous to 7, free, imbricate, usually several-seriate, the outermost often small and bracteole-like, inner gradually larger, becoming ligulate and thin to fleshy and ovate to suborbicular, the innermost often reduced. Stamens numerous to 4, several to 1-seriate, connective sometimes glandular, loculi introrsely lateral, dehiscing lengthwise. Carpels 21–5, free, in a single whorl, mostly closely appressed laterally, erect or somewhat spreading, narrowed into a slender or stout style stigmatic on the ventral side; ovule 1, attached ventrally near the base. Fruits follicular, dehiscing ventrally. Seeds glossy, with copious endosperm and minute embryo.

CLASSIFICATION. A. C. Smith, The families *Illiciaceae* and *Schisandraceae*, Sargentia, 7: 1 (1947); Lawrence, Taxon. Vasc. Pl. 505, fig. 141 (1951); Hutch., Fam. Fl. Pl. ed. 2, 1: 125, fig. 2 (1959).

ADDITIONAL LITERATURE. I. W. Bailey & C. G. Nast, Morph. and relationships of *Illicium, Schisandra,* and *Kadsura,* Journ. Arn. Arb. 29: 77 (1948); Hoh, Star Anise tree in Kwangsi, Sunyatsenia, 4: 272 (1940).

ANATOMY. Stomata are confined to the lower surface of the leaves, the surrounding cells not very clearly differentiated from the remainder. See Metcalfe & Chalk, Anat. Dicots. 1: 23, where *Illicium* is included in the *Schisandraceae.* POLLEN. Erdt. 254.

Economic Properties. Chinese Star Anise, the fruits and seeds of a small evergreen tree of S. China, *Illicium verum* Hk. f., are aromatic with a flavour similar to Anise (*Pimpinella anisum* Linn., *Apiaceae*); oil from both used as a flavouring agent and carminative. The Japanese Star Anise is *Illicium anisatum* Linn., the oil of the fruits of which has an odour and taste of bay leaves and is poisonous. Bastard Star Anise is derived from *I. religiosum* Sieb. & Zucc., E. Asia.

The single genus *Illicium*, formerly placed in the *Magnoliaceae*, has an interesting distribution closely resembling that of *Magnolia* and *Liriodendron*, but more subtropical. It is a natural genus of very closely allied species and must be of great age phylogenetically. It is confined to the Northern Hemisphere, from Assam to Japan and Korea and south to Borneo in the Old World, and in America it occurs in Florida, Mexico, and the West Indies.

Illicium Linn., Syst. Nat. ed. 10: 1050 (1759). *Badianifera* Linn. ex O. Ktze., Rev. Gen. Pl. 1: 6 (1891). *Skimmi* Kaempf. ex Adans., Fam. Fl. Pl. 2: 364 (1763). About 42 spp., E. Asia, Malaya, SE. North America, Mexico, West Indies; type *I. anisatum* Linn., Japan, Korea. B.H. 1: 17 (in *Magnoliaceae*). *Characters of the family.*

3. WINTERACEAE[1]

Lindl., Introd. Nat. Syst. ed. 2: 17 (1836)

Trees and shrubs with aromatic alternate or rarely subverticillate exstipulate pellucid-punctate evergreen leaves. Flowers rather small, bisexual, dioecious or polygamo-dioecious, in axillary or terminal fascicles or umbellate cymes, of various colours; floral axis very short, with the parts arranged more or less in whorls. Sepals 6–2, valvate. Petals in several to 2-series, imbricate, often conspicuous in bud. Stamens several, in several to 1-series, hypogynous; anthers introrse. Carpels in a single whorl or rarely subbiseriate, many to one, free or united, many to 1-ovuled; stigma sessile and long or on a distinct style. Fruits capsular, follicular, or baccate. Seeds with copious endosperm; embryo minute, very rarely medium-sized. Type genus *Drimys* Forst. (*Wintera* Murr., illeg. name).

Genera 8; species about 70.

DISTRIBUTION. Malay Archip., New Guinea, E. Australia, New Caledonia, New Zealand, Lord Howe's Island, Fiji, Cent. and South America.

CLASSIFICATION. Lindl., Nat. Syst. Bot. 26 (1830); ed. 2: 17 (1836); Veg. Kingd. 417 (1846) (in *Magnoliaceae*); Miers, On the *Winteraceae*, Ann. & Mag. Nat. Hist. ser. 3, 2: 33, 109 (1858), and Contrib. to Bot. 1: 123, pls. 25–27 (1851–61); Endlicher, Gen. Pl. 836 (1836) (in *Magnoliaceae*); Eichler, Mart. Fl. Bras. 13, 1: 129, tt. 30–32 (1841); Benth. & Hook. f., Gen. Pl. 1: 17 (in *Magnoliaceae*); Prantl, Engl. & Prantl, Nat. Pflanzenfam. 3, 2: 18, fig. 17 (1891); Nachtr. 2: 108 (1906) (in *Magnoliaceae*); Parmentier, Histoire des Magnoliacées (Tribe Illiciées), Bull. Sci. Fr. et Belg. 27: 159 (1895); van Tieghem, Journ. de Bot. 14: 275 et seq. (1906); Hutch., The family *Winteraceae*, Kew Bull. 1921: 185; Dandy, The *Winteraceae* of New Zealand, Journ. Bot. 1933: 119; Bailey & A. C. Smith, *Degeneriaceae*, A new family of flowering plants from Fiji, Journ. Arn. Arb. 23: 356–65, pls. i–v (1942); A. C. Smith, Taxonomic notes on the Old World species of *Winteraceae*, Journ. Arn. Arb. 24: 119 (1943); I. W. Bailey & C. G. Nast, Comparative morphology of *Winteraceae*: 1, Pollen and stamens, Journ. Arn. Arb. 24: 340, tt. 1–3 (1943); 2, Carpels, loc. cit. 472, tt. 1–6 (1943); Lawrence, Taxon. Vasc. Pl. 506 (family mentioned); Hutch., Fam. Fl. Pl. ed. 2, 1: 126, fig. 3

---

[1] Not to be confused with *Winteranaceae*, another name for the *Canellaceae*.

(1959); Tucker, Ontogeny of the inflorescence in *Drimys winteri* var. *chilensis*, Univ. Calif. Publ. Bot. 30: 257 (1959).

ANATOMY. Sol. 27 (in *Magnoliaceae*); M.C. 1: 25. POLLEN. Erdt. 258.

ADDITIONAL LITERATURE. J. Miers & van Tieghem (above); J. Tambon, Des Illicium en général de la Badiane et de son huille essentielle en particulier, pp. 77, pls. 1–4 (Montpellier 1886); Thompson & Bailey, Are *Tetracentron*, *Trochodendron*, and *Drimys* specialized or primitive types?, Mem. N. York Bot. Gard. 6: 27 (1916); T. W. Whitaker, Chromosome number and relationship in the *Magnoliales*, Journ. Arn. Arb. 14: 376, figs. 1–4, t. 80 (1933); A. C. Smith, Geographical distribution of the *Winteraceae*, Journ. Arn. Arb. 26: 48 (1945); A. C. Smith, *Illiciaceae* and *Schisandraceae*, Sargentia, 7: 1–224 (1947).

Characters occurring in few Genera and Species. **Leaves** subverticillate (in threes) in *Drimys rosea* Ridl. (New Guinea). **Inflorescence** a single terminal sessile flower in *Zygogynum vieillardii*, Baill. (New Caledonia); of three simple terminal pedicels in *Exospermum* and *Zygogynum* spp.; of several pedicels in *Drimys* spp.; a terminal cluster of cymes in *Bubbia* and *Drimys* spp.; pedicels narrowly winged in *Drimys parviflora* Ridl. **Calyx** completely closed in bud in *Drimys*. **Carpels** united in tribe *Exospermeae*; reduced to one in *Drimys dipetala* F. Muell., *Degeneria* Bailey & A. C. Smith, and *Zygogynum pomiferum* Baill.

Economic Properties. 'Winter's Bark', *Drimys winteri* Forst., South America; much used in Brazil as an astringent and stimulant. Captain Winter, from whom it takes its name, commanded the *Elizabeth* under Sir Francis Drake, and he used the bark 'as a spice and medicine for scurvy'. *Pseudowintera axillaris* (Forst.) Dandy is aromatic and pungent and its wood serviceable for inlaying (Cheeseman, Fl. N. Zeal. 29—as *Wintera axillaris*).

Phylogeny and Morphology. The family *Winteraceae*, as here understood, has usually been regarded as a tribe of *Magnoliaceae*, and it stands as such in the classifications of Bentham and Hooker (Gen. Pl. 1: 17), and Engler and Prantl (Die nat. Pflanzenfam. 3, 2: 18). In a short paper in the Kew Bull. 1921: 185–90, the present writer gave reasons for separating the group from the true *Magnoliaceae*, represented at that time by the genera *Michelia* Linn., *Manglietia* Bl., *Talauma* Juss., *Aromadendron* Blume, *Magnolia* Linn., and *Lioriodendron* Linn. This segregation had become more imperative since the *Trochodendraceae* and *Himantandraceae* had been taken out of *Magnoliaceae*, and some degree of uniformity of treatment was necessary.

Robert Brown[1] was the first to point out that the genera *Illicium* and *Drimys* should be distinguished as a separate family from *Magnoliaceae*, and for them he proposed the name *Wintereae*. Lindley, for a time, and J. Miers took a similar view, as did also Endlicher, who expressed the opinion (Enchir. Bot. 428) that the group ought to rank as an independent family, although later (Gen. Pl. 836), he included them as a subfamily of *Magnoliaceae*. Even J. D. Hooker and T. Thomson (Fl. Ind. 72), said that 'the *Wintereae* form a very questionable tribe of *Magnoliaceae*, and may with reason be

[1] R.Br. apud DC. Syst. Veg. 1: 548 (1818); de Candolle, however, treated them as a tribe, *Illiceae* of *Magnoliaceae*.

separated from them'. Bentham and Hooker, however, as already indicated, included them in the *Magnoliaceae*.

Although *Winteraceae* are clearly related to the *Magnoliaceae* and may have had a similar origin, they are considerably more advanced from an evolutionary point of view, and they are very definitely distinguished from them by the following characters: (1) absence of stipules; (2) secretory cells filled with resin or ethereal oil in the leaves, appearing as transparent dots; (3) very short and small floral axis; (4) relatively few stamens with small divergent anther-loculi; (5) few carpels in a single whorl (or very rarely in 2 whorls), sometimes reduced to a single carpel; and there are corresponding differences in the fruits.

Our knowledge of the family *Winteraceae* is still far from complete and much more collecting of the Australasian and South American species is desirable. The late Prof. van Tieghem separated two or three small genera from *Drimys*, which are here maintained and which further material and study will probably show to be justified.

Geographical Distribution. *Winteraceae* have, in contrast with the true *Magnoliaceae*, a more tropical and southerly distribution. They are absent from Europe, Africa, Central Asia, and W. North America. The largest and most widely spread genus is *Drimys*, representing, however, a very homogeneous group of species distributed from the Malay Archipelago through E. Australia to Tasmania, and ranging widely in South America, from Costa Rica to Tierra del Fuego, including the island of Juan Fernandez. The distribution of *Drimys*, therefore, seems to point to considerable antiquity, occurring as it does in two widely separated areas in the Southern Hemisphere; and in floral structure it has a slight tendency to unisexuality and reduction so fully carried out in the case of the *Schisandraceae*.

KEY TO TRIBES

Carpels free and remaining so in fruit.   1. DRIMYEAE
Carpels more or less united, especially in fruit, or carpel solitary
                                                                     2. EXOSPERMEAE

Tribe 1. DRIMYEAE

Calyx enclosing the petals in bud and at length rupturing irregularly
                                                                     1. **Drimys**
Calyx exposing the petals in bud, small and more or less cup-like or short and
    dentate:
Flowers solitary and axillary; petals 5–6   2. **Pseudowintera**
Flowers in a terminal cluster of many-flowered cymes or cymules; petals
    10–14:
    Inner series of petals 4–6; stamens with two widely divergent anther-
        loculi not exceeded by the connective   3. **Bubbia**
    Inner petals 10; stamens with linear and parallel contiguous anther-loculi
        exceeded by the connective   4. **Belliolum**

Tribe 2. Exospermeae

Stamens numerous (more than 12): flowers solitary:
Staminodes absent:
   Carpels 8–7, with conspicuous grooves between them in fruit, partially
      united **5. Exospermum**
   Carpels 4–1, closely united, each separated by a very thin wall
      6. Zygogynum
Staminodes present; carpel solitary **7. Degeneria**
Stamens about 12; flowers in a terminal panicle **8. Tetrathalamus**

Tribe 1. Drimyeae

1. **Drimys** J. R. & G. Forst., Char. Gen. 42 (1776). *Wintera* Murr. (1784).
About 20 spp., Malay Archip. to E. Australia, New Caledonia, Cent. and
South America; type *D. winteri* J. R. & G. Forst., South America. *D. con-
fertifolia* Phil., Juan Fernandez. For Amer. spp. see A. C. Smith, Journ. Arn.
Arb. 24: 1 (1943); for Old World spp. also A. C. Smith, loc. cit. 119 (1943).

Trees or shrubs; leaves evergreen, pellucid-punctate; flowers bisexual or sometimes
polygamo-dioecious; calyx closed in bud, bursting irregularly when opening, deciduous;
petals 6 or more, imbricate; stamens with rather thick filaments, anther-loculi lateral, parallel or divergent; carpels free, berry-like in fruit; stigmas sessile; seed with shining testa.

2. **Pseudowintera** Dandy, Journ. Bot. 1933: 121. *Wintera* Forst. f. ex Van
Tiegh. (1900), not Murr. (1784). 2–3 spp., New Zealand; type *P. axillaris*
(Forst.) Dandy, N. Isl.; *P. colorata* (Raoul) Dandy, N. Isl. *P. traversii* (Buch.)
Dandy, S. Isl. Cheesman, Fl. New Zeal. 29 (as *Drimys*); A. C. Smith, Journ.
Arn. Arb. 24: 153 (1943).

Small trees or shrubs; leaves alternate, pellucid-punctate; flowers axillary, fasciculate,
paired or solitary; calyx cup-shaped, margin shortly and irregularly dentate or lobate or
entire; petals 6–5, spreading; stamens 15–5; anther-loculi divergent; carpels 5–1, free;
ovules few; fruit berry-like.

3. **Bubbia** Van Tiegh., Journ. de Bot. 14: 278, 293 (1900). About 30 spp.,
some very imperfectly known, New Guinea, E. Australia, New Caledonia,
2 in Lord Howe Isl.; type *B. howeana* (F. Muell.) Van Tiegh., Lord Howe Isl.
Burtt, Ic. Pl. t. 3315 (1936); A. C. Smith, Journ. Arn. Arb. 23: 426 (1942); 24:
141 (1943).

Trees or shrubs; leaves entire, with pinnate nervation; flowers bisexual, in a terminal
cluster of many-flowered cymes; sepals 4, short, outer 2 reflexed, inner 2 erect, persistent;
outer petals 4, biseriate, very hard, larger, inner 6, 1-seriate, imbricate in bud; stamens 25–28,
2–3-seriate, outer shorter than the inner, anther-loculi widely divergent; carpels 4, free;
stigma sessile, linear, radiate; ovules numerous, 2-seriate, horizontally disposed; berries
4 or fewer, calyx persistent; seeds with oily endosperm and small embryo.

4. **Belliolum** Van Tiegh., Journ. de Bot. 14: 278, 330 (1900). 8 spp. New
Caledonia, Solomon Isls.; type *B. pancheri* (Baill.) Van Tiegh., New
Caledonia. A. C. Smith, Journ. Arn. Arb. 23: 437 (1942).

Trees; leaves alternate, oblanceolate to narrowly obovate, entire, pinnately nerved;
flowers bisexual, in a terminal cluster of pedunculate cymules of 1–3 flowers; sepals 3–4;
petals several, the 10 innermost free, fleshy; stamens numerous with linear and parallel
anther-loculi exceeded by the connective; carpels 1 or few, free, with numerous ovules on
the inner angle; fruits obovoid; seeds 10 or more (few by abortion), with oily endosperm
and small embryo.

Tribe 2. Exospermeae

5. **Exospermum** Van Tiegh., Journ. de Bot. 14: 279, 333 (1900). 2 spp., New Caledonia; type *E. stipitatum* (Baill.) Van Tiegh. A. C. Smith, Journ. Arn. Arb. 24: 159 (1943).

Leaves deciduous, alternate, oblong-oblanceolate, pinnately nerved; flowers terminal, solitary, long-pedicellate, pedicels triangular, gradually thickened upwards; calyx saucer-shaped, undulate; petals coriaceous, closely imbricate in bud; stamens numerous; anthers short, loculi divergent; carpels 8–7, loosely connate in fruit, subglobose, stigmas free, linear, sessile.

6. **Zygogynum** Baill. Adans. 7: 298, t. 4 (1867). 6 spp., New Caledonia; type *Z. vieillardii* Baill. A. C. Smith, Journ. Arn. Arb. 24: 162 (1943).

Trees; leaves evergreen, entire; flowers solitary, terminal, pedicels thick; calyx small, obscurely sinuate; petals 5–4, imbricate; stamens numerous, 5–4-seriate, anthers extrorse, opening laterally; carpels connate and 1-locular; styles short, free, depressed-capitate; fruiting carpels connate.

7. **Degeneria**[1] Bailey & A. C. Smith, Journ. Arn. Arb. 23: 357, tt. i–v (1942). 1 sp., *D. vitiensis* Bailey & A. C. Smith, Fiji Isls.; A. C. Smith, loc. cit. 30: 1 (1949); Swamy, Morphology of *Degeneriaceae*, Journ. Arn. Arb. 30: 10 (1949).

Trees; leaves alternate, pinnately nerved; flowers solitary, subaxillary, bisexual; sepals and petals dissimilar; sepals 3, much smaller than the petals; petals 13–12, 3–4-seriate, fleshy, imbricate; torus coriaceous, subglobose or convex; stamens several, fleshy, flattened, loculi 4, parallel in pairs, extrorse, opening by slits lengthwise; staminodes among the stamens and fewer than they, similar in structure; carpel 1, unequally ellipsoid, ventral part spreadingly stigmatose; loculus 1, ovules numerous, 2-seriate, placentas 2 parallel with the ventral suture; fruit indehiscent; seeds numerous, 2-seriate, alternately sessile and suspended on a filiform funicle.

8. **Tetrathalamus** Lauterbach in Lauterbach & K. Schum., Nachtr. Fl. Deutsch. Schutzegeb. Südsee 319 (1905) (in that work placed in *Guttiferae*). 1 sp., *T. montanus* Lauterbach, New Guinea. Burtt, Kew Bull. 1938: 458.

Shrub; branches terete; leaves petiolate, oblong, entire, with close oblique nerves arcuate and looped near the margin; panicle terminal, oliganthous, flowers pedicellate; bracteoles 3, triangular; sepals 4, imbricate, at length reflexed; petals 4, smaller than the sepals, spreading; stamens about 12, truncate, almost free, inserted above a fleshy disk; filaments thick, short; ovary sessile above the disk, 4-locular; ovule in each loculus attached to the inner angle; stigmas 4, sessile, minute.

4. CANELLACEAE

Martius, Nov. Gen. et Sp. 3: 170 (1829) (*Winteranaceae*[2])

Glabrous aromatic trees. Leaves alternate, exstipulate, entire, penninerved, marked with pellucid dots. Flowers cymose, axillary or terminal, bisexual, actinomorphic; bracts 3, orbicular, much imbricate, persistent. Sepals 5–3, free, thick, deciduous, imbricate, the innermost narrower. Petals the same number as the sepals or more, thin, imbricate. Stamens hypogynous, 20–5, the filaments united into a tube produced above the anthers; anthers

---

[1] Proposed by its authors as the type of a new family *Degeneriaceae*. I consider it to be closely related to *Exospermum* and *Zygogynum*, but hardly separable as a family.

[2] Not to be confused with *Winteraceae*.

sometimes linear, opening lengthwise; disk absent. Ovary free, 1-locular, with 2–6 parietal placentas, and 2 or more ovules on each placenta; style short, thick, or stigmas free, 2–5; ovules ascending or horizontal, anatropous. Fruit a berry; seeds 2 to many; testa crustaceous, shining; embryo short or curved within the oily or fleshy endosperm; radicle short, near the hilum; cotyledons oblong.—Type genus *Canella* P. Browne.

Genera 5; species 9.

DISTRIBUTION. Tropical and subtropical E. Africa, Madagascar, Florida to E. tropical South America and West Indies.

CLASSIFICATION. Bentham & Hooker f., Gen. Plant. 1. 121 (1862); O. Warburg, Engl. & Prantl, Nat. Pflanzenfam. 3, 6: 314 (1893); Miers, Ann. Nat. Hist. ser. 3, 1: 348; Contrib. to Bot. 1: 112 (1851); Baillon, Sur une canellacée de l'ancien continent, Adansonia, 7: 217–20, t. 5 (1867); Gilg, Engl. & Prantl, loc. cit. ed. 2, 21: 327 (1925); Occhioni, Contrib. ao estudo da fam. *Canellaceae*, Arch. Jard. Bot. Rio de Janeiro, 8: 3, figs. 1–70 (1948); Lawrence, Taxon. Vasc. Pl. 611, fig. 220 (1951); Verdcourt, Kew Bull. 1954: 541; Melchior & Schultze-Motel, E. P. ed. 2, 7a, 2: 221 (1959); T. K. Wilson, Synop. of genera and wood anatomy, Trop. Woods, 112: 1 (1960).

ANATOMY. Sol. 1: 86; M.C. 1: 109. POLLEN. Erdt. 94.

Economic Properties. Canella Bark (Wild Cinnamon bark, Cortex Canellae) is obtained from *Canella winterana* (Linn.) Gaertn. (*Canella alba* Murr.), a native of Florida and the West Indies. The bark was formerly confused with that of *Drimys winteri*, the true Winter's Bark. *Canella Bark* is used by the negroes as a condiment, and possesses aromatic, stimulant, and tonic properties. It contains about 1 per cent. of volatile oil with a pungent aromatic taste (see Greenish, Mat. Med. 274). According to Dawe (Herb. Kew.), *Warburgia ugandensis* Sprague is a most important timber tree in Uganda, the bark being used as a purgative, and the resin for fixing tools in handles. In the Transvaal the bark of *W. breyeri* Pott has been used by the natives as a remedy for low fever. The scented wood, Santal Vert, *Cinnamosma fragrans* Baill., is exported from Madagascar to E. Africa and thence to India and used in religious ceremonies. Bark of Red Canella or Mountain Cinnamon, *Cinnamodendron corticosum* Miers, is aromatic and was formerly used as a substitute for Winter's Bark.

Phylogeny and Morphology. Canellaceae is a small family considered by J. Miers[1] to be allied to the *Winteraceae*. Although having several characters in common with that family they differ particularly in their cymose inflorescences, united stamens, and the solitary unilocular ovary with 2–6 parietal placentas showing the union of as many carpels. A solitary ovary sometimes occurs in *Winteraceae*, namely in the genera *Zygogynum* and *Degeneria*, but in those it is composed of a single carpel. Furthermore, the sympetalous corolla of the genus *Cinnamosma* seems to point to a closer relationship with the more primitive sympetalous families such as *Ebenaceae*,

---

[1] For an account of the treatment accorded this small family up to 1850 see J. Miers, Ann. Nat. Hist. ser. 3, 1: 342–53 (1858).

of which they may well represent the polypetalous ancestors, and with which they show a decided link. The most advanced character in the flowers is the androecium, the stamens being completely connate into a tube produced above the anther-loculi; the latter are often separate and appear to be unilocular.

Geographical Distribution. Canellaceae are remarkably scattered in their distribution, Florida to central east tropical South America and the West Indies including the Bahamas, tropical and subtropical E. Africa and Madagascar. Regarding their supposed close relationship with the family *Winteraceae* we should note that the latter family is entirely absent from Africa and Madagascar as are also their near relatives the *Magnoliaceae*. The gap between the families is therefore considerable, both from a morphological standpoint, as noted above, and also geographically.

Petals free from one another; stamens 40–10:

Flowers axillary:
    Petals 12, in four series; stamens 12; stigma 6-lobed; leaves with numerous much-branched lateral nerves   **1. Pleodendron**
Petals usually 10, the 5 inner narrower than the 5 outer:
    Ovules 2-seriate on the 2–6 placentas; stamens 40–20

              2. Cinnamodendron
    Ovules 1-seriate on each of the 5 placentas; stamens 10

              3. Warburgia
Flowers in a terminal cyme; stamens 10; petals free from one another

              4. Canella
Petals united into a tube; stamens 7–9; flowers axillary, solitary, subsessile

              5. Cinnamosma

Excluded—*Tardiella* Gagnep., Lecomte Not. Syst. 15: 32 (1954) = *Casearia* (*Flacourtiaceae*).

1. **Pleodendron** Van Tiegh., Journ. de Bot. 13: 271 (1899). 1 sp., *P. macranthum* (Baill.) Van Tiegh., Porto Rico.

Tree; leaves oblong-elliptic, with numerous much-branched nerves; flowers axillary, solitary; sepals 3, shortly connate at the base; petals 12, free, in 4 rows, the outer largest; stamens 12, connate; ovary with 6 placentas; ovules numerous, semi-anatropous; style 6-lobed; fruit not seen.

2. **Cinnamodendron** Endl., Gen. 1029 (1840). *Capsicodendron* Hoehne (1933). 3 spp.; type *C. axillare* (Nees et Mart.) Endl., Brazil; *C. corticosum* Miers, Jamaica; *C. cubense* Urb., Cuba. B.H. 1: 121; E.P. 3, 6: 318; ed. 2, 21: 328; J. Miers, Ann. Nat. Hist. ser. 3, 1: 349.

Shrubs or small trees; leaves elliptic or obovate; flowers arranged in small axillary cymes; bracts and bracteoles very small, soon falling off; sepals 3, coriaceous, connate at the base, persistent; petals 12–8, deciduous; stamens 40–20, connate; anthers linear; ovary with 6–2 placentas; ovules numerous to 2, in 2 to many rows; style 1, short, thick, stigma 4–6-lobed; fruit a berry; seeds several, with shining testa; embryo small, with thick semi-orbicular cotyledons.

3. **Warburgia** Engl., Pflanzenw. Ostafr. C. 276 (1895). 3 spp.; type *W. stuhlmannii* Engl., Tanganyika Territ. *W. ugandensis* Sprague, Uganda, Kenya. *W. breyeri* Pott, Transvaal. E.P. 3, 6: 318; ed. 2, 21: 328.

Trees; leaves coriaceous, oblanceolate; flowers arranged in small axillary bracteolate cymes; sepals 3, suborbicular; outer 5 petals twice as long as the sepals, obovate-spathulate, the inner 5 slightly narrower than the outer, spathulate; stamens 10, connate into a cylindric column as long as the petals; anthers linear-oblong; ovary elongated; placentas 5; ovules in 1 row, anatropous; styles connate almost to the top; stigmas 5; fruit ellipsoid, pruinose and plum-like.

4. **Canella** P. Br. Hist. Jamaica 275, t. 27, fig. 3 (1756). *Winterana* Linn. (1759). *Winterania* Linn. (1762). 1 sp., *C. winterana* (Linn.) Gaertn. (*C. alba* Murr.), S. Florida, West Indies, Colombia. B.H. 1: 121; E.P. 3, 6: 317; ed. 2, 21: 326, fig. 145; J. Miers, Ann. Nat. Hist. ser. 3, 1: 346.

Tree, with aromatic bark; leaves oblanceolate, punctate; cymes terminal, subcorymbose, few-flowered; bracts and bracteoles deciduous; sepals 3, imbricate, rounded, persistent; petals 5, thick, imbricate, at length deciduous; stamens 10, connate, tube wavy at the top; anthers linear; ovary with 2 placentas; ovules 2–3 on each placenta; style short, thick, truncate at the apex; berry subglobose, 4–6-seeded; seeds subglobose, shining; embryo small in oily-fleshy endosperm; cotyledons half-orbicular.

5. **Cinnamosma** Baill., Adansonia, 7: 219 (1866–7). 3 spp., Madagascar; type *C. fragrans* Baill. B.H. 1: 970; E.P. 3, 6: 319; ed. 2, 21: 326, figs. 144c, 146E; Danguy, Lecomte, Not. Syst. 1910, 236; P. de la Bathie, Bull. Soc. Bot. Fr. 94: 212 (1947) (revision).

Small trees; flowers axillary, solitary, subsessile; sepals 3; petals 6–4, united high up into a tube with 3–1 inner lobes reflexed after flowering; stamens hypogynous, the filaments and anthers with their connectives united into a tube embracing the gynoecium; anthers 9–7, linear, adnate to the tube on the back, opening by slits lengthwise; ovary with 4–3 placentas; ovules 2 on each placenta, pendulous on a short funicle; style short, conical; berry pulpy inside.

5. SCHISANDRACEAE

Blume, Fl. Jav. Schizandr. 3 (1830); G. Don, Gen. Syst. 1: 101 (1831) *Schizandriaceae*

Climbing or trailing shrubs with often pellucid-punctate, alternate, frequently toothed leaves; stipules absent. Flowers unisexual, small to medium-sized, axillary, solitary; floral axis short, the parts hypogynous. Sepals and petals 9–15, imbricate, the outer more or less sepaloid, the inner gradually petaloid. Stamens numerous, short, partially connate or almost wholly united into a fleshy, globose mass; anthers short, 2-locular, introrse or lateral, opening lengthwise. Carpels numerous, 2–3-ovuled, in fruit either spreading out on the then much elongated axis or crowded into a fleshy mass; stigmas sessile on the inner edge of the carpels. Fruit baccate. Seeds immersed in the fleshy pulp, with a membranous or crustaceous testa; embryo small in copious uniform endosperm. Type genus *Schisandra* Michx.

Genera 2; species about 27.

DISTRIBUTION. Indo-Malaya, China, Japan, and SE. United States.

CLASSIFICATION. Endl., Gen. Pl. 835; Lindl., Veg. Kingd. 305; Benth. & Hook. f., Gen. Pl. 1: 17; Engl. & Prantl, Nat. Pflanzenfam. 3, 2: 12; A. C. Smith, Sargentia, 7: 79 (1947); Lawrence, Taxon. Vasc. Pl. 506, fig. 142 (1951); Hutch., Fam. Fl. Pl. ed. 2, 1: 129, fig. 5 (1959).

ANATOMY. Sol. 1: 27 (in *Magnoliaceae*); M.C. 1: 21 (partly). POLLEN. Erdt. 255.

Economic Properties. The mucilaginous berries of some species are edible, but almost tasteless. A few species are cultivated for their neat attractive flowers and fruits.

Phylogeny and Morphology. The absence of stipules separates this family from *Magnoliaceae*, but otherwise their close affinity is obvious. In their unisexual flowers they are considerably more advanced, this character being rare in *Magnoliaceae*, and the climbing or trailing habit is distinctive, a similar and parallel development having also occurred in the herbaceous phylum, for example the genus *Clematis*, in *Ranunculaceae* and the derived family *Menispermaceae*.

Geographical Distribution. Schisandra shares a similar distribution with some genera of *Magnoliaceae*, i.e. SE. Asia and the SE. United States. There are no species common to the two areas, though some are widely spread in their own particular part of the world. For example *Schisandra axillaris* Miq. ranges from the Khasia Hills in E. India, to Hupeh in Central China, and to Sumatra and Java.

Carpels in fruit scattered or crowded along the much elongated axis
1. **Schisandra**
Carpels in fruit in a globose or ellipsoid head   2. **Kadsura**

1. **Schisandra** Michx., Fl. Bor. Amer. 2: 218, t. 47 (1803) (conserved name). *Schizandra* of authors. *Stellandria* Brickell (1803). *Sphaerostema* Bl. (1825). *Sphaerostemma* Reichb. (1828). *Maximowiczia* Rupr. (1856). *Maximovitzia* Benth. & Hook. f. (1862). *Trochostigma* Auct. 12 spp., SE. Asia and SE. United States; type *S. coccinea* Michx., Atlantic coast from S. Carolina to Florida and Louisiana. B.H. 1: 19; E.P. 3, 2: 18.

Trailing shrubs; leaves thin, pellucid-punctate; sepals and petals together 12–9, gradually increasing in size to the inner petaloid; stamens 15–5, more or less connate into a globose mass; anthers small, loculi introrse or lateral; carpels numerous, 2-ovulate, at first capitate, at length laxly spicate, berry-like when mature; seeds reniform.

2. **Kadsura** Kaempfer ex Juss., Ann. Mus. Paris 16: 340 (1810). *Pulcheria* Nor. (1790). *Cadsura* Spreng. (1825). *Sarcocarpon* Bl. (1825). *Cosbaea* Lem. (1855). *Panslowia* Wight ex Pfeiff. (1874). 15 spp., Indo-Malaya, China, Japan; type *K. japonica* (Linn.) Dunal, Japan, Korea. B.H. 1: 19; E.P. 3, 2: 18.

Climbing shrubs; leaves mostly coriaceous; sepals and petals 15–9, gradually increasing in size to the inner petaloid; stamens numerous, separate or connate into a ball; antherloculi with a broad connective; carpels numerous, capitate, 3–2-ovulate, berry-like when mature and free but crowded into a globose head.

6. HIMANTANDRACEAE

Diels, Engl. Bot. Jahrb. 55: 126 (1917)

Aromatic trees covered with peltate scaly indumentum. Leaves alternate, entire, pinnately nerved; stipules absent. Flowers bisexual, solitary or paired on short axillary branches, at first enclosed by two calyptriform leathery deciduous sepals; inner sepals the one within the other. Petals about 7, lanceolate, very similar in size and shape to the numerous (about 40) stamens which have the anther-loculi separated on each side towards the base, opening lengthwise; staminodes several, subulate. Carpels 10–6, contiguous, free except at the base but soon united; ovule solitary and pendulous from the apex of each carpel, anatropous. Fruit globose, gall-like, fleshy, 10–7-locular by the late coalescence of the carpels. Seed pendulous; endosperm oily, embryo small. Type genus *Himantandra* F. von Muell.

Genus 1; species 3–4.

DISTRIBUTION. Moluccas, New Guinea, NE. Australia.

CLASSIFICATION. I. W. Bailey, Nast & A. C. Smith, The family *Himantandraceae*, Journ. Arn. Arb. 24: 190, tt. 1–6 (anat.) (1943).

ANATOMY. M.C. 1: 36. POLLEN. Erdt. 204.

A small and curious relic with petaloid stamens; remarkable in the Magnolian group in having peltate scaly indumentum, which is also characteristic of a few genera of *Annonaceae*. The leaves are also pellucid-punctate, owing to secretory oil-cells in the mesophyll.

Himantandra F. von Muell., Austral. Journ. Pharmac. 2: 5 (1887), and Bot. Centralbl. 30: 326 (1887); Pap. Pl. 2: 54 (1890); Diels, Ber. Deutsch. Bot. Ges. 34: 771 (1916), and Engl. Bot. Jahrb. 49: 164, fig. 6 (1912); 52: 185 (1915); 55: 126, fig. 1 (1917); Hutch., Fam. Fl. Pl. ed. 2, 1: 130, fig. 6 (1959). *Galbulimima* Bailey (1894); Sprague, Hook. Ic. Pl. t. 3001 (1915).—3–4 spp., Malaya to Australasia; type *H. belgraveana* (F. von Muell.) F. von Muell., Moluccas and New Guinea. *Characters of the family.*

7. LACTORIDACEAE

Engl., Engl. Bot. Jahrb. 8: 53 (1887)

Shrubs with alternate, small, obovate, emarginate, entire leaves with numerous, minute, pellucid dots; stipules large, intrapetiolar, membranous. Flowers polygamous-monoecious, small, solitary or two or three on a very short axillary inflorescence bearing one or two small leaves. Sepals 3, free. Petals 0. Stamens 6, in two whorls; anthers extrorse, short, 2-locular. Carpels 3, nearly free from one another, narrowed into short beak-like styles stigmatose within; ovules 6 in each carpel, arranged in two vertical series on the intruded margins of the carpel. Follicles introrsely dehiscent, beaked. Seeds in each carpel 4–6; testa thin, striate; endosperm copious, oily; embryo minute, near the apex of the endosperm. Type genus *Lactoris* Philippi.

Genus 1; species 1.

DISTRIBUTION. Endemic in the island of Juan Fernandez, off the coast of Chile.

ANATOMY. M.C. 38. POLLEN. Erdt. 220.

This interesting family, represented by a monotypic genus, is confined to the island of Juan Fernandez. It was at first described by Philippi as being probably allied to *Magnoliaceae*, a view supported by Engler, who made it the type of a separate family. Bentham and Hooker included it in the *Piperaceae*, a family with which it seems to have little in common. The affinity with *Winteraceae* is very marked, and it is probably a much reduced relative of that family.

Lactoris Philippi, Verh. Zool. Bot. Wien 15: 521, t. 13 (1865); B.H. 3: 127 (1880) (in *Piperaceae*); Engl., Bot. Jahrb. 8: 53; Hemsl., Bot. Chall. Exped. 1: t. 59; E.P. 3, 2: 19–20, f. 18; Johow, Fl. Juan Fernand. 114 (1896); Hutch., Fam. Fl. Pl. ed. 2, 1: 131, fig. 7 (1959). 1 sp., *L. fernandeziana* Philippi. *Characters of the family.*

8. TROCHODENDRACEAE

Seem., Journ. Bot. 2: 238 (1864) (*Trochodendreae*)

Trees with whorled exstipulate long-petiolate serrate evergreen or deciduous leaves and perulate buds. Flowers bisexual or polygamous, racemose or subfasciculate from perulate buds, rather small. Perianth 0 (perhaps sometimes represented by very minute bracteoles towards the apex of the pedicels). Stamens numerous, hypogynous or inserted in about 3–4 series on the outside of the expanded obconic torus; anthers short, or linear, extrorse, on long slender filaments. Carpels 6–10, more or less in a single whorl, rather loosely united, or quite free, divergent or stipitate, each stigmatose on the inner side; ovules one to several in each carpel, pendulous. Fruit dehiscent, carpels opening on the inner side, radiate, or stipitate and ascending and samaroid. Seeds few, linear, pendulous, with a thin testa; embryo minute in copious uniform endosperm. Type genus *Trochodendron* Sieb. & Zucc.

Genera 2; species 5.

DISTRIBUTION. Assam to Japan.

CLASSIFICATION. Benth. & Hook. f., Gen. Pl. 1: 954 (as tribe of *Magnoliaceae*); Engl. & Prantl, Nat. Pflanzenfam. 3, 2: 21; Hutch., Fam. Fl. Pl. ed. 2, 1: 132, fig. 8 (1959).

ANATOMY. Sol. 1: 31; M.C. 1: 39. POLLEN. Erdt. 439.

ADDITIONAL LITERATURE. Thompson & Bailey, Are *Tetracentron*, *Trochodendron* and *Drimys* specialized or primitive types?, Mem. N. York Bot. Gard. 6: 27 (1916); Bailey & Nast, Morph. & relationsh. of *Tetracentron* and *Trochodendron*, Journ. Arn. Arb. 26: 143; 267 (1945). A. C. Smith, Taxonom. rev. of *Trochodendron* and *Tetracentron*, Journ. Arn. Arb. 26: 123 (1945); Taxonom. rev. of *Euptelea*, Journ. Arn. Arb. 27: 175 (1946); morphology by Nash & Bailey, p. 186; Croizat, Bull. Torr. Cl. 74: 60 (1947); Lawrence, Taxon. Vascul. Pl. 492, fig. 132 (1951).

A small family with a restricted distribution, related to but more advanced and reduced than the *Winteraceae*; allied especially to *Illicium* which occurs in the same area. This family is probably something of a link with the *Hamamelidales*. There are no vessels in the xylem of *Trochodendron*, which thus resembles the true Gymnosperms and the genus *Drimys* (*Winteraceae*).

The stomata are not surrounded by cells of any special form as in *Magnoliaceae*.

Leaves evergreen, leathery; flowers racemose, androdioecious, with a broad
    torus bearing the stamens; carpels radiate   **1. Trochodendron**
Leaves deciduous, chartaceous; flowers precocious, subfasciculate, poly-
    gamous; carpels ascending samaroid, with a membranous wing
                                                  2. Euptelea

1. **Trochodendron** Sieb. & Zucc., Fl. Jap. 83, t. 39, 40 (1835). *Gymnanthus*
Jungh. (1840). The single species of this remarkable genus, *T. aralioides*
Sieb. & Zucc., occurs only in the forests of Japan and Formosa. In the
latter island it forms pure forests between the conifer belt and the broad-
leaved tree region, where specimens occur with trunks as much as 15 ft. in
diameter. B.H. 1: 954; E.P. 3, 2: 21; Hook. f., Bot. Mag. t. 7375; Keng,
Journ. Arn. Arb. 40: 158, t. 1 (1959).

Large tree; trunk up to 5 m. diam.; buds perulate; leaves alternate, evergreen, broadly
rhomboid, crenulate; stipules absent; flowers androdioecious, in short racemes from perulate buds; sepals and petals absent; stamens numerous, filaments filiform; anthers oblong,
muticous, loculi lateral, adnate and parallel; carpels numerous, radiate-verticillate, sessile,
connate; ovules numerous; styles short, free; fruit composed of the connate carpels.
Known as the Birdlime tree, the birdlime being made from the bark.

2. **Euptelea** Sieb. & Zucc., Fl. Jap. 133, t. 72 (1835). 4 spp.,[1] Assam to Japan;
type *E. polyandra* Sieb. & Zucc., Japan. *E. pleiosperma* Hk. f. & Thoms.,
N. Assam; *E. minor* Ching, NW. Yunnan; *E. davidiana* Baill., W. Szechuan,
Yunnan. *E. franchetii* Van Tiegh., Hupeh to E. Szechuan. B.H. 1: 954; E.P.
3, 2: 23.

Trees; buds perulate; leaves alternate, deciduous, suborbicular, sharply serrate; stipules
absent; flowers precocious, subfasciculate, polygamous; sepals and petals absent; stamens
numerous, filaments filiform; anthers linear, connective apiculate; carpels numerous,
subsimply verticillate, stipitate, 4–1-ovulate; stigmas sessile, introrsely decurrent; fruits
stipitate, samaroid, with a membranous wing; seeds 4–1, pendulous from the inner angle;
testa black, crustaceous, shining.

9. CERCIDIPHYLLACEAE

Engl., Syll. Pflanzenfam. ed. 6: 132 (1909)

Tree up to 100 ft. high. Leaves deciduous, opposite, or sometimes on the
sterile branchlets alternate, involute in bud, petiolate, rounded, cordate and
digitately nerved at the base, stipulate; stipules slightly adnate to the petiole,
caducous. Flowers dioecious; male flowers axillary, subsessile, solitary or
fascicled. Calyx small, scarious, divided to the base into 4 acute apiculate
segments. Stamens 15–20; filaments long and slender, inserted on a small
conical receptacle; anthers oblong-linear, basifixed, slightly apiculate, opening

[1] Opinions vary as to the number of species of this interesting genus. At any rate the
NE. Indian species, *E. pleiosperma*, is not identical with the Chinese *E. davidiana*, as supposed by some authors. The winter-buds distinguish them at once, those of the Indian
species being narrow and acute and the scales glabrous on the margin, of the Chinese plant
ovoid, subobtuse, with the scales constantly ciliate.

by longitudinal slits. Female flowers solitary, axillary, pedicellate. Sepals a little longer than in the male and with laciniate margins. Carpels 4–6, slightly stipitate, gradually narrowed into elongated slender styles stigmatic on their inner face; ovules in two rows on the placenta, descending, anatropous. Fruit a cluster of 2–6 slightly spreading follicles, splitting down the ventral suture, which by twisting becomes external; exocarp thin, endocarp woody and shining within. Seeds pendulous in two rows, compressed, nearly square, winged at one end; embryo medium-sized in copious endosperm; cotyledons flat. Type genus *Cercidiphyllum* Sieb. & Zucc.

Genus 1; species 1.

DISTRIBUTION. China and Japan.

ANATOMY. M.C. 1: 30. POLLEN. Erdt. 106.

Cercidiphyllum Sieb. & Zucc., Abh. Math. Acad. Muench. 4, 3: 238 (1846); Sargent, For. Fl. Jap. 3–15, tt. 1, 6–7 (1894); E.P. 3, 2: 23 (in *Magnoliaceae*); Engl. & Gilg., Syllab., ed. 7: 187 (1912) (as a separate family); Harms, Über die Blütenverhältnisse und die systematische Stellung der Gattung *Cercidiphyllum*, Ber. Deutsch. Bot. Ges. 34: 272 (1916); McLaughlin, System. Anat. of woods of Magnoliales, Trop. Woods 34: 3 (1933); Swamy & Bailey, The morphology and relationships of *Cercidiphyllum*, Journ. Arn. Arb. 30: 187 (1949); Lawrence, Taxon. Vascul. Pl. 495, fig. 135 (1951); Hutch., Fam. Fl. Pl., ed. 2, 1: 132, fig. 9 (1959); Lindquist, Notes on *C. magnificum* Nakai, Bot. Tidskrift, 51: 212, figs. 1–4 and map (1954); Miyabe & Kudo, Ic. Ess. For. Trees, Hokkaido, 2, fasc. 14: tt. 42, 43 (1932). 1 sp., *C. japonicum* Sieb. & Zucc., Japan and W. China (incl. *C. ovale* Maxim., and *C. magnificum* Nakai). *Characters of the family.*

According to Sargent *Cercidiphyllum* is one of the most interesting trees of Japan, and gives to the forests of Yezo their peculiar appearance and character. It inhabits the slopes of low hills in a moist, deep, rich soil, associated with a growth of dwarf Bamboos. There it attains a height of 100 ft. and often develops clusters of stems 8–10 ft. through, and even greater dimensions in China, where E. H. Wilson found an old tree 55 ft. in girth. It is a valuable timber tree, producing soft, straight-grained, light yellow wood, like that of *Liriodendron*. In Yezo it is a favourite material for the interior finish of cheap houses and for packing cases, boxes, &c., and for various domestic utensils. As an ornamental tree in this country it is valuable mainly as a botanical curiosity, for its habit of growth, and for its *Cercis*-like foliage, which is bright red in spring and yellow in autumn, the flowers being much reduced and inconspicuous. At Kew after many years' growth *Cercidiphyllum* remains a mere shrub often injured by late spring frosts, but it grows much better in continental Europe.

Assigned first of all to the *Magnoliaceae*, then to the *Trochodendraceae* when that family was established, *Cercidiphyllum* was later treated by Engler as a distinct family, which appears to be its proper status. The genus is evidently a relatively ancient one, being a much reduced descendant of the *Magnoliaceae*, but distinct by its dioecious flowers, reduced perianth, and follicular fruits. It is perhaps most nearly related to the genus *Liriodendron*. Solereder's view that the female flowers are inflorescences is not accepted here. The 'bracts' are in my opinion just reduced sepals, and the carpels twist round in fruit, causing the dehiscence to be abaxial. There is no affinity with the *Hamamelidaceae* except a superficial resemblance, for in that family the ovary is *syncarpous* and composed of *two carpels* which are usually partially or completely inferior (see Solereder in Deutsch. Bot. Gesellsch. 17: 387–406, t. 28 (1899)). The view is taken here that the *Hamamelidaceae* are descended through and from the *Rosales* and not directly from the Magnolian stock.

Follows closely on to *Magnoliales*, but definitely more advanced phylogenetically and a climax group, with floral parts moved into whorls, mostly with two rows of petals, some valvate; numerous free stamens retained; apocarpous to rarely syncarpous and then with parietal placentation; seeds with *ruminate endosperm*; leaves always entire, exstipulate; more tropical than *Magnoliales*.

Carpels numerous or few, rarely solitary, free or rarely united and with parietal placentas, inserted on a flat or conical receptacle; styles usually free; fruit superior, of several free units or, rarely, these united into a mass; sepals and petals not merged into a calyptra   10. *Annonaceae*

Carpels numerous, immersed in the turbinate receptacle; styles connate into a mass; fruit several-locular and berry-like; sepals and petals merged together into a calyptra   11. *Eupomatiaceae*

10. ANNONACEAE

A. L. de Jussieu, Gen. Pl. 283 (1789) (*Anoneae*)

Trees, shrubs, or climbers with aromatic wood and leaves. Leaves alternate, entire, exstipulate. Flowers usually green, yellowish, or purple, terminal, leaf-opposed, axillary, extra-axillary, or borne in fascicles or panicles on the older wood, rarely on underground sucker-like shoots, usually bisexual, rarely unisexual; axis flat, hemispherical or conical. Sepals hypogynous, 3, rarely 2, distinct or variously united, imbricate or valvate, persistent or deciduous, rarely enlarging and enclosing the fruit. Petals hypogynous, usually 6 in two series, rarely 4 or 3, imbricate or valvate in each series, sometimes the outer valvate and the inner slightly imbricate, very rarely absent. Stamens hypogynous, numerous, rarely few, spirally imbricate in several series; filaments very short and thick; anther-loculi extrorse or lateral, very rarely introrse, adnate to the connective, contiguous or separate, opening by a longitudinal slit, rarely transversely locellate, often hidden by the expanded truncate connective, rarely the latter elongated or not produced. Carpels numerous or few, rarely solitary, free or rarely united into a 1-locular ovary with parietal placentas; styles short, thick, free or rarely connate; stigma capitate or oblong, sometimes sulcate or bilobed; ovules 1–2 and inserted at the base of the carpel or 1–several on the ventral suture in 1 or 2 series, anatropous. Fruiting carpels usually stipitate and free, rarely united together into a many- (rarely 1-) locular mass, dry or fleshy, indehiscent or rarely follicular. Seeds arillate or not; endosperm copious, conspicuously ruminate; embryo minute, near the hilum. Type genus *Annona* Linn.

Genera 122; species about 1,100.

DISTRIBUTION. Tropics of both hemispheres, mainly at low elevations in moist forest areas, a few in warm temperate E. North America, subtropical South America, S. Africa, and N. Australia; comparatively rare in Madagascar and in the islands of the Pacific.

CLASSIFICATION. Dunal, Monogr. de la famille des Anonacées, pp. 144, pls. 1–33 (1817); Blume, Fl. Java, 1; 1–108, pls. 1–53 (1828); Bentham, Notes on *Anonaceae*, Journ. Linn. Soc. 5: 67–72 (1860); On African *Anonaceae*, Trans. Linn. Soc. 23: 463–80, pls. 49–53 (1862); Benth. & Hook. f., Gen. Pl. 1: 20–29 (1862); Martius, Fl. Bras. 13: 1–64, pls. 1–14 (1841); Prantl in Engl. & Prantl, Nat. Pflanzenfam. 3, 2: 23–39, figs. 20–34 (1891); Nachtr. 159–61 (1897); King, *Anonaceae* of British India, Ann. Bot. Gard. Calcutta, 4: 169, pls. 1–220 (1893); Boerlage, Notes sur les Anonacées du Jard. Bot. Buitenz. Icon. Bogor. 1, pt. 2–3, pp. 79–480, pls. 26–75 (1899); Engl. & Diels, Monogr. Afr. *Anonac.* (1901); R. E. Fries, Beiträge zur Kenntnis der sud-amer. *Anonac.* (1901); Vet. Akad. Handl. Stockh. 34, n. 5, 1–58, tt. 1–7 (1900); Finet & Gagnep., Bull. Soc. Bot. Fr. 53: Mem. 4: 55–170 (*Anonac.* of E. Asia) (1906); Diels, Die Anonaceen von Papuasien, Engl. Bot. Jahrb. 49: 113–67 (1912); Merrill, loc. cit. (below); Diels, Revisio *Anonacearum madagascariensium*, Notizbl. Bot. Gart. Berl. 9: 334–57 (1925); Sprague & Hutch., Kew Bull. 1916: 145 (key to African genera); Hutch., The genera of *Anonac.*, Kew. Bull. 1923: 241; Chipp in Hutch. & Dalz., Fl. W. Trop. Afr. 1: 46 (1927); ed. 2 (Keay) 1: 34 (1954); Cavaco, Humbert Fl. Madag. Fam. 78*e Annonac.* 1, figs. 1–24 (1948); R. E. Fries, Revision der Arten einiger Anonaceen-Gattungen, Act. Hort. Berg. 10: 1–341, tt. 1–27 (1930–1); 10, 2: 129–341 (1931); 12, 1: 1–220 (1934) (mostly American genera); 12, 3: 289–577, tt. 1–40 (1939) (contains key to American genera, p. 567); Einige Gesichtspuncte zur system. Gruppierung der amerik. Annon.-Gattungen, Ark. für Bot. 30, no. 8: 1–13 (1943); Boutique, Fl. Congo Belge et du Ruanda-Urundi, 2: 256 (1951); Sinclair, Revision of Malayan *Annonaceae*, Gardens Bull. Singapore, 14: 149 (1955); Hutch., Fam. Fl. Pl. ed. 2, 1: 133, fig. 10 (1959); R. E. Fries in Engl. & Prantl, Nat. Pflanzenfam. ed. 2, 17*a*, 2: 1, figs. 1–40 (1959) (see this for further literature).

ANATOMY. Sol. 1: 34; M.C. 1: 44. POLLEN. Erdt. 49.

ADDITIONAL LITERATURE. Bentham, loc. cit. (above); Baillon, Mémoire sur la fam. des *Anonac.*, Adansonia, 8: 162–84, 295–344 (1867); Voight, Untersuchungen über Bau und Entwicklung von Samen mit ruminiertem Endosperm aus . . . *Anonaceae*, Ann. Jard. Bot. Buitenz. 7: 151–90, pls. 20–22 (1888); Baillon, De la valeur de la configuration des étamines pour la classif. des *Anonac.*, Bull. Soc. Linn. Par. 1: 377–8 (1889); Lecomte, Sur la formation du pollen chez les *Anonacées*, Bull. Mus. Hist. Nat. Par. 2: 152–3 (1896); W. E. Safford, The genus *Annona*, the derivation of its name, and its taxonomic subdivision, Journ. Wash. Acad. Sci. 1: 118–20 (1911); Merrill, Studies on Philippine *Anonaceae*, Philipp. Journ. Sci. 10: 227–64 (1915); Bowden, Chromosome numbers in the *Annonaceae*, Amer. Journ. Bot. 35: 377 (1948); Vanderwyk. & J. S. Canright, Anatomy and relationships of *Annonaceae*, Trop. Woods, 104: 1 (1956).

Characters occurring in relatively few Genera. **Habit :** remarkable in *Geanthemum*, the flowers borne on subterranean shoots. **Branchlets :** spiny in some *Artabotrys* spp. and some *Annona* spp., sometimes reflexed for climbing in *Popowia* spp. **Indumentum :** mainly stellate or lepidote in tribe *Uvarieae*, *Drepananthus*, and *Rauwenhoffia*; lepidote in *Meiocarpidium*. **Inflorescence :** peduncle recurved, thickened and hook-like in *Artabotrys*. **Flowers :** very large in *Sapranthus*, with a carrion-like odour resembling that of a *Stapelia* or *Aristolochia*; dioecious in *Tetrastemma*, *Thonnera*, *Ephedranthus*; monoecious in *Uvariopsis*, *Raimondia*. **Calyx :** enlarging and becoming membranous and enclosing the fruits in *Sphaerothalamus*; sepals striate in *Marcuccia* and *Sapranthus*. **Petals :** 6 in a single series in *Monanthotaxis*, *Haplostichanthus*, *Monocyclanthus*; 4 in two series in *Tetrapetalum* and in subtribe *Xylopineae*, group B; 8 in two series in *Tetrameranthus*; 3 in *Xylopineae*, group C; petals opposite the sepals (outer 3 absent) in *Enantia*; sympetalous in *Asteranthe*, *Enneastemon*, *Uvariopsis*, *Hexalobus*, *Stormia*, *Disepalum*, and *Papualthia* spp., and subfamily *Monodoroideae*; transversely plicate and crumpled in bud in *Hexalobus*; outer petals with wavy crinkly margins, inner with lateral hooks in *Monodora*; inner petals boat-shaped with inrolled margins in *Cymbopetalum*; outer petals with long dorsal appendages in *Rollinia*, *Stenanthera*, and a few other genera. **Anthers :** transversely locellate in *Porcelia*, *Froesiodendron*, *Xylopia*, *Cardiopetalum*, and *Hornschuchia*. **Connective :** prolonged but not truncate in *Oxandra*, *Cananga*, *Bocagea*, *Anaxagorea*, *Platymitra*, *Mosenodendron*, *Mezzettiopsis*, *Saccopetalum*, *Miliusa*, *Orophea*; not produced beyond the thecae in *Geanthemum*, *Tetrastemma*, *Thonnera*, *Raimondia*, *Alphonsea*. **Outer stamens :** sterile and subpetaloid in *Fusaea*. **Carpels :** on an elongated torus in *Mischogyne*; united into a 1-locular ovary with parietal placentas in subfamily *Monodoroideae*; united in fruit into a many-locular mass in subtribe *Annonineae*, *Pachypodanthium*, *Annonidium*; carpels dehiscing on the adaxial side in *Anaxagorea*, and by a lateral split in *Cymbopetalum*; solitary in *Kingstonia*, *Monocarpia*, *Mezzettia*, *Tridimeris*; sunk in the torus in *Pseudannona*. **Stigmas :** united in *Piptostigma*. **Seeds :** triquetrous and winged in *Richella*.

Economic Properties. Generally speaking the family *Annonaceae* is not of much economic importance. Some species of *Annona* have edible fruits, the West Indian Custard Apple or Bullock's Heart, *A. reticulata* Linn., and Sweetsop, *A. squamosa* Linn., being the most important. These two are widely cultivated and naturalized in many parts of India and Malaya, in some districts appearing as if they were native. The fruit of *A. squamosa* Linn. is highly esteemed in India (Watt), even more than in the West Indies, and in times of famine and scarcity has proved of great value to the people. In India the leaves and fruits are also put to many medicinal uses, and in the West Indies a drink like cider is made from the juice of the latter. Cherimoya is *Annona cherimolia* Mill., W. South America; Soursop or Guanabana, *Annona muricata* Linn., West Indies; American Papaw, *Asimina triloba* (Linn.) Dunal, E. United States. The bark of Annonaceous plants is usually aromatic, stimulant, and astringent, whilst the inner layer of the bark affords a useful bast fibre. The petals of Ylang-Ylang, *Cananga odorata* (Lam.) Hook. f. & Thoms., native of Indo-China and Malaya, are strongly perfumed and the oil is used in European perfumery. Xochinacaztli, Sacred Ear Flower of the Aztecs, *Cymbopetalum penduliflorum* Baill., Mexico and Cent. America, flowers used as a spice for flavouring chocolate and in cooking. *Xylopia aethiopica* A. Rich. supplied the ancients with Ethiopian pepper. Strong ropes are made from the bark of certain Brazilian species. Lancewood, *Oxandra lanceolata* (Sw.) Baill., West Indies, is put to many uses; also *Duguetia quitarensis* Benth., British Guiana.

Phylogeny and Morphology. During the last hundred years the family *Annonaceae* has received the attention of many systematists, prominent amongst them being Baillon (*Adansonia*, vols. 7–8), King (Monograph of Indian *Annonaceae*), Engler & Diels (Monograph of the African species), whilst R. E. Fries and W. E. Safford have independently done some admirable work on certain tropical American groups; and T. A. Sprague and the present writer published a revised key to the African genera (see literature). In spite of the vast amount of work done on the family, however, no classification has as yet very satisfactorily resolved the genera into tribes, and some of the genera remain rather ill-defined. These two points should especially be the aim of a future monographer, who will probably find it necessary to reduce considerably the number of genera. In the past, perhaps, rather too much stress has been laid on the shape and size of the top of the anther-connective, for tribal distinctions at any rate, this character being used very prominently by Bentham & Hooker.

For the present work the number of tribes in the subfamily *Annonoideae* is reduced to three, the first, *Uvarieae*, showing the most primitive features in that either one or both rows of petals are imbricate and the anther-connective almost invariably truncate and hiding the loculi. These truncate anther-tips are a very striking feature of the *Annonaceae*, and they may represent an ancient relict type of leaf-structure. *Superficially* they resemble very closely the microsporophylls of many *Gymnosperms*.

The second tribe, *Miliuseae*, is distinguished by its valvate petals, but more especially by the inner petals being longer than the outer ones, the latter often scarcely different from the sepals, resembling them in shape, texture, and possibly also in colour. This group may therefore be even more primitive than the *Uvarieae*, though the latter is given priority on account of the imbricate aestivation of the petals.

The third and by far the largest tribe is the *Unoneae*, in which the petals are valvate, equal or subequal in size, or the inner smaller and frequently of a different shape and as a rule more or less clawed and remaining connivent and closely adpressed over the stamens and carpels. I have had to content myself with arranging the genera of this tribe into two subtribes, *Xylopiineae* and *Annonineae*, determined by the apocarpous and falsely syncarpous gynoecium respectively, and the *Xylopiineae* into further purely artificial groups, A, B, and C, determined by the number of petals. This, though undoubtedly unnatural, should facilitate the determination of most of the genera.

No doubt the bad state of many dried specimens has contributed much towards the unsatisfactory classification of the family. This may be due to the fact that *Annonaceae* are found almost exclusively in dense, moist, tropical forests, wherein their preservation for herbarium purposes presents more than ordinary difficulty, the flowers being mostly fleshy and shrivelling when dry and becoming very brittle.

Since the family was first monographed by Dunal in 1817 our knowledge has increased enormously through further exploration of the tropics. At that date only 103 species were known to botanists, and most of these very imperfectly. In 1832 A. de Candolle's review brought to light 204 species, whilst Bentham and Hooker's estimate in 1862 was 400 species disposed through 40 genera. The present work accounts for 121 genera, with a total of something like 1,100 species. The botanical exploration of South America and of tropical Africa has brought to light a considerable number of new genera and species, especially the forest areas from Nigeria to the Congo, where many small endemic and peculiar types have been discovered.

Annonaceae is one of the most uniform and natural of families, both in anatomical and floral structure, as well as in habit and habitat. It is readily distinguished from its nearest relations by a combination of well-marked characters. In habit they are small trees, shrubs, or climbers (the last chiefly characteristic of the Old World species), not a single species being truly herbaceous or annual. The leaves are always exstipulate, a character at once separating them from the *Magnoliaceae*, and they are always alternate. The flowers are hypogynous, usually bisexual, and, with a few exceptions, trimerous, with the petals in two whorls, both rows or only the inner row being slightly imbricate, or more often both rows valvate. The petals are usually 6, rarely 4, and when reduced to 3, either the inner series or very rarely the outer series (*Dennettia*) is absent. The genus *Fenerivia* is remarkable in having 12 petals. Reduction in the number of petals is often accompanied by separation of the sexes. The small, closely packed, spirally arranged, extrorse, almost sessile stamens in several series with the often truncate connectives closely packed together and protecting and hiding the loculi, the variously stipitate carpels (especially in fruit), the remarkably uniform rumination of the endosperm, and the minute embryo are sure marks of the family.

Subfamily *Monodoroideae*, in which the carpels are united into a single ovary with parietal placentas, apparently represents the highest development of the family, in which even a sympetalous corolla is a not uncommon feature. It is interesting to note that within this undoubtedly natural family union of the carpels is accompanied by *parietal* placentation, a condition generally more primitive than *axile*.

Geographical Distribution. *Annonaceae* are almost wholly confined to the tropics where they nearly always grow at low elevations. For example, they are very abundant in the rain-forest area of W. Africa, and nearly unrepresented in the adjacent and more elevated savannah regions, except along rivers. In Ceylon they do not ascend the mountains higher than 2,000 metres, and in the Khasia Hills of Assam not beyond about 1,600 metres. In Brazil their greatest elevation is probably about 1,300 metres. The only genus extending for any distance into the temperate zone is *Asimina*, which occurs in E. North America as far north as the Great Lakes.

There is a marked contrast in the habit of the species of the two hemispheres. In the tropics of the Old World they are usually of climbing or straggling habit, and occur in dense forest areas; but in tropical America they are nearly all shrubby or arboreal and mostly grow on the *campos* or open grassy plains.

Examples of intercontinental distribution or affinity are not numerous, but they are of considerable interest. The only natural genus common to the tropics of both hemispheres is *Xylopia*, which is remarkable in having transversely septate anthers. A species discovered in the Cameroons (*X. hypolampra*) described by Mildbraed, shows marked affinity with certain Brazilian species. Another example is the genus *Guatteria*, all American except for one species in West Africa. But the most remarkable instance of discontinuous distribution in the case of a very natural and outstanding genus is *Anaxagorea*, which is common to Central and NW. South America and Indo-Malaya. Besides the genus *Xylopia*, there are two other notable examples of affinity between Africa and Indo-Malaya, namely, the relatively primitive and extensive genus *Uvaria* and the genus *Artabotrys* with its peculiar hooked inflorescences. A third genus, *Popowia*, is also common to these two regions, but with less significance from a geographical point of view, for *Popowia* cannot be described as a natural genus, as it has evidently been a 'dumping ground' for species not easily otherwise classified. In the Indo-Malayan region *Sageraea* conforms exactly with Wallace's western area, whilst *Phaeanthus* is common to both parts. Besides these comparatively widely spread genera already mentioned, only two genera occur both in Africa and Madagascar. These are *Monodora*, and *Isolone*, genera highly advanced, being already completely *syncarpous* with *parietal* placentas and with large, attractive flowers. A region in Africa with a strong endemic element of small genera is the rain-forest area from Sierra Leone to the Gaboon, and the Congo forests harbour several curious types. Most of the larger Indo-Malayan genera are fairly widely spread in that region. There are several small endemic genera in Borneo and in New Guinea; and *Richella*, as defined in the present work, is confined to the Fiji Islands. In Borneo, according to Beccari's estimate (Nuov. Giorn. Bot. Ital. 3: 177 (1871)), there were at that date 25 genera and 97 species, but many more have since been described.

Key to Subfamilies and Tribes

Carpels free from one another from the beginning (rarely only 1), or if at length united then forming a many-locular syncarp; stigmas more or less erect, rarely radiating   Subfamily I. **ANNONOIDEAE**
Petals, at least of one series, imbricate, always 2-seriate; indumentum of leaves (when present) often stellate or lepidote
                                     Tribe 1. UVARIEAE (genera 1–36)
Petals valvate, either 2-seriate or rarely 1-seriate, usually 6 (very rarely 12), rarely 4 or 3:
Outer 3 petals smaller than the inner and often scarcely distinguishable from the sepals   Tribe 2. MILIUSEAE (genera 37–48)

Outer petals as large as or larger than the inner and quite distinct from the
 sepals, or sometimes by reduction only one series of 3 petals present
                              Tribe 3. UNONEAE (genera 49–120)
Carpels united from the beginning into a 1-locular ovary with parietal placentas; stigmas radiating
                    Subfamily II. **MONODOROIDEAE** (genera 121–122)

Subfamily I. ANNONOIDEAE

Tribe 1. UVARIEAE

Petals 6; sepals 3:

 Flowers borne on the stem or branches, never from underground shoots:
 Sepals imbricate:
  Ovules several to numerous (5 or more):
  Petals not nervose:
   Flowers fasciculate on the older wood remote from the leaves; torus
    conical or hemispherical; carpels numerous; stigmas sessile,
    radiating   1. **Stelechocarpus**
   Flowers usually axillary; torus flat; carpels few (3–6); stigma obtuse
    or capitate   2. **Sageraea**
  Petals nervose; flowers solitary and leaf-opposed or on the trunk and
   branches   14. **Sapranthus**

  Ovules 2–1:
  Petals shorter than or equal to the sepals, all striate-nervose; anther-
   connective pilose; flowers on the leafless parts of the branchlets
                                                       3. **Marcuccia**
  Petals longer than the sepals:
   Calyx becoming membranous and much enlarged, hiding the fruit;
    sepals and petals striate   4. **Sphaerothalamus**
   Calyx not enlarging or only slightly so:
    Anther-connective truncate at the apex; stamens numerous:
    Flowers or inflorescence not leaf-opposed:
     Flowers on the young or one-year-old branchlets; petals not gibbous
      in the middle:
      Ovule or ovules erect; fruits ovoid, stipitate; seeds sulcate
                                                       5. **Griffithianthus**
      Ovule pendulous; stigma sessile, obconic, hairy
                                                       6. **Crematosperma**
      Ovule laterally attached, ascending; stigma sessile, minute
                                                       7. **Ruizodendron**
      Ovule lateral, pendulous; style present   8. **Pseudoxandra**
     Flowers borne on the main stem or leafless branches; petals gibbous
      in the middle; stigmas cuneate, deciduous in a sticky mass
                                                       9. **Enicosanthum**
    Flowers in a leaf-opposed inflorescence; stigmas clavate, sessile;
     ovule 1, erect; trop. America   10. **Malmea**

Anther-connective lanceolate; stamens 15–10; fruits shortly stipitate,
1-seeded; trop. America   11. **Oxandra**

Sepals valvate:

Carpels free from one another, at least in fruit:

Ovules several to numerous (6 or more):

Petals not united at the base or very shortly so:

Tropical America genera:

Anthers transversely locellate:

Flowers terminal or leaf-opposed; leaves densely pellucid-glandular-
punctate   12. **Porcelia**

Flowers axillary or supra-axillary; leaves not glandular-punctate
13. **Froesiodendron**

Anthers not transversely locellate:

Flowers small (about 2·5 cm. long); petals not striate 12. **Porcelia**

Flowers large (over 7 cm.); petals conspicuously striate; peduncle
jointed at the base, with an oblong-cordate bract above the
joint   14. **Sapranthus**

Old World genera; anthers not transversely locellate:

All the petals remaining incurved, without glands at the base;
flowers small; indumentum of simple hairs:

Climbing shrubs; flowers in pendulous cymes from the older wood;
ovules numerous   15. **Cyathostemma**

Erect shrubs; flowers few and shortly cymulose on the leafy shoots;
ovules 6   16. **Toussaintia**

Inner petals at length spreading; without glands at the base; indumentum when present of stellate hairs:

Carpels more than 1, mostly stipitate and berry-like in fruit
17. **Uvaria**

Carpel 1, not stipitate and not berry-like, warted   18. **Dasoclema**

Inner petals remaining erect, with two basal glands
42. **Anomianthus**

Petals united at the base into a distinct tube; carpels about 10, 2-seriate;
E. trop. Africa   19. **Asteranthe**

Ovules 3–1:

Ovule inserted above the middle of the carpel; petals rounded, inner
smaller; fruits oblique   20. **Ellipeia**

Ovules inserted near or towards the base of the carpel:

Fertile carpels more than 1:

Flowers bisexual:

Outer petals much longer than the inner and spreading, the inner
closely adpressed over the stamens and carpels; ovules 2–1;
fruits tuberculate; trop. Africa   21. **Cleistopholis**

Outer petals about equal to the inner in length or shorter, at length
all open; ovule 1–2:

Carpels sessile or nearly so in fruit:

Carpels numerous, beaked, crowded with several flattened sides;
indumentum stellate or lepidote; trop. America 22. **Duguetia**

Carpels numerous, not beaked; indumentum simple
23. Dukeanthus

Carpels not beaked, loose, rounded climbers; flowers leaf-
opposed   ·   24. Ellipeiopsis

Carpels more or less stipitate in fruit:

Ovules 2; flowers on leafless part of branchlets 25. Lettowianthus

Ovule 1   26. Guatteria

Flowers unisexual (dioecious?); carpels numerous; fruits stipitate,
1-seeded; Brazil   27. Ephedranthus

Fertile carpel 1, remainder abortive:

Flowers fasciculate on the older wood; stamens about 12; stigma
peltate   28. Kingstonia

Flowers axillary, solitary; stamens numerous; stigma clavate-capitate
29. Stenanona

Carpels united, especially in fruit:

All the stamens fertile; trop. Africa:

Ovules numerous; indumentum stellate; syncarp ellipsoid, muricate
30. Pachypodanthium

Ovule 1; indumentum not stellate:

Flowers borne on the young shoots, leaf-opposed; calyx circumscissile   31. Letestudoxa

Flowers on the old wood; calyx not circumscissile; flower-buds at
first enclosed by 2 opposite bracteoles   32. Anonidium

Outer stamens sterile, with petaloid appendages; syncarp globose,
smooth but pitted; flowers extra-axillary; trop. America 33. Fusaea

Flowers borne on underground sucker-like shoots; indumentum stellate-
lepidote; anther-connective not swollen above the loculi; carpels closely
crowded but free in fruit   34. Geanthemum

Petals 8; sepals 4; ovules 2; trees; flowers axillary, solitary
35. Tetrameranthus

Petals 4; sepals 2; ovules numerous; climber; flowers in dense spikes subopposite to the leaves; Borneo   36. Tetrapetalum

1. **Stelechocarpus** Hook. f. & Thoms., Fl. Ind. 1: 94 (1855). 5 spp., SE. India
to Java and New Guinea; type *S. buranol* Hook. f. & Thoms., Chittagong
and Java. B.H. 1: 22; E.P. 3, 2: 31; King, Ann. Bot. Gard. Calc. 4: 3;
Sinclair, Gard. Bull. Singap. 14: 182; R. E. Fries, E.P. ed. 2, 17*a*, 2: 73.

Trees; leaves coriaceous; flowers dioecious, fasciculate on the older wood; sepals 3,
imbricate, small; petals 6, biseriately imbricate, ovate or rounded, equal; stamens with
a truncate-capitate connective; torus conical or hemispherical; carpels numerous; stigmas
sessile, radiating; ovules 6 or more; fruits large and berry-like, globose, with 6–4 seeds.

2. **Sageraea** Dalz., Hook. Kew Journ. Bot. 3: 207 (1851). 7–9 spp., Indian
Penins., Ceylon, Burma to Malay Archip. and Philippine Isls.; type *S. lauri-
folia* (Grah.) Blatter (*S. laurina* Dalz.), Bombay. B.H. 1: 22; E.P. 3, 2: 29;
King, Ann. Bot. Gard. Calc. 4: 5; Sinclair, Gard. Bull. Singap. 14: 180;
R. E. Fries, E.P. ed. 2, 17*a*, 2: 72.

Trees; leaves coriaceous; flowers bisexual or unisexual, axillary or fasciculate on
woody tubercles remote from the leaves; sepals 3, orbicular, imbricate; petals 6, orbicular,

biseriately imbricate; stamens up to 20, connective truncate-dilated; torus flat; carpels 3–6, narrow; stigma obtuse or capitate; ovules 6–8, biseriate; fruits subglobose or ovoid, stipitate or nearly sessile.

3. **Marcuccia** Becc., Nuov. Giorn. Bot. Ital. 3: 181, t. 3 (1871). 1 sp., *M. grandiflora* Becc., Borneo. E.P. 3, 2: 273.

Shrub; leaves oblong-elliptic; flowers on leafless branches; sepals 3, large, ovate; petals 6, equal or larger, imbricate, herbaceous, nervose; petals 6, thick, biseriate, outer valvate, inner slightly smaller and slightly imbricate; stamens numerous; anther-connective truncate, pilose; torus globose; carpels many, with obcuneate truncate stigmas in a sticky mass and falling off; ovule solitary, erect. Included in *Enicosanthum* by R. E. Fries, E.P. ed. 2, 17*a*: 68.

4. **Sphaerothalamus**[1] Hook. f., Trans. Linn. Soc. 23: 156, t. 20 (1860). 1 sp., *S. insignis* Hook. f., Borneo. B.H. 1: 23; E.P. 3, 2: 31; Becc., Nuov. Giorn. Bot. Ital. 3: 189, t. 7 (1871).

Shrub; leaves subsessile, large, obliquely cordate at the base; flowers large, solitary or paired, extra-axillary; sepals 3, large, orbicular, ventricose, imbricate; petals 6, 2-seriate, spathulate, imbricate at the apex; torus globose; stamens numerous, connective truncate at the apex; carpels numerous, style obconic; ovules 3–2; fruit globose, 2–1-seeded, stipitate, pericarp fleshy, included by the accrescent membranous calyx. Included in *Polyalthia* by R. E. Fries, E.P. ed. 2, 17*a*: 93.

5. **Griffithianthus** Merr., Philipp. Journ. Sci. Bot. 10: 231 (1915). *Griffithia* Maing. ex King, Ann. Bot. Gard. Calc. 4: 8, tt. 218–20 (1893) not Wight & Arn. (1834). 3 spp., Malaya; type *G. magnoliiflorus* (Maing.) Merr., Malay Penins. and Thailand.

Trees or shrubs; flowers bisexual, rather large, axillary, solitary or paired; sepals 3, very imbricate; petals 6, biseriately imbricate, ovate, inner smaller, excavated at the base; stamens numerous, elongated, connective truncate but not produced; carpels numerous; ovules solitary or paired, basal; style filiform; stigma broadly elevated; fruits ovoid, stipitate; seed solitary, sulcate. Included in *Enicosanthum* by R. E. Fries, E.P. ed. 2, 17*a*: 68.

6. **Crematosperma** R. E. Fries, Act. Hort. Berg. 10: 46, fig. 6 (1931). 17 spp., trop. South America; type *C. pedunculatum* (Diels) R. E. Fries, Peru. R. E. Fries, E.P. ed. 2, 17*a*, 2: 63.

Trees, with simple hairs; flowers bisexual, medium-sized, 1–2 axillary; peduncle bracteate towards the base; sepals 3, imbricate; petals 6, biseriate, erect-spreading, much longer than the sepals, subequal, coriaceous, glabrous, nervose, imbricate; stamens numerous, connective dilated-disciform; torus concave at the apex; carpels numerous; stigma sessile, obconic, hairy; ovule 1, pendulous from above the middle or near the apex of the loculus.

7. **Ruizodendron** R. E. Fries, Act. Hort. Berg. 12: 542, fig. 40 (1939). 1 sp., *R. ovalis* (Ruiz & Pav.) R. E. Fries, Bolivia and Peru. R. E. Fries, E.P. ed. 2, 17*a*, 2: 65, fig. 17.

Tree; leaves reticulate, obtuse; flowers axillary; sepals 3, imbricate, subequal, linear-lanceolate; petals 6, equal, 2-seriate, narrowly lanceolate; stamens numerous, connective dilated-disciform at the apex; carpels numerous; stigma minute, sessile; ovule 1, inserted laterally below the middle of the loculus; fruits stipitate, fleshy, depressed-globose; seed 1, lateral.

8. **Pseudoxandra** R. E. Fries, Act. Hort. Berg. 12: 222 (1937). 6 spp., trop. South America; type *P. leiophylla* (Diels) R. E. Fries, Brazil. R. E. Fries, E.P. ed. 2, 17*a*, 2: 65, fig. 16.

[1] Included in *Polyalthia* by Airy-Shaw (Kew Bull. 1939: 279).

Trees or shrubs; leaves lanceolate-oblong; flowers small, solitary or collected into few-flowered inflorescences, axillary; pedicels articulated, 2-bracteate below the joint; sepals 3, minute, imbricate; petals 6, biseriate, subsimilar, concave, narrowly imbricate; stamens numerous, connective dilated, disk-like; carpels several to numerous, gradually narrowed into a short style; stigma truncate or laterally produced and more or less tongue-shaped; ovule 1, lateral, pendulous; fruits globose, shortly stipitate; seed oblique, hanging down.

9. **Enicosanthum** Becc., Nuov. Giorn. Bot. Ital. 3: 183, t. 5, ff. 14–18 (1871). 1 sp., *E. paradoxum* Becc., Borneo. Sinclair, Gard. Bull. Singap. 14: 186, in small part. R. E. Fries, E.P. ed. 2, 17*a*, 2: 68, partly.

Shrub; leaves large, elongated-oblong; flowers solitary or few together on tubercles from the trunk; sepals 3, ovate, imbricate at the base; petals biseriately imbricate, outer erect, gibbous in the middle, inner similar but smaller; stamens numerous; anthers with a depressed-conical connective; carpels numerous; stigma cuneiform, truncate, deciduous in a sticky mass; ovule solitary, erect.

10. **Malmea** R. E. Fries, Arkiv. Bot. Stockh. 5: n. 4, 3 (1916). About 13 spp., Mexico to Brazil and Peru; type *M. obovata* R. E. Fries, Bahia, Brazil. R. E. Fries, Act. Hort. Berg. 10: 37, 319 (1930–1), & E.P. ed. 2, 17 *a*, 2: 61.

Trees or shrubs, flowers medium-sized, in a leaf-opposed cincinnus; sepals 3, imbricate; petals 6, imbricate, much larger than the sepals, biseriate, subequal, rounded-oval, spreading; stamens numerous, connective truncate-dilated; carpels numerous; stigma clavate, sessile; ovule solitary, basal; fruit long-stipitate.

11. **Oxandra** A. Rich., Sagra Fl. Cuba 2: 20, t. 8 (1842). 22 spp., trop. America, West Indies; type *O. laurifolia* (Sw.) A. Rich., West Indies. B.H. 1: 29 (in *Bocagea*); E.P. 3, 2: 29; Fries, E.P. ed. 2, 17*a*: 66.

Trees; leaves elliptic; flowers bisexual, in small fascicles in the axils of fallen leaves; sepals 3, small; petals 6, subequal, outer imbricate; stamens 15–10, anthers ending in a lanceolate ligule, loculi separate; carpels 10–6; ovule 1, erect; fruits shortly stipitate, 1-seeded.

12. **Porcelia** Ruiz & Pav., Prodr. 84, t. 16 (1794). 5 spp., trop. South America; type *P. nitidifolia* Ruiz & Pav., Peru and Bolivia. B.H. 1: 23; E.P. 3, 2: 31, partly; R. E. Fries, Act. Hort. Berg. 10: 28 (1931), and E.P. ed. 2, 17*a*, 2: 161.

Trees; leaves densely pellucid-glandular punctulate; flowers terminal or leaf-opposed, medium-sized, bisexual or rarely polygamous; sepals 3, triangular-ovate; petals 6, biseriately imbricate, subequal, much larger than the sepals, tomentellous; torus depressed-globose; stamens very numerous, anthers transversely locellate, connective truncate-dilated; carpels numerous; stigma sessile; ovules numerous, biseriate; fruits large, ellipsoid-cylindric; seeds large, reniform.

13. **Froesiodendron** R. E. Fries, Arkiv. Botanik Stockh. 3: 439 (1955). 1 sp., *F. amazonicum* R. E. Fries, Brazil. R. E. Fries, E.P. ed. 2, 17*a*, 2: 160.

Tree or shrub; indumentum of simple hairs; leaves oblong-elliptic, acuminate, lateral nerves few; flowers bisexual, solitary, axillary or supra-axillary; pedicels ebracteate; sepals 3, valvate, coriaceous; petals 6, imbricate free or slightly connate at the base, subequal; stamens numerous; anthers linear, loculi transversely locellate; connective truncate above the loculi; torus setulose; carpels numerous, free; ovules several; stigma subsessile, clavate, truncate, recurved; fruiting carpels stipitate, clavate, pericarp woody; seeds few or several, large, erect.

14. **Sapranthus** Seem., Journ. Bot. 4: 369, t. 54 (1886). 7 spp., Mexico and Cent. America; type *S. nicaraguensis* Seem., Cent. America. R. E. Fries, Act. Hort. Berg. 10: 3, figs. 1–2 (1931), and E.P. ed. 2, 17*a*, 2: 50.

Shrubs or trees; leaves lanceolate-elliptic; flowers medium to large, dark violet or at length almost black, solitary and leaf-opposed or on the trunk and branches; peduncle jointed at the base, furnished with an oblong-cordate bract above the joint; sepals imbricate; petals biseriately imbricate, subequal, thin, densely hirsute on the conspicuous nerves outside; stamens numerous, sessile, connective truncate-dilated; carpels 6 or more, silky; stigmas sessile, globose, disk-like; ovules 5 or more, 2-seriate; fruits sessile or shortly stipitate; seeds flattened.

15. **Cyathostemma** Griff., Notul. 4: 707; t. 650 (1854). 7–8 spp., Malaya; type *C. viridiflorum* Griff., Malay Penins. King, Ann. Bot. Gard. Calc. 4: 11, tt. 37–41; Sinclair, Gard. Bull. Singap. 14: 219; R. E. Fries, E.P. ed. 2, 17*a*, 2: 73.

Climbing shrubs; flowers bisexual or unisexual, subglobose, in pendulous cymes from the older wood; sepals connate, hirsute; petals 6, biseriate, short, subequal, imbricate at the apex, remaining incurved; torus flat; stamens numerous, anthers subintrorse, connective oblique, incurved; carpels numerous; styles cylindric, glabrous, bifid; ovules numerous; fruits several-seeded, stipitate.

16. **Toussaintia** Boutique, Bull. Jard. Bot. Brux. 21: 97, with fig. (1951). 1 sp., *T. congolensis* Boutique, trop. Africa. R. E. Fries, E.P. ed. 2, 17*a*, 2: 52.

Shrub; indumentum of simple hairs; leaves oblong, equally rounded at the base, pinnately nerved; flowers bisexual, solitary or 2 or 3 together on the leafy shoots or at their base; pedicels stouter upwards; bracts and bracteoles present; sepals 3, valvate, thick, enclosing the petals in bud, margins recurved; petals 6, in 2 whorls, imbricate in each, subequal; floral axis very long, cylindric, bearing very numerous stamens spreading at a right angle; anthers oblong, connective thick and truncate, shortly produced above the loculi; carpels several at the top of the axis; style distinct, stigma linear-oblong; ovules 6; fruit not known.

17. **Uvaria**[1] Linn., Sp. Pl. 536 (1753); Gen. Pl. ed. 5: 240 (1754). About 110 spp., tropics and subtropics of Old World; type *U. zeylanica* Linn., Ceylon. B.H. 1: 23; E.P. 3, 2: 30; King, Ann. Bot. Gard. Calc. 4: 14; Engl., Monogr. Afr. Anonac. 7; Sinclair, Gard. Bull. Singap. 14: 199; R. E. Fries, E.P. ed. 2, 17*a*, 2: 45, fig. 13.

Climbing or straggling shrubs or small trees, often with stellate indumentum; leaves alternate; flowers often terminal or axillary, extra-axillary, or leaf-opposed, mostly solitary, rarely in short racemes or on the trunk or older branches; sepals 3, valvate; petals 6, biseriately imbricate, sometimes united at the very base; torus pubescent or tomentose; stamens numerous, connective truncate or subfoliaceous; carpels numerous, rarely few, narrow; style short, thick, often pilose outside; ovules numerous, biseriate; fruits berry-like, oblong or ovoid or subglobose, several-seeded or by abortion 1-seeded, mostly more or less stipitate; seed subhorizontal, with or without a short aril.

18. **Dasoclema** J. Sinclair, Gard. Bull. Singap. 14: 273 (1955). 1 sp., *D. marginalis* (Scheff.) Sinclair (*Monocarpia siamensis Craib*), Thailand, Borneo, Sumatra. R. E. Fries. E.P. ed. 2, 17*a*, 2: 91.

Woody climber; branches and young leaves with minute stellate hairs; leaves oblong-elliptic, obtusely acuminate, with numerous lateral nerves, reticulate; flowers solitary,

---

[1] Synonyms of *Uvaria*: *Narum* Adans. (1763). *Pyragma* Nov. (1790). *Porcelia* Ruiz & Pavon (1794). *Orchidocarpum* L. C. Rich. (1803). *Marenteria* Thou. (1806). *Fitzalania* F. Muell. (1863). *Armenteria* Thou. ex Baill. (1882). *Uvariella* Ridl. (1922).

leaf-opposed; pedicels with a minute deciduous bract near the base; sepals 3, valvate, broadly ovate, minutely stellate-pubescent; petals 6, imbricate, in 2 series, subequal in length, the inner a little narrower and shorter, outer broad at the base, oblong; stamens with truncate connective; carpel 1, sessile; stigma disk-like, subsessile, split on one side; ovules about 8; mature carpel scarcely stipitate, ellipsoid lengthwise, somewhat warted, rusty-furfuraceous.

19. **Asteranthe** Engl. & Diels, Monogr. Afr. Annonac. 30, t. 88 (1901). *Asteranthopsis* O. Ktze. (1903). 2 spp., trop. E. Africa, type *A. asterias* (S. Moore) Engl. & Diels, trop. E. Africa. R. E. Fries, E.P. ed. 2, 17*a*, 2: 75.

Shrub or small tree; leaves slightly cordate at the base, acuminate; flowers bisexual, subsessile; sepals valvate, triangular, acuminate; petals imbricate, very much longer than the sepals, spreading, oblong-oblanceolate, connate at the base, densely silky outside, nervose within; stamens numerous, connective rounded; carpels about 10, 2-seriate, silky; stigma oblong; ovules biseriate; fruit not seen.

20. **Ellipeia** Hook. f. & Thoms., Fl. Ind. 1: 104 (1855). 14 spp., Malaya; type *E. cuneifolia* Hook. f. & Thoms., Malay Penins. B.H. 1: 23; E.P. 3, 2: 31; King, Ann. Bot. Gard. Calc. 4: 32, tt. 29–33; R. E. Fries, E.P. ed. 2, 17*a*, 2: 48.

Climbing shrubs; flowers paniculate; sepals 3, valvate, small; petals 6, rounded, imbricate, inner smaller; stamens with a dilated truncate connective; carpels numerous; styles oblong, pubescent; ovule 1, inserted above the middle of the loculus; fruits oblique.

21. **Cleistopholis** Pierre ex Engl., Engl. & Prantl., Nat. Pflanzenfam. Nachtr. 160 (1897). 6 spp., trop. Africa; lectotype. *C. glauca* Pierre ex Engl., Gabon. Engl. Monogr. Afr. Anonac. 33, partly; Sprague & Hutch., Kew Bull. 1916: 150; R. E. Fries, E.P. ed. 2, 17*a*, 2: 69.

Trees; leaves oblong, shining; flowers bisexual, fasciculate in the leaf-axils; sepals 3; petals 6, biseriate, outer valvate, spreading, flat, oblong or ligulate, inner concave and much shorter; stamens numerous, connective truncate; carpels numerous, stigma sessile, punctiform, minute; ovules 2–1; fruits tuberculate, subsessile.

22. **Duguetia** St. Hil., Fl. Bras. Mer. 1: 35, t. 7 (1825) (conserved name). *Aberemoa* Aubl. (1775). *Alcmene* Urb. (1921). About 70 spp., Cent. & trop. South America; type *D. lanceolata* St. Hil., Brazil. B.H. 1: 23 (excl. *Cardiopetalum*); E.P. 3, 2: 32; R. E. Fries, Act. Hort. Berg. 12: 28 (1934), and E.P. ed. 2, 17*a*, 2: 53, fig. 14 (excl. *Geanthemum*).

Trees or shrubs with stellate or lepidote indumentum; inflorescence subleaf-opposed or rarely from the trunk or leafless branches; sepals 3, valvate; petals 6, biseriately imbricate; stamens numerous, connective mostly capitate; carpels numerous, ovule solitary, basal, erect; fruits woody or fleshy, sessile, separate or more or less connate, often beaked.

23. **Duckeanthus** R. E. Fries, Act. Hort. Berg. 12: 106, t. 5 (1934). 1 sp., *D. grandiflorus* R. E. Fries, Brazil. R. E. Fries, E.P. ed. 2, 17*a*, 2:58.

Tree; leaves large, young shoots clothed with simple hairs; flowers bisexual, large, supra-axillary, pedicels bracteate at the base and in the middle, articulated above the lowest bract; sepals 3, membranous, large, valvate, easily falling away from the orbicular disk; petals 6, biseriate, outer a little shorter, erect-patent, imbricate; stamens very numerous, with a discoid-dilated connective; carpels with a clavate stigma; ovule 1, erect.

24. **Ellipeiopsis** R. E. Fries, Arkiv. Bot. Stockh. andra, ser. 3: 41 (1955). 2 spp., E. India, Indo-China; type *E. ferruginea* (Ham.) R. E. Fries, E. Bengal, Burma. R. E. Fries, E.P. ed. 2, 17*a*, 2: 49.

Shrubs, sometimes climbing, stellate-tomentose; flowers leaf-opposed, usually solitary, shortly pedicellate, pedicels bracteolate in the middle; sepals 3, free, valvate, rounded-ovate, acute, stellate-tomentellous; petals 6, longer than the sepals, imbricate in 2 series, subequal, at length divergent, rounded-ovate, tomentellous outside; stamens numerous, connective produced into a subglobose fleshy appendage; carpels several, subterete; stigma cuneate; ovules 1–2, basal; fruiting carpels numerous, sessile or nearly so, ovoid or ellipsoid, verruculose, 1-seeded.

25. **Lettowianthus** Diels, Notizbl. Bot. Gart. Berl. 13: 266, t. 9, fig. 2 (1936). 1 sp., *L. stellatus* Diels, trop. E. Africa. R. E. Fries, E.P. ed. 2, 17*a*, 2: 76.

Tree, clothed with simple hairs; flowers solitary from the axils of fallen leaves; sepals 3, valvate; petals 7–6, free, slightly imbricate, at length spreading stellately; stamens numerous, connective truncate; carpels many; style large, clavate, truncate; ovules 2, collateral; fruit long-stipitate, globose, mostly 2-seeded.

26. **Guatteria** Ruiz & Pavon, Prodr. 85, t. 17 (1784) (conserved name). *Cananga* Aubl. (1775) (not Hook. f. & Thoms. (1855)). *Afroguatteria* Boutique (1951). About 250 spp., Cent. and trop. America, West Indies, trop. Africa (1 sp.); type *G. glauca* Ruiz & Pavon,[1] Peru. B.H. 1: 23. Revision by R. E. Fries, Act. Hort. Berg. 12: 291 (1939), and E.P. ed. 2, 17*a*, 2: 78, fig. 20.

Trees or shrubs; flowers axillary or lateral, solitary or fasciculate, covered outside with silky or villous indumentum; sepals 3, valvate; petals 6, biseriate, outer slightly imbricate, inner more imbricate, spreading when open, subequal or the inner larger; stamens numerous, connective truncate-dilated beyond the loculi; carpels numerous; stigma capitate; ovule 1, erect; fruits stipitate.

27. **Ephedranthus** S. Moore, Trans. Linn. Soc., ser. 2, 4: 296, t. 21 (1895). 4 spp., trop. South America; type *E. parviflorus* S. Moore, Brazil. R. E. Fries, Act. Hort. Berg. 10: 175 (1931); E.P. ed. 2, 17*a*, 2: 68.

Trees; flowers unisexual, axillary, solitary, pedicels very short, covered in bud by broad imbricate bracts; sepals valvate; petals 6, subequal, erect-patent, free, biseriate, all imbricate above, open below; stamens numerous, connective dilated-truncate; female flowers with numerous carpels; ovule 1, erect; stigma capitate, sessile; fruits stipitate, 1-seeded.

28. **Kingstonia** Hook. f. & Thoms., Fl. Brit. Ind. 1: 93 (1872); King, Ann. Bot. Gard. Calc. 4, 1: 167, t. 216A. 1 sp., *K. nervosa* Hk. f. & Thoms., Malay Penins. Sinclair, Gard. Bull. Singap. 14: 184; R. E. Fries, E.P. ed. 2, 17*a*, 2: 96.

Trees; leaves oblong, nerves parallel; flowers bisexual, fasciculate on tubercles on the stem; sepals 3, ovate, persistent, connate at the base; petals 6, outer valvate, inner smaller, oblong, imbricate; stamens about 12, connective obliquely truncate; carpel 1; stigma sessile, peltate, crenate; ovules few; fruits globose; seeds 2-seriate, oblong, compressed, separated in 2 rows by dissepiments.

29. **Stenanona** Standl., Field Mus. Chicago Bot. 4, 8: 205 (1929). 2 spp., Cent. America; type *S. panamensis* Standl., Panama. R. E. Fries, Act. Hort. Berg. 10: 151 (1931), and E.P. ed. 2, 17*a*, 2: 49.

Small trees; flowers medium-sized, axillary or cauliflorus, solitary; pedicels with 2 bracts; sepals 3, valvate, caudate-acuminate; petals 6, biseriate, subequal, long-caudate-acuminate at the apex, outer imbricate and inserted at the base with the inner ones; stamens numerous, connective produced above the loculi in a deltoid lamina; carpels several, adpressed-strigose, style very short; stigma clavate-capitate, glabrous; ovules 2–8; fertile fruit 1, remainder abortive.

[1] Not *G. eriopoda* DC., as proposed in International Rules 1935.

30. **Pachypodanthium** Engl. & Diels, Notizbl. Bot. Gart. Berl. 3: 55 (1900). 4 spp., trop. Africa; type *P. staudtii* Engl. & Diels, Sierra Leone to Cameroons and Congo. Engl. Monogr. Afr. Anonac. 32, t. xi; R. E. Fries, E.P. ed. 2, 17*a*, 2: 60.

Trees; leaves elongated, clothed with stellate hairs; flowers terminating short thick branchlets and furnished with numerous short soon deciduous bracts; peduncles short, broadly compressed, furnished with 2 opposite bracts enclosing the flower-bud; sepals triangular, coriaceous, valvate; petals very imbricate, inner a little smaller; stamens numerous, connective dilated; carpels very numerous, at length more or less connate among themselves; ovules numerous; fruit like a syncarp, ellipsoid, muricate.

31. **Letestudoxa** Pellegr., Bull. Mus. Hist. Nat. Par. 26: 654 (1920).   2 spp. lectotype *L. bella* Pellegr., and *L. grandifolia* Pellegr., Congo. Pellegr., Mém. Soc. Linn. Normandie, 26: 13, t. 4 (1924); R. E. Fries, E.P. ed. 2, 17*a*, 2: 59.

Climbing shrubs, with simple hairs; flowers bisexual, solitary, subterminal, rarely lateral or leaf-opposed; peduncles short, with alternate bracteoles; sepals united in a calyptra falling off by a circular slit; petals 6, biseriately imbricate, coriaceous, subequal, large, narrowed at the apex, cordate at the base, shortly clawed; stamens numerous, connective scarcely dilated; carpels numerous, paired from the first as if 2-locular, afterwards coherent at the base; styles elongated; stigmas oblong; ovule 1, erect; syncarp composed of the partly united carpels, globose, muricate; seeds ovoid.

32. **Anonidium** Engl. & Diels, Notizbl. Bot. Gart. Berl. 3: 56 (1900). 5 spp., trop. Africa; type *A. mannii* (Oliv.) Engl. & Diels, S. Nigeria, Cameroons, Congo, and E. Africa. Engl., Monogr. Afr. Anonac. 36, t. xiv; R. E. Fries, E.P. ed. 2, 17*a*, 2: 156.

Trees; leaves large, oblong; flowers unisexual, in bracteate cymes on the old wood; bracts very concave; pedicels with 2 opposite bracteoles which at first enclose the buds; sepals valvate, ovate, more or less half as long as the petals; petals 6, outer valvate, inner a little smaller, slightly imbricate; stamens with a dilated connective, those of the female flowers more or less deformed; carpels of the male flowers deficient, of the female numerous, connate and immersed in the torus; style conspicuous, rounded and thickened at the apex; ovule 1, basal; fruit a large syncarp, of numerous fleshy carpels; seeds large, somewhat kidney-shaped.

33. **Fusaea** Safford, Contrib. U.S. Nat. Herb. 18: 64, d, 73 (1914), 3 spp., trop. South America; type *F. longifolia* (Aubl.) Safford, Guiana to Peru. R. E. Fries, Act. Hort. Berg. 10: 4 (1931), and E.P. ed. 2, 17*a*, 2: 58, fig. 15.

Straggling shrubs; leaves oblong-lanceolate; flowers bisexual, extra-axillary, solitary or paired; pedicels with 1–2 bracteoles; calyx 3-lobed, lobes ovate; petals 6, silky, imbricate, spreading, inner slightly narrower; outer stamens sterile, petaloid, imbricate, inner fertile, connective dilated at the apex; syncarp globose, smooth, pitted, the carpels united into a solid mass; seeds small, surrounded by edible pulp.

34. **Geanthemum** Safford, Contrib. U.S. Nat. Herb. 18: 66, t. 41 (1914). 5 spp., trop. South America; type *G. rhizanthum* Safford, Rio Janeiro, Brazil. R. E. Fries, E.P. ed. 2, 17*a*, 2: 57 (as sect. of *Duguetia*).

Tree-like, young parts covered with stellate-lepidote hairs; inflorescence mostly from subterranean branches; flowers bisexual; peduncles 1–many-flowered; calyx 3-partite, stellate-lepidote outside; petals 6, biseriate, outer open, inner imbricate; stamens all fertile, connective not produced; carpels free; stigma incurved, acuminate; fruits close together but free and easily separated; seeds similar to those of *Annona*.

35. **Tetrameranthus** R. E. Fries, Act. Hort. Bergiani, 12: 554, fig. 41 (1939). 1–2 spp., trop. South America; type *T. duckei* R. E. Fries, Brazil. R. E. Fries, E.P. ed. 2, 17*a*, 2: 166, fig. 38.

Tree; leaves elongated-obovate; indumentum composed of stellate hairs; flowers axillary, solitary; pedicels with 4 subverticillate bracteoles below the middle, articulated above the bracteoles; sepals 4, imbricate, broadly ovate; petals 8, conspicuously longer than the sepals, imbricate, ovate-oblong, subsimilar; stamens numerous; anthers shortly linear; connective dilated and acuminate; carpels numerous, ovoid; stigma 3-lobed, adpressed, sessile; ovules 2, lateral; fruit not known.

36. **Tetrapetalum** Miq., Ann. Mus. Lugd.-Bat. 2: 1 (1865–6). 2 spp., Borneo; type *T. volubile* Miq. B.H. 1: 955; E.P. 3, 2: 31; R. E. Fries, E.P. ed. 2, 17*a*, 2: 48.

Shrub with rambling branches, branchlets tomentose; flowers in dense spikes subopposite to the leaves; sepals 2, imbricate; petals 4, biseriately imbricate; torus convex; stamens very numerous, truncate; carpels numerous; style short; ovules numerous, biseriate.

Tribe 2. Miliusieae

Anther-connective widened and truncate at the apex:
  Petals 12, rather thick, 3 outer subovate, 9 inner narrowly tongue-shaped; carpels 1-ovuled   37. **Fenerivia**
  Petals 6:
    Margins of inner petals not inrolled or only slightly so; petals scarcely boat-shaped:
    Flowers solitary or subsolitary:
      Inner petals not clawed; ovules 2 or 1:
        Inner petals thick and concave at the base; pedicels short:
          Inner petals more or less triangular in cross section in the upper part; trop. America   38. **Heteropetalum**
          Inner petals subterete and acuminate in the upper part; trop. Asia
                  39. **Marsypopetalum**
        Inner petals flat and rather thin; ovules 2 or 1   40. **Phaeanthus**
      Inner petals clawed:
        Leaves narrowed at the base; ovule 1, erect; fruit 1-seeded
                  41. **Trivalvaria**
        Leaves cordate at the base; ovules several; fruits septate between the seeds   42. **Anomianthus**
      Flowers on simple pedicels in fascicles; ovules 6–4, 2-seriate; fruits berry-like; trop. Africa   43. **Brieya**
      Flowers paniculate; styles united; fruits berry-like, coherent beyond the middle; trop. W. Africa   44. **Piptostigma**
    Margins of the inner petals much inrolled, the inner petals thick and boat-shaped; flowers solitary, extra-axillary on long slender stalks; fruits dehiscent; seeds with a 2-lobed aril   45. **Cymbopetalum**
Anther-connective not truncate, more or less pointed:
  Inner petals broad, thick, and concave at the base; flowers usually solitary on simple long slender pedicels, precocious; fruits subglobose
                  46. **Saccopetalum**

Inner petals flat and thin, broad at the base, often connivent at the apex;
flowers axillary or extra-axillary   **47. Miliusa**
Inner petals clawed at the base, more or less connivent at the apex; flowers
axillary, fasciculate or cymose-paniculate   **48. Orophea**

37. **Fenerivia** Diels, Notizbl. Bot. Gart. Berl. 9: 355 (1925). 1 sp., *F. hetero-
petala* Diels, Madagascar. R. E. Fries, E.P. ed. 2, 17*a*, 2: 97.

Shrub with persistent coriaceous leaves; flowers axillary, solitary, shortly pedicellate;
sepals 3, united, very small, valvate; petals 12, rather thick, the outer 3 ovate, the inner 9
longer than the outer, narrowly tongue-shaped; torus short, cylindric, flat at the top;
stamens numerous, with short filaments; connective thickened over the loculi; carpels
numerous, glabrous, somewhat prismatic, with 1 basal erect ovule; fruit not known.

38. **Heteropetalum** Benth., Journ. Linn. Soc. 5: 69 (1861). 1–2 spp., type
H. brasiliense Benth., N. Brazil, Guiana, Venezuela. B.H. 1: 27; E.P. 3, 2:
34; R. E. Fries, Act. Hort. Berg. 10: 73 (1931), and E.P. ed. 2, 17*a*, 2: 87.

Tree; leaves coriaceous; flowers axillary; sepals 3, valvate; petals 6, biseriately valvate,
outer scarcely larger than the sepals, inner much larger, coriaceous, concave at the base,
erect-connivent around the stamens and carpels; stamens numerous, connective truncate-
dilated; torus flat; carpels numerous; stigma capitate; ovule 1, erect; fruits stipitate, 1-
seeded.

39. **Marsypopetalum** Scheff., Tijdschr. Nederl. Ind. 31: 342 (1870). 1 sp., *M.
pallidum* (Bl.) Kurz (*M. ceratosanthes* Scheff.), Malaya. E.P. 3, 2: 174; R. E.
Fries, E.P. ed. 2, 17*a*, 2: 125.

Small tree; flowers bisexual, supra-axillary, solitary; sepals 3, valvate; petals 6, biseriately
valvate, outer smaller and like and scarcely larger than the sepals, inner much larger, thick
and fleshy, very concave at the very base, erect around the stamens and carpels, otherwise
terete and acute at the apex, recurved; stamens numerous, connective truncate-dilated;
carpels numerous; stigma capitate-pilose; ovule 1, erect; fruits stipitate, 1-seeded.

40. **Phaeanthus** Hook. f. & Thoms., Fl. Ind. 1: 146 (1855). About 12 spp.,
Lower Burma and Andamans to New Guinea; type *P. nutans* (Wall). Hook
f. & Thoms., Malay Penins. to Moluccas. B.H. 1: 27; E.P. 3, 2: 34; King,
Ann. Bot. Gard. Calc. 4: 152, tt. 200A–201B; R. E. Fries, E.P. ed. 2, 17*a*, 2:
140.

Trees or climbing shrubs; flowers solitary, terminal or in extra-axillary fascicles; sepals 3,
small, valvate; petals 6, biseriately valvate, outer small and similar to the sepals, inner large,
flat; stamens numerous, connective truncate-dilated; carpels numerous, style oblong;
ovules 2–1, ascending; fruits stipitate, 1-seeded, ellipsoid or globose.

41. **Trivalvaria** Miq., Ann. Mus. Bot. Lugd. Bat. 2: 19 (1856). 6 spp., Indo-
Malaya; type *T. macrophylla* Miq., Malay Penins., Java, Borneo, Sumatra.
Ic. Bogor. 1: 143, t. 48; Sinclair, Gard. Bull. Singap. 14: 195; R. E. Fries,
E.P. ed. 2, 17*a*: 140.

Trees; leaves alternate, obovate-elliptic, acuminate; flowers solitary, extra-axillary; sepals
3, ovate, free; petals 6, biseriate, broad at the base, sessile, valvate, scarcely longer than the
calyx, thick, concave, outer 3 shorter, inner thicker and more concave, rather boat-shaped;
stamens numerous, connective rhomboid; carpels numerous, villous; ovule 1, erect; style
oblong, stigma obtuse; fruit shortly stipitate, juicy, ellipsoid, 1-seeded.

42. **Anomianthus** Zoll., Linnaea 29: 324 (1857–8). 1 sp., *A. dulcis* (Dun.)
Sinclair (*A. heterocarpus* Zoll.), Thailand to Java. B.H. 1: 27; R. E. Fries,
E.P. ed. 2, 17*a*, 2: 48.

Low shrub, with stellate indumentum; leaves cordate at the base; sepals 3, triangular; petals 6, biseriately valvate, outer slightly smaller, gradually changed to the inner ones, the latter slightly larger and dilated in the upper part; stamens numerous, linear, connective truncate; torus hemispherical; carpels up to 12; fruits stipitate, septate between the seeds.

43. **Brieya** de Wild., Fedde Repert. 13: 383 (1914). 1 sp., *B. fasciculata* de Wild., Congo. R. E. Fries, E.P. ed. 2, 17*a*, 2: 115 (in *Piptostigma*)

Tree; leaves veluntinous below, with numerous lateral nerves; flowers bisexual, rather large, fasciculate and pedicellate; sepals 3, ovate, acute, free; petals 6, biseriately valvate, outer similar to the sepals, inner longer and very long, flat; stamens numerous, connective dilated-truncate; carpels 5–2, stigma shortly stipitate, subglobose, scarcely lobed, deciduous; ovules 6–4, biseriate; fruits 5–2, berry-like, free.

44. **Piptostigma** Oliv., Journ. Linn. Soc. 8: 158, t. 12, fig. 1 (1865). About 15 spp., W. trop. Africa; type *P. pilosum* Oliv., S. Nigeria. B.H. 1: 957; E.P. 3, 2: 34; Engl., Monogr. Afr. Anonac. 54, t. xx; R. E. Fries, E.P. ed. 2, 17*a*, 2: 115, partly (excl. *Brieya*).

Trees; branchlets long-pilose; flowers fairly large, in panicles of cymes; sepals 3, free; petals 6, biseriately valvate, outer like the sepals and only slightly larger, inner longer and thinner, concave at the base, flat above; stamens numerous, connective truncate; carpels 6–4; stigma subsessile, depressed-globose; ovules 10–6, biseriate; fruits berry-like, coherent beyond the middle; seeds oblong.

45. **Cymbopetalum** Benth., Journ. Linn. Soc. 5: 69 (1861). 11 spp., S. Mexico to Peru and Brazil; type *C. brasiliense* (Vell.) Benth., Peru and Brazil. B.H. 1: 27; E.P. 3, 2: 33; R.E. Fries, Act. Hort. Berg. 10: 180 (1931), and E.P. ed. 2, 17*a*, 2: 160.

Small trees or shrubs; flowers solitary, terminal or lateral; sepals 3, valvate; petals 6, biseriately valvate, outer sessile and like the sepals, inner large, thick, involute-boat-shaped, with inflexed mucro; stamens numerous, connective truncate-dilated; carpels numerous; ovules several (14–4), sub-biseriate; fruits stipitate, oblong-cylindric, at length opening by a lateral split; seeds with a 2-lobed aril.

46. **Saccopetalum** Benn., Pl. Jav. Rar. 165, t. 35 (1838). 8 spp., India to E. Australia; type *S. horsfieldii* Benn., Java.

Trees; leaves deciduous; flowers precocious, solitary or subfasciculate at the leafless nodes; sepals 3, small, valvate; petals 6, biseriately valvate, outer small, sepaloid, inner much larger, saccate or boat-shaped at the base; stamens numerous, connective apiculate; carpels numerous; style ovate or elongated; ovules 6 or more; fruits subglobose. Included in *Miliusa* by Sinclair, Gard. Bull. Singap. 14: 377.

47. **Miliusa** Leschen. ex A. DC., Mem. Anon. 37, t. 3 (1832). *Hyalostemma* Wall., nomen. About 30 spp., Ceylon to S. China and Java; type *M. indica* Leschen. ex DC., Ceylon and S. India. B.H. 1: 28; E.P. 3, 2: 29; King, Ann. Bot. Gard. Calc. 4: 154, tt. 189B–206; R. E. Fries, E.P. ed. 2, 17*a*, 2: 98, partly (excl. *Saccopetalum* Benn.).

Trees or shrubs; flowers mostly bisexual, axillary or extra-axillary, solitary, fasciculate or cymose; sepals 3, small, valvate; petals 6, biseriately valvate, outer smaller, like the sepals, inner thin, much larger, the margins at first coherent; stamens numerous, loculi elliptic, connective more or less apiculate; carpels numerous; style oblong; ovules 1 or more; fruits globose or oblong, 1–many-seeded.

48. **Orophea** Blume, Bijdr. 18 (1825). *Mezzettiopsis* Ridley (1912). *Phoenicanthus* Alston (1931). 65 spp., Indo-Malaya to Philippine Isls. and New Guinea; type *O. hexandra* Blume, Andamans, Malay Penins., Java. B.H. 1: 29;

E.P. 3, 2: 35; King, Ann. Bot. Gard. Calcutta, 4: 101, tt. 144–9; Sinclair, Gard. Bull. Singap. 14: 390; R. E. Fries, E.P. ed. 2, 17a, 2: 130.

Trees and shrubs; flowers axillary, fasciculate or cymose-paniculate; sepals 3, ovate, free; petals 6, biseriately valvate, outer oval, inner clawed, the laminas coherent into a cap; stamens definite in number, with a narrow connective; carpels few to several; stigma sessile or subsessile, capitate or oblong; ovules 4–1, ascending; fruits of free spherical carpels and 1–2-seeded, or cylindric and constricted between the several seeds.

Tribe 3. UNONEAE

Key to subtribes and artificial groups

Carpels not united, or if slightly so then always remaining quite free in fruit, or carpel rarely 1   Subtribe 1. *Xylopiineae*

Petals 6	Group A
Petals 4	Group B (p. 104)
Petals 3–2, or rarely absent	Group C (p. 105)

Carpels united into a fleshy mass, especially in fruit   Subtribe 2. *Annonineae*
(p. 106)

Subtribe 1. *Xylopiineae*. Group A

Connective truncate or expanded and more or less covering the tops of the anther-loculi (to p. 92):
Ovules several to numerous (at least more than 2) (to p. 91):
Petals of the two, or rarely one, series similar or subsimilar and approximately of equal size, usually free from each other (to foot of p. 90):
Anthers transversely septate:
Receptacle not expanded below the sepals; flowers axillary, solitary, or fasciculate   49. **Xylopia**
Receptacle expanded into a rim below the sepals; leaves pellucid-punctate; flowers solitary, supra-axillary   50. **Cardiopetalum**
Anthers not transversely septate:
Petals not united at the base, at most slightly connivent:
Indumentum, when present, of stellate hairs, or lepidote:
Flowers on the young shoots, solitary:
Trees; fruits subsessile:
Leaves densely lepidote below; flowers extra-axillary
51. **Meiocarpidium**
Leaves not lepidote; hairs if present forked   65. **Polyceratocarpus**
Scandent shrubs; fruits stipitate; leaves glabrous or nearly so; flowers leaf-opposed or pseudo-terminal   52. **Rauwenhofia**
Subscandent shrubs; fruits not known; flowers axillary; E. trop. Africa   53. **Dielsiothamnus**
Flowers several together on the old wood; petals sharply contracted at the base over the stamens and carpels; fruits globose
54. **Drepananthus**
Indumentum, when present, of simple hairs:
New World genera:

Flowers leaf-opposed or terminal; fruits more or less stipitate, sometimes constricted between the seeds   55. **Desmopsis**

Flowers axillary; petals short, broadly ovate; fruits shortly stipitate, obovoid   56. **Trigynia**

Flowers axillary; petals oblong-linear; fruits sessile, globose
          57. **Diclinanona**

Old World genera:

Fruiting carpels slender, very torulose, or berry-like, spherical and reduced to 1 seed   58. **Desmos**

Fruiting carpels thick, not torulose; petals more or less spreading in the upper part:

Petals triangular-lanceolate, pointed, gradually narrowed and divergent from a broader base upwards:

Stamens very numerous:

Pedicels bracteate; carpels sessile, villous   59. **Meiogyne**

Pedicels not bracteate; carpels shortly stipitate
          60. **Monocyclanthus**

Stamens 12, subsessile in one row; carpels stipitate, constricted between the seeds   61. **Gilbertiella**

Petals linear to obovate, spreading from above the broadened concave base which remains closely adpressed to the stamens; sepals free or connate into a 3-lobed cupule
          62. **Cyathocalyx**

Petals shortly triangular-lanceolate or rounded-ovate, very thick, with flattened sides:

Carpels 3–2, not constricted between the seeds:

Buds ovoid; small trees; fruits shortly stipitate; New Guinea
          63. **Oncodostigma**

Buds depressed-globose; scandent shrub; fruits sessile, globose, verrucose; trop. Africa   64. **Exellia**

Carpels 3 or more, curved and constricted in fruit between the seeds; trop. Africa   65. **Polyceratocarpus**

Carpels 6–8, terete in fruit   66. **Polyaulax**

Carpels about 12, in fruit slightly constricted between the seeds; Philipp. Isls.   67. **Guamia**

Carpels numerous; fruits ovoid or shortly cylindric; trop. Africa
          68. **Uvariodendron**

Petals united into a tube at the base:

Petals crumpled and transversely plicate in bud; flowers on short axillary branchlets; trop. and S. Africa, Madag.
          69. **Hexalobus**

Petals not as above:

Stamens numerous, in several series; flowers shortly pedicellate or sessile   70. **Papualthia**

Stamens 9, in one series; flowers axillary, fasciculate 71. **Enneastemon**

Petals of the two series very dissimilar and usually very unequal in length, free from each other:

Carpels not sunk in the torus:
  Australian genus; imperfectly known   72. **Haplostichanthus**
  Tropical Asian genera:
    Petals free to the base:
      Inner petals not clawed   73. **Fissistigma**
      Inner petals clawed:
        Flowers bisexual   74. **Mitrephora**
        Flowers unisexual   75. **Pseuduvaria**
    Petals shortly united at the base   70. **Papualthia**
  Tropical African genera; inner petals not clawed:
    Fruits shortly stipitate, densely rusty-pilose with simple and branched hairs   76. **Uvariastrum**
    Fruits sessile, globose, verrucose   64. **Exellia**
  North and Central American genera:
    Outer petals broad, much broader than the inner   77. **Asimina**
    Outer petals narrow and elongated, spreading and recurved   78. **Deeringothamnus**
Carpels sunk in the cavity of the receptacle; outer petals subspathulate; Mascarenes   79. **Pseudoannona**

Ovules 2–1:

Peduncles at length indurated and thickened, more or less recurved and hook-like; petals with a dorsal horn-like appendage; trop. Old World   80. **Artabotrys**
Peduncles not as above, or if hooked then not indurated:
  Carpels more than 1:
    Petals subequal in length:
    Petals 2-seriate:
      Tropical American genera:
        Fruiting carpels not compressed, berry-like flowers small   81. **Unonopsis**
        Fruiting carpels laterally compressed, with a thick hard resinous pericarp; flowers medium-sized, silky-tomentose   82. **Guatteriella**
        Fruiting carpels terete, pericarp not resinous   83. **Guatteriopsis**
      Tropical Old World:
        Style nearly as long as the carpel, slender and terete;
        Carpels numerous, free; New Guinea   84. **Schefferomitra**
        Carpels numerous, connate, immersed in the receptacle; peduncles hooked; trop. Africa   85. **Pseudartabotrys**
        Carpels 6–3, free; flowers solitary, long-pedicellate; New Guinea   86. **Oreomitra**
      Style very short or almost absent:
      Petals free:
        All the petals more or less opening out in flower:
          Indumentum not stellate; flowers axillary or leaf-opposed   87. **Polyalthia**
          Indumentum stellate, flowers 1–3 together on one-year-old leafless branchlets   88. **Neo-uvaria**

Inner petals remaining more or less incurved over the stamens and carpels and often somewhat connivent; inflorescence extra-axillary, few- to 1-flowered   89. **Popowia**

Petals united at the base into a short tube; flowers fasciculate on the stem   90. **Woodiella**

Petals 1-seriate; flowers small in racemes; half of the stamens sterile; fruits 1-seeded   91. **Monanthotaxis**

Petals very unequal:

Petals united at the base   70. **Papualthia**

Petals free or only slightly connivent:

Petals with a contracted concave base; flowers extra-axillary or leaf-opposed   92. **Neostenanthera**

Petals not concave at the base:

Inner petals not clawed; flowers single, leaf-opposed or extra-axillary   93. **Richella**

Inner petals clawed; flowers single or fasciculate, axillary or extra-axillary   94. **Goniothalamus**

Carpel 1; petals linear, flat, inner smaller; stamens 9; ovules 2, subbasal   95. **Mezzettia**

Connective lanceolate, or not produced beyond the anther-loculi (not hiding the latter):

Carpels dehiscent on the inner side; seeds black and shining; fruits with a club-shaped stipe   96. **Anaxagorea**

Carpels indehiscent:

Petals subequal:

Tropical American genera:

Petals not apiculate; carpels 6–3:

Flowers supra-axillary on the young shoots; buds depressed-globose; carpels subglobose   97. **Bocagea**

Flowers borne on older leafless branchlets:

Buds globose; anthers not locellate; carpels globose

98. **Bocageopsis**

Buds oblong-linear; anthers multilocellate; carpels linear

99. **Hornschuchia**

Petals with an inflexed apiculus; carpels 2–1   100. **Onychopetalum**

Tropical Asian genera:

Connective small and not conspicuous; petals more or less triangular and short   101. **Alphonsea**

Connective very sharply pointed; petals strap-shaped, long; flowers pendulous   102. **Cananga**

Tropical African genera:

Gynoecium stipitate, especially in fruit   103. **Mischogyne**

Gynoecium not stipitate   104. **Atopostema**

Petals very unequal:

Inner petals not longer than the outer, not clawed:

Flowers densely crowded in small corymb-like racemes; ovules about 10

105. **Platymitra**

Flowers solitary or 2–3 together; ovule 1, basal   106. **Rolliniopsis**

Inner petals longer than the outer, clawed:
Stamens definite in number, with a narrow connective   48. **Orophea**
Stamens very numerous, connective not produced   107. **Ophryopetalum**

49. **Xylopia**[1] Linn., Syst. ed. 10: 1250, 1378 (1759). About 160 spp., tropics;
type *X. muricata* Linn., West Indies. B.H. 1: 28; E.P. 3, 2: 36; Engl. & Diels,
Monogr. Afr. *Anonac.* 57, tt. xxi–xxii; R. E. Fries, Act. Hort. Berg. 10: 86
(1931) (revision of Amer. spp.). See also Safford, Bull. Torr. Club, 39: 504
(1912); Sinclair, Gard. Bull. Singap. 14: 335 (Malayan spp.).

Trees or shrubs; leaves mostly distichous; flowers axillary, solitary or fasciculate; sepals 3,
valvate, connate at the base or beyond; petals 6, biseriately valvate, outer elongated, thick,
narrowly concave, connivent or scarcely open, inner included, triquetrous in the upper
part; stamens numerous, oblong; anthers transversely septate, connective truncate-dilated;
carpels few; style elongated, exserted; ovules 6–2, ventral; fruits oblong or elongated, often
opening.

50. **Cardiopetalum** Schlect., Linnaea 9: 319 (1834); R. E. Fries, Act. Hort.
Berg. 10: 194 (1931). *Stormia* S. Moore (1895). 1 sp., *C. calophyllum*
Schlecht., Brazil, Bolivia. R. E. Fries, E.P. ed. 2, 17a, 2: 159.

Shrubs or small trees; leaves pellucid-punctate; flowers solitary, supra-axillary; receptacle dilated-laminate, produced into an annulus beyond the insertion of the sepals; sepals 3,
reduplicate-valvate, thick; petals 6, biseriate, imbricate, connate in the lower part, the inner
slightly smaller; stamens numerous, anthers transversely locellate, connective flat at the
apex; carpels 25–14, sessile, hirsute; style cylindric-clavate; ovules several; fruits irregularly
torulose.

51. **Meiocarpidium** Engl. & Diels, Notizbl. Bot. Gart. Berl. 3: 54 (1900).
1 sp., *M. lepidotum* Engl. & Diels, trop. Africa. Engl. & Diels, Monogr. Afr.
Anonac. 30, t. x; R. E. Fries, E.P. ed. 2, 17a, 2: 91.

Tree, more or less clothed with peltate scale-like indumentum; flowers bisexual, extra-
axillary, solitary; sepals small, valvate; petals 6, valvate, subequal; stamens numerous, connective slightly truncate-dilated; carpels few; stigma subcapitate; ovules biseriate; fruits
subsessile, shortly cylindric, covered with grey silvery scales; seeds 1-seriate, compressed,
rounded on one side, shining.

52. **Rauwenhoffia** Scheff., Ann. Jard. Buit. 2: 21 (1885). 5 spp., Indo-China
to New Guinea and E. Australia; type *R. siamensis* Scheff., Thailand to
Cambodia. E.P. 3, 2: 35; Sinclair, Gard. Bull. Singap. 14: 228; R. E. Fries,
E.P. ed. 2, 17a, 2: 90.

Climbing shrubs, young parts with stellate hairs; leaves glabrous or almost glabrous;
flowers solitary, leaf-opposed or pseudo-terminal; sepals 3, valvate; petals 6, biseriately
valvate, thick, outer broadly ovate, open, inner much narrower and valvately connivent;
stamens numerous, connective dilated-truncate beyond the loculi; carpels several; stigmas
large, convolute at the apex; ovules several; fruits shortly stipitate, ellipsoid.

53. **Dielsiothamnus** R. E. Fries, Arkiv. Bot. Stockh. Andra, ser. 3, 1: 35
(1952). 1 sp., *D. divaricatum* (Diels) R. E. Fries, E. trop. Africa. R. E. Fries,
E.P. ed. 2, 17a, 2: 107.

---

[1] Synonyms of *Xylopia*: *Xylopicrum* P. Br. (1756). *Xylopicron* Adans. (1763). *Waria* Aubl.
(1775). *Unona* Linn. f. (1781) (not of auth.). *Bulliarda* Neck. (1790). *Krockeria* Neck. (1790).
Habzelia A. DC. (1832). *Coelocline* A. DC. (1832), *Patonia* Wight (1838). *Parartobotrys*
Miq. (1860). *Xylopiastrum* Roberty (1953).

Subscandent shrub; leaves large; indumentum sparse, of fasciculate or single hairs; flowers bisexual or rarely male, axillary, shortly pedicellate, pedicels with scale-like deciduous bracts; indumentum stellate or with simple hairs mixed; sepals 3, valvate, broadly ovate, densely hirsute outside; petals 6, valvate, thick and fleshy, outer ovate from a broad base, stellate-hirsute, nude inside; inner petals suddenly contracted towards the base, rhomboid, a little smaller than the outer; torus shortly conical; stamens numerous, linear-obconic; anthers lateral; connective obliquely dilated, apiculate; carpel 1, cylindric; stigma sessile, bilobed; ovules numerous (up to 25), 2-seriate; fruit ellipsoid-oblong, several-seeded, warted; seeds oblong.

54. **Drepananthus** Maing. ex. Hook. f., Fl. Brit. Ind. 1: 56 (1872). 10 spp., Malaya, New Guinea, Polynesia; lectotype *D. pruniferus* Maing. ex Hook. f., Malay Penins. E.P. 3, 2: 36; King, Ann. Bot. Gard. Calc. 4: 48, tt. 65–66; R. E. Fries, E.P. ed. 2, 17a, 2: 125.

Trees; leaves large; indumentum stellate; racemes short, fasciculate on woody tubercles on the trunk; sepals almost free; petals 6, valvate, 2-seriate, subequal, concave at the base, connivent; stamens numerous, connective truncate, with lateral loculi; carpels 12–4; stigma subsessile; ovules 4 or more, 2-seriate; fruits globose.

55. **Desmopsis** Safford, Bull. Torr. Bot. Club, 43: 184, tt. 7–9 (1916). 16 spp., Mexico, Cent. America, and Cuba; type *D. panamensis* (Robinson) Safford, Panama. R. E. Fries, E.P. ed. 2, 17a, 2: 50.

Shrubs or medium-sized trees; flowers bisexual, medium-sized, 1–few together, rarely on the trunk; pedicels long, with 2 bracts, the lower usually foliaceous, the upper mostly scale-like; sepals 3, valvate; petals 6, subequal, biseriately valvate, ascending, linear-oblong or lanceolate; stamens numerous, connective truncate-dilated; torus pilose; carpels 20–7; stigma depressed-globose or clavate-capitate, sessile, densely pilose; ovules 8–2, 2–1-seriate; fruits more or less stipitate, 1–few-seeded, sometimes constricted between the seeds; seeds grooved around the margin.

56. **Trigynaea** Schlecht., Linnaea 9: 328 (1834). *Teigyneia* Reichb. (1837). 5 spp., trop. South America; type *T. oblongifolia* Schlect., Brazil. B.H. 1: 25 (partly); R. E. Fries, Act. Hort. Berg. 10: 130 (1931), and E.P. ed. 2, 17a, 2: 157.

Shrubs or trees; leaves simple; flowers small, bisexual, sessile and single between the nodes; bracts absent; sepals 3, united only at the base; petals 6, free, ovate to rounded-ovate, similar, valvate; torus conical; stamens numerous, linear, connective not expanded over the loculi, latter transversely locellate; carpels 1–6; seeds 6–10, 2-seriate; fruiting carpels free, shortly stalked, rounded to ovoid, hairy; seeds 2-seriate, horizontal, compressed.

57. **Diclinanona** Diels, Notizbl. Bot. Gart. Berl. 10: 174 (1927). 2 spp. type *D. tessmannii* Diels, Peru. R. E. Fries, Act. Hort. Berg. 12: 2 (1934), and E.P. ed. 2, 17a, 2: 114.

Small trees; leaves long-cuspidate at the apex; flowers dioecious, mostly borne on the older branchlets; male flowers: sepals 3, free, valvate, ovate, conspicuous; petals 6, in 2 whorls, valvate, very narrow, outer bicallose above the base, inner a little smaller, with 2 oblong marginal glands; stamens in the males numerous, fewer in the females, connective dilated above the loculi; carpels few, hairy; ovules 6–9, 2-seriate; fruits sessile, globose.

58. **Desmos** Lour., Fl. Cochinch. 352 (1790). *Unona* of most authors, not of Linn. f. About 25 spp., S. China, Indo-Malaya, to Pacific Isls. and N.

Australia; lectotype *D. chinensis* Lour., Hong Kong and Hainan, and from
India to the Philippine Isls. and Malay Archip. (cult.). B.H. 1: 24; E.P. 3, 2:
33; King, Ann. Bot. Gard. Calc. 4: 53 (as sect. of *Unona*); Safford, Bull. Torr.
Club 39: 50 (1912); Sinclair, Gard. Bull. Singap. 14: 261 (excl. *Dasymaschalon*)
R. E. Fries, E.P. ed. 2, 17*a*, 2: 88, fig. 21.

Trees and shrubs; leaves various; sepals 3; petals valvate in 2 series, nearly equal, flat,
sometimes only 3; stamens numerous, the connective expanded into a subglobose or truncate cap; torus flat or slightly concave; carpels numerous; ovules 2–1-seriate; style ovoid or
oblong, recurved; fruiting carpels numerous, elongate and constricted between the seeds
or berry-like and spheroid.

59. **Meiogyne** Miq., Ann. Mus. Bot. Lugd. Bat. 2: 12 (1865–6). About 8 spp.,
Indo-Malaya, New Guinea; type *M. virgata* (Bl.) Miq., Malaya, New Guinea.
B.H. 1: 956 (in *Unona*). Sinclair, Gard. Bull. Singap. 14: 276, fig. 17; R. E.
Fries, E.P. ed. 2, 17*a*, 2: 96.

Leaves with dense oblique transverse veins; sepals 3, connate at the base; petals 6, biseriately valvate, flat, outer a little longer; stamens numerous, connective rhomboid at the apex;
carpels 5–2, sessile, villous, biseriately several-ovuled; stigma subcapitate, sessile; fruits
oblong, several-seeded; seeds in 2 rows, separated by spurious transverse septa.

60. **Monocyclanthus** Keay, K. B. 1953: 69, fig. 1. 1 sp., *M. vignei* Keay, W.
trop. Africa. R. E. Fries, E.P. ed. 2, 17*a*, 2: 164; Hutch. & Dalz. Fl. W. Trop.
Afr. ed. 2 (Keay), 1: 48, fig. 11.

Tree; leaves alternate, oblong-elliptic, pointed; flowers bisexual, fasciculate on the older
branches, shortly pedicellate; calyx slightly 3-lobed, saucer-shaped; petals 6, in a single
series, equal, valvate, narrowed from the base upwards; receptacle vertically ellipsoid;
stamens very numerous, densely crowded, oblong-linear; connective truncate dilated above
the extrorse loculi; carpels free, few (about 7), shortly stipitate above the stamens; stigma
truncate, margins involute; ovules 6–8, 2-seriate; fruit not known.

61. **Gilbertiella** Boutique, Fl. Congo Belge 2: 375 (1951); Bull. Jard. Bot.
Brux. 21: 124 (1951). 1 sp., *G. congolana* Boutique, Congo. R. E. Fries, E.P.
ed. 2, 17*a*, 2: 163 (1959).

Climber; indumentum simple; leaves elliptic, broadly and obtusely acuminate, with about
6 pairs of lateral nerves and reticulate between them; inflorescence terminal or axillary or of
1 or 2–3 fasciculate cymes, or flowers solitary and axillary, bisexual; sepals small; petals 6,
free, subequal in a single series, valvate, long-pointed; stamens 12, subsessile in one series,
anthers linear-oblong, extrorse, connective slightly produced; carpels 7, oblong, hairy;
stigma 2-lobed; ovules 5–7, 1-seriate; fruiting carpels stipitate, constricted between the
seeds; seeds oblong-cylindric.

62. **Cyathocalyx** Champ., Hook. f. & Thoms., Fl. Ind. 1: 126 (1855). *Monocarpia* Miq. (1865–6). 20 spp., India and Ceylon to Malaya, Philippine Isls.
and New Guinea; type *C. zeylanicus* Champ, Ceylon. B.H. 1: 24; E.P. 3, 2:
36; King, Ann. Bot. Gard. Calc. 4: 36, tt. 42–45; Sinclair, Gard. Bull. Singap.
14: 233; R. E. Fries, E.P. ed. 2, 17*a*, 2: 126, fig. 29.

Trees; indumentum of simple hairs; flowers fasciculate, terminal or leaf-opposed; sepals
3, free or connate into a trilobed cupule; petals 6, biseriately valvate, subequal, concave and
connivent at the base, lamina flat, spreading to filiform; stamens numerous, elongated, connective truncate; carpels solitary or up to 6; stigma large, sulcate; ovules several; fruits
berry-like, ovoid or globose.

63. **Oncodostigma** Diels, Engl. Bot. Jahrb. 49: 143, fig. 2 (1912). 3 spp., Malaya, New Guinea, New Hebrides; type *O. leptoneura* Diels, New Guinea. Sinclair, Gard. Bull. Singap. 14:274; R. E. Fries, E.P. ed. 2, 17*a*, 2: 120, fig. 27.

Tree; leaves glabrous; flowers bisexual, solitary, pedicels short, bracteate at the base, borne on the leafy shoots; sepals short, broadly triangular; petals 6, valvate, subequal, thick and fleshy to coriaceous, narrowly triangular, outer silky-pilose, 3 inner minutely puberulous except for the concave base; stamens numerous, connective thickened at the apex; carpels 3–2, pilose; stigma sessile, large, ovoid; ovules numerous, 2-seriate; fruits very shortly stipitate, ellipsoid, rusty-tomentellous; seeds 3–5, transverse.

64. **Exellia** Boutique, Bull. Jard. Bot. Brux. 21: 117, with fig. (1951). 1 sp., *E. scamnopetala* (Exell) Boutique, SW. trop. Africa, R. E. Fries, E.P. ed. 2, 17*a*, 2: 135.

Scandent shrub, indumentum of simple hairs; leaves scattered, oblong-elliptic, shortly acuminate, base equal-sided, glaucous below, pinnately few-nerved; flowers bisexual, axillary, solitary or paired; pedicels bracteate at the base; buds depressed-globose; sepals 3, very small; petals 6, in 2 whorls, valvate in each, thick and coriaceous, the inner a little smaller than the outer; stamens 15–12, 2-seriate, connective dilated-truncate and concave; loculi 2, very short; carpels 3, free; stigma sessile, conical; ovules 20–15, 2-seriate; fruiting carpels sessile, globose, verrucose, with several transverse seeds.

65. **Polyceratocarpus** Engl. & Diels, Notizbl. Bot. Gart. Berl. 3: 56 (1900). *Dielsina* Ktze. (1903). *Alphonseopsis* Bak. f. (1913). 5 spp., trop. Africa; type *P. scheffleri* Engl. & Diels, trop. E. Africa. Engl. & Diels, Monogr. Afr. Annonac. 67, t. 23; Boutique, Fl. Congo Belge, 2: 362; R. E. Fries, E.P. ed. 2, 17*a*, 2: 105, fig. 24.

Trees; indumentum of simple hairs; leaves large, oblong, acuminate, pinnately nerved; flowers axillary, solitary or paired; bracteoles present; calyx orbicular, plate-like, spreading, much smaller than the petals; petals 6, in 2 whorls, valvate, free, coriaceous, the outer a little larger than the inner; receptacle subglobose or shortly cylindric; stamens numerous, subsessile; loculi linear; connective enlarged at the apex; carpels 9–5, cylindric-oblong; stigma sessile, pulvinate; ovules about 20, in 2 series; fruiting carpels sessile or subsessile, cylindric-oblong, recurved; seeds numerous, 2-seriate, thicker on one side, testa dull-purple, striolate.

66. **Polyaulax** Backer, Blumea 5: 492 (1945). 1 sp., *P. cylindrocarpa* (Burck) Backer, New Guinea, Java (Madoera). R. E. Fries, E.P. ed. 2, 17*a*, 2: 115.

Erect shrub; leaves reticulate; flowers axillary, solitary; pedicels very short, scaly; buds cone-like; sepals 3, triangular; petals 6, 2-seriate, free, valvate, all much larger than the sepals, 3 outer at first obliquely erect, then spreading, ovate, acute, a little fleshy, 3 inner erect, ovate-oblong, thickly fleshy, slightly excavated at the base, deeply many-grooved; torus convex, densely pubescent between the stamens; stamens numerous, cuneate, anther-loculi extrorse, connective broad, truncate; carpels 6–8, free; ovules 6–7, 1-seriate; stigma globose or oblong, caducous, fruiting carpels 1–7, shortly stipitate, terete; seeds 4–7, 1-seriate, vertically compressed.

67. **Guamia** Merrill, Philipp. Journ. Sci. Bot. 10: 243 (1915). 1 sp., *G. mariannae* Merrill, Marianne Isls. (W. Pacific). R. E. Fries, E.P. ed. 2, 17*a*, 2: 122.

Small tree; flowers solitary, shortly pedicellate, axillary or subterminal; sepals 3, valvate; petals 6, 2-seriate, valvate, thick; outer at length spreading, inner a little smaller, narrower, subconcave at the base, slightly connivent; stamens numerous, obconic, connective obliquely subtruncate; carpels about 20, pilose; stigma subcapitate, glabrous; ovules numerous; fruits stipitate, oblong-rounded, cylindric.

68. **Uvariodendron** R. E. Fries, Act. Hort. Berg. 10: 51 (1930). 11–12 spp., trop. Africa; lectotype *U. giganteum* (Engl.) Fries, Cameroons. R. E. Fries, E.P. ed. 2, 17*a*, 2: 103.

Erect trees or shrubs, young parts covered with simple hairs; leaves mostly large, lateral nerves numerous; flowers medium to large, bisexual, axillary or from the nodes of leafless branches or from the trunk, usually subsessile, pedicels sometimes with 2 series of bracts; sepals 3, valvate; petals 6, 2-seriate, free, thick, silky outside, subequal, rounded-ovate or oblong, valvate in each series, narrowed towards the base; stamens very numerous, linear, anthers nearly sessile, loculi narrowly linear; connective truncate-dilated at the top; carpels numerous, silky, style very short; stigma truncate; ovules several to numerous, 2-seriate; fruiting carpels subsessile, ovoid or shortly cylindric; seeds 2-seriate, flattened, reniform.

69. **Hexalobus** A. DC., Mem. Anon. 36, t. 5A (1832). 6 spp., trop. and S. Africa, Madagascar; type *H. monopetalus* (A. Rich.) Engl. & Diels (*H. senegalensis* A. DC.), Senegal to Niger and Nile and N. Transvaal. B.H. 1: 24; E.P. 3, 2: 26; Engl. & Diels, Monogr. Afr. *Anonac.* 55, t. xx. R. E. Fries, E.P. ed. 2, 17*a*, 2: 74, fig. 19; Cavaco, Humbert Fl. Madag. Fam. 78*e Annonaceae*: 40.

Trees or shrubs; flowers bisexual, often large, on short axillary branchlets; sepals 3, valvate; petals 6, biseriately valvate, connate at the base into a short tube, subequal, crumpled in bud; stamens numerous, connective truncate; carpels 12–3; style bilobed; ovules numerous, 2-seriate; fruits berry-like, few, sessile or shortly stipitate; seeds numerous.

70. **Papualthia** Diels, Engl. Bot. Jahrb. 49: 138, fig. 1 (1912). 8 spp., Philippine Isls. and New Guinea; lectotype *P. pilosa* Diels. R. E. Fries, E.P. ed. 2, 17*a*, 2: 97.

Trees; leaves more or less unequal-sided at the base; indumentum of simple hairs; flowers bisexual or dioecious, shortly stalked or sessile; sepals 3, united at the base; petals thick or coriaceous, sometimes connate at the base, subequal or the inner smaller, connivent; stamens numerous, connective broadened; carpels 3 or more; ovules several to 2; fruits free, subglobose.

71. **Enneastemon** Exell, Journ. Bot. 1932: suppl. 1: 209, fig. 1. About 10 spp., trop. Africa; type *E. angolensis* Exell, Angola. R. E. Fries, E.P. ed. 2, 17*a*, 2: 163.

Trees or shrubs, often climbing; hairs simple; leaves usually with two glands at the base; flowers bisexual, small, axillary; sepals 3, united at the base; petals 6, sessile in one series, valvate, free or shortly united at the base, 3 longer and covering the others in bud; stamens 9–11, rarely 6, in one series, connective ending in a thick 3-angled tip; carpels 6–11; style short, stigma bifid; ovules 3–8; fruits free, more or less stipitate, contracted between the seeds.

72. **Haplostichanthus** F. Muell., Vict. Nat. 7; 180 (1891). 1 sp., *H. johnsonii* F. Muell., Mt. Bartle Frere, N. Australia. E.P.N. 161; R. E. Fries, E.P. ed. 2, 17*a*, 2: 164.

Shrub; flowers bisexual, small; sepals 3, deltoid, valvate; petals 6, uniseriately valvate, connate towards the base, 3 deltoid, the other 3 twice as long and semi-elliptic, all for some time connivent; stamens about 30, connective almost truncate-peltate; carpels 6, stigmas 6, depressed; fruits not seen.

73. **Fissistigma** Griff., Notulae 4: 706 (1854). *Melodorum* Dunal ex Hook. f. & Thoms. (1855) (not Lour. 1790). *Kentia* Blume (1828), not Adans. (1763). *Schnittspahnia* Reichb. (1841). *Pyramidanthe* and *Mitrella* Miq. (1865). *Ancana* F. Muell. (1869). About 70 spp., E. India to S. Yunnan and to NE.

Australia; type *F. scandens* (Griff.) Merr., India. B.H. 1: 28 (excl. *Cyatho-stemma* Griff.); E.P. 3, 2: 34; Sinclair, Gard. Bull. Singap. 14: 349.

Climbing shrubs; flowers single or several together, terminal, leaf-opposed or axillary, covered with hairs; sepals 3, small, valvate; petals 6, biseriately valvate, outer lanceolate-ovate, fleshy, inner subsimilar and smaller or triquetrous in the upper part; stamens numerous, connective oval, oblong or truncate above the loculi; carpels usually numerous; style oblong; ovules 2 or more and 2-seriate; fruit stipitate, spherical or ovoid.

74. **Mitrephora** Hook. f. & Thoms., Fl. Ind. 1: 112 (1855). *Kinginda* O. Ktze. (1891). About 40 spp., S. India to S. Yunnan, Indo-China, Malaya, Philippine Isls. to NE. Australia; type *M. obtusa* Hook. f. & Thoms., Malay Penins. and Java. B.H. 1: 26; E.P. 3, 2: 35; King, Ann. Bot. Gard. Calc. 4: 111, partly, tt. 152B–155; Sinclair, Gard. Bull. Singap. 14: 463; R. E. Fries, E.P. ed. 2, 17a, 2: 136, fig. 32.

Trees, often very tall; leaves coriaceous, with conspicuous close parallel nerves; sepals 3, rounded; petals 6, biseriately valvate, outer ovate, inner clawed, lamina vaulted; stamens numerous, connective truncate at the top; carpels numerous, oblong; ovules numerous, 2-1-seriate; fruits free, ovoid to rounded, usually stipitate.

75. **Pseuduvaria** Miq., Fl. Ned. Ind. 1, 2: 32 (1858). 15 spp., Burma, Indo-China, Malaya, Philippine Isls., New Guinea; type *P. reticulata* (Bl.) Miq., Burma to Java. Merrill, Philipp. Journ. Sci 10: 255 (1915); Sinclair, Gard. Bull. Singap. 14: 401; R. E. Fries, E.P. ed. 2, 17a, 2: 134.

Shrubs or trees; flowers dioecious; calyx 3-partite; petals 6, biseriately valvate, outer ovate, inner clawed; stamens numerous, connective truncate-capitate; carpels several; 5-2-ovulate, with infertile stamens at their base in the female flowers; stigma small; sub-sessile; fruits stipitate.

76. **Uvariastrum** Engl., Monogr. Afr. Anonac. 31, t. 10, fig. b (1901). 7 spp., W. trop. Africa; type *U. pierreanum* Engl., Gabon. R. E. Fries, E.P. ed. 2, 17a, 2: 104.

Shrubs; flowers rather large, axillary or at the nodes of the branches, subreflexed; sepals 3, large, valvate; petals 6, valvate, inner usually smaller than the outer; stamens numerous, connective enlarged, transverse and rhomboid; carpels 7-3, oblong, long-pilose; ovules about 30, 2-seriate; style very short, stigma broad, bilobed, with involute verrucose margins; fruits large, very shortly stipitate, ovoid, subacute, densely rusty-pilose with simple and bunched hairs; seeds 30-18, oblong, compressed, the endosperm penetrated by numerous leathery layers from the testa.

77. **Asimina** Adans., Fam. 2: 365 (1763). *Orchidocarpum* Mich. (1803). *Pityothamnus* Small (1933). 8 spp., North America, West Indies; type *A. triloba* (Linn.) Dunal, Great Lake reg. to Texas. B.H. 1: 24; E.P. 3, 2: 31; Britt. & Brown, Fl. N. States and Canada, 2: 83; Small, Fl. SE. United States, 447; R. E. Fries, Act. Hort. Berg. 12: 546 (1939), and E.P. ed. 2, 17a, 2: 69, fig. 18.

Small trees or dwarf shrubs; flowers lateral or axillary, nodding; sepals 4-3, much shorter than the petals, ovate, valvate; petals 8-6, biseriate, inner series valvate, outer much broader and larger than the inner; stamens 15-3, connective glandular; carpels 15-3, free; ovules numerous, biseriate; fruits fleshy, oblong, berry-like; seeds flat, enclosed by a fleshy aril.

78. **Deeringothamnus** Small, Bull. Torr. Bot. Cl. 51: 389 (1924). 2 spp., Florida; type *D. pulchellus* Small. R. E. Fries, E.P. ed. 2, 17a, 2: 71. J. K. Small, Addisonia, 11: t. 369 (1926); loc. cit. 15: t. 489 (1930).

Low shrubs, with stems of two kinds fasciculate from a fusiform rhizome, some bearing leaves and some flowers; leaves spathulate-cuneate; flowers bisexual or polygamous, nodding, solitary or 3–2-together in the axils of leafy bracts; sepals 4–2, imbricate; petals 13–6, white or yellowish, elongated, biseriately valvate, recurved-spreading; stamens 21–14, connective gland-like; carpels 6–1; stigma subulate, deciduous; ovules 8–3; fruits berry-like, oblong, stipitate, 4–1-seeded, more or less torulose or constricted in the middle.

79. **Pseudannona** Safford, Journ. Wash. Acad. Sci. 3: 17 (1913). 2 (or 3) spp., Mauritius; type *P. amplexicaulis* (Lam.) Safford. R. E. Fries, E.P. ed. 2, 17*a*, 2: 113.

Shrubs or climbers; flowers solitary, axillary; calyx gamosepalous, subtriangular or 3-lobed; petals 6, biseriate, all valvate, outer 3 longer and broader, subspathulate, inner triquetrous at the apex; receptacle depressed in the middle; stamens numerous, with a broad connective; carpels immersed in the cavity of the receptacle, the styles emerging from it and slender with recurved stigmatose apex; ovules several, 2-seriate; fruits free, several-seeded.

80. **Artabotrys** R. Br., Bot. Reg. t. 423 (1820). *Ropalopetalum* Griff. (1845). *Parabotrys* C. Muell. (1868). About 100 spp., Old World tropics and subtropics; type *A. uncinatus* (Lam.) Merr. (*A. odoratissimus* R. Br.), widely cultivated S. India to Formosa. B.H. 1: 24; E.P. 3, 2: 35; Engl. & Diels, Monogr. Afr. *Anonac.* 70, t. 26; Sinclair, Gard. Bull. Singap. 14: 246; R. E. Fries, E.P. ed. 2, 17*a*, 2: 123.

Trailing or climbing shrubs; flowers solitary or fasciculate, the common peduncle often hardened and hook-like; sepals 3, valvate; petals 6, subequal, biseriately valvate, concave at the base, connivent around the stamens and carpels; stamens numerous, connective dilated and truncate, the outer sometimes transformed into staminodes; carpels numerous; ovules 2, erect or superposed from the base; style ovate or linear-oblong.

The generic name refers to the hooked inflorescence and not to any edible qualities as stated by both Wittstein and Fries.

81. **Unonopsis** R. E. Fries, K. Sv. Vet. Akad. Handl. 34: pt. 5, 26, t. 4, ff. 3–8 (1900). 12 spp., West Indies and trop. South America; type *U. angustifolia* R. E. Fries, Brazil. R. E. Fries, E.P. ed. 2, 17*a*, 2: 100.

Trees; flowers bisexual, small; sepals 3, valvate; petals 6, subequal, biseriately valvate, broadly ovate, concave, rather thick; stamens numerous, connective truncate-dilated; carpels few or numerous; ovules solitary or few; fruits berry-like, stipitate; seeds solitary or few and l-seriate, horizontal.

82. **Guatteriella** R. E. Fries, Act. Hort. Berg. 12: 540, fig. 39 (1939). 1 sp., *G. tomentosa* R. E. Fries, Brazil. R. E. Fries, E.P. ed. 2, 17*a*, 2: 87.

Small tree or shrub; leaves large, acuminate; flowers medium-sized, silky-tomentose, axillary, solitary; pedicels short, articulated, bracteolate towards the base; sepals 3, valvate; petals 6, valvate, subequal; stamens numerous; anthers linear, with a disk-like enlarged connective; carpels numerous; stigma clavate; ovules solitary, basal, erect; fruits shortly stipitate, clavate-ellipsoid or laterally compressed, tomentose, pericarp thick, hard, full of resin.

83. **Guatteriopsis** R. E. Fries, Act. Hort. Berg. 12: 108, tt. 6–8 (1934) and 275, t. 8 (1937). 4 spp., trop. America; type *G. sessiliflora* (Benth.) R. E. Fries, Brazil, Peru. R. E. Fries, E.P. ed. 2, 17*a*, 2: 87.

Trees with simple hairs; leaves medium to large, oblong-oblanceolate; flowers axillary, bisexual; pedicels short, jointed above the middle, lower part bracteate; sepals 3, free, thickly coriaceous, valvate; petals 6, valvate in 2 series, subequal, free, rhomboid-ovate, thick, rigid, spreading; torus shortly columnar-conical, concave at the apex; stamens numerous; filaments short; anthers linear, extrorse, connective dilated and disk-like above the loculi; carpels several; ovule 1, basal, erect; stigmas conglutinate, clavate, hairy at the truncate apex; fruiting carpels stipitate, fusiform or elongated-oval, terete.

84. **Schefferomitra** Diels, Engl. Bot. Jahrb. 49: 152, fig. 4 (1912). 1 sp., *S. subaequalis* (Scheff.) Diels, New Guinea. R. E. Fries, E.P. ed. 2, 17*a*, 2: 133.

Climbing shrub, young parts densely rusty-pubescent; flowers bisexual; sepals 3, triangular; petals valvate, 3 outer pilose, 3 inner slightly shorter than the outer, shortly clawed, coherent at the apex and forming a loose cap; stamens numerous, connective ovoid; carpels several; style subterete, grooved; ovule 1; fruits several, stipitate, somewhat rounded, apiculate.

85. **Pseudartabotrys** Pellegr., Bull. Mus. Hist. Nat. Paris, 26: 656 (1920). 1 sp., *P. letestui* Pellegr., Congo (Mayombe). R. E. Fries, E.P. ed. 2, 17*a*, 2: 124.

Trailing or climbing shrub; flowers bisexual, solitary, peduncles hooked but not indurated; sepals 3, valvate; petals 6, biseriately valvate, subequal, free, deltoid at the base, concave, connivent around the stamens and carpels, flat above, long and narrowly linear, open; torus very thick, convex with the carpels immersed; stamens numerous, connective truncate-dilated; carpels numerous, connate; styles fusiform, caducous; ovule 1, erect.

86. **Oreomitra** Diels, Engl. Bot. Jahrb. 49: 151, fig. 3 (1912). 1 sp., *O. bullata* Diels, New Guinea. R. E. Fries, E.P. ed. 2, 17*a*, 2: 133, fig. 31.

Erect or climbing shrubs, branches rusty-pilose; flowers solitary, long-pedicellate; sepals 3, triangular; petals 6, valvate, subequal in length, 3 inner with longer claws than the outer, connivent towards the apex; stamens numerous, connective truncate-dilated; carpels 6–3; style terete; ovule 1; fruits stipitate, subglobose.

87. **Polyalthia** Blume, Fl. Jav. Anonac. 68 (1829), partly. *Monoon* Miq. (1865–6). *Sphaerocoryne* Scheff. ex Ridl. (1917). About 90 spp., Old World tropics; type *P. subcordata* Blume, Java. B.H. 1: 25; E.P. 3, 2: 33; Sinclair, Gard. Bull. Singap. 14: 299; R. E. Fries, E.P. ed. 2, 17*a*, 2: 93.

Trees or shrubs; flowers sometimes unisexual, axillary or leaf-opposed; sepals 3, valvate or slightly imbricate; petals 6, biseriately valvate, flat, subequal; stamens numerous, connective truncate beyond the loculi; carpels numerous; style oblong; ovules 2–1, erect; fruits stipitate, globose or oblong, 1-seeded.

88. **Neo-uvaria** Airy Shaw, Kew Bull. 1939: 278. 2 spp., Indo-Malaya; type *N. foetida* (Maing. ex Hook. f. & Thoms.) Airy Shaw, Malacca. Sinclair, Gard. Bull. Singap. 14: 421; R. E. Fries, E.P. ed. 2, 17*a*, 2: 107.

Trees; leaves acuminate, stellate pubescent or fasciculate-tomentose; flowers small, yellowish, 1–3 together on one-year-old leafless branchlets, shortly pedicellate; sepals open in bud, spreading; petals 6, subequal, spreading, outer very open, inner valvate, slightly separated at the base, thicker at the apex, all densely tomentellous; stamens 30–20, connective very broad, convex-truncate; carpels 12–4, oblong-ovoid, pubescent; style clavate; ovules 2–1; fruits 12–1, medium-sized to large, oblong-ovoid, shortly stipitate or subsessile, tomentose; seed solitary, almost filling the carpel, testa bony.

89. **Popowia** Endl., Gen. 831 (1839). *Clethrospermum* Planch. (1848). *Cleistochlamys* Oliv. (1867). *Clathrospermum* Planch. (1862). About 100 spp., Old World tropics; type *P. piscocarpa* (Blume) Endl., Malaya, Philippine Isls. B.H. 1: 25; E.P. 3, 2: 35; Engl. & Diels, Monogr. Afr. *Anonac.* 43, tt. 17–19; Ridl., Fl. Mal. Penins. 1: 74; Sinclair, Gard. Bull. Singap. 14: 466; R. E. Fries, E.P. ed. 2, 17*a*, 2: 136.

Climbing shrubs; inflorescence extra-axillary, dichotomously branched, few-flowered, or 1-flowered; flowers sometimes unisexual; sepals 3, smaller than the petals; petals valvate, inner sometimes imbricate, 3 outer larger than the connivent inner ones; stamens numerous; carpels numerous or few; ovules 2–1, basal, or several and biseriate; stigma sometimes shortly bifid; fruits 1- or more-seeded.

90. **Woodiella** Merrill, Journ. R. As. Soc. Str. Br. 85: 187 (1922). 1 sp., *W. sympetala* Merrill, Borneo. R. E. Fries, E.P. ed. 2, 17*a*, 2: 98.

Small tree; flowers medium-sized, fasciculate on the stem, pedicellate; sepals valvate connate; petals valvate, thick, elongated, all connate up to 1 cm., outer elliptic or oblong-elliptic, inner narrower, oblanceolate; stamens numerous, oblong, connective obliquely truncate; carpels numerous; stigma orbicular, sessile, deciduous; ovule 1; fruiting carpels oblong-ovoid, shortly stipitate, narrowed at each end.

91. **Monanthotaxis** Baill., Bull. Soc. Bot. Par. 2: 878 (1890). 4 spp.; trop. Africa; type *M. congensis* Baill., Congo. E.P.N. 159; Engl. & Diels, Monogr. Afr. Anonac. 53; R. E. Fries, E.P. ed. 2, 17*a*, 2: 162.

Shrubs, young parts densely silky-pilose; leaves oblong or oblong-lanceolate; flowers small· in racemes, bisexual; sepals 3, ovate-triangular, coherent at the base; petals 6, 1-seriate thick, lanceolate, valvate; stamens 12 in one series and fertile, or 6 opposite the petals and 6 between the petals sterile; connective thick, obliquely truncate; carpels numerous (about 25), densely pilose; style long or short, slightly bilobed; ovule 1, inserted above the base; fruits shortly stipitate, ovoid, 1-seeded.

92. **Neostenanthera** Exell, Journ. Bot. 1935: Suppl.: 5. *Stenanthera* Engl. & Diels (1900), not of R.Br. (1810). 8 spp., trop. Africa; type *N. hamata* (Engl. & Diels) Exell, Sierra Leone to Ivory Coast, W. Africa. R. E. Fries, E.P. ed. 2, 17*a*, 2: 124.

Trees or shrubs, sometimes somewhat climbing; leaves acuminate, pubescent or glaucous below; flowers single or few together, leaf-opposed or extra-axillary, bisexual; sepals 3, valvate, nearly free, small; petals 6, valvate, outer very much longer than the inner, excavated at the base, suberect, inner excavated, thick, closely embracing the stamens; stamens numerous; anthers linear, connective elongated, dilated; carpels numerous, free, ovoid, produced into a linear style; ovule 1, erect; fruits stipitate, jointed at the insertion of the stipe and deciduous, broadly fusiform; stipes more or less persistent.

93. **Richella** A. Gray, Proc. Amer. Acad. 2: 325 (1852); Amer. Explor. Exped. 1: 28, t. 2 (1857). *Polyalthia* sect. *Oxymitra* Bl. (1829). *Oxymitra* Bl. ex Hook. f. & Thoms. (1855). *Friesodielsia* van Steenis (1948). About 45 spp., Old World tropics; type *R. monosperma* A. Gray, Fiji. B.H. 1: 26. For notes and other references see R. E. Fries, E.P. ed. 2, 17*a*, 2: 139.

Shrubs or climbers; flowers single, leaf-opposed or extra-axillary; bracts present; sepals large, valvate, free or united at the base; petals 6, free, valvate, 3 outer leathery, long and narrow, flat or 3-sided, broadened and concave at the base, inner much shorter than the outer, lanceolate or oblong, narrowed at the base and often open between, forming a pyramid above; stamens numerous, connective broadened over the loculi; carpels numerous, with club-shaped style and 1 ovule in the lower part; fruits free, stipitate, rounded or ellipsoid-cylindric.

94. **Goniothalamus** Hook f. & Thoms., Fl. Ind. 1: 105 (1855). *Atrutegia* Bedd. (1864). *Atrategia* Bedd. ex Hook f. (1872). *Beccariodendron* Warb. (1891). 50 spp., S. and E. India, Malaya, Philippine Isls., New Guinea, Polynesia; type *G. macrophyllus* Miq., Java. B.H. 1: 26; King, Ann. Bot. Gard. Calc.; Sinclair, Gard. Bull. Singap. 14: 423; R. E. Fries, E.P. ed. 2, 17*a*, 2: 133.

Small trees or shrubs; flowers solitary or fasciculate, axillary or extra-axillary; pedicels bracteate at the base; sepals 3, valvate; petals 6, biseriately valvate, outer thick, flat, inner smaller, shortly clawed, calyptrately coherent above the stamens; stamens numerous; anther-loculi remote, connective oblong or truncate; carpels numerous; style simple or bifid; ovules solitary or 4–2 and superposed; fruits 1–2-seeded.

95. Mezzettia Becc., Nouv. Giorn. Bot. Ital. 3: 187 (1871). *Lonchomera* Hook. f. & Thoms. (1873). 7 spp., Malaya; lectotype *M. umbellata* Becc., Borneo. E.P. 3, 2: 29; Sinclair, Gard. Bull. Singap. 14: 327; R. E. Fries, E.P. ed. 2, 17*a*, 2: 96.

Trees; flowers bisexual, small, greenish, axillary or fasciculate or umbellate at the defoliated nodes; sepals 3, ovate, valvate; petals 6, biseriately valvate, soon open and increasing in size, linear, flat, inner smaller; stamens 9, 2-seriate, anthers introrse, convex on the back, rounded-truncate beyond the loculi; carpel 1, ovate, apex marked by an excavated stigmatic cavity; ovules 2, subbasal; fruits berry-like, spherical, seeds 2, large, compressed.

96. Anaxagorea St. Hil., Bull. Soc. Philom. 91 (1825). *Rhopalocarpus* Teijsm. & Binn. ex Miq. (1865). *Eburopetalum* Becc. (1871). 27 spp., India, Malaya, Cent. and SE. America; type *A. prinoides* (Dun.) St. Hil. ex A. DC., Guiana and Brazil. B.H. 1: 25; E.P. 3, 2: 32; R.E. Fries, Act. Hort. Berg. 12: 6 (1934) (Amer. spp.); Sinclair, Gard. Bull. Singap. 14: 346; Fries, E.P. ed. 2, 17*a*, 2: 117, fig. 26.

Trees; flowers axillary, solitary, or fasciculate on the young branchlets, pedicellate; sepals 3, valvate, united at the base; petals 6, biseriately valvate, spreading, flat, subequal; stamens numerous, connective apiculate, inner sometimes deformed; carpels mostly few, style subglobose or oblong; ovules 2, erect from the base; fruits with a club-shaped stalk, dehiscent on the inner side; seeds not arillate, black and highly shining.

97. Bocagea St. Hil., Fl. Bras. Mer. 1: 41, t. 9 (1825), partly. 2 spp., Brazil; type *B. viridis* St. Hil. B.H. 1: 29 (excl. syn. *Oxandra* A. Rich.); E.P. 3, 2: 28; R. E. Fries, Act. Hort. Berg. 10: 139 (1931), and E.P. ed. 2, 17*a*, 2: 158.

Small trees or shrubs; flowers small, solitary, supra-axillary; sepals 3, united at the base; petals 6, subequal, biseriately valvate, inner more or less open towards the base; stamens 12–6, connective not thickened at the apex; carpels 4–3, style very short; stigma capitate; ovules 8–4, biseriate.

98. Bocageopsis R. E. Fries, Act. Hort. Berg. 10: 143 (1931). 3 spp., trop. South America; lectotype *B. multiflora* (Mart.), R. E. Fries, Brit. Guiana, Brazil. R. E. Fries, E.P. ed. 2, 17*a*, 2: 102.

Trees; leaves oblong-lanceolate, rigid; inflorescence sessile in the axils of fallen leaves; pedicels bracteolate and articulate at the base, with a bracteole above the joint; flowers very small ('minute'), bisexual; sepals 3, minute, united at the base; petals 6, rounded-ovate, biseriately valvate, inner open towards the base; stamens 23–16, connective produced beyond the anthers but not thickened; carpels 6–3, hirsute; stigma capitate-clavate, sessile; ovules 2, lateral; fruits globose, pisiform; seeds 2 or 1.

99. Hornschuchia Nees, Flora 4: 302 (1821). *Bocagea* St. Hil., partly (1825). *Mosenodendron* R. E. Fries (1900). 3 spp., trop. South America; type *H. bryotrophe* Nees. R. E. Fries, Act. Hort. Berg. 10: 132 (1931); van Steenis, Bull. Bot. Gard. Buitenz. 17: 458 (1948); R. E. Fries, E.P. ed. 2, 17*a*, 2: 159.

Shrubs or small trees with simple hairs; flowers small, cauliflorous or between the nodes; buds cylindric; bracts present; sepals 3, united high up with a cupular base; petals 6, free, linear-oblong, similar, valvate; stamens 6; anthers linear, locellate, connective not broadened, ending in a small tip; carpels 3, linear-oblong; stigma small; ovules 3–11, 2-seriate; fruiting carpels 3, or 1–2, shortly stipitate, narrowly ellipsoid or spindle-shaped; seeds arillate.

100. **Onychopetalum** R. E. Fries, Act. Hort. Berg. 10: 148, fig. 3 (1931). 4 spp., Brazil; type *O. amazonicum* R. E. Fries. R. E. Fries, E.P. ed. 2, 17*a*, 2: 102, fig. 23.

Trees; leaves oblong-elliptic; inflorescence many-flowered, sessile in the axils of fallen leaves; pedicels articulated above the basal bract; flowers minute, bisexual; calyx gamosepalous, margin sinuate; petals 6, concave, thick, inner valvate, with an inflexed apex, outer valvate, open towards the base; carpels 2–1, hirsute; style cylindric, stigma minute; ovules 4; fruit solitary, sessile, ellipsoid.

101. **Alphonsea** Hook. f. & Thoms., Fl. Ind. 1: 152 (1855). 20 spp., Indo-Malaya; lectotype *A. lutea* (Roxb.) Hook. f. & Thoms., SE. India and Malay Penins. to New Guinea. B.H. 1: 29; E.P. 3: 328; King, Ann. Bot. Gard. Calc. 4: 161, tt. 205*b*, 209–15; Sinclair, Gard. Bull. Singap. 14: 381; R. E. Fries, E.P. ed. 2, 17*a*, 2: 90.

Trees or shrubs; flowers crowded in pedunculate leaf-opposed or extra-axillary fascicles; sepals 3, small, valvate; petals 6, biseriately valvate, often saccate at the base, equal or the inner slightly smaller; stamens numerous, connective apiculate; carpels numerous to solitary; ovules few and 2-seriate or solitary and erect; fruits stipitate.

102. **Cananga** Hook. f. & Thoms. Fl. Ind. 1: 129 (1855) (conserved name) (not of Aubl. 1775). *Fitzgeraldia* F. Muell. (1867). *Canangium* Baill. (1868). 4 spp., Indo-Malaya; type *C. odorata* (Lamk.) Hook. f. & Thoms., widely cult. from S. India to New Guinea and Queensland. B.H. 1: 24; E.P. 3, 2: 33; King, Ann. Bot. Gard. Calc. 4; 49, tt. 67–68; Sinclair, Gard. Bull. Singap. 14: 323; R. E. Fries, E.P. ed. 2, 17*a*, 2: 92.

Tall trees; leaves large; flowers large, solitary or fasciculate, pendulous; sepals 3, valvate; petals 6, biseriately valvate, subequal, soon open, elongated, flat; stamens numerous, connective lanceolate and acute at the apex; carpels numerous; stigma subcapitate; ovules numerous, 2-seriate; fruits berry-like, stipitate or sessile; seeds immersed in pulp, testa punctate, with spine-like processes intruded into the endosperm.

103. **Mischogyne** Exell, Journ. Bot. Suppl. 1932: Suppl. 1: 213, fig. 2 (1932). 1 sp., *M. michelioides* Exell, Angola.

Shrub; leaves deciduous; flowers solitary on defoliated branches; sepals 3, valvate, thick, shortly connate at the base; petals 6, biseriately valvate, subequal; stamens numerous; anthers narrowly linear, filaments short, connective not produced; gynoecium stipitate, the stipe increasing in fruit; carpels numerous, free, about 20-ovuled, ovules 2-seriate; style truncate with involute margins; fruits subsessile, not constricted between the large seeds.

Fries has added a second species, *M. elliotiana* (Engl. & Diels) R. E. Fries, perhaps better left in *Uvariastrum* as placed by Sprague & Hutch.; the gynophore is very short and the style bilobed.

104. **Atopostema** Boutique, Bull. Jard. Bot. Brux. 21: 121, t. 4 (1951). 2 spp., trop. Africa; type *A. klainii* (Pierre) Boutique, Congo, Gabun. R. E. Fries, E.P. ed. 2, 17*a*, 2: 141.

Climbing shrub; hairs simple; leaves obovate-oblong to ovate-oblong, acuminate; flowers cauline, solitary or fascicled, bisexual, small, pedicellate; bracts and bracteoles present; sepals 3, much smaller than the petals; petals 6, in 2 whorls, valvate, contiguous at the apex, remote at the base, outer larger than the inner; stamens 9–8, alternating with as many appendages (staminodes); filaments connate into a short tube; loculi lateral and oblique, the connective not produced beyond the loculi; carpels 20, curved-sinuate; ovary cylindric, 2-ovuled; style distinct, stigma ellipsoid and more or less peltate; fruits shortly stipitate, 1-seeded, ellipsoid-globose, or 2-seeded and constricted between the seeds; seeds ellipsoid-globose.

The inflorescence and fruiting carpels greatly resemble those of *Bocageopsis* R. E. Fries (No. 98) from South America (Brazil, Guianas, and Venezuela), but *Atopostema* has 9–8 stamens (23–16 in *Bocageopsis*), and about 20 carpels with distinct styles (carpels 6–3 with sessile stigma in *Bocageopsis*).

105. **Platymitra** Boerl. Cat. Pl. Phan. Hort. Bot. Bog. 1: 33 (1899); Icon. Bogor. 1: 2–3, 179, t. 62 (1899). 2 spp.; type *P. macrocarpa* Boerl., Java, Sumatra. *P. siamensis* Craib, Thailand. R. E. Fries, E.P. ed. 2, 17*a*, 2: 130.

Trees; flowers small, long-pedicellate, densely crowded in small corymb-like racemes in the axils mostly of fallen leaves; sepals 3, connate into a 3-lobed cup; petals 6, valvate, 2-seriate, outer sessile, ovate, spreading when open, inner scarcely smaller, narrow at the base, coherent above the stamens and carpels, the margins at length a little divergent; stamens 24–20, connective narrow, not produced; carpels 3–2; ovules about 10, 2-seriate; stigma small, horseshoe-shaped; fruits large, globose or ovoid, solitary or paired, several-seeded.

106. **Rolliniopsis** Safford, Journ. Wash. Acad. Sci. 6: 197, figs. 1–2 (1916). 4 spp., Brazil; type *R. discreta* Safford, E. Brazil. R. E. Fries, Act. Hort. Berg. 12: 190 (1934). R. E. Fries, E.P. ed. 2, 17*a*, 2: 156.

Small trees or shrubs; flowers bisexual, solitary or 2–3 together; calyx 3-lobed; corolla sympetalous, lobes 6, valvate, the outer produced into rounded compressed wings, inner much smaller, connivent and almost hiding the carpels and stamens; stamens numerous, with a slender connective; carpels several to numerous; ovule 1, basal; receptacle at length indurated; fruits separate, small, pear-shaped or ovoid, 1-seeded; seeds marked by a line.

107. **Ophrypetalum** Diels, Notizbl. Bot. Gart. Berl. 13: 269, t. 9, fig. 1 (1936). 1 sp., *O. odoratum* Diels, trop. E. Africa (Tanganyika Territ.), R. E. Fries, E.P. ed. 2, 17*a*, 2: 76.

Shrub or weak-stemmed tree; flowers sometimes precocious, solitary or few, fasciculate on the branches; sepals 3, valvate, thick; petals 6, 3 outer subinduplicate-valvate, 3 inner long-clawed, contracted above the concave claw and below the apex into a broadly cordate-reniform lamina with the basal part covered with very numerous setae; torus almost flat under the stamens, but excavated under the carpels; stamens very numerous, connective not produced, obtuse; carpels 18–12, with 6–4 ovules, pilose, narrowed into a subterete slightly curved style; fruits subsessile, obliquely lanceolate.

Subtribe 1. *Xylopiineae.* **Group B**

Carpels more than 1:
Flowers bisexual; petals linear; anther-connective rounded-truncate; Malaya   108. **Disepalum**
Flowers dioecious; petals ovate, free, thick; connective of stamens not produced; carpels hexagonal; tropical Africa   109. **Tetrastemma**
Flowers monoecious?; petals ovate, connate into a tube; carpels terete; tropical Africa   110. **Uvariopsis**
Carpel 1; Mexico   111. **Tridimeris**

108. **Disepalum** Hook. f., Trans. Linn. Soc. Bot. 23: 156, t. 20 (1862). 4 spp., Malaya; type *D. anomalum* Hook. f., Borneo. B.H. 1: 25; E.P. 3, 2: 33; van Steenis, Bull. Bot. Gard. Buitenz. 17: 405 (1948); R. E. Fries, E.P. ed. 2, 17*a*, 2: 128.

Trees or shrubs; flowers solitary or paired, terminal, long-pedicellate; sepals 2 (3), valvate, large, ovate, at length reflexed; petals 4–8, linear-spathulate, remote from each other; torus concave in the middle; stamens numerous, connective orbicular-dilated at the apex; carpels

10 or more; style short and terete; ovule solitary, erect; fruits 1-seeded, long-stipitate, ellipsoid, inserted on the enlarged woody torus.

109. **Tetrastemma** Diels, Engl. Bot. Jahrb. 39: 475, fig. 1 (1907). 1 sp., *T. dioicum* Diels, Cameroons.

Cauliflorous trees; flowers dioecious, the female much larger than the male and on very long pedicels; calyx disk-like or saucer-shaped, obsoletely bilobed; petals 4, valvate, equal, very thick and fleshy, excavated on the inner side; torus remarkably convex; stamens very numerous, small, soon falling off; carpels numerous; stigma depressed-turbinate, rugose; ovules 2-seriate, numerous; fruit not known.

110. **Uvariopsis** Engl., Notizbl. Bot. Gart. Berl. 2: 298 (1899). 2 spp., type *U. zenkeri* Engl., and *U. longipes* Engl., Cameroons. Engl. & Diels, Monogr. Afr. Anonac. 38, t. 15A.

Shrubs; flowers solitary, unisexual; sepals 2, medium-sized; petals 4, valvate, equal, connate at the base; stamens numerous, connective not produced at the apex; carpels numerous, pilose; ovules numerous, 2-seriate.

111. **Tridimeris** Baill., Adansonia, 9: 219 (1869). 1 sp., *T. hahniana* Baill., Mexico. E.P. 3, 2: 273; R. E. Fries, Act. Hort. Berg. 10: 178 (1931). R. E. Fries, E.P. ed. 2, 17*a*, 2: 71.

Small tree or shrub; flowers bisexual, small, axillary, solitary, peduncle with 2–4 bracts near the base; sepals 2; petals 4, 2-seriate, free, much longer than the sepals, subequal, valvate; stamens numerous, short, connective truncate-dilated; carpel 1; ovules several, 2-seriate; fruit large; seeds applanate, semiorbicular.

Subtribe 1. *Xylopiineae*. Group C.

Ovules 2 or more:
Anther-connective truncate at the apex; flowers bisexual:
  Petals linear-lanceolate; tropical Asia and America   112. **Dasymaschalon**
  Petals ovate or suborbicular:
    Petals more or less keeled in the middle or sometimes absent
                                          96. **Anaxagorea**
      Petals not keeled:
        Petals large, subreniform, 3·5 cm. long; tropical Asia   113. **Petalolophus**
        Petals small, ovate-orbicular, about 1 cm. long; tropical Africa
                                          114. **Dennettia**
Anther-connective not produced at the apex; cauliflorous, the flowers dioecious on very long pedicels; tropical Africa   115. **Thonnera**
Ovule 1; petals opposite the sepals; tropical Africa   116. **Enantia**

112. **Dasymaschalon** Dalle Torre & Harms, Siphonog. 174 (1901): Finet & Gagnep., Bull. Soc. Bot. Fr. 53: Mem. 4: 143 (1906). About 15 spp., Indo-Malaya; type *D. blumei* Finet & Gagnep., Burma and Andamans to Java and Borneo. R. E. Fries, E.P. ed. 2, 17*a*, 2: 115.

Small trees; flowers solitary, axillary or leaf-opposed or subterminal; sepals 3, small; petals valvate, sometimes spirally twisted in the upper part, linear-lanceolate, coherent at the base; stamens numerous; connective truncate; carpels numerous, often stipitate; ovules 2 or more; fruits stipitate, mostly moniliform, rarely 1-seeded.

113. **Petalolophus** K. Schum. & Lauterb., Nachtr. Fl. Deutsch Schutzgeb. Sudsee, 265 (1905). 1 sp., *P. megalophus* K. Schum. & Lauterb., New Guinea. R. E. Fries, E.P. ed. 2, 17*a*, 2: 132, fig. 30 ('*Petalophus*').

Low tree; leaves linear-lanceolate, large; flowers bisexual, large, 2 or more together in the leaf-axils on long slender peduncles, long-pedicellate; sepals ovate, small; petals 3, large, valvate, cucullate at the base, lamina compressed laterally, suborbicular, crenulate; stamens numerous, connective truncate; carpels numerous, globose, separate; stigma rounded, sessile; ovules 9–8, 2-seriate.

114. **Dennettia** E. G. Baker, Cat. Talb. Nig. Pl. 5, t. 2 (1913). 1 sp., *D. tripetala* E. G. Baker, S. Nigeria. R. E. Fries, E.P. ed. 2, 17*a*, 2: 106.

Tree; flowers bisexual, solitary or paired, borne on the older branches; calyx very small, cup-shaped, splitting into 2 or rarely 3 semiorbicular sepals; petals 3, uniseriately valvate, free, thick, concave, equal, longer than the sepals; stamens very numerous, sessile, connective truncate; carpels 20–15, free; style truncate; ovules several, 2-seriate.

115. **Thonnera** De Wild., Ann. Mus. Congo, sér. 5, 3: 86, t. 15 (1909). 1 sp. *T. congolana* De Wild., Congo; Boutique, Fl. Congo Belge et du Ruanda-Urundi, 2: 383, fig. 37 (1951).

Tree, cauliflorous; flowers dioecious, extremely long-pedicellate, the female larger than the male; calyx disk-like or saucer-shaped, obscurely bilobed; petals 3, valvate, subequal, thick, fleshy; stamens very numerous; stigma sessile, almost nothing; ovules numerous, 2-seriate; fruits ellipsoid, slightly ribbed.

116. **Enantia** Oliv., Journ. Linn. Soc. Bot. 9: 174 (1867). 3 spp., trop. Africa; type *E. chlorantha* Oliv., W. trop. Africa. B.H. 1: 958; E.P. 3, 2: 53; Engl. & Diels, Monogr. Afr. *Anonac.* 68, t. 25; R. E. Fries, E.P. ed. 2, 17*a*, 2: 127.

Trees, with woody yellow or sulphur-coloured bark; leaves large; flowers solitary or paired, pedicellate; sepals 3, free, valvate, at first subequal to the petals, at length exceeding them and soon falling off; petals 3 (outer absent), opposite the sepals, valvate, thick, narrower and concave at the base, erect or somewhat spreading; stamens numerous, connective produced; carpels numerous; ovule 1, basal; fruits stipitate, 1-seeded; seeds oblong.

Subtribe 2. *Annonineae*

Petals subequal; ovules numerous	117. **Ararocarpus**
Petals unequal; ovule 1:	
Petals free:	
Connective produced beyond the anther-loculi	118. **Annona**
Connective not produced beyond the anther-loculi; flowers monoecious	
	119. **Raimondia**
Petals connate at the base, the 3 outer enlarged into a thick spreading appendage	120. **Rollinia**

117. **Ararocarpus** Scheff., Ann. Buitenz. Bot. Gart. 2: 10 (1885). 1 sp., *A. velutinus* Scheff., Java. R. E. Fries, E.P. ed. 2, 17*a*, 2: 114.

Small tree; flowers solitary, axillary; sepals 3, subcordate-ovate, acute; petals 6, subequal, 2-seriate, open, elongated, flat, the inner subconcave at the base; stamens numerous, connective truncate-dilated; torus covered with long hairs; carpels 12–8, subconnate; style oblong, strigose-pilose; ovules several, 2-seriate; fruiting carpels united into a many-sided depressed-globose berry-like mass.

118. **Annona** Linn., Sp. Pl. 536 (1753); Gen. Pl. ed. 5: 241 (1754). *Anona* of authors. *Guanabanus* Plum. (1703) ex Fries (1959). About 110 spp., mostly trop. America; a few in trop. Africa; type *A. muricata* Linn., trop. America. B.H. 1: 27; E.P. 3, 2: 37; Safford, Classif. gen. *Annona*, etc., Contrib. U.S. Nat. Herb. 18: 1 (1914); MacCaughey, Genus *Annona* in Hawaiian Isls., Torreya, 17: 69 (1917). Amer. spp., see R. E. Fries, Act. Hort. Berg. 10: 197 (1931), and E. P. ed. 2, 17*a*, 2: 142, figs. 33, 34.

Trees or shrubs with simple or stellate hairs; flowers solitary or few together, terminal, leaf-opposed or from between the nodes; sepals 3, small, valvate; petals 6, free or connate at the base, 2-seriate or the inner rudimentary or absent, outer fleshy, valvate, entirely concave or only so at the base, connivent or subspreading, the inner imbricate or valvate; stamens numerous, connective produced above the loculi into a dilated truncate disk, rarely apiculate; carpels numerous, often connate; ovule solitary, basal, erect; fruit fleshy, formed of the united monocarps.

119. **Raimondia** Safford, Contrib. U.S. Nat. Herb. 16: 217, pls. 52–53 (1913). 3 spp., trop. South America; type *R. charimolioides* (Tr. & Pl.) R. E. Fries (*R. monoica* Safford), Colombia. R. E. Fries, Act. Hort. Berg. 10: 81 (1931), and E.P. ed. 2, 17*a*, 2: 151.

Tree-like shrubs; leaves deciduous, minutely punctate; flowers monoecious, nodding, extra-axillary on the branchlets or from the older wood; sepals 3, valvate, much smaller than the petals, connate at the base; petals 6, 2-seriate, coriaceous, valvate, outer lanceolate, concave at the base, inner shorter, ovate, forming a covering over the androecium; stamens crowded into an ovoid mass, connective not produced; carpels numerous, connate; ovule 1; fruit oblong, the carpels concrete into a fleshy mass; seeds enclosed by a membranous aril.

120. **Rollinia** St. Hil., Fl. Bras. Mer. 1: 28, t. 5 (1825). About 65 spp., Cent. and trop. South America; type *R. dolabripetala* (Raddi) St. Hil. (*R. longifolia* St. Hil.), E. Brazil. B.H. 1: 27; E.P. 3, 2: 38; Safford, Journ. Wash. Acad. Sc. 6: 370 (1916); R. E. Fries, Act. Hort. Berg. 12: 112 (1934), and E.P. ed. 2, 17*a*, 2: 151, fig. 35.

Trees or shrubs, with simple or rarely stellate hairs; flowers few in an inflorescence or rarely solitary; sepals 3, small, valvate, free or rarely connate at the base into a cup; petals 6, biseriately valvate, connate at the base, outer 3 with a spur or wing on the back, inner 3 minute; stamens numerous, connective disk-like and dilated at the apex; carpels numerous; ovule 1, erect; fruits united into a globose or ovoid false fruit.

Subfamily II. MONODOROIDEAE

Petals all alike; corolla small, tube cylindric, with spreading lobes
121. **Isolona**
Inner and outer petals very dissimilar, the latter larger and with wavy margins
122. **Monodora**

121. **Isolona** Engl. & Prantl, Natürl. Pflanzenfam. Nachtr. 3, 2: 161 (1897); Engl. & Diels, Monogr. Afr. Anonac. 82, t. 27. About 20 spp., trop. Africa, Madagascar; lectotype *I. madagascariensis* (A. DC.) Engl., Madagascar. Cavaco, Humbert Fl. Madag. Fam. 78*e* Annonac. 3, fig. 1; R. E. Fries, E.P. ed. 2, 17*a*, 2: 168, fig. 40.

Small trees or shrubs; flowers bisexual, axillary, solitary or paired, erect or pendulous; peduncles bracteate; sepals 3, small; petals valvate, equal, all connate into a tube at the base or in the lower part, rather thick; stamens numerous, connective of the upper stamens long-produced; carpels all connate into a unilocular ovary; ovules numerous on parietal placentas, closely and irregularly inserted; stigmas numerous, subsessile, connate into a body excavated in the middle much thicker than the ovary and often at length irregularly folded, fruit ovoid or ellipsoid, many-seeded; seeds shining.

122. **Monodora** Dun., Monogr. Anon. 79 (1817). About 20 spp., trop. Africa, Madagascar; type *M. myristica* Dun., Sierra Leone to Uganda and Angola (cult. in West Indies). B.H. 1: 26; E.P. 3, 2: 38; Engl. & Diels, Monogr. Afr. *Anonac.* 84, tt. 28–30; R. E. Fries, E.P. ed. 2, 17*a*, 2: 167, fig. 39.

Trees or shrubs or climbers; flowers terminal or leaf-opposed or extra-axillary, solitary or few in an inflorescence, variegated; sepals 3, small; petals valvate, 3 outer overlapping the inner, spreading, 3 inner clawed and connivent at the apex; stamens numerous, connective thickened at the apex; carpels all connate into 1-locular ovary; stigma subsessile, peltate; ovules numerous, closely and irregularly inserted on the walls; placentas confluent; fruit large, globose or ellipsoid, woody; seeds numerous, immersed in a resinous pulp.

Imperfectly known genera

Pelticalyx Griff., Notulae 4: 706 (1854). **Nephrostigma** Griff., loc. cit. 717 (1854). **Tabraca** Nov. Verh. Batav. Gen. 5, ed. 1, Art. 4: 4 (1790).

11. EUPOMATIACEAE

Endl., Gen. Pl. 835 (1839); Ench. Bot. 425 (1841) (*Eupomatieae*)

Shrubs. Leaves alternate, entire, exstipulate, glabrous. Flowers perigynous, bisexual, solitary, fairly large. Sepals and petals not differentiated from each other, united into a deciduous cap (calyptra) on the rim of the expanded concave torus. Stamens numerous, perigynous, in several series, the inner ones sterile and petaloid, the outer ones in few series with two linear extrorse anther-loculi and acuminate connective. Carpels numerous, immersed in the turbinate receptacle; styles connate into a mass; ovules several on the ventral side. Fruit berry-like, truncate at the top, girt with the remains of the perianth, several-locular. Seeds 1–2 in each loculus, angular; endosperm copious, ruminate; embryo very small near the micropyle. Type genus *Eupomatia* R.Br.

Genus 1; species 2.

DISTRIBUTION. Coastal belt of E. Australia and in New Guinea.

ANATOMY. Sol. 1: 34 (in *Annonaceae*); M.C. 1: 50. POLLEN. Erdt. 175.

ADDITIONAL LITERATURE. Hotchkiss, Geogr. distrib. of *Eupomatiaceae*, Journ. Arn. Arb. 36: 385 (1955); Pollen and pollination in *Eupomatiaceae*, Proc. Linn. Soc. N.S.W. 83: 86 (1958): Uphof, E.P. ed. 2, 17*a*, 2: 173, fig. 41 (1959).

Eupomatia R.Br., App. Flind. Voy. 2: 597, t. 2 (1814); Bot. Mag. t. 4848; B.H. 1: 29 (in *Annonaceae*); E.P. 3, 2; 39, fig. 34; Uphof, loc. cit. (above); Hutch., Fam. Fl. Pl. ed. 2, 1: 134, fig. 11 (1959). 2 spp., type *E. laurina* R.Br., E. Australia, New Guinea. *E. bennettii* F. Muell., Queensland. Benth., Fl. Austral. 1: 54. *Characters of the family.*

Only two species of this interesting genus are known. It was formerly included in the family *Annonaceae*, its seeds as in that family having ruminate endosperm. But it differs in having markedly perigynous flowers and a calyptrate perianth, with a gradual transition of the sepals into petals. The immersion of the separate carpels in the expanded torus, perhaps a relatively advanced feature, is probably a parallel with the similar condition found in some genera of the *Nymphaeaceae*, in the **Herbaceae** phylum. The timber of *E. laurina* R.Br. is prettily marked.

ORDER 3. LAURALES

Regarded here as being reduced apetalous derivatives from the *Magnoliales* independently of the *Annonales* stock and more closely related to *Wintera-ceae*; flowers range from hypogynous to perigynous; apocarpous to one carpel; endosperm rarely ruminate; leaves exstipulate; mainly tropics.

Carpels free among themselves or rarely single; leaves often pellucid-punctate, mostly opposite; endosperm not ruminate:
Style entire   12. *Monimiaceae*
Style 2-lobed   13. *Austrobaileyaceae*
Carpels united into a single ovary:
Stamens free among themselves:
Ovary superior, rarely inferior; fruit not winged, either baccate or drupa-ceous:
Anthers opening by slits lengthwise   14. *Trimeniaceae*
Anthers opening from the base upwards by valves   15. *Lauraceae*
Ovary inferior:
Fruits winged or enclosed in the inflated perianth; leaves alternate
                                                                          16. *Hernandiaceae*
Fruits neither winged nor enclosed in the perianth; leaves opposite
                                                                          17. *Gomortegaceae*
Stamens connate into a column; seeds with copious often ruminate endo-sperm; leaves often with pellucid dots   18. *Myristicaceae*

12. MONIMIACEAE[1]

Jussieu, Ann. Mus. Hist. Nat. Paris, 14: 133 (1809) (*Monimieae*)

Trees or shrubs, rarely climbers, usually fragrant, with opposite or rarely alternate entire or serrate coriaceous exstipulate often pellucid-punctate leaves, rarely anisophyllous (*Glossocalyx*). Flowers actinomorphic, rarely oblique (*Glossocalyx*), bisexual, polygamous, or unisexual, often dioecious, cymose or racemose, rarely solitary, small or medium-sized; inflorescence axillary or rarely terminal; bracts small or none, rarely enclosing the young inflorescence; calyx globose, ovoid, turbinate, depressed or rarely campanu-late, with 4–many often connivent teeth or lobes in 2–many series and imbricate, equal or the outer sepaloid and the inner petaloid, rarely obso-lete. Staminal disk adnate to the calyx-tube, rarely slightly free at the apex. Male fl.: stamens numerous or few in 1–2 series; filaments very short, often flattened, with or without a gland on each side at the base; anthers erect, 2-locular, loculi distinct or connivent at the apex, opening by a longitudinal slit or by valves from the base upwards. Female fl.: staminodes present or absent. Carpels very numerous to several, free from one another, 1-locular, sessile inside the base of the calyx or somewhat immersed in the remains of the fleshy disk; style short or elongated and plumose in fruit, stigma terminal; ovule solitary, erect from the base or pendulous from the apex of the loculus,

[1] Including *Amborellaceae* and *Atherospermataceae* Pichon (1948).

anatropous or rarely orthotropous. Carpels separate in fruit, enclosed by the calyx or the latter deciduous, indehiscent, often drupaceous, with a juicy, fleshy, or membranous exocarp, and a bony crustaceous or membranous endocarp. Seed erect or pendulous; testa membranous; endosperm fleshy; embryo small to half as large as the endosperm; cotyledons erect or spreading. Type genus *Monimia* Thouars.

Genera 32; species about 350.

DISTRIBUTION: Tropics and subtropics, mainly of the Southern Hemisphere, especially South America and Malay Archipelago, New Caledonia, E. Australasia, New Zealand; absent from India (except Ceylon and Burma), and very rare in Africa.

CLASSIFICATION. Benth. & Hook. f. Gen. Pl. 3: 137 (1880); Pax, Engl. & Prantl, Nat. Pflanzenfam. 3, 2: 94 (1888); Perkins & Gilg, Engl. Pflanzenr. 4, 101, *Monimiaceae* (1901); Perkins, loc. cit., Nachträge (1911); Lawrence,Taxon. Vasc. Pl. 510, fig. 146 (1951); Hutch., Fam. Fl. Pl. ed. 2, 1: 136, fig. 12 (1959); Cavaco, Humbert Fl. Madag. Fam. 80e *Monimiaceae*, 1, figs. 1–10 (1959).

ANATOMY. Sol. 2: 699; M.C. 2. POLLEN. Erdt. 271.

ADDITIONAL LITERATURE. See Perkins & Gilg (above); L. L. Mooney, I. W. Bailey, & B. G. L. Swamy, The morphology and relationships of the *Monimiaceae*, Journ. Arn. Arb. 31: 372 (1950); G. A. Garratt, Systematic anatomy of the woods of *Monimiaceae*, Trop. Woods, 39: 18 (1934).

Characters occurring in relatively few Genera. **Leaves** alternate in *Amborella*, *Tambourissa* spp., *Hennecartia* (occasionally); anisophyllous in *Glossocalyx* (by early fall of small filiform leaves appearing to be alternate). Inflorescence involucrate with two valvate bracts in *Atherosperma* and *Doryphora*. **Flowers** bisexual in *Hortonia*, *Daphnandra*, *Nemuaron*, *Doryphora*; solitary in each involucre in *Atherosperma*. **Bracts** foliaceous in *Bracteanthus*. **Calyx** flat and disk-like in *Hennecartia*; oblique and like an *Aristolochia* in *Glossocalyx*; female calyx circumscissile in *Conuleum* and *Lauterbachia*. **Anthers** with a mushroom-like produced connective in *Hennecartia*; connate into a tube in *Tetrasynandra*. **Styles** plumose in *Doryphora*.

Phylogeny and Morphology. *Monimiaceae* is a fairly well-defined family, and on the whole seems most closely related to the *Lauraceae*. It shows, however, affinities with several other families. Like the *Lauraceae* they appear to be reduced representatives of the *Magnoliales*, especially of the *Winteraceae* and *Annonaceae*, which they resemble in their aromatic, often pellucid-punctate leaves and the absence of stipules, and they have a very similar distribution. The apocarpous gynoecium and small embryo in copious endosperm seem to be further points of affinity. The tendency to perigyny by the cupular expansion of the perianth is very strong in the family, and is a considerable advance on the hypogynous *Magnoliales*, where only one genus shows a tendency to perigyny, namely *Trochodendron* (*Trochodendraceae*).

The opposite leaves and the plumose styles of *Doryphora* seem to indicate a development parallel with that in the Ranalean group of families as exhibited by *Clematis*, whilst the fruits of *Laurelia* seem to have been developed on similar lines to those of the *Calycanthaceae* in the *Rosales*, the latter, however, being entirely destitute of endosperm. The glandular appendages of the filaments and the valvular dehiscence of the anthers of the subfamily *Atherospermoideae* connect this group most closely with the *Lauraceae*, the latter character being also a well-known feature of the family *Berberidaceae*, probably being nothing more than parallelism. The divarication of the cotyledons in the embryo of many *Monimiaceae* is a remarkable feature.

In the present work I have followed Bentham and Hooker in dividing the family primarily into two main groups, treating these two groups, however, as *subfamilies* after the manner of Perkins and Gilg in their monographs in Engler's *Pflanzenreich*. The character of most phylogenetic importance in the subfamily *Monimioideae* seems to be the enclosure of the fruits by the accrescent calyx in the advanced tribe *Monimieae*. In this character they somewhat resemble some *Lauraceae* and the *Pomoideae* in *Rosaceae*. The rest of the classification adopted here follows more or less that of Bentham and Hooker's *Genera Plantarum*.

Geographical Distribution. *Monimiaceae* are almost entirely tropical in their distribution, only a few occurring outside the southern and none beyond the northern tropic. Their entire absence from India proper is noteworthy, this being also the case with the allied *Winteraceae*. They are very sparingly represented in tropical and south-east extratropical Africa, although the Mascarene Islands as usual harbour a few distinct endemic genera, *Ephippiandra*, *Monimia*, and *Tambourissa*. Of particular interest is the distribution of *Laurelia*, a distinct genus of three species which connects the flora of New Zealand with that of far distant Chile and Patagonia.

The main centres of distribution of the family are SE. Brazil and the SE. Malay Archipelago. E. Australia possesses five endemic genera, *Wilkiea*, *Tetrasynandra*, *Daphnandra*, *Doryphora*, and *Atherosperma*, the last mentioned extending into Tasmania. In New Caledonia there are three endemic genera, *Amborella*, *Carnegiea*, *Nemuaron*, and two in New Guinea, *Anthobembix* and *Lauterbachia*. *Levieria* occurs in Amboina, New Guinea, and Queensland, *Hedycarya* in Polynesia and New Zealand, *Palmeria* from the Malay Archipelago to E. Australia, whilst *Steganthera*, *Matthaea*, and *Kibara* are Indo-Malayan genera. *Hortonia* occupies Ceylon. The peculiar genus *Glossocalyx* is confined to middle W. Africa.

Economic Properties. Boldo Leaves, *Peumus boldus* Molin., a Chilean shrub containing an essential oil and an extract used in medicine; the fruit is edible, and the bark has tanning properties. Tea is sometimes made from the bark of *Atherosperma moschatum* Lab., an Australian tree. The bark of *Doryphora sassafras* Endl. yields a tonic medicine. Peruvian Nutmegs, fruits of *Laurelia aromatica* Juss. Timbers of this family are mainly used locally in Australia: Grey or Black Sassafras, *Doryphora sassafras* Endl., Tasmanian Sassafras, *Atherospermum moschatum* Labill., and Yellow Sassafras, *Daphnandra micrantha* Bth.

KEY TO SUBFAMILIES AND TRIBES

Anthers opening by longitudinal slits; ovules pendulous
Subfamily I. MONIMIOIDEAE

Drupes not enclosed by the calyx, free on a disk-like receptacle; calyx usually
    deciduous   Tribe 1. Hedycaryeae
Drupes entirely enclosed by the persistent contracted calyx
                                                 Tribe 2. Monimieae
Anthers opening by valves from the base upwards (as in *Berberis* and *Laura-*
    ceae); ovules usually erect   Subfamily II. **ATHEROSPERMOIDEAE**
Flowers laxly cymose or shortly racemose, not involucrate
                                                 Tribe 3. Laurelieae
Flowers involucrate with two valvate bracts   Tribe 4. Atherospermeae

Subfamily I. MONIMIOIDEAE

Tribe 1. Hedycaryeae

Anther-loculi parallel, distinct from each other, not confluent into one:
  Stamens numerous, more than 12:
    Leaves alternate; flowers dioecious:
      Calyx-lobes 5–7, subbiseriate; New Caledonia   1. **Amborella**
      Calyx-lobes 8, the four outer 2-seriate, sepaloid, the four inner somewhat
        petaloid; Malaya and Australia   2. **Levieria**
    Leaves opposite:
      Filaments biglandular at the base; female flowers with staminodes;
        Chile   3. **Peumus**
      Filaments not glandular at the base:
        Flowers dioecious; Polynesia, E. Australia and New Zealand
                                                           4. **Hedycarya**
        Flowers monoecious; Madagascar:
          Flowers in spike-like or raceme-like inflorescences:
            Male calyx 10–15-lobed   5. **Decarydendron**
            Male calyx 4-lobed   6. **Phanerogonocarpus**
            Flowers subumbellate   7. **Hedycaryopsis**
  Stamens 12 or fewer:
    Stamens more than 4; flowers bisexual; Ceylon   8. **Hortonia**
    Stamens 4; flowers monoecious; Malaya   9. **Matthaea**
Anther-loculi confluent into one at the apex and opening by a continuous
  slit:
  Stamens more than 12; Central and South America:
    Calyx-tube shorter than or about as long as the lobes:
      Calyx-lobes imbricate-incurved, shorter than the receptacle; style mostly
        very short   10. **Mollinedia**
      Calyx-lobes straight, longer than the receptacle; style fairly long
                                                           11. **Macropeplus**
    Calyx-tube much elongated; Brazil   12. **Macrotorus**
  Stamens less than 12:
    Calyx-lobes 6:
      Stamens in the male flowers 4 large and opposite the calyx-lobes, with
        2 or 3 in the middle of the receptacle more or less reduced and often
        connate; Indo-Malaya, New Guinea   13. **Kibara**

Stamens 8–14, all fertile, arranged unequally over the whole receptacle
                                                                14. **Wilkiea**
Calyx-lobes 4:
Stamens in a longitudinal series on each spreading calyx-lobe; carpels
    spreading stellately in fruit   15. **Ephippiandra**
Stamens crowded and inclined towards the middle of the flower:
  Anthers free, flat:
    Flower globose or ovoid-globose; Malay Archipelago
                                                             16. **Steganthera**
    Flower turbinate, flat or concave on the top; New Guinea
                                                             17. **Anthobembix**
  Anthers connate into a tube; Australia   18. **Tetrasynandra**

1. **Amborella** Baill., Adans. 10: 354 (1869). 1 sp., *A. trichopoda* Baill., New Caledonia. B.H. 3: 142; E.P. 3, 2: 98; Perkins & Gilg, Pflanzenr. 4, 101: 17, fig. 3, A–C; I. W. Bailey & Swamy, Journ. Arn. Arb. 29: 245 (1948).

A somewhat straggling shrub; leaves alternate; flowers dioecious, small, arranged in short lax cymes; bracts none; male flowers: calyx hemispherical, lobes 7–5 in 2 series; disk lining the tube; stamens numerous, in several series; filaments eglandular; anthers oblong, introrse, opening by slits lengthwise; female flowers not known; fruiting carpels small, stipitate, scarcely drupaceous, reticulate-rugose, crowned by a short style, the pericarp dry, indurate-crustaceous; seed pendulous, with a membranous testa and minute embryo.

2. **Levieria** Becc., Malesia 192 (1877). *Dryadodaphne* S. Moore (1923). *Isomerocarpa* A. C. Smith (1941). 6 spp., Malaya, New Guinea, Queensland; type *L. montana* Becc., New Guinea and Amboina. B.H. 3: 142; E.P. 3, 2: 98; Perkins & Gilg, Pflanzenr. 4, 101: 20, fig. 3, P–S; Nachtr. 7, fig. 3, L–S; Kostermans, Meded. Bot. Mus. Rijks Univ. Utrecht, no. 42: 605 (1937).

Shrubs with young parts tomentose; leaves opposite; racemes axillary or terminal, shorter than the leaves, subsimple or slightly branched; flowers monoecious; male flowers: calyx-tube very short, segments 8, the outer 4 in 2 rows, subsepaloid, the inner 4 subpetaloid; stamens numerous, the size of the outer segments, the inner smaller and narrower, connectives subtruncate at the apex; anthers subsessile, with distinct lateral loculi opening by slits lengthwise; female flowers: calyx subglobose, urceolate, with 1 bract at the apex, 4-dentate-lobate, at length splitting irregularly; carpels numerous, ovoid-oblong; style thick, hornlike; ovule pendulous, anatropous; drupes ovoid, seated on a thickened receptacle with reflexed margin; endocarp crustaceous; embryo minute, axile; cotyledons ovate, divergent.

3. **Peumus** Mol., Saggio Chile 185 et 350 (1782) (conserved name). *Boldu* Adans. (1763). *Ruizia* Ruiz & Pav. (1794). *Boldea* Juss. (1809). *Boldus* Schult. f. (1829). *Boldoa* Endl. (1841). 1 sp., *P. boldus* Mol., Chile. B.H. 3: 141; E.P. 3, 2: 99; Perkins & Gilg, Pflanzenr. 4, 101: 16, fig. 2; Nachtr. 2.

A small evergreen fragrant tree; leaves opposite, coriaceous, scabrid, with elevated veins below; flowers white, arranged in terminal cymes, dioecious; male flowers: calyx-tube broadly campanulate, lobes 12–10, 3–2-seriate, imbricate, outer herbaceous or membranous, inner more petal-like; disk lining the calyx-tube; stamens numerous, in several series on the disk, included in the tube; filaments with a substipitate gland on each side at the base; anthers 2-locular, loculi separate, parallel, opening at the side by a slit lengthwise; female flowers: calyx smaller than in the male, lobes more unequal, separating by a circular slit above the base of the disk and falling off; staminodes few, small; carpels numerous, sessile at the base of the calyx, tomentose; styles very short; ovules pendulous, anatropous, drupes 5–2, rarely solitary, very shortly stipitate on the discoid receptacle, rather small; seed pendulous, with copious endosperm; cotyledons large, spreading.

4. **Hedycarya** Forst., Char. Gen. 127, t. 64 (1776). *Crinonia* Banks ex Tul. (1855). 15 spp., Polynesia to E. Australia and New Zealand; type *H. arborea* Forst., New Zealand. 9 in New Caledonia, 2 in Fiji. *H. denticulata* (A. Gray) Perkins & Gilg, Samoa and Tonga. *H. solomonensis* Hemsl., Solomon Isls. *H. angustifolia* A. Cunn., Victoria, New South Wales. B.H. 3: 141; E.P. 3, 2: 99; Perkins & Gilg, Pflanzenr. 4, 101; 18, fig. 3, D–C, Nachtr. 3, fig. 2.

Trees or shrubs; leaves opposite; flowers dioecious, arranged in axillary short cymes or raceme-like panicles; bracts small or absent; male flowers: calyx depressed or hemispherical, lobes 10–7, small, inflexed, almost closed; disk adnate; stamens numerous, almost covering the disk; anthers subsessile, with separate parallel loculi opening at the sides by a slit lengthwise; female flowers: calyx falling off by a circular slit above the disk-bearing base; staminodes absent; carpels numerous, covering the disk, sessile; style short, obtuse; ovule pendulous, anatropous; drupes medium-sized to small, stipitate or sessile on the disk-like receptacle; seed pendulous; embryo axile, short or half as long as the endosperm; cotyledons straight.

5. **Decarydendron** Danguy, Bull. Mus. Hist. Nat. Paris, 34: 279 (1928). 3 spp., Madagascar; type *D. helenae* Danguy. Cavaco, Humbert Fl. Madag. Fam. 80e. *Monimiaceae*, 8, fig. 2 (1959).

Trees; leaves opposite, ovate, slightly dentate; flowers monoecious; inflorescence spike-like; female flower terminal; male flowers: calyx concave, fleshy, segments up to 15; stamens numerous, outer largest; anthers 2-locular, extrorse; filaments short; female flowers: calyx cupular and 3-sided, fleshy, segments 12–9; carpels very numerous (over 300), more or less prismatic; style prismatic, stigma subbilobed; ovule 1, pendulous; fruit not known.

6. **Phanerogonocarpus** Cavaco, Bull. Soc. Bot. Fr. 104: 612 (1957). 2 spp., Madagascar; type *P. capuronii* Cavaco. Cavaco, Humbert Fl. Madag. Fam. 80e. *Monimiaceae*, 1, fig. 1, 1–6 (1959).

Large trees; leaves opposite, entire or coarsely dentate, persistent; inflorescence on the stem, raceme-like; flowers monoecious, the females uppermost, rarely the inflorescence unisexual: male buds ovoid, 4-lobed; stamens numerous, inserted on the calyx-lobes, without glands; anthers 2-locular, dehiscing lengthwise; staminodes present at the top of lobes; female flowers tubular, 4-toothed at the apex; carpels numerous; no staminodes; fruit oblong to cylindric, large, 4–5-ribbed, containing numerous drupes; endosperm abundant.

7. **Hedycaryopsis** Danguy, Bull. Mus. Hist. Nat. Paris, 34: 278 (1928). 1 sp.,*H. madagascariensis* Danguy, Madagascar. Cavaco, Bull. Soc. Fr. 105: 39 (1958), and Humbert Fl. Madag. Fam. 80e. *Monimiaceae*, 12, figs. 31–35 (1959).

A tall tree; leaves opposite or subopposite; flowers monoecious, axillary, often 3 together and subumbellate; peduncle inflated at the apex, compressed, bibracteate; female flower in the middle; male flowers: calyx globose, villous, segments 5, unequal; stamens numerous, eglandular, the outer subaborted and calyx-like; anthers 2-locular, sessile or subsessile, loculi 2, lateral or subextrorse, with a thick connective; female flowers: calyx flat, fleshy, villous, with 8–5 very small segments; carpels numerous (100–90), densely crowded, sessile; stigma sessile, short; ovule pendulous, solitary; drupes 40–30 above the flat or convex receptacle, ovoid, remainder abortive.

8. **Hortonia** Wight. ex Arn., Mag. Zool. & Bot. 2: 545 (1838). 3 spp., Ceylon; type *H. floribunda* Wight ex Arn. B.H. 3: 142; E.P. 3, 2: 97; Trimen, Fl. Ceyl. 3: 437; Perkins & Gilg, Pflanzenr. 4, 101: 14, fig. 1.

Fragrant shrubs; leaves opposite, entire; flowers bisexual, pale yellow, in lax short cymes; bracts small or absent; calyx-tube short, campanulate, lobes more than 20 in several series, imbricate, gradually changed from broad sepaloid outer ones to the petal-like spathulate or linear inner ones; disk lining the tube; stamens 12–5, inserted in 2–1-series on the margin of the disk; filaments short, narrow, provided with a gland on each side at the base; anthers ovate, with separate parallel loculi, opening extrorsely by a slit lengthwise; carpels numerous, sessile; style short, stigma slender or slightly dilated; ovule pendulous, anatropous; drupes oblique, ovate, shortly stipitate on the scarcely thickened receptacle, surrounded by the remains of the withered calyx; seed broadly ovate, compressed, with fleshy endosperm; embryo axile, short; cotyledons obovate, erect or spreading.

9. **Matthaea** Blume, Mus. Bot. 2: 89, t. 10 (1852–6). 11 spp., Malay Penins. and Archip.; type *M. sancta* Blume, Sumatra and Borneo; 8 in Philippine Isls.; *M. calophylla* Perkins, Borneo. *M. latifolia* Perkins, Malay Penins. B.H. 3: 141; E.P. 3, 2: 99; Perkins & Gilg, Pflanzenr. 4, 101: 51, fig. 10, Nachtr. 15, fig. 7.

Shrubs; leaves opposite; flowers monoecious, fasciculate in the leaf-axils or at the nodes of older branchlets, pedicellate; male flowers: calyx depressed-cup-shaped, lobes 4 in 2 series; stamens 4; filaments very short; anthers ovoid, 2-locular, loculi opening by a slit lengthwise; connective slightly produced; female flower: calyx depressed-globose, almost hemispherical, closed when young, opening by a circular slit in flower; carpels very numerous, densely covering the broad flat receptacle, sessile or shortly stipitate; style oblong, very short; ovule pendulous, anatropous; drupes fleshy, stipitate on the disk-like receptacle; seed pendulous, with hard fleshy endosperm; embryo terete, straight, cotyledons short and straight.

10. **Mollinedia** Ruiz & Pav., Fl. Per. et Chil. Prodr. 83, t. 15 (1794). *Tetratome* Poepp. & Endl. (1838). *Paracelsia* Mart. (1857). 75 spp., Mexico (22° N.) to SE. Brazil (30° S.) and Peru; type *M. repanda* Ruiz & Pav. with *M. ovata* Ruiz & Pav., Peru; most spp. in S. Brazil. B.H. 3: 140; E.P. 3, 2: 101; Perkins & Gilg, Pflanzenr. 4, 101: 26, fig. 6–7; Nachtr. 11.

Trees or shrubs; leaves opposite; flowers unisexual, often dioecious, small, arranged in axillary or subterminal short lax raceme-like or thyrsoid cymes; bracts small or absent; male flowers: calyx ovoid, globose, turbinate or rarely oblong, lobes 4, 2-seriate, imbricate, connivent or rarely somewhat spreading, equal or the inner larger and sometimes dentate; disk adnate to the tube; stamens numerous to few, several-seriate; anthers ovoid or oblong, sessile or nearly so, loculi opening by slits lengthwise confluent into one at the apex; female flowers: calyx after flowering falling off by a circular slit; carpels numerous, in many series; ovule pendulous, anatropous; drupes numerous, ovoid, sessile or stalked on the dilated disk-like receptacle; seed pendulous; embryo small, axile; cotyledons ovate, straight.

11. **Macropeplus** Perkins, Engl. Bot. Jahrb. 25: 557. 1 sp., *M. ligustrinus* Perkins, E. Brazil. Perkins & Gilg, Pflanzenr. 4, 101: 24, fig. 5; Nachtr. 11, fig. 6.

Shrub; leaves opposite, entire or dentate; flowers dioecious, cymose, axillary or terminal; male flowers: calyx shortly cup-shaped, lobes 4, 3–5 times as long as the tube, 2-seriate, valvate in pairs, erect; stamens about 25, lax, subsessile; anther loculi confluent at the apex; female flowers: carpels numerous, densely crowded; styles elongated.

12. **Macrotorus** Perkins, Engl. Bot. Jahrb. 25: 561 (1898). 1 sp., *M. utriculatus* Perkins, Rio de Janeiro Prov., Brazil. Perkins & Gilg., Pflanzenr. 4, 101: 50, fig. 8.

Habit?, leaves opposite, ovate-oblong, minutely serrate or entire; flowers dioecious; inflorescence paniculate, axillary or terminal; male flowers subumbellate, pedicellate; calyx tubular, elongated, papery, lobes 4, small, connivent in 2 imbricate series; stamens numerous, crowded from the base to the apex of the calyx-tube; anthers shortly stalked, opening at length by a horizontal slit; female flowers not known.

13. **Kibara** Endl., Gen. 314 (1837). *Brongniartia* Bl. (1825), not Kunth. *Sciadicarpus* Hassk. (1842). *Sarcodiscus* Griff. (1854). 30 spp., Indo-Malaya,

New Guinea; type *K. coriacea* (Bl.) Tul., Java, Sumatra. B.H. 3: 140; E.P. 3, 2: 100; Perkins & Gilg, Pflanzenr. 4, 101: 58, fig. 16; Nachtr. 28, fig. 11.

Trees or shrubs; leaves opposite; flowers monoecious or rarely dioecious, small, pedicellate in short axillary or lateral cymes or panicles; bracts small or absent; male flowers: calyx ovoid, globose or hemispherical, lobes or teeth 4 in 2 series, imbricate, connivent or rarely more open; disk adnate to the tube or free above, annular or tubular; stamens 8–5, in 2 series, 4 on the margin of the disk and opposite to the calyx-lobes or teeth, inner 1–4 smaller, all shorter than the calyx; anthers subsessile, opening by slits lengthwise, slits confluent at the apex; female flowers: calyx falling from the disk by a circumscissile slit; carpels many to about 7, crowded on the receptacle; ovule pendulous, anatropous; drupes numerous, ovoid, sessile or stalked on the dilated disk-like receptacle; seed pendulous; embryo small, axile; cotyledons ovate, straight.

14. **Wilkiea** F. Muell., Trans. Phil. Inst. Vict. 2: 64 (1858). 5 spp., E. Australia; type *W. macrophylla* F. Muell., Queensland, New South Wales. B.H. 3: 140; E.P. 3, 2: 100; Perkins & Gilg, Pflanzenr. 4, 101: 57, fig. 14; Nachtr. 26.

Trees or shrubs; leaves opposite; inflorescence paniculate, axillary or terminal, the upper branches mostly female and l-flowered; flowers monoecious; male flowers: calyx cup-shaped, lobes 4, small; stamens 14–8, subsessile; anther loculi horse-shoe-shaped, confluent at the apex; female flowers: carpels numerous (50–30), densely crowded; style rather elongated; drupes numerous, oblong.

15. **Ephippiandra** Decne., Ann. Sci. Nat., sér. 4, 9: 278, t. 7 (1858). 3 spp., type *E. myrtoidea* Decne., Madagascar. B.H. 3: 141; E.P. 3, 2: 101; Perkins & Gilg, Pflanzenr. 4, 101: 50, fig. 9; Cavaco, Humbert Fl. Madag. Fam. 80*e*, 6, fig. 1, 7–11 (1959).

Small trees; leaves opposite, entire, evergreen; flowers monoecious, 1–2 axillary, pedicellate; male flowers: calyx globose or pear-shaped, almost closed and 4-toothed when young, at length opening into 4 spreading valvate lobes; disk lining the calyx-tube, glabrous; stamens within the disk, 12–10, in 2–3 series; anthers 4, on the calyx lobes, and 6 at their base, transverse, somewhat kidney-shaped, 1-locular, opening at the top by a slit; female flowers: carpels 15–5, narrow, sessile and crowded on the fleshy plate-like receptacle with the persistent base of the calyx-tube; ovule pendulous, anatropous; drupes ovoid, black, inserted on the convex red fleshy receptacle.

16. **Steganthera** Perkins, Engl. Bot. Jahrb. 25: 564 (1898). 15 spp., type *S. warburgii* Perkins, S. Celebes, rest in New Guinea, Perkins & Gilg, Pflanzenr. 4, 101: 52, fig. 11; Nachtr. 20, figs. 8, 9.

Trees or shrubs; leaves opposite, entire or dentate; flowers monoecious, few, in raceme-like cymes or in many-flowered panicles; male flowers: calyx-tube globose or oblong, leathery or rather woody, very thick towards the base, lobes 4, imbricate in pairs, small; stamens 4, densely subsessile in the middle of the receptacle; anther loculi opening at the top by a horizontal slit; female flowers: calyx or obovate-top-shaped; carpels numerous, densely crowded; styles elongated.

17. **Anthobembix** Perkins, Engl. Bot. Jahrb. 25: 567 (1898). 4 spp., New Guinea; type *A. hospitans* (Becc.) Perkins. Perkins & Gilg, Pflanzenr. 4, 101: 54, 12; Nachtr. 25, f. 10.

Trees or shrubs; leaves entire or remotely denticulate; flowers monoecious, in many- or few-flowered cymes, racemes or panicles; male flowers: calyx broadly obconic-top-shaped, thick towards the base, broadly split at the top, the margins gradually thinner and acute; sepals 4, imbricate in pairs, small; stamens 4, subsessile in the middle of the receptacle; anther loculi opening at the top by a horizontal slit; female flowers: calyx as in the male; carpels numerous, pilose; styles elongated.

18. **Tetrasynandra** Perk., Engl. Bot. Jahrb. 25: 568, t. 6, C (1898). 3 spp., E. Australia; lectotype *T. laxiflora* (Benth.) Perkins, Queensland. Perkins & Gilg, Pflanzenr. 4, 101: 55, fig. 13.

Trees or shrubs; leaves opposite, entire or dentate; flowers monoecious, in terminal or axillary few- to many-flowered panicles, the lower branches bearing mostly males, the upper females; male flowers: calyx cup-shaped, lobes 4, small; stamens 4, connate into a short cylindric tube; anther loculi opening by two horizontal slits; carpels 15–10, pilose.

Tribe 2. MONIMIEAE

Calyx open in bud:
Anthers more or less ovoid with parallel loculi dehiscing lengthwise:
Stamens mostly biglandular at the base   19. **Monimia**
Stamens not glandular at the base:
Stamens numerous   20. **Tambourissa**
Stamens about 16; anthers apiculate   21. **Schrameckia**
Anthers stipitate, peltate, with a discoid connective, dehiscing by a circular slit; male calyx flat and disk-like   22. **Hennecartia**
Calyx closed in bud by the inflexed lobes: stamens without glands at the base:
Calyx urn-shaped, contracted at the apex   23. **Palmeria**
Calyx deeply concave-campanulate, depressed, and flat on top:
Female flower with a deciduous calyptrate circumscissile calyx; carpels elongate, hairy   24. **Lauterbachia**
Female with a persistent irregularly split calyx; carpels short, glabrous   25. **Carnegiea**

19. **Monimia** Thou., Hist. Veg. Afr. Austr. 35, t. 9 (1804). 4 spp., Mascarenes; type *M. ovalifolia* Thou., Mauritius. B.H. 3: 139; E.P. 3, 2: 101; Perkins & Gilg, Pflanzenr. 4, 101: 65, fig. 18, A–F.

Shrubs; leaves opposite, entire; flowers dioecious, small, in short axillary cymes; male flowers: calyx ovoid or globose, with a minute 6–4-lobed mouth, at length deeply split into 6–4 valvate lobes; disk completely lining the tube, glabrous within; stamens numerous, many-seriate, short, the filaments with a gland on each side at the base; anthers ovoid, loculi separate, parallel, opening subintrorsely by a slit lengthwise; female flowers: calyx globose, soon almost closed; disk pilose inside; staminodes absent; carpels few, sessile or slightly immersed in the receptacle; styles slender; ovule pendulous, anatropous; drupes small, included in the globose closed or irregularly split calyx; seed pendulous; embryo small.

20. **Tambourissa** Sonn., Voy. Ind. Orient. 3: 267, t. 134 (1782). *Mithridatea* Comm. (1791). *Ambora* Juss. (1789). *Tamboul* Poir. (1806). 25 spp., Mascarenes; type *T. quadrifida* Sonn., Mauritius. B.H. 3: 139; E.P. 3, 2: 101; Perkins & Gilg., Pflanzenr. 4, 101: 66, fig. 18, N–S; Nachtr. 39; Cavaco, Humbert Fl. Madag. Fam. 80e, *Monimiaceae*, 18, figs. V–X (1959).

Trees; leaves opposite or rarely alternate; flowers dioecious or monoecious, few in the axils or at the tops of the branches, cymose or racemose, rather large, rarely in a terminal panicle; male flowers: calyx ovoid or subglobose, fleshy, very obtuse, when young closed or minutely 6–4-dentate at the apex, at length deeply split into 6–4 valvate spreading lobes; disk adnate to the tube; stamens numerous, many-seriate, not glandular; anthers subsessile, oblong, loculi separate, parallel, lateral, often undulate, opening by a slit lengthwise; female flowers: calyx almost closed; carpels numerous, covering the inside of the fleshy glabrous disk; styles very short; ovule pendulous, anatropous; drupes included in the fleshy almost closed calyx, connate to the middle of the disk or free in pockets of the disk; seed pendulous; embryo short; cotyledons ovate or elliptic.

21. **Schrameckia** Danguy, Bull. Mus. Hist. Nat. Paris 28: 249 (1922). 1 sp., *S. madagascariensis* Danguy, Madagascar. Cavaco, Bull. Soc. Bot. Fr. 105: 39 (1958); Cavaco, Humbert Fl. Madag. Fam. 80*e*, *Monimiaceae*: 4 (as subgen. of *Tambourissa*).

Tree; leaves opposite or subopposite, obovate, entire; flowers unisexual; male flowers arranged in axillary or terminal elongated more or less leafy compound inflorescences; pedicels compressed; calyx quadrangular in bud; segments 4; stamens about 16; anthers sessile, ovate-acuminate, connective thick; loculi 2, elongated, opening by slits laterally; female flowers not known; fruiting calyx hemispherical, irregularly pouched, depressed at the apex, with a hole at the top; drupes very numerous, enclosed in the fleshy calyx.

22. **Hennecartia** Poisson, Bull. Soc. Bot. Fr. 32: 38 (1885). 1 sp., *H. omphalandra* Poisson, Paraguay, Brazil. Perkins & Gilg, Pflanzenr. 4, 101: 72, fig. 19.

A small tree; leaves mostly opposite; flowers dioecious, in axillary racemes; male flowers: calyx dilated, disk-like, flat, not lobed; stamens very numerous; anthers shield-like, the connective depressed, disk-like, opening by a circular slit; female flowers: calyx tongue-like, thick; carpels 2–1, inserted at the base of the calyx; style short, stigma papillous; ovule 1, pendulous, anatropous; fruiting calyx globose, closed before maturity, at length irregularly split into 5–4 segments.

23. **Palmeria** F. Muell., Fragm. Phyt. Austral. 4: 151 (1864); 5: 2 (1865–6). 7 spp., Malay Archip., E. Australia; type *P. scandens* F. Muell., Queensland, New South Wales. B.H. 3: 140; E.P. 3, 2; 101; Perkins & Gilg, Pflanzenr. 4, 101: 64, fig. 18, G–M; Nachtr. 37, fig. 13.

Scandent shrubs; leaves opposite, entire; flowers dioecious, small, in raceme-like or axillary panicles, pedicellate, ebracteate; male flowers: calyx hemispherical, lobes 6–4, slightly imbricate, flat and connivent and almost closed; disk lining the calyx-tube, shortly hairy within; stamens numerous, in many series, eglandular; anthers subsessile, lanceolate, loculi parallel, separate, opening on the inner side by a slit lengthwise; female flowers; calyx subglobose, with a minute mouth; carpels numerous, separate, included in the calyx; styles filiform, shortly exserted; ovule pendulous, anatropous; drupes enclosed by the irregularly globose or pear-shaped calyx; seed pendulous; embryo small; cotyledons flat, somewhat spreading.

24. **Lauterbachia** Perk., K. Sch. & Lauterb. Fl. Deutsch. Schutzgeb. Sudsee, 331 (1900). 1 sp., *L. novoguineensis* Perkins, New Guinea. Perkins & Gilg, Pflanzenr. 4, 101: 63, fig. 17.

Leaves opposite, pellucid-punctate, entire; flowers dioecious or monoecious, the male not known, female in axillary or terminal racemes; calyx almost flat, leathery; lobes 4, minute, the mouth wide open; tube splitting transversely at the base and falling off; carpels densely crowded, pilose; style elongated.

25. **Carnegiea** Perkins, Engl. Pflanzenr. 4, 101; Monim. Nachtr. 36, fig. 12 (1911). 1 sp., *C. eximia* Perkins, New Caledonia.

Tree or shrub; leaves opposite, entire; flowers dioecious or monoecious, solitary in the axils of the upper leaves, male not known; female flowers: calyx almost flat, leathery, lobes minute or obsolete, forming a membranous covering perforated by a broad mouth, irregularly split at flowering time; carpels densely crowded, numerous, sessile; style short, obtuse; ovule 1, pendulous.

Subfamily II. ATHEROSPERMOIDEAE

Tribe 3. LAURELIEAE

Disk of the female flowers not intruded between the carpels; Australasian–Chilean–Patagonian genera:

Ovule pendulous; flowers bisexual, anthers extrorse   26. **Daphnandra**

Ovule erect; flowers bisexual, anthers introrse; style nearly basal in fruit
27. **Nemuaron**

Ovule erect; flowers polygamo-monoecious or dioecious; anthers dehiscing at the side:

Styles long-pilose   28. **Laurelia**

Style very short, not pilose   31. **Bracteanthus**

Disk of the female flowers more or less intruded between the carpels; tropical American and W. tropical African genera:

Leaves not anisophyllous:

Male calyx closed before maturity, the female circumscissile; Guiana
29. **Conuleum**

Male and female calyx persistent; open or somewhat closed; tropical America:

Bracts obsolete or absent   30. **Siparuna**

Bracts large and foliaceous; pseudocarp indehiscent   31. **Bracteanthus**

Leaves anisophyllous and appearing to be alternate through the smaller filiform leaf falling off; male and female calyx oblique and produced into an acuminate cyathium; tropical Africa   32. **Glossocalyx**

26. **Daphnandra** Benth., Fl. Austral. 5: 285 (1870). 4 spp., E. Australia; type *D. micrantha* (Tul.) Benth., Queensland, N.S. Wales. B.H. 3: 145; E.P. 3, 2: 102; Perkins & Gilg, Pflanzenr. 4, 101: 75, fig. 20, C–K; Nachtr. 44, fig. 14.

Trees; leaves opposite; flowers bisexual, small, in axillary cymes or thyrsoid panicles; bracts small, very caducous; calyx-tube short, campanulate during flowering, at length narrowly cylindric; lobes several, the 4 outer herbaceous and opposite in pairs, 6–8 inner larger, subpetaloid, and in 2 series; perfect stamens 5–4; filaments flat, with a wing-like gland on each side; anthers short, extrorsely 2-locular, loculi opening by valves; staminodes within the stamens numerous, in about 2 series, inner gland-like; carpels numerous, glabrous, ending in a pilose style; ovule pendulous, orthotropous; fruiting calyx narrowly tubular; carpels few, included, narrow, the long plumose styles at length exserted; embryo very small, almost basal; cotyledons small.

27. **Nemuaron** Baill., Adans. 10: 351 (1871–3). 2 spp., New Caledonia; type *N. vieillardii* Baill. B.H. 3: 145; E.P. 3, 2: 102; Perkins & Gilg, Pflanzenr. 4, 101: 73, fig. 20.

Glabrous shrubs; leaves opposite, crenate-dentate; flowers bisexual, few, in short axillary cymes; calyx-tube short; lobes 8–6, 4–3-seriate; stamens 8–4; filaments with a gland on each side at the base; anthers introrsely 2-locular, loculi opening by valves, connective not produced; staminodes numerous, inner small; carpels few, narrowly conical, adnate to the calyx-tube; style long and fragile; ovule erect; fruiting calyx-tube enlarged, fleshy, splitting valvately into 3–2 parts; carpels laterally enlarged, somewhat horseshoe-shaped; style lateral and almost basal; pericarp adnate to the seed.

28. **Laurelia** Juss., Ann. Mus. Par. 14: 134 (1809) (conserved name). *Pavonia* Ruiz & Pav. (1794), not Cav. (1786). *Theyga* Mol. (1810). *Thiga* Mol. (1810). 3 spp., Chile, Patagonia, New Zealand; type *L. sempervirens* (Ruiz & Pav.)

Tul., Chile, Patagonia. *L. novae-zelandiae* A. Cunn., New Zealand, widely spread in North Isl., only on west and north coast of South Isl. B.H. 3: 145; E.P. 3, 2: 102; Perkins & Gilg, Pflanzenr. 4, 101: 76, f. 21; Nachtr. 46. E. W. Berry, The *Monimiaceae* and a new *Laurelia*, Bot. Gaz. 96: 751 (1935).

Tall trees, pleasantly odorous; leaves opposite; cymes or racemes axillary, shorter than the leaves; flowers polygamo-monoecious or dioecious; male flowers: calyx-tube short, campanulate; lobes 12–6, in 2–3 series, subequal or the outer shorter; stamens 12–6, filaments short, with an oblong gland on each side; anthers apiculate with a short connective, the loculi lateral, opening by oblong valves; female or bisexual flowers: calyx enlarged after flowering, ovoid-cylindric or narrowly tubular, at length split valvately into 3–2 parts; inner stamens or all of them reduced to small staminodes; carpels numerous, linear-fusiform, long-pilose, ending in long plumose at length exserted styles; ovule erect, anatropous; embryo short; cotyledons short, straight or slightly divergent.

29. **Conuleum** A. Rich., Mém. Soc. Hist. Nat. Par. 1: 391, t. 25 (1823). 1 sp., *C. guianense* A. Rich., Guiana. B.H. 3: 143.

Small tree, with the branchlets, leaves, and inflorescence lepidote like an *Elaeagnus*; leaves opposite, entire; flowers dioecious, small, arranged in short axillary cymes, the males pedicellate, the females subsessile; male flowers: calyx obovoid-club-shaped, entire; disk short, fleshy, slightly prominent; anthers sessile on the disk, 8–7, the 4 at the margin of the disk broad, apex introrsely 2-locular, loculi opening by valves, the 4–3 inner narrower, truncate with small empty loculi; female flowers: calyx ovoid, with a small orifice, splitting transversely at the apex of the tube; disk fleshy, intruded between the carpels and forming cavities, prominent above the tube; carpels more or less included in the pockets of the disk, ending in slender styles free or coherent above; ovule erect, anatropous.

30. **Siparuna** Aubl., Pl. Guian. 864, t. 333 (1775). *Citrosma* Ruiz & Pav. (1794). *Leonia* Mutis. (1822). *Angelina* Pohl (1855). 108 spp., Cent. and trop. South America; type *S. guianensis* Aubl., Trinidad to Brazil. B.H. 3: 144; E.P. 3, 2: 104; Perkins & Gilg, Pflanzenr. 4, 101: 80 figs. 23, 24, 25, 26, 27; Nachtr. 47, fig. 15. O. Heilborn, Studies on the taxon., geogr., distrib., and embryology of *Siparuna*, Svensk Bot. Tidskrift 25: 202 (1931).

Shrubs or small trees with a pleasant scent, indumentum of simple or rarely stellate hairs or lepidote; leaves opposite or verticillate; flowers monoecious or dioecious, laxly cymose, cymes paired and axillary or on older lateral branches, shorter than the leaves; calyx-tube ovoid, subglobose, obconic or urceolate, often fleshy above and much dilated; limb short, connivent, with an undulate mouth or shortly and broadly 6–4-lobed, rarely shortly expanded; disk adnate to the tube, in the male flowers annular or scarcely prominent, in the female fleshy, more or less intruded between the carpels within the tube, the cavity divided into chambers often prominent at the mouth and connivent around the styles; stamens in male flower few or numerous, included in the calyx; anthers sessile or with short filaments, 1-seriate at the margin of the disk, or 2- or more-seriate within the disk, introrsely 2-locular near the apex, opening by valves; inner ones if present often narrower; female flowers: carpels few or several, each more or less included in the pockets of the disk; styles free or connate at the apex, at length shortly exserted from the calyx; ovule erect from the base of the loculus, anatropous; fruit fig-like, the calyx and enlarged often fleshy disk irregularly divided into pockets; drupes free in fruit, endocarp sometimes echinate; seed erect, with embryo and abundant endosperm.

31. **Bracteanthus** Ducke, Arch. Jard. Bot. Rio de Janeiro, 5: 106 (1930). 1 sp., *B. glycycarpus* Ducke, Brazil.

Tree, with foetid vegetative parts; leaves opposite or rarely 3-verticillate; flowers monoecious, the sexes intermixed, in axillary little-branched dichasia with leafy ovate stalked bracts; ultimate branchlets 3–4-flowered; calyx campanulate-globose, with a small denticulate mouth; stamens 2 larger, 2–1 smaller or the latter absent; anthers included, 2-locular;

female flower: carpels 16–10, the styles united in the upper part into a short column; pseudo-carp globose-pear-shaped, narrowed at the base, depressed in the middle at the top, yellow when mature and full of sweet pulp, enclosing numerous drupes with woody endocarps.

32. **Glossocalyx** Benth., Hook. Ic. Pl. t. 1301, 1302 (1880). 3 spp., W. trop. Africa; type *G. longicuspis* Benth., Fernando Po, Cameroons to Gabon. B.H. 3: 144; E.P. 3, 2: 105; Perkins & Gilg, Pflanzenr. 4, 101: 115, f. 28, Nachtr. 67.

Trees with paired branchlets, the young parts pubescent with rigid hairs; leaves opposite, very unequal, alternately oblong or obovate-oblong, acuminate, pinnately nerved, and alternately filiform, soon deciduous; flowers dioecious, few in the axils, fasciculate, shortly pedicellate; male flowers: calyx-tube campanulate, with a rather wide mouth fleshy inside, the limb broadly and obliquely cyathiform, very unequally 5-toothed or sublobed, produced on one side into a short lanceolate or long tongue-shaped point; disk adnate to the tube, in male flowers the annulus often slightly prominent at the mouth, in the female flowers fleshy, within the tube more or less intruded between the carpels, the cavity divided into pockets, subdistinct from the mouth of the annulus; stamens numerous, included, 2–3-seriate within the disk; filaments short, broad, subconnate; anthers ovate, introrsely 2-locellate, opening by valves; carpels numerous, each carpel more or less included in the pockets of the disk; styles free, shortly exserted; ovule erect; immature fruit subglobose, angular, fleshy, crowned by the calyx.

Tribe 4. ATHEROSPERMEAE

Flowers 3 in each involucre, bisexual: anthers with a long subulate appendage; fruiting calyx narrow and tubular   33. **Doryphora**
Flowers solitary in each involucre, monoecious or polygamo-dioecious; anthers with a short tip; fruiting calyx depressed-globose   34. **Atherosperma**

33. **Doryphora** Endl., Gen. Pl. 315 (1836–40); Iconogr. t. 10 (1838). *Learosa* Reichb. (1841). *Doratophora* Lem. (1849). 1 sp., *D. sassafras* Engl., New South Wales. B.H. 3; 145; E.P. 3, 2: 104; Perkins & Gilg, Pflanzenr. 4, 101: 79, fig. 22, K–N.

Tree; leaves opposite, dentate; flowers bisexual, axillary, 3 within 2 boat-shaped valvate involucral bracts, sessile, in a shortly pedunculate head; calyx-tube during flowering very short and campanulate, afterwards enlarged and cylindric; lobes 6, imbricate in 2 series; disk adnate, thin; perfect stamens often 6, opposite to the calyx-lobes; filaments short, with a wing-like gland on each side at the base; anthers extrorsely 2-locellate, locelli opening by valves, the connective produced into a long subulate acumen; staminodes within the stamens 12–6; carpels numerous, sessile, separate; style elongated, soon lateral; ovule erect, anatropous; fruiting calyx cylindric, often split, lobes caducous; carpels with a long plumose at length almost basal style; pericarp thin; seed erect.

34. **Atherosperma** Labill., Pl. Nov. Holl. 2: 74, t. 224 (1806). *Antherosperma* Poir. (1840). *Dendrosma* R.Br. ex Crombie (1879). 2 spp., E. Australia; type *A. moschatum* Labill., Victoria, New South Wales, Tasmania. *A. repandulum* F. Muell., EN. Queensland. B.H. 3: 144; E.P. 3, 2: 103; Benth., Fl. Austr. 5: 284; Perkins & Gilg, Pflanzenr. 4, 101: 77, fig. 22, A–J.

Trees; leaves opposite, entire or dentate; flowers polygamo-monoecious or dioecious, axillary, solitary, shortly pedunculate, sessile within 2 boat-shaped valvate involucral bracts which fall away at length; male flowers: calyx-tube short, broadly campanulate; lobes 8, rarely 10, subequal, imbricate in 2 series, outer slightly broader; disk lining the tube; stamens 12–10, included, attached in 2–3 series to the margin of the disk; filaments short, flat, with a wing-like gland on each side; anthers short, broad, extrorsely 2-locellate, locelli opening by valves; female flowers: calyx-tube campanulate, lobes smaller than in the male, some or all often falling off or absent; staminodes numerous, in several series; carpels numerous in the bottom of the calyx, free, with long styles, ovule erect, anatropous; fruiting calyx depressed-globose, mouth slightly contracted, the staminodes persistent and resembling teeth; fruiting carpels narrow, ending in long plumose styles, dry, with a thin pericarp; seed erect.

Imperfectly known genus—*Canaca* Guillaumin, Arch. Bot. Caen Bull. 1927, 1: 74. 1 sp., *C. vieillardii* Guillaumin, New Caledonia.

13. AUSTROBAILEYACEAE

Croizat, Cact. Succ. Journ. Am. 15: 64 (1943)

Large climbing shrubs; leaves opposite or subopposite, coriaceous, entire, reticulate and pinnately looped-nerved; stipules small, deciduous; flowers bisexual, axillary, solitary, pedicellate, pedicels bracteate at the base and bracteolate in the upper part; sepals and petals together about 12, pale green, free, imbricate, gradually larger from the outer sepaloid to the inner petaloid and obovate or suborbicular with thin margins; stamens 25–12, petaloid (pale green), outer fertile, inner gradually smaller and sterile, densely purple-spotted; anthers 2-locular, loculi adnate to the connective, dehiscing lengthwise; carpels several (about 8), free on a slightly upraised torus; style 2-lobed; stigmas introrse, about half as long as the carpels; ovules 14–8, in 2 collateral series on the adaxial side; fruits not seen. Type genus *Austrobaileya* C. T. White.

Genus 1; species 2.

Austrobaileya C. T. White, Contrib. Arn. Arb. no. 4: 29 (1933). 2 spp., Queensland; type *A. scandens* C. T. White. Croizat, Notes on *Dilleniaceae* and allies, *Austrobaileyeae* subfam. nov., Journ. Arn. Arb. 21: 397 (1940); Hutch., Fam. Fl. Pl. ed. 2, 1: 137, fig. 13 (1959). *Characters of the family.*

14. TRIMENIACEAE

Gibbs, Phytogeogr. & Fl. Arfak Mts. 135 (1917)

Trees, shrubs, or climbers. Leaves alternate or opposite, simple, entire or toothed, sometimes glandular-toothed; stipules absent. Flowers bisexual or unisexual, sometimes polygamous or dioecious, small, arranged in axillary or terminal racemes or racemes of cymules or panicles; bracts small or absent. Calyx lobes or sepals 6 or 4, 2–1-seriate, imbricate, small. Petals absent. Stamens numerous to 6; anthers opening by slits lengthwise; loculi parallel. Rudimentary ovary present in the male flowers. Ovary superior, 2–1-locular; stigma sessile; ovule solitary, pendulous from the top of the ovary, anatropous. Fruit baccate, ellipsoid or subglobose. Seeds compressed; cotyledons equal. Type genus *Trimenia* Seem.

Genera 4; species 6.

DISTRIBUTION. Tropical and S. Africa, New Guinea, Fiji, New Caledonia, New South Wales.

This is a very small tropical and subtropical family about which little is known up to the present. For notes on the genera see Gibbs (above).

CLASSIFICATION. van Steenis, Act. Bot. Neerl. 1: 94 (1952); Bailey & Swamy, morphology and relationships of *Idenburgia* and *Nouhuysia*, Journ. Arn. Arb. 34: 77 (1953); van Steenis, Svensk. Bot. Tidskrift, 49: 19 (1955); I. W. Bailey, *Sphenostemon* and *Nouhuysia*, Journ. Arn. Arb. 37: 360 (1956); C. R. Metcalfe, Taxonomic affinities of *Sphenostemon* in the light of the anatomy of its stem and leaf, Kew Bull. 1957: 249; Hutch., Fam. Fl. Pl. ed. 2, 1: 138, fig. 14 (1959).

ANATOMY. M.C. 2: 1144 (in *Monimiaceae*). POLLEN. Erdt. 272 (in *Monimiaceae*).

Economic Properties. Lemon Wood, *Xymalos monospora* (Harv.) Baill., evergreen tree of forests of trop. and S. Africa, wood used locally for furniture.

Trees or shrubs; leaves serrate or dentate:
Stamens numerous; inflorescence axillary   1. **Xymalos**
Stamens 12–6:
Racemes terminal   2. **Sphenostemon**
Racemes both terminal and axillary   3. **Trimenia**
Scandent shrubs; stamens numerous; flowers polygamous; leaves entire
    4. **Piptocalyx**

1. **Xymalos** Baill., Bull. Soc. Linn. Paris 1: 650 (1887), *Paxiodendron* Engl. (1895). 2 spp.; type *X. monospora* (Harv.) Baill., S. Africa (Orange Free State) to Ruwenzori and Cameroon Mts. *X. ulugurensis*, Tanganyika Territ. Baker & Wright, Fl. Trop. Afr. 6, 1: 169 (in *Monimiaceae*); Perkins & Gilg, Pflanzenr. *Monimiac.* 23; Nachtr. 9, fig. 5.

Small trees or shrubs; leaves opposite or subopposite, dentate; flowers dioecious, small, in axillary racemes of cymes; male flowers: calyx-lobes 6–4; stamens numerous; anthers subsessile, opening by slits lengthwise; rudimentary ovary absent; female flowers: calyx-lobes 4–3; staminodes absent; ovary 1-locular, ovule solitary, pendulous, stigma thick, sessile, discoid; fruit baccate, ellipsoid or subglobose, stigma crown-like; seeds compressed, cotyledons oblique.

2. **Sphenostemon** Baill., Bull. Soc. Linn. Paris, 1: 53 (1875). *Nouhuysia* Lauterb. (1912). *Idenburgia* Gibbs (1917). 5 spp., New Caledonia, New Guinea; type *S. balansae* Baill., New Caledonia. Baill., Adansonia, 11: 307 (1875); Gibbs, Contrib. Phytogeogr. & Fl. Arfak Mts., &c., 136, with figs. (1917); Gilg & Schlechter, Engl. Bot. Jahrb. 58: 244 (1923) (*Idenburgia*); van Steenis, Act. Bot. Neerl. 1: 97 (1952).

Trees; leaves alternate or opposite, glandular-dentate, pinnately nerved; stipules absent; flowers bisexual or monoecious, few in terminal racemes; bracts and bracteoles absent; sepals and petals 4–8, in 2 series, the inner petaloid, imbricate, very caducous; stamens 10–6, hypogynous; filaments free, very short, broad and thick; anthers introrse, 2-locular, with a broad more or less petaloid connective produced or not beyond the loculi, opening by slits lengthwise; ovary sessile, grooved, 2-locular, stigma large, sessile and pileiform; ovule 1 in each loculus, pendulous from near the top of the loculi, anatropous; fruit not seen.

3. **Trimenia** Seem., Fl. Vit. 425, t. 99 (1865–73). 1 sp., *T. weinmanniifolia* Seem., Fiji Isls. B.H. 3: 143; E.P. 3, 2: 98; Perkins & Gilg, Engl. Pflanzenr. *Moniamiac.* 21, fig. 4, A–C; Nachtr. 9.

Tree; branchlets sometimes angular with lines decurrent from the petiole; leaves opposite, slightly serrate, penninerved, primary veins transverse and parallel; flowers laxly racemose, racemes in the upper axils or paniculate at the apex of the branches, panicles ebracteate or bracts minute and caducous; flowers mostly male, some bisexual or female, irregularly arranged in the panicle; perianth scales numerous, ovate, membranous, imbricate, gradually increasing in size and enclosing the stamens and pistil, soon dropping off; male flowers: stamens 12–9, 3–2-seriate, filaments free; anthers large, linear-oblong, subextrorsely opening by slits, connective produced beyond the loculi; rudimentary ovary small; female or bisexual flowers: stamens as in the male but smaller or anthers abortive; ovary 1-locular, stigma obliquely truncate, sessile, papillous-penicellate; ovules 1, pendulous, fruit not known.

4. **Piptocalyx** Oliv., Benth. Fl. Austral. 5: 292 (1870). *Muellerothamnus* Engl. (1897). 1 sp., N. *moorei* Oliv., New South Wales. B.H. 3: 143; E.P. 3, 2: 98; Perkins & Gilg, Engl. Pflanzenr. *Monimiac.* 22, fig. 4, D–F; Nachtr. 9, fig. 4 (1911).

Scandent shrub; leaves opposite, entire, acuminate, pinnately nerved; flowers racemose, polygamous, small, terminal bisexual, lateral female; sepals 6, biseriately imbricate, subequal, scale-like, soon falling off; male flowers: stamens 15 to 13, filaments short; anthers opening by a slit lengthwise, apiculate; rudimentary ovary absent; female and bisexual flowers: fertile stamens fewer; ovary oblong, 1-locular, sessile, stigma broad, sessile, densely papillous; ovule pendulous; fruit not known.

15. LAURACEAE

A. L. de Jussieu, Genera Pl. 89 (1789) (*Lauri*)

Trees or shrubs (except *Cassytha*), with very hard sometimes fetid wood; stems sometimes buttressed. Leaves alternate, very rarely opposite, mostly coriaceous and evergreen, often glandular-punctate, pinnately nerved or 3–5-nerved from the base, entire; stipules absent; indumentum when present of simple hairs. Flowers mostly bisexual, more rarely polygamous or dioecious, small and inconspicuous, green or yellow, cymose, umbellate, capitate or paniculate, rarely solitary; leaf- and flower-buds perulate; bracts small, caducous, or absent, in a few genera forming an involucre below the umbels or heads; bracteoles absent. Calyx-tube (perianth) short, sometimes enlarged in fruit; segments usually 6 (rarely 4), imbricate in 2 series or rarely subvalvate in 1 series, equal or the outer often smaller; petals absent. Stamens or staminodes mostly twice as many as calyx-segments, in 4 or rarely more whorls, usually the innermost whorl aborted and reduced to staminodes, rarely the 2 outer whorls also aborted, the third whorl always present (very rarely sterile), as a rule with 2 more or less stalked glands on each side of the filament or the stalks of the glands adnate to the filaments, rarely all stamens with basal glands; anthers erect, continuous with the filament, those of the outer series with 2 or 4 locelli on the inner face (introrse), dehiscing by as many valves from the base to apex; anthers of the third series in many genera extrorse. Ovary sessile, free, or in a few genera adherent to the calyx and appearing inferior, 1-locular and composed of 1 carpel; style terminal, simple, stigma entire to irregularly lobed, rarely stigma sessile; ovule 1, pendulous, anatropous. Fruit a fleshy berry or rarely a drupe or dry, indehiscent, nude or partly covered by the persistent calyx, fruiting pedicel sometimes much thickened. Seed pendulous, without endosperm, testa rarely intruded between the thick fleshy cotyledons of the straight embryo. Type genus *Laurus* Linn.

Genera 47; species about 1900.

GEOGRAPHICAL DISTRIBUTION. Mainly tropics and subtropics.

CLASSIFICATION. Nees, Systema Laurinarum, pp. 720 (Berlin, 1836). Benth. & Hook. f., Gen. Pl. 3: 146 (1880); Baill., Hist. Pl. 2: 429 (1870). Pax, Engl. & Prantl, Nat. Pflanzenfam. 3, 2: 106 (1889); Mez, Laur. Amer. Monogr., Jahrb .Bot. Gart. Berlin 5: 1–566, tt. 1–3 (1889); Stapf, Fl. Trop. Afr. 6, 1: 171 (1909); Liou, Contrib. Étud. Syst. et Phytogr. des Laurac. de Chine et d'Indochine (1932); Robyns & Wilczek, Bull. Jard. Bot. Brux., 19: 457 (1949) (Laurac. of Belg. Congo and trop. Africa); Kostermans, Rec. Trav. Bot. Neerl. 33: 719 (1936); 34: 500 (1937); 35: 56, 831 (1938); Rev. Univ. Chilena, 24: 201 (1939); Fl. Madag. 81e: 1 (1950); Bol. Techn. Inst. Agron. do Norte, 29: 49 (1955); Communic. For. Research Inst. Indonesia no. 57; 1 (1957); New generic key, Reinwardtia 4: 193 (1957); Hutch., Fam. Fl. Pl. ed. 2, 1: 139 (1959).

ANATOMY. Sol. 2: 702; M.C. 2: 1145. POLLEN. Erdt. 221.

ADDITIONAL LITERATURE. W. F. Chun, Prelim. notes to the study of *Lauraceae* of China, Contrib. Biol. Sci. Soc. China, 1: 1 (1925); Fernald, Nomencl. of *Sassafras*, Rhodora, 38: 178 (1936); Contrib. Gray Herb. 113: 178 (1936); G. V. Coy, Morphology of *Sassafras* in relation to phylogeny of Angiosperms, Bot. Gaz. 86: 149 (1928); C. K. Allen, Studies in *Lauraceae*, Journ. Arn. Arb. 26: 280 (1945); Lawrence, Taxon. Vasc. Pl. 512, fig. 147 (1951); Kasapligil, Morphology and otogeny studies in *Umbellularia* and *Laurus*, Univ. Calif. Public. Bot. 25: 115 (1951); Kostermans, Historical surv. of *Lauraceae*, Journ. Sci. Research Indonesia, 1: 83, 113, 141 (1952); Kostermans, Notas sobre las *Laurac.-Lauroid.* sul Amer., Bol. Techn. Inst. Agron. do Norte, n. 28: 49 (1953); W. L. Stern, Comparative anat. of xylem and phylogeny of *Lauraceae*, Trop. Woods, 100: 1 (1954); C. E. Wood, Citation of some genera of *Lauraceae*, Journ. Arn. Arb. 39: 213 (1958).

Characters occurring in relatively few Genera. Stems filiform twining and leaves reduced to scales in *Cassytha*; leaves sometimes subopposite in *Beilschmiedia*; mostly prominently 3-nerved from the base in *Cinnamomum*; flowers in *Misanteca* arranged in dense heads; male and female inflorescences dissimilar in *Endlicheria*; inflorescence enclosed up to flowering time by an involucre of bracts in tribe *Litseae*; flowers dimerous in *Potameia*; receptacle (or pedicel) of the Malayan genus *Dehaasia* swollen and resembling that of *Podocarpus* (*Taxaceae*); calyx persistent and reflexed in fruit in *Machilus*; outer sepals much smaller than the inner in *Dehaasia* and *Cyanodaphne*; anthers opening by minute pores in *Micropora*; annular disk present in *Synandrodaphne*; ovary inferior in *Hypodaphnis*; mature fruit completely or almost completely enclosed by the accrescent calyx-tube in tribe *Cryptocaryeae*; fruit supported on a double-margined receptacle in *Misanteca*; ruminate cotyledons noted in *Beilschmieda sikkimensis* King ex Hook. f.

Economic Properties. The genus *Cinnamomum* provides several. Camphor distilled from the wood of *Cinnamomum camphora* Nees. Cassia spice, *C. cassia* Nees, Burma, from the bark and flower-buds. Indian Cassia, from *C. tamala* (Buch.-Ham.) Nees & Eberm. Padang Cassia, *C. burmannii* (Nees) Blume, Indonesia. Oliver's Bark, *C. oliveri* Bailey, Australia, and Massoia

Bark, *C. massoia* Schewe, New Guinea. Cinnamon Oil, *C. zeylanicum* Breyn., produced from the sucker-shoots of the evergreen shrub or small tree, native of Ceylon and used in medicine and for flavouring. Saigon Cinnamon is *C. loureiri* Nees, French Indo-China. Sassafras, a flavouring material, is obtained from the bark of the roots of *Sassafras albidum* Nees, native of southeastern North America; wood used for fencing, &c. Sweet-bay, *Laurus nobilis* Linn., native of Asia Minor: leaves used for flavouring and yield an oil valued in perfumery. Avocado or Alligator Pear, *Persea americana* Miller (*P. gratissima* Gaertn.), trop. Amer. Greenheart, *Ocotea rodiei* (Schomb.) Mez (*Nectandra rodiaei* Schomb.), British Guiana, well known for its use in making fishing rods and structural timber of great value. The wood of *Aniba perutilis* Hemsl., a Columbian tree, is a valuable timber for building and for cabinet-making (Kew Bull. 1894: 197). *Endlicheria sericea* Nees, a forest tree of the West Indies and Venezuela, yields a good cabinet wood. Fruits of *Cryptocarya peumus* Nees eaten in Chile. Puchury Beans, *Nectandra puchury* Nees, aromatic and used as a tonic and astringent in Brazil. Nan-Mu wood, *Persea nanmu* Oliv., highly esteemed in China. Stinkwood, *Ocotea bullata* E. Mey., greatly prized in South Africa for furniture (now very scarce). The powerful odour of some *Lauraceae* is strikingly evident in *Licaria puchurymajor* (Mart.) Kosterm., a Brazilian tree, even when opening a herbarium cover of dried specimens which were collected 70–80 years ago. The scent is called 'Puxiri', and Richard Spruce says that every part of the plant is redolent of it. Kurumoji Oil, distilled from leaves and twigs of *Lindera sericea* Japan. Brazilian Walnut, *Phoebe porosa* Mez, furniture wood and for veneers.

   Phylogeny and Morphology. Like *Sapotaceae*, the family *Lauraceae* is remarkably homogeneous. It is closely related to *Monimiaceae*. As in other very natural families, for example *Asteraceae* (*Compositae*), the genera, such as they are, are separated sometimes by quite trivial characters. The earlier taxonomists, Bentham, Mez, and Pax, relied mostly on the characters derived from the stamens, chiefly the number of whorls and with regard to the amount of their fertility, and whether the anther-loculi were 2 or 4. Doubts as to the generic importance of some of these characters have been expressed by certain more recent authors, but as they rarely suggest any others to replace them, it seems desirable that most of the genera as understood by the earlier botanists should be maintained so far as possible. In spite of much recent work by Kostermans, there is still considerable confusion as to the conception of several of the genera.

   If I were a young man, with a good working knowledge of other families, I should take great pleasure in dissecting the *type species* of each genus and compiling a key from the results. Then I should dissect every one of the known species (where possible) and 'run them down' separately. The results would no doubt be very interesting!

   As shown in the key to the tribes given here, after separating the distinct genus *Cassytha*, the next important phylogenetic character seems to be the absence or presence of an involucre of bracts. Tribe *Litseae* is thus easily distinguished, and is placed in an advanced position. Then the next most definite character is the number of loculi in the fertile anthers, 2 in the *Apollonieae* and *Cryptocaryeae*, and 4 in the *Sassafrideae* and *Cinnamomeae*.

Four-locellate anthers are very rare in other flowering plants and I am doubtful whether they signify an ancient type or represent a more recent development. The same question as to which is more primitive arises concerning the orientation of the anther-loculi, whether all are *introrse*, or some introrse and some extrose in the same flower. There seems little doubt, however, that the *Apollonieae*, with the mature fruit free or only partially enclosed by the calyx-tube, should take precedence over the *Cryptocaryeae*, in which the fruit becomes completely or almost completely enclosed by the usually accrescent calyx-tube (perianth).

The anatomical structure also seems to be equally as uniform, as noted by Solereder and by Metcalfe and Chalk. The stomata are of the Rubiaceous type, i.e. they are accompanied by special subsidiary cells parallel to the pore, and the indumentum, when present, is very uniform, the hairs being mostly unicellular, and there are no glandular hairs.

Geographical Distribution. The family is most abundantly represented in the tropics of both hemispheres, with about 18 genera in tropical America and nearly as many in tropical Asia; few genera are common to both regions, though the large genus *Cryptocarya* is widely spread. They are very rare in tropical Africa and Madagascar, though in the latter one genus has about 18 species.

The Atlantic Islands claim 3 indigenous genera, *Persea*, *Laurus*, and *Apollonias*, *A. barbujana* constituting one of the chief arboreal elements of the evergreen forest belt of the Canary Islands and Madeira. There are very few *Lauraceae* in NE. Australia. *Sassafras* occurs both in E. Asia (China and Formosa) and Atlantic North America.

KEY TO TRIBES

Large trees and shrubs with well-developed green leaves:
  Inflorescence not enclosed in bud or during flowering by an involucre of bracts:
    Anthers 2-locular or rarely 1-locular:
      Mature fruit not or only partially enclosed by the calyx-tube
                                1. APOLLONIEAE
      Mature fruit completely or almost completely enclosed by the calyx-tube
                             2. CRYPTOCARYEAE
    Anthers 4-locellate:
      Anthers all introrse   3. SASSAFRIDEAE
      Anthers of at least one row extrorse   4. CINNAMOMEAE
  Inflorescence enclosed up to or during flowering time by an involucre of bracts; flowers umbellate or solitary within the involucre   5. LITSEAE
Leafless filiform twiners; anthers 2-locular, those of the outer row introrse, of the third row extrorse   6. CASSYTHEAE

Tribe 1. APOLLONIEAE

Flowers bisexual or rarely unisexual and monoecious:
  Fertile stamens 9:

Staminodes present; calyx usually persistent in fruit:
  Calyx persistent, more or less thickened in fruit:
    Fertile stamens with conspicuous filaments; glands of the staminodes shortly stipitate; flowers paniculate; calyx persistent and embracing the fruit base   **1. Apollonias**
    Fertile stamens subsessile; glands sessile; flowers racemose; fruit seated on the flat calyx   **2. Thouvenotia**
  Calyx deciduous or unchanged in fruit:
    Leaves often subopposite; filaments of the third row not connate; calyx deciduous   **3. Beilschmiedia**
    Leaves scattered; filaments of the third row connate into a tube
       4. Systemonodaphne
Staminodes absent or rarely solitary and stipiform; pedicels much thickened and fleshy in fruit; calyx caducous:
  Outer sepals much smaller than the inner; stamens of the first and second row without glands   **5. Dehaasia**
  Sepals equal; all of the fertile stamens with 2 glands at the base of each filament   **6. Urbanodendron**
  Sepals equal; stamens of the first and second row eglandular
       18. Aniba
  Outer sepals longer than the inner; stamens without glands
       7. Nobeliodendron
Fertile stamens 6–3:
  Stamens free from each other:
    Flowers 3-merous:
      Fertile stamens 6:
        Anthers opening by valves:
          Style distinct:
            Calyx-tube distinct; stamens of the first row fertile   **8. Aiouea**
            Calyx-tube absent; stamens of the first row sterile, changed into large foliaceous staminodes   **9. Phyllostemonodaphne**
          Style absent; stigma more or less sessile   **10. Brassiodendron**
        Anthers opening by minute pores   **11. Micropora**
      Fertile stamens 3:
        Calyx deciduous or if persistent then not changed in fruit, rarely disk-like; stigma sessile or contracted into a short style
            12. Endiandra
        Calyx cupular and hardened, often with double margin in fruit; style distinct, shortly exserted   **13. Licaria**
    Flowers 2-merous; perfect stamens 4; anthers introrse; staminodes of the third row narrow, 2-glandular at the base, of the fourth row very small or absent; ovary with a short style; calyx-segments at length reflexed; Madagascar   **14 Potameia**
  Stamens more or less connate, 4 or 3:
    Calyx-segments 6, very short; perfect stamens 3, anthers 2-locellate, extrorse:
      Leaves scattered   **15. Misanteca**
      Leaves subverticillate   **16. Mezilaurus**

Calyx-segments 4; perfect stamens 4; anthers 1-locellate, introrse

17. **Syndiclis**

Flowers dioecious or polygamous-dioecious; perfect stamens 9:

Male inflorescence similar to the female, paniculate 18. **Aniba**

Male and female inflorescences dissimilar, male laxly paniculate, female dense, interrupted, and spike-like 19. **Endlicheria**

1. **Apollonias** Nees, Laur. Expos. 10 (1833). 2 spp., Canaries, Madeira, S. India; type *A. barbujana* (Cav.) A. Braun, Canaries, Madeira. B.H. 3: 152; E.P. 3, 2: 120; Kostermans, Reinwardtia, 4: 228.

Trees; leaves pinnately nerved, coriaceous; panicles axillary and subterminal; flowers bisexual; calyx-tube short; segments 6, subequal, fertile stamens 9, filaments filiform, of the first and second row eglandular, anthers introrse and 2-locellate; those of the third row with a subsessile or shortly stipitate gland on each side, with extrorse 2-locellate anthers; staminodes of the fourth row ovoid or cordate, very shortly stipitate; ovary narrowed into the style; berry globose or ovoid, surrounded at the base by the persistent, hardened, and 6-fid, slightly enlarged calyx.

2. **Thouvenotia** Danguy, Bull. Mus. Hist. Nat. Paris, 26: 652 (1920). 6 spp., Madagascar: type *T. madagascariensis* Danguy. *Apollonias* Kosterm., Notulae System. 8: 67 (1939), partly, not of Nees. Included by Kostermans in *Beilschmiedia* (Reinwardtia, 4: 229).

Trees; leaves glaucous or softly tomentellous below, pinnately nerved; racemes axillary or subterminal; densely villous, bracteate; flowers bisexual, villous; calyx-segments 6, 2-seriate, thick, very short; stamens 9, subsessile, outer 6 introrse, inner 3 with 2 glands and subextrorse; anthers 2-locellate; staminodes 3, hirsute; ovary 1-locular, style very short, stigma subconical; fruit ovoid, inserted on the flat calyx; seed 1, pendulous, with a short large funicle.

3. **Beilschmiedia**[1] Nees, Wall. Pl. As. Rar. 2: 69 (1831). About 200 spp., trop. and subtrop. Asia to New Zealand, trop. Africa; type *B. roxburghiana* Nees, E. India. B.H. 3: 152; E.P. 3, 2: 120; Robyns & Wilczek, Bull. Jard. Bot. Brux. 19: 457 (1949); Kostermans, Comm. For. Research Inst. Indones. no. 57: 37, partly (1957); Reinwardtia, 4: 229 (partly) (1957).

Trees and shrubs; leaves often subopposite, coriaceous, pinnately nerved; panicles axillary, dense and fascicle-like, sessile, or lax and pedunculate; young inflorescence sometimes covered with caducous imbricate scales; flowers bisexual; calyx-tube short; segments 6, subequal; fertile stamens 9, those of the first and second rows not glandular, anthers 2-locular introrse, those of the third row extrorse, free, with often stipitate glands at the base and on each side and sometimes irregularly disposed between the filaments of the second and third rows; staminodes of the fourth row ovoid or cordate, very shortly stipitate; ovary narrowed into the style; berry nude at the base, the calyx deciduous.

4. **Systemonodaphne** Mez, Jahrb. Bot. Gart. Berlin, 5: 78 (1889). 2 spp., trop. South America; type *S. mezii* Kostermans, Guiana and Brazil. Kostermans, Rec. Trav. Bot. Néerl. 35: 104 (1938); Journ. Sci. Res. Indon. 1: 145; Bolet. Técn. Inst. Agron. do Norte Brasil, 28: 73 (1955); Reinwardtia, 4: 239 (1957).

Trees or shrubs; leaves scattered, pinnately nerved; inflorescence few-flowered, axillary, flowers bisexual, long-pedicellate; calyx-tube shorter than the lobes; segments 6, equal; outer 3 series fertile stamens 9, the fourth series aborted, densely pilose, the 2 outer rows

---

[1] Synonyms of **Beilschmiedia**: *Boldu* Nees (1833). *Hufelandia* Nees (1836). *Bellota* Gay (1849). *Nesodaphne* Hook. f. (1855). *Wimmeria* Nees (1864). *Bielschmeidia* Panch. & Sebert (1874). *Bernieria* Baill. (1884). *Tylostemon* Engl. (1889). *Afrodaphne* Stapf (1905). *Anaueria* Kosterm. (1938). *Purkayasthaea* Purkay (1938). *Lauromerrillia* Allen (1942).

free, eglandular, the third row with the filaments connate into a tube, distinctly 2-glandular; anthers 2-locular, of the outer row introrse, of the third row extrorse; ovary pilose, obovoid, stigma obtuse; berry ellipsoid, with a saucer-like cupule with a double margin, the outer margin crowned by the persistent calyx-lobes.

5. **Dahaasia** Blume, Rumphia, 1: 161, tt. 44, 45, 47 (1835). *Cyanodaphne* Blume (1851). *Haasia* Nees (1836). About 20 spp., E. India and Malaya; lectotype *D. incrassata* (Jack) Kostermans (*D. microcarpa* Blume), Java, Borneo. B.H. 3: 152; E.P. 3, 2: 120; Kostermans, Journ. Sci. Res. Indon. 1: 120 (1952); Comm. For. Res. Inst. Indon. no. 57: 36 (1957); Reinwardtia, 4: 228 (1957).

Trees; leaves alternate, coriaceous, pinnately nerved; panicles axillary, often long-pedunculate; flowers bisexual, small; calyx-tube very short; segments 6, 3 outer much smaller; perfect stamens 9, those of the first and second row not glandular; with introrse anthers; of the third row with a subsessile gland on each side at the base, with extrorse anthers; staminodes absent; ovary narrowed into a short style; berry oblong, the pedicel much thickened, fleshy and coloured, the calyx caducous.

6. **Urbanodendron** Mez, Jahrb. Bot. Gart. Berlin, 5: 80 (1889). 1 sp., *U. verrucosum* (Nees) Mez, Brazil. E.P. 3, 2: 276; Kostermans, Rec. Trav. Bot. Néerl. 35: 106 (1938); Journ. Sci. Res. Indon. 1: 146 (1952); Comm. For. Res. Inst. Indon. no. 57: 46 (1957); Reinwardtia, 4: 238 (1957).

Tree or shrub; leaves coriaceous, lanceolate, acuminate, pinnately nerved; flowers bisexual, in axillary panicles; pedicels long; calyx-tube short; lobes 6, subequal, deciduous; fertile stamens 9, free, with 2 glands at the base of each; anthers suborbicular-ovate, 2-locellate, outer 6 subintrorse, inner 3 extrorse; staminodes of the fourth row absent or rarely solitary and stipiform; ovary glabrous, ellipsoid-globose, narrowed into a slender style, stigma very small, discoid, obtuse; berry ellipsoid, smooth, with a large widely campanulate thick cupule at the base with a double margin; embryo with subequal cotyledons.

7. **Nobeliodendron** O. Schmidt, Fedde Repert. 27: 151 (1929). 1 sp., *N. cubense* O. Schmidt, Cuba. Included by Kostermans in *Licaria* (Reinwardtia, 4: 238).

Tree; leaves petiolate, lanceolate or elliptic-lanceolate; flowers bisexual, not involucrate; calyx-tube obconic or funnel-shaped; lobes unequal, the outer clearly longer, rather scale-like, incurved at the apex; 3 whorls of stamens fertile, anthers 2-locellate, extrorse, remainder aborted; staminodes and glands absent; ovary subsuperior, depressed-globose, contracted into a terete thick style, stigma obtuse; ovule 1, pendulous; berry ellipsoid.

8. **Aiouea**[1] Aubl., Pl. Guian. 1: 310, t. 120 (1775). 30 spp., trop. South America; type *A. guianensis* Aubl., Guianas and Venezuela. B.H. 3: 153; E.P. 3, 2: 121; Mez, Jahrb. Bot. Gart. Berl. 5: 28; Kostermans, Reinwardtia, 4: 236 (1957).

Trees and shrubs, often shining; leaves coriaceous, pinnately nerved; panicles axillary or subterminal, lax; flowers bisexual, often very small and numerous; calyx-tube ovoid or subcampanulate; segments 6, subequal; perfect stamens 6, fertile in the first and second rows, rarely a third row present; filaments not glandular, anthers introrse; staminodes of the third row narrow, with a large gland on each side at the base, rarely imperfectly 1–2-locellate towards the apex, the fourth row ovate-triangular, subsessile or rarely absent; ovary with the style more or less exserted; berry ovoid or oblong; pedicels thickened, often obconic, crowned with the remains of the hardened calyx.

---

[1] Synonyms of **Aiouea**: *Ehrhardia* Scop. (1777). *Ajovea* Juss. (1789). *Colomandra* Neck. (1790). *Douglassia* Schreb. (1791). *Apivea* Steud. (1821). *Ajuvea* Steud. (1821). *Endocarpa* Raf. (1838). *Ehrhardia* Benth. & Hook. f. (1880).

9. **Phyllostemonodaphne** Kostermans, Rec. Trav. Bot. Néerl. 33: 754 (1936); Meded. Bot. Mus. Herb. Rijks Univ. Utrecht, 37: 754 (1936). 1 sp. *P. gemini-flora* (Meisn.) Kostermans, Brazil. Kostermans, Comm. For. Res. Inst. Indon. no. 57: 47 (1957); Reinwardtia, 4: 238 (1957).

Tree or shrub; leaves scattered, chartaceous; inflorescence without an involucre, paniculate, very few-flowered; flowers bisexual; calyx-tube absent, segments subequal; stamens of the first series sterile, changed into very large foliaceous staminodes, of the second and third series fertile, 2-glandular at the base, with broad free filaments and 2-locular anthers, those of the second series introrse, of the third series extrorse-lateral, of the fourth series small or none; ovary superior, style rather shorter than the ovary; fruit ellipsoid, cupule with a double margin.

10. **Brassiodendron** Allen, Journ. Arn. Arb. 23: 153 (1942). 1 sp., *B. fragrans* Allen, New Guinea. Included in *Endiandra* by Kostermans, Reinwardtia, 4: 229 (1957).

Tree; leaves alternate or opposite, pinnately nerved; racemes or panicles axillary or subterminal, without an involucre; flowers bisexual; calyx-lobes 6, subequal, fleshy, tube short; stamens 6, outer anthers 2-locular, introrse, inner extrorse, third and fourth series absent; ovary ovoid; stigma subsessile; fruit not known.

11. **Micropora** Hook. f., Ic. Pl. t. 1547 (1886); Fl. Brit. Ind. 5: 862 (1890). *Hexapora* Hook. f., name only (1886). 1 sp., *M. curtisii* Hook. f., Malay Penins. E.P. 3, 2: 121; Kostermans, Journ. Sci. Res. Indon. 1: 144 (1952); Comm. For. Res. Inst. Indon. no. 57: 38 (1957); Kostermans, Reinwardtia, 4: 230 (1957) (as *Hexapora*).

Tree; leaves alternate, elliptic-oblong; flowers small, bisexual, in axillary racemes or subpanicles; calyx very short; lobes 6, orbicular; stamens 6, exserted, not glandular; anthers 2-locellate, extrorse, thick, sessile, subquadrate, tomentose, loculi opening by minute pores; staminodes 3, very short, thick, tomentose, within and opposite to the stamens; ovary sessile, smooth, narrowed into a very short style; stigma minute; fruit not known.

12. **Endiandra** R.Br., Prodr. Fl. Nov. Holl. 402 (1810). *Dictyodaphne* Blume (1850). *Brassiodendron* Allen (1942). 80 spp., India and Hainan to E. Australia, New Caledonia; type *E. glauca* R.Br. NE. Australia. B.H. 3: 154; E.P. 3, 2: 122; Kostermans, Reinwardtia, 4: 229 (1957).

Trees; leaves alternate or opposite, pinnately nerved, often copiously and minutely reticulate or glaucous; panicles axillary or pedunculate at the base of the new shoots, many-flowered or reduced to a single cyme; flowers small, unisexual; calyx-tube very short or campanulate; segments 6, subequal or the outer a little larger; perfect stamens 3 in the third row with sessile, extrorsely 2-locellate anthers; staminodes absent or rarely 3, small, in the fourth row, or composed of a fleshy ring at the base of the calyx-segments in place of the first and second rows; glands 6 at the base of the perfect stamens, or absent; ovary sessile; stigma small, sessile or contracted into a short style, berry oblong or subglobose, the calyx completely deciduous or rarely disk-like, or unchanged and subpersistent.

13. **Licaria**[1] Aubl., Pl. Guian. 1: 313, t. 121 (1775). About 40 spp., Cent. America, West Indies, E. trop. South America; type *L. guianensis* Aubl., Brit. and French Guianas. Mez, Jahrb. Bot. Gart. Berl. 5: 81; B.H. 3: 154; E.P. 3: 2: 123; Kostermans, Rec. Trav. Bot. Néerl. 34: 575 (1937); 35: 123 (1938); Journ. Sci. Res. Indon. 1: 89 (1952): Bol. Técn. Inst. Agron. do Norte Brasil,

[1] Synonyms of **Licaria**: *Acrodiclidium* Nees (1833). *Evonymodaphne* Nees ex Lindl. (1836). *Triplomeja* (*Triplomeia*) Raf. (1838). *Symphysodaphne* A. Rich. (1850). *Chanekia* Lundell (1937). *Clinostemon* Kuhlm. & Sampaio (1928).

28: 65 (1955); Comm. For. Res. Inst. Indon. no. 57: 46 (1957); Reinwardtia, 4: 238 (1957).

Trees or shrubs; leaves alternate or subopposite, pinnately nerved; panicles axillary or at the base of the new shoots, lax; flowers bisexual, small; calyx-tube fleshy, often constricted at the apex; segments 6, subequal; perfect stamens 3, in the third row, contracted at the base and with a sessile gland at the base on each side, anthers 2-locular, extrorse or sub-introrse; staminodes of the first and second rows sessile, ovate or minutely scale-like or absent, fourth row absent; ovary included in the perianth-tube, style shortly exserted; berry at first included in the globose calyx, at length semi-exserted, surrounded by the hardened cupular calyx with a simple or double margin.

14. **Potameia** Thou., Nov. Gen. Madag. 5: 16 (1806). *Potamica* Poir. (1826). 2 spp., Madagascar; type *P. thouarsii* Roem. & Schult. B.H. 3: 154; E.P. 3, 2: 121; Kostermans, Fl. Madag. 81e: 10 (1950); Journ. Sci. Res. Indon. 1: 144 (1952); Comm. 55 For. Res. Inst. Bogor. 3 (1957), partly (excl. *Syndiclis* Hook. f.).

Shrubs with erect branches; leaves alternate; panicles axillary, much branched; flowers bisexual, small, numerous; calyx-tube obconic; segments 4, subequal; perfect stamens 4, not glandular, filaments short and broad; anthers introrse; staminodes of the third row narrow, with a gland on each side at the base, of the fourth row very small or absent; ovary with a short style; berry seated on the slightly enlarged reflexed calyx-segments.

15. **Misantheca** Cham. & Schlechtd., Linnaea, 6: 367 (1831). 4 spp., Mexico, Cent. America, West Indies, Brazil; type *M. capitata* Cham. & Schlechtd., Mexico. Mez, Jahrb. Bot. Gart. Berl. 5: 100; B.H. 3: 155; E.P. 3, 2: 123. Included in *Licaria* by Kostermans, Reinwardtia, 4: 238 (1957).

Trees and shrubs; leaves scattered, coriaceous, pinnately nerved; panicles pedunculate at the base of the young shoots, the small cymes either many-flowered in globose heads or laxer and few-flowered; flowers bisexual; calyx-tube fleshy, ovoid or obovoid; segments 6, very short; perfect stamens 3, in the third row connate into a fleshy column around the pistil, shortly exserted from the perianth; one anther extrorsely 2-locellate, sometimes with 1–2 small lower ones; staminodes of the first and second rows short or obsolete, of the fourth row absent; ovary contracted into a short style, included in the staminal column; fruit not seen.

16. **Mezilaurus** Taubert, Bot. Zentralbl. 50: 21 (1892). *Silvia* Allemao (1854), not Benth. (1846). *Silvaea* Meisn. (1864). *Mezia* O. Ktze. (1891). *Neosilvia* Pax (1897). 9 spp., trop. South America; type *M. navalium* (All.) Taub. Kostermans, Rec. Trav. Bot. Néerl. 35: 109 (1938).

Trees and shrubs; leaves alternate, subverticillate, pinnately nerved; panicles axillary; bracts and bracteoles deciduous; flowers bisexual, without an involucre, usually in umbel-like clusters; sepals 6, equal or nearly so, small; stamens only of the third whorl fertile, more or less connate; anthers 2-locular, usually extrorse; ovary immersed in the calyx-tube; style short; berry ellipsoid, pedicel woody, cylindrical, surmounted by a minute saucer-shaped thin disk-like enlargement, with more or less persistent sepals.

17. **Syndiclis** Hook. f., Ic. Pl. t. 1515 (1886). 1 sp., *S. paradoxa* Hook. f., Bhutan. E.P. 3, 2: 121.

Tree; leaves alternate, pinnately nerved; flowers very small, bisexual, paniculate in the upper leaf-axils, glandular-punctate; calyx 4-partite, deciduous; segments transversely oblong, 2-seriate, subequal; perfect stamens 4, opposite the calyx-segments, short and broadly ovoid, thick, pubescent and glandular-punctate, 1-locular, loculus small, introrse; staminodes 4, minute, lanceolate, hirsute; ovary narrowed into the acute style equally long; fruit not known.

18. **Aniba** Aubl., Hist. Pl. Guian. Franc. 1: 327 (1775). *Cedrota* Schreber (1789). *Aydendron* Nees & Mart. (1833). About 40 spp., trop. America; type *A. guianensis* Aubl., French Guiana. Mez, Jahrb. Bot. Gart. Berlin, 5: 50; B.H. 3: 153 (*Aydendron*); E.P. 3, 2: 121; Kostermans, Rec. Trav. Bot. Néerl. 35: 866 (1938); Journ. Sci. Res. Indon. 1: 89 (1952); Bol. Técn. Inst. Agron. do Norte Brasil, 28: 52 (1955); Reinwardtia, 4: 236 (1957).

Trees; leaves scattered, coriaceous, pinnately nerved; panicles pedunculate, axillary or subterminal; flowers paniculate, bisexual or polygamo-dioecious, small; calyx-tube campanulate obovoid, at length often constricted at the apex; segments 6, subequal; perfect stamens 9, filaments broad or narrow, those of the first and second row eglandular, anthers introrsely 2-locular, those of the third row with a subsessile gland on each side at the base; staminodes of the fourth row few, small or absent, rarely large and capitate-cordate; ovary enclosed by the calyx-tube, style shortly exserted; berry at first enclosed by the subglobose calyx-tube, soon exserted, globose-ovoid or oblong, surrounded at the base by hardened cupular truncate calyx-tube with a simple or double margin, the limb deciduous.

19. **Endlicheria**[1] Nees, Linnaea 8: 37 (1833). About 40 spp., trop. America; type *E. hirsuta* (Schott) Nees. B.H. 3: 153; E.P. 3, 2: 122; Kostermans, Rec. Trav. Bot. Néerl. 34: 500 (1937); Journ. Sci. Res. Indon. 1: 17 (1952); Bol. Técn. Inst. Agron. do Norte Brasil, 28: 62 (1955); Allen, Journ. Arn. Arb. 26: 421 (1945); Comm. For. Res. Inst. Indon. no. 57: 45 (1957); Kostermans, Reinwardtia, 4: 237 (1957).

Trees and shrubs; leaves coriaceous, pinnately nerved; flowers dioecious, small, male in lax large panicles, female in dense almost short or long interrupted spike-like inflorescences; calyx-tube short; segments 6, subequal; perfect stamens in male flowers 9, those of the first and second rows not glandular, anthers introrse, of the third row with a sessile gland at the base on each side and anthers extrorse; staminodes absent; ovary abortive in the male flowers; staminodes in the female flowers 9 or 6, short, sessile, scale-like; ovary with a shortly exserted style; berry at length exserted from the calyx-tube, surrounded at the base by the cupular truncate scarcely indurated calyx-tube.

Tribe 2. CRYPTOCARYEAE

Testa of the seeds membranous, scarcely distinguishable from the pericarp, not intruded between the cotyledons   20. **Cryptocarya**
Testa of the seed divided from the apex into 6 lobes by spurious septa formed by the intrusive endocarp   21. **Ravensara**

20. **Cryptocarya**[2] R.Br., Prodr. 402 (1810). About 200 spp., Old World tropics and subtropics, few in trop. South America; lectotype *C. glaucescens* R.Br., Australia. B.H. 3: 150; E.P. 3, 2: 122. Kostermans, Meded. Bot. Mus. Rijks Univ. Utrecht No. 42: 557 (1937); Reinwardtia, 4: 243 (1957).

Trees and shrubs; leaves alternate, rarely subopposite, coriaceous, pinnately nerved or triplinerved; flowers bisexual, small, paniculate; calyx-tube constricted at the apex after flowering; segments 6, subequal; perfect stamens 9, those of the first and second rows not

[1] Synonyms of **Endlicheria**: *Goeppertia* Nees (1836). *Schauera* Nees (1836). *Schaueria* Nees ex Meisn. (1864). *Ampelodaphne* Meisn. (1864). *Huberodaphne* Ducke (1925).

[2] Synonyms of **Cryptocarya**: *Boldu* Nees (1836). *Caryodaphne* Blume ex Nees (1836). *Endocarpa* Raf. (1838). *Salgada* Blanco (1845). *Cryptocaria* Gay (1849). *Bellota* Gay (1849). *Icosandra* Philippi (1857). *Massoia* Becc. (1880). *Massoja* Kuntze (1904). *Pseudocryptocarya* Teschner (1923).

glandular, with introrse anthers, of the third row with a subsessile gland on each side at the base, with extrorse anthers; staminodes of the fourth row ovate, shortly stipitate; ovary with a shortly exserted style, stigma obtuse or discoid; fruit enclosed by the enlarged hardened or thinly subdrupaceous or rather fleshy, globose or oblong, smooth or with numerously ribbed calyx-tube, the latter closed at the mouth, the limb deciduous or rarely persisting for a time; pericarp membranous or hardened, adnate to or free from the calyx-tube.

21. **Ravensara** Sonnerat., Voy. Ind. Or. 3: 248, t. 127 (1782). *Agathophyllum* Juss. (1789). *Evodia* Gaertn. (1791). *Euodia* Gaertn. (1791). 18 spp., Mascarenes; type *R. aromatica* Sonnerat., Madagascar. B.H. 3: 151; E.P. 3, 2: 122; Kostermans, Humbert Not. Syst. 8: 96 (1939); *Ravensara* in Madagascar, Bull. Jard. Bot. Brux. 28: 173 (1958).

Strongly aromatic trees; leaves coriaceous, pinnately nerved; panicles few-flowered, pedunculate; flowers bisexual, small; calyx-tube turbinate or obovoid, constricted at the top after flowering; segments 6, subequal; perfect stamens 9, those of the first and second rows not glandular, with introrse anthers, of the third row with a subsessile gland on each side at the base, with extrorse anthers; staminodes of the fourth row ovate, shortly stipitate; ovary with a shortly exserted style; fruit enclosed by the globose fleshy oily or hardened calyx-tube, the mouth subclosed, the limb deciduous; pericarp confluent with the calyx-tube, divided inside from the base to beyond the middle by 6 intruded ribs connate in the middle and dividing it more or less perfectly into 6 loculi; seed pendulous from the undivided apex, divided into 6 lobes descending into the spurious loculi; testa membranous, free from or at length more or less adnate to the pericarp.

Tribe 3. SASSAFRIDEAE

Inflorescence a short lax raceme and almost umbel-like; flowers dioecious
22. **Sassafras**
Inflorescence laxly paniculate; flowers mostly bisexual   23. **Sassafridium**
Inflorescence sessile or densely fasciculate or very shortly racemose; flowers
    dioecious   24. **Actinodaphne**

22. **Sassafras** Trew, Herb Blackwell 3: sign. P. t. 267 (1757); Nees, Laur. Expos. 17 (1833). *Pseudosassafras* Lecomte (1912). *Yushunia* Kamikoti (1933). 3 spp., China, Formosa, Atlantic North America; type *S. albidum* (Nutt.) Nees (*Laurus sassafras* Linn.). B.H. 3: 160; E.P. 3, 2: 119; Rehder, Amer. and Asiat. spp. of *Sassafras*, Journ. Arn. Arb. 1: 242 (1920).

Trees; leaves alternate, deciduous, pinnately nerved, sometimes trilobed; racemes short, almost umbel-like, developing with the new shoots from buds covered by a few scales; flowers dioecious;[1] calyx-tube very short; segments 6, subequal; stamens in the male flowers, and staminodes often in the female flowers 9, those of the first and second rows not glandular, of the third row with a stipitate gland on each side at the base; filaments narrow; anthers all subsessile, introrse; staminodes of the fourth row subsessile, thick, capitate-cordate; ovary narrowed into a short to rather long style: berry inserted in the fleshy cupular truncate or sinuate calyx-tube.

23. **Sassafridium** Meisn., DC. Prodr. 15, 1: 171 (1864). *Dendrodaphne* Beurl. (1856). 1 sp., *S. veraguense* Meisn., Mexico. B.H. 3: 160; E.P. 3, 2: 118. Included in *Ocotea* by Kostermans, Reinwardtia, 4: 232 (1957).

[1] The flowers are undoubtedly *dioecious* as noted by Wilson & Hemsley and not *bisexual* as stated by Lecomte.

Tree or shrub; leaves coriaceous, pinnately nerved; panicles pedunculate, axillary or lateral; flowers bisexual or polygamo-dioecious; calyx-tube short; segments 6, subequal; perfect stamens 9, those of the first and second rows without glands, of the third row with a subsessile gland on each side at the base; anthers all subsessile, introrse; 4-locellate; staminodes of the fourth row subsessile, thick, capitate-cordate; ovary narrowed into a short or rather long style; berry enclosed by the truncate cupular calyx.

24. **Actinodaphne** Nees, Wall. Pl. As. Rar. 2: 68 (1831). *Iozoste* Nees (1831). *Iozosmene* Lindl. (1836). About 70 spp., E. Asia; type *A. pruinosa* Nees, Malaya. B.H. 3: 160; E.P. 3, 2: 119; Kostermans, Reinwardtia, 4: 234 (1957).

Trees and shrubs; leaves subopposite or crowded at the ends of the shoots, or almost verticillate, pinnately nerved; fascicles of flowers axillary or lateral; flowers dioecious, subsessile, subtended by a few caducous bracts; calyx-tube short; segments 6, subequal; perfect stamens in the male flowers and often staminodes in the female flowers 9, those of the first and second rows not glandular, of the third row with a stipitate gland on each side at the base; filaments narrow; anthers 4-locellate, all introrse; ovary narrowed into a rather long style, stigma dilated, peltate; berry inserted on the hardened spreading flat discoid or concave calyx-tube.

Tribe 4. CINNAMOMEAE

Perfect stamens 9; ovary superior:
  Tropical American genera:
    Flowers bisexual:
      Staminodes of the fourth whorl present and thickened at the apex:
        Disk not present or only slightly developed:
          Fruit immersed at the base in the persistent hardened calyx
                                        25. **Phoebe**
          Fruit surrounded by the unchanged base of the calyx, the latter at length falling off   26. **Persea**
          Fruit seated on the expanded 6-fid persistent calyx with more or less thickened pedicel   27. **Nothaphoebe**
        Disk well developed, 6-lobed   28. **Pleurothyrium**
      Staminodes of the fourth whorl subulate, small or absent:
        Disk absent; stamens of first and second rows eglandular
                                        29. **Nectandra**
        Disk present, annular; stamens of the first and second rows glandular on the back   30. **Synandrodaphne**
    Flowers dioecious or polygamous:
      Pairs of anther-loculi superposed   31. **Ocotea**
      Pairs of anther-loculi more or less at an equal level:
        Calyx truncate and often cupular in fruit   29. **Nectandra**
        Calyx rotate-spreading and persistent in fruit   32. **Dicypellium**
  Tropical Asian, African, Pacific Islands, and Australian genera:
    Leaves mostly prominently 3-nerved from the base:
      Calyx-lobes equal or subequal   33. **Cinnamomum**
      Calyx-lobes very unequal, the outer minute, inner much larger, valvate
                                      34. **Cardiodaphnopsis**
    Leaves not 3-nerved from the base:

Perianth, if persistent, not reflexed in fruit; flowers bisexual or very
rarely polygamous   26. **Persea**
Perianth persistent and reflexed in fruit; flowers bisexual   35. **Machilus**
Perianth not reflexed in fruit; flowers mostly dioecious:
  Ovary more or less immersed in the calyx-tube; berry subtended by the
    deciduous-limbed cupular or expanded calyx-tube   31. **Ocotea**
  Ovary free from the calyx-tube; berry subtended by the persistent calyx-
    lobes   36. **Stemmatodaphne**
Perfect stamens 6; ovary inferior; flowers dioecious   37. **Hypodaphnis**
Perfect stamens 3; flowers bisexual; Borneo   38. **Eusideroxylon**

25. **Phoebe** Nees, Syst. Laur. 98 (1836). 50 spp., trop. and subtrop. Asia and
America; lectotype *P. lanceolata* Nees, trop. Asia. B.H. 3: 157; E.P. 3, 2: 115.

Trees and shrubs; leaf-buds small, scales few, keeled, foliaceous; leaves pinnately nerved;
inflorescence paniculate or subcorymbose, axillary; flowers bisexual, paniculate, nude;
calyx persistent, becoming hardened and clasping the basal part of the fruit, lobes 6, subequal; fertile stamens 3-seriate, the inner 3 with a pair of substipitate glands; anthers 4-
locular, inner 3 extrorse; staminodes 3, stipitate; stigma depressed, discoid; fruit baccate,
immersed at the base in the 6-lobed rigid persistent hardened calyx.

26. **Persea**[1] Miller, Gard. Dict. Abr. ed. 4 (1754); Gaertn. f. Fruct. 3: 222,
t. 221 (1805). *Farnesia* Fabr. (1763). 10 spp., Atlantic Isls., trop. Asia and
America; type *P. americana* Miller (*P. gratissima* Gaertn. f.), Atlantic Isls.,
cult. in warm countries. B.H. 3: 156, partly (sect. *Eupersea* only); E.P. 3, 2:
114; Webb & Berthelot, Îles Canar. t. 204; Kostermans, Reinwardtia, 4:
225 (in very small part).

Tall tree; leaves alternate, large, pinnately nerved, flowers in axillary or terminal pedunculate cymes shorter than the leaves, bisexual, rarely dioecious; calyx deeply 6-partite, persistent, segments at length falling off; stamens 12, in 4 series, the filaments of the 2 outer
series nude, those of the third row with 2 sessile or shortly stipitate glands above the base;
the fourth with imperfect anthers like triangular glands; anthers introrse, oblong, 4-locellate;
stigma discoid; berry ovoid-elliptic, fleshy, surrounded by the unchanged base of the calyx,
at length nude.

27. **Nothaphoebe** Blume, Mus. Bot. 1: 328 (1851). About 60 spp., trop. and
subtrop. Asia and America; lectotype *N. umbelliflora* (Blume) Blume. B.H. 3:
157 (in *Persea*); E.P. 3, 2: 116. Included in *Persea* by Kostermans, Reinwardtia, 4: 227 (1957).

Trees; leaves alternate, pinnately nerved; flowers bisexual; panicles axillary and terminal,
the flowers subumbellate, small and yellowish; calyx 6-fid, 3 outer teeth smaller; stamens 12,
in 4 series, outer 9 fertile, inner 3 sterile; fertile filaments very short, flattened, inner 3 with
2 collateral glands; anthers rounded-quadrate, 4-locellate, opening by ascending valves, in
series 1 and 2 introrse, in series 3 extrorse, sterile shortly stipitate, eglandular with sagittate-
ovoid heads; ovary 1-locular, 1-ovuled; style short, stigma discoid; berry 1-seeded, seated
on the expanded 6-fid calyx with more or less thickened pedicel.

28. **Pleurothyrium** Nees. Syst. Laur. 349 (1836). *Pleorothyrium* Endl. (1841).
5 spp., trop. South America; lectotype *P. chrysophyllum* Nees, Peru. B.H.
3: 159; E.P. 3, 2: 116.

---

[1] Synonyms of **Persea**: *Farnesia* Heist. (1763). *Nyrophyllum* Necker (1790). *Menestrate*
Vellozo (1825). *Alseodaphne* Nees (1831). *Tamala* Raf. (1838). *Euphoebe* Bl. ex Meisn. (1864).

Trees; leaves alternate, large pinnately nerved; panicles large, many-flowered, ferruginous, axillary; flowers bisexual; calyx-tube short; segments 6, subequal, spreading; disk fleshy, divided into 6 teeth alternate with the stamens; perfect stamens 9; anthers 4-locellate, the lateral 2 locelli scarcely higher than the others, the first and second rows of stamens introrse, the third row extrorse; glands subsessile on each side at the base of the stamens of the third row; staminodes of the fourth row triangular or cordate; ovary sessile within the calyx-tube; style short; fruit not seen.

29. **Nectandra**[1] Roland ex Rottb., Acta Litt. Univ. Hafn. 1; 279 (1778) (conserved name). About 90 spp., trop. and subtrop. South America; lectotype *N. sanguinea* Roland, South America. B.H. 3: 159; E.P. 3, 2: 116; C. K. Allen, Journ. Arn. Arb. 26: 365 (prelim. surv. of Mexican and Cent. Amer. spp.).

Trees or shrubs; leaves alternate or rarely subopposite, pinnately nerved; panicles axillary or terminal, pedunculate; flowers bisexual or rarely polygamo-dioecious; calyx-tube short; segments 6, subequal; perfect stamens 9, those of the first and second rows eglandular, much shorter than the calyx, anthers broad, subsessile, introrsely 4-locellate, locelli inserted below the margin in a curve, those of the third row narrowed at the base and with a subsessile gland on each side, anthers extrorsely 4-locellate; staminodes of the fourth row absent or small, setaceous or clavate-capitate; ovary included or exserted from the bottom of the calyx-tube; style short; berry globose, ovoid or oblong, surrounded by or on the hardened truncate cupular or expanded calyx-tube from which the limb falls off.

30. **Synandrodaphne** Meisn., DC. Prodr. 15: 1; 176 (1864). 1 sp., *S. antillana* Meisn., West Indies. B.H. 3: 159.

Tree or shrub; leaves alternate, pinnately nerved, reticulate; flowers bisexual, medium-sized, in axillary or lateral pedunculate panicles; pedicels rather long; calyx-tube turbinate-campanulate; segments 6, subequal, shorter than the tube; perfect stamens 9, those of the first and second rows attached to a prominent annular disk each with a pair of small scales on the back; anthers broad, subsessile, introrsely 4-locellate, the third row narrower within the disk, with a small gland at the base on each side, the anthers extrorsely 4-locellate; staminodes of the fourth row short; ovary contracted into the style; fruit not seen. Retained here as in Benth. & Hook. f., but referred to *Nectandra* by some authors.

31. **Ocotea**[2] Aubl., Pl. Guian. 780 (1775). Probably about 200 spp., trop. America; type *O. guianensis* Aubl., trop. South America. For literature see Kostermans, Reinwardtia, 4: 232 (1957).

Trees or rarely shrubs; leaves alternate or rarely subopposite pinnately nerved; panicles axillary or subterminal, often lax, rarely contracted into heads; flowers small, polygamo-dioecious or rarely bisexual; calyx-segments 6, subequal; perfect stamens 9, of the first and second rows eglandular, with 4-locellate introrse anthers, locelli superposed in pairs; of the third row with a gland on each side at the base, the anthers extrorse and 4-locellate; of the fourth row minute or absent; stamens in the female flowers often reduced to antherless scales or obscurely locellate; ovary more or less immersed in the calyx-tube; berry globose, ovoid or oblong, at length exserted from the hardened truncate cupular or expanded calyx-tube, the limb deciduous. Description according to Bentham & Hooker's concept.

---

[1] Synonyms of **Nectandra**: *Porostema* Schreb. (1791). *Perostema* Raeuschel (1794). *Damburneya* Raf. (1838). *Pomatium* Nees (1866). *Nyctandra* Prior (1883–6).

[2] Synonyms of **Ocotea**: *Borbonia* Boehmer (1760). *Linharea* Arruda (1810). *Gymnobalanus* Nees & Mart. (1833). *Leptodaphne* Nees & Mart. (1833). *Mespilodaphne* Nees & Mart. (1833). *Oreodaphne* Nees & Mart. (1833). *Petalanthera* Nees & Mart. (1833). *Strychnodaphne* Nees & Mart. (1833). *Teleiandra* Nees & Mart. (1833). *Camphoromoea* Nees (1833). *Calycodaphne* Bojer (1837). *Balanopsis* Raf. (1838). *Damburneya* Raf. (1838). *Agathophyllum* Blume (1851) (partly). *Adenotrachelium* Nees ex Meisn. (1864). *Agriodaphne* Nees ex Meisn. (1864). *Aperiphracta* Nees ex Meisn. (1864). (1833). *Canella* Schott ex Meisn. (1864) not P.Br. (1756). *Ceramocarpium* Nees ex Meisn. (1864). *Ceramophora* Nees ex Meisn. (1864). *Nemodaphne* Meisn. (1864).

32. **Dicypellium** Nees, Laur. Expos. 14 (1833); Syst. Laur. 343 (1836). 1 sp., *D. caryophyllatum* Nees, trop. America. B.H. 3: 159; E.P. 3, 2: 117; Mez, Jahrb. Bot. Berl. 5: 472 (1889); Kostermans, Reinwardtia, 4: 235 (1957).

Tree; leaves scattered, pinnately nerved, long-acuminate; racemes lateral, without an involucre; flowers rather large, dioecious; male flowers: sepals 6 (*fide* Mez); first row of stamens like the calyx-lobes; second and third row of anthers foliaceous, fertile, ovate, 4-locellate, locelli superposed in pairs; female flowers: calyx-segments 6, subequal, rotate; staminodes 12, those of the first row petal-like, persistent, at length coriaceous, those of the second row normal, subspathulate, inflexed below the apex, obsoletely 4-locellate, of the third row smaller, subtruncate, of the fourth row scale-like, oblong, adpressed to the pistil; stigma acute; berry oval, dry, surrounded at the base by the hardened subfleshy spreading calyx and staminodes, inserted on the dilated flat 6-angled disk.

33. **Cinnamomum**[1] Blume, Bijdr. 568 (1825). About 110 spp., India to Cent. China, Japan, south to E. Australia and Fiji; lectotype *C. zeylanicum* Blume, Ceylon. B.H. 3:155; E.P. 3, 2: 113; Kostermans, Reinwardtia, 4: 233 (1957).

Trees and shrubs, often with aromatic bark, leaves opposite or occasionally alternate, mostly triplinerved, rarely pinnately nerved; flowers bisexual or by abortion polygamous, in axillary or subterminal panicles or lateral at the base of the young shoots; calyx-tube short, segments 6, subequal; perfect stamens 9 or fewer by abortion, those of the first and second rows not glandular, with introrse anthers, of the third row with subsessile or stipitate glands on each side at the base of the filaments, anthers extrorse, 4- or rarely 2-locellate; staminodes of the fourth row shortly stipitate and capitate-cordate or sagittate; ovary sessile, narrowed into the style, stigma discoid or obscurely 3-lobed; berry inserted on the expanded slightly or scarcely enlarged truncate or 6-lobed calyx-tube, its segments deciduous from the base or from the middle, or rarely subpersistent.

34. **Cardiodaphnopsis** Airy-Shaw, Kew Bull. 1940: 3 spp., China, Indo-China, Malay Archip., type *C. tonkinensis* (Lecomte) Airy-Shaw, Tonkin to Philippine Isls. and Borneo. Included by Kostermans in *Persea* (Reinwardtia, 4: 225).

Trees; leaves opposite or subopposite, triplinerved, thinly coriaceous; flowers bisexual, in lax axillary thyrses; calyx-tube almost nothing; segments 6, outer minute, open in bud, inner larger, broadly triangular-ovate, valvate; stamens 9, either clavate-oblong and scarcely distinct from the filaments, or quadrate and distinct from the filaments, flattened, 4-locellate, those of the first and second rows introrse, of the third row extrorse and with subsessile glands at the base; staminodes 3, shortly arrow-like, shortly stipitate; ovary small, ovoid, narrowed into a short style, stigma small 3-2-lobed; fruit large, obovoid or pear-shaped, drupaceous, hard, shining green, the pedicel more or less thickened, expanded at the apex; calyx-segments caducous; seeds large, shaped like the fruit.

35. **Machilus** Nees, Wall. Pl. Asiat. Rar. 2: 70 (1831). 46 spp., India to Korea and Japan, Malaya, type *M. odoratissima* Nees, W. Himalayas to Upper Burma. B.H. 3: 156; E.P. 3, 2: 115. Included in *Persea* by Kostermans, Reinwardtia, 4: 227 (1957).

Trees; leaves alternate, pinnately nerved; buds often with imbricate scales; panicles axillary, dense and subsessile or lax and long-pedunculate; flowers bisexual, small or fairly large; calyx-tube short; segments 6, subequal or the outer slightly smaller; perfect stamens 9, those of the first and second rows not glandular, filaments rather long and with introrse anthers, of the third row with a stipitate gland on each side at the base, with extrorse anthers; staminodes of the fourth row shortly stipitate and capitate-cordate; ovary sessile,

---

[1] Synonyms of **Cinnamomum**: *Camphorina* Nor., *nomen* (1790). *Septina* Nor., *nomen* (1790). *Camphora* (Linn.) Nees (1831). *Cecicodaphne* Nees (1831). *Cecidodaphne* Nees (1836). *Parthenoxylon* Bl. (1851). *Cynamomum* Deniker (1886). *Neocinnamomum* Liou Ho (1932).

stigma small or discoid; berry globose or oblong, inserted on the not or scarcely thickened pedicel, the calyx-segments persistent and reflexed below the berry.

36. **Stemmatodaphne** Gamble, Kew Bull. 1910: 227. 1 sp., *S. perakensis* Gamble, Malay Penins. Included in *Persea* by Kostermans, Reinwardtia, 4: 225 (1957).

    Tree; leaves alternate; flowers umbellate in lax panicles from the axils of the leaves; pedicels long; calyx-lobes 6, subequal; fertile stamens 9, anthers 4-locellate, those of the first and second row short, triangular, introrse on very short filaments, of the third row similar, extrorse, with 2 minute glands at the base of the filaments, of the fourth row triangular, sessile; ovary globose; style short, stigma small; berry large, globose, calyx-lobes suberect, persistent, pedicel clavate, thickened.

37. **Hypodaphnis** Stapf, Fl. Trop. Afr. 6, 1: 185 (1909). 1 sp., *H. zenkeri* (Engl.) Stapf, trop. Africa. Engl. Bot. Jahrb. 26: 385, t. 9, fig. A (*Ocotea*); Kostermans, Bull. Jard. Bot. Brux. 15: 88 (1938); Reinwardtia, 4: 244 (1957).

    Tree; leaves alternate, pinnately nerved; panicles subterminal, many-flowered; flowers dioecious, small; calyx 6-partite to the base; male flowers: stamens 6, 3-seriate; anthers 4-locellate with collateral valves, those of the outermost row 2, introrse, of the inner row extrorse; staminal glands 3, large, inserted below the filaments of the second row; staminodes absent; ovary inferior, turbinate; style cylindric; ovule sterile; female flowers: stamens sterile; ovary inferior; style with a subdiscoid stigma; ovule large; fruit not known.

38. **Eusideroxylon** Teijsm. & Binnend, Batav. Nat. Tijdschr. 25: 292, tt. 1–2 (1863) (conserved name). *Bihania* Meisn. (1864). 2 spp., Malaya; type *E. zwageri* Teijsm. & Binnend. B.H. 3: 155; E.P. 3, 2: 117; de Wit, Bull. Bot. Gard. Buitenz. 18: 200 (1949).

    Tall tree with very hard wood; leaves alternate, coriaceous, pinnately nerved; panicles axillary, branched almost from the base, lax; pedicels rather long; flowers bisexual, small, tomentellous; calyx-tube short; segments 6, subequal; perfect stamens 3, of the third row columnar, eglandular, equally 4-locellate, truncate at the apex, 2 locelli extrorse, 2 introrse; staminodes of the first and second rows scale-like, ovate-orbicular, shorter than the calyx-lobes, of the fourth row narrow, shorter than the stamens; ovary ovoid, scarcely enclosed by the calyx-tube, contracted into the style; fruit small, pedicel scarcely thickened, calyx deciduous.

Tribe 5. LITSEAE

Anthers 4-locellate:
  Flowers bisexual:
    Perfect stamens 12; flowers single within the 4–5 imbricate bracts
                                                     39. **Dodecadenia**
    Perfect stamens 9; flowers numerous in the umbels   40. **Umbellularia**
  Flowers unisexual:
    Fruit inserted in the small calyx-tube   41. **Litsea**
    Fruit on a disk-like cup   42. **Neolitsea**
Anthers 2-locular:
  Flowers 2 or more in each involucre:
    Calyx-segments 6 or more, more or less petaloid   43. **Lindera**
    Calyx segments 4, subequal   44. **Laurus**
  Flowers solitary in each involucre:
    Stamens 6–9 in more than one row; inflorescence bracteate
                                                    45. **Iteadaphne**
    Stamens 6 in a single row; inflorescence without bracts   46. **Valvanthera**

39. **Dodecadenia** Nees ex Wall., Pl. As. Rar. 2: 61 (1831). 3 spp., Himalayas; type *D. grandiflora* Nees. B.H. 3: 161; E.P. 3, 2: 119.

Trees; leaves crowded, coriaceous, pinnately nerved; buds covered with imbricate scales; flowers bisexual, in sessile axillary heads solitary or several together, solitary within the 4–5 imbricate bracts; calyx-tube short, segments 8–6, subequal; perfect stamens 12, those of the first and second rows not glandular, of the third and fourth rows with a large gland on each side at the base; filaments narrow; anthers all introrse; ovary narrowed into a rather long style, stigma much dilated; berry inserted on the thick almost flat and discoid persistent calyx-tube, the pedicel very short and rather thick.

40. **Umbellularia** Nutt., N. Amer. Sylv. 87 (1842). *Linharia Arruda* (1816). *Linharea* Arruda (1821). *Drimophyllum* Nutt. (1842). *Sciadiodaphne* Reichb. (1841). 2 spp., W. North America to Mexico; type *U. californica* (Hook. & Arn.) Nutt., California to Oregon; *U. parvifolia* Hemsl., Mexico. B.H. 3: 162; E.P. 3, 2: 116; Kostermans, Reinwardtia, 4: 235 (1957).

Trees or shrubs; leaves alternate, evergreen, pinnately nerved and strikingly reticulate, strongly scented; flowers enclosed by a very caducous involucre, solitary in the upper axils or forming a raceme and crowded at the apex of the branches, bisexual, numerous in the umbels, shortly pedicellate; calyx-tube very short, segments 6, subequal; stamens 9, those of the first and second row eglandular, with introrsely 4-locellate anthers, of the third row with a sessile gland on each side at the base, with extrorse anthers; staminodes of the fourth row absent; ovary exserted from the calyx-tube; stigma peltate-dilated; berry seated on the scarcely enlarged discoid perianth-tube, ellipsoid or ovoid.

41. **Litsea**[1] Lam. Dict. 3: 574 (1789) (conserved name). About 400 spp., trop. and E. Asia, Malay Archip., Australasia, North America; type *L. chinensis* Lam. B.H. 3: 161; E.P. 3, 2: 119; Kostermans, Reinwardtia, 4: 240 (1957).

Trees and shrubs; leaves alternate or rarely subopposite, pinnately nerved or triplinerved, coriaceous and evergreen or rarely thinner and deciduous; buds nude or covered with overlapping scales; flowers dioecious, umbellate or capitate; involucres globose, in sessile or shortly pedunculate axillary or lateral fascicles or racemes, persistent in flower; bracts of the involucre 4–6, broad, closely folded on themselves; calyx-tube ovoid, campanulate or very short; segments 6 or 4 or fewer, subequal or small, rarely minute or absent; stamens in the males, staminodes in the females often 12 or 9, or in 2-merous flowers only 6, sometimes more than 12, those of the first and second rows mostly not glandular, those of the third and fourth rows, when present, and rarely of the second row with an open stipitate gland on each side at the base; anthers 4-locellate, all introrse, or those of the third row with the lower loculi rarely lateral; ovary in the female flower narrowed into a short or long style; stigma often dilated and irregularly lobed; fruit inserted in the small calyx-tube, the latter either unchanged or enlarged, cupular.

42. **Neolitsea** Merr., Philipp. Journ. Sci. Bot. 1: Suppl. 56 (1906). *Tetradenia* Nees (1831), not Benth. (1830). *Balanopsis* Raf. (1838) (partly). *Bryantea* Raf. (1838). *Litsea* sect. *Neolitsea* Benth. (1880). About 80 spp., E. Asia and Malaya; lectotype *N. cassia* (Linn.) Kostermans. Lecomte, Fl. Gen. Indoch.

[1] Synonyms of **Litsea**: *Malapoenna* Adans. (1763). *Glabraria* Linn. (1771). *Tomex* Thunb. (1783). *Hexanthus* Lour. (1790). *Sebifera* Lour. (1790). *Quinquedula* Nor. (1790). *Fiwa* J. F. Gmel. (1791). *Tetranthera* Jacq. (1797). *Berrya* Klein (1800). *Lethedon* Spreng. (1807). *Litsaea* Pers. (1807). *Pipalia* Stokes (1812). *Darwinia* Dennst. (1818). *Cyclicodaphne* Nees (1831). *Lepidadenia* Nees (1833). *Bryantea* Raf., *Dipliathus* Raf., *Decapenta* Raf., *Heckeria* Raf. (1838). *Fiva* Steud. (1840). *Adenodaphne* S. Moore (1921). *Pseudolitsea* Yang (1945).

5: 142 (1914); Liou-Ho, Laur. Chine et Indochine, 139 (1932); Allen, Ann. Missouri Bot. Gard. 25: 415 (key to spp.) (1938); Kostermans, Journ. Sci. Res. Indon. 1: 147 (1952); Reinwardtia, 4: 241 (1957).

Shrubs or small trees; leaves alternate, pinnately or triplinerved; umbels sessile, mostly axillary, subglobose, surrounded by large persistent bracts; flowers dioecious, dimerous; fertile stamens in the male flowers 6, in 3 whorls, the innermost whorl with glands; anthers 4-locellate, introrse; stigma peltate; fruit on a disk-like cup, the pedicel often slightly thickened.

43. **Lindera**[1] Thunb., Nov. Gen. Pl. 3: 44 (1783) (conserved name). About 80 spp., E. Asia, North America; type *L. umbellata* Thunb., Japan. B.H. 3: 163; E.P. 3, 2: 123; Koorders & Valeton, Meded. Lands Pl. Buitenzorg, 58: 229 (1904); Lecomte, Fl. Indo-Chine, 5: 152 (1914); Liou-Ho, Laur. Chine et Indochine, 117 (1932); Kostermans, Journ. Sci. Res. Indon. 1: 90 (1952); Reinwardtia, 4: 241 (1957) (excl. *Iteadaphne* Blume).

Trees and shrubs; leaves alternate or subopposite, pinnately nerved or 3–5-nerved; buds nude or covered by imbricate scales; flowers dioecious, umbellate or capitate, involucres sessile or pedunculate, sessile in fascicles or rarely shortly racemose; umbels or heads included by a globose or rarely ovoid involucre, bracts of the involucre 4, rarely 5 or 2, broad, concave, closely folded; calyx-tube very short; segments 6, subequal, rarely fewer or 7–9, petaloid and often small; stamens in the male flowers, staminodes in the female flowers, mostly 9, rarely fewer or more, mostly not glandular in the first and second rows, in the third and rarely also in the second rows with a sessile or stipitate gland on each side at the base or above the base; anthers all introrse and 2-locular; no fourth row of stamens or staminodes; ovary in male flowers small and empty or absent, rarely here and there perfect, in the female flower narrowed into a short or long style, stigma dilated, entire or sublobate; berry globose or ovoid seated on a nude pedicel or on the slightly dilated or disk-like entire or lobed calyx.

44. **Laurus** Linn., Sp. Pl. 369 (1753); Gen. Pl. ed. 5: (1754). *Appella* Adans. (1763). *Adaphus* Neck. (1790). *Ajovea* Raf. (1838). 2 spp., Mediterr. reg., Atlant. Isls.; type *L. nobilis* Linn., Mediterr. reg. B.H. 3: 163; E.P. 3, 2: 124.

Trees; leaves alternate, evergreen, pinnately nerved; involucres of flowers shortly pedunculate in the leaf-axils, fasciculate or shortly racemose; flowers bisexual or dioecious, umbellate, the umbels enclosed by the globose involucre before flowering; calyx-tube short; segments 4, subequal; perfect stamens in male flowers 12 or more, rarely 8, all the filaments with a stipitate gland on each side in the middle or near the base, or rarely the stamens of the first and second rows eglandular; anthers all short, introrsely 2-locular; staminodes in the female flowers often 4; ovary with a short style; berry ovoid seated on the calyx-tube, which remains unchanged or slightly enlarged, disk-like, entire, or lacerate.

45. **Iteadaphne** Blume, Mus. Bot. Lugd. Bot. 1: 365 (1851). 2 spp., type *I. confusa* Blume, Malaya. B.H. 3: 162; E.P. 3, 2: 124.

Small trees; leaves evergreen, pinnately nerved; involucres very small, the males shortly pedunculate, racemose in the axils, the common rhachis bracteate; female and bisexual a little longer pedunculate, solitary or fasciculate; flowers dioecious or polygamous, solitary within the globose involucre; calyx-tube very short, segments 6, subequal; stamens 6–9, those of the first row eglandular, of the second row (and third if present) with a subsessile gland on each side at the base; anthers all introrse; ovary not immersed; style short; berry seated at the base of the disk-like perianth.

---

[1] Synonyms of **Lindera**: *Euosmus* Nutt. (1818). *Sassafras* Bercht. & Presl (1825). *Calosmon* Bercht. & Presl (1825). *Daphnidium* Nees (1831). *Polyadenia* Nees (1831). *Benzoin* Nees (1833). *Evelyna* Raf. (1838). *Evosmus* Raf. (1838). *Ozanthes* Raf. (1838). *Aperula* Blume (1851). *Parabenzoin* Nakai (1925).

46. Valvanthera[1] C. T. White, Proc. Roy. Soc. Queensland 1935, 47: 76 (1936). 1 sp., *V. albiflora* C. T. White, Queensland.

A tree; leaves alternate, entire; stipules absent; flowers in slender axillary panicles; bracts and bracteoles absent; flowers dimorphic, abortive ones pedicellate, ovoid; normal flowers sessile, bisexual, subtended by a calyx-like cupular tube (involucre); calyx 6–8-lobed, lobes imbricate, unequal; stamens 6, filaments short, anthers 2-locular, dehiscing by valves; ovary semi-inferior, with 1 pendulous ovule?; style columnar, stigma with 2 recurved lobes; fruit drupaceous, ellipsoid or ovoid; endocarp crustaceous; seed solitary, without endosperm.

Tribe 6. CASSYTHEAE

Only genus   47. **Cassytha**

47. Cassytha[2] Linn., Sp. Pl. 35 (1753); Gen. Pl. ed. 5: 22 (1754). 15 spp., warmer regions, mainly Australia; type *C. filiformis* Linn., Cosmopolitan in the tropics. B.H. 3: 164; E.P. 3, 2: 124; Kostermans, Reinwardtia, 4: 254 (1957) (see for further references).

Stems filiform, twining, adhering by haustoria to other plants; scales in place of leaves very small; flowers bisexual, sometimes dimorphous, spicate, capitate or racemose, sessile or shortly pedicellate within the scale-like bract; bracteoles 2, minute; calyx-tube very short, turbinate or ovoid; segments 6, outer 3 much smaller; perfect stamens 9, of the first and second rows eglandular, anthers introrse, or rarely of the second row reduced to narrow staminodes, of the third row with a subsessile gland on each side at the base, anthers extrorse; staminodes of the fourth row subsessile or stipitate; ovary in the flowering stage scarcely sunk in the calyx-tube, soon afterwards completely covered by the tube; stigma small or capitate, subsessile; fruit closely enclosed by the succulent tube of the calyx; seed with membranous testa.

16. HERNANDIACEAE

Blume, Bijdr. no. 11: 550 (1825) (*Hernandieae*)

Trees or shrubs, sometimes scandent, with alternate simple or digitately compound exstipulate leaves. Flowers bisexual, or monoecious or polygamous by abortion, actinomorphic, arranged in axillary corymbose or panicle-like cymes, bracteate or not. Calyx superior, with 3–5 imbricate or valvate subequal segments in two whorls, or rarely 4–8 in one whorl. Petals absent. Stamens 3–5 in a single whorl, when the calyx is double opposite the outer segments, often 4; anthers 2-locular, dehiscing introrsely or laterally by 2 valves; staminodes gland-like, in one cr two whorls outside the stamens, or absent, those of the outer whorl in pairs at the base of the

---

[1] I have been able to dissect only a single young male flower of this puzzling genus and found it to consist of a 1-flowered involucel with a calyx of 6 imbricate sepals, 6 introrse anthers opening by valves and with a large 2-lobed style. I consider it to be better in *Lauraceae* rather than *Hernandiaceae* (in which family it was doubtfully placed by White), and nearest *Iteadaphne*. Metcalfe reports that from an anatomical standpoint there is no fundamental objection to including it in *Lauraceae* except that it has a type of petiole structure not recorded in *Lauraceae*, and that its leaves bear sunken capitate glands with multicellular (usually 8-celled) heads.

[2] Synonyms of **Cassytha**: *Rombut* Adans. (1763). *Acatsjavalli* Adans. (1763). *Cassyta* Linn. (1764). *Cassita* Hill (1765). *Volutella* Forssk. (1775). *Calodium* Lour. (1790). *Rumputris* Raf. (1836).

filaments, those of the inner whorl alternate with the stamens. Ovary inferior, 1-locular; ovule solitary, pendulous, anatropous. Fruit dry, more or less ribbed, either with 2–4 wings on the body or with two terminal wings formed by enlarged perianth-segments, or without wings but enclosed in the inflated receptacle. Seed solitary, without endosperm; testa leathery; embryo straight; cotyledons large, plano-convex or flat and twisted around the radicle. Type genus *Hernandia* Linn.

Genera 4; species 44.

DISTRIBUTION. Tropics of both hemispheres, mainly near the coasts, and especially on oceanic islands.

CLASSIFICATION. Benth. & Hook. f., Gen. Pl. 1: 689 (1867); loc. cit. 3: 164 (1880); Pax, Engl. & Prantl, Nat. Pflanzenfam. 3, 2: 126, fig. 79 (1889); S. T. Dunn (revision of *Illigera*), Journ. Linn. Soc. 38: 290 (1908); Sprague, Fl. Trop. Afr. 6: 189 (1909); Gagnepain, Les affinités des *Hernandiaceae*, Bull. Mus. Nat. Hist. Paris, sér. 2, 6: 443 (1934); Lawrence, Taxon. Vasc. Pl. 513, fig. 148 (1951); Hutch., Fam. Fl. Pl. ed. 2, 1: 141, fig. 17 (1959).

ANATOMY. Sol. 2: 707; M.C. 2: 1157; POLLEN. Erdt. 202.

Cystoliths are a special feature of *Sparattanthelium* and *Gyrocarpus*. Hairy covering usually only of unicellular clothing hairs; glandular hairs occur in most species of *Illigera*, and consist of a short unicellular stalk and a 2-celled head. Stomata in most *Illigera* and *Hernandia* have subsidiary cells arranged parallel to the pore (Solereder, 2: 707). See reference to Shutts (below).

Phylogeny and Morphology. Hernandiaceae were formerly included in the *Combretaceae* and *Thymelaeaceae* (Lindley, Veg. Kingdom 530), and *Hernandia* in *Lauraceae* (Benth. & Hook. f., Gen. Pl.), but Pax's assignation in the *Pflanzenfamilien* to near the *Lauraceae* seems to be a better place. The family as at present constituted is not particularly homogeneous, the genera showing little close affinity with one another. It has recently been divided into two separate families, on anatomical grounds, by C. F. Shutts (*Tropical Woods*, no. 113: 85 (1960)).

Economic Properties. The rather soft woods of this small family are used locally for canoes, catamarans, clogs, drawing boards, and musical instruments.

Cymes bracteate; fruits with lateral wings or not winged:
 Leaves simple:
  Leaves often triplinerved, not peltate; fruits dry, ribbed; axis of infructescence indurated and dichotomously divided; flowers polygamo-dioecious   1. *Sparattanthelium*
  Leaves often peltate; fruits surrounded by the inflated perianth
                                                                    2. *Hernandia*
 Leaves digitately compound; fruits with 2–4 broad lateral wings; flowers bisexual   3. *Illigera*
Cymes ebracteate; fruits crowned by two terminal wings formed by the enlarged persistent calyx-segments, flowers unisexual; leaves simple
                                                                   4. *Gyrocarpus*

1. **Sparattanthelium** Mart., Flora, 24: 2; Beibl. 40 (1841). 8 spp., trop. South America; type *S. tupiniquinorum* Mart., Brazil. B.H. 1: 690; E.P. 3, 2: 129.

Trees or scandent shrubs; leaves entire, 3–5-nerved; flowers polygamo-dioecious, small, ebracteolate, numerous, arranged in terminal bracteate cymes; calyx-tube constricted above the ovary, 7–4-partite, segments imbricate; petals absent; stamens 7–4; anthers oblong or linear; ovary 1-locular, style rather thick, stigma oblique, capitate, emarginate; ovule 1, pendulous; fruit a drupe with a coriaceous or rather woody stone, 1-seeded; seeds with foliaceous cotyledons folded around the radicle.

2. **Hernandia** Linn., Sp. Pl. 981 (1753); Gen. Pl. ed. 5: 421 (1754). *Hertelia* Neck. (1790). *Hernandezia* Hoffmgg. (1824). *Biasolettia* C. Presl (1835–6). *Biassolettia* Endl. (1840). *Hernandiopsis* Meisn. (1864). 14 spp., maritime tropics and subtropics; type *H. sonora* Linn., West Indies. B.H. 3: 164; E.P. 3, 2: 129; Sprague, Fl. Trop. Afr. 6, 1: 191.

Trees; leaves undivided, ovate or peltate, 3–7-nerved; flowers monoecious, laxly paniculate, ultimate branches of the panicle ending in a 4–5-bracteate foliaceous involucre each containing 3 flowers, the middle flower female, sessile, the lateral male and shortly pedicellate; involucre in fruit inflated, often coloured, contracted at the mouth; male flowers: calyx-segments 8 or 6, subvalvate in each series; stamens as many as the outer segments and opposite to them; anthers 2-locular, opening laterally by valves; glands paired at the base of the stamens, or solitary or rarely absent; female flowers: calyx-lobes 10 or 8; ovary 1-locular, style short, geniculate about the middle, stigma dilated, toothed or lobed; fruit ribbed, enclosed by the enlarged thick fleshy involucre; seeds with hard testa and thick lobed subruminate cotyledons.

3. **Illigera** Blume, Bijd. 1153 (1826). *Henschelia* Presl (1835–6). *Gronovia* Blanco (1837). *Corysadenia* Griff. (1848). *Coryzadenia* Griff. (1854). 17 spp., Old World tropics, mainly Indo-Malaya; lectotype *I. appendiculata* Blume, Java, Sumatra, New Guinea. *I. pentaphylla* Welw., trop. Africa. B.H. 1: 689; E.P. 3, 2: 129; revision by Dunn, Journ. Linn. Soc. 38: 294; Sprague, Fl. Trop. Afr. 6, 1: 192.

Scandent shrubs; leaves digitately 3-foliolate; flowers cymose, branchlets bracteate at the forks; bracteoles at the base of the flowers 1–3; calyx 5-partite, lobes valvate, deciduous; petals 5, linear-oblong, inserted below the perigynous disk, valvate; stamens 5, alternating with as many glands, filaments with 2 spathulate or tubular staminodes at the base; anthers oblong, opening by 2 lateral valves; pollen echinulate; ovary 1-locular, style filiform, stigma reniform, undulate; ovule 1, pendulous; fruit broadly 2–4-winged lengthwise, wings veiny; seeds with plano-convex bilobed cotyledons.

4. **Gyrocarpus** Jacq., Stirp. Amer. 282, t. 178, fig. 80 (1763). 5 or more species, tropics; type *G. americanus* Jacq., Mexico to Venezuela. B.H. 1: 689; E.P. 3, 2: 129; Sprague, Fl. Trop. Afr. 6, 1: 189.

Trees; leaves entire or lobed; flowers polygamous, mostly male, in ebracteate corymbose cymes; male flowers: calyx 7–4-partite, lobes imbricate; petals absent; stamens 7–4, alternating with as many or more staminodes; anthers opening by 2 valves; pollen echinulate; female flowers: calyx-lobes 2, persistent, accrescent; petals and stamens absent; ovary 1-locular; stigma sessile; ovule 1, pendulous; fruit nut-like, with 2 terminal wings formed by the accrescent calyx, wings veiny; seeds with spirally twisted cotyledons.

Excluded—*Valvanthera* C. T. White, see *Lauraceae* (p. 143).

17. GOMORTEGACEAE

Reiche, Ber. Deutsch. Bot. Ges. 14: 232 (1896)

Large tree; wood heavy, durable, and beautifully figured; leaves opposite, petiolate, shining and aromatic, narrowly elliptic, pinnately nerved; stipules absent; racemes axillary and terminal; flowers bisexual, subtended by 2 opposite bracts; sepals 6–10, spirally arranged, epigynous; petals absent; stamens described as varying from 2–11, epigynous; filaments free; anthers 2-locular, introrse, dehiscing by valves from below; inner stamens with 2 shortly stalked glands at the base of each filament; ovary inferior, 2–3-locular; style 2–3-lobed; ovules 1 in each loculus, pendulous; fruit with a bony endocarp and fleshy exocarp; seed with large embryo in abundant oily endosperm. Type genus *Gomortega* Ruiz & Pavon.

CLASSIFICATION. B.H. 3: 149 (under *Lauraceae*); E.P.N. 172, 347; Hutch. Fam. Fl. Pl. ed. 2, 1: 140, fig. 16 (1959); W. L. Stern, Amer. Journ. Bot. 42: 874 (1955) (with full bibliography); Buchheim, Bemerkungen zum Andrözeum der *Gomortegaceae*, Willdenovia, 2: 27 (1958).

ANATOMY. M.C. 2: 1157. POLLEN. Erdt. 191.

Gomortega Ruiz & Pavon, Prodr. Fl. Peruv. 62, t. 10 (1794). *Adenostemum* Pers. (1800). *Keulia* Molina (1810). 1 sp., *G. keule* (Molina) I. M. Johnston (*G. nitida* Ruiz & Pavon), Peru. I. M. Johnston, Contrib. Gray Herb. N.S. 70: 92 (1924).

The wood of this little-known and puzzling tree has been described in detail by W. L. Stern (above) and he has also correlated the various descriptions by botanists since the genus was described by Ruiz and Pavon in 1794. After a careful investigation based on the floral morphology, including the pollen grains, and the xylem anatomy, Stern (last sentence of his summary) considers 'that most likely *Gomortegaceae* is closely allied to *Monimiaceae* through a *Hortonia*-like forebear with valvular anthers'.

18. MYRISTICACEAE

R.Br., Prodr. 1:399 (1810) (*Myristiceae*)

Trees and shrubs; sometimes young shoots with stellate or T-shaped hairs. Leaves alternate, sometimes falsely whorled and often horizontal, entire, pinnately nerved, often pellucid-punctate. Inflorescence axillary, rarely terminal, paniculate or racemose, rarely capitate or cymose; bracts mostly caducous; bracteoles often absent. Flowers dioecious, rarely monoecious. Calyx 3- rarely 2–5-lobed, lobes valvate; petals absent. Stamens about 40 to 2; filaments completely united into a column, very rarely only at the base; anthers 2-locular, either free or more or less adnate to the column, often closely connate, extrorse, dehiscing lengthwise by slits, muticous or shortly apiculate. Ovary superior, sessile, 1-locular; style absent or very short; stigmas 2, more or less connate, rarely expanded into a dentate disk; ovule 1, anatropous, attached near the base. Fruit coriaceous-fleshy or subwoody, nearly always at length dehiscing into 2 valves. Seed 1, mostly erect, more or less covered by a crustaceous-fleshy undivided or more or less deeply laciniate coloured aril; endosperm ruminate, with few exceptions. Type genus *Myristica* Gronov.

Genera 16; about 380 species.

DISTRIBUTION. Tropics.

CLASSIFICATION. Benth. & Hook. f., Gen. Pl. 3: 135 (1880); Prantl, Engl. & Prantl, Nat. Pflanzenfam. 3, 2: 40, fig. 35 (1891); Warburg, loc. cit. Nachtr. II–IV: 161 (1897); Warburg Monogr. *Myristicaceae*, Nova Act. Deutsch. Akad. Natürf. 68: 1–680, tt. 1–25 (1897); Stapf, Fl. Trop. Afr. 6, 1: 156 (1909), Lawrence, Taxon. Vasc. Pl. 509, fig. 145 (1951); Hutch., Fam. Fl. Pl. ed. a, 1: 142, fig. 18 (1959); A. C. Smith & Wodehouse, Amer. spp. of *Myristicaceae*, Brittonia, 2: 393 (1937), which see for additional literature: H. Perrier, Humbert Fl. Madag. Fam. 79e, *Myristic.* 1, figs. 1–2 (1952); Sinclair, Gard. Bull. Singap. 16: 205 (1958), revision of Malayan spp.

ADDITIONAL LITERATURE. Garrett, System. anat. of woods of *Myristicaceae*, Trop. Woods, 35: 6 (1933); Sinclair, loc. cit. (*supra*).

ANATOMY. M.C. 2: 1132. POLLEN. Wodehouse, Brittonia, 2: 397 (1937); Erdt. 202; Hoshi, Note on the development of pollen of *Myristica fragrans* and affinities of the fam. *Myristicaceae*, Journ. Indian Soc. Bot. 25: 139 (1946).

Economic Properties. The woods of this family are of little value as timber. The most important product is Nutmeg, the dried seeds and aril (mace) of *Myristica fragrans* Houtt., native of the Malay Archipelago and widely cultivated in most tropical countries; largely used for flavouring and as carminatives. Otoba Nutmeg, *Myristica otoba* Humb. & Bonpl., South America.

Phylogeny and Morphology. The family consists entirely of trees and shrubs, though never of great size. The principal authority on the family was the late O. Warburg, who in his monograph recognized fifteen genera instead of only one, *Myristica*, as in de Candolle's *Prodromus*, Bentham in the *Genera Plantarum*, and Prantl in Engl. & Prantl, *Nat. Pflanzenfamilien*. From seven to thirteen sections were recognized in these works and they were clarified and raised to generic rank by Warburg, thus bringing 'a considerable degree of order to the classification of the family' (A. C. Smith).

A. C. Smith (loc. cit.) made a detailed study of the American genera and a number of necessary reductions amongst the species, but retained the genera as delimited by Warburg. He gave three separate keys to the five American genera, based, 1, on the staminate (male) inflorescence, 2, on the fruits, and 3, on sterile branchlets and foliage. Amongst the latter, two genera have on the young branchlets and petioles (or sometimes on the lower surface of very young leaves) hairs which are 2-branched and of the so-called Malpighiaceous and *Indigofera* type, and two genera with stellate hairs, such as are found in *Sterculiaceae* and *Malvaceae*. Other useful characters are derived from the nervation of the leaves.

The Malayan species of the family have been revised by J. Sinclair (loc. cit.). He also upholds the genera established by Warburg, four of which occur in the region, *Knema, Myristica, Horsfieldia,* and *Gymnacranthera,* and he provides three keys to them, 1, for material with male flowers, 2, for those in fruit, and 3, for the identification of sterile material, the last mentioned perhaps of less value. Besides paragraphs on morphology he also deals with phylogeny and evolution.

Geographical Distribution. Five of the genera are confined to tropical America, ranging from S. Mexico and the lesser Antilles south to Bolivia, Brazil, and Santa Catharina. Most species occur in the low tropical plains, with only a few ascending the foothills of the Andes to an elevation of 1,500 metres. The centre of distribution in South America is in the Brazilian Amazon region. Only a single species, *Compsoneura sprucei* (A. DC.) Warb., is known from Mexico, and one from the lesser Antilles, *Virola surinamensis* Warb.

Most of the remainder of the genera are found in tropical Asia, from India to New Guinea and Polynesia. There is only one, *Mauloutchia,* in Madagascar, and the remainder are in tropical Africa.

KEY TO GENERA

Stamens 30–40; filaments connate only at the base; style long, columnar; aril rudimentary; inflorescence almost globose, flowers apparently capitate; Madagascar   1. **Mauloutchia**
Stamens 2–20; filaments completely united; style absent or very short; aril not rudimentary:
Anthers of the stalked column of stamens completely united to the apex:
Flowers (of the male) without a bracteole:
Inflorescence fasciculate, subcapitate; flowers very small, subsessile or shortly pedicellate; anthers 3–4; seed elliptic, aril not laciniate or toothed; endosperm not ruminate, starchy; Africa   2. **Staudtia**
Inflorescence cymose, once or twice divided; flowers relatively large, fasciculate; anthers 6–10; seed depressed-globose, aril not laciniate; endosperm coarsely ruminate, not starchy; Africa
3. **Scyphocephalium**
Inflorescence paniculate:
Flowers sessile, clustered into small heads:
Flowers depressed-globose, cup-shaped when open:
Anthers 6–10; flower-heads sessile, frequently crowded into a false spike; aril laciniate; endosperm not ruminate, starchy; Madagascar   4. **Brochoneura**
Anthers 3–4; flowers in dense interrupted masses   5. **Cephalosphaera**
Flowers clavate; anthers 2–4; flower-heads stalked, not crowded; aril laciniate; endosperm ruminate; Africa   6. **Pycnanthus**
Flowers stalked, fasciculate:
Branches of the inflorescence broadened at the end into a 'disk', these 'disks' bearing a fascicle of flowers; flowers cup-shaped; anthers 3–5; aril laciniate; endosperm ruminate only on the outside; smooth within, not starchy; Africa   7. **Coelocaryon**

Branches of the inflorescence not broadened into 'disks'; flowers funnel-shaped or urceolate; anthers 2–7; aril laciniate; endosperm ruminate, not starchy; America **8. Virola**

Flowers (of the male) with a bracteole:

Fruit transversely broader than long, subdidymous; aril not laciniate; inflorescence racemose:

Anthers 6, short; lateral nerves of the leaves united by arches within the margin; America **9. Iryanthera**

Anthers 12, long; lateral nerves not united within the margin; America **10. Osteophloeum**

Fruit vertically longer than broad; aril laciniate; the first branches of the inflorescence mostly corymbose or forked; Asia **11. Myristica**

Anthers of the stalked column of stamens partly united but free at the apex; inflorescence paniculate; flowers urceolate, without a bracteole; aril laciniate; endosperm ruminate, not starchy; Asia

12. Gymnacranthera

Anthers united into a nearly always sessile globose or cup-shaped mass; flowers without a bracteole, mostly globose, culular when open; inflorescence paniculate; aril not laciniate; endosperm ruminate, mostly without starch; Asia **13. Horsfieldia**

Anthers adnate only at the base to the margin of the staminal disk, radiating; flowers with a bracteole, globose or cupular; aril laciniate only in the upper part; endosperm ruminate, starchy; Asia **14. Knema**

Anthers free, sessile at the end of the staminal column; flowers without a bracteole; America:

Anthers 4–6; aril not laciniate; endosperm not ruminate, starchy; tertiary nerves of the leaves more or less parallel **15. Compsoneura**

Anthers 3; aril laciniate; endosperm ruminate, not starchy; tertiary nerves of the leaves more or less reticulate, scarcely conspicuous

16. Dialyanthera

1. **Mauloutchia** Warb., Ber. Deutsch. Bot. Ges. 13: 94 (1895). 1 sp., *M. chapelieri* (Baill.) Warb., Madagascar. E.P.N. 164; Warb. Monogr. *Myristic.* 128, 233.

Tree; leaves elliptic-lanceolate, coriaceous, lateral nerves close, oblique, anastomosing to the margin, densely rusty-pubescent below; inflorescence axillary and lateral on the wood, subspherical; flowers monoecious (?), subsessile, spuriously capitate; calyx deeply 3-lobed; stamens 40–30, filaments united only at the base, unequal; style columnar, apex obtuse, stigmatose; ovule ascending; seed the size of the European Olive, aril rudimentary, embracing the base of the seed.

2. **Staudtia** Warb., Nova Acta Acad. Nat. Cur. 68: 241 (1897). ? *Thespesocarpus* Pierre (1896). 4 spp., trop. Africa; type *S. kamerunensis* Warb. E.P.N. 164; Warb., Monogr. *Myristic.* 128, 241, t. 8; Stapf, Fl. Trop. Africa, 6, 1: 164; Hutch. & Dalz., Fl. W. Trop. Afr. 1: 65; ed. 2 (Keay), 1: 62.

Trees; leaves glabrous, not white below; lateral nerves not very close, bifurcate and reticulate far from the margin and scarcely stouter than the tertiary nerves; flowers dioecious, capitate, densely crowded, heads subspherical, almost sessile, scarcely pedunculate; bracts present; bracteole absent; calyx 4–3-fid; filaments connate into a column; anthers 4–3, linear, adnate to and longer than the short basal part of the column; stigmas sessile; fruit large, pericarp thick, fleshy; aril completely covering the seed or not quite to the apex, not laciniate; seed ovoid or oblong ellipsoid, testa woody, thick, endosperm not ruminate; cotyledons connate at the base, suberect, not divergent.

3. **Scyphocephalium** Warb., Ber. Deutsch. Bot. Ges. 13: 94 (1895). *Ochocoa* Pierre (1896). 7 spp., trop. Africa; type *S. ochocoa* Warb. E.P.N. 164; Warb. Monogr. *Myristic.* 129, 244, tt. 2, 9; Stapf, Fl. Trop. Africa, 6, 1: 160; Hutch. & Dalz., Fl. W. Trop. Africa, 1: 65; ed. 2 (Keay), 1: 61.

Trees; leaves elongate-oblong, acuminate, not white below; lateral nerves arcuate and looped near the margin; tertiary nerves scarcely distinct, reticulate; flowers dioecious, rather large, crowded, and pseudo-capitate; bracts present; bracteoles absent; male calyx funnel-shaped, 3–5-partite; filaments connate into a slender column; anthers 10–6, adnate to and rather shorter than the columnar stipe; female calyx as in the male but with minute triangular bracteoles at the base; fruit large, pericarp fleshy, very thick, not dehiscent; aril entire, completely covering the seed; seed depressed, testa woody, not very thick, endosperm very ruminate, embryo very small, basal, cotyledons divaricate.

4. **Brochoneura** Warb., Ber. Deutsch. Bot. Ges. 13: 94 (1895). 4–5 spp., Madagascar; type *B. madagascariensis* (Lam.) Warb. E.P.N. 165; Warb., Monogr. *Myristic.* 128, 234, tt. 2, 8.

Trees; leaves coriaceous, glabrous and not white below; lateral nerves and veins reticulate; inflorescence paniculate, flowers dioecious, sessile in dense clusters, the clusters often confluent; bracts present, bracteoles absent; calyx deeply 4–3-lobed; filaments connate into a short column, anthers 10–6, usually longer than the basal stipe; fruit large; pericarp thick, fleshy; aril laciniate; seed ovoid, testa woody, thick, endosperm not ruminate; cotyledons connate at the base, suberect, not divergent.

5. **Cephalosphaera** Warb., Engl. Bot. Jahrb. 33: 383 (1903). 1 sp., *C. usambarensis* Warb., E. trop. Africa.

Tall tree; leaves oblong or oblong-lanceolate, glaucous below, later nerves anastomosing well within the margin; veins loosely reticulate; panicles axillary, enclosed in the sessile flower-like head when young, at length branched into sessile dense clusters of small flowers; bracts present; bracteoles none; flowers dioecious; male calyx subglobose, 3–4-fid; filaments united into a long exserted column; anthers 3–4, adnate to the column; female flowers: fruit large, with thick fleshy pericarp; seed with laciniate aril, ovoid, testa thick, woody; endosperm not ruminate, full of fat and starch.

6. **Pycnanthus** Warb., Ber. Deutsch. Bot. Ges. 13: 94 (1895). 5–6 spp., trop. Africa; type *Angolensis* (Welw.) Warb. (*P. kombo* (Baill.) Warb.). E.P.N. 165; Warb., Monogr. *Myristic.* 130, 252, t. 10; Stapf, Fl. Trop. Africa 6, 1: 157; Hutch. & Dalz., Fl. W. Trop. Africa, 1: 64, fig. 15; ed. 2 (Keay), 1: 61.

Trees; leaves elongate-oblong, rounded or cordate at the base, not white below; lateral nerves numerous and closely parallel, arcuate and united near the margin, tertiary nerves slender, subparallel and scarcely reticulate; flowers dioecious, very small, sessile in small heads collected into panicles; bracts present; bracteoles absent; filaments connate into a slender column; anthers 4–2, small, adnate to the column, shorter than the basal stipe of the column; stigmas sessile; fruit not large, pericarp thick, fleshy; aril laciniate, seed oblong, testa thin, woody; endosperm ruminate; cotyledons scarcely connate at the base, suberect.

7. **Coelocaryon** Warb., Notizbl. Bot. Gart. Berlin, 1: 99 (1895). 7 spp., trop. Africa; type *C. preussii* Warb. E.P.N. 165; Warb., Monogr. *Myristic.* 129, 250, t. 10; Stapf, Fl. Trop. Africa, 6, 1: 162; Hutch. & Dalz., Fl. W. Trop. Africa, 1: 65; ed. 2 (Keay), 1: 61.

Trees; leaves obovate-oblong, acuminate, not white below; lateral nerves well spaced, curved, scarcely confluent towards the margin; male flowers: calyx cupuliform, 3–4-partite; filaments united in a column; anthers 3–5, adnate to the column; female flowers: calyx as in male; ovary ovoid-globose; stigma sessile, 2-lobed; fruits large, fasciculate at the end of the branches of the axillary panicles, long-pedicellate; pericarp thick, fleshy; aril laciniate; seed oblong, testa woody, thick; endosperm partly ruminate, empty inside; cotyledons not connate at the base, suberect.

8. **Virola** Aubl., Pl. Guy. 904, t. 345 (1775). *Otoba* Karst. (1897). About 40 spp., West Indies, trop. South America; type *V. sebifera* Aubl., Cent. and trop. South America. Warb. Monogr. *Myristic.* 127, 163, tt. 1, 5–7; A. C. Smith & Wodehouse, Brittonia, 2: 453, figs. 7–9.

Trees; leaves very rarely white below, often rusty-pubescent with stellate hairs; lateral nerves often at length confluent near the margin, tertiary nerves reticulate or sometimes parallel, usually rather impressed above; inflorescence usually axillary, rarely terminal, paniculate, single; flowers dioecious, distantly fasciculate; bracts deciduous; bracteoles absent; calyx deeply 3-lobed; filaments connate, anthers 3–6 (2–7) elongated, closely connate and adnate to the column, longer or shorter than the style; stigmas very small, almost sessile; fruit erect, pericarp thin, rather woody; seed globose or ovoid, testa thin; aril laciniate, sometimes only at the apex; endosperm ruminate; embryo with free or scarcely connate suberect cotyledons.

9. **Iryanthera** Warb., Ber. Deutsch. Bot. Ges. 13: 94 (1895). 20 spp., trop. South America; lectotype *I. hostmannii* (Benth.) Warb., Guianas and Venezuela. E.P.N. 166; Warb., Monogr. *Myristic.* 126, 154, t. 1, 4; A. C. Smith & Wodehouse, Brittonia, 2: 424 (1938).

Trees, branchlets sometimes with medifixed hairs; leaves mostly coriaceous, glabrous, not white below, vernation convolute; nerves impressed above, united near the margin; tertiary nerves reticulate, not parallel, sometimes indistinct; inflorescences axillary, mostly paired, racemose or paniculate; flowers dioecious or monoecious, distantly fasciculate; bracts caducous; bracteoles present; calyx deeply 3-lobed, lobes spreading; filaments connate into a column; anthers 6, adnate to the column, shorter or longer than the column; fruit transversely ellipsoid; pericarp thin, subwoody; aril undivided, quite enclosing the seed; testa thin, endosperm not or scarcely ruminate; cotyledons connate at the base, divaricate.

10. **Osteophloeum** Warb., Ber. Deutsch. Bot. Ges. 13: 94 (1895). 1 sp., *O. platyspermum* (A. DC.) Warb., Guianas, Brazil, and Colombia. E.P.N. 166; Warb. Monogr. *Myristic.* 127, 162, tt. 1, 4; A. C. Smith & Wodehouse, Brittonia, 2: 451, fig. 6.

Tree; leaves coriaceous, glabrous and not white below, vernation convolute; nerves not impressed above, rather indistinctly confluent at the margin; tertiary nerves reticulate, not parallel; inflorescences axillary, short; flowers fasciculate, dioecious; bracts deciduous or absent; bracteoles very small, deciduous; calyx 3-fid; filaments connate into a short column; anthers 12, connate amongst themselves and adnate to the column, longer than the stipitate base of the column; fruits transversely ellipsoid, pericarp thin, rather woody; aril undivided, quite enclosing the seed, testa thick, rugose.

11. **Myristica** Gronovius, Fl. Or. 141 (1755); Linn. ex Linn. f., Suppl. 40 (1781) (conserved name). *Palala* Rumph. (1741). *Comacum* Adans. (1763). *Aruana* Burm. f. (1769). *Aromatites* Endl. (1841). *Comacum* Adans. ex Steud. (1841). About 100 spp., India to Polynesia and NE. Australia; type *M. fragrans* Houtt., Malay Archip. and much cult. Warb., Monogr. *Myristic.* 131, 374, tt. 11–19; Gamble, Journ. & Proc. Asiat. Soc. Bengal, 75, 2: 226 (1912); Sinclair, Gard. Bull. Singap. 16: 333 (1958).

Trees; leaves mostly white or glaucous below, rarely with rusty indumentum; lateral nerves confluent near the margin, tertiary nerves scarcely distinct, reticulate or subparallel; flowers dioecious, urceolate or campanulate, rarely tubular, pedicellate; inflorescence axillary or supra-axillary, sometimes from the axils of old leaves; peduncle often bifurcate or trichotomous, the flowers racemose or pseudo-umbellate; bracts present; bracteoles embracing the base of the calyx, rarely caducous; filaments connate into a column often apiculate above the anthers; anthers elongated, 30–12, closely connate and with the column, usually longer than the stipe of the latter; style almost nothing, stigmas connate into a sulcate mass and not deeply bilobed; pericarp fleshy-crustaceous, thick, aril laciniate almost to the base; testa hard; endosperm ruminate; cotyledons connate at the base or by the margins, divaricate and forming a disk or saucer.

12. **Gymnacranthera** Warb., Ber. Deutsch. Bot. Ges. 13: 94 (1895). About 18 spp., trop. Asia, from India to Philippines and New Guinea; type *G. paniculata* (A. DC.) Warb., Malaya and Philippines. E.P.N. 166; Warb. Monogr. *Myristic.* 131, 354, t. 20; Gamble, Journ. & Proc. Asiat. Soc. Bengal, 75, 2: 222 (1912); Sinclair, Gard. Bull. Singap. 16: 434 (1958).

Trees; leaves sometimes reddish-white or glaucous below but glabrous; lateral nerves confluent at the margin, tertiary nerves scarcely distinct, reticulate; flowers dioecious, small, urceolate, pedicellate; inflorescence axillary, paniculate, the flowers fasciculate; bracts present; bracteoles absent; filaments connate into an oblong thick column; anthers 12–6, elongated, lower part adnate to the column, upper part free, often inflexed and almost covering the column; stigmas sessile, connate, bilobed; pericarp thick, fleshy-crustaceous; aril laciniate almost to the base; testa woody, endosperm ruminate, cotyledons connate at the base, divaricate.

13. **Horsfieldia** Willd., Sp. Pl. 4: 872 (1805). *Irya* Linn. (1746). *Iryaghedi* Linn. (1746). *Pyrrhosa* Endl. (1839). About 85 spp., trop. Asia from India to China, New Guinea, and Polynesia; type *H. iryaghedhi* (Gaertn.) Warb. (*H. odorata* Willd.), Ceylon. Warb., Monogr. *Myristic.* 130, 262, tt. 21–23; Gamble, Journ. & Proc. Asiat. Soc. Bengal, 75, 2: 206 (1912); Sinclair, Gard. Bull. Singap. 16: 368 (1958).

Trees; leaves glabrous, not white below; lateral nerves confluent near the margin, tertiary nerves mostly indistinctly reticulate; flowers dioecious, small, globose, pedicellate or rarely sessile in panicles; filaments connate into a globose or clavate column sometimes impressed at the apex; anthers 30–12, adnate to the column; stigmas sessile, connate; pericarp woody-crustaceous, not thick; aril complete, not laciniate; testa woody, thin; endosperm ruminate; cotyledons connate at the base, flat or spreading.

14. **Knema** Lour., Fl. Cochinch. 604 (1790). About 70 spp., trop. Asia, from India and China to the Philippines and New Guinea; type *K. globularia* (Lamk.) Warb. (*K. corticosa* Lour.), Indo-China. Warb., Monogr. *Myristic.* 132, 543, tt. 24, 25; Gamble, Journ. Asiat. Soc. Bengal, 75, 2: 236 (1912); Sinclair, Gard. Bull. Singap. 16: 261 (1958).

Trees; leaves white below or covered by rusty indumentum; lateral nerves confluent near the margin, tertiary nerves parallel, prominent on both sides, confluent with each other; flowers dioecious, rather large, subglobose, saucer-shaped or urceolate, pedicellate; inflorescence axillary, often in the axils of old leaves, rarely branched or furcate; peduncle, thick or pulvinate, very short, the flowers densely racemose or pseudo-umbellate; bracts caducous; bracteoles at or above the middle of the pedicels, never embracing the calyx.

15. **Compsoneura** Warb., Ber. Deutsch. Bot. Ges. 13: 94 (1895). 8 spp., trop. America; type *C. sprucei* (A. DC.) Warb., S. Mexico to Brazil. E.P.N. 165;

Warb., Monogr. *Myristic.* 125, 142, t. 3; A. C. Smith & Wodehouse, Brittonia, 2: 405 (1938).

Leaves glabrous below, lateral nerves few, gradually extended to close within the margin; inflorescence axillary, racemose or subpaniculate, racemes sometimes fasciculate; flowers dioecious, in distant fascicles; bracts caducous, bracteoles absent; calyx 3-lobed; filaments connate into a very short column disk-like at the top; anthers 7–4 or 16, free from each other; fruit ellipsoid, erect and subumbellate at the top of the peduncle; pericarp thin; aril undivided and completely enclosing the seed; testa very thin and smooth; endosperm not ruminate; embryo small, basal; cotyledons connate at the base, divaricate.

16. **Dialyanthera** Warb., Ber. Deutsch. Bot. Ges. 13: 94 (1895); Nova Acta Acad. Leop. Carol. 68: 126 (1897). *Otoba* Karst. (1890). 6 spp., Costa Rica, Panama, Peru, and Colombia; type *D. otoba* (Humb. & Bonpl.) Warb., Costa Rica to Colombia. E.P.N. 165; Warb. Monogr. *Myristic.* 126, 148, tt. 1, 3; A. C. Smith & Wodehouse, Brittonia, 2: 416 (1938).

Trees; leaves thick and coriaceous, glabrous below, vernation conduplicate; nerves impressed above scarcely confluent at the margin, tertiary nerves reticulate, not parallel; inflorescence axillary, raceme-like, the dioecious flowers in distant fascicles; bracts present, bracteoles absent; calyx deeply 3-lobed; filaments connate into a column; anthers 3, free, divergent, much shorter than the column; stigmas very small, connate, sessile; fruit globose; aril laciniate, testa very thick, endosperm ruminate, embryo with cotyledons connate by their margins.

A fundamentally woody to rarely herbaceous group considerably advanced from the *Magnoliales*, retaining well-developed petals, numerous free stamens and carpels, and seeds with copious endosperm, thus forming a link or half-way house between that group and the *Rosales, Bixales*, and *Tiliales*; leaves alternate, often with strong pinnate nerves or pinnately compound; stipules very rare; tropics.

Leaves alternate (very rarely opposite), simple or pinnate, often with strong parallel lateral nerves; stipules absent or wing-like and adnate to the petiole; seeds often arillate:

Stamens hypogynous:

Leaves simple, usually with prominent parallel lateral nerves

19. *Dilleniaceae*

Leaves pinnate, trifoliolate or unifoliolate   20. *Connaraceae*

Stamens perigynous, inserted on the calyx-tube   21. *Crossosomataceae*

Leaves opposite or verticillate, simple to trifoliolate or pinnate; stipules present; seeds not arillate   22. *Brunelliaceae*

19. DILLENIACEAE

Salisbury, Parad. Lond. 2 (1): sub t. 73 (1807) (*Dilleneae*)

Trees, shrubs, or twiners, very rarely shrublets with short stems or herbs with radical fern-like leaves; leaves alternate, entire or dentate, rarely pinnatifid or trilobed, usually with prominent parallel lateral nerves; stipules absent, or wing-like and adnate to the petiole, mostly deciduous; inflorescence various; flowers small to medium-sized, rarely large, white or yellow, bisexual or poly-gamous, rarely dioecious; sepals 5, rarely more or fewer, very imbricate, per-sistent; petals 5 or fewer, free, imbricate, often crumpled in bud, deciduous; stamens numerous, rarely few, hypogynous, free or variously united into bundles at the base, usually persisting in fruit; anthers 2-locular, with lateral or introrse (rarely some extrorse) short or elongated loculi, opening length-wise by slits or by apical pores, sometimes the connective produced at the apex; carpels free or slightly connate or very rarely completely connate (*Neowormia*), rarely reduced to 1; ovules many to 1, anatropous, erect from the base or arranged in 2 series on the adaxial angle of the carpel; styles separate, terminal or subdorsal, divergent, tipped by a single stigma; fruiting carpels dehiscent or berry-like; seeds few or 1, thick, mostly with a variously crested or laciniate aril; testa crustaceous, raphe short; endosperm fleshy, embryo minute near the hilum. Type genus *Dillenia* Linn.

Genera 18; species about 530.

DISTRIBUTION. Tropics generally and in the drier parts of Australia; com-paratively rare in Africa.

CLASSIFICATION. Benth. & Hook. f., Gen. Pl. 1: 10 (1862); Eichler, Mart. Fl. Bras. 13: 1: 66 (1841); Gilg, Engl. & Prantl., Nat. Pflanzenfam. 3, 6: 100 (1893); Nachtr. 218 (1907); van Tieghem, Journ. de Bot. 13: 170 (1899); Glig, *Dilleniac. Africanae*, Engl. Bot. Jahrb. 33: 194 (1902); Gilg & Werdermann, Engl. & Prantl, Pflanzenfam. ed. 2, 21: 7 (1925); Corner, *Wormia* and *Dillenia*, Gard. Bull. Singap. 10: 3 (1938); Lanjouw & van Heerdt, Pulle Fl. Surinam, 3: 386 (1941); Hoogland, Fl. Malesiana, 4: 141 (1951); H. Perr., Humbert Fl. Madag. 132*e*: 1 (1951); Lawrence, Taxon. Vasc. Pl. 598, fig. 207 (1951); Hutch., Fam. Fl. Pl. ed. 2, 1: 143, fig. 19 (1959).

ANATOMY. Sol. 1: 20; M.C. 1: 7. POLLEN. Erdt. 148.

Characters occurring in relatively few Genera and Species. Habit herbaceous in *Acrotrema*. **Stems** exuding water when cut from *Tetracera potatoria* Afz. and other spp., and *Doliocarpus calinea* J. F. Gmel. (Trinidad); stem and branches flattened in *Pachynema*. **Leaves** very rough and scabrid in *Curatella americana* Linn. and *Delima sarmentosa* Linn. (E. Asia); bullate in *Acrotrema* spp.; much reduced and scale-like in *Pachynema*; stipules large and adnate to the petiole in *Davilla vaginata* Eichl.; petiole winged in *Davilla multiflora* St. Hil., narrowly winged in *Wormia triquetra* Rottb. (Ceylon); lyrately lobed in *Acrotrema lyratum* Thw. (Ceylon). **Inflorescence** with somewhat scorpioid cymose branching in *Schumacheria castaneifolia* Vahl (Ceylon). **Sepals** more than 5 in *Empedoclea* and *Reifferschiedia*; of two kinds in *Davilla*, the inner two hard and accrescent, completely enclosing the fruit and resembling a globose capsule. **Petals** 3 in *Trisema*; very fugaceous in *Davilla multiflora* St. Hil. **Stamens** with the inner anthers introrse, the outer anthers extrorse in *Dillenia*; united in *Schumacheria* and in most of the tribe *Hibbertieae*; in two bundles in *Didesmandra*. **Carpel** 1 in *Trisema*, *Delima*, and *Doliocarpus* spp.; carpels completely connate in *Neowormia* (Seychelles). **Seeds** with a large laciniate aril in *Delima sarmentosa* Linn., and *Tetracera* spp.

Economic Properties. The rough leaves are used locally as sandpaper; timber of some spp. of *Dillenia* used locally for boat building and general construction.

Phylogeny and Morphology. *Dilleniaceae* appear to be a comparatively primitive group and fairly closely related to the *Magnoliaceae*, having had a somewhat similar origin to the *Winteraceae*, with an almost identical distribution. They are probably the basic stock of a large and prolific phylum, the same source from which the major portion of the great group *Rosales* originated, and which has spread all over temperate regions. Such families as *Ochnaceae*, *Saurauiaceae*, and *Actinidiaceae* were probably early offshoots, whilst the bulk of the catkin-bearing families, the so-called 'Amentiferae', represent the reduced examples descended through the *Rosales* and especially the *Hamamelidales*.

The strong parallel lateral nervation of the leaves of the *Dilleniaceae* is remarkably characteristic and persists more or less throughout the groups and families mentioned. The affinity of the *Dilleniaceae* and *Rosaceae* is very marked, the latter family being distinguished only by its non-endospermic seeds, and usually more perigynous or epigynous type of flowers.

The herbaceous habit of the genus *Acrotrema* is outstanding, though the rootstock is a woody rhizome and the leaves are fern-like. A similar tendency to reduction to a suffruticose habit occurs in *Tetracera* (*T. strigillosa* Gilg), which is found in the light deciduous forests of tropical Africa, surely a reduction from its tree congeners. Adaptation to the dry climate of N. Australia is shown by *Pachynema*, the species of which are low shrubs with minute scale-like leaves, the stems and branches flattened and bearing phylloclades.

Geographical Distribution. The family is fairly equally distributed throughout the tropics, but is comparatively rare in Africa, being represented there only by the genus *Tetracera*. This genus is the largest and most widely spread, occurring thoughout the tropics and also in subtropical N. Australia. Of particular interest is the distribution of the genus *Wormia*, which connects the flora of the Mascarene Islands with that of Indo-Malaya (recalling that of *Nepenthes*), three species occurring in Madagascar. Of equal interest is *Hibbertia*, common to Madagascar and Australasia, more largely represented in the latter region, with a strong endemic element in New Caledonia, and with but two endemic species in Madagascar.

Dillenia is spread over the whole of the Indo-Malayan region, including New Guinea; *Curatella, Davilla,* and *Doliocarpus* are widely distributed in tropical America. The remainder of the genera are mainly quite local, *Empedoclea,* SE. Brazil; *Reifferschiedia,* Philippine Islands; *Schumacheria* Ceylon; *Didesmandra,* Borneo; *Acrotrema,* S. India, Ceylon, and the Malay Peninsula; *Trisema,* New Caledonia. In Australia there are some remarkable endemic genera, *Candollea* in western, *Adrastea* in eastern, and *Pachynema* in northern and western Australia.

KEY TO TRIBES

Anther-loculi short and divergent, separated at the base by the thickened connective; trees, shrubs, or twiners with usually rough leaves and numerous strong parallel lateral nerves   1. DELIMEAE

Anthers linear or oblong, loculi closely contiguous and not divergent; habit various; leaves large, with strong parallel nerves   2. DILLENIEAE

Anthers oblong, with parallel contiguous loculi, the latter very rarely slightly divergent; leaves usually small, sometimes 1-nerved, or almost completely reduced   3. HIBBERTIEAE

Tribe 1. DELIMEAE

Sepals more than 10, imbricate; floral axis elongated; racemes axillary and terminal; anthers introrse   1. **Empedoclea**

Sepals 5 (rarely 4 or 6), all remaining alike in texture:

Panicles terminal (or only in the upper axils); carpels 5–1; ovules numerous (10–15), 2-seriate on the placentas or few and basal   2. **Tetracera**

Panicles or fascicles lateral:

Carpels 2, subglobose, united; flowers in dense branched panicles:

Carpels dehiscent; indumentum of leaves stellate   3. **Curatella**

Carpels indehiscent; leaves glabrous   4. **Pinzona**

Carpel 1, globose; flowers usually in more or less simple fascicles with slender pedicels; indumentum of simple hairs or absent

5. **Doliocarpus**

Sepals 5, of two kinds, the inner 2 hard and accrescent and completely enclosing the fruit; panicles terminal or in the axils of the young leaves of young shoots or rarely reduced to 1 flower　　　**6. Davilla**

1. **Empedoclea** St. Hil., Fl. Bras. Merid. 1: 19, t. 3 (1825). 1 sp., *E. alnifolia* St. Hil., Brazil. B.H. 1: 11; E.P. 3, 6: 111; ed. 2, 21: 16 (under *Tetracera*); Fl. Bras. 13, 1: 82, t. 20, fig. 2.

Shrub; leaves coarsely serrate; panicles axillary and terminal, shorter than the leaves; sepals about 13, closely imbricate; petals 3, narrowly obovate; stamens numerous, slightly thickened at the apex; anthers small; carpel 1; ovules 6; fruit not seen.

2. **Tetracera**[1] Linn., Sp. Pl. 533 (1753); Gen. Pl. ed. 5: 237 (1754). About 130 spp., tropics and subtropics, incl. N. Australia; type *T. volubilis* trop. South America. B.H. 1: 12; E.P. 3, 6: 110; ed. 2, 21: 16; Lanjouw & van Heerdt, Fl. Suriname, 3: 387; Hoogland, Fl. Malesiana, 4: 141 (1951); Reinwardtia, 1: 185 (1953).

Scandent shrubs, rarely trees or subshrubs from a woody rhizome; leaves often scabrid; petiole short, grooved; panicles terminal or in the upper leaf-axils; sepals 6-4, often 5, spreading or reflexed in fruit; petals 6-4, or fewer, caducous; stamens numerous, filaments free; connective broad, anther-loculi separate; carpels 5-1, free, with numerous to 2 ovules; fruiting carpels opening on the inner side, few–1-seeded; seeds glossy brown to black, surrounded by a cup-shaped lacerate or denticulate aril.

3. **Curatella** Linn., Loefl. Iter. Hispan. 260 (1758). 6 spp., trop. America, West Indies, type *C. americana* Linn., common savannah tree from Mexico to Brazil and Peru. *C. grisebachiana* Eichl., St. Domingo. B.H. 1: 12. E.P. 3, 6: 113; ed. 2, 21: 19; Lanjouw & van Heerdt, Fl. Suriname, 3: 399.

Trees or scandent shrubs, mostly with stellate indumentum; panicles many-flowered, sessile on the one-year-old or older branches; sepals 5-4; petals 5-4; filaments of the stamens slightly dilated at the apex, anthers oblong, the loculi subparallel; carpels 2, coherent; ovules 2, erect; seed almost completely enclosed by a membranous aril.

4. **Pinzona** Mart. et Zucc., Abh. Akad. München, 1: 371 (1832). 2 spp.; type *P. coriacea* Mart. & Zucc., Brazil; *P. calineoides* Eich., Porto Rico, Guadeloupe, and Trinidad. Mart., Fl. Bras. 13, 1: 71, t. 16.

Shrubs or climbers; branchlets angular; leaves entire or denticulate; stipules absent; petioles narrowly winged; panicles axillary, shorter than the leaves, sessile, scaly at the base; sepals 4-3, persistent; petals 4-2; stamens numerous, free; anthers small, with separate loculi; carpels 2, united to the middle, 2-ovulate; styles 2, persistent; fruit didymous, at length irregularly dehiscent; seeds 2 or 1, surrounded by an undivided aril.

5. **Doliocarpus** Roland., Vet.-Akad. Handl. Stockholm, 249 (1756). *Soramia* Aubl. (1775). *Mappia* Schreb. (1791). *Ricaurtea* Triana (1858). *Othlis* Schott (1827). 40 spp., Cent. and trop. South America; type *R. major* J. F. Gmel., Guatemala to the Guianas. B.H. 1: 12; E.P. 3, 6: 114; ed. 2, 21: 20 (partly); Mart., Fl. Bras. 13, 1: 73; Lanjouw & van Heerdt., Fl. Suriname, 3: 400.

Shrubs, sometimes climbing; indumentum of simple hairs; panicles few-flowered or flowers solitary, borne laterally on the one-year-old or older branches, rarely axillary;

---

[1] Synonyms of **Tetracera**: *Delima* Linn. (1754). *Korosvel* Adans. (1763). *Tigarea* Aubl. (1775). *Assa* Houtt. (1776). *Euryandra* Forst. (1776). *Calligonum* Lour. (1790). *Wahlbonie* Thunb. (1790). *Rhinium* Schreb. (1791). *Roehlingia* Demst. (1818). *Trachytella* DC. (1818). *Diploter* Raf. (1838). *Trachystella* Steud. (1841). *Eleiastis* Raf. (1838). *Gynetra* Raf. (1838). *Traxilisia* Raf. (1838). *Leontoglossum* Hance (1851). *Delimopsis* Miq. (1859).

sepals 5; petals 5–3; filaments of the stamens thickened at the apex; anthers short; carpel 1; ovules 2, erect; fruit berry-like or coriaceous and bivalved; seeds almost completely enclosed by an aril.

6. **Davilla** Vand., Roem. Script. 115 (1796). *Hieronia* Vell. (1827). 40 spp., Cent. and trop. South America, West Indies; type *D. rugosa* Poir., Cuba, Trinidad, to S. Brazil and Bolivia. B.H. 1: 12; E.P. 3, 6: 112; ed. 2, 21: 19; Lanjouw & van Heerdt, Fl. Suriname, 3: 391.

Trailing or scrambling shrubs; panicles terminal or in the upper leaf-axils, often few-flowered, sometimes reduced to one flower; sepals 5, very unequal, the inner 2 largest, accrescent and often crustaceous, enclosing the fruit and resembling a globose capsule; petals 6–1; filaments of the stamens thickened at the apex; anthers short, loculi divergent; carpels 3–1; ovules 2, erect; fruit indehiscent or opening irregularly; seeds almost completely enclosed by an aril.

Tribe 2. Dillenieae

Trees, shrubs, or climbers with woody stems:
  Stamens more or less free; trees:
    Sepals numerous (more than 5); petals large; anthers opening by apical
      pores   7. **Reifferscheidia**
    Sepals 5:
      Anthers opening by apical pores; carpels free or slightly united at the
        base; aril well developed   8. **Wormia**
      Anthers undulate, opening by slits; flowers in leaf-opposed racemes;
        carpels completely united   9. **Neowormia**
      Anthers opening by slits; flowers usually solitary or fasciculate; carpels
        more or less united; aril absent or pulpy   10. **Dillenia**
  Stamens more or less united; scandent shrubs or trees:
    Stamens more than 10, in one bundle, homomorphous, all fertile
           11. **Schumacheria**
    Stamens 10, in two bundles, heteromorphous, only the posterior fertile
           12. **Didesmandra**
  Herbs with woody rhizomes and radical fern-like leaves; sepals 5; stamens
    united into 3 bundles; carpels 3, partly united   13. **Acrotrema**

7. **Reifferscheidia** C. Presl, Rel. Haenk. 2: 74, t. 62 (1836). 1 sp., *R. speciosa* Presl, Philippine Isls. B.H. 1: 13; E.P. 3, 6: 124; ed. 2, 21: 36 (in *Dillenia*).

Tree; leaves large, dentate; stipules large, adnate to the petiole; peduncles leaf-opposed, 1-flowered, 2-bracteate above the middle; flowers large and showy; sepals about 15; petals 5, large; stamens almost free; anthers linear, opening by 2 apical pores; carpels numerous, united at the base; ovules numerous; styles spreading, star-like; fruit subglobose; seeds not seen.

8. **Wormia** Rottb., Nya Saml. Danske Vid. Selsk. Skrivt. 2: 532 (1783). *Lenidia* Thou. (1806). *Clugnia* Comm. ex DC. *Capellia* Bl. (1825). About 50 spp., trop. Asia to Australia, Fiji, Madag.; type *W. triquetra* Rottb., Ceylon. B.H. 1: 13; E.P. 3, 6: 123 (under *Dillenia*); ed. 2, 21: 33; H. Perrier, Humbert Fl. Madag. Fam. 132*e*: 2, fig. 1 (1951).

Trees, sometimes very tall; leaves large; petioles winged, the wings deciduous; flowers showy, few in terminal panicles; sepals 5; petals 5; stamens nearly free; anthers erect, linear, opening by 2 apical pores; carpels free; ovules numerous; fruit opening on the inner side; seeds arillate.

9. **Neowormia**[1] Hutch. & Summerh., Kew Bull. 1928: 388. 1 sp., *N. ferruginea* Hutch. & Summerh., Seychelles.

Tree with soft wood, young parts densely silky-villous; leaves elliptic, with numerous prominent parallel nerves; petioles with lateral stipuliform deciduous lobes; inflorescence leaf-opposed, racemose, villous; bracts soon deciduous; sepals gradually larger from the outside, very imbricate, villous outside; petals 5, free; stamens very numerous, free; carpels 10, connate to the apex; styles subulate, free, spreading; ovules 2-seriate.

10. **Dillenia** Linn., Sp. Pl. 535 (1753), Gen. Pl. ed. 5: 239 (1754). *Syalita* Adans. (1763). About 70 spp., Indo-Malaya, Philippine Isls.; type *D. indica* Linn., Nepal to S. Yunnan and to Java. *D. pentagyna* widely spread in India; remainder mainly restricted in distrib. B.H. 1: 13; E.P. 3, 6: 123; ed. 2, 21: 35 (partly); Hoogland, Fl. Malesiana, 4: 154 (partly) (1951); Blumea, 7: 2 (partly) (1952).

Trees; leaves large; flowers showy, lateral, solitary or fasciculate; sepals 5, spreading; petals 5, large; stamens almost free; anthers linear, inner erect and introrse, outer recurved and extrorse; carpels 20–5, adherent to the axis; ovules numerous; fruit globose, united to and enclosed by the berry-like calyx; seeds without an aril.

11. **Schumacheria** Vahl, Skrivt. Naturh. Selsk. Kjoebenhavn, 6: 122 (1810). *Pleurodesmia* Arn. (1834). 3 spp., Ceylon; type *S. castaneifolia* Vahl. B.H. 1: 13; E.P. 3, 6: 122; ed. 2, 21: 33, fig. 24.

Scandent shrubs, with rigid flexuous branches; leaves large; spikes axillary or paniculate at the ends of the branches; flowers secund, bibracteate; sepals 5; petals 5; stamens unilateral, the filaments united into a short oblique cylindric column; anthers erect, linear-oblong, opening by 2 slits; carpels 3, separate; ovule 1 in each carpel; fruit indehiscent; seed arillate.

12. **Didesmandra** Stapf, Hook. Ic. Pl. 2646 (1900). 1 sp., *D. aspera* Stapf, Borneo. E.P. ed. 2, 21; 33; Hoogland, Fl. Malesiana, 4: 152, fig. 7 (1951).

Branchlets and the serrate leaves rough; petioles sheathing at the base, amplexicaul; inflorescence paniculate, flowers subsecund; sepals 5, imbricate, outer 2 smaller; petals 5, imbricate, thin; stamens 10, united into 2 bundles in front of the carpels, the posticous bundle fertile, with the linear anthers curved and hooked in the upper part, the connective expanded into a membranous deltoid appendage; remainder of stamens sterile, with truncate or erose appendages; carpels 2, free; style very long, cirrhose; ovule 1, erect; seed arillate.

13. **Acrotrema** Jack., Malay. Misc. 1, No. 5: 36 (1820). 10 spp., S. India, Ceylon, Malay Penins.; type *A. costatum* Jack., Malay Penins.; remainder in Ceylon except *A. arnottianum* Wight, S. India. B.H. 1: 13; E.P. 3, 6: 121; ed. 2, 21: 30, fig. 23; Hoogland, Fl. Malesiana, 4: 151, fig. 6 (1951).

Subacaulescent herbs with a perennial woody rhizome; leaves large, with the nerves transversely venose, or pinnately lobed or dissected; petioles winged, the wings deciduous; inflorescence axillary, few-flowered or racemose and many-flowered; sepals 5, spreading; petals 5; stamens collected into 3 bundles; anthers opening by terminal pores or short terminal slits; carpels 3, partly united; ovules numerous to 2; fruit irregularly dehiscent or split; seed with a white membranous aril.

---

[1] Included in *Dillenia* by Hoogland in Fl. Malesiana, 4: 154 (1951).

Tribe 3. HIBBERTIEAE

Leaves neither minute nor scale-like; shrubs, undershrubs, or twiners:
Stamens free, numerous; petals 3; carpel 1   14. **Trisema**
Stamens free or variously united; petals 5; carpels 2 or more:
Stamens more than 10:
Stamens free or irregularly united towards the base; carpels usually 2–5
     15. **Hibbertia**
Stamens united into 5 bundles; carpels 3–5   16. **Candollea**
Stamens 10; flowers sessile; carpels 2; ovules 2   17. **Adrastaea**
Leaves minute and scale-like; low shrubs with stems and branches flattened
into phylloclades; stamens 10, or fewer by abortion; carpels 2; ovules 2
     18. **Pachynema**

14. **Trisema** Hook. f., Hook., Kew Journ. 9: 47, t. 1 (1857). *Vanieria* Montr. (1860). *Trisemma* Pancher & Seb. (1874). 7 spp., New Caledonia; type *T. coriaceum* Hook. f. B.H. 1: 14; E.P. 3, 6: 115; ed. 2, 21: 23 (as *Hibbertia*).

Shrubs; leaves entire, shining; flowers sessile along the branches of the terminal silky-hairy panicles, unilateral, with 1–2 bracteoles; sepals 5; petals 3; stamens numerous, free; anthers oblong, with parallel contiguous loculi; carpel 1; style subulate; ovules numerous; fruits not seen.

15. **Hibbertia** Andr., Bot. Rep. 2: C. 126 (1800). *Cistomorphe* Caley ex DC. (1818). *Trimorphandra* Brongn. & Gris. (1864). *Rossittia* Ewart & Davies (1917). 150 spp., New Guinea, New Caledonia, Australia, Madagascar; type *H. scandens* (Willd.) Dryand. (*H. volubilis* Andr.), Australia. B.H. 1: 14; E.P. 3, 6: 115; ed. 2, 21 (partly); Benth., Fl. Austral. 1: 17; Hoogland, Fl. Malesiana, 4: 150 (1951); H. Perrier, Fl. Madag. 132e: 6, fig. 2 (1951).

Undershrubs or much-branched shrubs, struggling or climbing; leaves entire or dentate, often ericoid, 1-nerved; flowers solitary, sessile or pedicellate; bracts often 2–3 at the base of the pedicel, with 1–3 under the calyx small or sepaloid; sepals 5; petals 5; stamens few or numerous; filaments free or shortly connate; anthers oblong or orbicular; carpels 5–2, rarely numerous or solitary; ovules various in number; seeds mostly solitary, with a cupular entire or jagged aril.

16. **Candollea**[1] Labill., Nov. Holl. Pl. Spec. 2: 33, t. 176 (1806). *Eeldea* Durand, nomen (1888). 20 spp., W. Australia; type *C. cuneiformis* Labill. B.H. 1: 14; E.P. 3, 6: 118; ed. 2, 21: 28 (in *Hibbertia*); Benth., Fl. Austral. 1: 41.

Shrubs or undershrubs, with the habit of *Hibbertia*; leaves flat or closely revolute; sepals 5; petals 5; stamens with the filaments united to the middle or higher into 5 bundles, in species with 5 styles 2- or more-anthered with a stamen free between each bundle, in species with 3 styles in 2–3 bundles reduced to 1 stamen, remainder with 2–6 anthers; anthers oblong, the loculi parallel and contiguous; carpels 5–3, 3–1-ovulate; styles filiform; fruit dry or somewhat fleshy; seed solitary, rarely paired, with a cupular entire or jagged aril.

17. **Adrastaea** DC., Syst. 1: 424 (1818). *Burtonia* Salisb. (1818). *Adrastea* Spreng. (1825). *Ochrolasia* Turcz. (1849). *Huttia* Drumm. ex Harv. (1855). *Warburtonia* F. Muell. (1858–9). 1 sp., *A. salicifolia* DC., E. Australia. B.H. 1: 15. E.P. 3, 6: 116; ed. 2, 21: 24 (in *Hibbertia*); Benth., Fl. Austral. 1: 46.

[1] This name needs conservation.

Silky-pubescent undershrub, habit of *Hibbertia*; leaves flat; flowers sessile; sepals 5; petals 5; stamens 10, in a single series; filaments very short, flattened, subconnate; anthers oblong, loculi parallel, contiguous; carpels 2; ovules 2; styles subulate; fruit as in *Hibbertia*.

18. **Pachynema** R.Br. ex DC. Syst. 1: 411 (1818). 5 spp., Australia; type *P. complanatum* R.Br., N. Australia. B.H. 1: 15; E.P. 3, 6: 121; ed. 2, 21: 30, fig. 22; Benth., Fl. Austral. 1: 47.

Herbs or undershrubs, with juncoid or flattened branches; leaves reduced to minute scales or rarely few at the base of the stem and 3-fid; pedicels lateral, short, recurved; bracts very small; sepals 5; petals 5; fertile stamens 10 or fewer by abortion, in a subsimple series; filaments very short and flattened with oblong anthers and parallel contiguous loculi, or ovoid and thickened at the base with small anthers with divergent loculi; staminodes 2, within the stamens and alternate with the carpels; carpels 2; ovules 2; styles subulate; fruit 1-seeded, dry; seed arillate.

20. CONNARACEAE

R.Br., Narr. Exped. Congo App. 5: 431 (1818)

Small trees, or erect, scandent, or subscandent shrubs. Leaves persistent or deciduous, alternate, without stipules, imparipinnate, trifoliolate or uni-foliolate; leaflets coriaceous, entire or rarely lobulate, rarely peltate. Flowers small, in panicles or racemes, bisexual or very rarely unisexual. Sepals 5 or 4, usually persistent and often embracing the base of the fruit, imbricate or valvate. Petals 5, free or rarely slightly connivent in the middle, imbricate, or valvate, rarely circinate. Stamens hypogynous, 10 or rarely 5 or 4+4, alter-nately longer and shorter; filaments shortly connate at the base; anthers short, introrse. Carpels free, usually 5, rarely 1, often hairy, 1-locular; style subulate or filiform; stigma more or less capitate; ovules 2, collateral, ascend-ing. Fruiting carpels often solitary, sessile or stipitate, follicular or more rarely indehiscent. Seed 1 or rarely 2, mostly arillate, the testa often thick and like an aril in the lower part; aril fleshy, coloured; endosperm present or absent; embryo straight. Type genus *Connarus* Linn.

Genera 24; species about 390.

DISTRIBUTION. Tropics generally, very few in the moist subtropics.

CLASSIFICATION. Benth. and Hook. f., Gen. Pl. 1: 430 (1862); Gilg in Engl. & Prantl, Nat. Pflanzenfam. 3, 3: 61 (1890); Nachtr. 1: 189 (1897); Nachtr. 2: 30 (1900): Nachtr. 4: 117 (1915); Schellenberg, Beitr. vergl. Anat. u. syst. *Connarac.* (1910), and in Engl., Pflanzenr. *Connarac.* 4: 127 (1938). Hutch., Fam. Fl. Pl. ed. 2, 1: 145, fig. 20 (1959).

ANATOMY. Sol. 1: 250; M.C. 1: 471. POLLEN. Erdt. 126.

ADDITIONAL LITERATURE. See Schellenberg, loc. cit. (above), and Die phylogenet. Entwicklung und die Wanderungen der Connaraceen, Engl. Bot. Jahrb. 60: 207 (1925).

Characters occurring in relatively few Genera and Species. The majority of the genera have imparipinnate leaves with two or more pairs of leaflets. **Leaves** trifoliolate in *Paxia* spp., *Agelaea*, *Castanola*, *Rourea* spp., *Connarus* spp., *Pseudoconnarus*; unifoliolate in *Schellenbergia, Burttia, Vismianthus, Rourea* spp., *Connarus* (rare), *Cnestis* spp., *Ellipanthus, Pseudellipanthus*; leaflet peltate in *Pseudellipanthus peltatus* Schellenb. **Flowers** unisexual in *Pseudellipanthus*. **Petals** loriform and circinate in bud in *Roureopsis, Taeniochlaena, Paxia*; shorter than or at most subequal to the sepals in *Cnestis*. **Stamens** 5, fertile, with 5 staminodes in *Hemandradenia* and *Ellipanthus*; 4 fertile and 4 staminodes in *Pseudellipanthus*. **Carpel** solitary in *Jollydora, Connarus, Santaloidella, Ellipanthus, Pseudellipanthus, Schellenbergia, Burttia, Vismianthus, Hemandradenia*; indehiscent in *Jollydora* and *Hemandradenia*.

Economic Properties. These are of very minor importance. The shoots of some are used by natives in Africa as chew-sticks, and the aril of the seed for rubbing the teeth. Other parts of the plants are used in native medicines. Zebra wood, *Connarus guianensis* Lamb., British Guiana. The seeds of *Connarus africanus* Lam. are ground up and used as a purge and vermifuge, said to be effective against tapeworm. The bark has tonic and astringent properties. *Byrsocarpus coccineus* Schum. & Thonn. has also several medicinal properties (see Dalziel, Useful Pl. West Trop. Afr. 342 (1937)).

Phylogeny and Morphology. Connaraceae is one of the most natural families, showing remarkably little diversity of structure. They are woody throughout and there are no herbs amongst them, not even reductions to a subherbaceous habit as in many other woody families. A few are small trees, but the majority are shrubs and often scandent or subscandent. On the whole it may be conjectured that the family is a completely climax one, from the stock of which no further evolution may be traced. I regard them as being related to, though considerably more advanced than, *Dilleniaceae*, with which they share an apocarpous gynoecium and arillate seeds, differing in their compound or unifoliolate leaves. They probably represent a parallel group with *Rosaceae*, though not directly related to that family; but unlike that group, they have not spread into temperate regions. Instead they have remained in tropical forests and have largely become scandent.

Bentham & Hooker said that their relationships were very complex, though they considered them to be related to the *Anacardiaceae*, differing from them by the bisexual flowers, pair of orthotropous ovules, and superior radicle; they remarked that they differed from *Leguminosae* by the two or more carpels, collateral ovules, the frequently endospermous seed, and the absence of stipules. They also noted their approach to *Oxalidaceae*, but give several very important differences. I consider their supposed affinity with the last mentioned to be superficial.

In recent years the late Dr. G. Schellenberg devoted much time to the study of the family, and elaborated it for Engler's Pflanzenreich. I have not adopted his classification, however, because I consider it hardly possible to arrange the genera satisfactorily into tribes, as he has done. And I certainly do not agree with him in regarding the genus *Jollydora*, the sole representative of his Subfamily *Jollydoroideae*, as being in any way primitive. To my mind most of its characters are quite advanced, such as the indehiscent single carpel and the cauliflorous habit. The fact that there are two seeds in the fruit does not seem to me of very great importance, because there are always two ovules in each of the carpels of all the family, though one usually becomes abortive.

The genera have been arranged in an ascending series, those with pinnate leaves being regarded as the most primitive, and they have mostly more than one carpel in the flowering stage, though often only one of them develops into fruit. The next reduction of the leaves are those genera with only 3 leaflets, and finally only 1 (unifoliolate). It is significant that most of the latter have only one carpel. The aestivation of the sepals also seems important, many of the pinnate-leaved genera being *imbricate*, whilst the more advanced genera have *valvate* sepals. Amongst the latter it should be noted there is one genus, *Pseudellipanthus*, which has unisexual (probably dioecious) flowers, and I should consider this genus to be the most recently evolved type in the family.

Geographical Distribution. The most striking fact about this is that the family is almost confined to the tropics, only a few occurring in the sub-tropics, in Assam and Yunnan, in Asia, in Natal, in Africa, and a few in sub-tropical SE. America. Most of the genera are endemic to one region. The more widely spread are *Cnestis* (Africa eastwards to the Philippines), *Santaloides* (Old World tropics), and *Connarus*, the most widely distributed of all, throughout the tropics of both hemispheres.

KEY TO GENERA

Sepals imbricate:
  Leaves imparipinnate (with more than 3 leaflets):
   Carpels more than 1 in the flowering stage:
    Petals circinate in bud, loriform; sepals enlarged in fruit; fruiting carpels
      not stipitate:
     More than one carpel maturing into fruit; leaflets in numerous pairs:
     Sepals erect in fruit   1. **Roureopsis**
     Sepals revolute in fruit   2. **Taeniochlaena**
     Only one carpel maturing into fruit; leaflets in few pairs   3. **Paxia**
    Petals more or less imbricate, not loriform; fruiting carpels not stipitate:
     Petals shorter than the sepals; seeds with fleshy endosperm   4. **Cnestis**
     Petals longer than the sepals; seeds without endosperm:
      Flowers produced before or with the young leaves:
       Sepals at length reflexed and deciduous; trop. America 5. **Bernardinia**
       Sepals not reflexed, persistent and enlarged in fruit; trop. Africa,
        Madagascar   6. **Byrsocarpus**
      Flowers produced after the leaves; petals glabrous:
       New World tropics; calyx enlarged after flowering; fruits not curved
                                       7. **Rourea**
       Old World tropics; fruits curved:
        Aril free, embracing the seed   8. **Santaloides**
        Aril adnate to the testa, the latter appearing berry-like   9. **Jaundea**
  Carpel solitary in the flowering stage:
   Seeds mostly 2 in the carpel, without an aril; sepals not enlarged in fruit;
    fruit narrowed at the base   10. **Jollydora**
   Seed solitary in the carpel:
    Sepals not enlarged in fruit; fruit more or less stipitate   11. **Connarus**

Sepals enlarged and rather woody in fruit   12. **Santaloidella**
Leaves trifoliolate:
Petals circinate in bud; long and narrow; fruits not stipitate   3. **Paxia**
Petals not circinate in bud:
Petals longer than the sepals:
Inflorescence terminal, paniculate; fruits contracted at the base
                                                            13. **Agelaea**
Inflorescence axillary:
Leaves not papillous below:
Old World tropics   14. **Castanola**
New World tropics   7. **Rourea**
Leaves papillous below   15. **Pseudoconnarus**
Petals shorter than or subequal to the sepals; seeds with fleshy endo-
sperm   4. **Cnestis**
Leaves unifoliolate:
Fertile stamens 10:
Petals longer than the sepals:
Inflorescence racemose or subracemose; carpel solitary:
Fruiting carpel with a slender stipe; filaments connate at the base
                                                        16. **Schellenbergia**
Fruiting carpel not stipitate; filaments scarcely united at the base
                                                        17. **Burttia**
Inflorescence paniculate or cymose:
Carpels 5; leaves not striate with glands   7. **Rourea**
Carpel 1; leaves striate with glands   18. **Vismianthus**
Petals shorter than or subequal to the sepals   4. **Cnestis**
Fertile stamens 5; fruits not stipitate; seed with a berry-like testa
                                                        19. **Hemandradenia**
Sepals valvate:
Leaves imparipinnate:
Flowers without an androgynophore:
Petals longer than the sepals; seeds without endosperm:
Sepals free:
Inflorescence axillary, short   12. **Santaloidella**
Inflorescence pseudoterminal, paniculate   20. **Cnestidium**
Sepals connate   21. **Spiropetalum**
Petals shorter than the sepals or subequal; seeds with fleshy endosperm
                                                        4. **Cnestis**
Flowers with an androgynophore; leaflets striolate between the veins;
petals hairy   22. **Manotes**
Leaves unifoliolate:
Petals shorter than or subequal to the sepals; fruits not stipitate; seeds with
fleshy endosperm   4. **Cnestis**
Petals longer than the sepals; fruits more or less stipitate; endosperm
thin:
Flowers bisexual, in short racemes or panicles; fertile stamens 5
                                                        23. **Ellipanthus**

Flowers unisexual, probably dioecious, in axillary clusters; usually only 4 fertile stamens, with small subulate staminodes between

24. **Pseudellipanthus**

1. **Roureopsis** Planch., Linnaea 23: 423 (1850). 8 spp., 2 W. trop. Africa, 6 trop. Asia; type *R. pubinervis* Planch., Malaya. Schellenberg, Engl. Pflanzenr. *Connarac.* 107, figs. 18–19.

Erect or scandent shrubs; leaves imparipinnate; lateral leaflets often very oblique; inflorescence axillary, racemose, racemes fasciculate or very short and densely glomerate; sepals 5, imbricate, bearded at the apex; enlarged under the fruit, erect, imbricate at the base, not connivent; petals 5, circinate in bud, loriform, much longer than the sepals, acute; stamens 10, filaments connate at the base, glabrous; carpels 5, glabrous inside; fruits mucronate, glabrous, not stipitate; seed solitary, with the aril adnate to the base; endosperm absent.

2. **Taeniochlaena** Hook. f., Benth. & Hook. f., Gen. Pl. 1: 433 (1862). 4 spp., Malaya; type *T. acutipetala* (Miq.) Kurz, Malay Penins., Sumatra. Schellenberg, Engl. Pflanzenr. *Connarac.* 167, fig. 30.

Erect or scandent shrubs; leaves imparipinnate; inflorescence axillary, racemose, racemes fasciculate; sepals 5, imbricate, tomentose outside, puberulous within the apex, slightly enlarged under the fruit, reflexed; petals 5, about twice as long as the sepals, circinate in bud, glabrous, linear, acute; stamens 10, filaments connate at the base, glabrous; carpels 5, glabrous within; styles glabrous; stigmas capitate; ovules 2, collateral, erect; fruits several, sessile, velutinous outside; seed solitary, with a split ventral aril at the base; endosperm absent.

3. **Paxia** Gilg, Engl. Bot. Jahrb. 14: 320 (1891). 8 spp., W. trop. Africa; type *P. myriantha* (Baill.) Pierre. Schellenberg, Engl. Pflanzenr. *Connarac.* 114, fig. 20.

Scandent or erect shrubs or small trees; leaves imparipinnate, rarely unifoliolate; inflorescence axillary, paniculate, panicles crowded; sepals 5, imbricate, puberulous or lepidote outside; petals 5, circinate in bud, loriform, much longer than the sepals, subacute, glabrous; stamens 10, filaments connate at the base, glabrous; carpels 5, hair outside, glabrous within; stigma lobed; ovules 2, collateral, erect; fruit composed of one carpel, sessile, mucronate or hooked at the apex, glabrous; seed solitary, testa dry, shining, black, with a split ventral aril at the base; endosperm absent.

4. **Cnestis** Juss., Gen. 374 (1789). *Spondioides* Smeathm. ex Lam. (1789). About 40 spp., East Indies, Philipp. Isls., Madagascar, trop. Africa; type *C. corniculata* Lam., W. trop. Africa. Schellenberg, Engl. Pflanzenr. *Connarac.* 28, figs. 3–6.

More or less scandent shrubs, rarely arborescent; leaves imparipinnate; inflorescence terminal, paniculate, or axillary and racemose, racemes often borne in the axils of fallen leaves on the older branches; sepals 5, valvate or imbricate, sometines petaloid; petals 5, half as long as the sepals, connate at the base; stamens 10, shortly connate; carpels 5, hirsute; stigmas globose; ovules 2, collateral, erect; fruits 5–1 developed, sessile, pyriform, often produced into horn-like processes, mostly velutinous outside, densely covered inside with stiff setae; seed solitary, mostly black or dark brown, shining; aril basal, oblique.

5. **Bernardinia** Planch., Linnaea, 23: 412 (1850). 4 spp., S. trop. America; type *B. comans* (Casar.) Schellenberg, S. Brazil. Schellenberg, Engl. Pflanzenr. *Connarac.* 100, fig. 16.

Small trees, or shrubs, or semiscandent; leaves imparipinnate; inflorescence axillary, paniculate; sepals 5, imbricate, petaloid, not accrescent, reclinate after flowering; petals 5, longer than the sepals, linear-oblong, recurved, gland-dotted; stamens 10, filaments glabrous; carpels 5, ovoid, hirsute, narrowed into a short style; stigmas capitate; fruit sessile, slightly curved, oblong, apiculate with the style, narrowed at each end, coriaceous, tardily dehiscent by the ventral suture; ovules 2, collateral; seed solitary, the shape of the fruit, testa dark, fleshy towards the arilliform base; endosperm absent.

6. **Byrsocarpus** Schum. & Thonn., Beskr. Pl. Guin. 226 (1827). 17 spp., trop. Africa, Madagascar; type *B. coccineus* Schum. & Thonn., trop. Africa. Schellenberg, Engl. Pflanzenr. *Connarac.* 146, figs. 26–28.

Small trees, erect or scandent shrubs; leaves imparipinnate, often produced after the flowers; inflorescence axillary, racemose, sometimes subumbellate, bracts scarious; sepals 5, imbricate; petals 5, longer than the sepals, glabrous; stamens 10, filaments connate at the base, glabrous; carpels 5, pilose outside, glabrous within; stigma capitate; ovules 2, collateral; fruiting carpel 1, sessile, supported at the base by the slightly accrescent spreading calyx, mucronate at the apex, glabrous; seed enclosed by the aril except at the apex; endosperm absent.

7. **Rourea** Aubl., Hist. Pl. Guiane, 1: 467, t. 187 (1775). *Robergia* Schreber (1789). *Malbrancia* Necker (1790). *Eichleria* Progel (1877). 32 spp., trop. America; type *R. frutescens* Aubl., Guianas and Trinidad. Schellenberg, Engl. Pflanzenr. *Connarac.* 194, figs. 37–41.

Small trees, erect or scandent shrubs; leaves imparipinnate, leaflets often many pairs, rarely 1-foliolate; inflorescence terminal or axillary, paniculate; sepals 5, imbricate, villous or puberulous outside and sometimes also glandular; petals 5, longer than the sepals, glabrous; stamens 10, filaments connate at the base, glabrous; carpels 5, villous outside, glabrous within; stigma capitate; ovules 2, collateral, erect; fruit solitary, sessile, obovoid, striate lengthwise, with enlarged coriaceous or villous-hirsute sepals at the base, sometimes also glandular, often surrounded by the campanulate calyx; seed solitary, testa shining, dark, with a cup-shaped fleshy adnate aril at the base; endosperm absent.

8. **Santaloides** Schellenberg, Beitr. 46, 76, 119 (1910). *Rourea* of many authors, not Aubl. (partly). *Santalodes* O. Ktze. (partly). 45 spp., trop. Asia, Australasia, trop. Africa, Madagascar; type *S. minus* (Gaertn.) Schellenberg, S. India, Ceylon. Schellenberg, Engl. Pflanzenr. *Connarac.* 19, figs. 21–25.

Erect or scandent shrubs; leaves imparipinnate; leaflets sometimes many-paired, rarely 1-foliolate; inflorescence axillary or pseudoterminal, paniculate; sepals 5, imbricate, often ciliate; petals 5, longer than the sepals, glabrous; stamens 10, filaments connate at the base, glabrous; carpels 5, hairy outside, glabrous within; stigma capitate; ovules paired, erect; fruit solitary, sessile, closely surrounded at the base by the enlarged rather woody very imbricate sepals, arcuate on the dorsal side, glabrous, often finely striate lengthwise, opening by the ventral suture or sometimes irregularly split from the base; seed solitary, testa yellowish-brown when dry, shining, almost quite free from the aril; endosperm absent.

9. **Jaundea** Gilg, Notizbl. Bot. Gart. Berl. 1, 2: 66 (1895). 6 spp., trop. Africa; type *J. pinnata* (P. Beauv.) Schellenberg. Schellenberg, Engl. Pflanzenr. *Connarac.* 161, fig. 29.

Trees, erect or scandent shrubs; leaves imparipinnate, developed with the flowers, leaflets with strong secondary nerves prominent below; inflorescence paniculate, axillary or terminal; sepals 5, imbricate, puberulous outside; petals 5, longer than the sepals, glabrous; carpels 5, pilose outside, glabrous within; stigma capitate; ovules paired, collateral, erect; fruit solitary, sessile, arcuate, glabrous, with the slightly enlarged more or less spreading calyx at the base; seed adnate to the aril, the testa becoming berry-like and mucronate at the apex; hilum basal, conspicuous; endosperm absent.

10. **Jollydora** Pierre, in Bull. Soc. Linn.; Paris, sér. 2: 1233 (1896), nomen; Gilg, Engl. Bot. Jahrb. 23: 217 (1896). *Anthagathis* Harms (1897); 3 spp., W. trop. Africa; type *J. duparquetiana* (Baill.) Pierre. Schellenberg, Engl. Pflanzenr. *Connarac.* 24, fig. 2.

Trees; leaves imparipinnate, clustered at the apex of the trunk; inflorescence racemose, short, axillary or arising on the trunk; sepals 5, imbricate, outer smaller; petals 5, twice as long as the sepals, glabrous; stamens 10, connate at the base; anthers dorsifixed; carpel solitary; style glabrous, stigma globose; ovules paired, collateral, erect; fruit solitary, indehiscent, narrowed at the base, cylindric or ellipsoid, shining; seeds mostly 2, cylindric, not arillate.

11. **Connarus** Linn., Sp. Pl. 674 (1753). *Omphalobium* Gaertn. (1788). *Erythrostigma* Hassk. (1842). *Anisostemon* Turcz. (1842). *Thysanus* Lour. (1790). *Tricholobus* Blume (1855). *Canicidia* Vell. (1827). 121 spp.; tropics; type *C. monocarpus* Linn., S. India, Ceylon. Schellenberg, Engl. Pflanzenr. *Connarac.* 216, figs. 42–48.

Small trees or erect or scandent shrubs; leaves imparipinnate or trifoliolate, rarely 1-foliolate; inflorescence mostly terminal, paniculate, large, or rarely axillary, subcymose or racemose; hairs simple, 1-celled, 2-armed or compound; sepals 5, rarely 4, broadly imbricate or subvalvate, more or less punctate; petals 5, longer than the calyx or rarely subequal to them, punctate, often coherent in the middle, at length free; stamens 10, filaments connate at the base, sometimes staminodal and gland-like or bearing sterile anthers; anther-loculi often glandular at the base; connective with a glandular apex; carpel solitary, stigma oblique, reniform; ovules 2, collateral; fruit narrowed at the base into a sometimes long and slender stalk, or this sometimes thick or almost absent; pericarp woody or coriaceous; seed solitary, testa mostly dark-purple, shining; aril cupular or lateral, crenulate or laciniate; endosperm absent.

12. **Santaloidella** Schellenberg, De Wild. Pl. Bequaert. 4, 4: 548, nomen (1929). 1 sp., *S. gilletii* Schellenb. ex De Wild., W. trop. Africa. Schellenberg, Engl. Pflanzenr. *Connarac.* 118.

Leaves imparipinnate, leaflets 6–8 pairs, elliptic, sides very oblique, long-acuminate; inflorescence axillary, short, only known in fruit; flowers unknown; fruit solitary, surrounded at the base by the rather woody accrescent imbricate sepals, elongate-cone-like, acute at the apex, very finely striate, dehiscing ventrally; seed with a dark testa when dry, with an adnate aril at the base; endosperm absent.

13. **Agelaea** Soland. ex Planch., Linnaea, 23: 437 (1850). 46 spp., trop. Africa, Mascarenes; type *A. trifolia* (Lam.) Gilg., W. trop. Africa. Schellenberg, Engl. Pflanzenr. *Connarac.* 65, figs. 26–28.

Scandent or subscandent shrubs; leaves trifoliolate, leaflets sometimes tricuspidate or repand-sinuate; inflorescence terminal, paniculate; hairs bunched together; sepals 5, imbricate, tomentose or rather silky outside, inner longer, the overlapped margins paler, ciliate with glands; petals 5, mostly longer than the sepals, glabrous; stamens 10, filaments glabrous, connate at the base; carpels 5, hairy outside, sometimes some sterile; style hairy, stigma globose; ovules 2, collateral, erect; fruit pear-shaped, rounded at the apex, contracted at the base, densely velutinous outside; seed solitary, shining, dark, with a small fleshy aril at the base; endosperm absent.

14. **Castanola** Llanos, Mem. Acad. Cienc. Madrid, 3, 2: 505 (1859). *Hemiandrina* Hook. f. (1860). *Troostwykia* Miq. (1860). *Erythrostigma* Zoll. (1857). *Agelaea* Soland. ex Benth. & Hook. f. (1862) (partly). 12 spp., trop. Asia and W. trop. Africa; type *C. trinervis* Llanos, Philippine Isls. Schellenberg, Engl. Pflanzenr. *Connarac.* 169, figs. 31–32.

Scandent or subscandent shrubs; leaves trifoliolate; inflorescence axillary, shorter than the leaves, often glomerate; sepals 5, narrowly imbricate, tomentose outside, not enlarged in fruit; petals 5, longer than the sepals, glabrous; stamens 10 or rarely 5, filaments connate at the base, glabrous; carpels 5, or rarely 3, hairy outside; stigma globose; ovules 2, collateral, erect; fruits several, pear-shaped, contracted at the base into a thick stipe, densely velvety outside, sometimes tuberculate; seed solitary, testa leathery, shining, dark when dry, with a fleshy aril at the base; endosperm absent.

15. **Pseudoconnarus** Radlk., Sitzungsber. Bayer. Akad. Wiss. München, 16: 356 (1886). 4 spp., trop. South America; type *P. macrophyllus* (Poepp. & Endl.) Radlk., Brazil. Schellenberg, Engl. Pflanzenr. *Connarac.* 93.

Erect or semiscandent shrubs; leaves trifoliolate; inflorescence axillary, paniculate; sepals 5, imbricate, scarcely enlarged but spreading in fruit; petals 5, clawed at the base, glabrous; stamens 10, filaments glabrous, connate at the base; carpels 5, glabrous, stigmas globose; ovules 2, collateral, erect; fruits several, clavate, stipitate, apiculate; seed solitary, testa coriaceous, dark, shining, with a fleshy aril at the base; endosperm abundant.

16. **Schellenbergia** Parkinson, Indian Forester, 42: 295 (1936). 1 sp., *S. sterculiifolia* (Prain) Parkinson, Lower Burma. Schellenberg, Engl. Pflanzenr. *Connarac.* 179, fig. 33.

Small tree or shrub; leaves unifoliolate; inflorescence axillary, subracemose, appearing with the young leaves; sepals 5, imbricate; petals 5, longer than the sepals, glabrous; stamens 10, filaments connate at the base, glabrous; carpel solitary, villous; stigma subdiscoid; ovules 2, collateral, erect; fruit with a slender stipe, beaked-acuminate, glabrous inside and out; pericarp coriaceous, endocarp separating from the exocarp when mature; seed solitary, testa dark, berry-like, covered at the base by an undulate aril forming a long filiform appendage; endosperm rudimentary.

17. **Burttia** Bak. f. & Exell., Journ. Bot. 59: 249 cum icon. (p. 250) (1931). 1 sp., *B. prunifolia* Bak. f. & Exell., E. trop. Africa (Tanganyika Territ.). Schellenberg, Engl. Pflanzenr. *Connarac.* 96, fig. 14.

Shrub; leaves unifoliolate; flowers in short axillary racemes; sepals 5, imbricate, not accrescent in fruit; petals 5, longer than the calyx, glabrous; stamens 10, filaments scarcely united at the base; carpel solitary, sessile, villous; style villous; ovules 2, 3, or 1, erect; fruit subcylindric, dehiscent, silky-tomentose; seed 1, with a lobed aril; endosperm abundant.

18. **Vismianthus** Mildbr., Notizbl. Bot. Gart. Berl. 12: 706 (1936). 1 sp., *V. punctatus* Mildbr., E. trop. Africa (Tanganyika Territ.). Schellenberg, Engl. Pflanzenr. *Connarac.* 98, fig. 15.

Shrubs, covered with 2-armed hairs; leaves unifoliolate, leaflet ovate, acuminate, striate with glands; inflorescence axillary, cymose; pedicels articulate; sepals 5, imbricate, glandular-punctate and striate; petals 5, longer than the sepals, glabrous, glandular-punctate and striate; stamens 10, filaments glabrous; carpel solitary, densely villous; style pubescent; ovules 2, collateral, one often aborted.

19. **Hemandradenia** Stapf, Kew Bull. 1908: 288. 3 spp., W. trop. Africa, Madagascar; type *H. mannii* Stapf, Gabon. Schellenberg, Engl. Pflanzenr. *Connarac.* 64.

Small trees; leaves unifoliolate; inflorescence axillary and glomerate or paniculate and terminal; sepals 5, slightly imbricate; petals 5, linear-oblong; stamens 5, opposite the sepals and fertile, with 5 opposite the petals and sterile with the anthers reduced to a glandular body; carpel solitary, tomentose; stigma lobulate; ovules 2, collateral; fruit ellipsoid, indehiscent; pericarp thinly crustaceous, glabrous within; seed solitary, testa berry-like.

20. **Cnestidium** Planch., Linnaea, 23: 439 (1850). 2 spp., trop. America; type *C. rufescens* Planch. Schellenberg, Engl. Pflanzenr. *Connarac.* 191, fig. 36.

Subscandent shrubs; leaves imparipinnate; inflorescence paniculate, pseudo-terminal; sepals 5, subvalvate, erect in fruit, not enlarged, tomentose on each side; petals 5, a little longer than the sepals, glabrous; stamens 10, filaments connate at the base, glabrous; carpels 5, shortly hispid outside; stigma capitate; ovules 2, collateral, erect; fruit mostly 1, velvety outside, glabrous within; seed solitary, testa coriaceous, dark, shining, with a cupular fleshy aril adnate to the base; endosperm rudimentary.

21. **Spiropetalum** Gilg, Engl. Bot. Jahrb. 14: 335 (1891). 4 spp., W. trop. Africa; type *S. odoratum* Gilg. Schellenberg, Engl. Pflanzenr. *Connarac.* 103, fig. 17.

Scandent or semiscandent shrubs; leaves imparipinnate; inflorescence axillary, paniculate, or racemose; sepals 5, connate at the base, valvate, triangular, tomentose outside; petals 5, circinate in bud, loriform, much longer than the sepals, acute, glabrous; stamens 10, connate at the base, filaments glabrous; carpels 5, hairy outside, glabrous inside; style glabrous, stigma lobed; ovules 2, collateral, erect; fruit often solitary but sometimes several maturing, velvety outside; seed solitary, testa leathery, black, shining, with a split aril at the base; endosperm absent.

22. **Manotes** Soland. ex Planch., Linnaea, 23: 438 (1850). *Dinklagea* Gilg. (1897). 10 spp., W. trop. Africa; type *M. expansa* Soland. Schellenberg, Engl. Pflanzenr. *Connarac.* 54.

Scandent or semiscandent shrubs; leaves imparipinnate, leaflets opposite or subopposite, striolate between the veins: inflorescence racemose and axillary or paniculate and terminal, laxly flowered; sepals 5, valvate; petals 5, longer than the calyx, tomentellous outside; stamens and carpels seated on a slender column; stamens 10, connate at the base; carpels 5, villous; stigmas globose; ovules 2, collateral, erect; fruits 5–1 maturing, pear-shaped, stipitate, reflexed, apiculate, velvety outside, glabrous inside; seed solitary, testa with a dorsal linear coriaceous zone, remainder fleshy and berry-like, often pale red.

23. **Ellipanthus** Hook. f., Benth. & Hook. f. Gen. Pl. 1: 434 (1862). 13 spp., trop. Asia; type *E. unifoliolatus* Thwaithes, Ceylon. Schellenberg, Engl. Pflanzenr. *Connarac.* 181, fig. 34.

Shrubs or small trees; leaves unifoliolate, petiole articulate; flowers glomerate racemes or short axillary panicles; sepals 5, valvate, soon open; petals 5, imbricate; stamens 5 opposite the sepals and fertile, 5 opposite the petals and staminodal, all connate at the base into a tube; carpel solitary, villous; stigma capitate; ovules 2, collateral, erect; fruit ovoid, often narrowed into a stipe, tomentose outside; pericarp woody; seed solitary, testa mostly black and shining; aril thin, half as long as the seed; endosperm not abundant.

24. **Pseudellipanthus** Schellenb., Mez, Bot. Archiv. 1: 314 (1922). 2 spp., Borneo; type *P. beccarii* (Pierre). Schellenberg, Engl. Pflanzenr. *Connarac.* 189, fig. 35.

Small slender trees; branchlets with tomentose nodules; leaves 1-foliolate, leaflet oblong; inflorescence axillary, glomerate; flowers unisexual, probably dioecious; sepals valvate, tomentose outside; petals imbricate, tomentose outside; stamens 4 fertile (rarely 5 or 3), with small staminodes between, the filaments connate into a tube villous inside; carpel solitary, villous; ovules 2, collateral; fruit solitary, the ventral suture much curved, compressed, apiculate, narrowed at the base into a long stipe; seed oblong, testa shining, with a small aril at the base; endosperm not abundant.

21. CROSSOSOMATACEAE

Engl., Engl. & Prantl, Nat. Pflanzenfam. Nachtr. [1], zum ii–iv: 185 (1897)

Small shrubs; leaves small, alternate, entire, more or less sessile; stipules absent. Flowers solitary, terminating short branchlets, white, showy, bisexual. Sepals 5, connate into a turbinate tube at the base. Petals 5, imbricate, nervose, orbicular. Stamens numerous, free, inserted on the calyx-tube; filaments slender; anthers oblong, dorsifixed; loculi contiguous, dehiscing lengthwise. Carpels 3–5, free from one another on a short stipe, oblong, with 1–2 series of ovules, narrowed into a short style; stigma oblique, discoid. Ovules with a ventral raphe and an inferior micropyle. Fruits follicular, splitting along the adaxial margin. Seeds numerous, globose, girt by a multifid aril; testa crustaceous, shining; endosperm thin and fleshy; embryo medium-sized, slightly curved; radicle cylindric, near the hilum; cotyledons oblong, a little shorter than the radicle. Type genus *Crossosoma* Nutt.

Genus 1; species 4.

LITERATURE. Small, *Crossosomataceae*, N. Amer. Fl. 22: 231 (1908); Lemesle, Posit. phylogénét. de l'*Hydrastis* et du *Crossosoma californicum*, &c., Paris Acad. Sci. Compt. Rend. 227: 221 (1948); Lawrence, Taxon. Fl. Pl. 540, fig. 165 (1951); Hutch., Fam. Fl. Pl. ed. 2, 1: 145, fig. 21 (1959).

ANATOMY. M.C. 1: 11. POLLEN. Erdt. 133.

Stomata are present on both surfaces of the leaves, and they are surrounded by several ordinary epidermal cells (ranunculaceous type) as in *Dilleniaceae*, in which family *Crossosoma* was included by Bentham & Hooker. But Metcalfe & Chalk consider that the absence of raphides as well as of tubes or sacs filled with raphides or crystal sand is a clear indication that the genus has no affinity with *Dilleniaceae*. Solereder considered it to be related to *Rosaceae*. On account of the absence of stipules, the follicular free carpels, and the strongly arillate seeds I prefer to retain it next to *Dilleniaceae*.

Crossosoma Nutt., Journ. Acad. Philadelphia, new ser. 1: 150 (1847). 4 spp., SW. United States, New Mexico; type *C. californicum* Nutt., New Mexico, Calif. B.H. 1: 15 (in *Dilleniaceae*); E.P.N. 186; Small, N. Amer. Fl. 22: 231 (1908). *Characters of the family.*

22. BRUNELLIACEAE

Engl., Engl. & Prantl, Nat. Pflanzenfam. Nachtr. [1], zum ii–iv: 182 (1897)

Trees, sometimes spiny, often tomentose. Leaves opposite or verticillate, simple, trifoliolate or imparipinnate; leaflets toothed; stipules and small stipels present. Flowers actinomorphic, dioecious, in axillary or terminal panicles. Calyx 5–4-partite, segments valvate. Petals absent. Stamens 10–8, inserted at the base of the disk; anthers dorsifixed; male flowers with sessile rudimentary ovary; rudiments of stamens in the female flowers. Carpels 5–4, free, sessile, 1-locular; styles subulate, recurved, with undivided stigmas;

ovules 2, collateral. Fruiting carpels 5–4 or fewer, spreading, more or less beaked, 2–1-seeded. Seeds often black and shining, with fleshy endosperm and flat cotyledons. Type genus *Brunellia* Ruiz & Pavon.

Metcalfe & Chalk remark that the scalariform perforation-plates of the vessels serve to differentiate *Brunellia* from the *Simaroubaceae*, in which family the genus was included by Bentham & Hooker. They continue: 'It is also of interest that the *Cunoniaceae*, near which the family is placed in the respective systems of Engler and Hutchinson, likewise possesses scalariform plates.' A further anatomical character of note are the thick-walled unicellular hairs.

The type of pollen apparently does not throw any particular light on the affinity of this genus, which has such a remarkable variety and combination of characters.

ANATOMY. M.C. 1: 326. POLLEN. Erdt. 82.

Brunellia Ruiz & Pavon, Fl. Peruv. et Chil. Prodr. 71, t. 12 (1794). *Brunelia* Pers. (1807). About 12 spp., Cent. America, West Indies, trop. South America; lectotype *B. aculeata* Ruiz & Pavon, Peru. B.H. 1: 313 (in *Simaroubaceae*); E.P.N. 184; Hutch., Fam. Fl. Pl. ed. 2, 1: 147, fig. 22 (1959). *Characters of the family.*

ORDER 5. CORIARIALES

A small group of species of a single genus widely distributed in warm temperate regions of the world; leaves opposite or verticillate; carpels free, adnate to a wide receptacle; styles free; seeds not arillate; a difficult family to place satisfactorily in any system.

Single family   *Coriariaceae*

23. CORIARIACEAE
A.P. DC., Prodr. 1: 739 (1824) (*Coriarieae*)

Shrubs with angular branchlets, the lower opposite or 3 in a whorl; buds covered with scales; no glandular hairs. Leaves opposite, rarely 3 in a whorl, ovate-cordate to lanceolate, entire, 3- or more-nerved from the base; stipules absent. Flowers bisexual or subpolygamous, axillary, solitary or racemose, or in a terminal raceme, small, green. Sepals 5, imbricate, ovate-triangular, persistent. Petals 5, shorter than the sepals, 3-angled, fleshy, keeled inside, thickened after flowering and intruded between the carpels. Stamens 10, hypogynous, free, or 5 of them adnate to the keels of the petals; anthers large, oblong, rough. Carpels 10–5, free, adnate to the conical torus, 1-locular; styles free, elongated, stigmatose all over; ovules solitary, pendulous from the apex of the loculi, anatropous, with a dorsal raphe. Fruiting carpels embraced by the very accrescent petals, often purplish. Seeds compressed, with very thin endosperm and large straight embryo. Type genus *Coriaria* Linn.

Genus 1; species 8.

DISTRIBUTION. Warm temperate regions from the Mediterranean to the Himalayas, China and Japan, Formosa, New Guinea, New Zealand, and Central and W. South America.

CLASSIFICATION. B.H. 1: 429; E.P. 3, 5: 128; Lawrence, Taxon. Vasc. Pl. 571, fig. 185 (1951); Hutch., Fam. Fl. Pl. ed. 2, 1: 147, fig. 23, with map.

ADDITIONAL LITERATURE. Good, Geography of genus *Coriaria*, New Phytol. 29: 170 (1930).

ANATOMY. Sol. 1: 249; M.C. 1: 467. POLLEN. Erdt. 129.

Phylogeny and Morphology. The relationships of *Coriariaceae* are rather obscure. Bentham & Hooker say of the family: 'A single genus, not closely allied to any other; from all the families related to the *Rutaceae* it differs by the pendulous ovule with a dorsal raphe and superior micropyle; from *Olacaceae*, *Sapindaceae*, and *Anacardiaceae* by the habit, the inner stamens often adnate to the petals, and the long-stigmatose styles; approaches *Phytolaccaceae* by several characters.'

The discontinuous distribution of *Coriaria* and the structure of the gynoecium suggest considerable antiquity. The carpels are not fully united and the styles are free, so that on these characters some intermediate position between the *Magnoliales* and the *Hamamelidales* is perhaps the best place for it.

The family resembles *Anacardiaceae* only in containing abundant tannin, but differs from them by the absence of resin-canals, and by the possession of the rubiaceous type of stomata, which are accompanied on each side by a single subsidiary cell parallel to the pore; also the wood lacks two of the most characteristic features of the *Anacardiaceae*, i.e. septate fibres and radial intercellular canals.

The morphological difference between the species in the northern hemisphere and those of the southern hemisphere mentioned by Solereder breaks down on account of *C. terminalis* Hemsl., China and Himalayas, with terminal inflorescence developed with leaves of the current season. Pollen grains give no special indication of affinity.

Geographical Distribution. The absence of the family from Africa south of the Sahara, and from Australia, is noteworthy. Of particular interest is the distribution of the two species *Coriaria ruscifolia* Linn. and *C. thymifolia* Humb. & Bonpl., the former common to New Zealand and the neighbouring islands and Chile, the latter to New Zealand and Central and W. tropical South America.

Economic Properties. Several species have poisonous properties and all are probably suspect. The young shoots of *C. sinica* Maxim., in Hupeh, China, are poisonous to cattle. In some districts of India *C. nepalensis* Wall. is said to be highly poisonous (Watt, Dict. Econ. Prod. India, 2: 570), whilst most parts of plants of *C. ruscifolia* Linn., New Zealand and Chile, contain the poison known as *tutin*, especially the young shoots and seeds (Cheesm., Fl. New Zeal. 106).

Coriaria Linn., Sp. Pl. 1037 (1753). *Heterocladus* Turcz. (1847). *Heterophylleia* Turcz. (1848). 8 spp., type *C. myrtifolia* Linn., S. Europe, N. Africa. *Characters of the family.*

ORDER 6. ROSALES

A prolific group largely found in more temperate regions; fundamentally woody with numerous perennial herbs, but annuals very rare; flowers perigynous to epigynous, apocarpous to syncarpous, with axile placentation; differs markedly from *Ranales* in the absence of endosperm from the seeds; leaves generally stipulate; basic group for *Hamamelidales*, the latter leading up to the 'Amentiferae'.

Leaves with stipules, these sometimes adnate to the petiole, alternate or very rarely opposite; stamens all fertile:
Stamens usually numerous and free among themselves; sepals, petals, and stamens mostly perigynous or epigynous; petals entire or at most shortly bilobed; leaves simple or compound   24. *Rosaceae*
Stamens 5 or 3, free or united; sepals, petals, and stamens hypogynous; petals often deeply bilobed or bipartite; leaves simple
    25. *Dichapetalaceae*
Leaves without stipules, opposite; stamens numerous, the inner ones sterile; carpels numerous, free, inserted on the inside of the hollowed out receptacle   26. *Calycanthaceae*

24. ROSACEAE

A. L. de Jussieu, Gen. 334 (1789)

Trees, shrubs, or herbs, sometimes straggling or climbing. Leaves alternate or rarely opposite, simple or compound, often glandular-serrate; petiole often 2-glandular at the apex; stipules paired, free or adnate to the petiole, rarely absent. Inflorescence various, from single flowers to corymbose, racemose, or paniculate. Flowers mostly actinomorphic and bisexual, rarely dioecious. Calyx free from or adnate to the ovary; tube ('hypanthium') short or elongated, lobes mostly 5, imbricate, sometimes with an epicalyx of bracteoles; disk lining the calyx-tube, usually entire. Petals (rarely absent) inserted below the margin of the disk, as many as the calyx-lobes, free, equal or rarely unequal, imbricate, deciduous. Stamens mostly numerous, usually in a complete ring at the margin of or above the disk; filaments usually free; anthers small, didymous, rarely elongated, 2-locular, dehiscing lengthwise. Carpels many to 1, free, or connate and then usually more or less adnate to the calyx-tube (the ovary then inferior); ovules often 2 (rarely 1 or several) in each carpel or ovary-loculus, superposed, anatropous. Fruits various, superior to inferior, nude or enclosed by the persistent calyx, drupaceous, pomaceous, follicular, or of an indefinite number of achenes or drupes, or very rarely capsular and 3- or more-locular and loculicidally or septicidally 3–many-valved. Seeds erect or pendulous, sometimes winged; endosperm absent or very rarely scanty; cotyledons mostly fleshy, plano-convex, rarely foliaceous or convolute. Type genus *Rosa* Linn.

Genera 124; species about 3,375.

DISTRIBUTION. World-wide, most numerous in north temperate regions.

CLASSIFICATION. Benth. & Hook. f., Gen. Pl. 1: 600 (1865); Focke, Engl. & Prantl, Nat. Pflanzenfam. 3, 3: 1 (1888); Schneid., Laubholtzk. 1: 440 (incl. *Spiraeaceae*) (1906); Rydb., Fl. N. Amer. 22: 239 (1908); Hauman, Fl. Congo Belge, 3: 1 (1952); Bull. Jard. Bot. Brux. 21: 167 (1951) (African *Chrysobalanaceae*); Jepson, Fl. Calif. 2: 160 (1936); Rehder, Trees and Shrubs, ed. 2: 322 (1940); Graham, Fl. Trop. East Afr. *Rosaceae* (1960); Allan, Fl. New Zeal. 351 (1961).

ADDITIONAL LITERATURE. K. Sax, Origin and relationships of the *Pomoideae*, Journ. Arn. Arb. 12: 3 (1931); Chromosome relationships in the *Pomoideae*, loc. cit. 13: 363 (1932); F. Bolle, Eine Übersicht über die Gattung *Geum* L. und die ihr nahestehenden Gattungen, Fedde Repert. Beih. 72: 1 (1933); G. Jackson, Morphology of the flowers of *Rosa* and certain closely related genera, Amer. Journ. Bot. 21: 453 (1934); Gajenski, Evolution in the genus *Geum*, Evolution, 13: 378 (1959).

ANATOMY. According to Metcalfe & Chalk there are very few anatomical features common to the whole family. Clothing hairs are generally unicellular and simple or more rarely united into tufts resembling stellate hairs; true stellate hairs occur in *Chrysobalanus*. Glandular hairs are common, and nectaries are often found on the petiole, on the leaf-surface, and on the leaf-margins. The stomata are either of the ranunculaceous or (in *Chrysobalaneae*) rubiaceous type. Vascular bundles are separated by either narrow or broad primary rays. They note that the rather scanty information available suggests that *Laurocerasus* and *Prunus* should be separate genera, also *Padus*, here distinguished by morphological characters. They also consider that the anatomy of *Lyonothamnus* (here assigned to the *Quillajeae*) 'is quite consistent with its being a member of the *Rosaceae*' rather than *Cunoniaceae*,[1] to which it was referred by Britton & Shafer. Sol. 1: 301; M.C. 1: 539, 550.

POLLEN. Erdt. 380. BIOLOGY. Knuth 2: 342.

Characters occurring in relatively few Genera. **Leaves** opposite in *Rhodotypus, Coleogyne, Potaninia, Lyonothamnus*; reduced in *Canotia*; indumentum stellate in *Chamaebatiaria*; stipules either obsolete or absent from a few *Chrysobalaneae, Osmaronia, Exochorda*, and all tribe *Spiraeeae*. **Flowers** asymmetric in some genera of *Chrysobalaneae*; unisexual in *Bencomia, Hagenia, Aruncus, Osmaronia, Cliffortia*, and some *Rubus*; males racemose and female solitary in *Kageneckia*; capitate in *Acaena* spp., *Poterium, Sanguisorba* spp.; receptacle convex and enlarged in fruit in *Rubus* spp., *Fragaria, Duchesnea, Comarum*. **Calyx** persistent around the base of seedlings of *Neurada*; calyx-tube armed with hooked bristles in *Acaena* spp. **Petals** absent from many *Chrysobalaneae* and often from *Pygeum, Neviusa, Cercocarpus*, and tribe *Poterieae*; more than 5 in a few *Pygeum* spp., and sometimes in *Maddenia, Potentilla*, and *Dryas*. **Stamens** either monadelphous or unilateral in some *Chrysobalaneae*, few in *Chamaerhodon*, various *Potentilla* spp., *Sibbaldia*, and in tribe *Poterieae*; 5 in *Euphronia* and *Canotia*; hypogynous

---

[1] See Millspaugh & Nuttall, Field Mus. Nat. Hist. 5: 126 (1923).

with persistent filaments and deciduous anthers in *Canotia* and *Stylobasium*; anthers much elongated in *Stylobasium*; opening by terminal pores in *Stellariopsis*; filaments circinate in bud in *Acioa, Hirtella, Parastemon*; connate into a unilateral sheath (thus resembling a few *Caesalpiniaceae* and many *Fabaceae*) in *Acioa*. Disk large and urn-shaped and enclosing the carpels in *Rhodotypos*. Ovary superior and at the same time syncarpous and 5-locular in *Lindleya, Euphronia*, and *Canotia*. Carpel solitary, 2-locellate and also 2-lobed and 2-locular in *Parinari*; unilaterally adherent to the throat of the calyx in various *Chrysobalaneae*; carpel solitary (or 2) in *Purshia, Chamaebatia, Adenostoma, Prinsepia, Plagiospermum*; style plumose in fruit in *Dryas, Cercocarpus*; hooked in fruit in *Geum, Oncostylis*; achenes numerous and enclosed in the berry-like 'fruit' (calyx-tube) in *Rosa*. **Fruit** a 5-coccous capsule in *Vanquelinia*; woody and loculicidally dehiscent in *Lindleya*; coriaceous and septicidally 5-valved in *Euphronia* and *Canotia*. **Seeds** winged in tribe *Quillajeae*; cotyledons convolute in *Osmaronia, Quillaja*, and *Chamaemelis*.

Economic Properties. Almond (Bitter and Sweet), *Prunus amygdalus* Batsch, Mediterranean countries, a medicinal oil. Apple, *Malus sylvestris* Mill. Apricot, *Prunus armeniaca* Linn., imported from many countries for dessert, and for extraction of oil. Attar or Otto of Roses, *Rosa damascena* Mill., Eur., especially Balkans; volatile oil obtained by distillation of the fresh flowers of this and *R. gallica* Linn., *R. alba* Linn., and *R. centifolia* Linn. Cherry, *Prunus avium* Linn. Cherry Laurel, *Laurocerasus officinalis* Roem. (*Prunus laurocerasus* Linn.); fresh leaves contain about 0·1 per cent. of hydrocyanic acid. Cherry Wood, *Prunus avium* Linn., Europe and W. Asia, used for smoking-pipes and walking-sticks. Coco Plum, *Chrysobalanus icaco*, W. Africa, trop. America; fruits eaten locally. Damson or Bullace, *Prunus insititia* Linn. Bitter Almond, *Prunus amygdalus* var. *amara*. Blackberry, *Rubus fruticosus*, Linn., &c. Kousso, Cusso, or Cousso, *Hagenia abyssinica* (Bruce) J. F. Gmel., NE. trop. Africa; flowers imported for use as an anthelmintic. Loganberry, *Rubus* spp. x. Loquat, *Eriobotrya japonica* (Thunb.) Lindl., imported from many countries. Mahaleb or St. Lucie Cherry, *Prunus mahaleb* Linn., Europe, India; kernels used as a condiment and perfume. Makita, *Parinari laurina* A. Gray, Pacific Isls.; oil seed. Marasco or Maraschino Cherry, *Prunus acida* var. *marasca*; Medlar, *Mespilus germanica* Linn., Europe, Asia; fruit edible only when over-ripe. Mirabelle, Myrobalan, or Cherry Plum, *Prunus cerasifera* Ehrh., France, whence candied plums are imported into England. Morello Cherry, *Prunus acida* Ehrh., imported from Europe, Argentine, and U.S.A. Mume Plum or Japanese Apricot, *Prunus mume* Japan. Nectarine, *Prunus persica*, var. *nectarina* Maxim. Niko or Nikko Nuts (PoYoak), *Afrolicania elaeosperma* Mildbr., an oil seed, W. trop. Africa. Peach, *Prunus persica* (Linn.) Sieb. & Zucc., cult. in many countries; trade sources France, U.S.A., South Africa; in America most important commercially of all stone fruits. Pear, *Pyrus communis* Linn.; widely grown; fresh fruit imported into Britain from Europe, Channel Isls., U.S.A. (especially California), Canada. Quillaia Bark, Soap Bark, Panama Bark, *Quillaja saponaria* Molina, South America; tree cult. in India and California; a drug in Europe but used where grown for washing silk and wool. Quince,

Cydonia oblonga Mill., Turkestan and N. Persia, cult. in other warm countries; fruits for preserves—jelly and marmalade; seeds used medicinally. Plum, *Prunus domestica* Linn. Prunes, dried plums of *Prunus domestica* Linn. Raspberry, *Rubus caesius* Linn. Rose Hips from the British country-side became important during the Second World War, incompletely ripe fruits of *Rosa*, especially the common Dog Rose, *Rosa canina* Linn., being rich in vitamin C (see Melville & Pyke, Proc. Linn. Soc. Lond. 1947: 159). Rose Petals, *Rosa gallica* Linn., Europe incl. Britain, cult. for medicinal purposes. Rose Water, *Rosa damascena* Mill., Turkey, Bulgaria, S. France; official source of Rose Water, producing Otto of Rose. Strawberry, *Fragaria vesca* Linn. Wild Black Cherry or Virginian Prune Bark, dried bark of *Prunus serotina* Ehrh., imported from U.S.A. for use in medicine; also a timber tree.

Phylogeny and Morphology. *Rosaceae* present some interesting problems in evolution and geographical distribution, and anyone who cares to study them in detail in a large herbarium will find much of interest. They can only be treated here briefly on very broad lines.

The first consideration is which group should be regarded as the oldest within the family. In the present classification the family is regarded as having been derived from the same stock as the *Dilleniaceae*, a woody family almost confined to the tropics. We might, therefore, expect to find the most primitive tribe also in the tropics. This seems to be tribe *Quillajeae*, the leaves of which are not unlike those of some *Dilleniaceae*, and whose carpels, often quite free, show unmistakable affinity. In *Quillaja*, for example, the carpels are *five* and *free*. In fruit they spread out in a stellate manner as in some *Dilleniaceae*, and they contain many ovules in two series. This tribe is confined to tropical America, where, significantly enough, there are also many *Dilleniaceae*. The winged seeds of tribe *Quillajeae*, however, show a relatively advanced character.

The next but much more advanced and closely related tribe is *Chrysobalaneae*, more widely spread than the *Quillajeae*, but mainly in the southern tropics. In *Chrysobalaneae* the ovary is reduced to one carpel, the style has become basal, and the ovules are reduced to two. One or other of these characters however, occurs in other tribes. In addition the symmetric flower of *Quillajeae* has mostly developed into an asymmetrical one, particularly with regard to the stamens, which are often unilateral, and in the most advanced genera, for example, *Parinari*, the carpel is laterally adnate to one side of the receptacular tube, as in several genera of *Caesalpiniaceae*. It is probably this tribe which shows the closest affinity with *Caesalpiniaceae*, especially with the entire-leaved species of *Bauhinia*. Some botanists are in favour of recognizing *Chrysobalaneae* as a separate family, but if this were done several other families of equal rank would have to be established.

The remainder of the tribes of *Rosaceae* are found mostly in more temperate regions, especially in the northern hemisphere. Probably tribe *Pruneae* should come next in phylogenetic sequence, because the ovary has remained superior, and it is reduced to 1 carpel; and *Pomeae* should follow with its inferior ovary, though 5 carpels have been retained.

More climax tribes are *Spiraeeae, Poterieae, Neuradeae, Rubeae,* and *Roseae,* the last mentioned consisting only of the genus *Rosa,* the species of which, like those of *Rubus*, appear to be still in an active state of evolution.

Geographical Distribution. The family *Rosaceae* is to be met with in most parts of the globe, though in some regions it is very sparsely represented. It is most abundant in the north temperate zone, where *Rosa, Rubus, Geum*, and *Potentilla* are often most conspicuous.

The Atlantic Islands harbour two endemic genera, *Bencomia*, Canary Islands and Madeira, and *Chamaemeles*, Madeira. *Hagenia* is confined to NE. tropical Africa, *Leucosidea* to SE. Africa, and *Cliffortia* almost entirely S. African. The genus *Acaena* is mostly in the southern hemisphere, whilst *Oncostylis* is common to Tasmania, New Zealand and Auckland Islands, and Magellan, South America.

Remarkably restricted in distribution is the genus *Lyonothamnus*, found only in the islands off the coast of California; also *Chamaebatia*, only in California. *Stylobasium* is found only in Australia, *Grangeria* in Madagascar.

Common to E. Asia and North America are *Physocarpus, Duchesnea, Chamaerhodos*, and *Photinia*, while spread right across the north temperate zone are *Spiraea, Aruncus, Padus, Prunus, Amelanchier, Sorbus, Crataegus, Sanguisorba, Alchemilla*, and *Cotoneaster*. And common to tropical Africa and tropical America are *Chrysobalanus, Acioa, Hirtella*, and *Parinari*.

KEY TO TRIBES

Fruits dehiscent, follicular:
  Gynoecium free from the calyx-tube:
    Seeds winged or apiculate   1. QUILLAJEAE, p. 179.
    Seeds not winged or only slightly so at each end:
      Carpels alternate with the calyx-lobes, or fewer in number; free from each other to the base:
        Stipules absent   2. SPIRAEEAE, p. 181.
        Stipules present, sometimes early deciduous   3. NEILLIEAE, p. 183.
      Carpels opposite the calyx-lobes, mostly connate at the base; stipules present, persistent   4. GILLENIEAE, p. 185.
  Gynoecium united with the calyx-tube (receptacle): annual herbs
                5. NEURADEAE, p. 186.
Fruits not (or rarely) dehiscent, composed of achenes, berries, drupes, or pomes:
  Carpels in fruit neither enclosed by nor merged with the calyx-tube (receptacle) (ovary or carpels superior), or if more or less enclosed (inferior) then the calyx-tube not becoming fleshy:
    Ovules 2 in each carpel:
      Calyx or calyx-lobes deciduous; trees and shrubs, rarely shrublets:
        Carpels 5, free; flowers polygamo-dioecious; leaves without stipules; cotyledons folded   6. OSMARONIEAE, p. 187.
        Carpel 1 or rarely 2:
        Style terminal, or lateral especially in fruit   7. PRUNEAE, p. 187.
        Style basal or nearly so from the beginning and remaining so
                8. CHRYSOBALANEAE, p. 190.

Calyx or calyx-lobes persistent:
Carpels indefinite in number:
Perennial herbs; receptacle flat in fruit   9. ULMARIEAE, p. 193.
Shrublets or straggling, rarely herbs; receptacle conical to globose,
    especially in fruit   10. RUBIEAE, p. 194.
Carpels definite in number:
Flowers paniculate; petals 5   11. HOLODISCEAE, p. 194.
Flowers solitary, terminal; petals 4   12. RHODOTYPEAE, p. 194.
Ovule solitary in each carpel:
Carpels more than 1:
Calyx-lobes not bracteolate (no epicalyx)   13. KERRIEAE, p. 195.
Calyx-lobes bracteolate (epicalyx present):
Style not or only slightly elongated in fruit, never hooked
    14. POTENTILLEAE, p. 195.
Style elongated and often hooked in fruit:
Ovary superior, not included in the calyx-tube 15. DRYADEAE, p. 199.
Ovary inferior or included in the calyx-tube, especially in fruit
    16. POTERIEAE, p. 203.
Carpel 1:
Ovule basal, erect or ascending; petals 3, or absent
    17. CERCOCARPEAE, p. 208.
Ovule apical, pendulous; petals 5   18. ADENOSTOMATEAE, p. 209.
Carpels in fruit enclosed by or merged with the more or less fleshy enlarged
    calyx-tube (receptacle) (ovary usually inferior):
Carpels numerous; fruits small and dry achenes free within the enlarged
    more or less fleshy receptacle   19. ROSEAE, p. 209.
Carpels 5–1; fruits fleshy and surrounded by or merged with the fleshy
    enlarged calyx (receptacle)   20. POMEAE, p. 210.

Tribe 1. QUILLAJEAE

Carpels 5; leaves scattered, very rarely opposite:
Carpels free or nearly so, especially in fruit, spreading stellately; flowers
    polygamous or dioecious:
Stamens 20–16, inserted at the mouth of the calyx-tube; calyx-lobes im-
    bricate   1. **Kageneckia**
Stamens 10, 5 opposite the calyx-lobes on the large adnate disk-lobes,
    5 alternating and hypogynous; calyx-lobes valvate   2. **Quillaja**
Carpels more or less united in the ovary stage or to the central axis; flowers
    bisexual:
Stamens 12; carpels connate only on the ventral side; petals persistent;
    leaves very narrow   3. **Vauquelinia**
Stamens 20–15; carpels completely connate; evergreen trees; flowers
    solitary, axillary   4. **Lindleya**
Stamens 15; carpels connate on the axis, at length separated; shrubs;
    flowers in terminal racemes   5. **Exochorda**
Carpels 2, glandular; stamens 15, in pairs opposite the petals, singly opposite the
    sepals; leaves opposite; flowers in large terminal cymes 6. **Lyonothamnus**

1. **Kageneckia** Ruiz & Pav., Fl. Peruv. et Chil. Prodr. 145, t. 37 (1794). *Lydea* Molina (1810). *Lydaea* Molina (1810). *Kagenackia* Steud. (1840). 6 spp., Bolivia, Peru, Chile; lectotype *K. oblonga* Ruiz & Pav., Peru, Chile. B.H. 1: 614; E.P. 3, 3: 17.

Evergreen trees; leaves scattered, serrate; stipules minute, caducous; flowers unisexual, terminal, male racemose or corymbose, female solitary; calyx-tube persistent, campanulate or turbinate; lobes 5, imbricate; petals 5, sessile orbicular; stamens 20–16, inserted at the mouth of the calyx, 1-seriate, filaments short, subulate, free, incurved or decurved; anthers eglandular; disk thinly lining the calyx-tube; carpels 5, free, gibbous; style inserted on the ventral suture, stigma obliquely dilated, 2-fid; ovules numerous, 2-seriate, ascending; follicles 5, tomentose, spreading stellately, gibbous, obtuse, style ventral; seeds many, 2-seriate, ascending, long- and broadly-winged in the upper part, imbricate, testa membranous; endosperm thin; cotyledons flat, convex.

2. **Quillaja** Molina, Saggio Chile, 354 (1782). *Smegmadermos* Ruiz & Pav. (1794). *Smegmaria* Willd. (1806). *Cullay* Molina ex Steud. (1840). *Fontenellea* Q. St. Hil. (1842). *Fontenella* Walp. (1842). 6 spp., South America; type *Q. saponaria* Molina, Chile and Peru. B.H. 1: 614; E.P. 3, 3: 17.

Evergreen trees, glabrous, with sometimes saponaceous bark; leaves scattered, almost entire or serrate, nervose; stipules small, caducous; peduncles axillary and terminal, 3–5-flowered, pedicels 2-bracteolate; flowers polygamo-dioecious, rather large, tomentose, the lateral male, the central fertile; calyx-tube persistent, leathery, small, subcupular; lobes 5, broadly ovate, valvate; petals 5, small, sessile, spathulate; disk thick, fleshy, lining the calyx-tube; lobes 5, thick, depressed, emarginate, adnate to the calyx-lobes; stamens 10, 5 opposite the petals and inserted at the base of the disk, 5 alternate and inserted at apex of the disk-lobes; filaments subulate, free; carpels 5, sessile, tomentose; styles 5, terminal, free; ovules numerous, flattened, subhorizontal, densely 2-seriate; follicles 5, spreading stellately, oblong, obtuse, coherent at the base, coriaceous, style subventral; seeds numerous, compressed, ascending, imbricate, long- and broadly-winged in the upper part; cotyledons convolute.

Bark of *Quillaja brasiliensis* (St. Hil.) Mart., trop. America, contains saponin and is used for cleaning fine textiles. *Q. saponaria* Molina, Soap Bark tree, Chile and Peru, inner bark source of emulsifying agent used for tars; employed instead of soap.

3. **Vauquelinia** Correa ex Humb. & Bonpl., Pl. Aequin. 1: 140, t. 40 (1808). 10 spp., Arizona, Mexico; type *V. corymbosa* Correa ex Humb. & Bonpl., Mexico. B.H. 1: 615; E.P. 3, 3: 18; Rydb., N. Amer. Fl. 22: 260; Schneid., Laubholtzk. 1: 492.

Trees; leaves alternate or rarely opposite, deeply serrate-dentate; stipules minute; corymbs terminal and axillary; flowers bisexual, white; calyx-tube persistent, hemispherical; lobes 5; petals 5, oblong, spreading; stamens 12, inserted at the mouth of the calyx, 1-seriate, filaments subulate, free; anthers small, eglandular; disk lining the calyx-tube; carpels 5, connate into a 5-locular ovary, silky; styles 5, short, with capitate stigmas; ovules 2, ascending from the base; capsule surrounded below the middle by the calyx, 5-angular, woody-coriaceous, at length dividing into five 2-valved, 2-seeded cocci; seeds collateral, erect, expanded into a membranous wing.

Vauquelinia corymbosa Correa, Mexico, W. Texas, bark source of yellow dye used to colour goat skins.

4. **Lindleya** H. B. & K. Nov. Gen. et Sp. 6: 239, t. 562 (1823) (conserved name). *Lindleyella* Rydb. (1908). *Neolindleyella* Fedde (1940). 2 spp., Mexico; type *L. mespilioides* H. B. & K. B.H. 1: 615; E.P. 3, 3: 18; Rydb., N. Amer. Fl. 22: 259 (*Lindleyella*); Schneid., Laubholtzk. 1: 492.

Evergreen trees; leaves scattered; stipules small, subulate; flowers bisexual, axillary towards the apex of the branchlets, solitary, white; pedicels 2-bracteolate; calyx-tube persistent, turbinate, lobes 5, imbricate; petals 5, orbicular, sessile, large; stamens 20–15, inserted at the mouth of the calyx, 1-seriate; filaments unequal, subulate, flattened at the base, free; anthers oblong-lanceolate, recurved, loculi rather unequal; disk lining the calyx-tube; carpels 5, connate into a 5-sided, 5-locular ovary; styles 5, free, terminal, erect, stigmas subclavate, obliquely truncate; ovules 2 in loculus, collateral, attached in the middle of the axis, ascending; capsule woody, oblong, 5-sided, 5-locular, loculicidally 5-valved, loculi narrow, 2-seeded, valves thick, 3-sided, woody; seeds much compressed, semiorbicular, thinly winged; endosperm absent; cotyledons flat, oblong, veiny.

5. **Exochorda** Lindl., Gard. Chron. 1858: 925. 6–7 spp., Cent. and E. Asia; type *E. racemosa* (Lindl.) Rehder (*E. grandiflora* Lindl.), China. B.H. 1: 612; E.P. 3, 3: 18; Rehder, Man. Trees and Shrubs, ed. 2: 345 (1940); Schneid. Laubholtzk. 1: 493.

Shrubs; leaves entire or serrate, membranous; stipules narrow, soon falling off; racemes terminal, elongated, few-flowered; flowers polygamo-dioecious, large, white; calyx bibracteolate at the base, tube turbinate, constricted in the middle; lobes 5 or 4, rounded; stamens 15, short, inserted in threes, 1-seriate, inserted at the mouth of the calyx; disk lining the tube of the calyx, margin large, free, flat or incurved; carpels 5, immersed in the calyx-tube but free from it, connate on the axis; styles short, free, channelled, stigmas dilated; ovules 2, collateral from the apex of the loculus, pendulous; mature carpels 5, bony, compressed, ribbed on the face, at first connate on the axis, at length separated, dehiscing when dry by the inner angles, splitting into 2, 1-seeded; seeds pendulous, compressed, winged.

6. **Lyonothamnus** A. Gray, Proc. Amer. Acad. 20: 291 (1885). 1 sp., *L. floribundus* A. Gray, St. Catalina, Santa Cruz, and San Clemente Isls. (off coast of California). E.P. 3, 3: 60; Britton, N. Amer. Fl. 22: 180; Isbell, Fl. Morph. of *Lyonothamnus*, Bot. Gaz. 91: 426 (1931); Jepson, Fl. Calif. 2: 162, fig. 158 (1936); F. Bolle, Notizbl. Bot. Gart. Berl. 14: 53 (1938).

Tree or shrub, with deciduous bark; leaves opposite, persistent, lanceolate, entire or deeply divided, pinnate and fern-like; stipules small, deciduous; cymes large, terminal, resembling *Sorbus* spp.; bracts minute, persistent; calyx-tube campanulate, bearing 3–1 bracteoles; sepals 5, persistent; disk woolly, slightly 10-lobed; petals 5, white, suborbicular, deciduous; stamens 15, two opposite each petal, one opposite each sepal; anthers oblong, introrse; carpels 2, free, glandular; styles stout, stigma subcapitate; ovules 4 in each carpel, anatropous, pendulous; fruit woody; seeds oblong, apiculate, endosperm thin; cotyledons oblong.

Tribe 2. SPIRAEEAE

Stamens inserted on the margin of the calyx-tube (receptacle); flowers bisexual or rarely polygamo-dioecious; shrubs or undershrubs with simple leaves:
  Filaments free; leaves entire or toothed:
  Carpels opening only by the adaxial suture or also at the top adaxially; shrubs with deciduous leaves:
    Carpels free; seeds without endosperm   7. **Spiraea**
    Carpels united at the base; seeds with endosperm   8. **Sibiraea**
  Carpels opening by both sutures; caespitose tufted undershrubs with persistent leaves:
    Flowers racemose or rarely paniculate; stamens about 20
                                                            9. **Petrophyton**

Flowers solitary, nearly sessile at the ends of short branchlets; stamens
about 10   10. **Kelseya**
Filaments united at the base; fertile stamens about 20; leaves 2 or 3 times
3-cleft; carpels opening from the base by both sutures   11. **Luetkea**
Stamens inserted on the inner side of the calyx-tube; flowers unisexual (dioecious); stamens 30–20; tall herbs with 2–3 times compound leaves
                                                          12. **Aruncus**
Imperfectly known genus in Bolivia with pinnate leaves, bisexual apetalous
flowers and hypogynous disk.   13. **Apopetalum**

7. **Spiraea**[1] Linn., Sp. Pl. 489 (1753); Gen. Pl. ed. 5: 216 (1754). About 120
spp., north temp. hemisphere; type *S. salicifolia* Linn., E. Europe to N. Asia.
B.H. 1: 611; E.P. 3, 3: 14; Rydb., N. Amer. Fl. 22: 245; Schneid., Laubholtzk. 1: 449; Rehder, Trees and Shrubs, ed. 2: 327 (1940).

Shrubs; leaves simple, serrate or incised-serrate; stipules absent; flowers bisexual, very
rarely polygamous, white or rose, arranged in an umbel or contracted corymb or panicle at
the ends of the new shoots; calyx-tube campanulate or shortly turbinate, lobes 5, valvate or
slightly imbricate, the tube lined by the disk; petals 5, imbricate or contorted; stamens 15 to
numerous; anthers didymous; carpels mostly 5 (8–3), free; styles terminal or subterminal,
stigmas capitellate or disciform; ovules several (rarely 3–2), pendulous; follicles bony,
opening by the adaxial suture and at length splitting abaxially at the top; seeds linear or
oblong, testa membranous; endosperm thin or absent.

8. **Sibiraea** Maxim., Act. Hort. Petrop. 6: 213 (1879). 5–6 spp., SE. Europe,
Siberia, China; type *S. laevigata* (Linn.) Maxim., Siberia. E.P. 3, 3: 15;
Schneid., Laubholtzk. 1: 485; Rehder, Trees and Shrubs, ed. 2: 342 (1940).

Shrubs with erect thick branches; leaves involute, deciduous, entire, subvaginate at the
base, closely venose, glaucous; stipules absent; flowers polygamous-dioecious, the sexes
different in appearance, ebracteolate, arranged in terminal racemes often branched at the
base and forming a panicle; calyx-tube campanulate; lobes 5, erect; petals imbricate;
stamens about 25; anthers didymous, in the male overtopping the petals, in the female half
as long as the petals and very small; carpels mostly 5, in the male flowers very minute, in
female flowers straight, connate at the base, when 5 then alternate with the calyx-lobes;
style terminal, stigma capitellate; ovules 6–4, pendulous; follicles cartilaginous, oblong,
opening along the adaxial suture, at length also splitting abaxially at the apex; seeds mostly
2, large, with thin endosperm.

9. **Petrophyton** Rydb., Mem. New York Bot. Gard. 1: 206 (1900). 5 spp.,
W. North America; type *P. caespitosum* (Nutt.) Rydb., W. North America.
Rydb., N. Amer. Fl. 22: 252 (1908).

Dense caespitose undershrubs; leaves oblanceolate or spathulate, entire, coriaceous,
persistent, crowded; stipules absent; inflorescence racemose, rarely branched; calyx-tube
hemispheric, lobes 5, valvate; petals 5, imbricate, white; stamens about 20; disk entire;
carpels 5–3, free; style filiform, terminal, stigma minute, entire; ovules 4–2, pendulous;
follicles coriaceous, opening ad- and abaxially; seeds linear.

10. **Kelseya** Rydb., Mem. New York Bot. Gard. 1: 207 (1900). 1 sp., *K.
uniflora* (S. Wats.) Rydb., Montana and Wyoming, U.S.A. Hitchcock,
Leafl. West Bot. 2: 177 (1939); Rydb., N. Amer. Fl. 22: 254.

[1] Synonyms of **Spiraea**: *Drymopogon* Rupp. (1745). *Alipendula* Neck. (1790). *Awayus* Raf.,
Eleiosina Raf., *Sericotheca* Raf., *Drimopogon* Raf., *Xamedryon* Raf. (1838). *Pentactina*
Nakai (1917).

A low caespitose cushion-like shrublet with very short branchlets; leaves entire, densely crowded, coriaceous, persistent; stipules absent; flowers solitary, subsessile; calyx-tube hemispheric; lobes 5, valvate; petals 5, imbricate; stamens about 10; anthers didymous; disk inconspicuous, entire; carpels 5; styles terminal; ovules 4–3, pendulous; fruit coriaceous, opening by both sutures; seeds elongate-fusiform.

11. **Luetkea** Bong., Mém. Acad. St. Petersb. 6, sér. 2: 130, t. 2 (1833). *Eriogynia* Hook. (1834). *Eriogenia* Steud. (1840). *Lutkea* Steud. (1841). 3 spp., North America; type *L. pectinata* (Pursh) Ktze., NW. America. Maxim., Act. Hort. Petrop. 6: 167; Rydb., N. Amer. Fl. 22: 254; Jepson, Fl. Calif. 2: 168 (1936).

Caespitose undershrubs with a slender creeping trunk; branches erect, leafy; stipules absent; leaves twice tripartite, petiole winged; racemes terminal, several-flowered, elongating in fruit; flowers bisexual, subsessile, ebracteolate, white; calyx-tube turbinate, adnate to the disk; lobes 5, valvate, erect in fruit; petals contorted; fertile stamens about 20; filaments connate at the base; anthers didymous; staminodes about 10, connate; carpels mostly 5 (6–4), free, alternate with the sepals, narrowed into the style; ovules several, pendulous from the apex; follicles opening from the base by both sutures; seeds linear; endosperm absent.

12. **Aruncus** Adans., Fam. 2: 295 (1763). 14 spp., north temp. regions; type *A. sylvester* Kostel, north temp. regions. Maxim., Act. Hort. Petrop. 6: 168; E.P. 3, 3: 16; Rydb., N. Amer. Fl. 22: 255.

Perennial herbs with a thick, many-headed horizontal rhizome; leaves 2–3 times ternately pinnatisect; stipules absent; flowers dioecious, small, white, in large leafless panicles; calyx-tube pelviform, adnate to the disk, lobes 5, valvate; petals spathulate, contorted, those of the male conspicuously larger; stamens 30–20, 3-seriate; anthers didymous; carpels in male flowers minute or obsolete, subastylous; female flowers: anthers minute, empty; carpels mostly 3, at times 5 and alternate with the sepals, free; style terminal, stigma capitellate; ovules few, pendulous; follicles cartilaginous, dehiscing adaxially the whole length and at length abaxially at the apex; seeds few, with thin endosperm.

13. **Apopetalum** Pax, Fedde Repert. 5: 226 (1908). 1 sp., *A. pinnatum* Pax, Bolivia.

Leaves pinnate; flowers bisexual, apetalous, perigynous; sepals 8–6, tomentose inside, valvate; stamens 24–18, outer 16–12 opposite in pairs to the sepals, inner 8–6 alternate with the sepals; anthers introrse, apiculate; disk hypogynous, lobulate; carpels 8–6, free, hispid; style simple, glabrous; ovules several in each carpel.

Tribe 3. NEILLIEAE

Calyx-lobes imbricate; carpels opening by the adaxial suture:
  Leaves alternate, entire or lobed; stipules large and deciduous; ovules several, 2-seriate   14. **Neillia**
  Leaves alternate, incised or pinnatifid; stipules persistent; ovules 2, collateral   15. **Stephanandra**
  Leaves opposite, entire, cordate-ovate, palmately nerved; stipules small and setaceous   16. **Guamatela**
Calyx-lobes valvate; leaves alternate, more or less lobed, usually with stellate hairs; stipules caducous; carpels opening by both sutures
                                                                17. **Physocarpus**

14. **Neillia**[1] D. Don, Prodr. Fl. Nepal. 228 (1825). About 20 spp., Himalayas, E. Asia, Malaya; lectotype *N. thyrsiflora* D. Don, E. Himalayas and Khasia Mts., and W. China, Malaya. B.H. 1: 612; E.P. 3, 3: 14; Schneid., Laubholtzk. 1: 446; Rehder, Trees and Shrubs, ed. 2: 326 (1940).

Branched shrubs or sometimes much reduced and herb-like; leaves simple, variously lobed and dentate; stipules large, deciduous; flowers bisexual, racemose or paniculate, rather large, white; calyx-tube persistent, campanulate or broadly turbinate; lobes 5, imbricate; petals 5, inserted in the throat of the calyx, orbicular; stamens 30–10, inserted with the petals, 1–3-seriate; anthers didymous; disk lining the calyx-tube, margin inconspicuous; carpels 2–1, sessile; style terminal, stigma capitellate; ovules several, 2-seriate; mature carpels coriaceous, opening by the adaxial suture; seeds several, obovoid, testa shining, raphe elevated; endosperm rather plentiful; cotyledons plano-convex.

15. **Stephanandra** Sieb. & Zucc., Abh. Akad. München, 3: 739, t. 4 (1843). 5 spp., Japan, Korea, China; type *S. incisa* (Thunb.) Zabel (*S. flexuosa* Sieb. & Zucc.), Japan. B.H. 1: 612; E.P. 3, 3: 14; Maxim., Act. Hort. Petrop. 6: 216; Schneid., Laubholtzk. 1:448; Rehder, Trees and Shrubs, ed. 2: 327 (1940).

Shrubs, with perulate buds; leaves alternate, cut-up or pinnatifid and incised-serrate; stipules leafy, persistent; flowers bisexual, small, in terminal racemes or panicles; pedicels slender, bracteate at the base; calyx persistent, tube obconic-campanulate, 5-sided; lobes 5, triangular-ovate, slightly imbricate; petals 5, small; stamens 20–10, inserted at the mouth of the calyx, 1-seriate, filaments subulate, dilated at the base; disk thin, pubescent, lining the calyx-tube; carpels sessile, turbinate-globose, villous; style terminal, filiform, stigma capitellate; ovules collateral near the apex of the loculus, pendulous; follicles small, included in the calyx-tube, depressed-globose, coriaceous or crustaceous, ribbed on one side, 1–2-seeded; seeds subglobose, testa crustaceous; endosperm rather plentiful, densely fleshy; cotyledons orbicular.

16. **Guamatela** Donn.-Smith, Bot. Gaz. 57: 420 (1914). 1 sp., *G. tuerckheimii* Donn.-Smith, Guatemala.

Shrub; leaves opposite, simple, cordate-ovate, serrulate, palmately nerved, white-tomentose below; stipules setaceous, free; flowers bisexual, in terminal racemes, red or pink; bracts filiform; calyx-tube short, lobes 5, imbricate; petals 5, inserted at the mouth of the calyx-tube; stamens 10, 1-seriate, opposite the petals and calyx-lobes; filaments free, anthers cordate-ovate, apiculate; carpels 3, free but at first united by the stigmas; style terminal, stigma capitellate; ovules several in each carpel, 2-seriate on the adaxial suture; fruiting carpel 1, membranous, dehiscing by the adaxial suture; seeds numerous, obovoid, without endosperm; testa bony, shining.

17. **Physocarpus** Maxim., Act. Hort. Petrop. 6: 219 (1879) (conserved name). *Opulaster* Medik. (1799). *Icotorus* Raf. (1830). *Epicostorus* Raf. (1832). *Physocarpa* Raf. (1838), not Neck. (1790). About 20 spp., North America and Mexico, E. Asia; type *P. opulifolius* (Linn.) Maxim., E. United States. Schneid., Laubholtzk. 1: 442 (*Opulaster*); Rydb., N. Amer. Fl. 22: 240; Rehder, Trees and Shrubs, ed. 2: 324 (1940); Jepson, Fl. Calif. 2: 163 (1936).

Shrubs, bark deciduous; leaves alternate, more or less lobed, mostly with stellate hairs; stipules caducous; corymbs terminating short one-year-old shoots; flowers white, long-pedicellate; calyx-tube campanulate; lobes 5, persistent, valvate; petals 5, spreading; stamens 40–20, inserted on the disk; filaments slender, filiform; anthers didymous; carpels 5–1, more or less connate at the base; styles filiform, terminal; stigmas capitate or bilobulate; ovules 4–2, upper ones pendulous; follicles membranous-inflated, opening on both sides; seeds 4–2, shining; endosperm copious.

---

[1] Synonyms of **Neillia**: *Adenilema* Blume (1826). *Icotorus* Raf. (1830). *Epicostorus* Raf. (1832). *Adenileima* Reichb. (1841). *Adenilemma* Hassk. (1844).

Tribe 4. GILLENIEAE

Leaves pinnate or subpinnate; shrubs or shrublets:
Stamens 60–20:
    Leaves imparipinnate, leaflets serrate; shrubs   **18. Sorbaria**
    Leaves bipinnatipartite; low shrublets, stellate-pubescent and glandular
                                      19. Chamaebatiaria
Stamens 25–20; leaves pinnate, leaflets entire; indumentum of scattered
    hairs and thick scales.   **20. Spiraeanthus**
Leaves 3-foliolate, subsessile; herbs with perennial rhizomes   **21. Porteranthus**

18. **Sorbaria** A. Braun, Aschers. Fl. Brandenb. 177 (1864) (conserved name). *Basilima* Raf. (1836). *Schizonotus* Lindl. (1830). 15 spp., Afghan. to E. Asia; type *S. sorbifolia* (Linn.) A. Braun. Maxim., Act. Hort. Petrop. 6: 222; Schneid., Laubholtzk. 1: 486; Rydb., N. Amer. Fl. 22: 256 (*Schizonotus*).

Shrubs; leaves imparipinnate, stipulate, leaflets serrate; inflorescence terminal, large, racemose-paniculate; flowers white; calyx-tube hemispherical, adnate to the disk; lobes 5, soon reflexed, imbricate; petals 5, rounded, imbricate; stamens 50–20; carpels 8–4, mostly 5 and opposite to the calyx-lobes, connate in the lower third part; styles terminal or subterminal, stigmas capitellate; ovules several, pendulous; follicles thinly cartilaginous; seeds few.

19. **Chamaebatiaria** Maxim., Act. Hort. Petrop. 6: 225 (1879). 2 spp., SW. United States: type *C. millefolium* (Torr.) Maxim. Rydb., N. Amer. Fl. 22: 257; Schneid., Laubholtzk. 1: 491; Jepson, Fl. Calif. 2: 167, fig. 161 (1936); Rehder, Trees and Shrubs, ed. 2: 345 (1940).

Low shrublets, stellate-pubescent and glandular; leaves alternate, stipulate, bipinnatipartite; panicles terminal; flowers white; calyx-tube turbinate; lobes 5, erect, imbricate; petals 5, rounded; stamens about 60, inserted on the margin of the disk; carpels 5, connate below; styles terminal; stigmas capitate; ovules about 8, pendulous; fruit adaxially dehiscent and abaxially at the apex; seeds few, terete; endosperm fleshy.

20. **Spiraeanthus** Maxim., Act. Hort. Petrop. 6: 226 (1879). 1 sp., *S. schrenchkianus* (Fisch. et Mey.) Maxim., Soongarian desert. E.P. 3, 3: 16.

Much-branched shrub; buds ovoid, densely covered with overlapping scales; indumentum of scattered hairs and thick scales intermixed; leaves fasciculate from lateral buds, pinnate, leaflets numerous, small, entire, thickly coriaceous; panicles terminal, few-flowered; calyx-tube campanulate, 5–4-dentate, hispid within; petals 5–4, somewhat rounded, slowly deciduous; stamens 25–20, subbiseriate, filaments subulate, here and there 2 or 3 connate to the middle; anthers oblong, versatile, introrse; carpels 5–2, opposite the calyx-lobes, adaxially connate by a line at the base, hispid; style terminal, short, stigma capitate; ovules 2, collateral, basal; follicles surrounded by the calyx and longer, 5–2, bony, connate at the base, hispid, adaxially dehiscent beyond the middle, and abaxially at the apex; seeds 2–1, shortly winged at each end; endosperm thin, fleshy.

21. **Porteranthus** Britton, Mem. Torr. Club 4: 115 (1894). *Gillenia* Moench., Meth. Suppl. 286 (1802), not Adans. (1763). 2 spp., North America; type *P. trifoliatus* (Linn.) Britton, E. United States. B.H. 1: 613; E.P. 3, 3: 16; Rydb., N. Amer. Fl. 22: 258.

Herbs with perennial rhizomes, erect, pilose; leaves subsessile, 3-foliolate, leaflets stalked, elongated, incised-serrate; stipules small or large; flowers bisexual, laxly corymbose-paniculate, pale rose or white; calyx persistent, tube 10-nerved, cylindric, subcontracted at the mouth, teeth 5, erect, margins glandular, imbricate; petals 5, linear-lanceolate, elongate;

stamens 20–10, included, irregularly 3-seriate, filaments short, incurved, free, glabrous; anthers rather large; disk thinly lining the tube of the calyx; carpels 5, free or at first joined to the axis, narrowed at each end, villous; styles terminal, filiform, acute; ovules 4 or 2 at the base of the loculus, ascending; follicles 5, coriaceous, linear-oblong, 4–1-seeded; seeds ovoid to terete, testa coriaceous; endosperm fleshy; cotyledons linear-oblong, flat.

Tribe 5. NEURADEAE

Petals large; calyx-lobes without bracteoles between them; calyx in fruit covered with short knobs   **22. Grielum**

Petals large; calyx-lobes without bracteoles; calyx in fruit covered with stout spines   **23. Neuradopsis**

Petals small; calyx-lobes with bracteoles between them, echinate   **24. Neurada**

22. Grielum Linn., Gen. Pl. ed. 5: 578 (1754): 5–6 spp., S. Africa; type *G. tenuifolium* Linn. B.H. 1: 626; E.P. 3, 3: 49.

Annual low herbs, woolly-tomentose; leaves alternate, pinnatifid-lobate or pinnately compound, segments linear; stipules obsolete; flowers axillary, long-pedunculate, solitary, large, yellow; calyx-tube very short, concrescent with the carpels; lobes 5, ebracteolate, at length increasing in size, spreading; petals 5, large, convolute; stamens 10, inserted in the throat of the calyx; anthers oblong; carpels 10–5, verticillate, radiating, concrete amongst themselves and with the tube of the calyx; styles 10–5, filiform, short, stigmas capitate; ovule solitary, pendulous; fruit depressed, orbicular, broadly winged by the calyx-limb, 10–5-locular; carpels radiating horizontally, coriaceous; seeds horizontal, testa membranous; cotyledons plano-convex, auriculate at the base.

23. Neuradopsis Bremek. & Obermeyer, Ann. Transv. Mus. 16: 415 (1935). 3 spp., S. Africa; lectotype *N. austro-africana* (Schinz) Bremek. & Obermeyer.

Annual low herbs, diffusely branched, woolly-tomentose; leaves alternate, pinnately lobed; stipules absent; flowers axillary, solitary, large, yellow; calyx-tube expanded, flat at the base, echinate, concrescent with the carpels in fruit and often persistent around the seedling; lobes 5, oblong, ebracteolate; petals 5, large; stamens 10, 2-seriate; filaments filiform, anthers ovoid; carpels 10, verticillate, radiating, concrete amongst themselves and with the calyx-tube; styles 10, filiform, persistent, stigmas capitate; ovule solitary, pendulous; fruit discoid, with strong spines on the sides, calyx closed; fruiting carpels 10, radiating, coriaceous; seeds without endosperm.

24. Neurada Linn., Sp. Pl. 441 (1753); Gen. Pl. ed. 5: 199 (1754). *Neuras* Adans. (1763). *Figaraea* Viv. (1831). *Tribulastrum* B. Juss. ex Pfeiffer (1874). 1 sp., *N. procumbens* Linn., N. Africa to India. B.H. 1: 625; E.P. 3, 3: 49.

Annual herb, woolly, depressed, branches at length woody; base of stem often surrounded by the persistent calyx; leaves alternate, ovate, lobed; stipules minute or obsolete; flowers axillary, solitary, pedicellate; calyx-tube broadly expanded, flat at the base, at length conical, echinate, concrescent with the carpels; lobes 5, triangular, alternating with 5 subulate bracteoles; petals 5, small; stamens 10, inserted in the contracted throat of the calyx; anthers ovoid; carpels 10, verticillate, concrete among themselves and with the calyx, spreading horizontally; styles subulate from a broad base, persistent, stigma capitellate; ovule solitary, pendulous; fruit persistent around the collum, orbicular, depressed-conical, smooth from a flat broad base, with lateral stout spines on the sides; fruiting carpels 10, horizontally spreading, gaping above, terminated by the spinescent style; seeds curved, without endosperm, testa membranous; cotyledons linear-oblong, auriculate at the base. Used as a source of fodder for camels.

Tribe 6. Osmaronieae

25. **Osmaronia** Greene, Pittonia, 2: 189 (1891). *Nuttallia* Torr. & Gray (1840), not DC. (1821). 1–2 spp., type *O. cerasiformis* (Torr. & Gray) Greene, NW. America. B.H. 1: 611; E.P. 3, 3: 51; Schneid., Laubholtzk. 1: 650; Rydb., N. Amer. Fl. 22: 482; Rehder, Trees and Shrubs, ed. 2: 481 (1940).

Shrubs or small trees; winter buds stalked, covered with few imbricate scales; leaves deciduous, entire; stipules absent; flowers polygamo-dioecious, greenish white, few in short racemes, fragrant, appearing with the leaves; bracts and bracteoles thin, elongated; calyx-tube campanulate, with 5 short triangular lobes; petals 5, shortly clawed; stamens 15, in 2 series, 10 inserted with the petals, 5 below in the middle of the tube; disk lining the tube; carpels 5, free; styles short, articulate towards the base, stigma dilated; ovules 2, collateral, pendulous; fruit of 5–1, oblong, with thin flesh and a smooth stone, 1-seeded; seed pendulous, testa membranous; cotyledons convolute, fleshy.

Tribe 7. Pruneae

Style terminal:
    Carpels in the female flowers 2, in the male flowers 1; leaves with gland-
        tipped teeth; stipules large, glandular-dentate; racemes terminal
                26. **Maddenia**
    Carpel solitary; flowers mostly bisexual:
      Petals showy; drupe bony; calyx 5-lobed:
        Flowers (more than 12) arranged in elongated racemes:
          Racemes terminating the young leafy shoots; leaves mostly deciduous
              27. **Padus**
          Racemes in the axils of the leaves or fallen leaves of the previous year's
            shoot; leaves sometimes evergreen   28. **Laurocerasus**
        Flowers solitary or in umbel-like clusters, or rarely in very short few-
          flowered racemes separate from the leaves and bracts then usually
          conspicuous   29. **Prunus**
      Petals very small or absent; drupe coriaceous; calyx 10–5-toothed
              30. **Pygeum**
Style lateral, especially in fruit; carpel 1; shrubs with spiny branchlets;
      branchlets with transversely septate pith; stipules very small, deciduous:
    Flowers arranged in racemes; branchlets of one kind; buds perulate; leaves
      exstipulate; stamens numerous; anther-loculi separate   31. **Prinsepia**
    Flowers fasciculate with the leaves on very short arrested branchlets; stipules
      present, persistent; stamens 10; anther-loculi contiguous
              32. **Plagiospermum**

26. **Maddenia** Hook. f. & Thoms., Kew Journ. Bot. 6: 381, t. 12 (1854). 5 spp., Himalayas, China; type *M. himalaica* Hook. f. & Thoms., E. Himalayas. B.H. 1: 610; E.P. 3, 3: 51.

Small trees; leaves alternate, ciliate-denticulate, teeth glandular; stipules large, glandular-dentate; flowers polygamo-dioecious, fairly large, white, arranged in short terminal dense-flowered racemes; calyx deciduous, tube broadly campanulate, 10-fid, lobes short, some elongated and petaloid; petals mixed with the calyx-lobes, linear; stamens 30–20, more or less in 2 series, inserted at the mouth of the calyx; carpels in the male flower solitary, sessile, with a slender style and capitate stigma, in the female flowers 2, oblong, truncate, the stigma sessile and oblique; ovules 2, collateral, pendulous; drupes 2, oblong, subcompressed, purple, fleshy; stone ovoid, acute, 3-keeled on one side, 1-seeded, seed pendulous, testa membranous; cotyledons plano-convex.

27. **Padus**[1] Borckh., Moench Meth. 671 (1794), partly; Roem. Archiv. 1, 2: 38 (partly) (1797). About 27 spp.,[1] north temp. zone; type *P. racemosa* (Lam.) C. K. Schneid. (*Prunus padus* Linn.), Europe to N. Africa, N. Asia and Japan, Virginia, New Mexico. Schneid., Laubholtzk. 1: 637; Wooton & Standley, New Mexican spp. of *Padus*, Contrib. Un. St. Nat. Herb. 16: 132 (1913); Emberger, *Prunus padus* in the Atlas Mts., Bull. Soc. Bot. Fr. 77: 29 (1930).

Small much-branched trees; leaves deciduous, rarely evergreen, toothed, 2-glandular at the base, rarely not glandular; racemes leafy at the base, pendulous at the end of annual shoots; flowers white, small; calyx 5-partite, segments rounded, spreading; petals 5, denticulate; stamens numerous; ovary inferior; style 1; fruit a 1-seeded drupe, very bitter.

28. **Laurocerasus**[2] M. Roem., Syn. Monogr. 3: 5, 89 (1847). About 26 spp., Atlantic Isls., S. Europe to China and Japan, Malaya, New Guinea; type *L. officinalis* M. Roem. (*Prunus laurocerasus* Linn.), SE. Europe and Asia Minor. Schneid., Laubholtzk. 1: 645; Rehder, Trees and Shrubs, ed. 2: 452 (in *Prunus*) (1940).

Trees or shrubs; leaves evergreen or deciduous, serrate, dentate, or entire; flowers bisexual, arranged in leafless racemes in the axils of the leaves or in the axils of fallen leaves of the previous season's shoots; bracts small; calyx 5-lobed, lobes inflexed; petals showy, white; stamens about 20, in two whorls, the inner whorl shorter; carpel 1; style terminal, stigma disk-like; ovules 2, collateral; fruit bony, conical-ovoid, dark purple, stone hard and smooth, indehiscent 1-seeded; seed pendulous.

29. **Prunus**[3] Linn., Sp. Pl. 473 (1753); Gen. Pl. ed. 5: 213 (1754). Over 100 spp., north temp. zone; type *P. domestica* Linn. B.H. 1: 609; E.P. 3, 3: 51; Schneid., Laubholtzk. 1: 589; Rehder, Trees and Shrubs, ed. 2: 452 (1940);

[1] To **Padus** belong the following, in addition to the type species: *P. acrophylla* C. K. Schneid.; *P. alabamensis* (Mohr) Small; *P. australis* Beadle ex Small; *P. brachypoda* C. K. Schneid.; *P. calophylla* Wooton & Standl.; *P. capollin* (DC.) C. K. Schneid.; *P. capuli* (Cav. ex Spreng.) Moldenke; *P. cornuta* (Steud.) Carr.; *P. cuthbertii* Small; *P. eximia* Small; *P. grayana* (Maxim.) C. K. Schneid.; *P. melanocarpa* Shafer; *P. mescaleria* Wooton & Standl.; *P. napaulensis* (Ser.) C. K. Schneid.; *P. obtusata* (Koehne); *P. pubigera* (Koehne); *P. punicea* Wooton & Standl.; *P. rufomicans* (Koehne); *P. rufula* Wooton & Standl.; *P. salicifolia* (Kunth) C. K. Schneid.; *P. sericea* (Koehne); *P. serotina* (Ehrh.) Agardh; *P. ssiori* (Schmidt) C. K. Schneid.; *P. valida* Wooton & Standl.; *P. velutina* Batalin; *P. virens* Wooton & Standl.; *P. virginiana* (Linn.) Roem.; *P. wilsonii* (Koehne) C. K. Schneid.

[2] To **Laurocerasus** belong the following, in addition to the type species: *L. acuminata* (Wall.) Roem.; *L. annularis* (Koehne) Kovalev; *L. brasiliensis* (Cham. & Schl.) Roem., *L. brittoniana* (Rusby) C. K. Schneid., *L. buergeriana* (Miq.) C. K. Schneid.; *L. caroliniana* (Mill.) Roem.; *L. cortapico* (Kerber ex Koehne) Kovalev; *L. erythroxylon* (Koehne) Kovalev; *L. guanaiensis* (Rusby) C. K. Schneid.; *L. ilicifolia* (Nutt.) Roem.; *L. javanica* (Miq.) C. K. Schneid.; *L. limbata* Cardot.; *L. lusitanica* (Linn.) Roem.; *L. maackii* (Rupr.) C. K. Schneid.; *L. macrophylla* (Sieb. & Zucc.) C. K. Schneid.; *L. martabanica* (Wall.) C. K. Schneid.; *L. meyeri* (Rehd.); *L. microbotrys* (Koehne) Kovalev; *L. occidentalis* (Swartz) Roem.; *L. perulata* (Koehne); *L. phaeosticta* (Hance) C. K. Schneid.; *L. reflexa* (Gardn.) Roem.; *L. samydoides* (Schlecht.) Roem.; *L. sphaerocarpa* (Swartz) Roem.; *L. spinulosa* (Sieb. & Zucc.) C. K. Schneid.; *L. stellipila* (Koehne); *L. tuberculata* (Koehne) Kovalev; *L. venosa* (Koehne).

[3] Synonyms of **Prunus**: *Amygdalus* Linn. (1753). *Armeniaca* Juss. (1789). *Cerasus* Adans. (1789). *Prunophora* Neck. (1790). *Microcerasus* M. Roem. (1847). *Emplectocladus* Torr. (1854). *Amygdalopsis* Carr. (1862). *Aflatunia* Vassilcz (1955).

Mason, North America spp. of *Prunus*, Bull. U.S. Dept. Agr. 179: 1 (1915); Meyer, Kulturgeschichte und System. Beiträge zur Gattung *Prunus*, Fedde Repert. Beih. 22: 1 (1923).

Trees or shrubs, sometimes spiny; leaves deciduous, alternate, simple, often serrulate, convolute or conduplicate in bud; flowers solitary or fasciculate-corymbose or in very short racemes with conspicuous bracts, white, rose, or purple, sometimes precocious; calyx deciduous; tube obconic, urceolate or tubular; lobes 5, imbricate; petals 5, inserted at the mouth of the calyx; stamens 20–15, inserted with the petals; filaments filiform, free; carpel 1; style terminal; stigma peltate or truncate; ovules 2, collateral; drupe fleshy, stone hard and smooth, indehiscent, 1-seeded; seed pendulous, testa membranous, endosperm thin or absent; cotyledons flat.

To bring our classification approximately into line with the treatment accorded to *Pyrus*, now usually divided into several genera, I have done the same for *Prunus*, but less drastically. Even the gardener-botanist, George Nicholson, author of the *Gardener's Dictionary*, was dissatisfied with *Prunus* in Bentham & Hooker's *Genera Plantarum*. Nicholson remarked: 'The genus as arranged by Bentham & Hooker includes *Amygdalopsis*, *Amygdalus*, *Armeniaca*, *Ceraseidos*, *Cerasus*, *Laurocerasus*, and *Persica*, making a total of about 80 species; but for horticultural purposes it is, in most cases, deemed proper to treat these genera separately in this work.' Nicholson, therefore, treated as separate genera *Amygdalus*, *Armeniaca*, *Cerasus*, and *Persica*, besides *Prunus* (*sensu stricto*). In *Cerasus* he included also *Padus* and *Laurocerasus*. The whole group needs intensive monographic study.

30. **Pygeum**[1] Gaertn., Fruct. 1: 218, t. 46 (1788). About 110 spp., trop. and S. Africa, S. Asia, Ceylon, Malay Archip., New Guinea; type *P. wightianum* Bl. (*P. ceylanicum* Gaertn.), Ceylon. B.H. 1: 610; E.P. 3, 3: 51; Koehne, Die Gattung *Pygeum*, Engl. Bot. Jahrb. 51: 177 (1913); Graham, Fl. Trop. East Afr. *Rosaceae*, 45, fig. 6 (1960).

Trees or shrubs; leaves alternate, persistent, entire or very rarely serrulate, blade often with an impressed gland on each side at the base; stipules small, deciduous or rarely persistent; racemes axillary and lateral, solitary or fasciculate; flowers sometimes polygamodioecious; calyx deciduous; tube obconic or cyathiform, with a persistent annular base, teeth 12–10–5, small; petals as many as the calyx-teeth or absent, inserted at the mouth of the calyx, small, often deformed or mixed with the calyx-lobes; stamens 20–12, inserted with the petals; anthers didymous; ovary sessile, narrowed into the style, stigma capitate; ovules 2, pendulous, collateral; fruit dry, coriaceous or drupaceous, often transversely oblong, 1-seeded; seed transversely oblong, glabrous or silky; cotyledons very thick.

31. **Prinsepia** Royle, Ill. Pl. Himal. 206, t. 38, fig. 1 (1834). *Cycnia* Lindl. (1847). 1 sp., *P. utilis* Royle, Himalayas, China. B.H. 1: 611; E.P. 3, 3: 55.

Shrubs with spiny branchlets and septate pith; leaves deciduous, lanceolate to elliptic, serrulate; stipules minute, deciduous; racemes axillary, short, few-flowered; calyx-tube persistent, cyathiform; lobes 5, unequal, rounded, imbricate; petals 5, inserted in the throat of the calyx, rounded, shortly clawed; stamens numerous, inserted with the petals, in several series, filaments very short; anther-loculi separate, often unequal; carpel 1, sessile, style subterminal, stigma capitate; ovules 2, collateral, pendulous; drupe oblique, purple, style basal, supported on the flattened calyx, oblong-cylindric, pulpy; stone coriaceous, 1-seeded; seed oblong-cylindric, testa membranous; cotyledons oily, plano-convex.

32. **Plagiospermum** Oliv., Hook. Ic. Pl. t. 1526 (1886). 2 spp., type *P. sinense* Oliv., N. China. *P. uniflorum* (Batal.) Stapf, NW. China, Mongolia. Stapf, Bot. Mag. t. 8711 (1917); E.P.N. 186; Schneid., Laubholtzk. 1: 651.

Spiny shrubs; branchlets long and short; leaves crowded on the short branchlets; stipules minute; spines axillary, short; flowers fasciculate or subsolitary, pedicellate; calyxtube turbinate, lobes 5, ovate-deltoid; petals 5, rounded; stamens 10; anther-loculi contiguous; disk rather fleshy; carpel 1, free, 1-locular; ovules 2, collateral, spreading from a suprabasal placenta; style lateral, stigma truncate; drupe pruinose.

---

[1] Synonyms of **Pygeum**; *Polydontia* Bl. (1826). *Polystorthia* Bl. (1828). *Polyodontia* Meisn. (1837). *Germaria* C. Presl (1850). *Digaster* Miq. (1860).

Tribe 8. CHRYSOBALANEAE

Anthers large and elongated-linear, basifixed; ovary at the base of the calyx-tube; petals absent; stamens 10   33. **Stylobasium**
Anthers small, short, medifixed, didymous or suborbicular:
  Ovary inserted at the base of the calyx-tube:
    Petals present; flowers in short cymes; stamens 15 or more:
      Trees and shrubs; inflorescence axillary; petals clawed   34. **Chrysobalanus**
      Shrublets with underground rootstock; inflorescence terminal; petals not clawed   35. **Geobalanus**
    Petals present, minute, or absent; flowers in panicles; stamens 10–3   36. **Licania**
    Petals absent; flowers polygamous, in terminal panicles; stamens 20   37. **Afrolicania**
    Petals present or absent; flowers bisexual; stamens 8 or more   38. **Moquilea**
    Petals 5; stamens 15; flowers in racemes   39. **Grangeria**
  Ovary inserted unilaterally at the mouth or side of the calyx-tube:
    Perfect stamens 10 or more:
      Stamens free from one another or united only at the base:
        Carpels completely or incompletely 2-locular; drupe mostly 2-locular   40. **Parinari**
        Carpels 1-locular:
          Stamens arranged in a complete ring; Malay Archipelago 41. **Angelesia**
          Stamens in a ring or unilateral; tropical America   42. **Couepia**
      Stamens connate into a unilateral ligulate sheath; filaments circinate in bud   43. **Acioa**
    Perfect stamens usually less than 10; filaments circinate in bud:
      Calyx-tube elongated; perfect stamens 10–3   44. **Hirtella**
      Calyx-tube short; perfect stamens 2   45. **Parastemon**

33. **Stylobasium** Desf., Mém. Mus. Paris, 5: 37, t. 2 (1819). *Macrostigma* Hook. (1842). 2 spp., SW. and N. Australia; type *S. spathulatum* Desf. B.H. 1: 609; E.P. 3, 3: 57.

Undershrubs; leaves scattered, linear or narrowly obcuneate, nerveless, emarginate; stipules small, subulate or absent; flowers axillary, solitary or paniculate, bracteolate; calyx turbinate-campanulate, 5-lobed, lobes imbricate; petals absent; disk none; stamens 10, hypogynous, filaments persistent; anthers large, linear, basifixed, exserted; ovary sessile at the base of the calyx, 1-locular; style basal, curved, stigma large, peltate, coarsely glandular; ovules 2, basal; fruit globose, supported by the enlarged calyx, coriaceous or bony, 1-seeded; seed erect, subglobose, testa membranous; endosperm very scanty; embryo transversely induplicate.

34. **Chrysobalanus** Linn., Sp. Pl. 513 (1753); Gen. Pl. ed. 5: 229 (1754). *Icaco* Adans. (1763). About 15 spp., trop. Africa, America; type *C. icaco* Linn., trop. and subtrop. America. B.H. 1: 606; E.P. 3, 3: 57.

Small trees or shrubs; leaves alternate, coriaceous; stipules small, deciduous; cymes axillary, silky-pubescent, bracteate; flowers white, smallish; calyx turbinate-campanulate, lobes 5, subequal, imbricate; petals 5, inserted in the throat of the calyx, clawed, deciduous; stamens 15 or more, 1-seriate, inserted with the petals, all bearing anthers or sometimes some without anthers; filaments free or nearly so; anthers didymous; carpel sessile at the base of the calyx, 1-locular; style basal, filiform; ovules 2; drupe often edible, subpulpy, at length dry, indehiscent, with a fluted stone, 1-seeded; seed suberect; cotyledons thick and fleshy.

35. **Geobalanus** Small, Fl. Miami 80 (1913). 2 spp., Florida; type *G. oblongifolius* (Michx.) Small.

Shrublets from underground stems; leaves oblong to oblanceolate; indumentum when present of stellate hairs; cymes terminal, lax-flowered; bracts small, triangular; calyx 5-lobed, lobes imbricate; petals not clawed; filaments markedly united; carpel 1, sessile at the base of the calyx; style basal; stone of the fruit terete, not pointed at the base.

36. **Licania** Aubl., Hist. Pl. Guian. Franç. 1: 119, t. 45 (1775). *Dahuronia* Scop. (1777). *Hedycrea* Schreb. (1789). *Lincania* G. Don (1832). About 140 spp., trop. America, New Caledonia; type *L. incana* Aubl., Guianas, Brazil. B.H. 1: 606; E.P. 3, 3: 58.

Trees or shrubs; leaves alternate, persistent; petiole sometimes 2-glandular at the apex; stipules subulate or lanceolate, deciduous or persistent, free or connate; flowers small, paniculate or spicate, bracteolate; calyx-tube globose to hemispheric; lobes 5, small, imbricate or subvalvate; petals 5, minute or absent; stamens 10–3, rarely more, inserted in the throat of the calyx, scattered to one side or arranged in a ring; filaments often unequal, free and separated or connate into a membranous ring; anthers small; ovary sunk in the base of the calyx, 1-locular; style basal, short or subulate, enclosed by the calyx; ovules 2, basal; fruit 1-seeded, coriaceous to woody, terete and obovoid-clavate or pear-shaped or globose, sometimes coarsely ridged, often villous inside; seed erect, testa membranous; cotyledons thick and fleshy.

37. **Afrolicania** Mildbr., Notizbl. Bot. Gart. Berlin 7: 483 (1921). 1 sp., *A. elaeosperma* Mildbr., W. trop. Africa (Sierra Leone to Gabon).

Tree; leaves alternate, entire, stipulate; flowers small, in terminal panicles, polygamous; calyx-tube widely turbinate; sepals 5, imbricate or subvalvate, persistent; petals absent; stamens small, about 20, inserted on the margin of the calyx-tube, 5 alternate with the sepals, 15 in three opposite the sepals; anthers small, semiglobose; ovary sessile at the base of the calyx-tube, 1-locular; ovules 2, basal; style basifixed, shortly filiform; in male flowers ovary absent or reduced to a rudimentary style; fruit dry, ovoid, 1-seeded; seed erect, testa membranous; cotyledons thick and fleshy, oily, very concave.

38. **Moquilea** Aubl., Pl. Guian. 1: 521, t. 208 (1775). About 35 spp., trop. America; type *M. guianensis* Aubl., Guianas. B.H. 1: 606; E.P. 3, 3: 58 (in *Licania*).

Trees or shrubs; leaves alternate, persistent, petiole often 2-glandular at the apex; stipules 2, subulate, deciduous or rarely persistent; flowers paniculate, spicate, racemose or fasciculate, small; calyx-tube campanulate to hemispheric, lobes 5–4, imbricate, spreading, throat villous or woolly; petals 5 or 4, orbicular, or absent; stamens 10 or more, rarely fewer, inserted in the throat of the calyx, filaments filiform and long-exserted, often twisted; anthers small, didymous; ovary globose, at the base of the calyx-tube, 1-locular; style basal, slender, long-exserted, stigma undivided; ovules 2, basal; fruit various, globose or terete, 1-seeded, coriaceous, sometimes large and lobulate.

39. **Grangeria** Comm. ex Jussieu, Gen. 340 (1789). 3 spp., Mascarenes; type *G. borbonica* Lam., Mauritius. B.H. 1: 607; E.P. 3, 3: 58.

Small trees; leaves alternate, small; stipules small, caducous; racemes axillary and terminal; pedicels bracteolate; flowers small; calyx-tube shortly turbinate, gibbous, lobes 5, imbricate; petals 5, inserted in the throat of the calyx; stamens up to 15, inserted with the petals, 1-seriate in a ring; filaments free, all bearing short didymous anthers; ovary inserted to one side at the base of the calyx-tube, 1-locular; style basal, short; drupe obovoid, 3-sided, rather dry, shell bony, 1-seeded, woolly inside; seed erect, testa membranous.

40. **Parinari**[1] Aubl., Hist. Pl. Guian. Franç. 1: 514 (1775). About 130 spp., tropics, subtropics, Australia; lectotype *P. campestris* Aubl., Guianas, Brazil. B.H. 1: 607; E.P. 3, 3: 60; van Steenis, Bull. Bot. Jard. Buitenz. 17: 461 (1948); Graham, Fl. Trop. East Afr. *Rosaceae*, 48, fig. 7 (1960).

Trees, often tall; leaves alternate, persistent, sometimes 2-glandular at the base below; stipules subulate to lanceolate, sometimes large; flowers racemose-corymbose or paniculate, 2-bracteolate, white or rose; calyx-tube short or elongated, lobes 5, imbricate; petals 5–4, inserted in the calyx-throat, sessile or clawed, deciduous; stamens 10 or more, inserted with the petals, shortly connate at the base into a ring or more highly united and unilateral, usually all bearing short anthers; ovary adnate to one side of the throat of the calyx, often exserted, 2–1-locular, the septum sometimes imperfect; style basal, filiform, often hairy; stigma truncate; ovule 2–1, erect in each loculus; drupe sometimes edible, ovoid or spherical, shell fibrous or pulpy, stone bony and often villous or woolly inside; seed erect.

41. **Angelesia** Korth., Nederl. Kruidk. Arch. 3: 384 (1855). *Diemenia* Korth. (1855). *Trichocarya* Miq. (1855). *Coccomelia* Ridl. (1920). 3 spp., Malay Penins. and Archip., New Guinea; type *A. splendens* Korth., Malay Archip. B.H. 1: 607; E.P. 3, 3: 60; van Steenis, Bull. Jard. Bot. Buitenz. ser. 3, 13, pt. 2: 284 (1934).

Trees or shrubs; leaves strongly nerved; panicle raceme-like; flowers with short bracteate articulated pedicels; calyx-tube cylindric, angular, limb subcupular, lobes 5; petals ovate, shorter than the calyx-lobes; stamens 25, arranged in a ring, filaments connate at the base; anthers globose; ovary inserted at the apex of the calyx-tube, 1-locular; style basal, short; ovule solitary; drupe obovoid-globose, stone densely hairy inside; seed erect, obovoid.

42. **Couepia** Aubl., Hist. Pl. Guian. Franç. 1: 519, t. 221 (1775). *Dulacia* Neck. (1790). *Cuepia* J. F. Gmel. (1791). About 60 spp., South America; type *C. guianensis* Aubl., Guianas. B.H. 1: 608; E.P. 3, 3: 59.

Trees or shrubs; leaves alternate, petiole sometimes 2-glandular towards the apex; stipules often setaceous and deciduous; racemes or panicles axillary and terminal, bracteate; bracts large or small, persistent or caducous; calyx-tube elongated, often gibbous at the base, lobes 5, imbricate, hispid inside with deflexed hairs; petals 5, very rarely absent, a little longer than the calyx; stamens 15 or more, inserted at the mouth of the calyx, arranged in a complete or incomplete ring, 1- or more-seriate, the filaments more or less monadelphous, incurved and flexuous; anthers small; ovary adnate to the throat of the calyx, villous, 1-locular; style elongated, often villous, stigma very small; ovules 2, collateral, basal; drupe often edible, ovate to reniform, dry or fleshy; stone woody, 1-seeded.

43. **Acioa** Aubl., Hist. Pl. Guian. Franç. 2: 698, t. 280 (1775). *Acia* Schreb. (1791). *Dactyladenia* Welw. (1859). *Griffonia* Hook. f. (1856). About 35 spp., trop. Africa, trop. America; type *A. guianensis* Aubl., Guiana. B.H. 1, 608; E.P. 3, 3: 60.

Small trees, erect or scandent shrubs; leaves alternate; stipules subulate, deciduous; racemes simple or branched, axillary and terminal, many-flowered; flowers clothed with

---

[1] Synonyms of **Parinari**: *Parinarium* Juss. (1789) et Auct.; *Ferolia* Aubl. (1775). *Dugortia* Scop. (1777). *Neou* Adans. (1789). *Petrocarya* Schreb. (1789). *Thelira* Thou (1806). *Thelyra* DC. (1825). *Balantium* Desv. (1825). *Maranthes* Blume (1825). *Exitelia* Blume (1828). *Maranthus* Reichb. (1828). *Mampata* Adans. (1841). *Cyclandrophora* Hassk. (1842). *Grymania* C. Presl (1849). *Lepidocarpa* Korth. (1855). *Ledpiocarya* Korth. (1855). *Entosiphon* Bedd. (1864). *Exiteles* Miers (1879).

reflexed hairs inside; calyx-tube narrow, lobes 5, unequal, imbricate; petals 5, inserted at the mouth of the calyx, scarcely longer than the calyx, deciduous; disk expanded into a dentate corona, produced unilaterally into a ligule; stamens 10 or more, unilateral, 1-seriate, the filaments partially connate into a narrow much elongated ligule circinately coiled in bud; anthers small, didymous; ovary inserted on one side of the mouth of the calyx, woolly at the apex, 1-locular; style basal, capillary, very long, glabrous, dilated at the base, stigma minute; ovules 2, ascending; fruit dry, oblong or pear-shaped, 1-seeded, hispid within; seed erect, testa hairy.

44. Hirtella Linn.,[1] Sp. Pl. 34 (1753); Gen. Pl. ed. 5: 20 (1754). About 100 spp., Cent. and South America, trop. Africa, Madag.; type *H. americana* Linn., trop. America. B.H. 1: 608; E.P. 3, 3: 59; Hauman, Bull. Jard. Bot. Brux. 21: 167 (1951); Graham, Fl. Trop. East Afr. *Rosaceae*, 54 (1960).

Trees or shrubs; leaves alternate; stipules subulate or lanceolate, caducous; racemes simple or branched, axillary and terminal; bracts sometimes with sessile or stipitate glands; flowers usually small, white, rose, or blue, some sterile; calyx-tube often gibbous at the base, lobes 5, subequal, imbricate or very rarely valvate; petals 5, obovate, inserted at the mouth of the calyx, deciduous; stamens 8-3 (rarely more), unilateral, filaments connate at the base into a ring shorter on one side and circinate in bud; anthers small; ovary unilaterally inserted at the mouth of the calyx, 1-locular; style filiform, basal, elongated, stigma minute; ovules 2, ascending; berry or drupe obovoid, dry, 1-seeded; seed erect, testa membranous.

45. Parastemon A. DC., Ann. Sc. Nat. sér. 2, 18: 208 (1842). 2 spp., Burma, Malaya, New Guinea; type *P. urophyllus* A. DC., Burma, Malaya, New Guinea. B.H. 1: 607; E.P. 3, 3: 60.

Shrub; leaves alternate, persistent; racemes axillary and terminal, slender, many-flowered; flowers polygamous-dioecious, very small; pedicels minutely bracteate at the base; calyx-tube short, campanulate, lobes 5, imbricate; petals 5, imbricate, inserted in the throat of the calyx-tube, deciduous; perfect stamens 2, unilateral, inserted on an annulus crowning the throat of the calyx, filaments circinate in bud; anthers short; ovary minute, hirsute, inserted at one side of the throat of the calyx, 1-locular; style basal; fruit oblong, 1-locular, 1-seeded; seed erect, testa pubescent.

Tribe 9. ULMARIEAE

46. Filipendula Adans., Fam. 2: 295 (1763). *Ulmaria* Hill (1786). *Thecanisia* Raf. (1837). 8 spp., temp. northern hemisphere; type *F. vulgaris* Moench, Europe, N. Asia. Maxim., Act. Hort. Petrop. 6: 245 (1879); Rydb., N. Amer. Fl. 22: 266.

Perennial herbs with short oblique rhizomes clothed with fibres and here and there thickened into tubers; leaves pinnatisect or palmately lobed; rhachis appendaged; stipules large, semicordate; flowers bisexual or subpolygamous, white or red, paniculate, the central peduncle shortened and flowering first; calyx 5-partite, at length reflexed; petals 5, clawed, imbricate; disk obsolete; stamens 40-20; anthers didymous; carpels 15-5, 2-ovulate, stigma capitate; fruits free, compressed, crowned by the base of the style, 1-seeded, indehiscent; seeds pendulous, terete, with very little endosperm.

---

[1] Synonyms of **Hirtella** : *Causea* Scop. (1777). *Cosmibuena* Ruiz & Pav. (1794). *Brya* Vell. (1825). *Hirtellia* Dumort. (1829). *Sphenista* Raf. (1838). *Zamzela* Raf. (1838). *Magnistipula* Engl. (1905).*

* *Magnistipula* was retained as a separate genus by Graham in the *Flora of Tropical East Africa*; the relative length of the stamens appears to be of little generic value; also the presence or absence of glands on the calyx-lobes.

Tribe 10. RUBIEAE

47. **Rubus**[1] Linn., Sp. Pl. 492 (1753); Gen. Pl. ed. 5: 218 (1754). Over 200 spp., nearly world-wide; type *R. caesius* Linn., Europe to N. Asia. B.H. 1: 616; E.P. 3, 3: 28; Focke, *Species Ruborum* Monogr. generis *Rubi* Prodromus, Bibl. Bot. Heft 72 (1910); L. H. Bailey, Monogr. of *Rubus* in North America, Gentes Herb. 5: 1–932 (1941–5): Gustafsson, Genesis of Eur. Blackberry flora, Lunds Univ. Arssk. N.F. Avd. 2: 39, 6: 1–199 (1943).

Shrubs often straggling and prickly or creeping or dwarf herbs, glabrous, tomentose or pubescent, rarely woolly or glandular; leaves scattered, alternate, simple, lobed, 3–5-foliolate or imparipinnate; stipules adnate to the petiole; flowers in terminal and axillary panicles or corymbs, rarely solitary, white or rose; calyx expanded, with a short tube, ebracteolate; lobes 5, persistent; petals 5; stamens numerous, rarely few, inserted at the mouth of the calyx, filaments filiform; anthers didymous; disk lining the calyx-tube; carpels numerous, rarely few, inserted on the convex receptacle; style subterminal, filiform, stigmas simple or capitellate; ovules 2 in each carpel, collateral, pendulous; achenes drupaceous, rarely dry, crowded on the conical dry or spongy receptacle, 1-seeded; seed pendulous, testa membranous; cotyledons plano-convex.

Tribe 11. HOLODISCEAE

48. **Holodiscus** Maxim., Act. Hort. Petrop. 6: 253 (1879) (conserved name). *Sericotheca* Raf. (1838). *Schizonotus* Raf. (1838), not Lindl. (1830). About 12 spp., British Columbia (N. Amer.) to Colombia (S. Amer.); type *H. discolor* (Pursh) Maxim., British Columbia to California and Montana. E.P. 3, 3: 18; Rehder, Trees and Shrubs, ed. 2: 346 (1940); Rydb., N. Amer. Fl. 22: 261 (*Sericotheca*); Schneid., Laubholtzk. 1: 495; Jephson, Fl. Calif. 2: 166, fig. 160 (1936); Ley, Bull. Torr. Cl. 70: 275 (1943).

Shrubs; leaves subpinnatilobed, parallel-nerved; stipules absent; panicles or racemes terminal; flowers very numerous, small; calyx deeply 5-lobed; lobes valvate; disk totally adnate to the calyx-tube; petals 5, rounded; stamens about 20, 2-seriate; anthers didymous; carpels 5, alternate with the calyx-lobes; ovules 2, collateral, pendulous; achenes enclosed by the calyx, shortly stipitate, styles coronate at the base, woolly, caducous, 1-seeded; seed pendulous, with thin endosperm.

Tribe 12. RHODOTYPEAE

49. **Rhodotypos** Sieb. & Zucc., Fl. Jap. 1: 187, t. 99 (1835). *Rhodotypus* Endl. (1842). 1 sp., *R. scandens* (Thunb.) Makino (*R. kerrioides* Sieb. & Zucc.), Japan and China. B.H. 1: 613; E.P. 3, 3: 28; Schneid., Laubholtzk. 1: 501; Rehder, Trees and Shrubs, ed. 2: 406 (1940).

Shrub with perulate buds; leaves opposite, simple, ovate, sharply serrate; stipules free, linear; flowers bisexual, solitary, terminal; calyx-tube spreading, persistent, with 4 bracteoles at the base; lobes 4, large, leafy, serrate, imbricate; petals 4, large, obovate-orbicular, shortly clawed; disk thick, large, crowning the calyx-tube, constricted at the top into a 4-toothed urn; stamens numerous, several-seriate, filaments filiform, free; anthers broadly didymous; carpels 4, enclosed in the top of the disk; styles filiform, exserted, stigma capitate; ovules 2, pendulous; drupes 4–1, small, epicarp dry, shining 1-seeded; seed pendulous, obovoid; cotyledons plano-convex, 3-nerved inside.

---

[1] Synonyms of **Rubus**: *Dalibarda* Linn. (1753). *Chamaemorus* Ehrh. (1789). *Cylactis* Raf. (1819). *Cylastis* Raf. (1838). *Ametron, Ampomele, Cumbata, Dyctisperma, Manteia, Selnoration* all Raf. (1838). *Batidaea, Cardiobatus, Comarobatia, Melanobatus, Parmena, Psychrobatia* all Greene (1906).

Tribe 13. KERRIEAE

Carpels 8–5; petals present; flowers large and solitary   50. **Kerria**
Carpels 4–2; petals absent; flowers subcorymbose   51. **Neviusia**

50. **Kerria** DC., Trans. Linn. Soc. 12: 156 (1817). *Keria* Spreng. (1818). 1 sp., *K. japonica* DC., China and Japan. B.H. 1: 613; E.P. 3, 3: 28; Schneid., Laubholtzk. 1: 501.

Shrub, with slender virgate branchlets arising from scaly buds; leaves simple, long-acuminate, coarsely and unequally serrate; stipules linear-subulate; flowers large, solitary, yellow, terminal; calyx-tube short, persistent; lobes large, spreading, serrulate, imbricate; petals 5, large, oblong or rounded, shortly clawed; stamens numerous in several series, filaments filiform, free, flexuous; disk lining the calyx-tube, pilose; carpels 8–5, included in the calyx-tube, free; glabrous; styles filiform, erect, truncate at the apex; ovule 1, laterally attached to the middle of the suture; achenes small, dry.

51. **Neviusia** A. Gray, Mem. Amer. Acad. New Ser. 6: 374 (1858). *Neviusa* Benth. & Hook. f. 1 sp., *N. alabamensis* A. Gray, Alabama. B.H. 1: 613; E.P. 3, 3: 28; Rydb., N. Amer. Fl. 22: 481; Schneid., Laubholtzk. 1: 502; Rehder, Trees and Shrubs, ed. 2: 406 (1940).

Shrub; leaves alternate, doubly serrate; stipules small, free; flowers terminal subcorymbose, ebracteate, bisexual, white; calyx persistent, tube short, lobes 5, large, spreading, leafy, incised-serrate, imbricate; petals absent; stamens numerous, in several series, persistent; anthers small, eglandular; disk flat, lining the calyx-tube; carpels 4–2, sessile, silky; styles subterminal, filiform; ovule solitary, pendulous from the apex of the loculus; achenes drupaceous, small, included in the enlarged calyx, epicarp thin and fleshy, endocarp crustaceous; seed with very thin endosperm; cotyledons flat, radical inflexed.

Tribe 14. POTENTILLEAE

Style terminal or nearly so; ovule pendulous:
  Anthers opening by slits lengthwise:
    Stamens separated from the receptacle by a space, with no annular disk at the base of the filaments:
      Calyx-tube saucer-shaped to deeply campanulate; petals never linear; carpels usually more than 2:
        Filaments filiform or subulate, not petaloid:
          Carpels inserted at the bottom of the calyx-tube; epicalyx present
                       52. **Ivesia**
          Carpels inserted on a stalked receptacle; epicalyx absent   53. **Purpusia**
        Filaments dilated, petaloid:
          Stamens 20; carpels numerous; sepals reflexed in flower 54. **Horkeliella**
          Stamens 10; sepals not reflexed   55. **Horkelia**
      Calyx-tube wheel-shaped; petals narrowly linear; carpels 2; filaments filiform   56. **Comarella**
    Stamens inserted near the base of the receptacle or a more or less distinct annular thickening; filaments filiform   57. **Potentilla**
  Anthers opening by subterminal pores; carpel 1; filaments filiform
                      58. **Stellariopsis**
Style lateral to subbasal; ovule ascending:
  Shrubs or undershrubs; achenes hairy:

Style filiform; leaves trifoliolate   59. **Sibbaldiopsis**
Style club-shaped; leaves pinnate   60. **Pentaphylloides**
Herbs; achenes glabrous:
  Stamens about 20; achenes numerous:
    Leaves pinnate:
      Receptacle not enlarged in fruit; petals yellow, obtuse or retuse; leaves
        interruptedly pinnate   61. **Argentina**
      Receptacle somewhat enlarged in fruit, becoming spongy; petals red,
        acute or acuminate; leaves regularly pinnate   62. **Comarum**
    Leaves trifoliolate; receptacle much enlarged and usually red in fruit:
      Receptacle not pulpy; petals yellow   63. **Duchesnea**
      Receptacle pulpy; petals white or pinkish   64. **Fragaria**
  Stamens 5; achenes 15–10; leaves trifoliolate   65. **Sibbaldia**
Style basal or nearly so; ovules ascending or nearly erect:
  Stamens and carpels numerous; epicalyx present; leaves pinnate
                                           66. **Drymocallis**
  Stamens 5; epicalyx absent; leaves twice or thrice ternate   67. **Chamaerhodos**

52. **Ivesia** Torr. & Gray, Newb. Pacif. R.R. Rep. 6: 72 (1857). About 35 spp.,
North America; type *I. gordonii* (Hook.) Torr. & Gray, Washington to California and Montana. Rydb., N. Amer. Fl. 22: 283; Keck; Lloydia, 1: 75
(1938) (revision).

    Perennial herbs with thick erect rootstocks; leaves mostly basal and numerous, pinnately
divided usually into numerous small more or less crowded and imbricate leaflets; flowers in
cymes; calyx-tube deeply campanulate or turbinate to saucer-shaped; epicalyx of 5 bracteoles; calyx-lobes 5; petals 5, usually clawed, white or yellow; stamens 20–5, inserted in the
throat of the calyx-tube; filaments filiform or subulate; carpels 15–3, surrounded by a ring
of prominent bristles; styles long and slender, terminal or nearly so, sometimes slightly
thickened and glandular below; ovules and seeds pendulous.

53. **Purpusia** Brand., Bot. Gaz. 27: 446 (1899). 3 spp., North America;
type *P. saxosa* Brand., Nevada. Rydb., N. Amer. Fl. 22: 291.

    Caespitose glandular perennials with thick roots and short caudices; leaves imparipin-
nate, mostly basal; flowers in cymes; calyx-tube deeply campanulate; epicalyx absent; calyx
lobes 5, valvate; petals 5, white, oblanceolate, acuminate; stamens 5, opposite the sepals,
inserted at the mouth of the calyx-tube; anthers didymous; carpels 7–6, on a stalked receptacle; styles nearly terminal, filiform articulate at the base; embryo curved.

54. **Horkeliella** Rydb., N. Amer. Fl. 22: 282 (1908). 3 spp., North America;
type *H. purpurascens* (S. Wats.) Rydb., California.

    Perennial herbs with scaly rootstock and short erect caudex; leaves pinnate, with numer-
ous crowded deeply cleft leaflets; flowers few in open cymes; calyx-tube deeply campanulate;
epicalyx of 5 bracteoles; calyx-lobes 5, reflexed in flower; petals 5, oblanceolate or cuneate,
white; stamens 20, inserted in the throat of the calyx-tube; filaments dilated, white, subulate
or lanceolate; receptacle conical or hemispheric; carpels numerous; style long and slender,
terminal, slightly thickened and glandular below.

55. **Horkelia** Cham. & Schlechtd., Linnaea, 2: 26 (1827). 12 spp., North
America; type *H. californica* Cham. & Schlechtd., California. B.H. 1: 621
(in *Potentilla*); E.P. 3, 3: 35; Rydb., N. Amer. Fl. 22: 269 (1908); Keck,
Lloydia, 1: 75 (1938) (revision).

Perennial herbs; rhizome or rootstock scaly; leaves pinnate, leaflets mostly numerous; inflorescence cymose-paniculate, calyx 5-bracteolate, tube deeply campanulate to saucer-shaped, lobes 5, erect; petals linear or spathulate, white or pale yellow; stamens 10; filaments dilated and more or less petaloid, persistent, with a distinct midrib; receptacle conical or hemispherical; carpels 15–3; styles long and slender, articulated at the base and at length deciduous; ovule pendulous.

56. **Comarella** Rydb., Mem. Dep. Bot. Columbia Univ. 2: 156 (1898). 2 spp., North America; type *C. multifoliolata* (Torr.) Rydb., Arizona. Rydb., N. Amer. Fl. 22: 291.

Perennial herbs with very thick woody taproots and short thick scaly caudices; leaves pinnate with numerous crowded leaflets; flowers in cymose panicles with slender branches; calyx-tube wheel-shaped, the central portion turbinate, enclosing the carpels and beset on the inner surface with long bristles, the surrounding portion flat, pentagonal in outline, making nearly a right angle with the pedicel; petals dark-purple, narrowly linear, shorter than the calyx; stamens 5, inserted at the outer margin of the flat portion of the calyx-tube; filaments filiform; anthers small; carpels 2; styles long and filiform, terminal; fruiting carpels spreading nearly horizontally rather flat; seed inserted near the base of the style, pendulous.

57. **Potentilla**[1] Linn., Sp. Pl. 495 (1753); Gen. Pl. ed. 5: 219 (1754). About 200 spp., north temp. and Arctic regions; type *P. reptans* Linn., Europe, N. Asia. B.H. 1: 620; E.P. 3, 3: 34; Rydb., N. Amer. Fl. 22: 293; T. Wolf, Monogr. der Gattung *Potentilla*, Biblioth. Bot. Heft 71: 1–714, tt. 1–20 (1908) (partly).

Perennial or annual herbs, the perennials with scaly more or less caespitose rootstocks; leaves digitately compound, inflorescence usually cymose-paniculate; calyx-tube concave, mostly hemispheric; bracteoles, sepals and petals 5 (more rarely 4), petals deciduous, obcordate to rounded, usually not clawed, yellow, white, or dark-purple; stamens usually about 20, in 3 series, often 10, 5 and 5 inserted near the axis; anthers more or less didymous; filaments filiform or subulate, receptacle hemispheric or conical; carpels usually numerous (rarely 10 or fewer); style attached near the apex of the carpel, jointed with it and deciduous, long and filiform or short; seed inserted near the base of the style, pendulous.

58. **Stellariopsis** Rydb., Mem. Dep. Bot. Columbia Univ. 2: 155 (1898). 1 sp., *S. santolinoides* (A. Gray) Rydb., California. Rydb., N. Amer. Fl. 22: 292.

Perennial herbs with thick woody roots and short erect caudices covered with numerous leaves; leaves pinnate, with numerous minute crowded imbricate leaflets; flowers in open cymose panicles; calyx-tube saucer-shaped, small; epicalyx of 5 bracteoles; calyx-lobes 5; petals 5, white, elliptic or rounded-ovate, slightly clawed; stamens 15, inserted on the margin of the disk, separated some distance from the carpels; filaments filiform, long; anthers purplish, didymous, obcordate, each half nearly pear-shaped, opening by a subterminal pore; carpel 1, surrounded by numerous bristles; style long and slender, terminal; fruit large for the size of the flower, at length becoming more or less horizontal; seed inserted near the base of the style, pendulous.

59. **Sibbaldiopsis** Rydb., Mem. Dep. Bot. Columbia Univ. 2: 187 (1898). 1 sp., *S. tridentata* (Soland.) Rydb., N. North America, Britain. Rydb., N. Amer. Fl. 22: 365.

[1] Synonyms of **Potentilla**: *Tormentilla* Linn. (1753). *Quinquefolium* Adans. (1763). *Pentaphyllum* Gaertn. (1788). *Tridophyllum* Neck. (1790). *Jussiea* Linn. ex Sm. (1811). *Fraga* Lapeyr. (1813). *Trichothalamus* Spreng. (1818). *Bootia* Bigelow (1824). *Lehmannia* Tratt. (1824). *Chionice* Bunge (1844). *Potentillopsis* Opiz (1857). *Fragariastrum* Schur. (1866) *Coelas* Dulac (1867). *Chamaephyton* Fourr. (1868). *Dynamidium* Fourr. (1868). *Callionia* Greene (1906). *Tylosperma* Botsch. (1952).

Caespitose undershrubs with leathery ternate leaves; calyx-tube almost flat; bracteoles, sepals and petals 5 each; petals white, obovate or elliptic, not clawed; stamens about 20, in 3 series, inserted near the base of the receptacle; anthers rounded, cordate at base; receptacle hemispheric; carpels numerous, with lateral filiform styles; stigmas truncate; achenes turgid, villous; seeds ascending.

60. **Pentaphylloides** Duhamel, Traité des Arbres, 2: 99 (1755). *Dasiphora* Raf. (1838). 4 spp., north temp. region; type *P. fruticosa* (Linn.) O. Schwarz (*Potentilla fruticosa* Linn.), circumpolar distrib. Rydb., N. Amer. Fl. 22: 366 (as *Dasiphora*).

Shrubs with scarious sheathing stipules; leaves pinnate, leathery; flowers axillary; calyx-tube saucer-shaped; bracteoles, sepals and petals 5; petals yellow, orbicular, not clawed; stamens about 25, in 5 bundles on a pentagonal disk surrounding the receptacular column, anthers oblong, flat, not didymous, dehiscent by a slit lengthwise; receptacle hemispheric; carpels numerous; styles club-shaped, thick and glandular upward, inserted near or below the middle of the carpels; stigmas large and more or less 4-lobed; achenes densely covered with long straight hairs; seed ascending.

61. **Argentina** Lam., Fl. Fr. 3: 118 (1778). *Dactylophyllum* Spenn. (1829), partly. 12 spp., temp. northern hemisphere; type *A. anserina* (Linn.) Rydb., Europe, Asia, natural. elsewhere. Rydb., N. Amer. Fl. 22: 352.

Perennial herbs with slender prostrate stolons; leaves interruptedly pinnate, with many leaflets; flowers solitary in the axils of small leaves or scales on the stolons; calyx-tube almost flat; epicalyx usually of 5 bracteoles, sepals usually 5; petals usually 5, yellow, broadly elliptic or almost orbicular, not clawed, scarcely emarginate; stamens 25–20, in 3 series, inserted closely around the base of the receptacle as in *Potentilla*; filaments filiform, rather short; anthers slightly didymous, opening by a slit lengthwise; calyx-tube hemispheric; carpels numerous; styles filiform, lateral, attached almost at the middle of the carpel, scarcely deciduous; fruits with thick pericarp; seeds ascending.

62. **Comarum** Linn., Sp. Pl. 502 (1753); Gen. Pl. ed. 5: 220 (1754). *Pancovia* Heist. (1763). About 5 spp., temp. northern hemisphere; type *C. palustre* Linn., temp. northern hemisphere. Rydb., N. Amer. Fl. 22: 355.

Marsh perennials with long creeping rootstocks and pinnate leaves; flowers in cymes; calyx-tube almost flat or slightly saucer-shaped, enlarging in fruit, more or less tinged with red; epicalyx of 5 bracteoles; sepals 5; petals 5, red, ovate, acuminate; stamens 25–20, inserted near the base of the calyx-tube; filaments filiform; anthers flat, orbicular, cordate at the base, opening by marginal slits; receptacle hemispheric, enlarging in fruit and becoming ellipsoid or hemispheric and springy; carpels numerous; style lateral, filiform.

63. **Duchesnea** Smith, Trans. Linn. Soc. 10: 372 (1811). 5–6 spp., S. Asia, China, North America; type *D. indica* (Andr.) Focke (*D. fragiformis* Smith), Indo-Malaya, China. B.H. 1: 602 (in *Fragaria*); E.P. 3, 3: 33; Rydb., N. Amer. Fl. 22: 355.

Perennial herbs; stems several, procumbent, filiform, subsimple; radical leaves several, cauline long-petiolate, ternate; leaflets dentate; stipules paired, adnate at the base to the petiole, incised, persistent; pedicels leaf-opposed, solitary, ebracteate; calyx persistent, 5-bracteolate, bracteoles larger than the 5 calyx-lobes and incised; petals 5, yellow, obovate; stamens numerous; anthers subrounded, 2-lobed; carpels numerous, inserted on a convex receptacle; styles ventral, deciduous, stigma undivided; receptacle pulpy; achenes minute, ovate-compressed; seeds solitary, reniform, smooth.

64. **Fragaria** Linn., Sp. Pl. 494 (1753); Gen. Pl. ed. 5: 218 (1754). *Dactylophyllum*, Spenn., partly (1829). 8 spp., temp. northern hemisphere, Himalayas,

Mexico, Chile, Brazil; type *F. vesca* Linn., temperate regions. B.H. 1: 620; E.P. 3, 3: 33; Rydb., N. Amer. Fl. 22: 356.

Herbs, mostly stoloniferous; leaves alternate, 3-foliolate, very rarely becoming pinnate with a few additional lateral leaflets or 1- or 5-foliolate; stipules adnate to the base of the petiole, often membranous, sheathing; inflorescence erect, few-flowered, flowers polygamo-dioecious, cymose, white, rarely yellow; calyx persistent, tube obconic or turbinate, 5-bracteolate; lobes 5, valvate; petals 5, broadly obovate; stamens numerous, 1-seriate, persistent; anthers didymous; disk lining the calyx-tube; carpels numerous, borne on a convex receptacle, free from each other; styles ventral, short, persistent; ovule solitary, ascending from the middle of the loculus; achenes numerous, minute, seated in pits on the enlarged fleshy oblong or globose receptacle, dry and crustaceous.

65. Sibbaldia Linn., Sp. Pl. 284 (1753); Gen. Pl. ed. 5: 137 (1754). *Dactylophyllum* Spenn., partly (1829). *Coelas* Dulac (1876). *Sibbaldianthe* Juzepczuk (1941). About 20 spp., northern temp. and alpine regions; type *S. procumbens* Linn., Arct. and alpine regions of northern hemisphere. Rydb., N. Amer. Fl. 22: 365.

Low tufted perennial herbs with short caespitose caudices or rootstocks; leaves ternate; calyx-tube saucer-shaped or cup-shaped; epicalyx of 5 bracteoles; calyx-lobes 5; petals 5, yellow, obovate to oblanceolate, scarcely equalling the sepals; stamens 5, inserted away from the small receptacle; carpels 20–5; styles lateral; ovule and seed attached near the base of the style, ascending.

66. Drymocallis Fourr., Ann. Soc. Linn. Lyon, 2, 16: 371 (1868). *Bootia* Bigel. (1824). About 30 spp., North America; type *D. rubricaulis* Fourr. Rydb., N. Amer. Fl. 22: 366.

Perennial herbs with scaly rootstocks, glandular pinnate leaves and cymose inflorescence; calyx-tube saucer-shaped or hemispheric, bracteoles, sepals and petals 5 each; petals obovate to orbicular, not clawed, yellow or white; stamens 30–20 in 5 bundles in the much thickened margin of a pentagonal disk around the receptacle; anthers oblong, truncate at each end or cordate at the base, dehiscent by a marginal slit; receptacle hemispheric or semiellipsoid; carpels numerous; style nearly basal, thickened and glandular a little below the middle and tapering to each end, rather persistent; stigma minute; seed attached near the base of the style, ascending.

67. Chamaerhodos Bunge, Ledeb. Fl. Altaic. 1: 429 (1829). 5 spp., N. Asia, China, Tibet, North America; type *C. altaica* Bunge, Siberia. B.H. 1: 621; E.P. 3, 3: 36; Rydb., N. Amer. Fl. 22: 376.

Herbs, woody at the base, glandular-pilose or pubescent, leaves alternate, 3-partite or 2–3 times divided into narrow segments; stipules membranous at the base, adnate to petiolar sheath; inflorescence or flowering stem erect, slender, corymbosely branched, bracteate; flowers erect, small, white or purple; calyx persistent, tube obconic or campanulate, ebracteolate; lobes 5, erect, valvate; petals 5; stamens 5, opposite the petals, filaments subulate; anthers didymous; disk lining the base of the calyx-tube, margin thickened, setose with long rigid hairs; carpels 10–5 or more, inserted at the base of the calyx, sessile or on the narrow receptacle; style basal, articulated at the base, deciduous, stigmas capitellate; ovule solitary, ascending from the base of the loculus; achenes few or many, dry, glabrous, enclosed by the calyx; seed erect.

Tribe 15. DRYADEAE

Carpels numerous to several:
  Shrubs; leaves dissected into narrow lobes:
    Bracteoles present; carpels numerous; calyx-lobes imbricate   68. **Fallugia** --

Bracteoles absent; carpels few; calyx-lobes valvate   69. **Cowania** -

Perennial herbs with underground rootstocks or low prostrate shrublets; calyx-lobes valvate:

Carpels in fruit caudate or beaked with the whole or part of the persistent style:

Epicalyx double, composed of 10–5 bracteoles; disk absent; leaflets of basal leaves always entire or nearly so; whole plant covered with long rusty hairs   70. **Novosieversia**

Epicalyx composed of 10–4 bracteoles in a single series or absent; leaflets of basal leaves crenate, dentate, serrate, or laciniate:

Disk free from the calyx-tube and forming a distinct annulus between the stamens and carpels; filaments often pilose; petals narrowly elliptic or oblong   71. **Sieversia**

Disk united with the calyx-tube or not evident:

Style in fruit hooked at the apex   72. **Geum** .

Style in fruit not hooked at the apex:

Style glabrous in fruit; petals 5   73. **Acomastylis**

Style with reflexed hairs (barbate) at the apex in fruit petals 5   74. **Orthurus**

Style plumose in fruit; petals 10–8   75. **Dryas** -

Carpels in fruit without a persistent style; petals 5:

Basal leaves pinnatisect with several leaflets   76. **Coluria** -

Basal leaves ternate or simple and lobed   77. **Waldsteinia** -

Carpels usually solitary, rarely 2; petals 5:

Calyx-lobes imbricate; leaves crowded, 3-fid or pinnatifid, white below   78. **Purshia**

Calyx-lobes valvate; leaves three times pinnatisect, viscid, the lobes terminated by a gland   79. **Chamaebatia**

68. **Fallugia** Endl., Gen. 1246 (1840). 1 sp., *F. paradoxa* (D. Don) Endl., Mexico and S. United States. B.H. 1: 618; E.P. 3, 3: 38; Rehder, Trees and Shrubs, ed. 2: 423 (1940); Rydb., N. Amer. Fl. 22: 414; Schneid., Laubholtzk. 1: 526; Jepson, Fl. Calif. 2: 206 (1936).

Erect shrub, much branched; leaves alternate, 3–7-lobed, rarely some entire, lobes linear, margins recurved, white below; stipules adnate to the petiole; flowers bisexual or polygamous, white, terminal, ebracteate; calyx-tube cupular, 5-bracteolate at the apex; lobes 5, ovate, imbricate; petals 5, suborbicular; stamens numerous, filaments connate into a ring at the base; anthers small; carpels numerous, inserted on a small conical receptacle; style terminal, villous; ovule solitary, ascending; achenes numerous, terminated by the long very plumose persistent style; seed erect; cotyledons linear-oblong.

69. **Cowania** D. Don, Trans. Linn. Soc. 14: 574, t. 22 (1825). *Greggia* Engelm. (1848). 3–4 spp., Mexico, NW. America; type *C. mexicana* D. Don, NW. America. B.H. 1: 618; E.P. 3, 3: 38; Rehder, Trees and Shrubs, ed. 2: 423 (1940); Rydb., N. Amer. Fl. 22: 414; Schneid., Laubholtzk. 1: 527; Jepson, Fl. Calif. 2: 207, fig. 165 (1936).

Much-branched leafy shrubs, branches thick, woody; leaves alternate, small, cuneate, 3–5-fid or partite or lobulate, plicate, margins revolute, snowy white below with thick nerves; stipules adnate to the petiole; flowers sessile, terminal, solitary, large, sulphur-yellow or rose; calyx-tube turbinate, persistent; lobes 5, valvate; petals 5, spreading, obovate; stamens numerous, 2-seriate, inserted at the mouth of the calyx; anthers eglandular; disk lining the tube of the calyx, margin thickened; carpels 12–5, inserted at the base of the calyx, free, villous, 1-locular; style short, villous; ovule solitary, ascending; achenes 12–5, enclosed by the calyx; styles plumose, long-exserted; seed erect, testa membranous; endosperm thin; cotyledons oblong.

70. **Novosieversia** F. Bolle, Fedde Repert. Beih. 72: 23 (1933). 1 sp., *N. glacialis* (Adams) F. Bolle, NE. Asia.

Perennial herbs; basal leaves subequally pinnatisect or pinnate; leaflets mostly entire or subentire; stem with 3–5 leaves or bracts, 1-flowered; calyx-tube saucer-shaped; epicalyx double, the 10 lower bracteoles small, upper 5 medium and 5 large; petals large, entire or slit at the top, rounded or shortly clawed; disk absent; stamens numerous; carpels many; receptacle mostly long; style long-plumose, not jointed.

71. **Sieversia** Willd., Ges. Nat. Freunde Berlin Mag. 5: 397 (1811). *Adamsia* Fisch. (1821). *Erythrocoma* Greene (1906). *Parageum* Nakai & Hara (1935). *Woronowia* Juzepczuk (1941). 25 spp., north temp. and Arctic zone; type *S. pentapetala* (Linn.) Greene (*S. anemonoides* Willd.), N. Asia to Arctic America. B.H. 1: 619; E.P. 3, 3: 36 (in *Geum*); Bolle, Fedde Repert. Beih. 72: 24 (1933) (as *Erythrocoma*).

Perennial herbs with rootstocks or suffruticose bases; basal leaves lyrately or odd-pinnately divided, usually with smaller segments interposed; stem leaves reduced; stipules usually large, adnate to the petioles; flowers solitary or cymose; calyx-tube turbinate or hemispherical; bracteoles usually present; sepals 5, valvate; petals 5, white, light yellow, or pink, or purplish; stamens numerous, in several series on a disk at the mouth of the calyx; carpels numerous, free; styles not articulated, the lower portion plumose, elongated in fruit, not hooked, the upper portion glabrous, persistent or withering and then deciduous; fruit a hairy achene; seed erect, basal.

72. **Geum** Linn., Sp. Pl. 500 (1753); Gen. Pl. ed. 5: 220 (1754). *Caryophyllata* Mill. (1754). *Oreogeum* Ser. (1823). *Stylypus* Raf. (1825). *Oncostylus* Bolle (1933). About 70 spp., world distrib.; type *G. urbanum* Linn., north temp. zone. B.H. 1: 619; E.P. 3, 3: 36; F. Bolle, Eine Übersicht über die Gattung *Geum* L. und die ihr nahestehenden Gattungen, Fedde Repert. Beih. 72: 1–119 (1933); Rydb., N. Amer. Fl. 22: 401; Gajenski, Monographiae Botan. 4 (1957). See also Additional Literature, p. 175.

Herbs with a perennial rhizome, sometimes stoloniferous; radical leaves crowded, imparipinnate, alternate pairs often smaller, the terminal one the largest; stem-leaves few, often 3-foliolate or bract-like; stipules adnate to and sheathing the petiole; flowers on a scape or solitary or rarely corymbose, rather large, white, yellow, or red; calyx-tube persistent, turbinate, or hemispheric, 5-bracteolate at the apex, rarely nude; lobes 5, valvate; petals 5, orbicular or obovate; stamens numerous, crowded; disk lining the calyx-tube, smooth or ribbed; carpels numerous; style filiform, kneed, stigma minute, slightly recurved or hooked; ovule solitary, ascending; achenes small, sessile or stipitate, dry, style elongated, becoming kneed and hooked at the apex; seed erect, testa membranous; cotyledons oblong.

73. **Acomastylis** Greene, Leaflets 1: 174 (1906). 15 spp., type *A. rossii* (R.Br.) Greene, Arctic America, NE. Asia. Rydb., N. Amer. Fl. 22: 412 (1913); Bolle, Fedde Repert. Beih. 73; 78 (1933).

Low caespitose perennial herbs with stout rootstocks; basal leaves pinnately divided with numerous cleft or toothed divisions; stem-leaves few, reduced; flowers terminal, solitary or very few in cymes; calyx-tube more or less turbinate; lobes valvate; bracteoles present; petals 5, obovate, yellow; stamens numerous, inserted at the mouth of the calyx; carpels numerous, hirsute, tapering into the glabrous persistent styles, these not elongating in fruit; ovule basal.

74. **Orthurus** Juzepczuk, Komarov Fl. URSS. 10: 262, 616 (1941). 2 spp., Mediterranean to Turkestan; type *O. heterocarpus* (Boiss.) Juzepczuk, Mediterranean region.

Perennial herbs with a rosette of lyrate radical leaves; flowers few in cymes; calyx-tube funnel-shaped or subcampanulate; sepals and bracteoles 5 each, sepals valvate, erect; petals 5; stamens numerous; carpels 10–4, shortly stipitate, spreading stellately in fruit; style straight, articulate in the middle, the upper part caducous and glabrous or pilose, the lower part accrescent in fruit not hooked but provided with stiff reflexed hairs (barbate as in some *Bidens* (*Asteraceae*)).

75. **Dryas** Linn., Sp. Pl. 501 (1753); Gen. Pl. ed. 5: 220 (1754). *Ptilotum* Dulac. (1867). *Dryadea* Linn. ex Kuntze (1891). 3–4 (or more) spp., Europe east to temp. and Arctic America; type *D. octopetala* Linn., north temp. zone. B.H. 1: 618; E.P. 3, 3: 38; Rydb., N. Amer. Fl. 22: 399; Schneid., Laubholtzk. 1: 525. See Juzepczuk, Bull. Gard. Bot. Princ. URSS. 28: 306 (1929), who enumerates 18 spp.!

Low prostrate shrublets; leaves alternate, entire to subpinnatifid, margins recurved, whitish below; stipules adnate to the petiole; flowers solitary, pedicellate, white or yellowish white; calyx-tube short, concave, glandular; lobes 10–8, valvate; petals 10–8, broadly obovate; stamens numerous, 2-seriate; disk lining the calyx-tube; carpels numerous, free, sessile on the flat receptacle; style terminal, plumose; ovules solitary, ascending; achenes numerous, terminated by the plumose style; seed ascending, testa membranous; cotyledons linear-oblong.

76. **Coluria** R. Br., Parry Voy. App. 276 (1824). *Laxmannia* Fisch. (1812). *Stictogeum* Ser. (1823). 7 spp., Siberia, China; type *C. geoides* (Pall.) Ledeb. (*C. potentilloides* R. Br.), Siberia. B.H. 1: 619; E.P. 3, 3: 36; Evans, Edinb. Notes, 15: 47 (1925); Bolle, Fedde Repert. Beih. 72: 90 (1933).

Low herbs, softly tomentose, with a rhizome; leaves mostly radical, interruptedly pinnatisect, lobes obovate, crenate, those on the stem sessile among the connate stipules and entire or 3-fid; inflorescence erect, bracteate, few-flowered; flowers yellow; calyx persistent, at length elongated, 10-ribbed, 5-bracteolate at the apex; lobes 5, valvate; petals 5, larger than the calyx-lobes; stamens numerous, crowded in 2–3 series; anthers rather large, loculi oblong; disk lining the calyx-tube; carpels numerous, inserted on a short receptacle; styles subterminal, erect, deciduous; ovule solitary, ascending from the base of the loculus; achenes numerous, on a columnar receptacle, included in the calyx-tube, compressed, rugose.

77. **Waldsteinia** Willd., Neue Schrift. Ges. Naturf. Fr. Berlin, 2: 105, t. 4 (1799). *Comaropsis* Rich. (1816). 6–7 spp., north temp. hemisphere; type *W. geoides* Willd., SE. Europe. B.H. 1: 619; E.P. 3, 3: 36; Rydb., N. Amer. Fl. 22: 398; Bolle, Fedde Repert. Beih. 72: 93 (1933).

Creeping herbs; leaves alternate, entire, lobed, 3–5-fid or 3–5-foliolate, leaflets crenate or incised; stipules rather large, membranous; inflorescence bracteate, 5–2-flowered; flowers bisexual, rather large, yellow; calyx persistent, tube elongate-obconic or turbinate; bracteoles 5, minute, or absent; lobes 5, spreading, valvate; petals 5, obovate, subequal to the calyx-lobes; stamens numerous, crowded into 3 series, filaments persistent; anthers didymous, small; disk lining the tube of the calyx, margin crenulate; carpels 6–2, inserted on the short villous receptacle, small; styles subterminal, filiform, deciduous, stigma undivided; ovule solitary, ascending; achenes obliquely obovoid, dry or fleshy, hairy, scarred at the apex; seed erect.

78. **Purshia** DC., Trans. Linn. Soc. 12: 157 (1817). *Tigarea* Pursh (1814). *Kunzia* Spreng. (1825). 2 spp., North America; type *P. tridentata* (Pursh) DC., W. North America. B.H. 1: 617; E.P. 3, 3: 40; Schneid., Laubholtzk. 1: 528; Rydb., N. Amer. Fl. 22: 416; Rehder, Trees and Shrubs, ed. 2: 425 (1940).

Shrubs; buds small, scaly; leaves, pedicels, and calyx glandular-pilose; leaves small, alternate, crowded, cuneate, 3-lobed, lobes linear, with recurved margins; stipules small, adnate to the petiole; flowers bisexual, yellowish, solitary and subsessile at the ends of short branchlets; calyx-tube elongated, ebracteolate; lobes 5, imbricate; petals 5, spathulate; stamens about 25, 1-seriate; anthers large; disk lining the calyx-tube; carpel 1 (rarely 2) free; style short, curved, persistent; ovule solitary, erect from the base; fruit coriaceous, pubescent, tipped by the persistent style; seed with dark shining testa; endosperm thin; cotyledons flat, obovate.

79. **Chamaebatia** Benth., Pl. Hartweg. 308 (1849). 2 spp., Calif.; type *C. foliolosa* Benth. B.H. 1: 617: E.P. 3, 3: 40; Schneid., Laubholtzk. 1: 532; Rydb., N. Amer. Fl. 22: 417; Jepson, Fl. Calif. 2: 213 (1936); Rehder, Trees and Shrubs, ed. 2: 425.

Glandular-pubescent shrubs, with resinous odour; leaves fern-like, alternate, 3-pinnatisect, lobes small, crowded, terminated by a gland; stipules small, dentate, adnate to the base of the petiole; cymes terminal, few-flowered, bracts leafy, pinnatifid; flowers white; calyx-tube campanulate, lobes 5, imbricate; petals 5, obovate; stamens numerous, in many series; disk thin, lining the tube of the calyx; carpel 1, villous, style short, stigmatose on one side; ovule 1, ascending; achene coriaceous, enclosed by the calyx-tube; seed erect, hilum broad; endosperm thin; cotyledons flat and broadly oblong.

Tribe 16. POTERIEAE (*Sanguisorbeae*)

Trees, shrubs, or shrublets, with more or less woody but not spiny branches; petioles sometimes spiny:
Petals present, sometimes rudimentary:
Stamens about 20; tree with pinnate leaves with large stipules adnate to the petiole; flowers paniculate   80. **Hagenia** ·
Stamens 12–10; flowers spicate; shrubs   81. **Leucosidea** ··
Petals absent:
Flowers bisexual or rarely polygamous and then corymbose:
Flowers in pendulous spikes; calyx-tube winged; stamens 5 or more
                                                                82. **Polylepis** ·
Flowers solitary; stamens 3–1:
Calyx-tube winged   83. **Tetraglochin** ⁝
Calyx-tube not winged   84. **Margyricarpus**
Flowers unisexual, dioecious or monoecious; stamens numerous:
Flowers solitary; leaves 1–3-foliolate   85. **Cliffortia**
Flowers spicate; leaves pinnate   86. **Bencomia**
Herbs, perennial with underground rhizomes, or rarely annuals, if rather woody then with spiny branches:
Petals present:
Bracteoles not connate into an epicalyx   87. **Agrimonia** ·
Bracteoles connate into an epicalyx:
Involucre 10–12-fid; stamens 10–5   88. **Aremonia** ·

Involucre sharply 4–5-dentate; stamens 40–35   89. **Spenceria**
Petals absent:
Calyx-lobes imbricate, without bracteoles between:
Flowers monoecious or polygamous; stamens 30–20:
Perennial herbs with annual stems from underground rhizomes; fruits
dry; leaflets toothed   90. **Poterium** ·
Perennial or annual herbs with tap roots; leaflets deeply pinnatisect
     91. **Poteridium**
Spiny undershrubs; fruits succulent; inflorescence leaf-opposed
     92. **Sarcopoterium**
Flowers bisexual; stamens few (15–4); herbs with underground rhizomes
     93. **Sanguisorba** ⸱
Calyx-lobes valvate:
Calyx-lobes 1-seriate; style terminal or nearly so   94. **Acaena**
Calyx-lobes 2-seriate; style basal or lateral   95. **Alchemilla**

80. **Hagenia** J. F. Gmel., Syst. 2: 613 (1791). *Banksia* Bruce (1805). *Bankesia*
Bruce (1808). *Hagea* Poir. (1818). *Brayera* Kunth. ex Brayer (1822). *Bracera*
Engelm. (1839). 1 sp., *H. abyssinica* (Bruce) J. F. Gmel., Abyssinia to
Nyasaland. B.H. 1: 622; E.P. 3, 3: 43; Graham, Fl. Trop. E. Africa *Rosaceae*,
43, fig. 5 (1960).

Tall tree; branchlets villous, ringed by the scars of the fallen leaves; leaves crowded, interruptedly imparipinnate, leaflets oblong; stipules large, adnate to the semiamplexicaul
dilated petiole; panicles large, axillary, branched, hirsute; bracts subfoliaceous; flowers
polygamo-dioecious; bracts membranous, 2–3 at the base of the calyx; calyx-tube turbinate,
throat constricted into a membranous wing; lobes 10, 2-seriate, outer (bracteoles) membranous, inner spathulate; petals 5, small, linear; disk lining the calyx-tube, constricted at the
apex into a membrane embracing the styles; stamens up to 20, small, inserted in the throat
of the calyx; anthers minute; carpels 2–3, included in the calyx-tube; styles terminal, short,
stigmas broadly spathulate-dilated, villous; ovule solitary, pendulous; achenes reticulate.

81. **Leucosidea** Eckl. & Zeyh., Enum. Pl. Cap. 265 (1836). *Nestlera* E. Mey.
ex Walp. (1852). 1 sp., *L. sericea* Eckl. & Zeyh., S. Rhodesia, S. Africa. B.H.
1: 622; E.P. 3, 3: 43.

Densely leafy shrub, silky-villous; bark deciduous; leaves alternate, imparipinnate;
leaflets few pairs, incised-dentate, alternate ones sometimes smaller; stipules adnate to the
sheathing base of the petiole; flowers densely crowded into terminal villous shortly pedunculate spikes, green, 2-bracteolate; calyx persistent, tube obconic, constricted at the throat;
lobes 12–10, 2-seriate, outer (bracteoles) short, inner lanceolate and valvate; petals 5,
obovate, deciduous; disk lining the calyx-tube; stamens 12–10, inserted on the annular disk;
anthers didymous; carpels 4–2, villous at the apex; styles terminal, filiform, exserted stigmas hooked at the apex; ovule solitary, pendulous; achenes membranous, included in the
indurated almost bony calyx-tube; seed oblong, testa membranous; cotyledons plano-
convex.

82. **Polylepis** Ruiz & Pavon, Prodr. 34, t. 15 (1794). *Quinasis* Raf. (1838).
About 38 spp., trop. South America; type *P. racemosa* Ruiz & Pavon, Peru.
B.H. 1: 623; E.P. 3, 3: 45, fig. 22: Bitter, Engl. Bot. Jahrb. 45: 564 (revision).

Small trees or shrubs; branches twisted with scars of fallen leaves; leaves alternate,
3-foliolate or imparipinnate, leaflets in few pairs, leathery; petiole broadly membranous-
sheathing at the base; racemes slender, laxly flowered, mostly pendulous; flowers rather
large, bracteate; calyx persistent, tube turbinate, 3–4-winged, constricted at the throat;

lobes 5–3; petals absent; disk lining and almost closing the calyx-tube; stamens numerous to 5, inserted in the throat of the calyx; anthers small, didymous, often pilose or villous; carpel 1, included in the calyx-tube; style short or long-exserted, stigma peltate, dilated, fimbriate or penicellate; ovule solitary, pendulous; achene coriaceous, included in the hardened angular spiny or winged calyx-tube; seed pendulous, ovoid, testa membranous; cotyledons plano-convex.

83. Tetraglochin Kunze ex Poepp., Fragm. Synop. Phaner. Chile, 26 (1833). 3–4 spp., South America; type *T. strictum* Poepp., Peru, Chile, Bolivia. E.P. 3, 3: 45; Rothmaler, Darwiniana, 3: 429 (1939).

Shrubs, branched, erect, with long and short shoots; petiole very spiny, with a broad base; young branchlets very short, axillary, leafy; leaflets rigid, oblong-elongate, mucronate, margins revolute; flowers bisexual; calyx 4–5-partite, persistent; petals absent; stamens 2 or 1, with very short filaments; carpel solitary; style simple, stigma multifid-flabelliform; fruit drupaceous, cylindric, 3–4-winged, crowned by the persistent calyx-limb, wings broad and membranous.

84. Margyricarpus Ruiz & Pavon, Fl. Peruv. et Chil. Prodr. 7, t. 33 (1794). 1 sp., *M. setosus* Ruiz & Pav., South American Andes. B.H. 1: 623, partly; E.P. 3, 3: 45; Schneid., Laubholtzk. 1: 535.

Branched, rigid, leafy shrub; leaves alternate, crowded and overlapping, imparipinnate, with a broadly sheathing petiole; flowers sessile in the leaf-axils, solitary, small, inconspicuous; calyx persistent, tube ovoid or compressed-4-sided, tuberculate, constricted in the throat; lobes 5–4; petals absent; disk lining the calyx-tube and almost closing it; stamens 3 or 2, inserted in the calyx-throat, filaments short, glabrous; carpel 1, included in calyx-tube; style very short, stigma dilated, penicellate; ovule solitary, pendulous; achene coriaceous, included in the leathery or nut-like tuberculate or subdrupaceous calyx-tube; seed oblong, testa membranous; cotyledons plano-convex.

85. Cliffortia Linn., Sp. Pl. 1038 (1753); Gen. Pl. ed. 5: 460 (1754). *Morilandia* Neck. (1790). *Monographidium* C. Presl (1850). About 80 spp., S. Africa, 1 in trop. E. Africa; type *C. polygonifolia* Linn. B.H. 1: 624; E.P. 3, 3: 46; Weimarck, Monogr. *Cliffortia* (1934); Graham, Fl. Trop. E. Africa *Rosaceae*, 40, fig. 4 (1960).

Erect or procumbent shrubs or shrublets or rarely trees; leaves alternate, 3–2-foliolate or 1-foliolate, flat, ericoid or acicular, serrate, lobed or entire, articulate at the base; sheaths with often connate margins; stipules either scarious and thin or foliaceous or subulate, rigid and pungent, rarely deficient; flowers unisexual, sometimes with rudiments of the other sex, very rarely bisexual, dioecious or monoecious, axillary, solitary or fasciculate, sessile to long-stalked; bracteoles embracing the base of the pedicels; calyx-tube enclosing the achene, ovoid, oblong, fusiform or cylindric, smooth, ribbed or 2–4-winged; sepals 4 or 3, deciduous or persistent, often coherent; petals absent; stamens 20–8 or 3–4–6, or up to 50; filaments filiform, glabrous; anthers yellow to purple-violet, usually glabrous; achenes 2 or 1; styles filiform, stigma dull-purple, lacerate-multifid.

86. Bencomia Webb & Berth., Phyt. Canar. 2: 10, t. 39 (1846). *Marcetella* Svent. (1948). *Dendriopoterium* Svent. (1948). 3 spp., Canary Isls., Madeira; type *B. caudata* Webb & Berth., Canary Isls. B.H. 1: 624; E.P. 3, 3: 46.

Sparingly branched shrubs, branchlets leafy to the apex, bark caducous; leaves alternate, imparipinnate, petiole elongated, with sheathing overlapping bases; leaflets membranous, oblong, serrate or dentate; stipules adnate to the petiole sheath; spikes long, axillary, pedunculate; flowers dioecious, sessile, bracteolate and 2-bracteolate; male flowers: sepals 4–5, penicellate at the apex, revolute after flowering, membranous, imbricate; petals absent; stamens numerous, filaments filiform, twisted; anthers ovate-rounded; female flowers: calyx-tube globose, constricted at the throat; lobes 5–4, deciduous; petals absent; stamens absent; carpels 4–2, included in the calyx-tube, sessile; styles filiform, terminal, stigma aspergilliform; ovule solitary, pendulous; achenes 4–2, coriaceous, narrowly ovoid, closely concrescent with the globose calyx-tube into a hardish 2–4-locular drupe; seeds not known.

87. **Agrimonia** Linn., Sp. Pl. 418 (1753); Gen. Pl. 5: 206 (1754). *Amonia* Nestl. (1816). About 25 spp., temp. regions and mts. of tropics, and South America; type *A. eupatoria* Linn., north temp. regions. B.H. 1: 622; E.P. 3, 3: 43; Rydb., N. Amer. Fl. 22: 391.

Tall herbs with creeping roots; leaves alternate, imparipinnate, leaflets several pairs, incised-serrate; stipules adnate to the base of the petiole; flowers rather small, usually in terminal spike-like racemes, yellow; pedicels bracteate at the base, 2-bracteolate in the middle; calyx persistent, tube turbinate, provided below the limb outside with hooked spinules or 5 teeth, constricted at the throat; lobes 5, imbricate, at length connivent; petals 5, larger, than the calyx-lobes, orbicular or oblong; disk lining the calyx-tube, margin thickened, annular, glandular; stamens 10–5 or more, inserted at the mouth of the calyx, 1-seriate; carpels usually 2, included in the calyx-tube, sessile; styles filiform, exserted, stigma dilated; ovule pendulous; achenes 2–1, included in the closed calyx-tube clothed above with hooked prickles; seed pendulous, testa membranous.

88. **Aremonia** Neck. Elem. 2: 100 (1790) (conserved name). *Agrimonoides* Mill. (1754). *Spallanzania* Pollini (1816). 1 sp., *A. agrimonoides* (Linn.) DC., S. Europe, Asia Minor. E.P. 3, 3: 43.

Perennial herb; leaves imparipinnate, leaflets dentate, lower small, upper larger with intermediate smaller ones; flowers small, yellow, subfasciculate; involucre calyx-like, 10–12-fid; calyx-limb 5-fid; petals 5, obovate; stamens 10–5; carpels 2, styles terminal; achene often 1 by abortion, included in the globose calyx-tube, 1–2-seeded.

89. **Spenceria** Trimen, Journ. Bot. 17: 97, t. 201 (1879), *Spencera* Stapf (1924). 2 spp., China; type *S. ramalana* Trimen. Stapf, Bot. Mag. t. 9007.

Perennial herbs, pilose-villous, caespitose from a several-headed rhizome densely covered with the remains of the old leaves; basal leaves imparipinnate, sheathing at the base; leaflets 7–4-pairs, coarsely 2–3-toothed at the apex; stem-leaves few- to 1-pairs, 3-sect or dentate; stipules herbaceous, adnate to the rhachis; inflorescence laxly racemose; bracts 3-fid or 3-lobed; bracteoles 2, opposite, connate into an involucre close to the petals, sharply 4–5-toothed, glandular-pubescent; receptacle obconic, densely white-silky outside; sepals lanceolate; petals golden or cream, obovate; stamens 40–35; filaments persistent; anthers rounded; carpels 2, included in the tubular receptacle; style filiform, stigma minute; ovule solitary, pendulous; spurious fruit deciduous, dry and somewhat hardened; perfect achene 1, subglobose, enclosed in the receptacle; seed without endosperm; cotyledons large, almost square.

90. **Poterium** Linn., Sp. Pl. 994, partly (1753) (conserved name); Gen. Pl. ed. 5: 430 (1754). *Leiopoterium* DC. (1825). About 25 spp., Europe, N. Africa, Orient; lectotype *P. sanguisorba* Linn., Europe, Orient. B.H. 1: 624, partly; Rydb., N. Amer. Fl. 22: 389.

Perennial herbs; leaves alternate, imparipinnate, petioles elongate, sheathing at the base; leaflets serrate; stipules adnate to the petiole; flowers densely capitate at the ends of the scapes, bracteate and bracteolate, monoecious or polygamo-dioecious or some bisexual; calyx-tube turbinate, persistent, constricted at the throat; lobes petaloid, deciduous, imbricate; petals absent; disk lining the calyx and almost closing the tube; stamens 30–20, inserted in the throat of the calyx, filaments elongated, filiform, weak; anthers didymous; carpels 3–1, included in the calyx-tube; style terminal, filiform, stigma dilated, penicellate or laciniate; ovule solitary, pendulous; achene coriaceous, included by the 4-sided hardened calyx-tube; seed oblong.

91. **Poteridium** Spach, Ann. Sci. Nat. 3, 5: 43 (1846). 2 spp., North America; type *P. annuum* (Nutt.) Spach, S. United States. Rydb., N. Amer. Fl. 22: 388.

Leafy branched annuals and biennials with tap-roots; leaves imparipinnate; leaflets pectinately pinnate; stipules adnate to the petiole; flowers greenish, bisexual, in dense oblong spikes; calyx urn-shaped, contracted at the mouth, 4-winged; lobes 4, green with white scarious margins; petals absent; stamens 4 or 2, opposite all or the inner 2 sepals; carpel 1; style terminal, stigma brush-like; ovule 1, pendulous; achenes enclosed by the 4-winged hardened dry calyx-tube.

92. **Sarcopoterium** Spach, Ann. Sci. Nat. 3, sér. 5: 43 (1846). 1 sp., *S. spinosum* Spach (*Poterium spinosum* Linn.), E. Mediterranean. Sibth., Fl. Graeca t. 943. E.P. 3, 3: 45 (in *Poterium*).

Branched rigid intricate shrub; branches in lower part ending in branched spines; leaves coriaceous, pinnate, very narrow; stipules rigid, tooth-like; leaflets in many pairs, rounded, dentate; flowers unisexual, spicate; peduncle leaf-opposed; bracts 4; calyx 4-partite, segments oblong, coloured on the margin, at length reflexed; petals absent; stamens numerous, exserted; anthers rounded; carpels often 2, free; style filiform, stigmas exserted, penicellate, rosy; fruit spicate, testaceous, spherical, small, fleshy, calyx-limb deciduous but enclosed by the tube.

93. **Sanguisorba** Linn., Sp. Pl. 116 (1753); Gen. Pl. ed. 5: 53 (1754). *Pimpinella* Adans. (1763). *Poterion* St. Lag. (1880), About 12 spp., temp. northern hemisphere; type *S. officinalis* Linn., Europe to NE. Asia. B.H. 1: 624 (in *Poterium*); E.P. 3, 3: 44; Rydb., N. Amer. Fl. 22: 386.

Perennial herbs; leaves alternate, imparipinnate, petiole sheathing and imbricate at the base; leaflets serrate; stipules sheathing, adnate to the petiole; flowers densely capitate or spicate at the apex of the elongated scapes, bracteate and bracteolate; flowers bisexual; calyx-tube constricted at the throat, lobes petaloid, deciduous, imbricate; petals absent; disk lining the calyx-tube; stamens few (15–4), inserted in the throat of the calyx; filaments free or rarely partly united; anthers didymous; carpels 2–1, included in the calyx-tube; style terminal, filiform, stigma penicellate; achene dry, 1-seeded, included in the hardened muricate or winged calyx-tube.

94. **Acaena** Linn., Mant. 2: 145 (1771). *Ancistrum* Forst. (1776). *Lasiocarpus* Banks & Soland. (1847). *Sphaerula* Anders. ex Hook. f. (1847). 40 spp., mostly southern hemisphere, Mexico, California, New Guinea, Hawaii; type *A. elongata* Linn., Mexico. B.H. 1: 623; E.P. 3, 3: 46; Rydb., N. Amer. Fl. 22: 389; Bitter, Die Gattung *Acaena*, Bibl. Bot. 17 (74): 1–336 (1911); Fedde Repert. 10: 489 (1912); Allan, Fl. New Zeal. 355 (1961).

Herbs often rather woody at the base, decumbent or spreading, with the flowering branches often scape-like and erect; leaves alternate, imparipinnate, leaflets incised or serrate, often multifid; stipules sheathing at the base, adnate to the petiole; flowers capitate or interruptedly spicate at the apex of stem or scape, small, green, red, or white, bracteate; calyx-tube persistent, nude or tuberculate, or armed with spreading hooks or spines; lobes 7–3, valvate, persistent or deciduous; petals absent; stamens 10–1, inserted in the throat of the calyx, sessile; styles subterminal, short, stigmas peltate, spathulate or dilated and fimbriate or penicellate; ovule solitary, pendulous; achenes dry, included in the indurated, smooth, tuberculate, or bristly calyx-tube; seed pendulous; cotyledons plano-convex; fruiting head often bristling with spines or hooks.

95. **Alchemilla**[1] Linn., Sp. Pl. 123 (1753); Gen. Pl. ed. 5: 58 (1754). *Percepier*

---

[1] Classified by Rydberg in N. Amer. Fl. 22: 377 (1908) into 4 genera, *Alchemilla* Linn., *Aphanes* Linn., *Lachemilla* Rydb., and *Zygalchemilla* Rydb. From an American point of

Moench (1794). *Aphanes* Linn. (1753). *Lachemilla* Rydb. (1908). *Zygalchemilla* Rydb. (1908). About 60 spp. or more, America, Africa, Europe, Asia; type *A. vulgaris* Linn., north temp. regions. B.H. 1: 621; E.P. 3, 3: 43; T. C. E. Fries, Species of Afr. Mts., Ark. Bot. 18: 11 (1923); Graham, Fl. Trop. E. Africa *Rosaceae*, 2, figs. 1, 2 (1960).

Perennial herbs, rarely annual, decumbent to erect; branches often densely covered with overlapping leaves; leaves alternate, orbicular, lobed, digitate or palmatipartite; stipules adnate to the sheathing petiole; flowers very small; mostly crowded into dense corymbs, rarely laxly cymose or solitary, ebracteate; calyx-tube urceolate, persistent, with constricted throat; lobes 10–8, 2-seriate, inner (sepals) valvate, outer (bracteoles) small; petals absent; stamens 4–1, inserted in the throat of the calyx, filaments short, free; disk lining the calyx-tube, margin thickened, closing the calyx; carpels 4–1, sessile or substipitate, free; style basal or ventral, filiform, glabrous, stigma capitellate; ovule solitary, ascending from the base of the loculus; achenes 4–1, enclosed by the calyx, membranous; seed basal, testa membranous; cotyledons, linear-obovoid.

Tribe 17. CERCOCARPEAE

Style not elongated in fruit; shrubs with small crowded opposite leaves:
Flowers solitary, terminal; stipules small, persistent; petals absent; stamens
40–20   96. **Coleogyne**
Flowers axillary; stipules large, hyaline, persistent; petals 3; stamens 3
97. **Potaninia**
Style elongated, long-plumose; shrubs with alternate simple leaves and solitary
or fasciculate flowers; petals absent; stamens 25–15   98. **Cercocarpus**

96. **Coleogyne** Torr., Smithson. Contrib. 6: 4, t. 4 (1854). 1 sp., *C. ramosissima* Torr., California, Nevada, Colorado. B.H. 1: 617; E.P. 3, 3: 39; Jephson, Fl. Calif. 2: 222 (1936); Rydb., N. Amer. Fl. 22: 397; Schneid., Laubholtzk. 1: 533.

Much-branched spinescent shrub; leaves opposite, small, entire, coriaceous, hairs medi-fixed; stipules small, persistent; flowers solitary, terminal, bracteate, bracts 3-fid; calyx-tube very short, lobes 4, large, yellowish inside, persistent; petals absent; stamens 40–20, filaments inserted at the base of the tubular disk which encloses the ovary; anthers oblong, cordate at the base; disk lining the calyx and 4-dentate at the apex; carpel 1, sessile in the base of the tubular disk but free, 1-locular; style lateral, villous at the base, twisted, exserted, persistent; ovule 1, in the middle of the loculus; fruit a coriaceous glabrous achene.

97. **Potaninia** Maxim., Bull. Acad. St. Petersb. 27: 465 (1881). 1 sp., *P. mongolica* Maxim., Mongolia. E.P. 3, 3: 36.

Shrublet with thick underground stock and with spine-like branchlets; leaves minute, ternate or 5-nate, the leaflets jointed with the apex of the petiole; stipules adnate to the petiole, large, hyaline; flowers axillary, ebracteate, minute, white; calyx-tube persistent, funnel-shaped, 3-bracteolate; lobes 3, deltoid; petals 3, scarcely larger than the calyx-lobes, deciduous; stamens 3, alternate with the petals; filaments short, inserted at the glabrous margin of the swollen disk densely silky inside; anthers ovate, not exserted, dorsifixed, introrse; carpel 1, central, oval, densely silky; style basal, stigma capitate; ovule 1, inserted laterally next to the style, ascending.

view this may seem feasible, but I prefer to accept the genus in its wider concept until monographic treatment of the world species is carried out. This needs a botanist of wide experience in other families as well as in *Rosaceae*.

98. **Cercocarpus** H. B. & K., Nov. Gen. et Sp. 6: 232, t. 559 (1823). *Bertolonia* Moç. & Sessé (1825). About 20 spp., W. North America, Mexico; type *C. fothergilloides* H. B. & K., Mexico. B.H. 1: 618; E.P. 3, 3: 38; Schneid., Laubholtzk. 1: 529; Jephson, Fl. Calif. 2: 216 (1936); Rehder, Trees and Shrubs, ed. 2: 424 (1940); Rydb., N. Amer. Fl. 22: 418; Martin, Brittonia, 7: 91 (1950) (revision).

Small trees or shrubs with spur-like branchlets; leaves alternate, simple, leathery, with straight nerves; stipules adnate to the base of the petiole; flowers sessile or shortly pedicellate, solitary or fasciculate, terminal; calyx-tube persistent, narrowly tubular and pedicel-like, sometimes split on one side in fruit; limb deciduous, cup-shaped; lobes 5, small, valvate; petals absent; stamens 25–15, 2–3-seriate; anthers often hairy; disk conspicuous, lining the calyx-tube; carpel 1, included in the calyx-tube, narrow and terete, silky; style terminal, filiform, villous, stigma obtuse; ovule solitary, suberect; achene villous, linear-oblong, enclosed by the calyx-tube, narrowed into a very long plumose twisted persistent style; seed linear; cotyledons linear-elongate.

Tribe 18. ADENOSTOMATEAE

99. **Adenostoma** Hook. & Arn., Bot. Beech. Voy. 139 (1832). 3 spp., W. North America; type *A. fasciculatum* Hook. & Arn., California, N. Mexico. Rydb., N. Amer. Fl. 22: 396; Schneid., Laubholtzk. 1: 533; Jepson, Fl. Calif. 2: 219 (1936).

Shrubs with fasciculate or alternate, rigid, filiform or clavate leaves; inflorescence paniculate with short spike-like branches and numerous very small flowers; calyx-tube urceolate or obconic, 10-angled, in fruit enclosing the single achene, often with 5 glands in the throat alternate with the sepals; sepals 5, rounded, mucronate; petals 5, orbicular, spreading; stamens 15–10, 2 or 3 opposite each sepal; anthers subglobose; carpel solitary; ovary obliquely obovoid, covered at the top by a hairy cushion; style lateral, inserted below the edge of the cushion, twice bent; stigma capitate; ovule solitary, pendulous; fruit an achene, covered by the indurated calyx-tube.

Tribe 19. ROSEAE

100. **Rosa**[1] Linn., Sp. Pl. 491 (1753); Gen. Pl. ed. 5: 217 (1754). Over 150 spp., Europe, Asia, Ethiopia, North America; type *R. centifolia* Linn., Caucasus region. B.H. 1: 625; E.P. 3, 3: 46; Crépin, Journ. Roy. Hort. Soc. London, 11: 217 (1889); Boulenger, Les Roses d'Europe de l'herb. Crépin, Bull. Jard. Bot. Brux. 10 (1924); Revision des roses d'Asie à la sect. des *Synstylae*, Ann. Soc. Sci. Brux. 53: (1933): Liste des roses d'Asie, &c., Ann. Soc. Sci. Brux. 56: (1936).

Erect trailing or scandent shrubs, mostly armed with prickles, glabrous to glandular-pilose; leaves alternate, imparipinnate, rarely 1-foliolate or leaves reduced to connate leaf-like stipules; leaflets mostly serrate; stipules adnate to the petiole; flowers solitary or corymbose, showy, white, yellow, rose, or red; calyx ebracteolate, tube globose to ventricose, constricted at the throat; lobes 5, rarely 4, spreading, more or less foliaceous, often pinnatisect, deciduous or persistent, imbricate; petals 5, very rarely 4, spreading, imbricate; disk lining the calyx-tube, often silky, the mouth annular and almost closing the calyx; stamens numerous in several series, inserted on the disk, filaments filiform; carpels numerous, rarely few, sessile inside the calyx-tube, free; styles ventral, exserted, free or connate in the upper part; ovules solitary, pendulous; achenes numerous, included in the berry-like calyx-tube; seed pendulous.

---

[1] Synonyms of **Rosa**: *Rhodophora* Neck. (1790). *Hulthemia* Dumort. (1824). *Lowea* Lindl. (1837). *Hultenia* Reichb. (1837). *Rhodopsis* Reichb. (1841). *Saintpierrea* Germ. de St. Pierre (1878). *Ernestella* Germ. de St. Pierre (1878). *Platyrhodon* Houst. (1927). *Hesperhodos* Cockerell (1913).

P

Tribe 20. Pomeae

Carpels drupaceous and bony when mature, the fruit containing 5–1 stones:
  Leaves simple or at most lobed (not pinnate):
    Leaves entire or rarely serrulate; branches unarmed:
      Flowers solitary, large and showy (3–5 cm. diam.); carpels 5
                                                   101. **Mespilus**
      Flowers small (less than 1 cm. diam.), usually in several- to many-flowered corymbs:
        Carpel 1, remaining free from the fleshy calyx   102. **Dichotomanthes**
        Carpels 2–5, united with the calyx-tube:
          Ovary 5–2-locular   103. **Cotoneaster**
          Ovary incompletely 10–6-locular   104. **Malacomeles**
      Flowers in racemes; carpel 1, united with the calyx-tube
                                               105. **Chamaemeles**
    Leaves crenate, dentate, or lobed, rarely entire; branches usually armed with spines:
      Leaves persistent; carpels 5, each with 2 fertile ovules   106. **Pyracantha**
      Leaves deciduous or subpersistent; carpels 5–1, with 1 sterile and 1 fertile ovule   107. **Crataegus**
      Leaves persistent; carpels 5, 1-locular, 1-ovuled   108. **Hesperomeles**
  Leaves pinnate; leaflets small, entire; ovary 5-locular, each loculus with 1 ovule   109. **Osteomeles**
Carpels with leathery or papery walls in fruit, the latter with often fleshy endocarp:
  Flowers in corymbs or panicles:
  Carpels partly free from each other:
    Carpels in fruit free to the middle (from above), endocarp dehiscent when mature; leaves persistent, entire or serrulate; flowers in corymbs
                                          110. **Stranvaesia**
    Carpels in fruit free only at the apex or at most to one-third of its height; flowers in corymbs or short panicles:
      Leaves pinnate or simple and then often coarsely lobed or toothed, deciduous, usually with straight excurrent nerves, not glandular on the rhachis above   111. **Sorbus**
      Leaves never pinnate, with glands on the midrib above, deciduous, with curving nerves; calyx-lobes persistent   112. **Aronia**
      Leaves never pinnate, without glands on the midrib above, sometimes evergreen   113. **Photinia** ˒
  Carpels wholly connate and inferior; leaves evergreen, dentate, with straight strong nerves ending in teeth; flowers in panicles (often woolly)
                                              114. **Eriobotrya**
  Flowers in umbels, racemes, or solitary:
  Carpels many- to 4-seeded:
    Styles connate at the base; leaves serrate or crenate, rarely entire:
      Ovules numerous in each loculus; calyx-lobes deciduous:
        Flowers in leafless clusters, appearing before or with the leaves; calyx-lobes entire   115. **Chaenomeles**

Flowers solitary on leafy shoots; calyx-lobes serrulate
116. **Pseudocydonia**
Ovules 10–4 in each loculus; calyx-lobes persistent · 117. **Docynia** ·
Styles free; sepals persistent, reflexed; leaves entire; ovules numerous in
each loculus   118. **Cydonia** ·
Carpels 2–1-seeded:
Ovary and fruit 5–2-locular; loculi 2-ovuled:
Leaves evergreen; ovary 2-locular; flowers in upright racemes or
panicles   119. **Raphiolepis** ·
Leaves deciduous; ovary 5–2-locular; flowers in umbel-like racemes:
Styles connate at the base; fruit usually globose or depressed-globose,
without or with very few grit-cells   120. **Malus**
Styles connate at the base; fruit with numerous grit-cells; leaves pal-
mately lobed like some spp. of *Acer*   121. **Eriolobus**
Styles free to the base; fruit usually pear-shaped, its flesh with numerous
grit-cells   122. **Pyrus** ·
Ovary and fruit incompletely 10–6-locular, loculi 1-ovulate:
Flowers usually in racemes; styles usually 5; petals longer than broad
123. **Amelanchier** ·
Flowers solitary or few in umbel-like corymbs; styles 3–2; mature fruits
yellowish, bitter; petals pink or rose, obovate   124. **Peraphyllum**

101. **Mespilus** Linn., Sp. Pl. 478 (1753); Gen. Pl. ed. 5: 214 (1754). 1 sp.,
M. germanica Linn., SE. Europe to Persia (cult. and naturalized in Cent.
Europe and Britain). B.H. 1; 626 (in *Pyrus*); E.P. 3, 3: 26; Schneid., Laub-
holtzk. 1: 764; Rehder, Trees and Shrubs, ed. 2: 358 (1940).

Tree, sometimes spiny; buds covered with imbricate scales; leaves deciduous, alternate,
serrulate; stipules deciduous; flowers solitary, showy, white, terminal on short leafy branches;
calyx-lobes large; petals broad; stamens 40–30; anthers red; carpels 5, connate; styles 5,
free; ovules paired; fruit apple-like, gaping at the apex, crowned by the leafy sepals; drupes 5,
bony.

102. **Dichotomanthes** Kurz, Journ. Bot. 11: 194, t. 133 (1873). 2 spp., China;
type *D. tristaniicarpa* Kurz, Yunnan. Hemsl., Hook. Ic. Pl. t. 2653; E.P.N. 260;
N. 2: 48.

Trees, young parts woolly-tomentose; leaves alternate, entire; flowers white, in terminal
corymbs; calyx with 2 bracteoles at the base, 5-toothed; fleshy and enlarged in fruit; petals 5,
rounded; stamens 20–15 inserted on a perigynous annulus, filaments alternately shorter;
anthers didymous; carpel 1 at the base of the calyx-tube, 1-locular; style lateral, stigma
capitate, lobulate; ovules 2, collateral, erect; fruit dry, oblong, slightly exserted from the
fleshy calyx, often 1-seeded, pericarp coriaceous.

103. **Cotoneaster** Medik., Phil. Bot. 1: 155 (1789). About 50 spp., north
temp. region and Mexico; type *C. integerrimus* Medik., Europe (incl. Brit.)
to N. Asia and Altai. B.H. 1: 627; E.P. 3, 3: 21; Schneid., Laubholtzk. 1: 744;
Rehder, Trees and Shrubs, ed. 2: 347 (1940).

Shrubs or erect small trees, sometimes decumbent; leaves alternate, leathery, often evergreen, entire or serrulate; stipules subulate, deciduous; flowers in axillary or terminal
cymes, rarely solitary; calyx-tube turbinate or campanulate, adnate to the ovary; lobes 5,
short, persistent; petals 5, erect or spreading, subsessile; stamens numerous, inserted at the

mouth of the calyx; ovary inferior, or the carpels free at the apex, 5–2-locular; styles 5–2, free, dilated at the apex; ovules 2 in each carpel, erect; fruit a small drupe, red or black, ovoid, globose or turbinate, containing 5–2 pyrenes, these bony, 1-seeded; seeds compressed; cotyledons plano-convex.

104. **Malacomeles** G. N. Jones, Madrono 8: 35 (1945). *Nagelia* Lindl. (1845). *Nägelia* Lindl. (1846), not Rabenhorst (1844). *Cotoneaster* sect. *Malacomeles* Decne. (1874). 2 spp., Mexico, S. United States, Cent. America; type *M. denticulata* (Kunth) G. N. Jones, Texas, Mexico, Cent. America.

Unarmed shrubs; leaves simple, alternate, entire or denticulate; stipules small; flowers corymbose or paniculate, terminating short new leafy branchlets; bracts persistent; calyx-tube more or less adnate to the carpels, lobes 5, imbricate, persistent; disk nectariferous; petals 5, white, suborbicular; stamens 20, inserted on the rim of the calyx-tube; styles 5–3, free to the base; carpels 5–3, cartilaginous or membranous, not bony; ovary inferior, incompletely 10–6-locular; styles 5–3; ovule 1 in each loculus; loculi of the fruit nearly divided by a false partition growing from the back of each carpel with 1 seed in each partition; fruit berry-like, juicy and edible; seeds brown, flattened, smooth; endosperm none.

105. **Chamaemeles** Lindl., Trans. Linn. Soc. 13: 104, t. 11 (1821). 1 sp., *C. coriacea* Lindl., Madeira. B.H. 1: 628; E.P. 3, 3: 27.

Glabrous shrub; leaves subfasciculate, thick, obovate to oblanceolate, crenulate; stipules small, deciduous; flowers small, in terminal and axillary racemes; pedicels bracteolate; calyx-tube turbinate, shortly adnate to the base of the ovary; lobes 5, short; petals suborbicular, clawed, erose; stamens 15–10; ovary inferior, 1-locular; style rather thick, stigma obtuse; ovules 2, basal, erect; drupe small, thinly fleshy, ovoid, crowned by the small calyx-limb; stone bony, 1-seeded; seed erect, obovoid; cotyledons closely much folded.

106. **Pyracantha** M. Roem., Synops. Monogr. 3: 104, 219 (1847). *Timbalia* Clos. (1871). *Sportella* Hance (1877). 6 spp., SE. Europe to Himalayas and Cent. China; type *P. coccinea* (Medik.) M. Roem. Schneid., Laubholtzk. 1: 761; Rehder, Trees and Shrubs, ed. 2: 357 (1940).

Shrubs, mostly spiny; leaves evergreen, alternate, narrow, entire or serrulate; stipules minute, caducous; corymbs compound, terminal; flowers white; calyx-lobes short; petals suborbicular, spreading; stamens 20; anthers yellow; carpels 5, ventrally free, dorsally half-adnate to the calyx-tube; fruit small, globose, red or orange, calyx persistent; pyrenes 5.

107. **Crataegus**[1] Linn., Sp. Pl. 475, partly (1753); Gen. Pl. ed. 5: 213, partly (1754). About 1,000 (or more) spp. (descr.), north temp. regions; type *C. oxyacantha* Linn., Europe, N. Africa. B.H. 1: 626; E.P. 3, 3: 26 (as *Mespilus*); Schneid., Laubholtzk. 1: 766; Rehder, Trees and Shrubs, ed. 2: 359 (1940); Palmer, Synop. North Amer. *Crataegus*, Journ. Arn. Arb. 6: 5 (1–25); see also Brittonia, 5: 471 (1946).

Shrubs or trees, branchlets often spiny; leaves alternate, simple, lobed or pinnately lobed, coriaceous or membranous, often deciduous; stipules usually small and deciduous; cymes corymbose, terminal, large, bracteate; bracts caducous; flowers white, rose, or red, scented; calyx-tube urceolate or campanulate, adnate to the carpels, lobes 5, persistent or deciduous; petals 5, inserted in the mouth of the calyx, spreading, orbicular; stamens numerous; ovary inferior or free at the top, 5–1-locular; styles 5–1, free, dilated at the apex; ovules 2 in each loculus, erect; fruit drupaceous, drupes usually small, red or black, rarely yellow, ovate to globose; stone bony, 5–1-locular, loculi 1- rarely 2-seeded; seeds erect, compressed; cotyledons plano-convex.

---

[1] Synonyms of **Crataegus**: *Lazarolus* Medik. (1789). *Oxyacantha* Medik. (1789). *Azarolus* Borkh. (1803). *Anthomeles* M. Roemer (1847). *Halmia* M. Roemer (1847).

108. **Hesperomeles** Lindl. Bot. Reg., sub t. 1956 (1837); Hook., Ic. Pl. t. 846; Wedd., Chlor. And. 2: 229. About 15 spp., Cent. and South America; lectotype *H. cordata* Lindl. Schneid., Engl. Bot. Jahrb. 42: 85 (1909).

Shrubs, sometimes spiny; leaves simple, toothed, sometimes bullate; flowers in terminal corymbs; calyx short, rigid, very open, 5-toothed; petals 5, concave, longer than the calyx-teeth; stamens 20; anthers short, didymous; ovary inferior, carpels 5, adnate to the calyx-tube, free on the inner angles, 1-locular ovule 1; styles 5, free, glabrous; fruit turbinate or globose, 5-locular, endocarp bony.

109. **Osteomeles** Lindl., Trans. Linn. Soc. 13: 98, t. 8 (1821). *Eleutherocarpum* Schlechtd. (1857). 4–5 spp., Burma and China to Polynesia; type *O. anthyllidifolia* Lindl., Hawaii. B.H. 1: 628; E.P. 3, 3: 22; Schneid., Laubholtzk. 1: 762.

Trees or shrubs; leaves alternate, evergreen, imparipinnate, leaflets entire; stipules small; flowers corymbose, bracteolate; calyx-tube campanulate or turbinate, adnate to the carpels; lobes 5, lanceolate or subulate, acute, persistent; petals 5; spreading; stamens numerous to 10, inserted in the throat of the calyx; carpels 5, more or less united and joined to the calyx-tube; styles 5, stigmas thickened; ovule solitary in each loculus, erect; drupe rather fleshy, with 5 pyrenes, the latter bony or crustaceous, often free from the calyx at the top; seed erect, compressed; cotyledons plano-convex.

110. **Stranvaesia** Lindl., Bot. Reg. t. 1956 (1837). 5 spp., Himalayas to China; type *S. glaucescens* Lindl., Himalayas. B.H. 1: 627; E.P. 3, 3: 26; Schneid., Laubholtzk. 1: 712; Rehder, Trees and Shrubs, ed. 2: 385 (1940).

Trees; leaves alternate, simple, evergreen; stipules setaceous; corymbs axillary and terminal, many-flowered; flowers white, woolly in bud; calyx-tube campanulate, half adnate to the base of the ovary; lobes 5, short, erect, persistent; petals 5, spreading; stamens up to 20, inserted in the mouth of the calyx; ovary villous, semi-inferior, 5-locular; styles 5, connate at the base, dilated at the apex, 2-lobed; ovules 2 in each loculus, ascending; drupe small, orange, ovoid or spherical, fleshy, endocarp 5-locular, crustaceous, loculi dorsally loculicidally dehiscent, valves septate in the middle; seeds oblong, compressed; cotyledons nearly flat.

111. **Sorbus**[1] Linn., Sp. Pl. 477 (1753); Gen. Pl. ed. 5: 213 (1754). About 80 spp., northern hemisphere, in America south to Mexico, in Asia south to Himalayas; type *S. domestica* Linn., S. Europe, N. Africa, W. Asia. B.H. 1: 626; E.P. 3, 3: 22 (in *Pyrus*); Schneid., Laubholtzk. 1: 667; Rehder, Trees and Shrubs, ed. 2: 373 (1940); Jones, Synop. North Amer. spp. of *Sorbus*, Journ. Arn. Arb. 20: 1 (1939).

Trees or shrubs; leaves deciduous, alternate, simple and often toothed or pinnately lobed, or imparipinnate or imperfectly so, plicate or rarely convolute in bud; corymbs terminal; flowers mostly white, rarely rose; calyx-lobes 5, mostly triangular; petals 5; stamens 20–15; anthers small, rounded; carpels 5–2, semi-inferior to inferior; styles free or connate at the base; ovules paired; fruit usually small, apple-shaped, very rarely pear-shaped, 5–2-locular, loculi with cartilaginous walls and 2–1-seeded.

112. **Aronia** Pers., Synop. 2: 39 (1807). *Adenorachis* Nieuwl. (1825). *Xeromalon* Raf. (1836). 3 spp., N. America; type *A. arbutifolia* (Linn. f.) Ell., E. North America. Rehder, Trees and Shrubs, ed. 2: 382 (1940).

Shrubs; leaves deciduous, glandular-denticulate, midrib black-glandular above, convolute in bud; stipules small, deciduous; corymbs small; flowers white or rose; calyx-lobes

---

[1] Synonyms of **Sorbus**: *Aucuparia* Riv. ex Ruppius (1745). *Chamaemespilus* Medik. (1789). *Aria* DC. (1825). *Cormus* Spach (1834). *Micromeles* Decne. (1874). *Ariosorbus* Koidz. (1934).

persistent; petals 5, spreading; stamens numerous; anthers purple; ovary 5-locular, woolly at the apex; styles 5, connate at the base; fruit very small, apple-like, with persistent calyx-lobes.

113. **Photinia** Lindl., Trans. Linn. Soc. 13: 103, t. 10 (1821). *Heteromeles* Roem. (1847). *Pourthiaea* Decne. (1874). *Myriomeles* Lindl. (1847). 60 spp., E. Asia, North and Cent. America; type *P. arbutifolia* Lindl., California. B.H. 1: 627; E.P. 3, 3: 25; Schneid., Laubholtzk. 1: 706.

Shrubs or trees; leaves alternate, evergreen or deciduous, simple; stipules sometimes rather leafy; flowers in terminal corymbs or panicles, often white; calyx-tube campanulate or turbinate, adnate to the ovary or free above; lobes 5, ovate, obtuse; petals 5, spreading; stamens up to 20, inserted in the throat of the calyx; ovary inferior or free at the top, 5–2-(rarely 1-) locular; styles 5–2, rarely 1, free or connate at the base, dilated at the apex; ovules 2 in each loculus, erect; drupe or berry ovoid, 5–1-locular, loculi 2–1-seeded; seeds erect; cotyledons plano-convex.

114. **Eriobotrya** Lindl., Trans. Linn. Soc. 13: 102 (1821). 15 spp., S. and E. Asia; type *E. japonica* Lindl., Japan and China. B.H. 1: 627 (in *Photinia*); E.P. 3, 3: 25; Nakai, Journ. Arn. Arb. 5: 67 (1924); Schneid., Laubholtzk. 1: 711; Rehder, Trees and Shrubs, ed. 2: 385 (1940).

Trees or shrubs; leaves large, dentate, with conspicuous parallel nerves; panicles broad, terminal, usually woolly; calyx-lobes acute; petals 5, clawed; stamens 20; anthers rounded; ovary inferior, 5–2-locular; styles 5–2, connate below; ovules paired; fruit apple-like, edible, with persistent incurved calyx-teeth.

115. **Chaenomeles** Lindl., Trans. Linn. Soc. 13: 97 (1822). 2 spp., E. Asia; type *C. japonica* (Thunb.) Lindl., Japan. Schneid., Laubholtzk. 1: 728; Rehder, Trees and Shrubs, ed. 2: 28 (excl. *Pseudocydonia* Schneid.) (1940).

Shrubs with spiny branches; buds small, with about 2 outer scales; leaves deciduous, appearing before or with the flowers, simple, toothed, often clustered on short shoots; stipules large, leafy, rounded; flowers in leafless clusters; calyx-lobes 5, upright, entire; petals 5, large, obovate-rounded; stamens 20 or more; styles 5, connate at the base; ovary 5-locular, loculi many-ovuled; fruit a large many-seeded pome; seeds brown.

116. **Pseudocydonia** C. K. Schneid., Fedde Repert. 3: 180 (1906). 1 sp., *P. sinensis* (Thouin) C. K. Schneid., China.

Shrub or small tree without spines; leaves obovate-elliptic, simple, with numerous gland-tipped teeth continued on the margin of the petiole; stipules rather large, elliptic, glandular-toothed; flowers solitary on leafy short shoots; calyx-lobes 5, serrulate, becoming reflexed; petals 5, rounded; stamens 20 or more; styles 5, connate at the base; ovary 5-locular, loculi many-ovuled; fruit globose to ovoid, very hard, fragrant; seeds brown.

117. **Docynia** Decne., Nouv. Arch. Mus. Par. 10: 131 (1874). 5 spp., China, Himalayas, Thailand, Annam; type *D. indica* Decne., Upper Burma, Thailand. Rehder, Trees and Shrubs, ed. 2: 399 (1940).

Trees, unarmed; leaves evergreen or semi-evergreen, ovate-elliptic to lanceolate, entire or serrate, stipulate; flowers 2–5 in umbels; calyx-lobes lanceolate; petals obovate, clawed; stamens 50–30; ovary 5-locular, each loculus with 10–3 ovules; styles 5, connate at the base, villous below; fruit more or less stipitate, ovoid to narrowly pear-shaped, fleshy, the calyx persistent.

118. **Cydonia** Mill., Gard. Dict. Abridg. ed. 4 (1754). 1 sp., *C. oblonga* Mill., Persia to Turkestan, and much cult. and naturalized. Schneid., Laubholtzk. 1: 654; Rehder, Trees and Shrubs, ed. 2: 400 (1940).

Shrub or small unarmed tree; buds small, with few scales; leaves deciduous, ovate-elliptic, entire, woolly below; stipules present, large, glandular-toothed; flowers terminal on short lateral leafy shoots, white or pink, showy; calyx-lobes 5, large, glandular-toothed, soon reflexed; petals 5, rounded-obovate, contorted; stamens 20, filaments free, glabrous; anthers cordate at the base, dorsifixed; ovary inferior, 5-locular, each loculus with numerous ovules; styles 5, free, villous in the lower half; fruit a large pear-shaped many-seeded pome; cotyledons fleshy.

119. Raphiolepis Lindl., Bot. Reg. t. 468 (1820) (conserved name). *Opa* Lour. (1790) partly. *Rhaphiolepis* Poir. (1827). About 15 spp., subtrop. E. Asia; type *R. indica* (Linn.) Lindl., S. China, Indo-China. B.H. 1: 627; E.P. 3, 3: 25; Nakai, Journ. Arn. Arb. 5: 61 (1924); Schneid., Laubholtzk. 1: 70; Rehder, Trees and Shrubs, ed. 2: 385 (1940).

Trees or shrubs; leaves alternate, evergreen, very coriaceous, serrate or entire; stipules subulate; inflorescence racemose, paniculate or corymbose; bracts subulate, deciduous; flowers white or red; calyx-tube adnate to the ovary, transversely splitting in the upper part, the 5 subulate lobes and stamens deciduous; petals 5, clawed; stamens numerous, inserted in the mouth of the calyx; ovary inferior, 2-locular; styles 2, elongated, connate at the base, obliquely thickened at the apex; ovules 2 in each loculus, erect; berry pulpy, 2–1-locular, mostly 1-seeded, scarred at the apex, often black; seeds globose or turgid; cotyledons thick, plano-convex or hemispherical.

120. Malus Mill., Gard. Dict. ed. 7 (1759). *Sinomalus* Koidz. (1932). *Docyniopsis* Koidz. (1934). About 25 spp., temp. northern hemisphere; type *M. sylvestris* Mill., Europe, W. Asia. B.H. 1: 626; E.P. 3, 3: 22 (in *Pyrus*); Schneid., Laubholtzk. 1: 714; Rehder, Trees and Shrubs, ed. 2: 389 (1940).

Trees and shrubs, branches rarely spiny; leaves deciduous or rarely subpersistent, plicate or convolute in bud, stipulate; racemes very short and umbelliform; flowers white, rose, or crimson; calyx-lobes persistent; petals suborbicular or obovate; stamens 50–15; anthers small, rounded; ovary inferior, 5–3-locular; styles 5–2, connate at the base; fruit pomaceous (apple), fleshy, calyx mostly persistent, 5–2-locular, loculi with cartilaginous shiny endocarp; seeds with cartilaginous testa becoming brown or blackish; cotyledons plano-convex.

121. Eriolobus Roemer, Synop. Monogr. 3: 216 (1847). 1 sp., *E. trilobatus* (Poir) Roemer, SE. Europe, Orient. Stapf, Bot. Mag. t. 9305 (1933); Schneid., Laubholtzk. 1: 725; Rehder, Trees and Shrubs, ed. 2: 398 (in *Malus*) (1940).

Medium-sized tree; buds perulate; leaves petiolate, resembling some spp. of *Acer*, crowded at the ends of the branchlets, palmately and subpinnately lobed, serrulate; stipules filiform, caducous; flowers showy, crowded in a terminal sessile or subsessile umbel-like corymb; bracts filiform, caducous; receptacle campanulate, tomentose; calyx-lobes soon strongly reflexed; petals orbicular, shortly clawed; stamens about 20; filaments free, glabrous, anthers dorsifixed, cordate at the base; ovary inferior, 5-locular; styles 5, united at the base; stigma capitate: fruit more or less globose, with persistent calyx and columnar part of styles; usually only 1 loculus fertile in each fruit, with 2–1 seeds; seeds compressed.

122. Pyrus Linn., Sp. Pl. 479 (1753); Gen. Pl. ed. 5: 214 (1754). About 25 spp., Europe to E. Asia, south to N. Africa, Persia, and Himalaya; type *P. communis* Linn., Europe, W. Asia. B.H. 1: 626 (partly); E.P. 3, 3: 22 (partly); Schneid., Laubholtzk. 1: 655; Rehder, Trees and Shrubs, ed. 2: 401 (1940); Rubstov, Geogr. distrib. of *Pyrus* and trends in its evolution, Amer. Nat. 78: 358 (1944).

Trees and shrubs, sometimes spinescent; leaves alternate, deciduous, simple, often serrate; stipules deciduous; racemes umbelliform; flowers white or rarely rose; bracts subulate, deciduous; calyx-lobes 5, reflexed, persistent or deciduous with the apex of the tube and stamens; petals 5, suborbicular, shortly clawed; disk lining the calyx-tube or thickened and spread over the top of the ovary; stamens 30–20; ovary inferior, 5–2-locular; styles free, stigmas truncate; ovules 2 in each loculus, ascending; fruit fleshy, 5–2-locular, endocarp of the loculi cartilaginous; seeds with an often cartilaginous and black testa; cotyledons plano-convex.

123. **Amelanchier** Medik., Phil. Bot. 1: 135 (1789). *Aronia* Pers., partly (1807). *Xeromelon* Raf. partly (1836). 25 spp., temp. northern hemisphere; type *A. ovalis* Medik., Cent. and S. Europe. B.H. 1: 628; E.P. 3, 3: 26; Wiegand, Genus *Amelanchier* in E. North Amer., Rhodora 14: 117 (1912); Schneid., Laubholtzk. 1: 731; Rehder, Trees and Shrubs, ed. 2: 386 (1940); Jones, North American spp. of *Amelanchier*, Illinois Biol. Monogr. 20, no. 2: 1 (1946).

Small trees or shrubs with slender branches; leaves alternate, simple, deciduous; stipules subulate, elongated, or small or absent; flowers in slender racemes; bracts narrow, deciduous; calyx-tube campanulate or urceolate, more or less adnate to the ovary; lobes 5, subulate or lanceolate, recurved, persistent; petals 5, erect or spreading, small or large or elongated; stamens numerous, inserted in the mouth of the calyx; ovary inferior or semi-inferior, 5–2-locular, loculi often partly divided by spurious septa; styles 5–2, connate and villous at the base, dilated and obliquely truncate at the apex; ovule solitary in each loculus, erect; berry small, 5–2- or spuriously 10–4-locellate, loculi 2–1-seeded, with membranous or coriaceous septa and endocarp; carpels free or connate within, often villous; seed erect; cotyledons plano-convex.

124. **Peraphyllum** Nutt. ex Torr. & Gray, N. Amer. Fl. 1: 474 (1840). 1 sp., *P. ramosissimum* Nutt., Oregon to Calif. and Colorado. Schneid., Laubholtzk. 1: 713; Jepson, Fl. Calif. 2: 233 (1936); Rehder, Trees and Shrubs, ed. 2: 389 (1940).

Shrub; leaves simple, deciduous, partly fasciculate; stipules minute, caducous; racemes umbelliform, terminal; flowers few, white or tinged with rose; calyx-lobes lanceolate, entire; petals 5, obovate, spreading; stamens 20; anthers small, rounded; ovary inferior, 3–2-locular, loculi with 2 ovules separated by a false septum; fruit small, apple-like, 6–4-locular, loculi 1-seeded, crowned by the persistent calyx-lobes.

Genera previously included in *Rosaceae*: *Atomostigma* O. Ktze. = **Myrcia** (*Myrtaceae*). *Canotia* Torr. = *Rutaceae*. *Euphronia* = *Trigoniaceae*. *Lecostemon* Sesse & Mocino = **Sloanea** (*Tiliaceae*). *Pterostemon* Schau. = **Canotia** (*Rutaceae*).

25. DICHAPETALACEAE[1]

Engl., Engl. & Prantl, Nat. Pflanzenfam. 3, 4: 345 (1896)

Trees, shrubs, or rarely subshrubs from a woody rootstock. Leaves alternate, pinnately nerved, entire; stipules usually deciduous. Inflorescence axillary but the peduncle mostly concrescent with the petiole, corymbose-cymose or subcapitate, or the flowers fasciculate. Flowers small, bisexual or unisexual; pedicels often articulated towards the top. Sepals 5, free or partly connate, sometimes unequal, imbricate. Petals 5, free and equal or connate and unequal, clawed, often narrow and 2-fid or 2-lobed or inflexed at the apex. Stamens 5,

---

[1] Conserved family name in favour of the older *Chailletiaceae* R.Br., Narr. Congo Append. 5: 442 (1818).

all or only 3 fertile, alternating with disk glands, free or adnate to the corolla-tube. Disk-glands free or united into a disk. Ovary free, 2–3-locular; styles 2–3, terminal, free or connate nearly to the apex; stigmas capitate or simple; ovules paired at the top of the loculi, pendulous, anatropous. Fruit a drupe, sometimes hispid, dry, 1–2-locular, loculi 1-seeded; seeds pendulous, without endosperm; embryo large. Type genus *Dichapetalum* Thouars.

Genera 4; species about 110.

DISTRIBUTION. Tropics; one species in extratropical S. Africa.

CLASSIFICATION. Benth. & Hook. f., Gen. Pl. 1: 340 (1862); Engl. & Prantl, Nat. Pflanzenfam. 3, 4: 345 (1896).

ADDITIONAL LITERATURE. De Wild., Rev. Zool. Afr. 6: Supp. Bot. (1919) ('Notes sur les espèces africaines du genre *Dichapetalum* Thonn.'); Engler, Bot. Jahrb. 46: 562–97 (1912), trop. Afr. spp.; M. B. Moss, Kew Bull. 1928: 115 (E. S. trop. & sub-trop. Afr. spp. of *Dichapetalum*); Leenhouts, Asian, Australian, and Polynesian spp. of *Dichapetalum*, Reinwardtia, 4: 75 (1956).

ANATOMICAL FEATURES. According to Solereder *Dichapetalaceae* are distinguished by a series of anatomical characters: the stomata have sub-sidiary cells parallel to the pore as in *Rubiaceae,* and occur only on the lower surface of the leaf; cork is superficial in origin; indumentum composed solely of simple unicellular hairs; no glandular hairs.

Metcalfe & Chalk state that the anatomical features are not sufficient to be of much assistance in determining the taxonomic position of this small family. For want of a better place it is put here next to the *Rosaceae.* Charac-ters to be noted are the presence of unicellular hairs with conical or wart-shaped papillae on the surface of the leaves and the rubiaceous type of stomata; also the frequent occurrence of mucilaginous cells in the epidermis, hypodermis, and sometimes ground tissue of the petiole and branch.

According to Erdtman pollen similar to that of *Dichapetalum* occurs in several other families and gives no particular indication of relationship.

ANATOMY. Sol. 1: 198; M.C. 1: 358. POLLEN. Erdt. 145.

Economic Properties. Several species are poisonous, particularly *Dicha-petalum cymosum* (Hook. f.) Engl., which is found in the High Veld of S. Africa, and is known as the Poison Leaf, Gifblaar, Gifblad, &c. In the past it caused annually great loss to farmers, because in spring it is one of the few plants available before the grass has grown. Other African species are poisonous (see Kew Bull. 1928: 115).

Phylogeny and Morphology. The most interesting morphological feature is the frequent concrescence of the petiole and the peduncle of the inflores-cence, the latter then apparently arising from the base of the leaf-blade. This is a feature more fully developed in some *Flacourtiaceae* (q.v.) and in *Helwingia* (*Araliaceae*). That the family is considerably advanced is shown by the sym-petalous corolla of two of the genera, with only three fertile stamens in *Tapura*. In this genus, also, the peduncle is always adnate to the petiole.

Bentham & Hooker f. placed the family at the end of their *Geraniales*, after *Meliaceae*, and considered it to be related to *Celastraceae* and *Rhamnaceae*. Engler included it in his Reihe *Geraniales*, between the *Polygalaceae* and *Euphorbiaceae*. I cannot see any relationship with any of these families. **Geographical Distribution.** *Dichapetalaceae* are nearly confined to the tropics, only one species occurring in extra-tropical S. Africa. The largest and most widely spread genus is *Dichapetalum*, which is found through most parts of the tropics, particularly in Africa. *Stephanopodium* occurs only in tropical S. America, but *Tapura* is both there and in tropical Africa.

Fertile stamens 5:

Petals usually free from one another; anthers not sessile   1. **Dichapetalum**

Petals partly united:

Anthers sessile   2. **Stephanopodium**

Anthers on slender filaments   3. **Falya**

Fertile stamens 3; anthers on slender filaments; petals united into a somewhat

zygomorphic corolla   4. **Tapura**

1. **Dichapetalum**[1] Thou., Gen. Nov. Madag. 23 (1806). *Chailletia* DC. (1811). About 100 spp., tropics and subtropics; type *D. madagascariense* Thou., Madagascar. B.H. 1: 341; E.P. 3, 4: 348; M. B. Moss, Kew Bull. 1928: 115; Leenhouts, *Dichapetalum* in Asia, Australia, and Melanesia, Reinwardtia, 4: 75 (1956).

Small trees or shrubs, erect or scandent, rarely undershrubs; leaves alternate, entire; stipules 2, caducous; inflorescence axillary, cymose or corymbose, often many-flowered, peduncle free or adnate to the petiole; flowers small, mostly white, sometimes polygamous or dioecious; calyx 5-partite; petals 5, free, broadly clawed, inflexed and 2-lobed at the apex, open in bud; stamens 5, equal; anthers broadly oblong, connective more or less thickened; disk glands 5, opposite the petals or connate into a sinuate disk; ovary free, subglobose, 3–2-locular; styles 3–1, free or partly connate; drupe coriaceous, stone 2–1-locular, crustaceous or bony.

2. **Stephanopodium** Poepp. & Endl., Gen. et Sp. 3: 40, t. 246 (1842). 4 spp., trop. South America; type *S. peruvianum* Poepp. & Endl., Peru. B.H. 1: 341; E.P. 3, 4: 350.

Erect trees; leaves entire, membranous; stipules deciduous; flowers crowded at the top of the petiole, small, white; calyx campanulate, 5-fid; corolla sympetalous, 5-fid, lobes subequal; stamens 5, alternate with the corolla-lobes; anthers sessile, with a thick connective; disk-glands 5; ovary 2-locular; styles 2, filiform, free or partly connate; drupe coriaceous, 2-locular; seeds not known.

3. **Falya** Descoings, Natural. Malgache, 9: 171, fig. 1 (1957), 1 sp., *F. leandriana* Descoings, Madagascar.

Small tree; leaves alternate, obovate, densely hairy on lower part of the midrib, stipulate; inflorescence axillary, from the petiole; flowers glomerate, bisexual, slightly zygomorphic; sepals 5, free, imbricate; petals 5, imbricate, united in the lower third, entire or bilobed; stamens 5, filaments adnate to the corolla-tube, then free above; anthers composed of 2 erect parallel laminas; disk annular; ovary 3-sided, 3-locular; ovule solitary in each loculus, pendulous; style undivided, stigma capitate; fruit drupaceous, 3-lobed, rather fleshy, with 2–3 endospermic seeds.

---

[1] Other synonyms of **Dichapetalum**: *Leucosia* Thou. (1806). *Symphyllanthus* Vahl (1810). *Plappertia* Reichb. (1828). *Moacurra* Roxb. (1832). *Quilesia* Blanco (1837). *Patrisia* Rohr. ex Steud. (1840). *Mestotes* Soland. ex Steud. (1842). *Pentastira* Ridley (1916).

4. Tapura Aubl., Pl. Guian. 1: 126, t. 48 (1775). *Rohria* Schreb. (1789). *Gonypetalum* Ule (1907). 8 spp., trop. America and trop. Africa; type *T. guianensis* Aubl., Guianas and Venezuela. B.H. 1: 341; E.P. 3, 4: 351.

Shrubs; leaves entire, coriaceous; stipules small, subpersistent: flowers white, axillary but peduncle adnate to the petiole, densely crowded, cymose; bracts minute and scale-like; calyx 5-partite, inner 2 segments larger; corolla sympetalous, irregularly 5-fid, outer 3 lobes narrow and entire, inner 2 broad and emarginate or 2-fid, hooded; stamens adnate to the apex of the corolla-tube, 3 perfect and exserted, 2 without anthers between the smaller corolla-lobes; disk semiannular or 2–3-partite; ovary globose, 3–2-locular; style filiform, 3–2-lobed at the apex; drupe coriaceous, stone 3–2-locular, crustaceous or bony.

26. CALYCANTHACEAE

Lindl., Bot. Reg. 5: no. 404 (1819) (*Calycantheae*)

Shrubs with aromatic bark; buds scaly or naked; leaves opposite, entire; stipules absent. Flowers bisexual, axillary, solitary, fragrant, sometimes precocious. Sepals and petals in several series, imbricate, the outer bract-like the remainder petaloid, inserted towards the top of a thick urceolate torus (receptacle). Stamens numerous, inserted at the top of the torus; filaments short and free; anthers 2-locular, extrorse, dehiscing lengthwise by slits, apiculate. Carpels numerous, free, inserted on the inside of the hollow torus; styles filiform, free. Ovules solitary or 2 superposed in each carpel, anatropous, ascending. Fruits 1-seeded, enclosed in the fleshy enlarged torus; seed erect, without endosperm, and with folded foliaceous cotyledons. Type genus *Calycanthus* Linn.

Genera 2; species 7.

DISTRIBUTION. NE. Asia and North America.

CLASSIFICATION. Benth. & Hook. f., Gen. Pl. 1: 16; Engl. & Prantl, Nat. Pflanzenfam. 3, 2: 94; Pollard, N. Amer. Fl. 22: 237 (1908); Lawrence, Taxon. Vasc. Pl. 507, fig. 143 (1951); Hutch., Fam. Fl. Pl. ed. 2, 1: 151, fig. 26, with map (1959).

ADDITIONAL LITERATURE. J. Peter, Zur Entwickelungsgeschichte einiger Calycanthaceen, Cohn Beitr. Biol. Pfl. 14: 59 (1920); Schurhoff, Zur Apogamie von *Calycanthus*, Flora 116: 73 (1923); Sax, Chromosome behaviour in *Calycanthus*, Journ. Arn. Arb. 14: 279 (1933).

ANATOMY. Aromatic early flowering garden shrubs characterized by four cortical vascular bundles inversely orientated as regards the position of the xylem and phloem groups, and by the presence of secretory cells; hairs unicellular, and lack of glandular hairs; the stomata are accompanied by two subsidiary cells parallel to the pore and confined to the lower surface. Apparently the anatomical characters do not favour the relationship accorded here to the family. The lack of endosperm in the seeds and the opposite leaves without stipules seem to warrant exclusion from near *Magnoliaceae*, as accorded them by Bentham & Hooker f. Sol. 1: 25; M.C. 1: 13.

Economic Properties. Both genera are cultivated for their fragrant flowers. Allspice, *Calycanthus floridus* Linn., bark aromatic.

Stamens numerous (30–10) in several series; flowers brownish-red or purplish
                                                    1. Calycanthus
Stamens few in 2 series; flowers yellowish-white   2. Chimonanthus

1. **Calycanthus**[1] Linn., Syst. ed. 10: 1066 (1759) (conserved name). 4 spp., North America; type *C. floridus* Linn., E. North America. B.H. 1: 16; E.P. 3, 2: 94; Rehder, Trees and Shrubs, ed. 2: 255 (1940).

Shrubs; leaves deciduous; flowers purple or reddish; sepals and petals in several series, the outermost bract-like, the inner petaloid; stamens in several series, outer fertile, inner gradually smaller and sterile; carpels and fruit as described for the family.

2. **Chimonanthus** Lindl., Bot. Reg. t. 451 (1819) (conserved name). *Meratia* Loisel. (1819). 3 spp., China; type *C. praecox* (Linn.) Lindl. Rehder, Trees and Shrubs, ed. 2: 256 (1940).

Shrubs; leaves deciduous or evergreen; flowers small, yellowish; outer sepals numerous, bract-like, somewhat distinct from the several series of petals; stamens 2-seriate, outer fertile, united at the base, inner sterile, united after flowering into a cone partially enclosing the torus; carpels and fruit as described for the family.

---

[1] Synonyms of **Calycanthus**: *Beureria* Ehret (1755). *Butneria* Duhamel (1755). *Basteria* Mill. ex Adans. (1763). *Buttneria* Duhamel (1801). *Pompadoura* Buc'hoz ex DC. (1828). *Byttneria* Steud. (1840). *Buerera* O. Ktze. (1891). *Buettneria* Kearney (1894). *Buettnera* Auth.

A large and very natural (homogeneous) assemblage of three closely related families and about 570 genera widely distributed over most of the world, with many of great economic importance; *Caesalpiniaceae* and *Mimosaceae* mainly in the tropics, with the most advanced family, *Fabaceae* (*Papilionaceae*), more widely spread into temperate regions; *Caesalpiniaceae* most closely related to the more primitive *Rosaceae*, the *Mimosaceae* being relatively more advanced, and the zygomorphic-flowered *Fabaceae* (*Papilionaceae*) the climax group; carpel reduced to 1, and seeds devoid of (rarely with scanty) endosperm.

Petals imbricate in bud, the adaxial (uppermost) overlapped on each side by the adjacent lateral petals (when these present); flowers more or less zygomorphic; anthers uniform (very rarely dimorphic), dehiscing lengthwise or by terminal pores; leaves mostly pinnate or bipinnate (very rarely simple), without stipels; radicle never folded   27. *Caesalpiniaceae*

Petals valvate or very rarely imbricate in bud, free or sympetalous; flowers actinomorphic; anthers uniform, dehiscing lengthwise, sometimes with a deciduous gland at the apex; leaves bipinnate (rarely simply pinnate); radicle never folded   28. *Mimosaceae*

Petals imbricate in bud (rarely absent), the adaxial (uppermost) outside the adjacent lateral (wing) petals and forming with the keel petals a strongly zygomorphic corolla (very rarely actinomorphic), usually free or only weakly united along one margin; stamens rarely free, monadelphous in a closed tube or more usually the adaxial (vexillary) filament free and the remainder connate into a unilateral sheath, open on the adaxial or rarely also on the abaxial side; anthers either uniform or dimorphic and then mostly alternately basifixed and dorsifixed; radicle sometimes folded   29. *Fabaceae* (*Papilionaceae*)

27. CAESALPINIACEAE

R.Br., Flinders Voy. Terra Austr. 2: 551 (1814) (*Caesalpineae*)

Trees, shrubs, or very rarely herbs. Leaves nearly always alternate, pinnate or bipinnate, pinnae or leaflets 1-many-pairs, rarely leaves simple or 1-foliolate, sometimes with translucent dots; stipules paired, mostly caducous; stipels absent or rarely present and minute. Flowers zygomorphic, very rarely actinomorphic, usually 5-merous, mostly bisexual, some large and showy, others very small; inflorescence racemose or paniculate, axillary, terminal or rarely leaf-opposed. Sepals 5, or 4 by the union of 2, free or partly united, imbricate or rarely valvate, often much reduced when the bracteoles are large and calyx-like and covering the bud. Petals 5 or fewer, rarely absent, the adaxial innermost, the others variously imbricate. Stamens 10 or fewer,

[1] *Leguminales*, a New Ordinal Name, G. N. Jones, Taxon. 4: 188 (1955).

rarely numerous, free to variously connate; anthers various, usually dehiscing lengthwise, rarely by terminal pores, 2-locular; extra-staminal disk sometimes present. Ovary free or when stipitate the stipe sometimes more or less adnate to the calyx-tube, of 1 carpel, 1-locular with a ventral suture; style single, undivided. Ovules many to 1, superposed. Fruit 2-valved, or indehiscent and drupaceous or samaroid. Seeds sometimes arillate, rarely with endosperm; cotyledons fleshy or foliaceous; radicle straight or rarely slightly oblique, never folded.

Genera 152; species nearly 2800.

DISTRIBUTION. Mostly tropical and subtropical, most numerous in tropical America.

CLASSIFICATION AND ADDITIONAL LITERATURE. Benth. & Hook. f., Gen. Pl. 1: 434 (1865) (as suborder of *Leguminosae*); Taubert, Engl. & Prantl., Nat. Pflanzenfam. 3, 3: 125 (1894); E. G. Baker, Legum. Trop. Afr. (1926); Britton & Rose, N. Amer. Fl. *Caesalpiniaceae*, 23: 201 (1930); Ducke, Legum. Amaz. Brasil. Bot. Técn. Inst. Agron. do Norte no. 18: 71 (1949); Hutch. & Dalz., Fl. W. Trop. Afr. 1: 325 (1928); ed. 2 (Keay), 1: 439 (1958); J. Léonard, Les *Cynometra* et les genres voisins en Afrique tropicale, Bull. Jard. Bot. Brux. 21: 372 (1951); Wilczek, J. Léonard, Hauman & Hoyle, Fl. Congo Belge, 3: 234 (1952); Burkart, Legum. Argent. ed. 2: 149, figs. 23–41 (1952); J. Léonard, Genera des *Cynometreae* et des *Amherstieae* africaines, Mém. Acad. Roy. Belg. Cl. Sci. 30: fasc. 2, with numerous figures (1957); Senn, Relations of and cytology to the classification of *Leguminosae*, Chron. Bot. 7: 306 (1943).

ANATOMY. According to Solereder only a few anatomical features are common to *Caesalpiniaceae*. These are simple perforations in the vessels, wood-prosenchyma with simple pits, superficial development of cork, and a composite and continuous sclerenchymatous ring at the outer margin of the bast. Simple unicellular hairs are very common. Tannin-sacs, noted for *Fabaceae* (*Papilionaceae*) (p. 297), are almost entirely absent. The stomata vary, and they may or may not be accompanied by subsidiary cells parallel to the pore. Clothing and glandular hairs are very varied in their structure. Sol. 281. M.C. 1: 487. POLLEN. Erdt. 227.

Characters occurring in relatively few Genera. **Leaves** bipinnate and simply paripinnate on the same plant in *Gleditsia*; also in *Haematoxylon*; leaf-rhachis very short and ending in a sharp spine-like point in *Parkinsonia*; leaves and other parts gland-dotted in *Hoffmanseggia* and *Cordeauxia*; indumentum of stellate hairs in *Cenostigma*. **Stipules** pinnate in *Jacqueshuberia* and *Sclerolobium*; large, long, linear, and spirally folded around the apical bud in *Hylodendron* and *Daniellia*; peduncles extremely long (up to 2·5 m.) and pendulous in *Eperua* spp. **Bracts** large and coloured in *Lysidice*, *Maniltoa*, *Plagiosiphon*, *Neochevalierodendron*, *Brownea*, *Elizabetha*, *Paloue*, *Amherstia*, *Humboldtia*, *Daniellia*, *Hymenostegia*, and *Berlinia* spp. **Flowers** polygamous in *Gleditsia*, *Gymnocladus*, *Arcoa* (or dioecious), *Apuleia* spp.; dioecious in *Tetrapterocarpon*. **Petal** 1 in *Aprevalia*, *Afzelia*, *Julbernardia*, *Monopetalanthus*,

Cryptosepalum, Macrolobium Campsiandra, Brownea. **Stamens** numerous (more than 15) in *Polystemonanthus, Schizoscyphus*; 5 in *Koompassia, Didelotia, Acrocarpus, Duparquetia, Zenia, Androcalymma*; 4 in *Tetrapterocarpon*; 3 or 2 in *Distemonanthus, Cryptosepalum, Dialium, Dicorynia, Apuleia, Labichea, Petalostylis*; **anthers** dimorphic in *Moldenhauera*; anthers opening by pores in *Storkiella, Kalappia, Androcalymma, Labichea, Martiodendron, Duparquetia, Distemonanthus, Cassia, Baudoniniana,* and *Koompassia*. **Style** dilated and petaloid in *Petalostylis*. **Fruit** 1-seeded at the base and with a terminal oblique wing at the top in *Pterolobium*; **seeds** winged in *Melanoxylon*.

Economic Properties. These are mainly useful timbers, and are noted at the end of the descriptions of the various genera.

Phylogeny and Morphology. It is merely a matter of opinion or convenience (or even of prejudice!) whether *Caesalpiniaceae* should be treated as a separate family from *Mimosaceae* and *Fabaceae* (*Papilionaceae*) or all three regarded as subfamilies of *Leguminosae*. It is a fallacy to assume that all of this group have the fruit a *legume*, as botanically defined.[1] Very many have not. Quite a number of families are less easy to separate, and I prefer to continue to treat these three, each already unwieldy enough, as separate families, as in my *Families of Flowering Plants*, in the *Flora of West Tropical Africa*, and in other works such as the *Flore du Congo Belge*. Botanists fortunately are not hidebound by rules in such matters and are free to please themselves. No one is 'correct' in such cases, and nowadays there is a strong tendency amongst taxonomists to reduce the size of families and genera, especially those depending on a *single character*.

As noted under *Rosaceae*, considered to be a basic group for the *Leguminales*, one of the most advanced tribes of that family is *Chrysobalaneae*, in which the flowers are usually somewhat zygomorphic or asymmetric, with the fruit tending towards the leguminous type. All its genera are confined to the tropics and subtropics, like most of the *Caesalpiniaceae*. There seems to be rather a close connexion between this tribe of *Rosaceae* and the genus *Bandeiraea*, W. African, with simple undivided leaves and with the same general facies as some *Chrysobalaneae*. I regard this genus, and also *Bauhinia* (*sensu* Bentham and Taubert), as something of a connecting link between the two families. A longitudinal section of a flower of *Bauhinia maximilianii* Benth., seemingly a primitive species of the genus with undivided leaves, bears a great resemblance to that of several species of *Parinari* in *Chrysobalaneae*.

The different types of leaves in *Caesalpiniaceae* may provide an indication of the general trend of evolution within the family. Those with simply pinnate leaves, and amongst them those that have retained an odd terminal leaflet (imparipinnate) are perhaps the most primitive. This would appear to be the first stage in the evolution of a simply pinnate leaf, the separation of the lateral nerves into leaflets and the retention of the upper part of the midrib as the backbone of a terminal leaflet. It may be observed that the terminal leaflet of

---

[1] Daydon Jackson's Glossary of Botanic Terms says of a *legume*: 'the seed vessel of *Leguminosae, one-celled and two-valved,* but various in form.' The italics are mine.

a simply pinnate leaf is usually larger and of a different shape from the lateral ones, even in many cases conforming more or less to the general shape of the leaf as a whole.

A further stage is the suppression of either, (1) the terminal leaflet, giving the *paripinnate* leaf (often a barren tip of the rhachis is present, indicating the suppression of the terminal leaflet), or, (2) the reduction of the lateral leaflets, leaving only the terminal one, the *unifoliolate* leaf. The latter is much more common in *Fabaceae*. By further subdivision of the leaflets of paripinnate and imparipinnate leaves, the evolution of various types of bi-pinnate leaves is easily understood.

Another very interesting feature which has arisen in the flowers of several genera is the complete or almost complete reduction of the calyx. Compensation for the loss of this protective envelope, however, is provided for by the *enlargement of the bracteoles*. These in several genera have become thick and *valvate* and entirely cover the remaining parts of the flower whilst in bud, often resembling an old-fashioned purse and simulating an ordinary calyx to a marked degree. Examples are the well-known genera *Berlinia*, *Brachystegia*, and several others which I have grouped together into a newly named sub-family, the *Brachystegioideae*, representing in my opinion the most recently evolved group of the family.

In the partly phylogenetic and partly artificial diagnostic key, therefore, those genera with simply pinnate leaves precede those that are twice pinnate, those with petals precede those without petals, those with imbricate sepals or calyx-lobes come before those with valvate sepals or calyx-lobes, and im-paripinnate take precedence over paripinnate leaves.

Caesalpiniaceae are almost without exception trees and shrubs, but in the African genus *Cryptosepalum* the habit varies from trees to shrubs and to her-baceous annual shoots from an underground rootstock; reduction in the number of petals and stamens also accompanies this reduced habit.

Notes on the tribes of suborder **Caesalpinieae** in Bentham & Hooker's *Genera Plantarum*

Unfortunately it has not been possible to continue to use the tribes employed by Bentham & Hooker, not only because the differences amongst them were often very slight and over-lapping, but also because the number of genera has increased twofold (76 in B. & H., and over 150 in the present work). Many of these genera are new discoveries, others are splits from older conceptions, most of them no doubt quite justified. Here follows a translation of Bentham & Hooker's tribes so that a student may see for himself how slight the differences appear to be.

Tribe *Sclerolobieae*. Leaves imparipinnate or rarely paripinnate; ovary-stipe free from the base of the calyx; ovules 3–numerous.

Tribe *Eucaesalpinieae*. Leaves all or mostly bipinnate; ovary-stipe free from the base of the calyx; ovules numerous or rarely 1–2.

Tribe *Cassieae*. Leaves imparipinnate or paripinnate; ovary-stipe free from the base of the calyx; anthers opening by 2 pores or short slits, or when longitudinally dehiscent erect, basifixed, and not versatile.

Tribe *Bauhinieae*. Leaves simple, entire, 2-lobed or rarely 2-foliolate; calyx gamosepalous above the disk or valvately partite; stipe of ovary free or adnate to the calyx-tube; ovules 2–numerous.

Tribe *Amherstieae*. Leaves paripinnate or rarely imparipinnate, 3-numerous or very
rarely 1-foliolate; stipe of the ovary adnate here and there to the calyx-tube; ovules
3-numerous.

Tribe *Cynometreae*. Leaves abruptly pinnate, 2-numerous-foliolate; ovary 1–2-ovuled;
flowers often small.

Tribe *Dimorphandreae*. Leaves bipinnate, very rarely imparipinnate; flowers small, spicate;
calyx gamosepalous beyond the disk; ovules numerous.

GEOGRAPHICAL DISTRIBUTION. The greatest number of genera occur in
tropical Africa and tropical America, in the former about 56, in the latter
about 40 being endemic in each region. Only about 8 additional genera
occur in both regions. In Malaya and New Guinea there are only about
11 genera, in tropical Asia about an equal number, and in Madagascar there
are 9 endemic genera. The family is very poorly represented in Polynesia, S.
China, Australia, and extra-tropical South America, whilst in the north
temperate zone only about 3 genera occur, *Cercis* from S. Europe through
Central and E. Asia to Japan and in North America; *Ceratonia* in the E.
Mediterranean (and cult.), and *Gleditsia* in North and South America,
temperate and subtropical Asia, and the Malay Archipelago.

Only a few genera call for special mention. *Dalhousiea*, very natural, in
India and W. tropical Africa; *Bowringia*, E. Asia and W. tropical Africa;
Calpurnia, S. India and Africa; and *Cladrastis*, NE. America and E. Asia.

KEY TO SUBFAMILIES AND ARTIFICIAL GROUPS OF GENERA

Subfamily I. CAESALPINIOIDEAE. Bracteoles usually quite small and often
soon falling off, neither resembling nor taking the place of the calyx, the
latter normally developed and more or less conspicuous; if bracteoles
larger then mostly more or less petaloid and at length deciduous. Type
genus *Caesalpinia*.

Subfamily II. BRACHYSTEGIOIDEAE.[1] Bracteoles large (rarely small), opposite, valvate, not petaloid (or if so then calyx obsolete), persistent, enclosing or mostly enclosing the remainder of the flower in bud and
often resembling a calyx, the latter then usually reduced or obsolete.
Type genus *Brachystegia*.

Subfamily 1. **Caesalpinioideae**—key to artificial groups, though these are
arranged phylogenetically

Leaves once pinnate (vary rarely subdigitate) or reduced to one leaflet, or
leaves primitively simple (sometimes deeply bilobed):
Petals or petal present, though sometimes some or all variously reduced:
Sepals imbricate in bud:
Leaves imparipinnate (i.e. with an odd terminal leaflet), neither uni-
foliolate nor simple   Group 1 (genera 1–21)

---

[1] BRACHYSTEGIOIDEAE, subfam. nov.—Bracteolae magnae (raro parvae), oppositae, val-
vatae, haud petaloideae (vel si petaloideae tum calyce deficiente), persistentes, ceterum
florem in alabastro omnino vel pro maxima parte includentes et calycem simulantes, tum
calyce plerumque reducto vel deficiente.

Leaves paripinnate (i.e. without an odd terminal leaflet), sometimes
   simple, entire or bilobed, 1-foliolate, or rarely reduced to phyllodes
                                        Group 2 (genera 22–64)
Sepals valvate or open in bud   Group 3 (genera 65–78)
Petals absent   Group 4 (genera 79–95)
Leaves twice pinnate   Group 5 (genera 96–125)

Subfamily II. **Brachystegioideae**   (genera 126–152)

GROUP 1

Stamens 20–15; filaments long-exserted; racemes short, corymbose-paniculate;
   petals obovate-oblong; fruit large, flat, 2-valved; trop. South America
                                              1. **Campsiandra**
Stamens 10–8, sometimes some reduced to staminodes:
Filaments free among themselves:
Fruits splitting to the base by both margins into 2 valves (not samaroid);
  Seeds winged; filaments villous at the base; fruits septate between the
    seeds; petals orbicular; trop. South America   2. **Melanoxylon**
  Seeds subkeeled on one side; filaments glabrous; fruits not septate be-
    tween the seeds; petals clawed; trop. South America
                                          3. **Recordoxylon**
Seeds neither winged nor keeled but fruits winged on one side; filaments
   glabrous; petals oblong; anthers opening at the apex by pores or
   short slits; Pacific Islands region.   4. **Storkiella**
Seeds not winged; fruits not winged; anthers opening by slits:
  Flowers in 2 ranks (distichous); leaflets with translucent dots
                                    5. **Gilletiodendron**
  Flowers in more than 2 ranks; leaflets without dots   6. **Scorodophloeus**
Fruits splitting only along one margin (follicular); seeds not winged:
  Petiole (rhachis) not glandular between the leaflets; ovules 3–2:
    Stipules intrapetiolar, short, triangular; stamens 10, free, all fertile;
      anthers opening by slits; stipe of ovary obliquely dilated at apex
                                          7. **Batesia**
    Stipules obscure; 2 stamens fertile, remainder abortive or reduced to
      staminodes; anthers opening by terminal pores; ovary sessile
                                        8. **Kalappia**
  Petiole (rhachis) glandular between all or only the lower leaflets; ovule 1;
    petals subspathulate; fruit unequally obovate, long-narrowed at the
    base; ovary shortly stipitate   9. **Vouacapoua**
Fruits indehiscent, winged at the base with the single seed at the top or base;
   filaments elongated, thread-like and conspicuous, glabrous; ovules few,
   2-seriate:
  Filaments elongated, thread-like and conspicuous, glabrous; ovules few,
    2-seriate; sepals 5; seed at the top of the fruit   18. **Bathiaea**
  Filaments not as above; seed at the base of the fruit   11. **Pterogyne**
Filaments united at the base into a short tube; flowers in thick hairy clusters
   on the branches or stem; ovules 2; calyx-segments 5
                                        12. **Anthagathis**

Stamens 5–4, sometimes with 2 or 1 staminodes:
Anthers opening lengthwise; staminode 1; fruit broadly winged along the
    adaxial suture; stipules absent   13. **Zenia**
Anthers opening by terminal pores or a short pore-like slit:
Anthers not bilobed; staminodes absent; stipules absent; fruit not known
                                                    14. **Androcalymma**
Anthers deeply bilobed, each lobe pointed and opening by a pore-like slit;
    staminodes 2, petaloid, margined with glands; fruit longitudinally 4-
    winged   15. **Duparquetia**
Stamens 3–2:
Fruit dehiscent; Australian genera:
Style short, not dilated; perfect stamens 2; anthers opening by terminal
    pores; flowers in axillary racemes; leaflets sometimes subdigitate or
    leaf 1-foliolate   16. **Labichea**
Style dilated and petaloid, saccate above the ovary; perfect stamens 3,
    anthers opening by slits; flowers solitary, axillary   17. **Petalostylis**
Fruit indehiscent:
Fruit not winged, more or less rounded and only slightly compressed, 1-
    seeded; petals 2, 1 or none; anthers opening by a slit; tropics generally
                                                    18. **Dialium** (part)
Fruit not winged, compressed, reticulate; petals 3; anthers opening by a
    pore at the apex; trop. Africa   19. **Distemonanthus**
Fruits narrowly winged, compressed; trop. America:
Sepals 5; anthers shortly slit at the apex; petals 3; ovary free from the
    calyx-tube   20. **Dicorynia**
Sepals 3; anthers opening from top to base; ovary-stipe more or less adnate
    to the calyx; petals 3   21. **Apuleia**

1. **Campsiandra** Benth., Hook. Journ. Bot. 2: 93 (1840). 3 spp., trop. South
America; type *C. comosa* Benth., Guiana, Brazil, Venezuela. B.H. 1: 563;
E.P. 3, 3: 180; Amshoff, Pulle Fl. Suriname, 2, 2: 93.

Trees, unarmed; leaves imparipinnate, leaflets coriaceous; stipules small or very caducous;
flowers yellow or rose; racemes short and paniculate; bracts small, caducous; bracteoles
minute or absent; calyx-tube campanulate; lobes 5, short, imbricate; petals 5, slightly unequal, obovate-oblong, imbricate; stamens 20–15, free, filaments elongated; anthers ovate
or oblong, uniform; ovary shortly stipitate, free at the base of the calyx; ovules numerous;
style filiform, stigma terminal small or truncate-dilated; fruit large, straight or falcate,
plano-compressed, coriaceous, 2-valved; seeds large, compressed; testa thin.

Leaves and roots of *C. laurifolia* Benth. used in Brazil as febrifuge, as tonic, and for washing
ulcers.

2. **Melanoxylon** Schott, Spreng. Syst. Cur. Post. 406 (1827). *Perittium* Vogel
(1837). 2 spp., trop. South America; type *M. brauna* Schott, Brazil. B.H. 1;
563; E.P. 3, 3: 177.

Tall trees; leaves imparipinnate, leaflets in numerous pairs; flowers rather large; racemes
in a large terminal panicle; bracts minute, deciduous; bracteoles none; calyx-tube obliquely
campanulate; segments 5, very imbricate, outermost smaller; petals 5, broadly orbicular,
spreading, imbricate, uppermost slightly dissimilar; stamens 10, free; filaments villous at
the base; anthers oblong, uniform; ovary sessile, free at the base of the calyx; ovules numerous; style short, thick, incurved, stigma truncate-concave, ciliolate; fruit broadly oblong-
falcate, compressed, coriaceous-subwoody, 2-valved, filled inside between the seeds; seeds

transverse, compressed, with a falcate wing at the apex; endosperm thin, cotyledons flat, oblong, cordate at the base.

Brauna, Granna, wood of *M. brauna* Schott, heavy, tough, very hard; used for spokes, bridges, beams, posts, &c.; bark used in tanning.

3. **Recordoxylon** Ducke, Trop. Woods, 39: 16 (1934). 2 spp., trop. America; type *R. amazonicum* (Ducke) Ducke, Brazil. Archiv. Jard. Bot. Rio de Janeiro, 6: (1933).

Large trees; leaves imparipinnate, leaflets mostly opposite; panicles terminal, rufous-tomentellous, composed of few-flowered racemes; bracts and bracteoles very small and caducous; sepals 5, imbricate, deciduous; petals 5, golden-yellow, subequal, shortly clawed; stamens 10, free, filaments glabrous; ovary shortly stipitate, free, silky; fruit small, flat, linear-oblong, very narrowly winged along the adaxial suture, valves thinly coriaceous, tardily but not elastically dehiscent, not filled between the seeds; seeds subkeeled on one side.

R. amazonicum: wood hard, heavy, durable, resistant to insects; used for construction.

4. **Storkiella** Seem., Bonplandia, 9: 363, t. 6 (1861). *Doga* Baill. (1869). 2 spp., type *S. vitiensis* Seem., Fiji. *S. pancheri* Baill., New Caledonia. B.H. 1: 571; E.P. 3, 3: 164.

Tall trees; leaves imparipinnate, with globose buds in their axils, leaflets coriaceous; stipules minute or caducous; flowers yellow, paniculate at the apex of the branches; bracts and bracteoles very caducous; calyx-tube shortly turbinate; segments 5–3, slightly unequal, imbricate; petals 5–3, oblong, imbricate, the upper inner petal often deficient; stamens 10, free, filaments filiform; anthers linear, basifixed, loculi opening at the apex by pores or short slits; ovary subsessile, free at the base of the calyx, ovules numerous; style shortly subulate, stigma terminal, obtuse; fruit oblong or subfalcate, flat and compressed, thinly coriaceous, 2-valved, broadly winged on the upper suture; seeds transverse, suborbicular, compressed; cotyledons broad, foliaceous, cordate at the base.

5. **Gilletiodendron** Vermoesen, Man. Essences Forest. Congo Belge, 85 (1923). *Microstegia* Pierre ex Harms (1907). 5 spp., trop. Africa, type *G. klainei* (Pierre) Vermoesen, Congo. J. Léonard, Bull. Jard. Bot. Brux. 21: 400, figs. 108, 109 (1951); Mém. Acad. Roy. Belg. Cl. Sci. 30, 2: 61 (1957).

Trees; leaves imparipinnate; leaflets numerous to few, alternate or a few opposite, asymmetric, pellucid-punctate; midrib usually eccentric, rhachis ending in a bristle-point; stipules linear, very caducous; flowers small, in axillary and terminal panicles, many-flowered; bracts small, very caducous; bracteoles 2, subopposite at the base of the pedicel, very caducous; sepals 4, free, imbricate, at length reflexed, unequal, one much larger, glandular; petals 5, free, equal; stamens 10, free, alternately longer and shorter; anthers dorsifixed, opening lengthwise; ovary stipitate; style filiform, stigma terminal; ovules 5–2; fruit compressed, oblique, stipitate, opening by 2 glandular-verrucose or smooth valves; seeds compressed.

6. **Scorodophloeus** Harms, Engl. Bot. Jahrb. 30: 77 (1901). 2 spp., trop. Africa; type *S. zenkeri* Harms, Cameroons and Congo. J. Léonard, Fl. Congo Belge, 3: 327, fig. 22; Mém. Acad. Roy. Belg. Cl. Sci. 30, 2: 102 (1957).

Trees; leaves, usually imparipinnate, rarely paripinnate, leaflets numerous (about 18–20), mostly alternate; stipules very caducous; racemes terminal or axillary, many-flowered; bracteoles paired below the middle of the pedicels, linear-lanceolate, not forming an involucre; calyx-tube elongated, narrowly subcylindric-turbinate; lobes 4, ovate, imbricate; petals 5, obovate or oblong-obovate, almost equal, longer than the calyx-lobes, clawed, obtuse, margins fimbriate; stamens 10, exserted, filaments filiform, glabrous, free;

ovary stipitate, lower part of the stipe adnate to the calyx-tube, 2-ovulate; style elongated, filiform, stigma small, capitellate; fruit stipitate, 2-valved, curled on dehiscence, transversely nerved; seeds flat, suborbicular.

7. Batesia Spruce ex Benth., Benth. & Hook. f., Gen. Pl. 1: 563 (1865). 1 sp., *B. floribunda* Spruce ex Benth., Brazil. E.P. 3, 3: 178.

Tall tree; leaves large, imparipinnate, leaflets coriaceous; stipules intrapetiolar, short, triangular; flowers yellow, in panicles of racemes at the apex of the branches; bracts and bracteoles, narrow, very caducous; calyx-tube campanulate; segments 5, imbricate; petals 5, slightly unequal, ovate, imbricate; stamens 10, free, filaments villous at the base; anthers uniform; ovary shortly stipitate, free at the base of the calyx, few-ovuled, stipe obliquely dilated at the apex, subjointed; style very short, thick, stigma terminal, truncate, concave, and ciliate; fruit short, subfalcate, compressed-turgid, rather woody, with elevated ribs, dehiscent by only 1 margin; seeds 3–2, transverse, suborbicular, thick and compressed, pale red and shining.

8. Kalappia Kostermans, Reinwardtia, 1: 451, fig. 1 (1951). 1 sp., *K. celebica* Kostermans, Celebes.

Tall unarmed tree; leaves imparipinnate; leaflets alternate, about 5, elliptic, entire; stipules obscure; bracts and bracteoles soon falling; sepals 5, subequal, imbricate; petals 5, clawed, erect-patent, 2 lateral outermost, larger; stamens 10, free, 2 fertile, remainder abortive or reduced to staminodes; anthers basifixed though also versatile, opening by terminal pores, shortly apiculate; ovary sessile, 3–5-ovuled; style incurved, stigma small, terminal; fruit flat, narrowly winged along the ventral suture, dehiscing by the dorsal suture, valves thin, smooth inside; seeds 3–1, flat, disk-like; cotyledons flat, broad.

9. Vouacapoua Aubl., Pl. Guian. Suppl. 9, t. 373 (1775). 4 spp., trop. South America; type *V. americana* Aubl., Guianas, Brazil. Baill., Adans. 9: 206, t. 4 (1868–70); E.P.N. 4: 130 (1914); Amshoff, Pulle Fl. Suriname, 2, 2: 87.

Trees; leaves imparipinnate; leaflets 4–2-pairs, opposite, glabrous; petiole glandular between all or below the lower two leaflets; stipules caducous; flowers small in terminal panicles; receptacle concave, clothed within by a thin obscurely 10-crenate disk; sepals 5, equal, imbricate; petals 5, imbricate, equal, slightly longer than the sepals, subspathulate; stamens 10; filaments dilated at the base; anthers subsagittate, linear; ovary shortly stipitate; ovule 1; fruit unequally obovate, long-narrowed at the base, dehiscent by only 1 margin; seed 1: radicle very short, straight.

10. Bathiaea Drake, Hist. Madag. 1: 205 (1902). 1 sp. *B. rubriflora* Drake, Madagascar.

Tree; leaves alternate, imparipinnate; leaflets alternate, elliptic, pinnately nerved; flowers in dense short axillary panicles with the long thread-like filaments of the stamens conspicuous; bracts deciduous; sepals 5, imbricate, obovate; petals 5, slightly unequal, the upper one interior; disk annular; stamens 10, unequal, the posterior a little shorter; filaments elongated and filiform; anthers ellipsoid, connective apiculate; ovary stipitate; ovules few, in 2 series; style filiform, elongated, stigma terminal; fruit indehiscent, samaroid, unequal-sided, unequally narrowed to the base, anterior suture thickened towards the upper part; seed pendulous from the top of the fruit, oblong; cotyledons thick.

11. Pterogyne Tul., Ann. Sci. Nat. sér. 2, 20: 140 (1843). 1 sp., *P. nitens* Tul., South America. B.H. 1: 586; E.P. 3, 3: 130; Burkart, Legum. Argent. ed. 2, 156, fig. 25.

Tree; leaves imparipinnate, leaflets mostly alternate, oblong, shining; stipules minute; flowers small in short lax axillary racemes, catkin-like in bud; bracts small, scale-like, deciduous, the young racemes catkin-like; bracteoles absent; calyx-tube very short; segments 5, subpetaloid, subequal, imbricate; petals 5, subequal, imbricate; stamens 10, free; ovary 1-ovuled, winged on the upper side; style short, stigma terminal, truncate; fruit samaroid, compressed, not dehiscent, with a seed at the base, obliquely ovate-acuminate, coriaceous, reticulate, wing thin and rigid, falcate-oblong, with incurved veins; seed pendulous, oblong-obovate, compressed.

P. nitens Tul.: wood pinkish-brown, heavy, hard, used for cabinet work, railroad ties, and cooperage.

12. **Anthagathis** Harms, Engl. & Prantl, Nat. Pflanzenfam. Nachtr. 1: 195 (1897). 1 sp., *A. monadelphia* Harms, W. trop. Africa (Gabun).

Tree or shrub; leaves imparipinnate; leaflets 9, alternate or subopposite, large, acuminate, pinnately nerved; rhachis somewhat thickened at the insertion of the leaflets; flowers shortly pedicellate, in thick hairy clusters on the branches or stem; bracts small, almost orbicular, scale-like; calyx-tube very short, segments 5, broadly imbricate, more or less oval; petals 5, imbricate, oblong, somewhat longer than the sepals; stamens 10, filaments united at the base into a short tube; anthers oval, dorsifixed near the base, opening lengthwise; ovary small, narrowed into the style hairy at the base; stigma disk-like; ovules 2; fruit not seen.

13. **Zenia** Chun, Sunyatsenia, 6: 195, fig. 24 (1946). 1 sp., *Z. insignis* Chun, China.

Tall unarmed tree; buds with few perulae; leaves imparipinnate, deciduous, not stipulate; leaflets 9–13 pairs, alternate, entire, not stipellate; inflorescence cymose-paniculate, terminal, long-pedunculate; flowers red, bracteolate, bisexual, subactinomorphic; sepals 5, free, imbricate, unequal, the 5th much smaller; petals 5, imbricate, slightly unequal, strongly keeled; perfect stamens 4, the 5th reduced to a short filiform staminode, rarely 5, all subequal or the lower shorter, free, inserted on the margin of the sinuate-lobate disk; anthers uniform, linear-oblong, basifixed, opening lengthwise; ovary few- (about 9-) ovuled, shortly stipitate, stipe free; style short, stigma subterminal; fruit indehiscent, membranous, compressed, elliptic-oblong, falcate, acuminate at the apex, reticulate-venose, broadly winged along the upper (adaxial) suture; seeds few, orbicular, compressed, smooth, shining, dark-brown, with long slender funicles.

14. **Androcalymma** Dwyer, Ann. Miss. Bot. Gard. 44: 295, fig. 1 (1957). 1 sp., *A. glabrifolium* Dwyer, Brazil.

Tree; leaves imparipinnate; leaflets 4–5, alternate, ovate-elliptic, shortly acuminate, pinnately nerved and reticulate, coriaceous; stipules not seen; cymes terminal, many-flowered; flowers very small; bracts very small and early caducous; pedicels very short; sepals 5, very imbricate; petals 5, imbricate, elliptic, a little longer than the sepals, keeled inside; stamens 4, free, equal, filaments thick, short, abruptly contracted at the top; anthers bilocular, opening by terminal pores; ovary with 2 ovules; style very short and subulate; fruit not known.

15. **Duparquetia** Baill., Adans. 6: 189, t. 4 (1865). *Oligostemon* Benth. (1865), not Turcz. (1858). 1 sp., *O. orchidacea* Baill., trop. Africa. B.H. 1: 570; E.P. 3, 3: 166; Steyaert, Fl. Congo Belge, 3: 544.

Tall shrub; leaves imparipinnate, leaflets large, obovate-oblong; stipules ovate; flowers in a terminal panicle; pedicels jointed in the middle, lower half persistent; bracts and bracteoles minute, scale-like; sepals 4, free, large, very imbricate; petals 5, rose, smaller than the sepals, upper 3 lanceolate or ovate lanceolate, finely veined and with a few marginal glands, lower petals larger; stamens 4, filaments very short, free; anthers arched over the ovary, basifixed, deeply 2-lobed, loculi acuminate, opening by a short pore-like slit at the apex; staminodes, 2, spathulate-oblanceolate, margined with large glands; ovary shortly stipitate, 4-winged, 2-ovuled; style thick, stigma small, terminal; fruit elongated, 2-valved, 4-winged lengthwise, valves spirally coiled, fibrous within; seeds 2.

16. **Labichea** Gaudich. ex DC., Prodr. 2: 507 (1825), and Freyc. Voy. 485, t. 112 (1826). 7 spp., Australia; type *L. cassioides* Gaudich. B.H. 1: 573; E.P. 3, 3: 156.

Shrubs or undershrubs; leaves imparipinnate or petiole very short and leaflets subdigitate or 1-foliolate, leaflets small, rigid; stipules small, caducous; flowers yellow, in axillary racemes; bracts small, caducous; bracteoles absent; calyx-tube very short; segments 5 or 4, imbricate, slightly unequal; petals 5 or 4, imbricate, spreading, subequal; stamens 2, filaments very short; anthers basifixed, oblong-linear, opening by terminal pores, uniform or some produced into a beak at the apex; ovary sessile or shortly stipitate, free, 3–2-ovuled; style short, stigma small, terminal; fruit oblong or lanceolate, compressed, 2-valved; seeds transverse or oblique, compressed, funicle dilated into a small fleshy aril.

17. **Petalostylis** R.Br., Append. Sturt Exped. 17 (1849). *Petalogyne* F. Muell. (1856). *Petalostyles* Benth. (1864). 2 spp., Australia; type *P. labicheoides* R. Br. B.H. 1: 573; E.P. 3, 3: 156.

Shrubs; leaves imparipinnate, leaflets small, rhachis sometimes becoming spine-like; stipules narrow, very caducous; flowers axillary, solitary, yellow; bracts very small; bracteoles small, caducous; calyx-tube very short; sepals 5, imbricate; petals 5, imbricate, spreading, subequal; perfect stamens 3; anthers linear, basifixed, opening by slits lengthwise; staminodes 2, small, with acuminate imperfect anthers; ovary subsessile, free, many-ovuled; style dilated and petaloid, saccate above the ovary, 3-lobed, middle lobe longer and terminated by a small stigma; fruit oblong-linear, compressed, obliquely 2-valved; seeds oblique, compressed, funicle dilated into a small fleshy aril.

18. **Dialium** Linn., Mant. 1: 3 (1767). *Arouna* Aubl. (1775). *Aruna* Schreb. (1789). *Cleyria* Neck. (1790). *Codarium* Sol. ex Vahl (1805). *Andradia* Sim (1909). About 70 spp., tropics, very few in trop. America; type *D. indum* Linn., Malaya. B.H. 1: 574; E.P. 3, 3: 155; E. G. Bak., Legum. Trop. Africa, 3: 643; Amshoff, Pulle Fl. Suriname, 2, 2: 52; Steyaert, Bull. Soc. Roy. Bot. Belg. 84: 29, t. 1 (1951); Fl. Congo Belge, 3: 531, t. 39; Hutch. & Dalz., Fl. W. Trop. Africa ed. 2 (Keay), 1: 448.

Trees; leaves imparipinnate, leaflets usually few, mostly alternate; stipules small; flowers small, in axillary or terminal cymes; bracts and bracteoles small, caducous; calyx-tube very short; segments 5, very imbricate, herbaceous or petaloid; petals 2–1, small, or absent; stamens 2, rarely 3, free, filaments short; anthers oblong, erect; ovary sessile at the base of the calyx-tube, or shortly stipitate with the stipe shortly adnate to the tube, 2-ovulate; style shortly subulate, stigma terminal, small; fruit ovate-orbicular, rather compressed, or ovoid-globose or globose, not dehiscent; endocarp often pulpy; seed 1, more or less compressed.

D. *indum*: Tamarind Plum, Malay Archip.; fruits edible; wood very hard, heavy, used for houses and boats; fruits also edible of *D. maingayi* Baker, Malay Penins.; *D. ovoideum* Thwaites, Ceylon; *D. platysepalum* Baker, Malaya.

19. **Distemonanthus** Benth., Benth. & Hook. f., Gen. Pl. 1: 573 (1865). 1 sp., *D. benthamianus* Baill., trop. Africa. E.P. 3, 3: 156; Hutch. & Dalz., Fl. W. Trop. Afr. ed. 2 (Keay), 1: 449.

Tree; leaves imparipinnate, leaflets few, alternate; stipules small, very caducous; flowers in axillary cymes, produced more or less before the leaves; bracts small, narrow, very caducous; bracteoles absent; calyx-tube shortly turbinate; segments 5–4, membranous, marginate, slightly imbricate; petals 3, sessile, scarcely imbricate, upper lanceolate, lateral linear; perfect stamens 2, inserted between the upper and lateral petals; anthers linear, erect, opening by an oblique pore at the apex; staminodes 3, opposite the petals, petaloid; ovary shortly stipitate, stipe obliquely adnate to the calyx-tube; ovules several; style shortly filiform, stigma terminal, oblique; fruit compressed, thin, not dehiscent, reticulate.

20. **Dicorynia** Benth., Hook. Journ. Bot. 2: 82 (1840). *Dicorynea* Lindl. (1847). 4 spp., Guianas, N. Brazil; type *D. paraensis* Benth., N. Brazil. B.H. 1: 571; E.P. 3, 3: 165; Amshoff, Pulle Fl. Suriname, 2, 2: 79.

Trees; leaves imparipinnate, leaflets few; stipules very caducous; flowers white, numerous in terminal panicles; bracts and bracteoles ovate, very caducous; calyx-tube very short; sepals 5, ovate, very imbricate; petals 3, obliquely orbicular; stamens 2, free, unequal; anthers oblong, thick, shortly dehiscent at the apex; ovary sessile, ovules few; style filiform, inflexed, stigma small, terminal; fruit not dehiscent, obliquely ovate, plano-compressed, narrowly winged on the upper surface; seeds 2–1, transverse, suborbicular, compressed; cotyledons cordate.

21. **Apuleia** Mart., Herb. Fl. Bras. 123 (1837) (conserved name), not Gaertn. (1791). *Zenkeria* Arn. (1838). *Apoleya* Gleason (1935). 2 spp., trop. America, Argentina; type *A. leiocarpa* (Vog.) Macbr. (*A. praecox* Mart.), Brazil to Argentina. B.H. 1: 574; E.P. 3, 3: 156; Burkart, Legum. Argent. ed. 2: 162, fig. 28.

Trees; leaves imparipinnate, leaflets alternate, coriaceous; stipules minute or absent; flowers rather small, white, often polygamous, in small axillary cymes, produced whilst the leaves are scarcely developed; bracts minute; bracteoles absent; calyx-tube shortly turbinate; segments 3, very imbricate; petals 3, subsessile, oblong, narrowed at the base, slightly imbricate; stamens 3, rarely 2, filaments abruptly narrowed at the apex; anthers linear-oblong, erect, basifixed; ovary shortly stipitate, stipe adnate to the tube; ovules 3–2; style rather thick, stigma terminal, truncate or dilated; fruit obliquely ovate or oblong, compressed, thinly coriaceous, not dehiscent, narrowly winged on the upper suture; seeds 2–1, transverse, ovate or orbicular, compressed.

A. leiocarpa: wood yellow, hard and durable; used for flooring, door frames, and heavy construction work.

GROUP 2

Anthers opening lengthwise by slits, often attached near the middle and more or less versatile (to p. 235):
Fertile stamens 5 or more (to p. 235):
Bracteoles or bracts usually small or absent, not petaloid, often deciduous or caducous (to foot of page 234):
Sepals free to the base or nearly so (not forming a distinct tube):
Stamens free among themselves or only slightly connate at the base:
Ovary not stipitate:
Indumentum when present not stellate:
Inflorescence a raceme;
Stamens with woolly filaments; fruit oval or oval-orbicular, indehiscent; leaflets with scattered black glands below   22. **Stahlia**
Stamens with glabrous filaments; fruit arcuate-ovoid or subreniform, rarely straight, often warted or wrinkled, 2-valved
23. **Cynometra**
Inflorescence a panicle; stamens with glabrous filaments; fruit arcuate:
Leaves not glandular-punctate; fruit compressed, thin, 1-seeded, dehiscent   24. **Umtiza**
Leaves glandular-punctate; fruit more than 1-seeded
5. **Gilletiodendron**

Indumentum stellate; stamens with woolly filaments; fruit oblanceo-
late, 2-valved; racemes terminal, simple or branched
                                                      25. **Cenostigma**
Ovary stipitate:
  Fruits not samaroid:
    Leaflets numerous pairs:
      Stipe of the ovary free and not partly adnate to the calyx-tube:
        Filaments pilose or villous near the base; calyx-lobes or segments
          5; fruit indehiscent:
          Fruit hard, not bladder-like; trop. America   26. **Sclerolobium**
          Fruit bladder-like; Madagascar   27. **Denisophytum**
        Filaments glabrous; calyx-segments 4; leaves pellucid-punctate;
          fruit dehiscent   5. **Gilletiodendron**
      Stipe of the ovary partly adnate to the calyx-tube; filaments glabrous;
        fruit-valves curled on dehiscence   6. **Scorodophloeus**
    Leaflets 4–1-pairs, or rarely leaves 1-foliolate:
      Filaments pilose or villous at the base:
        Racemes in terminal panicles; bracteoles subulate; fruit indehiscent
                                                         26. **Sclerolobium**
        Racemes axillary; bracteoles absent:
          Fruit splitting along the middle of the valves
                                                         28. **Haematoxylon**
          Fruit not splitting along the middle of the valves:
            Leaflets minutely pellucid-punctate   29. **Diptychandra**
            Leaflets not punctate   30. **Eurypetalum**
      Filaments glabrous:
        Stipe of the ovary free or nearly so from the calyx-tube
                                                         23. **Cynometra**
        Stipe of the ovary partly adnate to the calyx-tube:
          Leaves with 2 pairs of leaflets; trop. Africa 31. **Lebruniodendron**
          Leaves 1-foliolate: Malaya   32. **Uittienia**
      Leaves simple   33. **Zenkerella**
  Fruits winged and samaroid, 1-seeded, the seed at the basal end;
    flowers small, in short lax axillary racemes   11. **Pterogyne**
Stamens united into a sheath or only the upper stamen free:
  Stamens numerous, more than 30; ovary 1-ovuled   34. **Schizoscyphus**
  Stamens 10; fruit winged along the upper suture; ovary few-ovuled
                                                         35. **Phyllocarpus**
Sepals more or less united into a distinct tube:
  Petals equal or subequal in size and shape, always more than 1:
    Leaflets 2 or more-pairs:
      Calyx-lobes or teeth 5:
        Branchlets spine-tipped; leaves very small, borne with the flowers on
          short arrested branchlets:
          Fruits 4-winged, wings crested; seeds several   36. **Lophocarpinia**
          Fruits not winged; seed 1   24. **Umtiza**
        Branchlets not spine-tipped; leaves paripinnate:

Petals free from each other; filaments more or less hairy:
Densely glandular shrubs; fruit short, subovate, 2-valved, long-
setose   37. Zuccagnia
Not glandular:
Flowers densely spicate, the spikes collected into terminal pani-
cles; fertile stamens 5   38. Mora
Flowers racemose or racemose-paniculate; fertile stamens 10:
Fruit subvesicular; ovary-stipe free from the calyx
27. Denisophytum
Fruit not vesicular; ovary-stipe partly adnate to the calyx-tube
39. Tachigalia
Petals connate at the base into a short tube; fertile stamens 10, fila-
ments glabrous   40. Sympetalandra
Calyx-lobes or teeth 4; stipe of the ovary adnate to the calyx-tube:
Flowers crowded in short panicles or racemes; leaflets few pairs
41. Schotia
Flowers in spikes fasciculate at the tops of the branches; leaflets
2 pairs   42. Goniorrhachis
Flowers in heads borne on the trunk or branches; leaflets 3–4 pairs
43. Browneopsis
Leaflets a single pair; stipe of ovary often adnate to the calyx-tube:
Leaves pellucid-punctate; seeds few, variously shaped
44. Hymenaea
Leaves not punctate; seed often solitary, suborbicular, compressed
45. Peltogyne
Leaves 1-foliolate:
Stamens 10, all with anthers; calyx-lobes 5; petals 5   46. Griffonia
Stamens 9, sometimes some antherless; calyx-lobes 4; petals 3
47. Paloue
Petals very unequal or petal only 1; calyx-lobes 4:
Stipules large and folded around the terminal bud   48. Daniellia
Stipules not as above:
Leaves simple, entire or usually variously deeply bilobed
49. Bauhinia
Leaves compound:
Leaves 2-foliolate; stipules very caducous   50. Trachylobium
Leaves more than 2-foliolate:
Stipules not intrapetiolar, minute and early deciduous:
Seeds thick and turgid, arillate, the aril often at first enveloping the
seed; petal 1, suborbicular or reniform, the others rudimentary
or absent   51. Afzelia
Seeds flat and disk-like, suborbicular, not arillate; petals 5, 3 larger
and similar to one another, 2 minute   52. Loesenera
Stipules intrapetiolar, foliaceous or small; racemes with sometimes
long pendulous peduncles   53. Eperua
Bracts or bracteoles large and petaloid, more or less persistent:
Petals more or less equal in size:
Stamens 15–10, filaments free or connate:

Stipe adnate to the calyx-tube; filaments pilose at the base; fruit com-
pressed   54. **Plagiosiphon**
Stipe free from the calyx-tube; filaments glabrous; fruit turgid
55. **Maniltoa**
Stamens 9, filaments free or shortly connate only at the base
47. **Paloue**
Stamens 6; stipe of ovary adnate to the calyx-tube; fruit large, flat,
2-valved, valves curling when open   56. **Lysidice**
Petals very unequal in size or only 1 petal present:
Stipe of ovary only shortly adnate to the calyx-tube   57. **Hymenostegia**
Stipe of ovary totally adnate to the calyx-tube 58. **Neochevalierodendron**
Fertile stamens 3–2; filaments more or less connate in the lower part:
Stipules large, foliaceous, intrapetiolar, connate at the base; seeds not
arillate:
Flowers in fascicles of racemes on the older wood   59. **Leucostegane**
Flowers in terminal racemes or panicles   60. **Intsia**
Stipules small, minute, or caducous; seeds often arillate:
Seeds not arillate:
Leaflets in numerous pairs; filaments connate high up into a sheath open
above   61. **Tamarindus**
Leaflets 3 pairs; filaments connate only at the base into a ring around the
base of the ovary   62. **Endertia**
Seeds with a large often brightly coloured aril   51. **Afzelia**
Anthers opening by terminal pores, the loculi attached at or near the base:
Leaves pinnate or rarely reduced to phyllodes   63. **Cassia**
Leaves unifoliolate   64. **Baudouinia**

22. **Stahlia** Bello, Anal. Soc. Espan. Hist. Nat. 255 (1881); Urban, Symb.
Antill. 1: 313 (1899). 1 sp., *S. maritima* Bello, Porto Rico.

Tree; leaves paripinnate; leaflets 4–6-pairs, rather unequal-sided, the broader half facing
the rhachis, with scattered prominent black glands below; stipules not seen; flowers
medium-sized, in axillary and terminal racemes; bracts not imbricate, connate at the base
into an obconic receptacle, coriaceous; calyx-lobes large, imbricate; petals 5, inserted in the
throat of the receptacle, imbricate, subequal, densely covered on the back with subclavate
papillae; stamens 10, free, connivent above; filaments woolly, linear-subulate; anthers
uniform; ovary sessile 2-ovulate; style filiform, truncate at the apex; fruit oval or oval-
orbicular, plano-convex, smooth, indehiscent; seed filling the cavity, compressed; cotyledons fleshy.

23. **Cynometra** Linn., Sp. Pl. 382 (1753). *Iripa* Adans. (1763). *Cynomora* Hedw.
(1806). *Metrocynia* Thou. (1806). *Cymonetra* Roberty (1954). About 150 spp.,
tropics; type *C. cauliflora* Linn., Indo-Malaya. B.H. 1: 586; E.P. 3, 3: 129;
Amshoff, Pulle Fl. Suriname, 2, 2: 15; J. Léonard, Bull. Jard. Bot. Brux. 21:
373; Fl. Congo Belge, 3: 309; Burkart, Legum. Argent. ed. 2: 154, fig. 23.

Trees and shrubs; leaves paripinnate, leaflets 1–few-pairs, coriaceous, oblique, sometimes with a gland at the base; stipules caducous; flowers small, racemose, racemes short,
often fasciculate, axillary, lateral on the branches or on the trunk; lower bracts ovate, dry,
imbricate, at length deciduous, remainder small; bracteoles membranous and coloured, or
absent; calyx-tube short; segments 5–4, thin, imbricate, reflexed during flowering; petals
5, subequal or the lower minute, imbricate; stamens 10 or rarely numerous, free; filaments filiform; anthers small, uniform; ovary sessile or shortly stipitate, free or nearly so,

2-ovulate; style filiform, stigma terminal, truncate or capitate; fruit arcuate-ovoid or subreniform, rarely straight, thick, turgid or subcompressed, rugose, verrucose or rarely smooth, 2-valved; seed filling the cavity, thick and compressed; cotyledons thick and fleshy.

C. cauliflora: Indo-Malaya; fruits edible; *C. cubensis* Rich.: wood dark reddish, used in carpentry; *C. sessiliflora* Harms: Congo, source of a copal gum.

24. **Umtiza** T. R. Sim, For. Fl. Cape Col. 205 (1907). 1 sp., *U. listeriana* T. R. Sim, S. Africa. Phillips, Gen. S. Afr. Pl. ed. 2: 394 (1951).

Evergreen tree, branches and twigs often transformed into strong spines with or without leaves; leaves paripinnate, leaflets sessile, shining, oblong, oblique, side veins ascending and much branched; stipules and stipels absent; panicles terminal on lateral branches; flowers small, actinomorphic, bisexual; calyx campanulate, with 5 short equal segments; petals 5, perigynous, free, equal, slightly imbricate; stamens 10, perigynous, equal, free, spreading equally or slightly declinate; anthers reniform, versatile; ovary sessile, style exserted, stigma capitate; ovules 2; fruit compressed, thin, pointed, firmly membranous, 1-seeded, dehiscent.

25. **Cenostigma** Tul., Ann. Sci. Nat. sér. 2, 20: 140, t. 3 (1843). 6 spp., Brazil, Paraguay; type *C. macrophyllum* Tul. B.H. 1: 564; E.P. 3, 3: 177.

Trees, mostly with more or less stellate indumentum; leaves paripinnate, leaflets coriaceous; stipules small; flowers rather large, racemose at the apex of the branches, or racemes branched; bracts small and deciduous; calyx-tube short; segments 5, imbricate, lowermost boat-shaped and larger; petals 5, slightly unequal, obovate, imbricate; stamens 10, free, declinate, filaments woolly; anthers uniform; ovary subsessile, free, few-ovuled; style filiform, subclavate at the apex, stigma terminal, small; fruit oblanceolate, flat, rather woody, reticulate, 2-valved, thinly filled between the seeds; seeds transverse, orbicular, compressed.

26. **Sclerolobium** Vogel, Linnaea, 11: 395 (1837). *Cosymbe* Tul. (1884). *Amorphocalyx* Klotzsch (1848). About 25 spp., N. trop. South America; type *S. denudatum* Vogel, Brazil. B.H. 1: 562; E.P. 3, 3: 180; Amshoff, Pulle Fl. Suriname, 2, 2: 90; Dwyer, Lloydia, 20: 67; 266 (1957) (revision).

Trees; leaves pari- or rarely imparipinnate; indumentum simple or stellate; stipules minute or absent, or foliaceous, 1–3-foliolate, sometimes pinnatipartite; rhachis sometimes with a barren tip; flowers yellow or white, small, densely racemose, racemes in terminal panicles; bracts minute or subulate-lanceolate and conspicuous in bud; bracteoles subulate or absent; calyx-tube short; segments 5, imbricate, slightly unequal; petals 5, small, slightly unequal, imbricate; stamens 10, free, filaments pilose at the base, plicate in bud; anthers uniform; ovary stipitate, free, few-ovuled; style filiform, glabrous, stigma small, terminal; fruit shortly stipitate, compressed, indehiscent, 2–1-seeded, mesocarp thinly fibrous-subwoody, endocarp thin and hard, fibrous; seeds large, flat, orbicular-reniform.

27. **Denisophytum** R. Vig., Humbert Not. System. 13: 349 (1949). 1 sp., *D. madagascariense* R. Vig., Madagascar.

Small tree; leaves paripinnate, deciduous; leaflets 6–10, elliptic, margins parallel, auriculate on one side at the base; stipules deciduous; racemes small, lax; bracts stipule-like, tomentose; calyx-tube very short, posterior teeth rounded at the apex, anterior narrow, thickened; corolla yellow; petals subobovate, clawed, subequal to the sepals but broader; stamens 10, unequal, filaments villous and thick at the base; anthers dorsifixed; ovary shortly stipitate, few-ovuled; style short, cylindric; fruit subvesicular, indehiscent, shortly stipitate, beaked; seeds lenticular, flattened, with a small rounded hilum.

28. **Haematoxylon** Linn., Sp. Pl. 384 (1753) ('Haematoxylum'). *Haematoxyllum* Scop. (1777). *Cymbosepalum* Baker (1895). 3 spp., Mexico, trop. America, West Indies, S. Africa; type *H. campechianum* Linn., trop. America. B.H. 1: 567; E.P. 3, 3: 171; Amshoff, Pulle Fl. Suriname, 2, 2: 83.

Trees with coloured wood and often spiny branchlets; leaves paripinnate or bipinnate by the lower pinnae again divided, leaflets in few pairs, obovate; stipules either spinous or small and deciduous; flowers small, yellow; racemes axillary; bracts minute or inconspicuous; bracteoles absent; calyx-tube short; segments 5, slightly unequal, very imbricate; petals 5, oblong, spreading, slightly unequal, imbricate; stamens 10, free, filaments pilose at the base; anthers uniform; ovary shortly stipitate, free, 3–2-ovuled; style filiform, stigma small, terminal; fruit lanceolate, compressed, membranous, sutures splitting along the middle of the valves; seeds transversely oblong; cotyledons divaricately 2-lobed.

H. brasiletto Karsten: Brazil-wood, Nicaragua-wood, trop. America; wood bright orange, becoming red, hard, source of Brasilin, a dye. *H. campechianum* Linn.: Logwood, Lignum Campechianum, Palo Campechio; wood brownish-red to blood-red, hard, used for furniture; heartwood source of dye 'Haematoxylin', used in wool industry and as stain for microscopical objects and in the manufacture of inks; flowers source of honey.

29. **Diptychandra** Tul., Ann. Sci. Nat. sér. 2, 20: 139 (1843), and Arch. Mus. Paris, 4: 127, t. 8 (1844). 3 spp., Brazil, Paraguay; lectotype *D. epunctata* Tul., Brazil, Paraguay. B.H. 1: 562; E.P. 3, 3: 180.

Small trees or shrubs; leaves paripinnate, leaflets minutely pellucid-punctate; stipules minute or absent; flowers yellow, small, laxly racemose, racemes axillary and terminal; bracts and bracteoles absent or early caducous; calyx-tube short; segments 5, imbricate, slightly unequal; petals 5, small, ovate, slightly unequal, imbricate; stamens 10, free, filaments pilose at the base, biplicate in bud; anthers ovate, versatile; ovary stipitate, free, few-ovuled; style filiform, inflexed, stigma terminal, small or truncate; fruit shortly stipitate, short or elongated, compressed, 2-valved, bare inside, valves coriaceous, margins nerve-like; seeds 3–1, transverse, orbicular or reniform, much compressed, testa expanded into a wing on one side or all around.

30. **Eurypetalum** Harms, Engl. Bot. Jahrb. 45: 293 (1910). 3 spp., W. trop. Africa; type *E. tessmannii* Harms, Gabon. E. G. Bak., Legum. Trop. Afr. 3: 769; J. Léonard, Mém. Acad. Roy. Belg. Cl. Sci. 30, 2: 118 (1957).

Trees; leaves paripinnate; leaflets 1–2-pairs; flowers paniculate; bracts and bracteoles very small; calyx-tube shortly cupular; sepals 4, almost equal in length; petals 5, one large and broad, subreniform, broader than long, broad at the base and sessile, rounded, margin undulate, often emarginate, wrinkled and plicate in bud; other petals much smaller, hyaline, scale-like, rounded; stamens 10, filaments subulate, hirsute-villous at the base and very shortly connate; anthers versatile, equal; ovary shortly stipitate, small, densely villous; style short, incurved, glabrous, stigma small, capitellate; ovules 2–1; fruit 2-valved, stipitate, apiculate.

31. **Lebruniodendron** J. Léonard, Bull. Jard. Bot. Brux. 21: 420, t. 8 (1951); Fl. Congo Belge, 3: 329, t. 24; Mém. Acad. Roy. Belg. Cl. Sci. 30, 2: 96 (1957). 1 sp., *L. leptanthum* (Harms) J. Léonard, trop. Africa.

Tree; leaves paripinnate, leaflets 2 pairs, opposite, pinnately nerved; stipules united, intrapetiolar, very caducous; stipels very minute; inflorescence a short raceme, axillary or terminal, with numerous imbricate bud-scales at the base; bracts small, scarious, caducous; flowers small; bracteoles subopposite, membranous, not petaloid, small, caducous; sepals 4, free, imbricate, reflexed; petals 5, free, equal; stamens 10; filaments free; anthers dorsifixed, versatile; disk none; ovary stipitate, stipe partly adnate to the receptacle; ovules 2; fruit asymmetric, flattened, apiculate, stipitate, reticulate.

32. **Uittienia** van Steenis, Bull. Bot. Gard. Buitenz. ser. 3, 17: 416 (1948). 1 sp., *U. modesta* van Steenis, Borneo.

Tree; leaves 1-foliolate, ovate to lanceolate; petiole thickened each end; stipules minute, linear, early caducous; flowers in short axillary thyrses; calyx-lobes 5, free, deciduous, narrowly imbricate in bud; petals 5; stamens 7; filaments free; anthers basifixed, uniform, ovate, dehiscing lengthwise; disk distinct, cushion-shaped, hairy; ovary terete, stipitate;

style filiform; ovule 1; fruit[1] indehiscent, subobliquely globular, very large (6 × 6 cm. diam.), woody, with a softish pulp around the single subglobular seed; endosperm almost filling the seed, the embryo a tiny conical body.

33. **Zenkerella** Taub., Engl. & Prantl, Nat. Pflanzenfam. 3, 3: 386 (1894). *Podogynium* Taub. (1896). 6 spp., trop. Africa; type *Z. citrina* Taub. E.P. Nachtr. 194; J. Léonard, Bull. Jard. Bot. Brux. 21: 373 (1951): Mém. Acad. Roy. Belg. Cl. Sci. 30, 2: 94 (1957); Hutch. & Dalz., Fl. W. Trop. Afr. ed. 2 (Keay), 1: 458.

Trees; leaves simple, entire, shortly petiolate; stipules caducous or rarely large, foliaceous and persistent; flowers fasciculate-racemose, axillary; bracteoles caducous; calyx-tube cupular, turbinate, or cylindric-funnel-shaped; sepals 4–5, imbricate, reflexed; petals 5, subequal; stamens 10, free or shortly united at the base; disk absent; ovary stipitate, stipe partly adnate to the calyx-tube; ovules 1–3; fruit stipitate, almost semi-orbicular, dehiscent by 2 coriaceous valves with prominent transverse nerves; seed solitary, compressed, semiorbicular to reniform.

34. **Schizoscyphus** Taub., Bot. Centrabl. 41: 265 (1890). *Schizosiphon* K. Schum. (1889). 1 sp., *S. roseus* (K. Schum.) Taub., New Guinea. E.P. 3, 3: 130.

Tree up to 9 m. high; leaves subsessile, paripinnate; leaflets 6–8-pairs, sessile, very unequal-sided, with one gland towards the base above; racemes terminal, many-flowered, shortly pedunculate; bracts caducous; flowers rose; calyx obliquely and narrowly turbinate, striate, unilaterally split in front; lobes 4, reflexed, oblong, membranous; petals 3, narrowly lanceolate, equal in length; stamens over 30, connate beyond the calyx-tube, sheath equally split like the calyx; filaments long-exserted; anthers apiculate, versatile; ovary sessile, 1-ovuled; style elongated, curved, stigma turbinate-tubulose; fruit not seen.

35. **Phyllocarpus** Riedel ex Tul., Ann. Sci. Nat. sér. 2, 20: 142 (1843). 2 spp., trop. America; type *P. riedelii* Tul., Brazil and Peru. B.H. 1: 564; E.P. 3, 3: 179.

Tall trees; leaves paripinnate, leaflets ovate, in numerous pairs; stipules erect and conspicuous or small and inconspicuous; flowers purple or red; racemes short, often fasciculate at the nodes of leafless one-year-old branches; bracts and bracteoles very caducous; calyx-tube very short; segments 4, subequal, imbricate; petals 3, obovate, imbricate; stamens 10, filaments free at the top, otherwise connate into a sheath split on the upper side; anthers uniform, ovate, versatile; ovary stipitate, free, few-ovuled; style filiform, slightly clavate at the apex, stigma terminal, small; fruit oblong, subfalcate, compressed, thin, winged along the upper suture; seed solitary, compressed, reniform, testa shining.

36. **Lophocarpinia** Burkart, Darwiniana, 11: 256, figs. 1, 2 (1957). 1 sp., *L. aculeatifolia* Burkart, Argentina, Paraguay.

Shrub with hard divaricate branchlets ending in a spiny tip; leaves very small, borne with the flowers on arrested short branchlets, simply paripinnate, leaflets 2–3 pairs, sessile, obovate; stipules ovate, tip setose; stipels very small, subulate; flowers at the base of the arrested branchlets, pedicellate; bracts very small; bracteoles absent; calyx widely campanulate at the base, deeply 5-lobed, lobes imbricate, lowermost large, boat-shaped, enclosing the stamens during flowering; petals 5, free, imbricate, the uppermost innermost, fleshy and coloured, distinct from the lateral; stamens 10, free, declinate, filaments pilose; anthers dorsifixed, opening by slits; ovary shortly stipitate; ovules several; stigma small, terminal; fruit incurved or falcate, jointed, joints elongated, 4-winged, wings cristate; seeds elongate-reniform, with thin endosperm; cotyledons transversely elongated with the radicle formed like the letter T.

[1] I am indebted to Dr. van Steenis for the description of the fruit and seed.

37. **Zuccagnia** Cav., Ic. Pl. 5: 2, t. 403 (1799) (conserved name). 1 sp., *Z. punctata* Cav., Chile, Argentina. B.H. 1: 587; E.P. 3, 3: 173; Burkart, Legum. Argent. ed. 2, 184, fig. 37.

Glutinous shrub; leaves paripinnate, leaflets small, about 10–12 pairs, coriaceous, densely glandular; stipules minute; flowers yellow in terminal racemes, often transformed into head-like galls with filiform filaments; bracts small, very caducous; bracteoles absent; calyx-tube turbinate; segments 5, imbricate, slightly unequal, lowermost outside; petals 5, obovate-orbicular, slightly unequal, imbricate, uppermost inside, broader; stamens 10, free, declinate, filaments pilose at the base; anthers ovoid, uniform; ovary shortly stipitate, free, 1-ovuled; style filiform, stigma concave, ciliolate; fruit short, subovate, compressed, 2-valved, long-setose, seed flat.

38. **Mora** Schomb. ex Benth., Trans. Linn. Soc. 18: 210, tt. 16 and 17 (1839). About 9 spp., West Indies, trop. South America; type *M. excelsa* Benth., Trinidad, Venezuela, Guiana. Ducke, Arch. Jard. Bot. Rio de Janeiro, 4: 44 (1925); Sprague & Sandw., Kew Bull. 1932: 395; Amshoff, Pulle Fl. Suriname, 2, 2: 12.

Gigantic trees; leaves paripinnate, glabrous; leaflets 3–4-pairs, opposite; stipules caducous; flowers in very dense spikes, the spikes collected into terminal panicles; bracts small, scale-like; bracteoles absent; calyx urceolate-campanulate, shortly 5-toothed, imbricate; petals obovate-oblong, about twice as long as the calyx, subequal, shortly clawed; fertile stamens 5, opposite the petals, anthers covered with long deciduous white hairs, 5 sterile alternate with the petals, with glabrous clavate empty anthers; ovary shortly stipitate, with several ovules; style glabrous, equal to the stamens; stigma terminal; seeds 1–6, large, reniform, without endosperm; testa thin and fragile; fruit elliptic or oblong, woody, dehiscent.

Mora Wood, *M. excelsa* Benth., large timber tree used for shipbuilding and railway sleepers.

39. **Tachigalia**[1] Aubl., Hist. Pl. Guian. Franc. 1: 372, t. 143 (1775). About 22 spp., Cent. America and trop. South America; type *T. paniculata* Aubl., Guiana, Brazil, Peru. B.H. 1: 582; E.P. 3, 3: 137; Amshoff, Pulle Fl. Suriname, 2, 2: 89; J. D. Dwyer, Ann. Missouri Bot. Gard. 41: 223 (revision) (1954).

Trees; leaves paripinnate, leaflets coriaceous, rhachis often angular; stipules linear or small, or pinnately partite, caducous; racemes elongated, solitary and axillary, or paniculate at the ends of the shoots; bracts subulate or lanceolate, caducous; bracteoles absent; flower-buds remarkably incurved-clavate; calyx-tube obliquely turbinate; segments 5, unequal, very imbricate, lower smaller and exterior; petals 5, slightly unequal, obovate, imbricate, uppermost inside the others and less oblique; stamens 10, filaments mostly villous at the base, upper 3 often thicker and shorter; anthers ovate or oblong, uniform, or of the upper stamens smaller; ovary shortly stipitate, stipe adnate to the middle or to the apex of the calyx-tube; ovules numerous; style filiform, stigma terminal, small; fruit oblong, compressed, membranous, valves coriaceous, completely separating when mature; seeds ovate, compressed with thin endosperm, enclosed by the fibrous endocarp.

40. **Sympetalandra** Stapf, Hook. Ic. Pl. t. 272 (1901). 1 sp., *S. borneensis* Stapf, Borneo.

Small tree; leaves paripinnate; leaflets 2 pairs, coriaceous, pellucid-punctate, opposite; flowers small; racemes dense, axillary and extra-axillary collected into a panicle towards the tops of the shoots; bracts minute; bracteoles absent; calyx campanulate, broad, shortly 5-lobed, lobes imbricate; petals 5, equal, oblong, imbricate, connate at the base into a

---

[1] Synonyms of **Tachigalia**: *Tachigali* Aubl. (1775). *Cuba* Scop. (1777). *Cubaea* Schreb. (1789). *Valentinia* Neck. (1790). *Tachia* Pers. (1805). *Tassia* Rich. ex DC. (1825).

short tube; stamens 10, free, alternately shorter; anthers uniform, basifixed, with a deciduous gland at the apex, opening by slits lengthwise; ovary stipitate, 2-ovulate; style with a terminal punctiform stigma; fruits not seen.

41. **Schotia** Jacq., Collect. 1: 93 (1786) (conserved name), *Theodora* Medik. (1786). *Scotia* Thunb. (1798). *Omphalobium* Jacq. ex DC. (1825). *Schottia* Brongn. (1843). 20 spp., trop. and S. Africa; type *S. afra* (Linn.) Thunb. (*S. speciosa* Jacq.), S. Africa. B.H. 1: 581; E.P. 3, 3: 138; E. G. Bak., Legum. Trop. Afr. 3: 708; J. Léonard, Fl. Congo Belge, 3: 330, fig. 23; Mém. Acad. Roy. Belg. Cl. Sci. 30, 2: 97 (1957).

Small trees or shrubs; leaves paripinnate; stipules short; flowers red, showy, crowded in short panicles or racemes; bracts and bracteoles ovate or oblong, membranous, very caducous; calyx-tube turbinate, shortly or long-attenuated at the base; segments 4, very imbricate; petals 5, slightly unequal, subsessile, imbricate, uppermost inside the others, ovate or oblong, or minute and scale-like; stamens 10, free, or shortly connate at the base; anthers uniform; ovary stipitate, stipe adnate to the calyx-tube, many-ovuled; style elongated, stigma small, terminal; fruit oblong or broadly linear, often falcate or curved, compressed, coriaceous, subindehiscent, sometimes margined or winged along the upper suture; seeds orbicular, compressed, funicle sometimes expanded into a large cupular aril.

42. **Goniorrhachis** Taub., Flora, 77: t. 3 (1892). 1 sp., *G. marginata* Taub., Brazil. E.P. 3, 3: 137.

Shrub; stipules very caducous; leaves paripinnate; leaflets 2-pairs, obliquely ovate or oblong, unequal-sided at the base; spikes flexuose, few-flowered, fasciculate at the tops of the branchlets, bracteate at the base; bracts suborbicular, forming a cup, at length deciduous; flowers obliquely zygomorphic, white, medium-sized, with 2 alternating thick orbicular-ovate concave bracteoles at the base, persistent during flowering; calyx-tube subcylindric, segments 4, imbricate, ovate, lowermost exterior; petals 5, imbricate, subequal, obovate, shortly clawed, uppermost interior; stamens 10, 5 slightly longer, filaments free; anthers dorsifixed, uniform; ovary stipitate, stipe adnate to one side of the calyx-tube, many-ovuled; style filiform, shorter than the ovary, stigma small, terminal; fruit not seen.

43. **Browneopsis** Huber, Bol. Mus. Para, 4: 197, 565 (1906). 1 sp., *B. ucayalina* Huber, Amazon.

Tree; leaves paripinnate; leaflets 3–4-pairs, opposite or subopposite, oblong, shortly jointed-petiolulate; common petiole jointed at the base; inflorescences borne on the trunk and branches, subsessile, capitellate; bracts very accrescent from below upwards, the lowermost very short, intermediate larger and very broadly rounded, coriaceous, striate, uppermost ovate, oblong at the top and thinner, obtuse, all minutely tomentellous outside; bracteoles absent; flowers densely crowded in heads covered with the bracts; calyx-tube fleshy, segments 4, petaloid, free or more or less connate; petals 4–3, rudimentary, ligulate; stamens 15–12, filaments connate to the middle into a tube split on the upper side; anthers oblong, medifixed, subversatile; ovary stipitate, stipe adnate to the calyx-tube, linear, style elongated, stigma capitate.

44. **Hymenaea**[1] Linn., Sp. Pl. 1192 (1753); Gen. Pl. ed. 5: 499 (1754). About 30 spp., trop. America; type *H. courbaril* Linn., S. Mexico, Cent. America, West Indies, and cult. B.H. 1: 583; E.P. 3, 3: 135; Amshoff, Pulle Fl. Suriname, 2, 2: 22.

Trees; leaves 2-foliolate, pellucid-punctate; stipules broadly linear, very caducous; flowers white, in terminal densely corymbose panicles; bracts and bracteoles very caducous;

---

[1] Synonyms of **Hymenaea**: *Coubari* Adans. (1763). *Hemenaea* Scop. (1777). *Tanroujou* Juss. (1789). *Courbaril* Plum. ex Endl. (1841). *Hymenia* Griff. (1854).

calyx-tube thick and campanulate, subsolid; segments 4, very imbricate, coriaceous; petals 5, sessile, oblong or obovate, slightly unequal, the uppermost inside and often larger; stamens 10, free, glabrous; anthers oblong, uniform; ovary shortly stipitate, stipe adnate to the calyx-tube, few-ovuled; style filiform, stigma terminal, small; fruit obliquely obovoid or oblong, short or rather long, thick or subterete and drupe-like, woody, not dehiscent; seeds few, of various shapes.

Coubaril, *H. coubaril* Linn.; wood very hard, like Mahogany; used for shipbuilding, furniture, and by Indians for canoes; pulp around the seeds edible; also yields a gum-resin (Copal); Copal also from *H. stilbocarpa* Hayne, Brazil, and *Trachylobium verrucosum* (Gaertn.) Oliv., Madagascar.

45. Peltogyne Vogel, Linnaea, 11: 410 (1837). About 27 spp., West Indies, trop. America; type *P. discolor* Vogel, Brazil. B.H. 1: 582; E.P. 3, 3: 135; Amshoff, Pulle Fl. Suriname, 2, 2: 24.

Trees; leaves 2-foliolate; stipules not seen; flowers usually white, in short racemes collected into dense or large panicles at the ends of the branches; bracts small, very caducous; bracteoles short, caducous, or rarely shortly connate and persistent for some time; calyx-tube thick and campanulate, subsolid; segments 4, very imbricate; petals 5, sessile, oblong or obovate, slightly unequal, the uppermost inside and often narrower; stamens 10, free, glabrous; anthers oblong, uniform; ovary shortly stipitate, stipe adnate to the calyx-tube, few-ovuled; style filiform or short, stigma terminal, capitate-dilated; fruit obliquely orbicular, acinaciform or subtriangular, compressed, coriaceous, 2-valved, narrowly winged along the upper suture or not winged; seed often solitary, suborbicular, compressed.

P. paniculata Benth., Purple Heart, Brazil, Guiana; wood black in water, heavy, hard, durable; used for interior finish; other spp. also timber trees.

46. Griffonia Baill., Adans. 6: 188, t. 2 (1865), not Hook. f. (1865). *Schotiaria* DC. (1825). *Bandeiraea* Welw. ex Benth. (1865). *Bandereia* Baill. (1870). 3–4 spp., trop. Africa; type *G. simplicifolia* Baill. E. G. Bak., Legum. Trop. Afr. 3: 660 (*Bandeiraea*); J. Léonard, Fl. Congo Belge, 3: 265, t. 21 (1952); Hutch. & Dalz., Fl. W. Trop. Afr. ed. 2 (Keay), 1: 444.

Tall climbing shrubs; leaves 1-foliolate, with a very short stalk; stipules minute; flowers showy, red, recurved or pendulous, in terminal racemes or panicles; calyx-tube elongated; limb openly campanulate, lobes 5, short, broad, subimbricate; petals 5, oblong, erect, subequal, imbricate; stamens 10, free, subdeclinate; anthers uniform, versatile; ovary long-stipitate, stipe adnate to the calyx-tube and long-exserted; ovules numerous; style short, stigma small, terminal; fruit long-stipitate, obliquely oblong, compressed or turgid, with a persistent style hooked below the apex, coriaceous, 2-valved; seeds few to 1.

47. Paloue Aubl., Hist. Pl. Guian. Franç. 1: 365, t. 141 (1775). *Palovea* Auct. *Ginannia* Scop. (1777). *Paloveopsis* Cowan (1957). 5 spp., trop. South America; type *P. guianensis* Aubl., French Guiana. B.H. 1: 578; E.P. 3, 3: 144; Amshoff, Pulle Fl. Suriname, 2, 2: 38.

Small trees; leaves 1-foliolate, large, coriaceous, pinnately nerved, petiole very short; stipules minute; flowers red, showy, shortly racemose at the ends of the shoots; bracts short, persistent; bracteoles connate into a 2-lobed involucel, shorter than the calyx, the latter conspicuous in bud; calyx-tube elongate-turbinate; segments 4, slightly unequal, imbricate; petals 3, slightly unequal, oblong, subsessile; stamens 9, free, filaments elongated or scimitar-shaped, sometimes some without anthers; anthers oblong, uniform; ovary stipitate, stipe adnate to the calyx-tube; ovules numerous; style filiform, stigma small, subcapitate, terminal; fruit long and narrow, straight or scimitar-shaped, 2-valved, compressed, rather woody, the upper suture thicker; seeds ovate, compressed.

48. Daniellia J. J. Benn., Pharm. Journ. 14: 251 (1854). *Daniella* Auth. *Paradaniellia* Rolfe (1912). *Cyanothyrsus* Harms (1897). 12 spp., trop. Africa; type *D. thurifera* J. J. Benn. E. G. Bak., Legum. Trop. Afr. 3: 694; Hutch. &

Dalz., Fl. W. Trop. Afr., 1: 340 (1928); ed. 2 (Keay), 1: 461 (1958); J. Léonard, Fl. Congo Belge, 3: 341, t. 25 and fig. 26 (1952); Mém. Acad. Roy. Belg. Cl. Sci. 30, 2: 110 (1957).

Large timber trees; leaves paripinnate, leaflets petiolulate, opposite, pinnately nerved; stipules large and lanceolate, folded around the terminal bud, soon deciduous and leaving a circular scar; flowers in a terminal panicle of racemes, the branches at length scarred by the fallen bracts; bracts and bracteoles early deciduous; calyx-lobes 4, broadly lanceolate, deciduous and leaving a truncate tube, imbricate; petals 5, imbricate, sessile, unequal, usually 2 large and 3 smaller, rarely 1 large and 4 small; stamens 10, filaments free, or 9 united at the base; anthers dorsifixed; ovary stipitate, stipe partly adnate to the calyx-tube; ovules numerous; style exserted, stigma capitate, terminal; fruit stipitate, compressed, boat-shaped, 2-valved, endocarp thin, separating from the exocarp; seed solitary, elliptic, flattened, attached to a long funicle near the top of the suture and with a cupular aril.

D. thurifera J. J. Bennett; stem source of Ogea Gum of Sierra Leone, a Frankincense; sold as body perfume; also called Illorin Gum and Balsam of Copaiba; other sources are *D. oblonga* Oliv., *D. ogea* Rolfe, and *D. similis* Craib.

49. Bauhinia[1] Linn., Sp. Pl. 374 (1753).

About 570 spp., tropics and warm temperate regions; type *B. divaricata* Linn., South America. B.H. 1: 575; E.P. 3, 3: 147; E. G. Bak., Legum. Trop. Afr. 3: 651; Wilczek, Fl. Congo Belge, 3: 269, t. 22 (1952); Burkart, Legum. Argent. ed. 2, 158, fig. 26.

Trees and shrubs, sometimes straggling or climbing; stem often flattened, and sometimes with undivided tendrils at the base of the racemes; leaves simple, 3–many-nerved, entire or 2-lobed or almost 2-foliolate, with the midrib bristly between the lobes; stipules various, caducous; flowers in terminal or rarely axillary racemes or in terminal rarely axillary panicles or corymbs; calyx-tube shortly turbinate, sometimes elongated, limb entire or closed at the apex or shortly 5-toothed, teeth imbricate, variously split during flowering, spathaceous or valvately 5-lobed or partite; petals 5, slightly unequal, erect or spreading, imbricate, upper within in bud; perfect stamens 10 or fewer with some reduced to staminodes or deficient, free or shortly connate; anthers ovate, oblong or linear, versatile, opening lengthwise; ovary usually stipitate, stipe free or adnate, 2–many-ovuled; style filiform or short, stigma terminal, often peltate or oblique; fruit oblong or linear, rarely falcate, membranous to hard, indehiscent or 2-valved, continuous within or filled or septate; seeds orbicular or ovate, compressed, with endosperm; cotyledons flat; radicle straight or nearly so, never inflexed.

---

[1] Above is a translation of Bentham's description of *Bauhinia* (*sensu lato et auct. plur.*), representing a concept which remained acceptable to most botanists until a few years ago. de Wit,* in a Revision of Malayan *Bauhinieae*, separated several genera from *Bauhinia* (*sensu* de Wit) by rather slender characters, some of them appearing twice in his small artificial key. Pending a comprehensive re-examination of the whole world species, including a great range of characters in Africa and America, I prefer to follow the example of the de Candolles, Bentham & Hooker, Taubert, and others. For notes on the status of *Piliostigma*, recently also treated as a separate genus, see Wilczek (above).

Synonyms of **Bauhinia** (*sensu* Benth. & Hook. f.): *Phanera* Lour. (1790). *Pauletia* Cav. (1799). *Amaria* Mutis (1810). *Schnella* Raddi (1820). *Lacara* Spreng. (1822). *Casparea* H. B. & K. (1824). *Caulotretus* Rich. (1827). *Perlebia* Mart. (1828). *Binaria, Cansenia, Elayuna, Mandarus, Monoteles, Telestria* all Rafin. (1838). *Casparia* D. Dietr. (1840). *Piliostigma* Hochst. (1846). *Lasiobema* Miq. (1855). *Alvesia* Welw. (1858). *Locellaria* Welw. (1859). *Gigasiphon* Drake (1902). *Cardenasia* Rusby (1927). *Caspareopsis* Britt. & Rose (1930). *Bracteolanthus* de Wit (1956). *Lysiphyllum* de Wit (1956). *Adenolobus* Torre & Hillcoat (1955). *Tylosema* Torre & Hillcoat (1955).

* de Wit, Revision of Malaysian *Bauhinieae*, Reinwardtia, 3: 381 (1956).

Leaves and pods of *B. variegata* Linn., eaten as vegetable, China, Indo-Malaya; bark tonic, alterative and astringent, used for tanning and dyeing; *B. reticulata* DC., trop. Africa, roots give mahogany-coloured pigment; bark a fibre for clothes and ropes; pods and seeds source of black and blue dyes. Chrysanthemum Wood. *B. championii* Benth., Japan and Hong Kong. Formosa; cross-section of wood marked like a *Chrysanthemum* flower. Several species cultivated for ornament.

50. **Trachylobium** Hayne, Flora, 10: 743 (1827). 1 sp., *T. verrucosum* (Gaertn.) Oliv. (*T. hornemannianum* Hayne), trop. Africa, Mascarene Isls. B.H. 1: 583; E.P. 3, 3: 135; J. Léonard, Mém. Acad. Roy. Belg. Cl. Sci. 30, 2: 115 (1957).

Tree; leaves 2-foliolate, leaflets coriaceous, pellucid-punctate; stipules very caducous; flowers white, in terminal panicles; bracts and bracteoles ovate or orbicular, concave, caducous before flowering; calyx-tube narrowly turbinate; segments 4, very imbricate; petals 5, either 3 of the upper ones clawed, suborbicular and subequal, with the 2 lower minute and scale-like, or all clawed and subequal, imbricate; stamens 10, free, filaments villous at the base; anthers oblong, uniform; ovary shortly stipitate, stipe adnate to the calyx-tube; ovules few; style filiform, stigma small, terminal; fruit drupaceous, ovoid-oblong, thick and coriaceous, coarsely verrucose-rugose, not dehiscent; seeds thick, not arillate.

T. verrucosum (Gaertn.) Oliv.; root, trunk, and fruits the source of Zanzibar Copal, much of it found as semi-fossil in the soil; Gum Copal of Madagascar.

51. **Afzelia** Smith, Trans. Linn. Soc. 4: 221 (1798) (conserved name). *Pahudia* Miq. (1855). *Afrointsia* Taub. ex Dalla Torre & Harms (1901). *Afrafzelia*, Pierre (1899). About 30 spp., S. China, Indo-Malaya, trop. and S. Africa, Madagascar; type *A. africana* Smith. B.H. 1: 580; E.P. 3, 3: 140; E. G. Bak., Legum. Trop. Afr. 3: 699; J. Léonard, Reinwardtia, 1: 63 (1950), Fl. Congo Belge, 3: 350, t. 26 and fig. 27 (1952), and Mém. Acad. Roy. Belg. Cl. Sci. 30, 2: 106 (1957); Hutch. & Dalz., Fl. W. Trop. Afr. ed. 2 (Keay), 1: 459.

Trees; leaves paripinnate or rarely subimparipinnate; leaflets few pairs, coriaceous; stipules very minute and early deciduous, linear-subulate on seedlings; flowers rather large, in paniculate racemes at the ends of the shoots; bracts ovate, concave, deciduous or reflexed; bracteoles ovate, concave, subpersistent, shorter than the flower-buds; calyx-tube elongated; segments 4, slightly unequal, very imbricate; petal 1, clawed orbicular or reniform, the others rudimentary or absent; stamens 8–3, free or partly united, filaments elongated, declinate; anthers ovoid; staminodes 4–2, small or absent; ovary stipitate, stipe more or less adnate to the calyx-tube; ovules numerous; style elongated, stigma truncate and subcapitate; fruit obliquely oblong, compressed, thick and often rather woody, 2-valved or subindehiscent, transversely septate between the seeds or filled with thin pulp; seeds transverse, ovoid or orbicular, thick, arillate, the aril often at first completely enveloping the seed.

A. africana Smith, wood hard, exported to Europe as African or Rhodesian Mahogany; used for cabinet work, turnery, &c.; burnt pods used in the Sudan for manufacture of native soap; seeds used for handles of hatpins.

52. **Loesenera** Harms, Engl. & Prantl, Nat. Pflanzenfam. Nachtr. 197 (1897); Engl., Bot. Jahrb. 26: 268 (1899). *Ibadja* A. Chev. (1938). 4 spp., W. trop. Africa; type *L. kalantha* Harms. J. Léonard, Mém. Acad. Roy. Belg. Cl. Sci. 30, 2: 120 (1957); Hutch. & Dalz., Fl. W. Trop. Afr. ed. 2 (Keay), 1: 461.

Shrubs or small trees; leaves paripinnate; leaflets 1–5 pairs, obliquely oblong or lanceolate, acuminate, coriaceous; stipules striate, deciduous; racemes terminal; bracts and bracteoles almost the same size, ovate, velvety outside; bracts soon deciduous; bracteoles 2 at the base of the calyx, enclosing the flower-bud and persisting for a long time; calyx-tube funnel-shaped; segments 4, imbricate, broadly oval or ovate, velvety outside; petals 5, membranous, 3 larger and similar to one another, obovate, shortly clawed, 2 minute and narrowly lanceolate, acute; stamens 10, filaments filiform, free; anthers ovoid; ovary stipitate, stipe more or less adnate to the receptacle; stigma minute, capitellate; ovules very few; fruit compressed, broadly oblong, woody, very hard, often velvety-hairy, the pericarp separating into two lamellae; seeds flat and disk-like, suborbicular.

53. **Eperua**[1] Aubl., Hist. Pl. Guian. Franç. 1: 369, t. 142 (1775). 6 spp., E. trop. South America; type *E. falcata* Aubl., Trinidad, Guianas. B.H. 1: 580; E.P. 3, 3: 141; Sandw., Kew Bull. 1931: 364 (Guiana spp.); Amshoff, Pulle Fl. Suriname, 2, 2: 28.

Tall or slender trees paripinnate or rarely subimparipinnate, leaflets coriaceous, in few pairs; stipules foliaceous or small, intrapetiolar; flowers showy, purple-red or white; racemes often short and shortly paniculate, sometimes on very long pendulous peduncles; bracts and bracteoles caducous; calyx-tube turbinate-campanulate; segments 4, ovate or oblong, very imbricate; petal 1, sessile, large and very broad; stamens 10, free or shortly connate at the base; filaments elongated, alternate ones rarely smaller and without anthers; ovary shortly stipitate, stipe adnate to one side of the calyx-tube; ovules numerous; style elongated, involute in bud, stigma small, terminal; fruit large, oblong or elongated, often oblique or scimitar-shaped, plano-compressed, rather woody, 2-valved; seeds few, compressed; cotyledons fleshy.

E. falcata Aubl., Wallaba, Bootlace tree; wood hard, made into shingles, telegraph poles, and used for construction.

54. **Plagiosiphon** Harms, Engl. & Prantl, Nat. Pflanzenfam. Nachtr. 194 (1897), and Engl. Bot. Jahrb. 26: 263 (1899). *Tripetalanthus* A. Chev. (1946). 5 spp., trop. Africa; type *P. discifer* Harms, Cameroons. J. Léonard, Bull. Jard. Bot. Brux. 21: 425, and Mém. Acad. Roy. Belg. Cl. Sci. 30, 2: 92 (1957); Hutch. & Dalz., Fl. W. Trop. Afr. ed. 2 (Keay), 1: 464.

Shrubs; leaves paripinnate with 2–1 or numerous pairs of leaflets; leaflets opposite, subcoriaceous, sessile; racemes axillary, elongated, several-flowered; bracts absent or very minute; bracteole at the base of the flowers large, petaloid, suborbicular; calyx-tube rather long and obliquely cylindric, slightly ventricose on one side at the base; disk at the base of the calyx thick, deeply channelled inside; sepals 4, imbricate, oblong, obtuse; petals 5, as long as the sepals or a little longer, oblong, subspathulate; stamens 10, filaments filiform, pilose at the base; anthers small, oblong; ovary obliquely oblong, stipitate, stipe adnate to the calyx-tube, free part densely pilose; style filiform, pilose only in the lower part, stigma small, subcapitellate; ovules 5–2; fruits compressed, obliquely oblong, mucronate.

55. **Maniltoa** Scheff., Ann. Jard. Biutenzorg 1: 20 (1876). *Pseudocynometra* O. Ktze. (1903). 4–5 spp., E. India, Malay Archip., New Guinea, Fiji Isls.; type *M. grandiflora* Scheff., New Guinea, Fiji. E.P. 3, 3: 129; Nachtr. 193.

Trees; young leaves enclosed in a bud several cm. long; bud-scales imbricate, cartilaginous, lower subrotundate, upper long-contracted and membranous towards the base, dilated at the apex, subrotundate, all coarsely serrate at the apex; stipules linear, suddenly dilated towards the apex, very caducous; leaves paripinnate, leaflets 2–5-pairs, opposite or subopposite, very unequal-sided, acuminate, glaucous below; racemes dense, on the defoliated branches; pedicels 2-bracteate at the base, outer bract lanceolate, rounded at the apex, half-embracing the pedicel, inner much narrower, linear; calyx ebracteolate, tube very short, campanulate, segments 4, subequal; petals 5, subequal, narrowly linear, equal in length to the calyx-segments; stamens 15–10; ovary shortly stipitate, stipe free from the calyx, 2-ovulate, style elongated, stigma capitate; fruit arcuate-ovoid, thick, turgid, rugose; seeds 2, transverse; testa hard.

56. **Lysidice** Hance, Seem. Journ. Bot. 5: 298 (1867). 1 sp., *L. rhodostegia* Hance, S. China, Tonking.

---

[1] Synonyms of **Eperua**: *Parivoa* Aubl. (1775). *Adleria* Neck. (1790). *Rotmannia* Neck. (1790). *Dimorpha* Schreb. (1791). *Panzera* Willd. (1799).

Shrub; leaves paripinnate; stipules small, intrapetiolar; panicles axillary and terminal, the peduncles with large coloured bracts at the base; calyx bibracteolate at the base, coloured, funnel-shaped, tube rather fleshy, 4-partite, segments imbricate, reflexed during flowering; petals 3, slightly shorter than the calyx, of equal length, long-clawed; stamens 6; filaments connate at the base into a short ring, 2 minute and bearing abortive anthers; ovary stipitate, exserted, about 12-ovuled, stipe adnate to the calyx-tube; style long, filiform, circinate in bud, stigma simple; fruit large, flat, apiculate, 2-valved, valves curling after opening; seeds compressed, transversely oblong.

57. **Hymenostegia** Harms, Engl. & Prantl, Nat. Pflanzenfam. Nachtr. 193 (1897); Engl. Bot. Jahrb. 26: 263 (1899). *Dipetalanthus* A. Chev. (1946). About 20 spp., trop. Africa; type *H. floribunda* (Benth.) Harms. Hutch. & Dalz., Fl. W. Trop. Afr. 1: 331 (1928); ed. 2 (Keay) 1: 464 (1958); E. G. Bak., Legum. Trop. Afr. 3: 764; J. Léonard, Bull. Jard. Bot. Brux. 21: 433, fig. 116 (1951); Fl. Congo Belge, 3: 336, figs. 24, 25 (1952); Mém. Acad. Roy. Belg. Cl. Sci. 30, 2: 122 (1957).

Trees and shrubs; leaves paripinnate, leaflets few- to many-pairs, opposite to alternate; stipules small to large, usually very caducous, sometimes auriculate at the base; racemes or panicles axillary or terminal; bracteoles opposite, large and ovate to linear-filiform, petaloid, usually persistent; calyx-tube cupular or cylindric; disk absent or very small; sepals 4, imbricate; petals 5–1, very unequal, entire; stamens usually 10, rarely 16–26, free; anthers dorsifixed; ovary stipitate, stipe shortly adnate to the calyx-tube; ovules 2–3; style filiform, stigma terminal; fruit coriaceous, compressed, stipitate, 2-valved; seeds not arillate.

58. **Neochevalierodendron** J. Léonard, Bull. Jard. Bot. Brux. 21: 428, fig. 114 (1951). 1 sp., *N. stephanii* (A. Chev.) J. Léonard, Gabon, W. trop. Africa. J. Léonard, Mém. Acad. Roy. Belg. Cl. Sci. 30, 2: 119 (1957).

Tree; leaves alternate, paripinnate; leaflets 4 or rarely 2, lower alternate, upper opposite, obliquely obovate; petiolules twisted; racemes axillary or terminal, shorter than the leaves; bracts caducous; bracteoles broadly ovate-rounded, 1-nerved, more or less petaloid, caducous, not covering the bud; pedicels compressed, sepals 4, free, very imbricate, coriaceous; petals 5, 2 minute, 3 larger and suborbicular, cordate, shortly clawed, densely tomentose within; stamens 10, all with anthers; filaments connate at the base; anthers dorsifixed, opening lengthwise; ovary stipitate, stipe totally adnate to the side of the calyx-tube; ovules 2–4; fruits very large, stipitate, 2-valved, transversely nerved.

59. **Leucostegane** Prain, Ann. Bot. Gard. Calc. 9: pt. 1: 37, t. 46 (1901). 2 spp., Malaya; type *L. latistipulata* Prain, Malay Peninsula.

Trees; leaves paripinnate, stipellate; stipules large, foliaceous, intrapetiolar, connate; flowers in fascicles of racemes on older wood; bracteoles deciduous; pedicels bracteate; calyx infundibuliform with somewhat fleshy tube, limb 4-partite, lobes obtuse, imbricate, reflexed in flower; petals 2, small, much shorter than calyx-lobes, inserted in the calyx-throat between upper and lateral sepals, the upper if present a staminode-like process; stamens only 2 perfect, opposite the lateral sepals, with large ovoid anthers, decurved plicate in bud, and with two erect short sterile staminodia between and above the fertile stamens; ovary stipitate, exserted, oblong, the stipe adnate to calyx-tube, style filiform, circinate in bud, stigma oblique; fruit oblong, compressed, apiculate.

60. **Intsia** Thouars, Gen. Nov. Madag. 22 (1806). *Macrolobium* Zipp. ex Miq. (1855), not Schreb. (1789). About 6–7 spp., Madagascar, Indo-Malaya, Indo-China, Formosa, Philippine Isls., New Guinea, Pacific Isls.; type *I. bijuga* (Colebr.) O. Ktze. (*I. madagascariensis* Thouars), throughout the region. Dress, Bull. Jard. Bot. Buitenz. ser. 3, 16, 1: 83 (1938); de Wit, loc. cit. 17, 1: 139 (1941).

Trees; leaves paripinnate; leaflets 2–5 pairs, opposite, rounded to elliptic; stipules connate at the base; flowers in terminal racemes or panicles; bracts and bracteoles deciduous; calyx-tube elongated; segments 4, imbricate; petal 1, clawed, orbicular or reniform, others rudimentary; fertile stamens 3, declinate, filaments long, connate at the base, with 4–7 staminodes; anthers dorsifixed; ovary stipitate, adnate to the calyx-tube; ovules several, 1-seriate; style elongated, stigma terminal; fruit compressed, flat and thin, 2-valved, transversely nerved; seeds few, flat and compressed, elliptic or rounded, not arillate.

I. bijuga (Colebr.) O. Ktze., Fiji Intzia, Molucca Ironwood; wood strong, durable, used for building houses, ships, telegraph poles, furniture, bridges, &c.; also Kava bowls of Samoans.

61. **Tamarindus** Linn., Sp. Pl. 32 (1753); Gen. Pl. ed. 5: 20 (1754). *Cavaraea* Speg. (1916). 1 sp., *T. indica* Linn., trop. Asia and Africa. B.H. 1: 581; E.P. 3, 3: 139; J. Léonard, Fl. Congo Belge, 3: 436 (1952); Mém. Acad. Roy. Belg. Cl. Sci. 30, 2: 200 (1957); Roti-Michelozzi, Webbia, 13: 134, fig. 1 (1957).

Tree; leaves paripinnate, leaflets in numerous pairs, small; stipules minute, caducous; flowers yellowish, tinged with red, racemose at the ends of the shoots; bracts and bracteoles ovate-oblong, coloured, caducous; calyx-tube narrowly turbinate; segments 4, very imbricate, membranous; upper 3 petals about equal in length, imbricate, the uppermost inside narrower and subsessile, lower 2 minute, setaceous or scale-like; perfect stamens 3, connate high up into a sheath open above, filaments short; anthers oblong; staminodes few, minute, at the apex of the sheath; ovary stipitate, stipe adnate to the calyx-tube; ovules numerous; style elongated, rather thick, stigma terminal, truncate, subcapitate; fruit oblong or linear, incurved, thick, subcompressed, not dehiscent, epicarp thin, mesocarp pulpy, endocarp thick and coriaceous, septate between the seeds; seeds obovate-orbicular, compressed.

Tamarind, large tree frequently cult.; pulp of fruits used fresh, in beverages, for preserving, and in medicine; used as an ingredient of confection of Senna; grown also for shade and ornament.

62. **Endertia** van Steenis & de Wit, Bull. Bot. Gard. Buitenz. ser. 3, 17: 323, fig. 1 (1947). 1 sp., *E. spectabilis* van Steenis & de Wit, Borneo.

Tree; leaves paripinnate, leaflets 3 pairs, elliptic, acuminate; stipules axillary, small, early-deciduous; bracts and bracteoles long-persistent; calyx-tube cupular, lobes 4, imbricate; petals 2 or 1, lateral, rounded, shortly clawed; perfect stamens 2, filaments connate at the base into a ring around the base of the ovary; anthers dorsifixed, suborbicular; ovary 5–3-ovuled; style recurved, glabrous; stigma small, terminal; fruit oblong, shortly beaked, dehiscent, the valves at length twisted; seeds flat and discoid; cotyledons flat.

63. **Cassia**[1] Linn., Sp. Pl. 376 (1753). About 600 spp., tropics and subtropics; lectotype *C. fistula* Linn., trop. Asia. B.H. 1: 571; E.P. 3, 3: 157; Benth., Trans. Linn. Soc. 27: 503 (1871); Amshoff, Pulle Fl. Suriname, 2, 2: 54; E. G. Bak., Legum. Trop. Afr. 3: 626; Steyaert, Fl. Congo Belge, 3: 496, tt. 35–38 (1952); Burkart, Legum. Argent. ed. 2, 162, fig. 29 (1952); Neal, Common and Aberrant Flowers of *C. fistula*, Pacific Science, 5: 82 (1951); de Wit, *Cassia* in Malaysia, Webbia, 11: 197, figs. 1–3 (1955); Hutch. & Dalz., Fl. W. Trop. Afr. ed. 2 (Keay), 1: 450.

[1] Synonyms of **Cassia**: *Senna* Mill. (1754). *Chamaecrista* Moench (1794). *Grimaldia* Schrank (1805). *Sooja* Sieb. (1830). *Chamaefistula* G. Don (1832). *Chamaesenna* Raf. (1838). *Herpetica* Raf. (1838). *Emelista* Raf. (1838). *Adipera* Raf. (1838). *Panisia* Raf. (1838). *Plisanisia* Raf. (1838). *Ditremexa* Raf. (1838). *Isandrina* Raf. (1838). *Cathartocarpus* Pers. (1805). *Lenocassia* Britt. (1930). *Gaumerocassia* Britt. (1930). *Palmerocassia* Britt. (1930). *Vogelocassia* Britt. (1930). *Leonocassia* Britt. (1930). *Sciacassia* Britt. (1930). *Psilorhegma* Britt. (1930). *Desmodiocassia* Britt. & Rose (1930). *Pseudocassia* Britt. & Rose (1930). *Pterocassia* Britt. & Rose (1930). *Cowellocassia* Britt. (1930). *Phagmocassia* Britt. & Rose (1930). *Sericeocassia* Britt. & Rose (1930). *Xerocassia* Britt. & Rose (1930). *Tharpia* Britt. & Rose (1930). *Earleocassia* Britt. (1930). *Echinocassia* Britt. & Rose (1930).

Trees, shrubs, and herbs; leaves paripinnate or rarely reduced to phyllodes; stipules various; petiolar glands often present, wart-like or shield-like; flowers bisexual, yellow or rarely white or rosy, in axillary or terminal racemes, terminal panicles, or axillary and sub-solitary; bracts and bracteoles various; calyx-tube very short; segments 5, imbricate; petals 5, imbricate, spreading, subequal or the lowermost larger, the uppermost inside the others; stamens 10, all perfect and subequal or the upper ones smaller or imperfect, or stamens only 5; anthers uniform or those of the lower stamens larger, loculi opening at the apex by a pore or short slit; ovary sessile or stipitate, free within the calyx: ovules numerous; style with a terminal stigma; fruit very various in shape and size, terete or compressed, woody, coriaceous or membranous, often 2-valved, sometimes indehiscent, rarely winged length-wise, continuous within or septate or pulpy between the seeds; seeds transverse or rarely placed lengthwise, compressed or rarely tetragonous-subterete, with endosperm.

Several species are medicinal: *C. absus* Linn., tropics, seeds used in S. Africa for ringworm and ophthalmia; as cathartic in India; *C. angustifolia* Vahl, Tennevelley Senna, dried leaves used as laxative; Alexandrian Senna, *C. acutifolia* Del., NE. trop. Africa to Egypt and Arabia; *C. fistula* Linn., tree, cult. in tropics, source of Purging Cassia, Indian Laburnum, Cassia Pods; dried fruit used as purgative; *Cassia obovata* Collad, Dog Senna or Italian Senna; *C. occidentalis* Linn., Coffee Senna, seeds as substitute for Coffee called Mogdad or Negro Coffee; also medicinal.

64. **Baudouinia** Baill., Adans. 6: 193, t. 5 (1866). 2 spp., Madagascar; type *B. sollyiformis* Baill. B.H. 1: 1003; E.P. 3, 3: 165.

Small tree; leaves 1-foliolate, obovate, entire; stipules very caducous, striate; peduncles axillary, slender, 1–3-flowered; bracts very small; flowers subactinomorphic; calyx 5-partite, segments subequal, lanceolate, imbricate; petals similar to the calyx-segments, thinner, imbricate; stamens 10, free, obpyramidate, thickened and truncate at the apex; anthers basifixed, introrse, 2-locular, sagittate, opening by apical pores; ovary shortly stipitate, villous; ovules mostly 3, subhorizontal or obliquely descending; style slender, scarcely thickened at the apex; fruit woody, drupaceous, stipitate; seeds solitary in spurious loculi between the oblique dissepiments of the thickened endocarp.

GROUP 3

Stamens 12–10, rarely one reduced to a staminode; anthers opening by slits
    lengthwise;
Flowers very large with subequal petals; sepals 4; upper filament free,
    remainder connate at the base; ovary stipitate, stipe adnate to the calyx-
    tube; trop. Africa   **65. Baikiaea**
Flowers medium-sized to small; other characters above not associated.
  Leaves 2- or more-foliolate:
    Petals 5:
      Leaves imparipinnate; ovules several to numerous:
        Calyx-tube not elongate-turbinate; segments 5 or 4:
          Calyx-segments 5, not warted; leaflets numerous and small, not
            punctate; filaments free; fruits elongated, neither verrucose nor
            setose   **66. Poeppigia**
          Calyx-segments 4, warted; leaflets fairly large, punctate; filaments
            partly connate into a sheath; fruits obliquely oblong to sub-
            orbicular, verrucose or strongly setose   **67. Tessmannia**
        Calyx-tube elongate-turbinate, at length valvately 3–4-partite; fila-
          ments free; fruit obliquely ovate, with thickened sutures
                                   68. Exostyles

Leaves paripinnate:

Inflorescence racemose, terminal or subterminal; filaments hairy towards the base:

Stipules absent; flowers yellow; bracts minute, very caducous; ovules 2
69. **Stuhlmannia**

Stipules small, persistent; flowers white; bracts thick and spine-like,
very caducous; ovules numerous   70. **Lemuropisum**

Inflorescence paniculate; stipules small, caducous; flowers red, pedicels
fasciculate; filaments glabrous; ovules numerous   71. **Chidlowia**

Inflorescence corymbose; low densely branched shrublet; leaflets with
numerous purple glands below; filaments barbate below the middle
72. **Cordeauxia**

Petal 1; stamens shortly and obliquely united, the adaxial free or reduced
to a staminode:

Stipules foliaceous; flowers in terminal panicles of racemes; fruits often
prickly   73. **Sindora**

Stipules deciduous; flowers in axillary racemes; fruits not prickly;
leaflets pellucid-punctate   74. **Sindoropsis**

Leaves 1-foliolate (simple):

Ovules several; stipules scale-like or membranous; flowers on the one-
year-old or older branches; fruit oblong or broadly linear   75. **Cercis**

Ovules 1–3; stipules caducous or rarely large, foliaceous and persistent;
flowers axillary, fasciculate-racemose; fruit semi-orbicular to reniform   33. **Zenkerella**

Stamens 5–4:

Anthers opening by pores at the apex or base; seeds compressed; branchlets
not cladodiform:

Ovules few; fruit lined with 2 ribs lengthwise; trop. South America
76. **Martiodendron**

Ovule 1; fruit surrounded by a wing; Malaya   77. **Koompassia**

Anthers opening by slits lengthwise; branchlets flattened and cladodiform;
Madagascar   78. **Brenierea**

Stamens 2; anthers opening by terminal pores   19. **Distemonanthus**

65. **Baikiaea** Benth., Benth. & Hook. f., Gen. Pl. 1: 581 (1865). 6 spp., trop.
Africa, SW. Africa; type *B. insignis* Benth., W. trop. Africa. E.P. 3, 3: 138;
E. G. Bak., Legum. Trop. Afr. 3: 703; J. Léonard, Fl. Congo Belge, 3: 296,
t. 23 (1952); Mém. Acad. Roy. Belg. Cl. Sci. 30, 2: 72 (1957); Hutch. &
Dalz., Fl. W. Trop. Afr. ed. 2 (Keay), 1: 456.

Trees; leaves paripinnate or imparipinnate, leaflets 1–5-pairs, large and coriaceous;
stipules short; flowers very large, crowded in short subterminal racemes; pedicels very
short; bracts and bracteoles short, caducous; calyx-tube turbinate; segments 4, long, thick,
abruptly narrowed to the margins, valvate; petals 5, clawed, obovate-spathulate, subequal,
the uppermost inside, subequal-sided, remainder oblique; stamens 10, upper one free, remainder connate at the base; alternate filaments villous at the base, the others thinner and
glabrous; anthers linear, versatile; ovary densely villous, stipitate, stipe adnate to the
calyx-tube; ovules 1 to many; style glabrous, elongated, stigma small; fruit stipitate, dehiscent by 2 valves, woody, flat, unequal-sided at the base, valves becoming spirally twisted;
seeds compressed, elliptic or suborbicular.

66. Poeppigia C. Presl, Symb. Bot. 1: 15, t. 8 (1830). *Ramirezia* A. Rich. (1855). 1 sp., *P. procera* C. Presl, W. Indies, trop. America. B.H. 1: 562; E.P. 3, 3: 179.

Tall tree; leaves imparipinnate, leaflets numerous, small; flowers in paniculate cymes, terminal; bracts and bracteoles narrow, membranous, very caducous; calyx-tube campanulate; segments 5, subequal, valvate, mostly connate above the disk; petals 5, imbricate, slightly unequal, oblong; stamens 10, free, filaments glabrous, almost straight; anthers ovate or oblong, versatile; ovary stipitate, stipe obliquely inserted in the calyx-tube; style short, conical or incurved, stigma terminal, small; ovules numerous; fruit elongated, membranous, flat and compressed, narrowly winged along the upper suture; seeds transverse, ovate, compressed.

67. Tessmannia Harms, Engl. Bot. Jahrb. 45: 295, fig. 2 (1910). About 12 spp., trop. Africa; type *T. africana* Harms, W. Trop. Africa. E. G. Bak., Legum. Trop. Afr. 3: 705; J. Léonard, Bull. Jard. Bot. Brux. 19: 384 (1949); Fl. Congo Belge, 3: 287, figs. 15, 16; Mém. Acad. Roy. Belg. Cl. Sci. 30, 2: 66; Hutch. & Dalz., Fl. W. Trop. Afr. ed. 2 (Keay), 1: 455.

Trees; leaves imparipinnate; leaflets several, alternate to opposite, often emarginate, pinnately nerved, translucently punctate, subsessile; racemes or panicles axillary or terminal; bracts small, caducous; sepals 4, slightly imbricate or valvate, verrucose or strongly warted; petals 5, subequal, longer than the sepals, narrowly oblanceolate, broadly clawed, corrugated-plicate on the margin; stamens 10, inverted in bud, one filament quite free, glabrous, the remainder connate into a thick sheath hairy outside; anthers all dorsifixed, versatile, opening lengthwise; ovary stipitate; ovules several; style lateral, long, circinately coiled, glabrous; stigma small, capitate; fruits woody, flat, obliquely oblong, suborbicular to obovate, smooth, verrucose or strongly setose; seeds hard, shining.

68. Exostyles Schott ex Spreng., Syst. Cur. Post. 4: 406 (1827). *Exostylis* G. Don (1832). 2 spp., Brazil; type *E. venusta* Schott ex Spreng. B.H. 1: 560; E.P. 3, 3: 184.

Small trees; leaves imparipinnate; leaflets alternate, toothed or crenulate; stipules small, subulate-setaceous, caducous; stipels subulate; flowers rose or purple, racemose, racemes axillary, short, lax; bracts and bracteoles lanceolate-setaceous or acuminate, rigid, small, subpersistent; calyx-tube elongate-turbinate, limb before flowering acuminate and entire, at length valvately 3–4 partite; petals 5, erect, slightly unequal, imbricate, 4 often convolute, the uppermost within the others; stamens 10, equal; anthers uniform, linear, acuminate, attached near the base, loculi opening by slits lengthwise; ovary stipitate, ovules numerous; style straight, elongated, stigma terminal, small; fruit obliquely ovate, compressed, leathery, 2-valved, with thickened sutures; seeds 3–1, ovate, compressed, not arillate.

69. Stuhlmannia Taub., Engl., Pflanzenw. Ost-Afr. C: 201 (1895). 1 sp., *S. moavi* Taub., E. trop. Africa.

Tree; bark very rough; leaves alternate, paripinnate; leaflets 3–6-pairs, subopposite, subsessile, unequal-sided at the base; stipules and stipels absent; racemes terminal; flowers yellow, aromatic; bracts minute, very caducous; bracteoles absent; sepals 5, narrow, free nearly to the base, valvate; petals 5, obovate, clawed, subequal; stamens 10, filaments united at the base into a ring, setose-pilose towards the base; anthers oblong, dorsifixed near the base, opening lengthwise; ovary shortly stipitate, free, glandular; ovules 2; style glabrous; fruit (young) compressed, shortly stipitate.

70. Lemuropisum H. Perrier, Bull. Soc. Bot. Fr. 85: 494 (1939). 1 sp., *L. edule* H. Perrier, SW. Madagascar.

A much-branched shrub; leaves paripinnate, with few leaflets; stipules small, persistent; flowers white, subactinomorphic, in terminal racemes; bracts thick, spine-like, very caducous;

calyx-tube cupular; segments 5, equal, valvate; petals 5, subequal, very imbricate; stamens 10, filaments pilose towards the base; ovary sessile, many-ovuled; style slender, elongated, capitate-papillous at the apex; fruit elongated, subcylindric, submembranous, depressed between the seeds, 2-valved, valves at length twisted; seeds lengthwise, thick and reniform; hilum ventral, small.

71. **Chidlowia** Hoyle, Kew Bull. 1932: 101, pl. 1. 1 sp., *C. sanguinea* Hoyle, W. trop. Africa. J. Léonard, Mém. Acad. Roy. Belg. Cl. Sci. 30, 2: 276 (1957); Hutch. & Dalz., Fl. West Trop. Afr. ed. 2 (Keay), 1: 456 (1958).

Tree; leaves paripinnate, leaflets coriaceous; stipules small, caducous; flowers red, crowded in elongated panicles; pedicels fasciculate; bracts and bracteoles minute, very caducous; calyx-tube campanulate, equally shortly dentate, teeth open in bud; disk fleshy, adnate to the calyx-tube; petals 5, subequal, sessile, very imbricate, much longer than the calyx; stamens 10, free, filaments glabrous, filiform; anthers uniform, opening lengthwise; ovary stipitate, many-ovuled; style filiform, stigma small, terminal; fruit oblong-linear, large, compressed, coriaceous-woody, elastically dehiscent; seeds orbicular, compressed, with a short thick funicle.

72. **Cordeauxia** Hemsl., Kew Bull. 1907: 361. 1 sp., *C. edulis* Hemsl., Somaliland, Ethiopia. Roti-Michelozzi, Webbia, 13: 187, with map (1957).

Densely branched shrub up to 3 m.; branches very hard; leaves paripinnate; leaflets mostly 4 pairs, ovate-oblong, dotted with numerous purple glands below; corymbs terminal, few-flowered; sepals 5, valvate, glandular, at first connivent; petals almost equal, clawed, and spathulate; stamens 10, free; filaments barbate below the middle; anther ellipsoid, dorsifixed; ovary shortly stipitate, densely glandular like the style; stigma terminal, obtuse; ovules 2; fruit coriaceous, compressed-ovoid, curved, beaked, dehiscent, 2-valved; seed mostly solitary, large (3·5–5 cm. long), without endosperm, edible; cotyledons thick and fleshy.

Yeheb Nuts, seeds used as food by natives.

73. **Sindora** Miq., Fl. Ind. Bat. Suppl. 287 (1860) (conserved name). *Galedupa* Lam. (1786). *Echinocalyx* Benth. (1865). *Grandiera* Lefèvre ex Baill. (1871) 18–20 spp., Indo-Malaya, Indo-China, trop. Africa; type *S. sumatrana* Miq., Sumatra. B.H. 1: 584; E.P. 3, 3: 132; de Wit, Bull. Bot. Gard. Buitenz. ser. 3, 18: 5, figs. 1–15 (1949) (revision); Pellegrin, Lég. Gabon, 133 (1949).

Trees; leaves paripinnate, leaflets 2–10 pairs, coriaceous; stipules foliaceous; flowers small, in terminal panicles of racemes; bracts and bracteoles ovate, caducous; calyx-tube very short, segments valvate, more or less covered with soft bristles; petal 1, sessile, oblong, folded; stamens 10, rarely 9, shortly and obliquely united, declinate; upper stamen reduced to an antherless staminode, the next 2 perfect with elongated filaments and ovate anthers, the 7 lower shorter with small empty anthers or without anthers, anthers dorsifixed; ovary shortly stipitate, free, 2–5-ovuled; style long, filiform, with a small terminal stigma; fruit flat, 2-valved, often prickly; seeds black, shining, with a large fleshy aril at the base.

S. inermis Merrill, and *S. supa* Merrill, Philippine Isls., source of Kayu-gala oil, a perfume and illuminant and remedy for skin diseases; timber hard, heavy, used for many purposes.

74. **Sindoropsis** J. Léonard, Mém. Acad. Roy. Belg. Cl. Sci. sér. 2, 30, fasc. 2: 81 (1957). 1 sp., *S. letestui* (Pellegr.) J. Léonard, trop. Africa.

Leaves imparipinnate, leaflets several, alternate, elliptic, acuminate, closely pinnately nerved, densely pellucid-punctate, each with a marginal gland near the base, the midrib ending at the tip in a pore-like gland visible below; stipules deciduous; bracts and bracteoles small, early deciduous; racemes axillary, much shorter than the leaves; sepals 4, valvate; petal 1, elliptic clawed, caducous; stamens 10, the adaxial subfree, the others united at the base; filaments longer and shorter; anthers uniform; disk absent; ovary shortly stipitate;

ovules 5–7; fruits oblong-lanceolate, acuminate, much compressed, 2-valved, coriaceous, reticulate; seeds 1–2, oblong, thick, not arillate; testa shining.

75. **Cercis** Linn., Sp. Pl. 374 (1753). *Siliquastrum* Adans. (1763). *Circis* Chapman (1860). 6 spp., from S. Europe through Cent. and E. Asia to Japan, North America; type *C. siliquastrum* Linn., Europe, Near East. B.H. 1: 576; E.P. 3, 3: 146; Hopkins, *Cercis* in N. Amer., Rhodora, 44: 93 (1942).

Trees and shrubs; leaves simple, broad, entire or emarginate or 2-lobed, 3- or more-nerved; stipules scale-like or membranous, caducous; flowers rose, in short fascicle-like racemes on the year-old or older branches; bracts scale-like, small, often imbricate at the base of the racemes; bracteoles minute or absent; calyx-tube oblique, shortly turbinate or campanulate, very shortly and broadly 5-toothed; petals 5, 'falsely papilionaceous', the adaxial inside the others; stamens 10, free, declinate; anthers short, uniform, versatile; ovary shortly stipitate, free, many-ovuled; style filiform, with a terminal obtuse stigma; fruit oblong or broadly linear, flat and compressed, thin, tardily 2-valved, the upper suture narrowly winged; seeds transverse, obovate, compressed, with endosperm.

Judas Tree, *C. siliquastrum* Linn., wood used by cabinet-makers; seed a substitute for Capers.

76. **Martiodendron** Gleason, Phytol. 1: 141 (1935). *Martiusia* Benth. (1840), not Schultes (1822). *Martia* Benth. (1840). *Martiusa* Benth. & Hook. f. (1865). 2 spp., trop. South America; type *M. excelsum* (Benth.) Gleason. B.H. 1: 571; E.P. 3, 3: 166; Amshoff, Pulle Fl. Suriname, 2, 2: 81 (*Martiusia*).

Trees; leaves imparipinnate; leaflets alternate, ovate or elliptic, pinnately nerved; stipules very caducous; flowers showy, yellow, paniculate at the ends of the shoots; buds incurved-acuminate; bracts and bracteoles very caducous; calyx-tube very short, segments narrow, acuminate, subequal, subvalvate; petals 5, oblong, very imbricate, the uppermost inside and rather broader; stamens 4 or rarely 5, free; anthers unequal, elongated, acuminate, opening by terminal pores; ovary sessile, free, few-ovuled; style subulate, stigma small, terminal; fruit large and oblong, compressed, thinly coriaceous, not dehiscent, marked by 2 ribs lengthwise; seed often 1 in the middle of the fruit, flat, reniform or subrhomboid.

77. **Koompassia** Maingay, Hook. Ic. Pl. t. 1164 (1873). *Abauria* Becc. (1877). 2 spp., Malaya; type *K. malaccensis* Maing., Malacca, Malay Archipelago. E.P. 3, 3: 155; de Wit, Bull. Bot. Gard. Buitenz. 17: 309 (1947) (revision).

Trees; leaves imparipinnate; leaflets alternate; flowers small, in small axillary or terminal panicles of cymules; calyx-tube almost none; segments 5, valvate, rather thick; petals 5, subequal; stamens 5, filaments very shortly filiform; anthers ovate, basifixed, opening by terminal and basal pores; ovary sessile, 1-ovuled; style very shortly subulate, stigma terminal, small; fruit oblong, compressed, surrounded by a wing, not dehiscent; seed 1, flat and compressed.

78. **Brenierea** Humbert, Compt. Rend. Paris, 249: 1599, with fig. (1959). 1 sp., *B. insignis* Humbert, Madagascar.

Small tree; branchlets flattened into cladodes closely dotted with gland-like scales; leaves alternate, 2-foliolate, leaflets obovate, entire, with few ascending nerves, punctate; stipules minute; flowers in very short axillary spiciform clusters, slightly zygomorphic; bracts and bracteoles minute; calyx campanulate, 5-toothed, teeth valvate, with minute scales outside; petals ('staminodes' ??) 5, linear, exserted; stamens 5, free, opposite the calyx-teeth; anthers medifixed, versatile, dehiscing lengthwise; ovary subsessile, compressed; stigma capitate, sessile; ovules 2; fruit flat and compressed, stipitate, elliptic-orbicular, 2-seeded, probably indehiscent; seeds flat, suborbicular, cotyledons flat, thick, radicle almost straight.

GROUP 4

Leaves imparipinnate:
Ovules numerous to few (more than 2):
Stipules linear, very long, spirally folded around the apical bud; flowers in
    axillary or terminal short racemes, covered in bud by leathery closely
    imbricate bracts; stamens 8; fruit oblong   79. **Hylodendron**
Stipules not as above; fruit suborbicular or obliquely elliptic:
Leaves pellucid-punctate; sepals 4, unequal, subvalvate   80. **Copaifera**
Leaves not punctate; sepals 4, imbricate, reflexed during flowering; fruit
    obliquely orbicular, ovate or broadly oblong   81. **Crudia**
Ovules 2:
Bracts boat-shaped, broad and ovate at the base, margins inflexed; ovary
    shortly stipitate; panicles terminal, few-flowered; fruit oblong, flat and
    thin, with 1–2 seeds near the middle   82. **Stemonocoleus**
Bracts minute:
Racemes elongated, slender, collected into panicles; stamens 10; fruit
    drupaceous, rounded-obovate, hard and corrugated   83. **Oxystigma**
Cymes axillary or terminal; stamens 3 or 2; fruit ovate-orbicular
                                                         18. **Dialium**
Ovule 1:
Ovary sessile; flowers very small, racemose-paniculate; fruit obovate; seed
    solitary, bulging in the fruit   84. **Kingiodendron**
Ovary stipitate; racemes spike-like, elongated, shortly paniculate; seed at
    top of fruit   85. **Gossweilerodendron**
Leaves paripinnate:
Stamens 25–20, anthers dorsifixed; leaves 2-foliolate, leaflets obliquely ovate,
    parallel-nerved from the base; ovule 1, lateral; fruit stipitate, indehiscent
                                              86. **Colophospermum**
Stamens 12 or fewer:
Calyx-lobes or segments imbricate:
Calyx-segments 5:
Ovules numerous; leaflets few-pairs, coriaceous; flowers small, poly-
    gamous or dioecious, racemose; stamens 5; fruit elongated, thick
    and coriaceous, divided between the seeds, edible   87. **Ceratonia**
Ovules 2:
Flowers in interrupted spikes, the spikes paniculate at the ends of the
    branchlets; fruits 2-valved; leaflets 1–2-pairs   88. **Prioria**
Flowers in panicles of racemes:
Fruits 2-valved, 1-seeded at the apex; leaflets 1-pair   89. **Hardwickia**
Fruits drupaceous; leaflets 3–1-pairs   83. **Oxystigma**
Calyx-segments 4:
Leaves several-foliolate:
Inflorescence paniculate; fruit 2-valved; calyx-segments petaloid; stipe
    of ovary adnate to the calyx-tube   90. **Saraca**
Inflorescence racemose:
Stipe of ovary short, free from the calyx-tube; bracts and bracteoles
    caducous; anthers didymous, very small   91. **Apaloxylon**

Stipe of the ovary adnate to the calyx-tube; bracteoles 2, linear-
oblong, borne towards the apex of the pedicels; anthers versatile
                                   92. Talbotiella
Leaves 2-foliolate; inflorescence paniculate; its branches strobiliform
when young; disk present, fleshy; ovary stipitate or sessile; fruit
winged on one side   **93. Guibourtia**
Calyx-lobes valvate:
  Disk absent; fruit indehiscent, drupaceous   **94. Detarium**
  Disk present; fruit dehiscent; seeds arillate   **80. Copaifera**
Leaves 1-foliolate, ovate to lanceolate; petiole short, jointed at base and apex;
stipules linear, caducous; calyx 3-lobed, outer lobe hooded; anthers
opening by pores; fruits 1-seeded   **95. Dansera**

79. Hylodendron Taub., Engl. & Prantl, Nat. Pflanzenfam. 3, 3: 386 (1894).
1 sp., *H. gabunense* Taub., W. trop. Africa to Congo. J. Léonard, Fl. Congo
Belge, 3: 302, fig. 17; Mém. Acad. Roy. Belg. Cl. Sci. 30, 2: 75 (1957); Hutch.
& Dalz., Fl. W. Trop. Afr. ed. 2 (Keay), 1: 456.

    Large tree; leaves imparipinnate; leaflets 9–15, alternate, oblong; stipules large, very long,
linear, spirally folded around the apical bud, at length deciduous; flowers small, in axillary
or terminal short racemes, covered in bud by leathery closely imbricate, striate broadly
ovate bracts; bracteoles 2, linear, at the base of the calyx; calyx-tube short, lobes 4, slightly
imbricate, concave; petals absent; stamens 8, alternately longer and shorter; ovary sessile,
with numerous ovules; style linear-subulate, with terminal capitellate stigma; fruit indehiscent, narrowly oblong, slightly curved, flat, thin, laxly reticulate, 2–1-seeded towards
the distal end, glabrous; seeds smooth.

80. Copaifera Linn., Sp. Pl. ed. 2: 557 (1762) (conserved name). *Copaiva*
Jacq. (1760). *Copaiba* Adans. (1763). *Pseudosindora* Symington (1944). About
25 spp., trop. America, trop. Africa, Malay Archipelago; type *C. officinalis*,
(Jacq.) Linn., trop. South America. Amshoff, Pulle Fl. Suriname, 2, 2: 17;
J. Léonard, Bull. Jard. Bot. Brux. 19: 396 (1949); Fl. Congo Belge, 3: 304;
Mém. Acad. Roy. Belg. Cl. Sci. 30, 2: 84 (1957). J. D. Dwyer, Cent. Amer. &
West Ind. & S. Amer. spp., Brittonia, 7: 143–72 (1951); de Wit, Genus *Copai-
fera* in Borneo, Webbia, 9: 459 (1953); Burkart, Legum. Argent. ed. 2: 155,
fig. 24.

    Trees, shrubs, or subshrubs; leaves alternate, pari- or imparipinnate; leaflets several,
opposite or alternate, usually pellucid-punctate; stipules small, very caducous; stipels
absent; inflorescence recemose or paniculate; bracts usually small and caducous; bracteoles,
2, caducous; flowers small; sepals 4, unequal, subvalvate; petals absent; stamens 10–8,
free, usually longer and shorter; anthers dorsifixed; ovary stipitate or sessile; ovules 7–2,
superposed; style filiform, stigma terminal; fruit more or less stipitate, suborbicular or
obliquely elliptic, compressed or more or less dilated, dehiscing by 2 valves; seed 1, rarely 2,
nude or more or less arillate; cotyledons flat.

    Maracaibo Copaiba Balsam, Oleoresin, *C. officinalis*; also obtained by incision from the trunks
of various other species, such as Cupahyba Oil, *C. multijuga* Hayne, Brazil.

81. Crudia[1] Schreb., Gen. 1: 282 (1789) (conserved name). About 55 spp.,
trop. America, trop. Africa, trop. Asia; type *C. spicata* (Aubl.) Willd.,

   [1] Synonyms of **Crudia**: *Apalatoa* Aubl. (1775). *Opalatoa* Aubl. (1775). *Touchiroa* Aubl.
(1775). *Waldschmidtia* Scop. (1777). *Cyclas* Schreb. (1789). *Crudya* Batsch (1802). *Pryona*
Miq. (1855). *Tuchiroa* O. Ktze. (1891).

Guiana. B.H. 1: 584; E.P. 3, 3: 134; E. G. Bak., Legum. Trop. Afr. 3: 738; J. Léonard, Fl. Congo Belge, 3: 366 (1952); de Wit, Genus *Crudia* in Malay Archip. south of Philippine Isls., Bull. Bot. Gard. Buitenz. ser. 3, 18: 407 (1950); Amshoff, Gen. *Crudia* na Amér. do sul, Bol. Técn. Inst. Agron. do Norte no. 28: 77 (1953); Hutch. & Dalz., Fl. W. Trop. Afr. ed. 2 (Keay), 1: 466.

Trees; leaves imparipinnate, leaflets alternate; stipules small and caducous or foliaceous and persistent for a time; flowers small, in terminal racemes or these lateral on the one-year-old branchlets; bracts and bracteoles small, caducous, rarely ovate, membranous and persistent for a time; calyx-tube short; segments 4, membranous, imbricate, reflexed during flowering; petals absent; stamens 10 or fewer, free; anthers ovate or oblong; ovary shortly stipitate, stipe free or attached to the calyx-tube; ovules few; style filiform, stigma small; fruit obliquely orbicular, ovate or broadly oblong, compressed, rigidly coriaceous, 2-valved, margins often thickened; seeds 2–1, large, orbicular or subreniform, compressed, emarginate with a lateral hilum.

82. **Stemonocoleus** Harms, Engl. Bot. Jahrb. 38: 76, fig. 2 (1905). 1 sp., *S. micranthus* Harms, W. trop. Africa. J. Léonard, Mém. Acad. Roy. Belg. Cl. Sci. 30, 2: 156 (1957).

Tree; leaves imparipinnate; leaflets alternate, 8–10, oblong or ovate, oblique at the base, emarginate at the apex; panicles terminal, few-flowered; bracts boat-shaped, broad and ovate at the base, margins inflexed; bracteoles 2, narrowly oblong to lanceolate, slightly keeled on the back, slightly fimbriolate towards the apex; calyx-tube shortly funnel-shaped, with the staminal disk exserted and sheath-like with one side open; sepals 5–4, imbricate, slightly unequal; petals absent; stamens 4, filaments inserted below the outer side of the disk; anthers dorsifixed; ovary shortly stipitate, 2-ovuled; style elongated, involute, stigma minute, capitellate; fruits 2-valved oblong, flat and thin, with 1–2 seeds near the middle, laxly reticulate; seeds oblong, compressed, shining.

83. **Oxystigma** Harms, Engl. & Prantl, Nat. Pflanzenfam. Nachtr. 195 (1897); Engl. Bot. Jahrb. 26: 264 (1899). *Eriander* Winkler (1908). *Pterygopodium* Harms (1913). 5 spp., trop. Africa; type *O. mannii* (Baill.) Harms. E. G. Bak., Legum. Trop. Afr. 3: 772; J. Léonard, Fl. Congo Belge, 3: 369, figs. 29, 30; Mém. Acad. Roy. Belg. Cl. Sci. 30, 2: 128 (1957).

Trees and shrubs; leaves pari- or imparipinnate; leaflets 3–1-pairs, coriaceous; flowers small, racemose-paniculate, racemes elongated, very slender; bracts minute; bracteoles minute and scale-like at the base of the flowers; calyx-tube very short; segments 5, orbicular, petaloid, subequal, broadly imbricate in bud; petals absent; stamens 10, filaments filiform, anthers small; ovary sessile, 2-ovuled; style filiform, subulate, acute at the apex; fruit drupaceous, rounded-obovate, very corrugated, hard, and indehiscent, or flat and wing-like with the seed at the top; seed solitary.

84. **Kingiodendron** Harms, Engl. & Prantl, Nat. Pflanzenfam. Nachtr. 194 (1897). 4 spp., India to Polynesia; type *K. pinnatum* (Roxb.) Harms, India. de Wit, Bull. Bot. Gard. Buitenz. 18: 211 (1949).

Trees; leaves imparipinnate, leaflets 5–6, alternate; flowers racemose-paniculate, very small; calyx-tube very short; segments 5, rounded, broadly imbricate; petals absent; stamens 10; ovary sessile, 1-ovuled; style filiform, stigma obtuse, shortly capitate; fruit obovate, coriaceous or woody, often apiculate; seed solitary, bulging.

85. **Gossweilerodendron** Harms, Notizbl. Bot. Gart. Berlin, 9: 457, fig. 9, F–L (1925). 1 sp., *G. balsamiferum* (Vermoesen) Harms, Congo. J. Léonard, Fl. Congo Belge, 3: 375, t. 28 (1952); Mém. Acad. Roy. Belg. Cl. Sci. 30, 2: 133 (1957); Hutch. & Dalz., Fl. W. Trop. Afr. ed. 2 (Keay), 1: 466.

Tall tree; leaves imparipinnate, leaflets alternate or rarely opposite, oblong to obovate, pellucid-punctulate; racemes spike-like, elongated, shortly paniculate; flowers small; bracts and bracteoles minute, deciduous; calyx-tube broad and very short; sepals 4, imbricate, rounded, pellucid-punctulate; petals absent; stamens 10 (rarely 9–8); filaments free, densely villous at the base; anthers small, oval-subquadrate, dorsifixed; ovary stipitate, villous, obliquely ovoid; style short; ovule 1, pendulous; fruit shortly stipitate, samaroid, basal part flattened into a wing with a single seed at the top end.

Stem source of a copal-resin used for illumination; wood used for table tops, furniture, and construction.

86. **Colophospermum** Kirk ex J. Léonard, Bull. Jard. Bot. Brux. 19: 390 (1949). 1 sp., *C. mopane* Kirk (*Copaifera mopane* Kirk ex Benth.), S. trop. Africa and subtrop. Africa. J. Léonard, Mém. Acad. Roy. Belg. Cl. Sci. 30, 2: 159 (1957).

Small tree; leaves alternate, 2-foliolate, leaflets opposite, obliquely ovate, parallel-nerved from the base without midrib, coriaceous; stipules caducous; flowers small, in racemes or panicles; bracts minute; bracteoles absent; sepals 4; petals absent; stamens 25–20, free, equally long; anthers dorsifixed; ovary compressed; ovule 1, lateral; style lateral; fruit stipitate, compressed, indehiscent; seed flat, kidney-shaped, wrinkled, spotted with resin; cotyledons much corrugated.

87. **Ceratonia** Linn., Sp. Pl. 1020 (1753). *Ceratia* Adans. (1763). 1 sp., *C. siliqua* Linn., E. Mediterranean and cult. B.H. 1: 574; E.P. 3, 3: 154.

Medium-sized or small tree, with a dense evergreen crown; leaves paripinnate, leaflets few pairs, coriaceous; stipules minute or absent; flowers small, polygamous or dioecious, racemose, racemes short, lateral on the one-year-old branchlets, solitary or fasciculate; bracts and bracteoles minute, scale-like, deciduous; calyx-tube shortly turbinate; segments 5, short, tooth-like, imbricate, deciduous; petals absent; stamens 5, filaments filiform; anthers ovate, versatile; disk horizontally spread within the stamens; ovary shortly stipitate in the middle of the disk; ovules numerous; style very short, stigma peltate; fruit elongated, compressed, thick and coriaceous, not dehiscent, thickened on each suture, divided within between the seeds by pulpy areas continuous with the endocarp; seeds transverse, obovate, compressed.

The Carob or Johanna Fruit, *Ceratonia siliqua* Linn., produces tragasol, a mucilaginous hemi-cellulose occurring in the fruits; a native of Syria and generally cultivated in Mediterranean countries; these pods were the 'locusts', the food of John the Baptist and the Prodigal Son; for a long period they have been a favourite food for farm animals, and incidentally for schoolboys in country districts; according to Hill (Econ. Bot. ed. 2, 346), trees of this species are grown in California; the dried pods are rich in sugar; seeds contain a useful gum, Tragasol.

88. **Prioria** Griseb., Fl. Brit. West Ind. 215 (1860). 1 sp., *P. copaifera* Griseb., Panama, Costa Rica, Jamaica, Colombia. B.H. 1: 585; E.P. 3, 3: 131; Fawcett & Rendle, Fl. Jamaica, 4: 123, fig. 37.

Tall tree; leaves paripinnate; leaflets 1–2-pairs, coriaceous; stipules scale-like, caducous; flowers small, sessile in interrupted spikes, the spikes paniculate at the apex of the branchlets; bracts inconspicuous; bracteoles connate into a 2-lobed cup; calyx-tube short; segments 5, orbicular, subpetaloid, very imbricate; petals absent; stamens 10, free, subequal; anthers uniform, connective thick, apiculate; ovary sessile or shortly stipitate, free, 2-ovuled; style shortly subulate, stigma terminal, minute; fruit obliquely obovate-orbicular, flat and compressed, coriaceous-woody, 2-valved; seed 1, pendulous, large, flat.

Cativo, Cantivo, timber used for rough furniture, boxes, crates, and in the U.S.A. as a veneer.

89. **Hardwickia** Roxb., Hort. Beng. 33 (1814), and Pl. Corom. 3: 6, t. 209 (1819). 1 sp., *H. binata* Roxb., India. B.H. 1: 586; E.P. 3, 3: 130.

Trees; leaves paripinnate; leaflets 1 pair, coriaceous; flowers small, in small axillary and terminal panicles of racemes; bracts minute; bracteoles scale-like below the calyx;

calyx-tube very short; segments 5, orbicular, petaloid, subequal, very imbricate; petals absent; stamens 10, alternately a little shorter, all perfect; ovary sessile, free, 2-ovuled; style filiform, stigma large, peltate, fruit lanceolate, flat and compressed, 2-valved and 1-seeded at the apex; thin and not dehiscent towards the base, nerved lengthwise; seed pendulous, obovate, flat and compressed.

90. **Saraca** Linn., Mant. 1: 13 (1767). *Jonesia* Roxb. (1795). *Arisaca* Pierre ex Dalla Torre & Harms (1901). About 25 spp., trop. Asia; type *S. indica* Linn., Indo-Malaya. B.H. 1: 583; E.P. 3, 3: 134.

Trees; leaves paripinnate, leaflets mostly few pairs, coriaceous; stipules small, caducous; flowers yellow, rose, or red, in lateral paniculate corymbs or on the older branches; bracts small, deciduous; bracteoles persistent for some time, coloured, much shorter than the calyx-tube; calyx-tube elongated; segments 4, petaloid, ovate, subequal, much imbricate; petals absent; stamens 9–3, free; filaments elongated; anthers oblong, subequal; ovary stipitate, stipe adnate to the calyx-tube; ovules numerous; style filiform, stigma terminal, obtuse; fruit oblong or elongated, compressed or almost turgid, coriaceous to rather woody, 2-valved; seeds compressed or subterete, ovoid or subglobose; testa thin.

91. **Apaloxylon** Drake del Castillo, Hist. Pl. Madag. 1, 1: 75, 206 (1902). 1 sp. 1 sp., *A. madagascariensis* Drake del Castello, Madagascar.

Tree; leaves paripinnate; leaflets small; racemes axillary; bracts and bracteoles caducous; calyx-tube concave, with an annular disk within; sepals 4, white, imbricate, ovate; petals absent; stamens 10, yellow, unequal; anthers didymous, very small, dorsifixed; ovary linear, shortly stipitate; style elongated; fruit oblong, samaroid, narrowed at the base, not dehiscent, unequal-sided; seed 1, pendulous from the top of the fruit.

92. **Talbotiella** E. G. Bak., Journ. Bot. 52: 2 (1914). 3 spp., W. trop. Afr.; type *T. eketensis* E. G. Bak., S. Nigeria. E. G. Bak., Legum. Trop. Afr. 3: 768; J. Léonard, Mém. Acad. Roy. Belg. Cl. Sci. 30, 2: 125 (1957).

Shrubs; leaves paripinnate; leaflets many, opposite; racemes axillary, laxly several- to many-flowered; bracteoles 2, submembranous, linear-oblong, not forming an involucre, borne towards the apex of the pedicels; scales at the base of the peduncles scarious, brownish, imbricate, boat-shaped, shining on the back; calyx-tube shortly funnel-shaped; sepals 4, suborbicular, broadly imbricate, subequal; petals absent; stamens 10–8, filaments filiform, free; anthers versatile; ovary stipitate, villous, 2-ovuled, stipe adnate to the calyx-tube; style terminal, elongated, stigma small, capitellate; fruit flattened, 2-valved, oblong, transversely nervose, valves strongly curled after dehiscence; seeds rather compressed, suborbicular.

93. **Guibourtia** J. J. Benn. emend. J. Léonard, Bull. Jard. Bot. Brux. 19: 400 (1949); ibid. 20: 282 (key to Afr. spp.). *Pseudocopaiva* Britt. & Wils. (1929). 17 spp., trop. Africa and trop. America; type *G. copallifera* J. J. Benn, trop. Africa. J. Léonard, Fl. Congo Belge, 3: 359, figs. 27, 28; Mém. Acad. Roy. Belg. Cl. Sci. 30, 2: 137 (1957); Hutch. & Dalz., Fl. W. Trop. Afr. ed. 2 (Keay), 1: 465.

Trees or shrubs; leaves 2-foliolate, leaflets opposite, sessile, unequal-sided, entire, rarely with a terminal leaflet; inflorescence paniculate, terminal, its branches strobiliform when young; bracts mostly small; flowers in more than 2 rows, small; bracteoles 2, small; sepals 4, subequal, imbricate; petals absent; stamens 12–8, free, alternately longer and shorter; anthers ovoid, dorsifixed; disk present, fleshy; ovary stipitate or sessile; ovules 4–1; style filiform, glabrous; stigma capitellate, terminal; fruit more or less stipitate, suborbicular to obliquely elliptic, flat or dilated, coriaceous or membranous, dehiscent or not, unilaterally winged; seeds 2 or 1, nude or arillate; cotyledons flat or folded.

Sierra Leone Copal, *G. copallifera* J. J. Benn. and *G. salikounda* Heckel. Congo Copal derived from *G. demeusii* (Harms) J. Léonard.

94. **Detarium** Juss., Gen. 365 (1789). 3–4 spp., trop. Africa; type *D. senegalense* J. F. Gmel. (*D. microcarpum* Guill. & Perr.). B.H. 1: 585; E.P. 3, 3: 132; E. G. Bak., Legum. Trop. Afr. 3: 747; J. Léonard, Fl. Congo Belge, 3: 308 (1952), and Mém. Acad. Roy. Belg. Cl. Sci. 30, 2: 89 (1957); Hutch. & Dalz., Fl. W. Trop. Afr. ed. 2 (Keay), 1: 457.

Trees; leaves paripinnate; leaflets few pairs, alternate; stipules inconspicuous; flowers small, in axillary panicles or on lateral one-year-old branchlets; bracts and bracteoles small, ovate, concave, very caducous; calyx-tube short or almost nothing; segments 4, valvate; petals absent; stamens 10, free, alternately shorter; anthers versatile, ovate; disk absent; ovary sessile, free, 2-ovuled; style filiform, stigma small, terminal; fruit sessile, orbicular, thick, compressed, drupaceous, not dehiscent, with fibrous exocarp and bony endocarp; seed orbicular, thick and compressed.

D. senegalense J. F. Gmel., source of African Mahogany used for carpentry; produces a fragrant resin, and the sweet pulp of fruits sold in the markets of Senegal.

95. **Dansera** van Steenis, Bull. Bot. Gard. Buitenz. ser. 3, 17: 414, fig. 1 (1948) *Rhynchocarpa* Backer ex Heyne (1927). 1 sp., *D. procera* van Steenis, Sumatra.

Tree; leaves 1-foliolate, ovate to lanceolate; petiole short, jointed at the base and apex; stipules linear, caducous; flowers cymose, axillary, small; bracts and bracteoles minute, fugacious; calyx 3-lobed, lobes free, imbricate, outer hooded; petals absent; stamens mostly 6, rarely 5 or 7, 2 with longer filaments, all fertile, basifixed, opening by an apical-lateral pore, soon dehiscing to the base; disk none; ovary 1-ovuled; style straight, with a recurved tip; fruit 1-seeded, indehiscent, ovoid, exocarp hard, mesocarp pulpy and enveloping the seed, the latter with a punctiform hilum.

GROUP 5

Fertile stamens 12–10 (to p. 259):
  Calyx-lobes or teeth imbricate (to p. 258):
    Leaf-rhachis not ending in a spine-like sharp point:
      Branchlets and leaf-rhachis prickly:
        Flowers crowded in simple spikes, or these paniculately branched; fruits oblong-linear, transversely depressed between the seeds, not winged   96. **Wagatea**
        Flowers in racemes or panicles of racemes:
          Fruits not winged, often filled with pulp between the seeds:
            Ovary stipitate, ovules numerous   97. **Erythrophloeum**
            Ovary sessile, ovules few   98. **Caesalpinia**
          Fruits winged:
            Fruits winged lengthwise along the upper suture; ovules 2 or more   99. **Mezoneuron**
            Fruits compressed and samaroid, with the single seed at the base and obliquely winged above; ovule 1   100. **Pterolobium**
      Branchlets and leaf-rhachis not prickly:
        Ovules numerous to several (6 or more):
          Fruits dehiscent, not winged:
            Calyx-segments 5:
              Stipules absent:
                Tall trees, not glandular; stipules absent   101. **Schizolobium**
                Low shrubs or herbs, often very glandular; stipules present, small   102. **Hoffmanseggia**

Stipules present:
Stipules persistent on the flowering branchlets, foliaceous, pin-
nately divided; filaments partly connate into a split tube
103. **Jacqueshuberia**
Stipules not as above; filaments more or less free
104. **Stenodrepanum**
Calyx-segments 4; petiole of the leaf jointed at the base and with a
cupular gland above; seeds on slender funicles   105. **Brandzeia**
Fruits not dehiscent, flat and often more or less winged:
Fruits at most 2-winged:
Fruits not transversely divided within; leaflets small and numerous:
Branches all of one kind; anthers shorter than the filaments; fruit
compressed   106. **Peltophorum**
Branches dimorphous, the leaves clustered on lateral spur-like
branchlets; anthers as long as the filaments; fruit oblong,
subterete   107. **Arcoa**
Fruits transversely divided within into 10–15 loculi; leaflets 2–4-
pairs, large; fruit compressed, hard and very thick; seeds large,
transverse, with a slender flexuous funicle   108. **Pachyelasma**
Fruits 4-winged, resembling those of some *Combretum* spp.
109. **Tetrapterocarpon**
Ovules 3–2:
Some filaments dilated; pinnae 2 pairs:
Leaves not punctate   110. **Stachyothyrsus**
Leaves minutely punctate   111. **Kaoue**
Filaments not dilated:
Stipules spiny, recurved; filaments glabrous; fruits subwinged on each
side   112. **Peltophoropsis**
Stipules not spiny; filaments densely villous or pilose at the base:
Fruits deeply sulcate in the middle, not splitting along the middle of
the valves   113. **Bussea**
Fruits splitting along the middle of the valves   28. **Haematoxylon**
Leaf-rhachis very short and ending in a sharp spine-like point, flat and
leaf-like; leaflets very small; fruit linear, torulose; filaments villous at
the base   114. **Parkinsonia**
Calyx-lobes valvate:
Flowers bisexual:
Anthers uniform in size:
Petals 5:
Calyx more or less equally lobed, not 2-lipped:
Spiny trees and shrubs; fruit linear-oblong, flat and compressed, valves
obliquely venulose; filaments pilose at the base   115. **Cercidium**
Not spiny:
Inflorescence a raceme:
Racemes axillary and clustered at the ends of the shoots; fruits
compressed, narrowly winged on each side   116. **Conzattia**
Racemes terminal or leaf-opposed; fruits with valves often glandular
or with scattered short plumose bristles   102. **Hoffmanseggia**

Inflorescence a corymb of racemes; flowers orange or red, very
   showy; filaments villous at the base; fruits elongated, filled
   within between the seeds   **117. Delonix**
Inflorescence an interrupted spike; flowers white, small; anther-
   connective with a glandular appendix   **118. Burkea**
Calyx 2-lipped; flowers in dense racemes, showy, scarlet; bracts membranous, coloured, very caducous; filaments pilose at the base;
   fruit elongated, turgid   **119. Colvillea**
Petal 1; flowers precocious, shortly racemose-paniculate; anthers long-
   exserted; tree with twisted branches; pinnae 1–3-pairs
                           120. Aprevalia
Anthers not uniform, the longest elongated and sterile; flowers in sub-
   panicles of racemes at the ends of the branchlets; fruit oblong, com-
   pressed; seeds ovoid; pinnae both paripinnate and imparipinnate
                         121. Moldenhauera
Flowers polygamous; fruit mostly pulpy within between the seeds:
  Branches not spinous; fruits turgid or subterete, 2-valved
                         122. Gymnocladus
  Branches and trunk armed with simple or branched spines; fruits com-
   pressed, indehiscent or tardily 2-valved   **123. Gleditsia**
Fertile stamens 5 or 4, rarely 6:
  Fruits not winged:
   No spines; flowers bisexual   **124. Dimorphandra**
   Spiny trunk and branches; flowers polygamous   **123. Gleditsia**
  Fruits narrowly winged along the adaxial suture; no spines; flowers preco-
   cious, bisexual; fruit long-stipitate, elongated   **125. Acrocarpus**
  Fruits 4-winged, 1-seeded, ovoid, with endosperm; flowers unisexual,
   dioecious, very small, pale-green, racemose   **109. Tetrapterocarpon**

96. **Wagatea** Dalz., Hook. Kew Journ. 3: 90 (1851). 1 sp., *W. spicata* Dalz.,
India. B.H. 1: 568; E.P. 3, 3: 170.

Tall climbing shrub or low bush, armed with sharp prickles; leaves bipinnate; leaflets
numerous; stipules inconspicuous; flowers crowded in simple elongated spikes or these
paniculately branched; rhachis thick; calyx scarlet; tube campanulate; segments scarcely
longer than the tube, imbricate, the lowermost outside and concave; petals 5, oblong, erect,
imbricate, the uppermost inside and rather broader; stamens 10, free, slightly declinate,
short; filaments pilose at the base; anthers uniform; ovary sessile, free; ovules numerous;
style slightly clavate at the apex, stigma oblique, concave, subbilabiate; fruit oblong-linear,
acute, coriaceous, transversely depressed between the seeds; sutures thickened; seeds
obovate-oblong, testa thick and bony.

97. **Erythrophloeum** Afz. ex R. Br., Tuckey Congo 430 (1818). *Erythrophlaeum*
Reichb. (1828). *Fillaea* Guill. & Perr. (1833). *Mavia* Bertol. (1850). *Laboucheria*
F. Muell. (1859). 15 spp., trop. Africa, Seychelles, trop. and temp. E. Asia,
Australia; type *E. guineense* G. Don, trop. Africa. B. H. 1: 588; E.P. 3, 3: 126;
E. G. Bak., Legum. Trop. Afr. 3: 777; J. Léonard, Fl. Congo Belge, 3: 242,
t. 18 (1952); Hutch. & Dalz., Fl. W. Trop. Afr. ed. 2 (Keay), 1: 483.

Trees; leaves bipinnate, pinnae few pairs; leaflets often alternate, coriaceous; flowers in
terminal panicles of racemes; bracts small; bracteoles absent; calyx-tube short; limb

campanulate, with 5 short subequal teeth; petals 5, equal, slightly imbricate; stamens 10, free, equal or alternately shorter; anthers uniform; ovary stipitate, stipe free; ovules numerous; style short, stigma terminal, obtuse; fruit oblong, compressed, thick and coriaceous, 2-valved, pulpy within between the seeds; seeds transverse, ovate, compressed.

E. guineense G. Don, Redwater tree, Sasswood or Sassy Bark; decoction of the bark used as arrow-poison, an 'ordeal', and to stupefy fish in West Africa, and as a medicine; wood hard, durable, used for construction.

98. **Caesalpinia**[1] Linn., Sp. Pl. 380 (1753); Gen. Pl. ed. 5: 178 (1754). About 280 spp., tropics and subtropics; type *C. brasiliensis* Linn.,[2] West Indies. B.H. 1: 565; E.P. 3, 3: 173; E. G. Bak., Legum. Trop. Afr. 3: 613; Amshoff, Pulle Fl. Suriname, 2, 2: 85; J. Léonard, Fl. Congo Belge, 3: 249, fig. 13 (1952); Burkart, Legum. Argent. ed. 2, 173, fig. 31; Synop. espec. Argent., Physis, 12: 166 (1936).

Trees, shrubs, or tall climbers, unarmed or armed with sharp prickles; leaves bipinnate, leaflets few to many; stipules various; flowers yellow or red, often showy; racemes paniculate in the upper leaf-axils or at the ends of the shoots; calyx-tube short; teeth 5, imbricate, the lowest outside, concave or boat-shaped, often larger; petals 5, orbicular or oblong, spreading, very imbricate, slightly unequal or the uppermost smaller; stamens 10, free, declinate; filaments often villous or glandular at the base; anthers uniform; ovary sessile, free, few-ovuled; style filiform, rarely clavate at the apex, stigma terminal, truncate, concave or minute; fruit compressed, ovate to lanceolate or falcate, not winged, sutures nervelike or thickened, sometimes turgid and 2-valved, or indehiscent, often filled between the seeds; seeds transverse, ovate to orbicular or globose; cotyledons flat.

Sappanwood and Brazilwood, two soluble wood dyes, from the heartwood of *Caesalpinia sappan* Linn., India and Malaya, and *C. echinata* Lam., trop. America and the West Indies, respectively; wood also used for making violin bows. Tara fruits, *C. spinosa* (Mol.) Ktze., trop. America, are rich in tannin, used for tanning high-grade leather, for ink, and as a black dye. Algarobilla, *C. brevifolia* Baill., Chile, pods used for tanning. Celavina seed, *C. tinctoria* DC., Peru, pods also used for tanning. Divi-Divi, *C. coriaria* Willd., trop. America, pods important source of supply for the same purpose.

99. **Mezoneuron** Desf., Mém. Mus. Par. 4: 245, tt. 10, 11 (1818) ('Mezonevron'). *Mezoneurum* Auct. About 35 spp., Old World tropics, China; type *M. glabrum* Desf., Burma, Malaya. B.H. 1: 565; E.P. 3, 3: 176; J. Léonard, Fl. Congo Belge, 3: 258, t. 20 (1952).

Tall climbing shrubs or rarely trees, the branchlets and petioles, especially at the base of the leaf-pairs, often very prickly; leaves bipinnate, leaflets small and numerous or larger and shining; stipules small; racemes axillary or paniculate at the ends of the shoots; bracts narrow, rarely persistent; bracteoles absent; calyx-tube short, very oblique; segments 5, imbricate, the lowermost exterior, larger, concave or boat-shaped, rarely all connate into a tube; petals 5, orbicular, spreading, very imbricate, subequal or the uppermost inner one slightly dissimilar; stamens 10, free, declinate; anthers uniform; ovary sessile or shortly stipitate, free, 2- or more-ovuled; style subulate, often obliquely clavate at the apex, stigma sometimes ciliolate; fruit compressed, membranous or rarely coriaceous,

---

[1] Synonyms of **Caesalpinia**: *Poinciana* Linn. (1753) (not of 1760). *Guilandia* P.Br. (1756). *Guilandina* Linn. (1753). *Bonduc, Campecia, Ticanto,* Adans. (1763). *Pseudosantalum* Mill. (1768). *Poincia* Neck. (1790). *Pomaria* Cav. (1799). *Tara* Molina (1810). *Coulteria* H. B. & K. (1823). *Adenocalyx* Bert. (1823). *Libidibia* Schlechtd. (1830). *Cladotrichium* Vog. (1837). *Erythrostemon* Klotzsch (1841). *Cinclidocarpus* Zoll. (1846). *Balsamocarpon* Clos. (1846). *Lebidibia* Griseb. (1860). Also *Guaymasia, Moparia, Nicarago, Poincianella, Russellodendron, Biancaea* of Britt. & Rose (1930).

[2] *Caesalpinia brasiliensis* of Linn. Sp. Pl. 380 consists, according to Urban (Symb. Antill. 2: 286 (1900)), of three species as follows: (*a*) Plumier's plant, the type of the genus; (*b*) *Peltophorum brasiliense* (Sw.) Urb., and (*c*) *Caesalpinia bahamensis* Lam.

not dehiscent or only tardily 2-valved, winged lengthwise along the upper suture; seeds few to 1, transverse, compressed, orbicular or reniform.

M. kauaiense (Mann) Hbd., Hawaii Isls.; wood very hard and durable, almost black; used by the islanders for spears and the Laau melo-me-lo, an implement for fishing. *M. scortechinii* F. Muell., Australia, source of Barrister Gum.

100. **Pterolobium** R.Br., Salt Abyss. App. 64 (1814) (conserved name). *Kantuffa* Roth (1821). *Reichardia* Roth (1821). *Quartinia* A. Rich. (1840). 5 spp., Old World tropics and subtropics; type *P. stellatum* (Forssk.) Brenan (*P. exosum* (Gmel.) Bak. f.; *P. lacerans* R. Br.), trop. Africa and subtrop. S. Africa. B.H. 1: 567; E.P. 3, 3: 172; Roti-Michelozzi, Webbia, 13: 181, fig. 7 (1957).

Trees or tall climbing shrubs, armed with recurved prickles; leaves bipinnate; leaflets numerous, small; stipules and stipels aculeate; flowers rather small, white, in terminal panicles of racemes; bracts very caducous; bracteoles absent; calyx-tube short; segments 5, imbricate, the lowermost concave and larger; petals 5, spreading, slightly unequal, imbricate; stamens 10, free, declinate or subequal, filaments sometimes villous at the base; anthers uniform; ovary sessile, free, 1-ovuled; style short or elongated and clavate at the apex, stigma terminal, truncate or concave; fruit red, sessile, compressed and samaroid, indehiscent, the seed-bearing base obliquely ovate or elliptic, the upper part produced into an oblique oblong or falcate membranous wing; seed pendulous, very compressed, without endosperm.

101. **Schizolobium** Vogel, Linnaea, 11: 399 (1837). 2–3 spp., Cent. America, Brazil; type *S. parahybum* (Vell.) Blake (*S. excelsum* Vogel), Brazil. B.H. 1: 569; E.P. 3, 3: 170; Britton & Rose, N. Amer. Fl. 23: 304.

Tall trees; leaves bipinnate, large, pinnae several pairs, leaflets numerous, small; stipules absent; flowers yellow, in axillary racemes or terminal panicles; bracts small; bracteoles absent; calyx-tube obliquely turbinate; segments slightly unequal, imbricate, reflexed; petals 5, clawed, ovate or rounded, slightly unequal, imbricate; stamens 10, free, sub-declinate, filaments scabrid at the base; anthers uniform; ovary scarcely stipitate, laterally attached to the calyx-tube; ovules numerous; style filiform, stigma minute, terminal; fruit compressed, obovate, 2-valved, 1-seeded, with a firm coriaceous outer coat strongly reticulate inside separating from the inner thin one; seed at the apex of the fruit and enclosed by a membranous wing-like layer of the inner pericarp, large, oblong, compressed.

102. **Hoffmanseggia** Cav., Ic. 4: 63, tt. 392, 393 (1797). *Larrea* Orteg. (1797). *Hoffmannsegia* Broun (1822). *Melanosticta* DC. (1825). *Schrammia*, Britton & Rose (1930). About 45 spp., Texas to Patagonia, and in S. and S. trop. Africa; type *H. falcaria* Cav., Chile, Peru. B.H. 1: 567; E.P. 3, 3: 173; Britton & Rose, N. Amer. Fl. 23: 309 (as *Larrea*); Burkart, Legum. Argent. ed. 2, 176, figs. 32, 33.

Low shrubs or herbs, often very glandular; leaves bipinnate, leaflets small; stipules small; stipels when present small and setaceous; flowers yellow, in terminal or leaf-opposed racemes; bracts deciduous; bracteoles absent; calyx-tube very short; segments 5, valvate; petals 5, spreading, imbricate, uppermost inside the others and often dissimilar; stamens 10, free, filaments often glandular at the base; anthers uniform; ovary subsessile, free; ovules numerous; style often incurved and clavate upwards, stigma terminal; fruit subsessile, linear or ovate, straight or falcate, compressed, 2-valved, valves often glandular or with scattered short plumose setae; seeds transversely or obliquely ovate.

103. **Jacqueshuberia** Ducke, Arch. Jard. Bot. Rio de Janeiro, 3: 118 (1922). 2 spp., Brazil; type *J. quinquangulata* Ducke.

Small trees; stem and branches distinctly 5-angled; stipules persistent on the flowering branchlets, large, foliaceous, pinnate; leaves bipinnate, pinnae and leaflets in many pairs;

bracts long-setaceous; flowers without bracteoles, in short terminal subcorymbose racemes; calyx-tube cupular or campanulate, obsoletely ribbed; segments 5, imbricate, ovate; petals 5, imbricate, erect, ovate, slightly unequal, sessile; stamens 10, equal, elongated, filaments connate for one third their length into a tube deeply split on the anticous side; anthers dorsifixed; ovary sessile, 8-ovuled; style filiform, much elongated, spirally coiled in bud; stigma terminal, obliquely capitate; fruit woody, linear, straight, rather compressed, 2-valved, valves elastically opening from the apex to the base, deeply sulcate outside the middle, obliquely septate within between the seeds; seeds 8–4, compressed, oblong-rhomboid.

104. **Stenodrepanum** Harms, Notizbl. Bot. Gart. Berlin, 7: 500 (1921). 1 sp., *S. bergii* Harms, Argentina. Burkart, Legum. Argent. ed. 2, 178, fig. 34.

Erect shrub; leaves bipinnate, leaflets very small; flowers racemose; calyx-tube short and cupular; segments 5, subequal, one slightly broader than the others, oblong-obovate or oblong, others oblanceolate or oblong; petals 5, subequal, slightly longer than the sepals, 4 oblong-oblanceolate, narrowed into a claw, the fifth broader, obovate, and a broader limb, claws slightly glandular-verruculose; stamens 10, filaments hirsute, slightly glandular; ovary shortly stipitate, rather densely glandular-verruculose; stigma small, obliquely capitellate; ovules about 8; fruit very narrowly linear-lanceolate, more or less falcate, somewhat beaked, obliquely striate lengthwise, slightly torulose, slightly constricted between the 5–9 seeds; seeds narrow, shining, brownish-black.

105. **Brandzeia** Baill., Adansonia, 9: 217 (1896). 1 sp., *B. filicifolia* Baill., Seychelles and Madagascar.

Tree with hard reddish wood; leaves bipinnate; pinnae 6–9 pairs, opposite or sub-opposite; leaflets very small, crowded, subsessile, oblong, very unequal-sided at the base and auriculate; petiole articulated at the base and with a cupular gland above; stipules very small; flowers racemose-cymose on the year-old wood, crowded and small; buds subglobose; calyx-tube cupular, lined with a glandular crenate disk; segments 4, very imbricate; petals 5 (rarely 4 or 6), subequal, at length longer than the calyx, long-clawed, imbricate; stamens 10 or 8; filaments free, very long, long-inflexed in bud; anthers ellipsoid, connective glandular; ovary stipitate; ovules 12–8, 2-seriate; style slender, stigmatose at the apex; fruit stipitate, rather large, oblong or obovate, compressed, each suture more or less sinuate and thickened, often empty at the base; mesocarp fibrous, endocarp forming incomplete septa between the seeds; seeds on slender funicles.

106. **Peltophorum** Walp., Repert. 1: 811 (1842) (conserved name). *Baryxylum* Lour. (1790). *Brasilettia* DC. ex O. Kuntze (1891). About 15 spp., tropics and subtropics, incl. N. Australia; type *P. dubium* (Spreng.) Taub. (*P. vogelianum* Walp.), trop. South America. B.H. 1: 565; E.P. 3, 3: 176; Burkart, Legum. Argent. ed. 2: 179.

Tall trees; leaves bipinnate; leaflets small and numerous, opposite; stipules small, caducous; flowers yellow, in terminal panicles of racemes; bracts narrow to lanceolate, often caducous; bracteoles absent; calyx-tube very short; segments 5, imbricate, subequal; petals 5, orbicular, spreading, slightly unequal, very imbricate; stamens 10, free, declinate, filaments pilose at the base; anthers uniform; ovary sessile, free, 2- or more-ovuled; style filiform, stigma broadly peltate; fruit oblong-lanceolate, rarely elongated, compressed, indehiscent, veiny in the middle, with thin nerve along the margins as if 2-winged; seeds 4–1, transverse, compressed.

P. dubium (Spreng.) Taub., tree, wood durable, used locally for carpentry, furniture, vehicles, &c. *P. pterocarpum* Backer, SE. Asia, N. Australia, shade tree in coffee plantations; bark gives a yellow dye employed in batik work in Java.

107. **Arcoa** Urb., Fedde Repert. 19: 4 (1923). 1 sp., *A. gonavensis* Urb., West Indies. Urban, Ark. for Bot. 22A, n. 8: 34, tt. 1, 2 (1928).

Tree or shrub with dimorphous branches; leaves bipinnate, clustered on short lateral spur-like branchlets; leaflets numerous, opposite, small, oblong; flowers polygamous or dioecious, yellow, sessile in clustered spikes, also on the spur-like branchlets; bracts present; calyx-tube cupular, lined with the disk inside; lobes 5, semiorbicular petals 5 or 6, oblong, all alike, imbricate; stamens 12, short; anthers versatile, as long as the free filaments; ovary narrowly oblong; stigma broad, sessile, subpeltate; fruit oblong-ellipsoid, subterete, fleshy, indehiscent, 6–1-seeded; seeds obovate, with fleshy endosperm.

108. Pachyelasma Harms, Engl. Bot. Jahrb. 49; 428 (1913). 1 sp., *P. tessmannii* (Harms) Harms, Spanish Guinea and Cameroons (trop. Africa). J. Léonard, Fl. Congo Belge, 3: 240 (1952); Hutch. & Dalz., Fl. W. Trop. Afr. ed. 2 (Keay), 1: 484.

Tree; leaves large, bipinnate; pinnae 2–4 pairs, opposite or rarely alternate; leaflets alternate, oblong or oblanceolate-oblong, subcoriaceous; flowers in elongated spiciform racemes; calyx-tube broadly cupular; segments 5, imbricate, broad, shortly ciliolate; petals 5, imbricate, obovate-oblong or obovate, about 2 times as long as the calyx-segments; stamens 10, free, filaments glabrous; anthers small, dorsally attached near the base; connective shortly produced at the apex; ovary shortly stipitate; ovules numerous, 2-seriate; fruit large, lanceolate or oblong-lanceolate, hard and very thick, compressed, straight or slightly curved, divided transversely into 10–15 loculi, each enclosing a seed; seeds transverse, compressed laterally, with a slender flexuous funicle, oblong, about 2 cm. long and 1 cm. broad; embryo narrow in the middle of endosperm, cotyledons cordate at the base.

109. Tetrapterocarpon Humbert, Compt. Rend. Acad. Sci. Paris, 208: 374 (1939). 1 sp., *T. geayi* Humbert, Madagascar.

Small tree; leaves alternate, bipinnate; leaflets often alternate, the end ones paired; stipules caducous; flowers unisexual, dioecious, very small, pale-green, in axillary racemes; bracts and bracteoles very small; pedicels articulate towards the base; calyx-tube concave; segments 4, equal; petals 4, imbricate, equal; stamens 4, free, equal; anthers dorsifixed; filaments hairy at the base and apex; staminodes in the female flower 4, and ovary rudimentary; ovary of female flowers stipitate, free, with 4 folds, 1-ovuled; style short, stigma capitate-reniform; fruit indehiscent, membranous, obovate, dorsiventrally compressed and 4-winged (about 30 × 25 mm.), outer wings broader; seed 1, ovoid, with endosperm; cotyledons flat; radicle straight.

110. Stachyothyrsus Harms, Engl. & Prantl, Nat. Pflanzenfam. Nachtr. 198 (1897); Engl. Bot. Jahrb. 26: 277 (1899). 1 sp., *S. staudtii* Harms, W. trop. Africa.

Tree; leaves bipinnate; pinnae opposite, 2 pairs; leaflets 3–4 pairs, opposite or subopposite, oblong, acuminate; panicles large, pyramidal, terminal, composed of 10–20 elongated many-flowered spikes; bracteoles absent; calyx-tube shortly cupular; lobes 5, imbricate, broad, rounded, semiorbicular; petals 5, equal, imbricate, oblong, rounded at the apex, 2–3 times as long as the calyx; stamens 10, 5 alternate with the petals subequal to them or a little longer, with filaments filiform and clavate-dilated towards the apex, 5 opposite the petals with shorter filaments; anthers basifixed, ovoid, shortly apiculate; ovary obliquely oblong, style short, stigma terminal; ovules 2–3, superposed; fruit oblong-oblanceolate, flat, coriaceous, nervose, woody, 2-seeded.

111. Kaoue Pellegr., Bull. Soc. Bot. Fr. 80: 462 (1933). 2 spp., trop. Africa; type *K. stapfiana* (A. Chev.) Pellegr. Wilczek, Bull. Jard. Bot. Brux. 21: 353 (1951); Fl. Congo Belge, 3: 238, t. 17; Hutch. & Dalz., Fl. W. Trop. Afr. ed. 2 (Keay), 1: 456.

Trees; leaves bipinnate, rarely some pinnate, minutely translucid-punctate; pinnae 2 pairs; leaflets opposite; inflorescence spike-like, racemose, terminal, slender, long-pedunculate;

bracts very small, flowers small; calyx campanulate, equally 5-lobed, imbricate; petals 5, subequal, imbricate; stamens 10, unequal, the 5 outer with thick filaments swollen upwards and with ovate anthers, the 5 inner much shorter, with narrow filaments and oblong anthers; ovary subsessile, 3–2-ovuled; style short and stout; fruit stipitate, dehiscent, oblong-oblanceolate, woody, flattened; seeds 2–1, oblong or elliptic, flattened.

112. **Peltophoropsis** Chiov., Ann. Bot. Roma, 13: 385 (1915). 1 sp., *P. sciona* Chiov., NE. trop. Africa. Roti-Michelozzi, Webbia, 13: 220, fig. 223.

Shrub with swollen nodes; leaves bipinnate; pinnae 2–4 pairs; leaflets 3–6 pairs, small, elliptic; stipules spiny, recurved; racemes lax and few-flowered; bracts minute; calyx-tube obconic; segments 5, lanceolate, subequal, imbricate; petals 5, unequal, uppermost large, ovate, shortly clawed, the other 4 shorter and much narrower, lanceolate, shortly clawed; all yellow; stamens 10, free, equal; anthers very small, attached in the middle, apiculate; ovary shortly stipitate; style thick, stigma small, subpeltate; ovules 2–3, attached to the middle of the ovary; fruit indehiscent, lanceolate, narrowed at each end, compressed, upper suture thick and expanded, subwinged on each side; seeds 1–3, elliptic, compressed, suspended on a rather long funicle, mottled; endosperm present.

113. **Bussea** Harms, Engl. Bot. Jahrb. 33: 159 (1902). 6 spp., trop. Africa; type *B. massaiensis* (Taub.) Harms, Tanganyika Territory and N. Rhodesia. Harms, E.P. Nachtr. 3: 154, fig. 22 (1906); E. G. Bak., Legum. Trop. Afr. 3: 616; J. Léonard, Fl. Congo Belge, 3: 255, t. 19 (1952).

Trees and shrubs; leaves bipinnate; racemes paniculate; bracts deciduous; calyx-tube obliquely cupular; segments 5, imbricate, hyaline on the margin; petals 5, longer than the calyx, broadly clawed, rather broadly spathulate, corrugated, one smaller and narrower with an irregularly crenate margin, villous in the lower part; stamens 10, filaments densely villous at the base; ovary shortly stipitate, oblique, 2-ovuled; style pilose, stigma peltate-capitellate; fruit woody, laterally compressed, oblanceolate, gradually narrowed to the base, shortly apiculate on one side; valves 2, elastically recurved, deeply sulcate in the middle; seeds 2, compressed, oblong.

114. **Parkinsonia** Linn., Sp. Pl. 375 (1753). *Cercidiopsis* Britton & Rose (1930). 2–3 spp., America, S. Africa; type *P. aculeata* Linn., trop. America, and cult. B.H. 1: 570; E.P. 3, 3: 171; Amshoff, Pulle Fl. Suriname, 2, 2: 82; Johnston, Taxonomy of *Parkinsonia* and *Cercidium*, Contrib. Gray Herb. 70: 61 (1924); Burkart, Legum. Argent. ed. 2, 181, fig. 36.

Trees; leaves at first pinnate and fasciculate, later bipinnate, with a very short spine-like rhachis; pinnae 2–4, very long and flattened, with numerous small leaflets; stipules short, spinescent; racemes lax, axillary; bracts small, caducous; bracteoles absent; calyx-tube short; segments 5, membranous, slightly unequal, narrowly imbricate; petals 5, spreading, slightly unequal, the uppermost within and broader; stamens 10, free, filaments villous at the base; anthers uniform, ovoid, versatile; ovary shortly stipitate, free, many-ovuled; style filiform, twice folded in bud, stigma small, terminal; fruit linear, torulose, sub-2-valved, valves thinly coriaceous or rather thick, striate over the seeds; seeds oblong, lengthwise, hilum small, near the apex.

115. **Cercidium** Tul., Arch. Mus. Par. 4: 133 (1844). *Hoopesia* Buckl. (1862). *Rhetinophloeum* Karst. (1862). *Retinophleum* Benth. & Hook. f. (1865). 9 spp., N. America to Chile; type *C. praecox* (R. & P.) Harms (*C. spinosum* Tul.), Brazil. B.H. 1: 570: E.P. 3, 3: 172; Johnston, Taxonomy of *Parkinsonia* and *Cercidium*, Contrib. Gray Herb. 70: 61 (1924); Burkart, Legum. Argent. ed. 2, 180, fig. 35.

Trees and shrubs; branches often twisted, armed at the nodes with short straight spines; leaves small, bipinnate; pinnae 1–2 pairs; leaflets small, in few pairs; flowers yellow, in short lax racemes at the often leafless nodes; pedicels slender; bracts small, membranous; bracteoles minute or absent; calyx-tube shortly campanulate; segments 5, slightly unequal, valvate; petals 5, clawed, oblong or orbicular, imbricate, the uppermost inside the others and dissimilar; stamens 10, free, slightly declinate, filaments pilose at the base; anthers uniform, ovate, versatile; ovary shortly stipitate; ovules numerous; style involute, stigma minute, terminal; fruit linear-oblong, flat and compressed, membranous or subcoriaceous, 2-valved, sutures nerve-like, valves obliquely venulose; seeds longitudinal, ovate, compressed.

116. Conzattia Rose, U.S. Dep. Agric. Contrib. Nat. Herb. 12: 407, t. 69 (1909). 3 spp., Mexico; type *C. multiflora* (Robinson) Standl. (*C. arborea* Rose).

Small trees and shrubs; leaves large, bipinnate; pinnae and leaflets numerous; stipules minute; racemes clustered at the ends of the shoots and axillary, slender, many-flowered; calyx-tube campanulate, very short; lobes valvate, subequal, at length reflexed; petals 5, yellow, equal; stamens 10, erect; filaments free, pubescent at the base; ovary white-woolly; fruit compressed, narrowly winged on each side; seeds few, oblong, with distinct endosperm.

117. Delonix Raf., Fl. Tellur. 2: 92 (1836). *Poinciana* Linn. (1760), not of 1753. 3 spp., trop. Africa, Madagascar, Asia; type *D. regia* (Boj.) Raf. (*Poinciana regia* Boj.), Madagascar, widely grown in the tropics as an ornamental tree, the *Flambouyant* or *Flame of the Forest*. B.H. 1: 569; E.P. 3, 3: 172; Amshoff, Pulle Fl. Suriname, 2, 2: 84; E. G. Bak., Legum. trop. Afr. 3: 623; Burkart, Legum. Argent. ed. 2, 183, fig. 35, D.

Trees; leaves bipinnate; leaflets numerous, small; stipules inconspicuous; stipels absent; flowers showy, orange or red, corymbose-racemose at the ends of the branches; bracts small, very caducous; bracteoles absent; calyx-tube shortly turbinate or very short; segments valvate, subequal; petals 5, orbicular, imbricate, subequal or the uppermost dissimilar; stamens 10, free, declinate, filaments shortly villous at the base, inflexed in the upper part; ovary sessile, free; ovules numerous; style filiform or short, slightly clavate at the apex, stigma truncate, ciliolate; fruit elongated, compressed, hard, thinly and obliquely venose, 2-valved, filled within between the seeds; seeds transverse, oblong, with endosperm; testa hard, with a small hilum.

118. Burkea Benth., Hook., Ic. Pl. t. 593 (1843). 1 sp., *B. africana* Hook., trop. and S. Africa. B.H. 1: 587; E.P. 3, 3: 128; Wilczek, Fl. Congo Belge, 3: 237; Hutch. & Dalz., Fl. W. Trop. Afr. ed. 2 (Keay), 1: 483, fig. 154, C.

Trees or tall shrubs with very thick branchlets; leaves silky when young, bipinnate; pinnae few pairs; leaflets alternate, coriaceous; stipules deciduous; flowers white, small, in interrupted spikes, spikes elongated, simple or paniculately branched; bracts small; calyx-tube very short, campanulate, equally 5-lobed; petals 5, subequal, obovate, imbricate; stamens 10, subequal, filaments very short; anthers uniform, ovate, connective with an inflexed glandular appendix; ovary sessile or shortly stipitate, villous, 2-ovuled; style very short, thick, stigma terminal, concave; fruit stipitate, oblong, compressed, thinly coriaceous, reticulate, 1-seeded, indehiscent; seed suborbicular, compressed, with a filiform funicle.

B. africana Hook., source of soluble gum; bark employed for tanning in E. Africa.

119. Colvillea Boj. ex Hook., Bot. Mag. tt. 3325–6 (1834). 1 sp., *C. racemosa* Boj., Madagascar. B.H. 1: 569; E.P. 3, 3: 172.

Tree; leaves bipinnate; leaflets numerous, small; stipules minute, caducous; flowers showy, scarlet, in dense racemes; rhachis thickened; bracts membranous, coloured, very caducous; bracteoles absent; calyx-tube very short, limb ventricose, 2-lipped, segments induplicate-valvate, upper 4 connate high up, lowermost more separate; petals 5, imbricate, uppermost inside and very broad, lateral obovate, lower outside and narrow; stamens 10, free, declinate, filaments pilose at the base; anthers large, uniform; ovary subsessile, free; ovules numerous; style filiform, stigma, small, terminal; fruit elongated, straight, turgid, 2-valved; seeds transverse, oblong, hilum small.

120. **Aprevalia** Baill., Bull. Soc. Linn. Paris, 1: 428 (1884). 1 sp., *A. floribunda* Baill., Madagascar E.P. 3, 3: 387.

Tree with twisted branches; leaves bipinnate; pinnae 1–3 pairs; leaflets 5–7 pairs, oblong-obovate; flowers precocious, numerous, green and yellow, shortly racemose-paniculate; bracts deciduous; calyx-tube subcampanulate, lobes valvate; petal 1, small, clawed; stamens 2-seriate, unequal; anthers dorsifixed, versatile, long-exserted; ovary sessile, tomentose; ovules numerous, 2-seriate; style dilated at the apex; fruit not seen.

121. **Moldenhauera** Schrad., Goett. Anzeig. 1821: 718 (1821). *Dolichonema* Nees (1821). *Moldenhaweria* Steud. (1841). 5 spp., Brazil, Venezuela; type *M. floribunda* Schrad., Brazil. B.H. 1: 569; E.P. 3, 3: 170.

Trees; leaves bipinnate and at the same time paripinnate or imparipinnate; stipules narrow, small, caducous; flowers in subpanicles of racemes at the ends of the branches; bracts small, narrow, caducous; bracteoles absent; calyx-tube very short; segments 5, at first connate, at length separating valvately, subequal; petals 5, long-clawed, ovate-oblong, fimbriate on the margin, imbricate, spreading, slightly unequal; stamens 10, free, filaments glabrous, 9 short and straight with anthers attached above the base, the tenth lowermost and much longer, incurved-ascending, with a smaller empty anther glabrous or pilose; ovary sessile, free; ovules numerous; style elongate, filiform, stigma truncate, ciliolate; fruit oblong, compressed, coriaceous, 2-valved; seeds transverse, ovoid.

122. **Gymnocladus** Lam., Encycl. 1: 733, t. 823 (1783). 3 spp.; type *G. dioica* (Linn.) Koch (*G. canadensis* Lam.), North America; *G. chinensis* Baill., China; *G. burmanicus* C. E. Parkinson, Burma. B.H. 1: 568; E.P. 3, 3: 169; Burkart, Legum. Argent. ed. 2, 187, fig. 39.

Trees; leaves bipinnate; leaflets ovate or oblong; stipules absent; flowers polygamous, whitish, in simple terminal racemes or panicles; bracts and bracteoles absent; calyx-tube elongated; segments 5, narrow, subequal, open in bud; petals 4 or 5, oblong, slightly unequal, imbricate, the uppermost inside the others or sometimes absent; stamens 10, free, shorter than the corolla; filaments slightly pilose; anthers uniform; ovary in the male flower rudimentary, minute or absent, in the bisexual or female flowers sessile; ovules numerous; style straight, compressed, stigma thick, oblique; fruit sessile, oblong, subfalcate, thick, turgid or subterete, 2-valved, full of pulp inside between the seeds; seeds thick, ovoid or subglobose, on stout funicles.

G. dioica (Linn.) Koch, Kentucky Coffee tree, E. United States; wood strong, heavy, durable, used for railroad ties, cabinet work, fences; roasted seeds used at one time as a substitute for coffee. *G. chinensis* Baill., crushed pods used in laundry work and the ground seeds as an ingredient in perfumed soap.

123. **Gleditsia** Linn., Sp. Pl. 1056 (1753). *Gleditschia* Scop. (1777). *Gleditzia* J. St. Hil. (1805). *Asacara* Raf. (1825). *Garugandra* Griseb. (1879). *Caesalpinioides* O. Ktze. (1891). *Pogocybe* Pierre (1899). About 12 spp., North and South America, temp. and subtrop. Asia, Malay Archip.; type *G. triacanthos* Linn., North America. B.H. 1: 568; E.P. 3, 3: 168; Gagnep., Bull. Soc. Bot. Fr. 81: 672 (1934); Burkart, Legum. Argent. ed. 2, 185, fig. 38.

Trees; trunk and branches armed with stout simple or branched spines; leaves bipinnate and simply paripinnate on the same specimen; leaflets small or medium-sized; stipules small; flowers polygamous, small, greenish or whitish, racemose, fasciculate or in small cymes; bracts small, scale-like; bracteoles absent; calyx-tube turbinate-campanulate; segments 5–3, narrow, subequal, open in bud or subimbricate; petals 5–3, sessile, slightly unequal, imbricate; stamens 10–6, free, rather straight; anthers uniform; ovary in male flowers rudimentary, minute or absent, in bisexual flowers subsessile, free; ovules numerous to 2; style short, stigma terminal; fruit ovate or elongated, straight, compressed, coriaceous or subfleshy, indehiscent or tardily 2-valved, often pulpy within; seeds transverse, obovate or orbicular, compressed.

G. amorphoides Taub., Brazil; wood very durable used for general carpentry; also that of *G. sinensis* Lam., China; pods of this broken up and used in washing and for tanning hides; pods of *G. triacanthos* Linn., the Honey Locust, E. United States, contain 29 per cent. of sugar readily eaten by animals; wood very durable in soil, used for railroad ties, wheels, and fence posts.

124. Dimorphandra Schott, Spreng. Syst. 4: Append. 404 (1827). About 25 spp., Cent. America, trop. South America; type *D. exaltata* Schott, Brazil. Ducke, Arch. Jard. Bot. Rio de Janeiro, 4: 39 (1925); Sprague & Sandwith, Kew Bull. 1932: 395; Ducke, Journ. Wash. Acad. Sci. 25: 193 (1935); Amshoff, Pulle Fl. Suriname, 2, 2: 9.

Trees, some very large and of immense girth; leaves bipinnate, leaflets usually hairy; stipules small and caducous; flowers small, in dense often paniculate racemes or spikes; bracts small and soon deciduous; bracteoles absent; calyx-tube more or less campanulate, shortly 5-lobed; petals spathulate; fertile stamens 5, opposite the petals, alternating with 5 staminodes; anthers oblong, versatile, glabrous; staminodes usually free, more or less broadened and thickened at the apex, sometimes coherent and bearing a rudimentary anther; ovary sessile or shortly stipitate; style very short; stigma small, terminal; fruit flat, linear or broadly falcate, fleshy or woody, indehiscent or elastically 2-valved; seeds small, cylindric or oval and flattened, hard, with coriaceous testa and some endosperm.

D. gonggrijpii (Kleinh.) Sandw., N. trop. South America; wood heavy, hard, durable, used for construction work and shipbuilding. *D. mora* Benth., Trinidad, trop. South America; wood resistant to Teredo and other marine borers; used for ships, railroad ties, paving blocks, &c.

125. Acrocarpus Wight ex Arn., Magaz. Zool. et Bot. 2: 547 (1839). 2 spp., trop. Asia; type *A. fraxinifolius* Wight & Arn., India to Malay Archip. B.H. 1: 568; E.P. 3, 3: 170.

Trees; leaves large, bipinnate; leaflets ovate, acuminate; stipules minute, caducous; flowers opening before the leaves, rather large, scarlet, densely racemose, becoming reflexed, like a bottle-brush, racemes axillary and solitary or 2–3 at the ends of the branches; bracts and bracteoles small, oblong, caducous; calyx-tube campanulate; lobes 5, short, lanceolate; petals 5, narrow, subequal; stamens 5, free, filaments elongated; anthers oblong-linear, versatile; ovary stipitate, free; ovules numerous; style short, inflexed, stigma small, terminal; fruit elongated, long-stipitate, narrowly winged along the adaxial suture; seeds obovate, rather compressed, narrowed at the base.

A. fraxinifolius Wight & Arn., Pink Cedar, Red Cedar, Shingle tree; wood hard, brown with stripes, used for tea-boxes, boards, furniture, and buildings.

Subfamily II. BRACHYSTEGIOIDEAE

Petals present, equal or subequal in size and shape, never reduced to 1 (to pp. 268, 269):
Stamens numerous (more than 15); leaves paripinnate (without an odd terminal leaflet); leaflets 5–7 pairs; flowers in terminal panicles of racemes; bracteoles with a broad thick apiculus   **126. Polystemonanthus**
Stamens up to 15:
Leaves imparipinnate (with an odd terminal leaflet); leaflets 2–5; sepals 4, imbricate; stipules connate, enclosing the terminal bud; panicles axillary and terminal   **127. Oddoniodendron**
Leaves paripinnate (without an odd terminal leaflet):
Calyx fairly well developed and distinct (to p. 268):
Posterior petal or petals sessile or subsessile:

Lowest pair of leaflets smallest and resembling stipules; leaf-rhachis sometimes winged; calyx-segments 4, coloured, imbricate; ovary-stipe adnate to the calyx-tube; fruits oblong, compressed
128. **Humboldtia**
Lowest pair of leaflets not as above:
Fruits marked with a nerve along the middle of each valve; leaflets unilaterally auriculate; panicles terminal or subterminal
129. **Michelsonia**
Fruits without a middle nerve:
Fruits transversely nerved; flowers in racemes or corymbose panicles; stipe of ovary free from the calyx-tube   130. **Dicymbe**
Fruits not transversely nerved; flowers densely racemose or capitate; stipe of ovary adnate to the calyx-tube; fruit elongated, falcate:
Leaflets many-pairs; flowers densely racemose or capitate; sepals 4
131. **Elizabetha**
Leaflets mostly 4 pairs; flowers in terminal panicles of racemes; sepals 5   132. **Isoberlinia**
Posterior petal or petals with a more or less distinct claw:
Fertile stamens 15–5:
Stipules foliaceous or coloured, caducous; stipe of ovary adnate to the calyx-tube; racemes short, sessile, or flowers sometimes densely capitate with an involucre of bracts; calyx-segments petaloid
133. **Brownea**
Stipules neither foliaceous nor coloured, mostly inconspicuous:
Calyx-segments 6–7; petals 6; only half of the 13–12 stamens fertile; filaments shortly villous in the lower part; ovary shortly stipitate
134. **Englerodendron**
Calyx-segments 5; anthers all fertile, uniform; ovary subsessile
135. **Thylacanthus**
Calyx-segments 4:
Leaflets 4–5 pairs, acuminate, curved; stipules deciduous; adaxial suture of fruits thickened   52. **Loesenera**
Leaflets numerous pairs, emarginate at the apex; stipules intra-petiolar, large, soon falling off; adaxial suture 2-ridged
136. **Microberlinia**
Fertile stamens 3:
Calyx obsolete or very rudimentary:
Fertile stamens usually 10, rarely 9 or up to 18   137. **Brachystegia**
Fertile stamens 4–5   138. **Didelotia**
Petals present, very unequal, or only 1 petal present:
Petals 5, sometimes some reduced or rudimentary:
Fertile stamens more than 3:
Calyx distinct and well developed:
Stamens free or subequally connate only at the base:
Sepals or calyx-lobes 5:
Ovary sessile, 4-ovuled   139. **Julbernardia**
Ovary stipitate, stipe adnate to the calyx-tube:
Flowers bisexual; leaves not dotted with glands:

Stamens 8–13, all fertile   140. **Berlinia**
Stamens 3–10, usually 3 larger and fertile, exserted, the others
    reduced to staminodes or absent   141. **Gilbertiodendron**
Flowers polygamous; leaves marked with translucent dots; leaflets
    2–3 pairs; 2 petals reduced to scales   142. **Pseudomacrolobium**
Sepals or calyx-lobes 4:
Lowest pair of leaflets smaller and resembling stipules
                       128. **Humboldtia**
    Lowest pair of leaflets not resembling stipules:
    Stipules striate, deciduous   52. **Loesenera**
    Stipules united and intrapetiolar, semi-cylindric, persistent; inflores-
      cence corymb-like, compact   143. **Paramacrolobium**
    Stipules minute and early caducous; inflorescence racemose-panicu-
      late   51. **Afzelia**
Stamens more or less connate into a unilateral sheath; calyx-lobes
    petaloid, tube elongated:
    Stamens 10; upper petal broadly obcordate   144. **Amherstia**
    Stamens 9; upper petal ovate   145. **Heterostemon**
Calyx obsolete or absent:
    Leaflets more than 1 pair, often brightly coloured when young; stipules
      small; ovules numerous   137. **Brachystegia**
    Leaflets 1 pair, coriaceous, 2–3-nerved; ovules 2   146. **Aphanocalyx**
Fertile stamens 3:
    Stipules not intrapetiolar, minute or long and linear; trees, shrubs, or
      herbs from a woody rootstock   147. **Cryptosepalum**
    Stipules intrapetiolar, connate, ribbed or nervose:
    Leaves 2-foliolate; leaflets with numerous pinnate nerves
              148. **Pellegriniodendron**
    Leaves about 10-foliolate; leaflets closely reticulate
             143. **Paramacrolobium**
Petal 1:
    Fertile stamens 10; leaves fern-like; stipules large, cordate at the base and
      auricled; ovary stipitate; fruit with elastically coiled valves
             149. **Monopetalanthus**
    Fertile stamens 3; ovary stipitate; leaves paripinnate or falsely so, sometimes
      punctate below; stipules sometimes foliaceous.   150. **Macrolobium**
Petals absent; ovary 2-ovuled:
Leaves imparipinnate; stipules intrapetiolar, connate and subtruncate,
    persistent; sepals 2, small, subpetaloid; ovary shortly stipitate, stipe
    free from the tube   151. **Librevillea**
Leaves paripinnate; stipules very caducous or absent; calyx-segments 4;
    ovary sessile   152. **Augonardia**

126. **Polystemonanthus** Harms, Engl. & Prantl, Nat. Pflanzenfam. Nachtr.
197 (1897), and Engl. Bot. Jahrb. 26: 273 (1899). 1 sp., *P. dinklagei* Harms,
Liberia. J. Léonard, Mém. Acad. Roy. Belg. Cl. Sci. 30, 2: 169 (1957); Hutch.
& Dalz., Fl. Trop. West Afr. 1: 338, fig. 132; ed. 2 (Keay), 1: 467, fig. 151
(same figure).

Tree; leaves large, paripinnate, leaflets 5–7 pairs, oblong or oblong-elliptic, coriaceous, densely puberulous below; flowers in terminal racemose-panicles; bracteoles large, persistent for a long time, enclosing the flower-bud, rather thick, valvate, broadly oval, with an elevated line down the middle and a broad obtuse thick apiculus; calyx-tube campanulate-funnel-shaped, thick; sepals 4, imbricate, broadly oval or obovate-oval, rounded, outermost broad at the base, inner a little narrowed to the base or shortly clawed, densely silky outside; petals 5, imbricate, membranous, almost equal in length, otherwise slightly unequal in shape, outer 2 long-clawed, lateral 2 shortly clawed, innermost with a narrow limb; stamens very numerous, filaments elongated; anthers linear, sagittate; ovary on an elongated stipe inserted on one side and near the base of the calyx-tube, densely silky; style rather long, stigma minute; ovules 12–10; fruit shortly stipitate, compressed; seeds not seen.

127. **Oddoniodendron** De Wild., Pl. Bequaert. 3: 222 (1925). 1 sp., *O. micranthum* (Harms) Bak. f. (*O. gilletii* De Wild.), trop. Africa. J. Léonard, Fl. Congo Belge, 3: 408 (1952), and Mém. Acad. Roy. Belg. Cl. Sci. 30, 2: 173 (1957).

Tree; leaves imparipinnate; leaflets 2–5, alternate, elliptic; stipules connate, enclosing the bud; panicles axillary and terminal; bracts small and caducous; bracteoles 2, opposite, concave, valvate, sepaloid, enclosing the bud, persistent; sepals 4, imbricate; petals 5, imbricate, entire, equal; stamens 10–8, free, all fertile; anthers dorsifixed; ovary villous; style filiform; ovules 2–5; fruit dehiscent, compressed, woody; seeds compressed.

128. **Humboldtia** Vahl, Symb. Bot. 3: 106 (1794) (conserved name). *Batschia* Vahl (1794). *Humboldia* Reichb. (1828). 8 spp., Ceylon, India; type *H. laurifolia* Vahl, Ceylon, India. B.H. 1: 579; E.P. 3, 3: 143.

Shrubs; leaves paripinnate; rhachis sometimes winged; leaflets sessile, coriaceous, venulose; lowest pair of leaflets much smaller and resembling stipules; stipules foliaceous, obliquely reniform or semisagittate; flowers orange; racemes dense, often reflexed, at the apex of the shoots or at older nodes; bracts ovate or oblong; bracteoles coloured, enclosing the flower-bud, spreading during flowering; calyx-tube turbinate or narrow; segments 4, subequal, coloured, imbricate; petals either 5 sessile, oblong and subequal, or 3 subequal, the uppermost inside and rather broader, the lower rudimentary or absent; perfect stamens 5, alternating with as many tooth-like staminodes; ovary stipitate, stipe adnate to the calyx-tube; ovules few; style filiform, stigma terminal, clavate-capitate; fruit oblong, oblique or falcate, compressed, coriaceous, 2-valved; seeds transverse, ovate, compressed.

129. **Michelsonia** Hauman, Bull. Inst. Col. Belg. 23: 478 (1952); Fl. Congo Belge, 3: 406, fig. 33. 2 spp., trop. Africa; type *M. microphylla* (Troupin) Hauman.

Trees; leaves paripinnate, leaflets 7–15 pairs, opposite, subsessile unilaterally auriculate; inflorescence terminal or subterminal, paniculate; flowers with 2 ovate, valvate bracteoles; 3 sepals free and 2 united, ciliate; petals 5, subequal, or the lateral smaller than the median; stamens 10, 9 united at the base; ovary few-ovuled; stigma capitate; fruit oblong, apiculate, flat, with a nerve along the middle of each valve.

130. **Dicymbe** Spruce ex Benth. & Hook. f., Gen. Pl. 1: 564 (1865). 7 spp., trop. South America; type *D. corymbosa* Spruce ex Benth., Brazil, British Guiana. E.P. 3, 3: 177.

Trees; leaves paripinnate, leaflets few, opposite, acuminate; stipules not seen; flowers white, rather large, racemose- or corymbose-paniculate; bracts thick, shell-like, very caducous; bracteoles 2, thick and coriaceous, valvate and enclosing the flower in bud, open during flowering and persistent; calyx-tube turbinate, thick; segments 4, oval-oblong, imbricate, often 2-fid at the apex; petals 5, ovate, slightly unequal, imbricate; stamens 10, free, filaments inflexed, pilose at the base; anthers linear, uniform; ovary shortly stipitate, free, many-ovuled; style elongated, involute in bud, stigma peltate; fruit compressed, transversely nerved, 2-ribbed along the adaxial suture.

131. **Elizabetha** Schomb. ex Benth., Hook. Journ. Bot. 2: 92 (1840). About 10 spp., trop. South America; type *E. princeps* Schomb. ex Benth., Guianas. B.H. 1: 577; E.P. 3, 3: 145; A. Ducke, Trop. Woods, 37: 18 (1934) (revision); Amshoff, Pulle Fl. Suriname, 2, 2: 41.

Trees; leaves paripinnate, leaflets in many pairs, very small, coriaceous; stipules large, intrapetiolar, caducous; flowers showy, scarlet, densely racemose or capitate at the apex of the shoots; bracts broad, coriaceous, imbricate or caducous; bracteoles coriaceous, coloured, connate at the base, enclosing the calyx; calyx-tube elongated, segments 4, petaloid, slightly unequal, imbricate; petals 5, subsessile, oval-oblong, slightly unequal, imbricate, the uppermost interior and rather broader, scarcely oblique; stamens 9, free or very shortly connate at the base, the longest 3 perfect with oblong anthers, 6 smaller with empty anthers or without anthers; ovary stipitate, stipe adnate to the calyx-tube, ovules numerous; style filiform, stigma terminal, capitate or dilated; fruit elongated, falcate, compressed, rather woody, 2-valved, upper suture thickened-dilated; seeds transverse, ovate, very compressed.

132. **Isoberlinia** Craib & Stapf, Kew Bull. 1912: 93. 7 spp., trop. Africa; lectotype *I. dalzielii* Craib & Stapf, W. trop. Africa. J. Léonard, Fl. Congo Belg. 3: 376, fig. 31; Mém. Acad. Roy. Belg. Cl. Sci. 30, 2: 173 (1957); Hutch. & Dalz., Fl. W. Trop. Afr. ed. 2 (Keay), 1: 468.

Trees; leaves paripinnate; leaflets rigidly chartaceous, opposite or subopposite, mostly 4 pairs; flowers medium-sized, in terminal panicles of racemes; bracts small, deciduous; bracteoles large, concave, covering the flower-bud, more or less persistent after flowering; sepals 5; petals 5, subequal slightly longer than the sepals or subequal to them, the posticous one mostly slightly broader than the others, sessile or subsessile; stamens 10, all fertile; anthers oblong; ovary stipitate; ovules about 6; style elongated, filiform, stigma terminal; fruit woody, compressed, obliquely oblong, with 2 elastic valves; seeds compressed, rounded.

133. **Brownea** Jacq., Enum. Pl. Carib. 6 (1760) (conserved name). *Hermesias* Loefl. (1758). *Brownaea* Jacq. (1760). About 30 spp., North America, trop. America, West Indies; type *B. coccinea* Jacq., Venezuela. B.H. 1: 577; E.P. 3, 3: 145; Pittier, *Brownea* and *Browneopsis* in Panama, Colombia, and Venezuela, Contrib. U.S. Nat. Herb. 18: 145 (1916).

Trees, often low or weak; leaves paripinnate, leaflets coriaceous, often large; stipules foliaceous or coloured, caducous; flowers showy, rose or red, rarely white; racemes short, sessile at the apex of the shoots, or flowers sometimes densely capitate with an involucre of bracts; bracts either large, coloured, or smaller and caducous; bracteoles coloured, more or less connate, enclosing the calyx; calyx-tube turbinate-campanulate; segments mostly 4, petaloid, slightly unequal, imbricate; petals 5, clawed, ovate or oblong, slightly unequal, imbricate, uppermost inside, rather broader and scarcely oblique; stamens 15–10, free or more or less connate below the middle; anthers uniform, oblong; ovary stipitate, stipe adnate to the calyx-tube; ovules numerous; style filiform, stigma terminal, capitate-dilated; fruit oblong or elongated, straight or falcate, compressed, coriaceous-subwoody, 2-valved, upper suture often thickened or dilated; seeds transverse, ovate, much compressed.

134. **Englerodendron** Harms, Engl. Bot. Jahrb. 40: 27 (1902). 1 sp., *E. usambarense* Harms, E. trop. Africa. J. Léonard, Mém. Acad. Roy. Belg. Cl. Sci. 30, 2: 199 (1957).

Tree; leaves paripinnate; leaflets many pairs, symmetric at the base; flowers involucrate by the bracteoles, paniculate; calyx-tube shortly cupular; segments 6–7, subequal, imbricate; petals 6, about double the length of the sepals, subequal, clawed, limb oblong-oblanceolate; stamens 13–12, of which 6–8 are fertile, with elongated filaments and well-developed dorsifixed anthers, alternating with shorter filaments bearing minute anthers; filaments shortly villous in the lower part; ovary shortly stipitate, densely villous; style hairy at the base, stigma terminal, minutely capitellate; ovules 6–5; fruit very shortly stipitate, compressed, opening by 2 woody valves, obovate or obovate-oblong, obtuse or rounded at the base, rounded at the apex and shortly obliquely mucronate.

135. **Thylacanthus** Tul., Arch. Mus. Par. 4: 175 (1844). 1 sp., *T. ferrugineus* Tul., Brazil. B.H. 1: 564; E.P. 3, 3: 177.

Shrub; leaves paripinnate, leaflets few, mostly in 3 pairs, subcoriaceous, stipules not observed; flowers shortly paniculate at the ends of the branchlets; bracts thick, very caducous; bracteoles concave, thick, enclosing the young flower-buds, forming a 2-lobed involucre persisting below the flower; calyx-tube very short; segments 5, ovate-rounded, petaloid, ciliate, imbricate; petals 5, narrowly obovate, imbricate; stamens 10, shortly connate at the base, filaments inflexed at the apex; anthers short, uniform; ovary subsessile, free, few-ovuled; style elongated, involute in bud, stigma peltate; fruit not known.

136. **Microberlinia** A. Chev., Rev. Bot. Appliq. 26: 587, t. 21 B (1946). 2 spp., trop. Africa; lectotype *M. brazzavillensis* A. Chev. J. Léonard, Mém. Acad. Roy. Belg. Cl. Sci. 30, 2: 184 (1957); Hutch. & Dalz., Fl. W. Trop. Afr. ed. 2 (Keay), 1: 471.

Tall trees; leaves paripinnate, leaflets in numerous pairs, opposite, small, oblong, unequal sided at the base, apex emarginate, lateral nerves looped within the margin; stipules intra-petiolar, large, oblong-linear, free, soon falling off; panicles axillary; bracts very large in bud, imbricate, covering the whole inflorescence, soon deciduous; bracteoles obovate, enclosing the flower; sepals 4, imbricate, unequal; petals 5, subequal and clawed; stamens 10, in 2 bundles, 9 lower connate into a sheath split above, the 10th free; anthers uniform; ovary stipitate, inserted on the margin of the calyx-tube, 3–6-ovuled; style slender, truncate; fruit oblong, subfalcate, compressed, 2-valved, valves keeled, 2-ridged on the adaxial suture; seeds ovate or orbicular, compressed.

137. **Brachystegia** Benth., Benth. & Hook. f., Gen. Pl. 1: 582 (1865). About 70 spp., trop. Africa; type *B. spiciformis* Benth. B.H. 1: 582; E.P. 3, 3: 138; Nachtr. 196; Hutch. & Burtt Davy, Kew Bull. 1923: 129; E. G. Bak., Legum. Trop. Afr. 3: 711; Hoyle, Fl. Congo Belge, 3: 446, figs. 38–40 (1952); J. Léonard, Mém. Acad. Roy. Belg. Cl. Sci. 30, 2: 248 (1957); Hoyle, Monograph (*ined.*).

Trees; young branchlets often with brilliantly coloured leaves; bark fibrous; leaves alternate, paripinnate, leaflets very diverse in number and shape, normally opposite in 2 to numerous pairs, often pellucid-punctate; stipules free and lateral to connate and intra-petiolar, with or without basal auricles; racemes or panicles usually terminal, rarely lateral on older branchlets; bracts early deciduous; bracteoles 2, opposite, valvate, enclosing the flower in bud, persistent; sepals and petals together 1–11 often rudimentary or absent; stamens usually 10 (abnormally 9 or 13–18), sometimes with staminodes, free or shortly united, often obscurely diadelphous; disk sometimes present and formed of glandular swellings; ovary stipitate, stipe free from the receptacle; style glabrous, stigma small, subcapitate; ovules 4–10; fruit flat, woody, oblong or boat-shaped, beaked, dehiscing elastically; adaxial suture with a phlange-like wing on each side; seeds subdiscoid, almost flat. This description condensed from one kindly supplied by Mr. A. C. Hoyle of Oxford, who has prepared a monograph, not so far published.

The wood of *B. spiciformis* Benth. is hard and heavy; the bark of this and several other species used by Africans for making cloth and roofing for their huts, &c.

138. **Didelotia** Baill., Adansonia 5: 367, t. 8 (1865). *Zingania* A. Chev. (1946). *Toubaouate* Aubr. & Pellegr. (1958). 6–8 spp., trop. Africa; type *D. africana*

Baill., W. Africa. E.G. Bak., Legum. Trop. Afr. 3: 736; J. Léonard, Fl. Congo Belge, 3: 494, fig. 43; Mém. Acad. Roy. Belg. Cl. Sci. 30, 2: 265; Hutch. & Dalz., Fl. W. Trop. Afr. ed. 2. (Keay), 1: 480.

Large trees; leaves paripinnate, leaflets 1–many, opposite, oblique, unequal-side at the base; racemes paniculate, terminal, each raceme few-flowered; flowers bisexual; bracteoles rounded, valvate, enclosing the flower-bud; calyx obsolete; petals small, subulate; stamens 5; filaments soon elongated, exserted, inflexed in bud; anthers dorsifixed; ovary subsessile, few-ovuled, ovules 2-seriate; style excentric, slender, stigma obsolete, obtuse; fruit flat, oblong-oblanceolate, rounded on one side at the base, with a subconspicuous median nerve, apiculate at the end of the lower suture.

139. **Julbernardia** Pellegr., Boissiera Fasc. 7: 297 (1943). *Paraberlinia* Pellegr. (1943). *Pseudoberlinia* Duvign. (1950). *Seretoberlinia* Duvign. (1950). 9 spp., trop. Africa; type *J. hochreutineri* Pellegr., Gabon. J. Léonard, Fl. Congo Belge, 3: 399 (1952); Mém. Acad. Roy. Belg. Cl. Sci. 30, 2: 188 (1957).

Trees; leaves paripinnate; leaflets 2–5-pairs, opposite, coriaceous; stipules caducous or persistent; panicles lax, many-flowered, axillary or terminal; bracts soon deciduous; bracteoles 2, opposite at the base of the flower, suborbicular, keeled, valvate, enclosing the flower-bud, persistent, silky; calyx-tube flattened; segments 5, large, subequal, imbricate; petals 5, membranous, one about as long as the calyx-segments and long-clawed, the others minute, narrowly lanceolate, acute; stamens 10–9, long-exserted, one free, the others connate at the base; anthers elliptic, versatile; ovary sessile, 4-ovuled; style filiform, stigma capitellate; fruit dehiscent, 2-valved, oblong or oblong-linear, compressed, thickened on the margins; seeds oval, flattened.

140. **Berlinia** Soland. ex Hook. f. Hook. Niger Fl. 326 (1849) (conserved name). *Westia* Vahl (1810). *Tetraberlinia* Hauman (1952). *Macroberlinia* Hauman (1952). About 50 spp., trop. Africa; type *B. acuminata* Soland. ex Hook. f. B.H. 1: 579; E. G. Bak., Legum. Trop. Afr. 3: 680, partly; E.P. 3, 3: 141; Troupin, *Berlinia* and allied genera, Bull. Jard. Bot. Brux. 20: 285 (1950); J. Léonard, Fl. Congo Belge, 3: 387, t. 30; Mém. Acad. Roy. Belg. Cl. Sci. 30, 2: 180, 186 (1957); Hutch. & Dalz., Fl. W. Trop. Afr. ed. 2 (Keay), 1: 469.

Trees; leaves paripinnate; leaflets coriaceous; stipules intrapetiolar, often large, foliaceous, persistent or caducous; flowers in racemes or panicles at the ends of the branchlets; bracts coriaceous, ovate, caducous; bracteoles 2, large, concave, spathulate, enclosing the flower-buds, spreading during flowering or caducous; calyx-segments 5, thin, imbricate; upper petals largest, long-clawed, hooded and folded in bud; 2–4 lower petals small, linear, or absent; stamens 10 or rarely 5, 3 larger and exserted, free or slightly connate at the base; filaments elongated; anthers oblong, uniform; ovary stipitate, stipe adnate to the calyx-tube; ovules numerous; style filiform, stigma terminal; fruit compressed, woody and hard, 2-valved; seeds rounded and compressed.

B. acuminata, wood hard, used for carpentry, turnery, canoes, drums, naval construction.

141. **Gilbertiodendron** J. Léonard, Bull. Jard. Bot. Brux. 22: 188 (1952); 24: 57; Fl. Congo Belge, 3: 428, fig. 35: Mém. Acad. Roy. Belg. Cl. Sci. 30, 2: 232 (1957). 26 spp., trop. Africa; type *G. demonstrans* (Baill.) J. Léonard. Hutch. & Dalz., Fl. W. Trop. Afr. ed. 2 (Keay) 1: 474, fig. 152.

Trees; leaves paripinnate, rarely imparipinnate, leaflets usually several-pairs, opposite, rarely alternate, with one or more glands on the margin; stipules small to very large, sometimes foliaceous, often with a reniform foliaceous appendage at the base; stipels absent; inflorescence paniculate or racemose, axillary, terminal or on the old wood; bracts mostly small; flowers in more than 2 rows; bracteoles 2, opposite, concave, valvate, sepaloid, enclosing the bud, sometimes very large, persistent; sepals 5, imbricate, 4 subequal, the median larger, and 2-toothed or 2-fid; petals 5, the middle one largest, sometimes very large, rather fan-like, 2-lobed, clawed, remainder equal, small or scale-like; large outer stamens 3, rarely 4, 5, or 9, exserted, 6 others (rarely small or none) included, more or less reduced; anthers dorsifixed; ovary shortly stipitate, adnate to one side of the receptacle; ovules numerous to few; style filiform; stigma terminal; fruit dehiscent, compressed, mostly oblong, woody, with 1–3 prominent longitudinal nerves; seeds compressed.

142. **Pseudomacrolobium** Hauman, Bull. Inst. Col. Belge, 23: 477 (1952); Fl. Congo Belge, 3: 383, t. 29 (1952). 1 sp., *P. mengei* (De Wild.) Hauman, trop. Africa. J. Léonard, Mém. Acad. Roy. Belg. Cl. Sci. 30, 2: 179 (1957).

Tree; leaves paripinnate, leaflets 2–3 pairs, opposite or subopposite, equal-sided at the base, marked with translucent dots; inflorescence terminal, paniculate; bracts very small, caducous; flowers polygamous; bracteoles 2, opposite, valvate, free, covering the flower in bud; sepals 5, imbricate, 3 free, subcordate, 2 united almost to the apex; petals 5, 3 well developed, shortly clawed, other 2 reduced to scales; stamens about 10, free, all fertile, exserted; ovary stipitate, stipe adnate to one side of the receptacle; stigma capitate; ovules few; fruit flat, oblong, transversely septate between the seeds.

143. **Paramacrolobium** J. Léonard, Bull. Jard. Bot. Brux. 24: 348 (1954); Mém. Acad. Roy. Belg. Cl. Sci. 30, 2: 230 (1957). 1 sp., *P. caeruleum* (Taub.) J. Léonard, trop. Africa. Hutch. & Dalz., Fl. W. Trop. Afr. ed. 2 (Keay), 1: 474.

Tree; leaves paripinnate, leaflets 3–5 (rarely 2) pairs; stipules united and intrapetiolar, semi-cylindric, 2-fid, persistent; petiolules twisted; stipels absent; leaflets unequal-sided at the base, not glandular; inflorescence corymb-like, compact; bracteoles very long; sepals 4, unequal, the posterior longer and 2-toothed; petals 5, 1 largest, 2 smaller, 2 small; stamens 9, in a circle, unequally united at the base, 3–5 fertile and exserted, 6–4 staminodial and smaller; ovary long-stipitate, long-exserted, unilaterally attached to the calyx-tube; fruit winged along one suture, 2-valved, woody; seeds 3–8, very hard, areolate.

144. **Amherstia** Wall., Pl. As. Rar. 1: 1, tt. 1–2 (1830). 1 sp., *A. nobilis* Wall., Burma. B.H. 1: 578; E.P. 3, 3: 143.

Tree; leaves paripinnate, leaflets large, coriaceous; stipules narrow, foliaceous, caducous; flowers showy, scarlet, in large lax terminal pendulous racemes; pedicels very long; bracts very caducous; bracteoles persistent, large, coloured, spreading, free or nearly so; calyx-tube elongated; segments 4, petaloid, slightly unequal, imbricate; petals 5, 3 subequal in length, the uppermost inside and very broadly obcordate, the lateral oblong-cuneate, lower 2 minute or rudimentary; stamens 10, 9 connate into a sheath, 5 longer, 4 alternate shorter with small anthers, tenth stamen free upwards; anthers oblong; ovary stipitate, stipe adnate to the calyx-tube; ovules numerous; style filiform, stigma terminal, capitellate; fruit elongated, falcate, compressed, rather woody, 2-valved, thickened and dilated along the upper suture; seeds transverse, ovate-orbicular, much compressed.

145. **Heterostemon** Desf., Mém. Mus. Paris, 4: 241, t. 12 (1818). *Heterostemum* Steud. (1840). 7–8 spp., trop. South America; type *H. mimosoides* Desf., Brazil, Venezuela. B.H. 1: 578; E.P. 3, 3: 144; Amshoff, Pulle Fl. Suriname, 2, 2: 39; Sandw., Kew Bull. 1939: 9 (key to spp.).

Trees, sometimes low and weak; leaves paripinnate with opposite or alternate leaflets, or imparipinnate or unifoliolate; stipules often foliaceous, often caducous; flowers showy, purple or bluish, in short sessile racemes at the tops of the shoots or at defoliated nodes; bracts small; bracteoles persistent, connate, much shorter than the calyx-tube; calyx-tube elongated; segments 4, petaloid, slightly unequal, imbricate; upper 3 petals slightly unequal, ovate, imbricate, uppermost inside, lower 2 minute, rudimentary; stamens 9, connate into a sheath split on the upper side, filaments free at the apex, 3 longest (lower) stamens perfect, with oblong anthers, 6 shorter unequal and with anthers empty or without anthers;

ovary stipitate, stipe adnate to the calyx-tube; ovules numerous; style filiform, stigma terminal, capitate; fruit stipitate, elongated, straight or falcate, compressed, coriaceous, 2-valved; seeds transverse, ovate or orbicular, very compressed.

146. **Aphanocalyx** Oliv., Hook. Ic. Pl. 11: 53, t. 1066 (1867–71). 3 spp., trop. Africa; type *A. cynometroides* Oliv., trop. W. Africa. E.P. 3, 3: 132; J. Léonard, Fl. Congo Belge, 3: 438, fig. 36 (1952); Mém. Acad. Roy. Belg. Cl. Sci. 30, 2: 262 (1957).

Trees; leaflets 1-pair, coriaceous, 2–3-nerved; racemes axillary, short, flowers crowded; bracts scarious, deciduous; bracteoles enclosing the flower-bud, forming 2 valves, mucronulate, persistent during flowering; calyx obsolete or reduced to minute teeth; petal 1, posticous, overtopping the bracteoles, obovate-cuneate; lateral and anticous petals obsolete or sometimes 1 lateral petal subequal to the posticous one or shorter; stamens 10, all bearing anthers; filaments free or slightly united at the base; anthers small, versatile; ovary shortly stipitate, 2-ovuled; style filiform, stigma capitate; fruit compressed, dehiscing by 2 woody valves; seeds compressed, discoid.

147. **Cryptosepalum** Benth., Benth. & Hook. f., Gen. Pl. 1: 584 (1865). *Dewindtia* De Wild. (1902). *Pynaertiodendron* De Wild. (1902). About 12 spp., trop. Africa; type *C. tetraphyllum* (Hook. f.) Benth. E.P .3, 3138; E. G. Bak., Legum. Trop. Afr. 3: 741; J. Léonard, Fl. Congo Belge, 3: 485, t. 34 (1952); Mém. Acad. Roy. Belg. Cl. Sci. 30, 2: 270 (1957); Hutch. & Dalz., Fl. W. Trop. Afr. ed. 2 (Keay), 1: 480.

Small trees, much branched, or reduced to herbs with woody rhizomes; leaves paripinnate, leaflets 1–numerous pairs rarely unifoliate, oblique; stipules minute or long and linear; flowers small, whitish-rose, in short axillary or terminal racemes; bud-scales at the base of the young racemes imbricate, soon deciduous; floral bracts minute; bracteoles rather large, concave, valvate, enclosing the flower in bud; calyx-tube very short; segments 4, minute, scale-like; petal 1, sessile, orbicular; stamens 3; filaments short; anthers oblong, versatile; ovary shortly stipitate, free, 2-ovuled; style filiform, stigma terminal, truncate; fruit obliquely oblong, compressed, shortly beaked.

148. **Pellegriniodendron** J. Léonard, Bull. Jard. Bot. Brux. 25: 203 (1955). 1 sp., *P. diphyllum* (Harms.), J. Léonard, trop. Africa. J. Léonard, Mém. Acad. Roy. Belg. Cl. Sci. 30, 2: 245 (1957); Hutch. & Dalz., Fl. W. trop. Afr. ed. 2 (Keay), 1: 474.

Tree; leaves subsessile, 2-foliolate, leaflets opposite, oblong to oblong-oblanceolate, with numerous pinnate nerves, a little unequal at the base, with a pair of very obscure subulate stipels (? reduced leaflets) at the base; stipules intrapetiolar, connate, ribbed; panicles terminal, with short branches rough with the scars of the fallen striate bracts; bracteoles 2, obovate, nerved, enclosing the flower; sepals 5, narrowly lanceolate; petals 5, one large, long-clawed, deeply bilobed, lobes suborbicular, remainder like the sepals, almost equal among themselves; stamens 3; ovary very shortly stipitate 3-ovuled; style pilose at the base; fruits (imperfect) with thin crusty valves.

149. **Monopetalanthus** Harms, Engl. & Prantl, Nat. Pflanzenfam. Nachtr. 195 (1897); Engl. Bot. Jahrb. 26: (1899). 8 spp., trop. Africa; type *M. pteridophyllum* Harms, W. trop. Africa. E. G. Bak., Legum. Trop. Afr. 3: 734; Pellegrin, Bull. Soc. Bot. Fr. 89: 118 (1942); J. Léonard, Fl. Congo Belge, 3: 441, fig. 37 (1952), and Mém. Acad. Roy. Belg. Cl. Sci. 30, 2: 255 (1959); Hutch. & Dalz., Fl. W. Trop. Afr. ed. 2 (Keay), 1: 478, fig. 153.

Trees; leaves fern-like, paripinnate, leaflets many pairs, unequal-sided, subrectangular at the base; stipules large, membranous, scarious, obliquely oblong, cordate at the base and auricled; racemes strobiliform in bud, axillary, shorter than the leaves; bracts broadly ovate, imbricate, deciduous; bracteoles long-persistent, forming an involucel, oval, densely velvety; calyx-tube very short; segments 5, two connate to the middle and obliquely ovate, three similar to each other and minutely tooth-like, ferruginous-fimbriate; petal 1, much larger than the calyx, membranous, clawed, spathulate; stamens 10, filaments connate at the base into a tube; anthers broadly oval, dorsifixed; ovary stipitate; style filiform, elongated, hairy in the lower part, stigma minute, capitellate; ovules 3–2; fruit oblong or obovate-oblong, stipitate, elastically 2-valved, shortly ferruginous.

150. **Macrolobium**[1] Schreb., Gen. Pl. 1: 30 (1789) (conserved name). Over 130 spp., trop. America, trop. Africa; type *M. bifolium* (Aubl.) Pers., trop. America. B.H. 1: 579; E.P. 3, 3: 142; E. G. Bak., Legum. Trop. Afr. 3: 666; Amshoff, Pulle Fl. Suriname, 2, 2: 33; R. S. Cowan, Mem. N.Y. Bot. Gard. 8: 257 (revision of Amer. spp.); J. Léonard, Jard. Bot. Brux. 25: 201 (1955) (*Anthonota*); Hutch. & Dalz., Fl. W. Trop. Afr. ed. 2 (Keay), 1: 471 (*Anthonota*).

Large trees to small shrubs; leaves paripinnate or pseudo-imparipinnate; leaflets 1–45 pairs, opposite, mostly unequal-sided, sometimes punctate below; stipules sometimes foliaceous; inflorescence simply racemose, rarely racemes shortly branched; bracts usually caducous; bracteoles enclosing the flower in bud; sepals 5–4, sometimes unequal; petal 1, clawed or sessile, orbicular; stamens 3; filaments filiform, anthers dorsifixed versatile; stigma terminal; style filiform; ovary 8–1-ovuled, stipitate, stipe basal or adnate to the calyx-tube; fruit dehiscent or indehiscent, oval or orbicular to oblong, 1–few-seeded.

Zebra Wood, *Macrolobium* spp., trop. Africa; wood valued for cabinet work.

151. **Librevillea** Hoyle, Bol. Soc. Brot. 29: 17, tt. 1–3 (1955). 1 sp., *L. klainei* (Pierre) Hoyle, trop. Africa. J. Léonard, Mém. Acad. Roy. Belg. Cl. Sci. 30, 2: 254 (1957).

Tree with buttressed stem; leaves imparipinnate; leaflets alternate oblong-elliptic, acuminate, subequal-sided at the base, pinnately nerved and finely reticulate; stipules intrapetiolar, connate and subtruncate, persistent; panicles terminal and axillary; bracts very small; pedicels slender; bracteoles covering the flower, persistent, valvate; sepals 2, small, subpetaloid; stamens 10 (9), connate at the base; anthers subglobose, medifixed, pollen smooth; ovary shortly stipitate, stipe free from the tube; style filiform, stigma very small, ovules 2; fruit dehiscent, shortly stipitate, oblong, compressed, rather woody, shortly apiculate; sutures slightly thickened, not winged; seeds 2–1, flat, oblong-elliptic, hilum small.

152. **Augonardia** Pellegr., Bull. Soc. Bot. France, 71: 309 (1924). 1 sp., *A. letestui* Pellegr., Congo, Gabun, W. Africa. J. Léonard, Mém. Acad. Roy. Belg. Cl. Sci. 30, 2: 158.

Tree; leaves paripinnate; leaflets 4–5 pairs, opposite or subopposite, entire, elliptic, finely reticulate; stipules very caducous or absent; panicles terminal, many-flowered, dense; bracts caducous; bracteoles 2, slightly keeled on the back, enclosing the flower-bud; calyx shortly funnel-shaped, thickened at the base; segments 4, imbricate, subequal; petals absent; perfect stamens 3, long, connate at the base; anthers introrse, dorsifixed; staminodes 4, free, subulate; ovary sessile, 2-ovuled; style elongated, stigma minutely capitellate.

---

[1] Synonyms of **Macrolobium**: *Vouapa* Aubl. (1775). *Outea* Aubl. (1775). *Kruegeria* Scop. (1777). *Utea* St. Hil. (1805). *Anthonota* Beauv. (1805). *Vuapa* St. Hil. (1805). *Pseudovouapa* Britton & Killip (1936). *Triplisomeris* Aubrev. & Pellegr. (1958). *Isomacrolobium* Aubrev. & Pellegr. (1958).

28. MIMOSACEAE

R.Br., Flinders, Voy. Terra Austr. 2: 551 (1814) (*Mimoseae*)

Trees, shrubs, or very rarely herbs; leaves bipinnate, rarely once pinnate; stipules present, sometimes spine-like. Flowers actinomorphic, bisexual, unisexual, or some neuter and sterile, small and short or rarely elongated and tubular, usually sessile in cylindric spikes or globose heads, rarely racemose or in globose umbels; bracts small, often deciduous; bracteoles rarely present. Sepals usually 5, imbricate or valvate, connate into a toothed or lobed limb, rarely free. Petals as many as the sepals, valvate, free or connate into a lobed corolla, hypogynous or slightly perigynous. Disk usually absent. Stamens numerous to few and as many as the sepals or petals, free or monadelphous or adnate to the base of the corolla-tube; anthers small, versatile, often crowned by a deciduous gland, dehiscing lengthwise. Ovary free at the base of the calyx-tube, 1-locular; style usually filiform, stigma small, terminal; ovules mostly numerous. Fruit dehiscent or indehiscent, sometimes breaking into 1-seeded segments; seeds mostly ovate or orbicular, compressed, sometimes winged, hilum basal, rarely thick, globose or ovoid; aril rarely present; testa hard, endosperm none or very thin; cotyledons flat; radicle straight (not folded).

Genera 56; species about 2800.

DISTRIBUTION. Mainly tropics and subtropics, especially numerous in the southern hemisphere.

CLASSIFICATION. Benth. & Hook. f., Gen. Pl. 1: 592 (1865) (suborder *Mimoseae*); Benth., Revision of the Suborder *Mimoseae*, Trans. Linn. Soc. 30: 335 (1875); Taubert, Engl. & Prantl, Nat. Pflanzenfam. 3, 3: 99 (1891) (subfam. *Mimosoideae*); Britton & Rose, N. Amer. Fl., *Mimosaceae*, 23: 1 (1928); E. G. Bak., Legum. Trop. Afr. 3: 779 (1930); Burkart, Mat. para une monogr. del genero *Prosopis*, Darwiniana 4: 57 (1940); Las Legum. argent. silv. y cultiv. 1–590 (1943); Hutch. & Dalz., Fl. West Trop. Afr. 1: 351 (1928); ed. 2 (Keay), 1: 484 (1958); Ducke, Legum. Amaz. Brasil., Bol. Técn. Inst. Agron. do Norte, no. 18: 18 (1949); Gilbert & Boutique, Fl. Congo Belge, 3: 137 (1952); Kostermans, Monogr. Asiat., Malay., Austral., and Pacif. spp. of *Mimosaceae* formerly included in *Pithecolobium* Mart., Organiz. Sci. Res. Indones. Bull. 20: 1–122 (1954, see notes on p. 297); Brenan, Notes on *Mimosoideae*, Kew Bull. 2: 170 (1955); Fl. Trop. E. Afr. *Mimosoideae* (1959).

ANATOMY. Anatomically *Mimosaceae* share most of the important characters of *Caesalpiniaceae* and *Fabaceae*. The stomata are accompanied by subsidiary cells placed parallel to the pore. The vessels have simple perforations, and the wood-prosenchyma has simple pits. The simple clothing hairs are unicellular or uniseriate, and may be one-armed or hooked. The compound hairs are sometimes tufted. Glandular hairs are of varied form. M.C. 1: 476. POLLEN. Erdt. 225.

Characters occurring in relatively few Genera and Species. **Leaves** simply paripinnate in *Affonsea* and *Inga*. **Flowers** in the upper part of the spike bisexual, the lower neutral with long staminodes in *Dichrostachys*; spikes condensed into dense globose or clavate heads in *Parkia*. **Calyx-lobes** imbricate in tribes *Mimozygantherae* and *Parkieae*, valvate in other tribes; sepals united high up in tribe *Parkieae*. **Stamens** numerous (more than 10) in tribes *Acacieae* and *Ingeae*; usually with apical glands (sometimes deciduous) in tribes *Parkieae* and *Adenanthereae*; filaments more or less united into a tube in tribe *Ingeae*; staminodes present in *Pentaclethra*. **Ovule** reduced to 1 in *Xeroclada*. Valves of the **fruit** separating from the persistent sutures in *Mimosa*, *Schranckia*, and *Schranckiastrum*; splitting transversely into 1-seeded cocci in *Entada*, *Pseudentada*, *Plathymenia*; subturgid and/or angled or winged in *Stryphnodendron*, *Tetrapleura*, *Ambylogonocarpus*; 1-seeded in *Xeroclada*. **Seeds** winged in *Newtonia*, *Parapiptadenia* spp., *Piptadeniastrum*, *Monoschisma*, *Indopiptadenia*, *Cylicodiscus*, and *Fillaeopsis*.

Economic Properties. Notes on these will be found at the end of the generic descriptions.

Phylogeny and Morphology. *Mimosaceae* were the subject of a classical memoir by Bentham,[1] whose views on phylogeny would have been of infinite value had he been of a more speculative turn of mind. For the purpose of a phylogenetic study of this family we must shift from the African to the South American region, for most of the African genera seem to be more modern developments of the group, the headquarters of which is in South America.

The most primitive tribe and the connecting link with the *Caesalpiniaceae*, is tribe *Parkieae*, in which the calyx has remained imbricate. The other tribes and genera represent a very natural assemblage, and are divided upon what appear to be very trivial characters, such as the presence or absence of a small gland at the top of the anther. As a rule the genera with racemose or spicate inflorescence should be regarded as more primitive than those with a capitate inflorescence, although both these types occur in the same genus, for example in *Acacia* and to a less extent in *Albizia*. One of the more primitive genera is *Inga* (tropical America), which is exceptional, with *Affonsea*, in having *simply pinnate* leaves, and the flowers have *numerous stamens*. The latter genus shows also a very primitive character in the possession of 2–6 *free carpels* which it shares with the aptly named *Archidendron* from NE. Australia and New Guinea. The free carpels are no doubt a relict character and may indicate that the *Mimosaceae*, or a part of them, have been derived from the *Rosaceae* independently of the *Caesalpiniaceae*.

Of the genera with spicate flowers probably the most highly advanced is *Dichrostachys*, which has the upper flowers of the catkin-like spike bisexual and the lower ones neuter.

The majority of *Mimosaceae* are trees, shrubs, or climbers, but a few genera have one or two species which have become herbaceous, and in one case, *Neptunia oleracea* Lour., the habitat is aquatic, and on this account the species is almost unique in the family.

KEY TO TRIBES

Calyx-lobes or sepals imbricate; leaves bipinnate; stamens 10 or 5, sometimes with several staminodes, filaments free or connate only at the base:

[1] Benth., *Mimoseae*, Trans. Linn. Soc. 30: 335 (1875).

Sepals free; stamens without an apical gland; staminodes absent; ovules
numerous; stigma peltate, convex 1. MIMOZYGANTHEAE
Sepals united high up; stamens usually tipped with an apical gland; stami-
nodes present; ovules few; stigma concave 2. PARKIEAE
Calyx-lobes valvate:
Filaments free from one another or united only at the base:
Stamens numerous (more than 10); pollen-grains usually collected into
2–6 masses in each loculus 3. ACACIEAE
Stamens 10 or fewer; pollen-grains numerous and separate in each loculus:
Anthers without a gland at the apex 4. MIMOSEAE
Anthers with a (sometimes deciduous) gland at the apex
5. ADENANTHEREAE
Filaments more or less united into a tube; stamens numerous (more than
10); pollen-grains usually collected into 2–6 masses in each loculus
6. INGEAE

Tribe 1. MIMOZYGANTHEAE

1. **Mimozyganthus** Burkart, Darwiniana 3: 445, fig. 1 and photo. (1939).
1 sp., *M. carinatus* (Griseb.) Burkart, Argentina. Burkart, Legum. Argent. ed.
2: 146, fig. 22.

Shrubs or trees; stipules spiny; leaves bipinnate, pinnae few pairs; leaflets numerous,
minute, oblong, obtuse, opposite or alternate; rhachis glandular between the pinnae;
flowers capitate, minute, bisexual; heads axillary, globose, sessile between the pair of spines,
solitary or 2–4 together, shortly elongated after flowering; sepals 5, free, imbricate, oblong,
fleshy, incurved; petals 5, free, valvate, sometimes slightly overlapping in the middle;
stamens 10, free; anthers ellipsoid, eglandular, dorsifixed; ovary shortly stipitate; ovules 2;
style short, stigma large, peltate, thick, convex; fruit indehiscent, much compressed, elliptic, 1–2-seeded, exocarp thinly coriaceous, obliquely fibrous; placenta thick, narrowly
keeled; cotyledons orbicular, sagittate at the base.

Tribe 2. PARKIEAE

Spikes elongated, often paniculate; stamens 5 together with 15–5 staminodes
2. **Pentaclethra**
Spikes condensed into dense globose or clavate heads; stamens 10; staminodes
absent 3. **Parkia**

2. **Pentaclethra** Benth., Hook. Journ. Bot. 2: 127 (1840). 2 spp.; *P. macroloba*
(Willd.) Kuntze (*P. filamentosa* Benth.), trop. America and Africa (Congo
region). *P. macrophylla* Benth., W. trop. Africa. B.H. 1: 588; E.P. 3, 3: 125;
E. G. Bak., Legum. Trop. Afr. 3: 779; Gilbert & Boutique, Fl. Congo Belge,
3: 138; Hutch. & Dalz., Fl. W. Trop. Afr. ed. 2 (Keay), 1: 487.

Unarmed trees; leaves bipinnate, pinnae and leaflets in many pairs, shining; stipules
small; stipels setaceous; flowers bisexual or dioecious, whitish-yellow; spikes elongated and
often paniculate; calyx campanulate, teeth 5, very short and broad, imbricate; petals more
or less connate; stamens 5, exserted; anthers tipped by a deciduous gland; staminodes 15–5,
opposite the corolla-lobes, linear, coloured, elongated; corona sometimes present and
adnate to the inside of the stamens; ovary with numerous ovules; style filiform, stigma

terminal, concave; fruit elongated, oblique, plano-compressed, coriaceous to woody, 2-valved, valves elastically revolute; seeds large.

Owala Oil tree, *P. macrophylla*; the seeds are the source of Owala Butter or Oil, used for candles and soap; lotion of bark for sores; wood hard, used in turnery, for wheels, and in carpentry; *P. macroloba*, useful timber.

3. **Parkia** R.Br., App. Denh. & Clappert. 234 (1826). *Paryphosphaera* Karst. (1862). About 60 spp., tropics; type *P. filicoidea* Welw. (*P. africana* R.Br.), trop. Africa. B.H. 1: 588; E.P. 3, 3: 123; Gilbert & Boutique, Fl. Congo Belge, 3: 141, t. 10; Hutch. & Dalz., Fl. W. Trop. Afr. ed. 2 (Keay), 1: 487, fig. 155; Brenan, Fl. Trop. E. Afr. *Legum.-Mimosoid.* 7, fig. 1 (1959).

Trees, unarmed; leaves bipinnate, with numerous pinnae and leaflets; flowers very numerous in large clavate or depressed-globose heads; peduncles solitary and axillary, or several at the tops of the branches; upper flowers in the heads yellow to red, lower sterile and white or red; calyx cylindric, teeth 5, very short and imbricate; petals 5, linear-spathulate, free or connate to the middle; stamens 10, free or connate at the base and adnate to the corolla; anthers oblong, usually tipped by a gland; ovary sessile or stipitate; ovules numerous; style filiform, stigma terminal; petals of the sterile lower flowers often free; staminodes 10, in a long bundle, free above, filiform and coloured; fruit oblong or elongated, straight or curved, compressed, rather woody or fleshy, 2-valved; seeds transverse, thick, ovoid or compressed.

P. filicoidea, fruits edible, with sweet yellow pulp; seeds used as condiment and as coffee called Café du Sudan; bark for tanning to give red colour to leather; wood for carpentry; *P. speciosa* Hassk., Malaya, and *P. javanica* Merr., pods used for flavouring; seeds edible.

Tribe 3. ACACIEAE

Only genus   4. Acacia

4. **Acacia**[1] Mill., Gard. Dict. Abridg. ed. 4 (1754); Willd., Sp. Pl. 4, 2: 1049 (1806). About 900 spp., tropics and subtropics, especially Africa and Australia; type *A. arabica* Willd., trop. Africa and Asia. B.H. 1: 594; E.P. 3, 3: 108; E. G. Bak., Legum. Trop. Afr. 3: 815; Gilbert & Boutique, Fl. Congo Belge, 3: 145, with figs.; Burkart, Legum. Argent. ed. 2, 95, figs. 7, 8; Physis, 19: 104 (1941); Hutch. & Dalz., Fl. W. Trop. Afr. ed. 2 (Keay), 1: 496, fig. 159; Brenan, Fl. Trop. E. Afr. *Legum.-Mimosoid.* 49, fig. 14–18 (1959).

Trees, shrubs, or very rarely herbs, often very prickly or spinose; leaves bipinnate, leaflets mostly small and in numerous pairs, or leaves completely reduced to phyllodes; petiolar gland often present; stipules sometimes spinescent, rarely membranous; flowers in cylindric spikes or globose heads; peduncles axillary and solitary or fasciculate or paniculate at the ends of the branches; bracts often 2, connate, scale-like, under the head or in the middle or at the base of the peduncle, often linear-cuneate under the flowers or peltately dilated at the apex; flowers small, 5–3-merous, bisexual or polygamous; calyx campanulate, dentate, lobed or divided into sepals; petals usually more or less united, rarely absent; stamens numerous in each flower, exserted, free or partly united, yellow or white; ovary sessile or stipitate, 2- or more-ovulate; style filiform; fruit ovate to linear, straight, arcuate or variously

---

[1] Synonyms of **Acacia**: *Sassa* Bruce (1791). *Phyllodoce* Link (1831). *Vachellia* Wight & Arn. (1834). *Farnesia* Gasparr. (1838). *Cuparilla, Drepaphyla, Eburnax, Esclerona, Gumifera, Hecatandra, Poponax, Senegalia, Zigmaloba*, all of Rafin (1838). *Chitonanthus* Lehm. (1847). *Tetracheilos* Lehm. (1847). *Arthrosprion* Hassk. (1855). *Hoopesia* Buckl. (1862). *Tauroceras, Bahamia, Feracacia, Lucaya, Fishlockia, Myrmecodendron, Aciopsis, Aciella*, all of Britton & Rose (1928). *Manganaroa* Speg. (1923). *Nimiria* Craib (1927). *Siderocarpos* Small (1901). *Faidherbia* A. Chev. (1934). *Dugandia* Britton & Killip (1936). *Pithecodendron* Speg. (1923).

contorted, flat to terete, membranous to woody, 2-valved or indehiscent, rarely articulated or moniliform; seeds transverse or lengthwise, compressed, with a filiform funicle or fleshy aril.

A large number of species of *Acacia* are of economic use; for details see Uphof, Dict. Econ. Pl. 2 (1959); especially important are *A. arabica* Willd. (*A. nilotica* Del.), Babul Acacia, trop. Africa; wood put to many uses; leaves and green pods for camels, sheep, and goats; stem exudes gum. *A. catechu* Willd., Catechu of India; extract of heartwood used for tanning, toilet preparations, dyeing, staining wood, and medicinal purposes.

Tribe 4. MIMOSEAE

Fruits dehiscent:
  Valves of the fruit remaining attached to the sutures; unarmed trees, shrubs, or herbs:
    Fruits opening by both sutures:
      Fruits linear, straight or slightly falcate, spreading or rarely densely crowded; seeds arranged lengthwise or very oblique to the sutures
                                                             5. Desmanthus
      Fruits broadly linear; seeds transverse to the length of the fruit or only slightly oblique   **6. Leucaena**
    Fruits opening by only one suture   **7. Anadenanthera**
  Valves of the fruit separating from the persistent sutures; leaves often stipellate; flowers in globose heads or cylindric spikes; often armed with prickles:
    Fruit-valves entire or jointed, breaking away from and broader than the persistent replum   **8. Mimosa**
    Fruit-valves subtetragonous, entire, narrower than the persistent replum
                                                             9. Schranckia
    Fruits subtetragonous, more or less torulose; valves entire, separating from the jointed dilated sutures   **10. Schranckiastrum**
  Fruits indehiscent, very broad and thin; flowers racemose or racemose-paniculate; unarmed trees:
    Racemes single or paired; flowers polygamous; petals free   11. **Dinizia**
    Racemes paniculate; flowers bisexual; petals shortly united 12. **Aubrevillea**

5. **Desmanthus** Willd., Sp. Pl. 4, 2: 1044, partly (1806) (conserved name). *Acuan* Medik. (1786). *Darlingtonia* DC. (1825). *Acuania* O. Ktze. (1891). 22 spp., subtrop. of North America, West Indies, Argentina, Madagascar; type *D. virgatus* (Linn.) Willd., North America, West Indies, naturalized elsewhere. B.H. 1: 592; E.P. 3, 3: 117; Burkart, Legum. Argent. ed. 2, 117, fig. 15.

Trees, shrubs, or perennial herbs; leaves bipinnate, leaflets small; stipules setaceous, persistent; petiolar gland often between the lower jugae; capitula ovate-globose, axillary, solitary; flowers all bisexual, or the lower neuter and sometimes without petals but with short staminodes; calyx campanulate, shortly dentate; petals free or nearly so; stamens 10 or 5, free, exserted; anthers eglandular at the apex; ovary subsessile; ovules numerous; style subulate or thickened above, stigma terminal; fruit linear, straight or falcate, plano-compressed, 2-valved, continuous within or subseptate between the seeds; seeds placed lengthwise or oblique, ovate, compressed.

6. **Leucaena** Bent., Hook. Journ. Bot. 4: 416 (1842). *Ryncholeucaena* Britton & Rose (1928). *Caudoleucaena* Britton & Rose (1928). 50 spp., Polynesia,

trop. America; type *L. glauca* (Willd.) Benth., trop. America, a shade tree introduced into other tropical countries. B.H. 1: 594; E.P. 3, 3: 115; Burkart, Legum. Argent. ed. 2, 118, fig. 16.

Unarmed trees or shrubs; leaves bipinnate, leaflets numerous and small or few and larger, oblique; petiole often glandular; stipules setaceous or small; capitula globose; peduncles axillary, subfasciculate or the upper ones in a terminal leafless 'raceme'; bracts often 2, below the capitula or below the apex of the peduncle; flowers 5-merous, sessile, usually bisexual; calyx tubular-campanulate, dentate; petals free; stamens 10, free, exserted; anthers ovate, oblong or globose, often pilose, not glandular; ovary stipitate, ovules numerous; style filiform; fruit stipitate, broadly linear, plano-compressed, rigidly membranous, 2-valved, continuous within; seeds transverse, ovate, compressed.

7. **Anadenanthera** Speg., Physis, 6: 313 (1923). *Schleinitzia* Warb.? (1891). *Niopa* Britton & Rose (1927). 4 spp., trop. and subtrop. America; type *A. peregrina* (Linn.) Speg., West Indies to Brazil. (1) Britton & Rose, N. Amer. Fl. 23: 189 (1928) (*Niopa*).

Unarmed trees; petiole with a gland above the base; rhachis not glandular between the pinnae; leaves large, bipinnate; pinnae opposite or nearly so; leaflets many-pairs; flowers in globose heads; calyx 5-toothed; corolla sympetalous; disk absent; stamens 10; anthers not glandular at the apex; ovary sessile or nearly so; fruit straight, opening by only one suture, the valves remaining attached along the other, not twisting, very coriaceous, flattened, with a straight margin or more or less constricted between the seeds; seeds flat, not winged, suborbicular or elliptic, shining; funicle in the middle of the seed.

8. **Mimosa** Linn., Sp. Pl. 516 (1753). *Panthocarpa* Raf. (1825). *Eburnax* Raf. (1836). *Lomoplis* Raf. (1838). *Sensitiva* Raf. (1838). About 600 spp., tropics and subtropics; type *M. pudica* Linn., tropics. B.H. 1: 593; E.P. 3, 3: 115; Burkart, Legum. Argent. ed. 2, 119, fig. 17; Brenan, Fl. Trop. E. Afr. *Legum.-Mimosoid.* 42, fig. 13 (1959).

Trees, shrubs (sometimes climbing), or herbs, mostly armed; leaves bipinnate, often sensitive, rarely absent and reduced to phyllodes; petiolar glands rarely present; secondary rhachides mostly 2-stipellate; capitula globose or spikes cylindric; peduncles axillary, solitary or fasciculate, upper ones sometimes in a raceme; flowers small, sessile, the stamens often twice as long as the corolla, 6–3-merous, bisexual or polygamous, or some neutral in a few species with filiform staminodes subpetaloid at the apex; calyx usually minute, sometimes paleaceous, ciliate, and pappus-like; petals more or less connate; stamens double the number of the petals, or equal, free, exserted; anthers small, not glandular; ovary usually sessile, 2- or more-ovuled; style filiform; fruit oblong or linear, usually plano-compressed, membranous or coriaceous, valves 2, separating from the persistent margins, entire or divided transversely into segments, continuous or subseptate within; seeds ovate or orbicular, flat.

9. **Schranckia** Willd., Sp. Pl. 4, 2: 1041 (1806) (conserved name), not Medik. (1792). *Leptoglottis* DC. (1825). *Schrankia* Benth. (1842). *Morongia* Britton (1894). 20 spp., trop. America; type *S. quadrivalvis* (Linn.) Merrill (*S. aculeata* Willd.), Cent. America. B.H. 1: 593; E.P. 3, 3: 115; Burkart, Legum. Argent. ed. 2: 116, fig. 15.

Undershrubs or herbs, often prostrate, armed with recurved prickles; leaves bipinnate, often sensitive; rhachis not glandular, often setose between the pinnae; leaflets small; stipules setaceous; capitula globose or spikes cylindric; peduncles axillary, solitary or fasciculate; flowers 5–4-merous, sessile, bisexual or polygamous, rose or purplish; calyx very small; petals connate to the middle; stamens as many as or double the number of the petals, free, exserted, the filaments of the males often flattened, in bisexual flowers filiform;

anthers small, not glandular; ovary subsessile, ovules numerous; style filiform; fruit linear, acute or acuminate, prickly all over, valves breaking away from the dilated persistent margins; seeds lengthwise, oblong, sub-4-sided, funicle short.

10. **Schranckiastrum** Hassler, Fedde Repert. 16: 151 (1919). 1 sp., *S. insigne* Hassler, Paraguay.

Shrub or small tree; leaves bipinnate, stipellate; flowers capitate, heads in elongated cylindric leafy 'spikes'; flowers 4-merous, bisexual; calyx valvate, campanulate, 4-lobed; corolla sympetalous, valvate, 4-lobed to the middle; stamens 8, exserted, free, almost 3 times as long as the corolla; anthers small, eglandular; ovary shortly stipitate, many-ovuled; style filiform, stigma small, terminal; fruit linear, subquadrangular, more or less torulose, very elongated, beaked, contracted at the base into a stipe, valves entire, separating from the septate jointed dilated sutures, elastically dehiscent; seed oblong.

11. **Dinizia** Ducke, Arch. Jard. Bot. Rio de Janeiro, 3: 76, t. 4 (1922). 1 sp., *D. excelsa* Ducke, Brazil, Brit. Guiana.

Large tree, unarmed; leaves bipinnate; pinnae 7–11-pairs, alternate; leaflets 8–10-pairs; racemes terminal, solitary or paired; flowers polygamous; calyx shortly 5-toothed, valvate; petals 5, free; stamens 10, free, long-exserted; anthers not glandular; ovary shortly stipitate; style long-exserted; fruit very broad and thin, brown, shining, not dehiscent, rugose-venose to the margins, stipitate about 2 cm. at the base; seeds transverse, compressed, testa hard and shining, nearly black, the embryo enclosed by thick semi-translucent endosperm.

12. **Aubrevillea** Pellegr., Bull. Soc. Bot. Fr. 80: 466 (1933). 2 spp., trop. Africa; type *A. kerstingii* (Harms) Pellegr. Gilbert & Boutique, Fl. Congo Belge, 3: 227; Hutch. & Dalz., Fl. W. Trop. Afr. ed. 2 (Keay), 1: 492.

Unarmed tall trees; leaves bipinnate; pinnae 4–8 pairs; leaflets numerous, sessile, oblong, small; inflorescence of spike-like racemes grouped in panicles; bracts caducous; flowers bisexual; calyx cupular, shortly 5-toothed, valvate; petals united in the lower part into a tube and with the base of the filaments; stamens 10–8, rarely 6–7; filaments united at the base; anthers eglandular; ovary 5–7-ovuled, oblong, stipitate; style short; ovules 7–4; fruit oblong, flat, papyraceous, oblong or elongated, indehiscent; seeds few to 1, reniform, flat.

Tribe 5. ADENANTHEREAE

Inflorescence spicate or racemose; spikes or racemes sometimes paniculate:
  Flowers all bisexual in the inflorescence (to p. 285):
    Fruits opening by a valve or valves (not splitting transversely), the valves remaining attached to the sutures (to p. 284):
      Leaflets opposite; disk absent from within the calyx:
        Flowers spicate (sessile on the axis):
          Fruits not spirally coiled after dehiscence:
            Fruits opening elastically from apex to base, falcate; pinnae 1 pair; seeds ellipsoid   13. **Calpocalyx**
          Fruits not opening elastically, opening laterally:
            Leaf-pinnae more than 2-foliolate:
              Fruit dehiscing along both sutures:
                Seeds at most margined but not winged; plants often prickly; corolla glabrous outside   14. **Piptadenia**
                Seeds distinctly winged; plants not prickly; corolla often pubescent outside   15. **Parapiptadenia**

Fruit dehiscing by only one suture; seeds winged:
  Fruit torulose; seeds attached in the middle   16. **Monoschisma**
  Fruit not torulose; seeds attached at the base   17. **Newtonia**
  Leaf-pinnae 2-foliolate:
    Leaflets with a fleshy gland between them; seeds not white, with a
      broad wing at each end   18. **Indopiptadenia**
    Leaflets without a gland; seeds white, not winged   19. **Goldmania**
  Fruit closely spirally coiled after dehiscence; seeds not winged
                                                          20. **Strombocarpa**
Flowers racemose (distinctly stalked on the axis):
  Trees; fruit often incurved or falcate, or elongated and straight; exocarp
    not separating from the endocarp:
    Seeds surrounded by a broad membranous wing   21. **Piptadeniastrum**
    Seeds not winged:
      Fruit dehiscing into 2 thin valves which spirally twist; seeds scarlet
        or bicolorous   22. **Adenanthera**
      Fruit dehiscing into 2 woody recurving valves, not twisted; seeds not
        coloured   23. **Pseudoprosopis**
  Undershrubs, unarmed, often with a thick woody rootstock and annual
    stems; fruit straight or nearly so; exocarp separating from the
    endocarp   24. **Elephantorrhiza**
Leaflets alternate; disk present and conspicuous within the calyx; seeds
  winged:
  Indumentum of stellate hairs; seeds attached at the base; flowers in
    racemes, pedicels jointed at the apex, persistent as 'pegs'
                                                          25. **Cyclicodiscus**
  Indumentum not stellate; seeds attached in the middle; flowers in
    spikes   26. **Fillaeopsis**
Fruits splitting transversely into 1-seeded cocci, the latter falling away from
  the persistent sutures:
  Both exocarp and endocarp breaking into 1-seeded segments:
    Unarmed shrubs or climbers; end pair of pinnae sometimes transformed
      into a leafless tendril; fruits sometimes very large and elongated
                                                          27. **Entada**
    Climbing shrubs armed with numerous reflexed prickles; end pair of
      pinnae not as above   28. **Pseudoentada**
  Only the endocarp breaking into 1-seeded segments; seeds transverse,
    with a long funicle   29. **Plathymenia**
Fruits indehiscent and not breaking up into segments:
  Fruits more or less compressed:
    Petals free or at length free:
      Fruits not winged; trees and shrubs unarmed or armed with prickles
        or axillary spines or spinescent stipules   30. **Prosopis**
      Fruits winged; unarmed trees   31. **Gagnebina**
    Petals remaining united; fruits not winged; shrubs or small trees armed
      with straight stipular spines   32. **Sopropis**
  Fruits subturgid or 4-angled or 4-winged (more or less quadrangular in
    section):

Fruits subturgid or moniliform; unarmed trees; America

33. **Stryphnodendron**

Fruits with 4 sharp wings; unarmed trees; Africa   34. **Tetrapleura**

Fruits with 4 rounded angles; unarmed trees; Africa

35. **Amblygonocarpus**

Flowers not all bisexual, the upper in the spike bisexual, yellow, the lower
neuter, pink, or white, with long staminodes; shrubs or small trees with
spiny branches; seeds obovate, compressed   36. **Dichrostachys**

Inflorescence capitate, globose or ovoid-globose:

Fruits dehiscent:

Fruits woody and elastically dehiscent from the apex to the base, septate
between the seeds; unarmed trees   37. **Xylia**

Fruits not elastically dehiscent, opening at each side:

Fruits not septate between the seeds; trees with spiny branches; petioles
glandular; leaflets numerous, small and narrow   38. **Delaportea**

Fruits subseptate between the seeds; perennial herbs or subshrubs,
sometimes aquatic; stipules obliquely cordate   39. **Neptunia**

Fruits not dehiscent:

Ovules several; fruit several-seeded, not winged:

Fruits not spirally twisted when ripe:

Fruits not breaking up into 1-seeded segments; trees and shrubs, unarmed or spinescent   30. **Prosopis**

Fruits breaking up into 1-seeded segments; stipules spinescent

40. **Piptadeniopsis**

Fruits soon closely spirally twisted; trees and shrubs armed with spiny
stipules   20. **Strombocarpa**

Ovule solitary; fruits 1-seeded, wing-like on the lower suture; rigid undershrubs armed with recurved spinescent stipules   41. **Xerocladia**

13. **Calpocalyx** Harms, Engl. & Prantl, Nat. Pflanzenfam. Nachtr. 191
(1897; Engl. Bot. Jahrb. 26: 257, t. 5, F–G (1899). 6 spp., W. trop. Africa;
type *C. dinklagei* (Taub.) Harms, S. Nigeria and Cameroons. E. G. Bak.,
Legum. Trop. Afr. 3: 798; Hutch. & Dalz., Fl. W. Trop. Afr. ed. 2 (Keay), 1: 487.

Trees; leaves bipinnate, pinnae 1 pair; leaflets opposite, several pairs, acuminate; spikes
pedunculate, paniculate, shortly catkin-like when young; calyx-tube campanulate-cylindric,
lobes 5, valvate; petals 5, connate towards the base, at length free, valvate; stamens 10; filaments filiform, inserted at the base of the petals; anthers glandular at the apex, glands soon
deciduous; ovary subsessile, style elongated, stigma terminal, subacute; ovules about 10–6;
fruit falcate, woody, narrowed at the base and opening elastically; seeds ellipsoid, slightly
compressed.

14. **Piptadenia** Benth., Hook. Journ. Bot. 2: 135 (1840), not of Journ. Bot. 4:
334 (1842). *Pityrocarpa* Britton & Rose (1928). 11 spp., trop. America; lectotype *P. latifolia* Benth., Brazil.

Trees and shrubs, rarely climbers, mostly armed with prickles on the stem or with spiny
stipules; leaves bipinnate, pinnae opposite; leaflets broad, several to many, pinnately
nerved; petiole with a gland above the base or rarely towards the apex; rhachis glandular or
not between the pinnae; flowers spicate, spikes axillary, elongated; calyx 5-toothed; corolla
sympetalous, 5-lobed; stamens 10, free or nearly so; anthers glandular at the apex; disk
very small; ovary stipitate; fruit straight or slightly curved, dehiscing by both margins,

valves rigid, either flattened and transversely plicate with straight margins or moniliform and deeply constricted between the seeds; seeds lenticular, not winged, shortly elliptic or suborbicular.

15. **Parapiptadenia** Brenan (*ined.*) *Piptadenia* Benth., Hook., Journ. Bot. 4: 334 (1842), not Journ. Bot. 2: 135 (1840). 2 spp., trop. South America; lectotype *P. rigida* (Benth.) Brenan, Brazil.

Trees or shrubs, unarmed or prickly; leaves bipinnate, leaflets small and in many pairs or rarely larger and in few pairs; petiolar and jugal glands usually present; flowers 5-merous, small, white or greenish, bisexual or subpolygamous, in cylindric spikes or globose heads; peduncles axillary, solitary or fasciculate, the upper ones often paniculate; calyx campanulate, slightly dentate; petals often connate to the middle; stamens 10, free, exserted; anthers crowned by a deciduous gland; ovary subsessile, 3- or more-ovuled; fruit stipitate or rarely sessile, broadly linear, flat, membranous or subcoriaceous, 2-valved, valves entire, continuous within, not pulpy; seeds compressed, sometimes elongated and winged, attached at the base or in the middle by a filiform funicle.

16. **Monoschisma** Brenan, Kew Bull. 1955: 179. 2 spp., South America; type *M. leptostachyum* (Benth.) Brenan.

Unarmed trees; petiole not glandular; rhachis glandular between the pinnae; pinnae mostly opposite; leaflets 1–several-pairs; flowers spicate; petals free; disk very inconspicuous; ovary shortly stipitate; fruits straight or more or less curved, dehiscing along one margin, valves twisted, coriaceous, flattened, torulose, deeply constricted between the seeds; seeds flat, narrowly winged, without endosperm, suborbicular or shortly elliptic, brown; cotyledons almost as broad as long; funicle obliquely attached in the middle of the seed.

17. **Newtonia** Baill., Bull. Soc. Linn. Paris, 1: 721 (1888). About 14 spp., trop. Africa, trop. America; type *N. duparquetiana* (Baill.) Keay (*N. insignis* Baill.), W. trop. Africa. Gilbert & Boutique, Fl. Congo Belge, 3: 213; Hutch. & Dalz., Fl. W. Trop. Afr. ed. 2 (Keay), 1: 489; Brenan, Fl. Trop. E. Afr. *Legum.-Mimosoid.* 23, fig. 6 (1959).

Trees; leaves alternate, bipinnate; pinnae opposite, often with a gland at the base, 2- or more-foliolate; leaflets opposite, obliquely elliptic or oblong to linear; spikes very slender, in a terminal panicle; flowers numerous and very small; bracts minute; calyx campanulate, 5-toothed; petals 5, valvate; stamens 10, alternately longer and shorter; filaments wrinkled in bud; anthers tipped by a small stipitate globular very fugacious gland; ovary many-ovuled; style with a cupular stigma; fruits broadly linear, compressed, straight, opening by sutures, valves chartaceous; seeds narrowly oblong, attached at the cordate base of the fairly narrow wing by a slender funicle.

18. **Indopiptadenia** Brenan, Kew Bull. 1955: 178. 1 sp., *I. oudhensis* (Brandis) Brenan, India.

Unarmed tree; leaves alternate, bipinnate, pinnae opposite, 2-foliolate; leaflets opposite, rather large, subsessile, obliquely rounded-elliptic, glaucous, pinnately nerved; flowers in pedunculate axillary spikes, these single or 2–3 together in a 'raceme'; calyx and corolla glabrous outside; petals free; disk inconspicuous; ovary shortly stipitate; fruits flat, mostly curved, long-stipitate, linear, dehiscing by both margins, continuous within; seeds numerous, parallel with the fruit margins, kidney-shaped, with a broad wing at each end with the funicle in the middle.

19. **Goldmania** Rose ex Micheli, Mem. Soc. Phys. Hist. Nat. Genève, 34: 274 (1903) (partly). 2 spp., Mexico and Cent. America; type *G. platycarpa* Rose ex Micheli. Brenan, Kew Bull. 1955: 177.

Small trees; branchlets sometimes spinescent at the apex; petiole not glandular; rhachis between the pinnae glandular; leaflets 1 (rarely 2) pairs; flowers spicate; corolla sympetalous, long-tubular, free from the stamens and disk, lobes valvate; stamens 10, free, anthers tipped by a gland; disk very small; ovary stipitate; fruit more or less falcate-curved, dehiscing along one margin only, valves thick, not or scarcely constricted between the seeds; seeds white, with endosperm, lenticular, not winged or margined, suborbicular or slightly irregular.

20. Strombocarpa[1] Engelm. & Gray, Bost. Journ. Nat. Hist. 5: 243 (1845). *Prosopis* sect. *Strombocarpa* Benth. (1841). 6 spp., America; type *S. strombulifera* (Willd.) A. Gray, extratrop. South America. Britton & Rose, N. Amer. Fl. 23: 183 (1928).

Trees or shrubs, armed with spiny stipules; leaves bipinnate, mostly glandular between the pinnae, glands sessile; pinnae 1–2 pairs; inflorescence spicate or capitate; calyx 5-toothed; petals 5, valvate; stamens 10, free; anthers with a deciduous gland at the apex; ovules numerous; style filiform; fruit elongated, closely spirally twisted, cylindric, not dehiscent; seeds with endosperm.

21. Piptadeniastrum Brenan, Kew Bull. 1955: 179. 1 sp., *P. africanum* (Hook. f.) Brenan (*Piptadenia africana* Hook. f.), trop. Africa. Hutch. & Dalz., Fl. W. Trop. Afr. ed. 2 (Keay), 1: 489.

Tall unarmed tree; leaves bipinnate; rhachis eglandular; pinnae about 10 pairs, often alternate; leaflets many pairs, very small and linear, auricled at the base; flowers in spike-like racemes collected into terminal panicles; pedicels jointed in the middle, lower joint persisting as a 'peg'; sepals 5, short; petals shortly united at the base; stamens 10, free or nearly so; anthers with a deciduous gland at the apex; ovary sessile or subsessile; fruit elongated, straight or curved, dehiscent by both margins; valves very coriaceous, flattened, obliquely nerved; seeds flat, surrounded by a broad membranous wing, more or less oblong, brown; cotyledons dilated, broader than long, funicle near the middle.

22. Adenanthera Linn., Sp. Pl. 384 (1753); Gen. Pl. ed. 5: 181 (1754). *Gonsii* Adans. (1763). *Pongelion* Adans. (1763). *Stachychrysum* Boj. (1837). 12 spp., trop. and subtrop. Asia to N. Australia and Polynesia, trop. Africa (introd.); type *A. pavonina* Linn., S. China, India, Burma, Malay Penins. and widely cult. B.H. 1: 590; E.P. 3, 3: 120.

Unarmed trees; leaves bipinnate; leaflets small, in many pairs; racemes elongated, slender, spike-like, axillary, or paniculate at the apex of the shoots; flowers 5-merous, white or yellowish, bisexual or polygamous; calyx campanulate, shortly dentate; petals coherent below the middle or soon free; stamens 10, free, scarcely exserted; anthers with a deciduous gland at the apex; ovary sessile, many-ovuled; style filiform; fruit linear, often incurved or falcate, compressed or turgid around the seeds, 2-valved, valves entire, often convex, at length mostly contorted, often divided between the seeds by a septum continuous with the endocarp; seeds thick, testa hard, scarlet or two-coloured, mostly enclosed by a thin pulp.

23. Pseudoprosopis Harms, Engl. Bot. Jahrb. 33: 152 (1902). 3–4 spp., trop. Africa; type *P. fischeri* (Taub.) Harms, Tanganyika, Congo, N. Rhodesia. E.P. Nachtr. 3: 147, fig. 20; Gilbert & Boutique, Fl. Congo Belge 3: 223; Brenan, Fl. Trop. E. Afr. *Legum.-Mimosoid.* 26, fig. 7 (1959).

Shrubs or climbing shrubs with zigzag branches; leaves bipinnate; leaflets very small, oblong, rounded or emarginate at the apex; flowers in simple lateral pedunculate racemes, densely arranged and catkin-like when young; buds oblique; calyx shortly cupular, teeth 5, unequal, the upper one often longer than the others; petals 5, free, valvate, inflexed at the

---

[1] The following belong to this genus: *S. cinerascens* A. Gray, Texas; *S. odorata* (Torr. & Frém.) A. Gray, SW. United States; *S. torquata* (DC.) Hutch. (*Prosopis torquata* DC.), extratrop. South America; *S. abbreviata* (Benth.) Hutch. (*Prosopis abbreviata* Benth.), South America. *S. reptans* A. Gray, South America.

apex; stamens 10; filaments elongated; anthers with a large deciduous gland at the apex; ovary shortly stipitate, villous, about 10-ovuled; style filiform, glabrous; fruit compressed, dehiscing by 2 recurved valves, woody, septate within between the seeds; seeds compressed, subquadrate-orbicular or rhomboid, shining, with an areole in the middle; no endosperm.

24. **Elephantorrhiza** Benth., Hook. Journ. Bot. 4: 344 (1842). 9–10 spp., E. and S. trop. and S. Africa; type *E. elephantina* (Burch.) Skeels (*E. burchellii* Benth.), S. Africa. B.H. 1: 590; E.P. 3, 3: 122; E. G. Bak., Legum. Trop. Afr. 3: 800; Brenan, Fl. Trop. E. Afr. *Legum.-Mimosoid.* 19, fig. 4 (1959).

Low unarmed undershrubs, with thick woody rhizomes; leaves bipinnate, leaflets small, in many pairs; petiolar glands absent; racemes spike-like, cylindric, axillary or on short leafless scapes; flowers 5-merous, small, uniform, bisexual or polygamous; calyx campanulate, shortly dentate; petals coherent below the middle, at length free; stamens 10, free, shortly exserted; anthers with a deciduous gland at the apex; ovary sessile, many-ovuled; style filiform; fruit straight, plano-compressed, thick and coriaceous, separating into valves, endocarp entire, breaking away from the exocarp; seeds transverse, orbicular, compressed, enclosed by thin pulp.

25. **Cyclicodiscus** Harms, Engl. & Prantl, Nat. Pflanzenfam. 3, 3: Nachtrag. 192 (1897), and Engl. Bot. Jahrb. 26: 256 (1899). *Cyrtoxiphus* Harms (1897). 1 sp., *C. gabunensis* (Taub.) Harms, W. trop. Africa. E. G. Bak., Legum. Trop. Afr. 3: 795; Hutch. & Dalz., Fl. W. Trop. Afr. ed. 2 (Keay), 1: 488.

Tree; leaves bipinnate; pinnae 1–2 pairs; leaflets alternate or subopposite, obliquely ovate or oblong; racemes spike-like, elongated, paniculate; bracts minute, deciduous; pedicels jointed at the apex, persistent as puberulous pegs on the axis; calyx-tube shortly campanulate, minutely 5-toothed; petals 5, free, valvate; stamens 10; anthers tipped by a small soon deciduous gland; disk conspicuous; ovary stipitate; ovules about 13; style short or elongated, filiform, stigma cupular; fruit large, 0·75 m. long, ensiform, densely covered with scales, with thickened margins; seeds thin, elongated, winged all around, wing unequally cordate at the base.

26. **Fillaeopsis** Harms, Engl. Bot. Jahrb. 26: 258, t. 6 (1899). 1 sp., *F. discophora* Harms, W. trop. Africa. Hutch. & Dalz., Fl. W. Trop. Afr. 1: 353; ed. 2 (Keay), 1: 490; E. G. Bak., Legum. Trop. Afr. 3: 796; Gilbert & Boutique, Fl. Congo Belge, 3: 216.

Tree; leaves bipinnate; pinnae opposite, 1–2 pairs; leaflets few, mostly alternate, elliptic, acuminate; spikes elongated, paniculate, terminal; flowers small; bracts very minute and scale-like; calyx minute, saucer-shaped, 5-toothed; petals 5, free, ovate, valvate; stamens 10, inserted at the base of the very thick cupular disk surrounding the ovary; anthers glandular at the apex, gland soon deciduous; ovary oblong, subsessile, style filiform, stigma cupular; ovules several; fruit large, broad, flat, sessile, oblong, very densely reticulate, transversely nerved, at length opening; seeds up to 10, flat, transverse, oblong, nearly surrounded by a membranous wing, attached to a slender funicle in the middle.

27. **Entada** Adans., Fam. 2: 318 (1763) (conserved name). *Pusaetha* O. Ktze. (1891). *Gigalobium* P.Br. (1756). *Perima* Raf. (1838). *Strepsilobus* Raf. (1838). *Adenopodia* C. Presl (1850). *Entadopsis* Britton (1928). 40 spp., tropics; type *E. gigas* (Linn.) Fawcett & Rendle. B.H. 1: 589; E.P. 3, 3: 122; E. G. Bak., Legum. Trop. Afr. 3: 784; Hutch. & Dalz., Fl. W. Trop. Afr. 1: 354, fig. 136; ed. 2 (Keay), 1: 490, fig. 156; Gilbert & Boutique, Fl. Congo Belge, 3: 220 (incl. *Entadopsis*, p. 203); Brenan, Fl. Trop. E. Afr. *Legum.-Mimosoid.* 9, figs. 2, 3 (1959).

Shrubs, often tall climbers, unarmed; leaves bipinnate, the end pair of pinnae sometimes changed into a leafless tendril; leaflets either fairly large and few or small and numerous; stipules small, setaceous; petiolar glands absent; spikes slender, solitary or paired, or sometimes short and arranged in a raceme-like panicle, the lower ones axillary; flowers bisexual or polygamous, 5-merous, sessile; calyx campanulate, shortly dentate; petals free or slightly united; stamens 10, free; anthers with a deciduous gland at the apex; ovary subsessile; ovules numerous; style filiform, stigma concave; fruit straight or curved, sometimes very large, plano-compressed, thin, coriaceous or woody, sutures thickened, persistent, continuous, valves breaking away from the sutures, transversely jointed, segments 1-seeded, endocarp persistent and separating from the exocarp; seed orbicular.

28. **Pseudoentada** Britton & Rose, N. Amer. Fl., 23: 191 (1928). 1 sp., *P. patens* (Hook. & Arn.) Britton & Rose, Nicaragua.

Climbing shrub, armed with numerous reflexed prickles; leaves bipinnate; pinnae 2–4 pairs; leaflets 3–6 pairs, broad; inflorescence paniculate, terminal, its branches spicate; calyx minute, 5-toothed; petals 5, connate at the base; stamens 10, exserted; fruit flat, valves separating from the sutures and transversely jointed, joints 1-seeded.

29. **Plathymenia** Benth., Hook. Journ. Bot. 4: 333 (1842) and 2: 134 in notes. *Platyhymenia* Walp. (1842). *Chrysoxylon* Casar. (1843). *Pirottantha* Speg. (1923). 3–4 spp., trop. South America; type *P. foliolosa* Benth., Brazil, Bolivia. B.H. 1: 589; E.P. 3, 3: 122; Burkart, Legum. Argent. ed. 2, 143.

Small trees or shrubs, unarmed; leaves bipinnate, leaflets and pinnae mostly in numerous pairs; petiolar and jugal glands very rarely absent; spikes cylindric, peduncles supra-axillary or the upper paniculate, with often a gland below the spike in the leaf-axil; flowers small, bisexual or polygamous, 5-merous; calyx campanulate, very shortly dentate; petals at length separate; stamens 10, free, shortly exserted; anthers crowned by a deciduous gland; ovary stipitate; ovules numerous; style filiform, stigma truncate, concave; fruit broadly linear, straight, plano-compressed, thin, exocarp continuous, 2-valved, endocarp falling away and jointed, joints 1-seeded and persistent around the seeds; seeds transverse, with a long funicle.

30. **Prosopis**[1] Linn., Mant. 1: 10 (1767). 45 spp., tropics and subtropics; type *P. cineraria* (Linn.) Druce (*P. spicigera* Linn.), Persia to India. B.H. 1: 591; E.P. 3, 3: 118; Burkart, Darwiniana, 4: 57, partly (1940); Gilbert & Boutique, Fl. Congo Belge, 3: 212; Brenan, Fl. Trop. E. Afr. *Legum.-Mimosoid.* 34, fig. 10 (1959).

Trees or shrubs, unarmed or armed with prickles or axillary spines or spinescent stipules; leaves bipinnate, pinnae 1–2 pairs or rarely in numerous pairs, leaflets few- or many-paired; stipules small or absent; petiolar and jugal glands small or obscure, rarely absent; flowers 5-merous, small, in axillary cylindric spikes or rarely globose heads; calyx shortly dentate; petals at first connate below the middle; stamens 10, free; anthers crowned with or rarely without a deciduous gland, ovary sessile or stipitate; ovules numerous; style filiform; fruit linear, thick and compressed to straight or falcate, not dehiscent; mesocarp thick and spongy, hard or rarely thin, endocarp cartilaginous or papery, continuous with the septa between the seeds or sometimes surrounding each seed; rarely the fruit more or less continuous within through the breakdown of the septa; seeds ovate, compressed.

31. **Gagnebina** Neck., Elem. 2: 458 (1790); DC. Mém. Lég. 423, t. 64. *Gagnebinia* Spreng. (1830). 2 spp., Mascarene Isls.; type *G. tamariscina* DC., Mauritius, B.H. 1: 591; E.P. 3, 3: 119.

[1] Synonyms of **Prosopis**: *Mitostax* Raf. (1838). *Neltuma* Raf. (1838). *Pleuromenes* Raf. (1838). *Algarobia* DC. (1839). *Lagonychium* Marsch.-Bieb. (1819). *Strombocarpus* Benth. & Hook. f. (1865). *Anonychium* Schweinf. (1868). *Strombocarpa* A. Gray (1845).

Unarmed trees; leaves bipinnate, leaflets small, like the pinnae in numerous pairs; stipules small, setaceous; petiolar glands large, jugal glands small; flowers 5-merous, small, in slender cylindric spikes, the peduncles in the upper axils fasciculate or subpaniculate; calyx shortly 5-toothed; petals free, valvate; stamens 10, free; anthers crowned with a gland; ovary stipitate; ovules numerous; style filiform, stigma obtuse; fruit oblong-linear, compressed, rather thick, not opening, sutures with a membranous wing, divided inside between the seeds by septa continuous with the endocarp; seeds transverse, compressed.

32. **Sopropis** Britton & Rose, N. Amer. Fl. 23: 182 (1928). 1 sp., *S. palmeri* (S. Wats.) Britton & Rose, Lower California.

Shrub or small tree armed with straight stipular spines, and with long shoots and short shoots; leaves bipinnate; pinnae 1 pair; leaflets alternate, oblong, small; flowers bisexual, in axillary spikes; calyx campanulate, 5-toothed; corolla sympetalous, shortly silky outside; stamens 10, free, long-exserted, anthers with a terminal deciduous gland; ovary many-ovuled, tomentose, stipitate; style filiform, loosely villous; stigma small, terminal; fruit linear, compressed, septate but not constricted between the seeds, mesocarp fibrous; seeds compressed.

33. **Stryphnodendron** Mart., Flora, 20, 2: Beibl. 117 (1837). *Folianthera* Raf. (1838). 15 spp., trop. America; type *S. barbadetimam* (Vell.) Mart., Brazil. B.H. 1: 590; E.P. 3, 3: 120.

Trees, often small, unarmed; leaves bipinnate, leaflets small, in numerous pairs often rather broad and barbate in the axils of the veins below; petiolar gland large, jugal glands few; flowers 5-merous, small, bisexual or subpolygamous; spikes cylindric, rather catkin-like, axillary, shortly pedunculate; calyx shortly dentate; petals connate to the middle or at length free; stamens 10, free; ovary shortly stipitate; ovules numerous; style filiform; fruit not opening, linear, compressed, thick, more or less divided within between the seeds by septa continuous with the endocarp, mesocarp fleshy and subpulpy; seeds transverse, funicle filiform.

34. **Tetrapleura** Benth., Hook. Journ. Bot. 4: 345 (1842). 1 sp., *T. tetraptera* (Schum. & Thonn.) Taub. (*T. thonningii* Benth.), W. & NE. trop. Africa. B.H. 1: 590; E.P. 3, 3: 120; Hutch. & Dalz., Fl. W. Trop. Afr. 1: 357, fig. 137; ed. 2 (Keay), 1: 493, fig. 157; Brenan, Fl. Trop. E. Afr. *Legum.-Mimosoid.* 32, fig. 8 (1959).

Tall unarmed tree; leaves opposite, bipinnate, leaflets small and numerous like the pinnae; flowers 5-merous, small, in axillary spike-like racemes; calyx campanulate, shortly dentate; petals free; stamens 10, free; anthers crowned by a globose gland; ovary sessile, ovules numerous; style filiform; fruit oblong, 4-sided, subfalcate, thick, not dehiscent, sutures rather acute, the sides produced into a thick longitudinal wing, divided within between the seeds by septa continuous with the endocarp; seeds transverse, ovate, compressed.

35. **Amblygonocarpus** Harms, Engl. & Prantl, Nat. Pflanzenfam. 3, 3, Nachtr. 191 (1897), and Engl. Bot. Jahrb. 26: 255, t. 5, A–D (1899). 1 sp., *A. andongensis* (Welw. ex Oliv.) Exell & Torre (*A. scheinfurthii* Harms), trop. Africa. Gilbert & Boutique, Fl. Congo Belge, 3: 217; Hutch. & Dalz., Fl. W. Trop. Afr. ed. 2 (Keay), 1: 492; Brenan, Fl. Trop. E. Afr. *Legum.-Mimosoid.* 32, fig. 9 (1959).

Tree or shrub; leaves bipinnate, pinnae 2–5-pairs, opposite or subopposite, without glands between; leaflets numerous, alternate, broadly obovate-elliptic, truncate or emarginate at the apex, glaucous below; racemes usually paired, dense and spike-like, slender, single or clustered amongst the leaves; calyx very short, 5-toothed; petals 5, valvate, oblong; stamens 10; anthers with a small deciduous gland at the apex; ovary shortly stipitate, style filiform, stigma minute; ovules several; fruit tetragonal, oblong, shortly stipitate, pericarp woody, shining, incompletely septate between the seeds; seeds smooth, slightly compressed, oval.

36. **Dichrostachys** Wight & Arnott, Prodr. 271 (1834) (conserved name). *Cailliea* Guill. & Perr. (1833). About 7 spp., trop. and S. Africa, Madagascar, trop. Asia, Australia; type *D. cinerea* (Linn.) Wight & Arnott, trop. and S. Africa, India, Malaya, and N. Australia. B.H. 1: 591; E.P. 3, 3: 118; Hutch. & Dalz., Fl. W. Trop. Afr. 1: 357, fig. 138; ed. 2 (Keay), 1: 494, fig. 158; Gilbert & Boutique, Fl. Congo Belge, 3: 198, t. 13.

Shrubs or small trees with spinescent branchlets, the flowering branchlets often fasciculate and axillary and covered with imbricate stipules; spikes axillary, cylindric, pedunculate, solitary or paired, often nodding, the upper flowers bisexual, yellow, the lower neuter, white, rose, or purplish; calyx shortly toothed; petals coherent below the middle; stamens in bisexual flowers 10, free; anthers crowned with a stipitate gland; ovary subsessile; ovules numerous; style filiform, stigma truncate; neuter flowers: staminodes 10, long and filiform; rudimentary ovary small; fruit linear, compressed, twisted, not dehiscent or the valves irregularly breaking away from the sutures, continuous inside; seeds obovate, compressed.

37. **Xylia** Benth., Hook. Journ. Bot. 4: 417 (1842). *Xylolobus* Kuntze (1903). About 12 spp., trop. Asia and Africa, Madagascar; type *X. xylocarpa* (Roxb.) Taub. (*X. dolabriformis* Benth.), India, Burma, Indo-China. B.H. 1: 594; E.P. 3, 3: 121; Gilbert & Boutique, Fl. Congo Belge, 3: 210, t. 15; Brenan, Fl. Trop. E. Afr. *Legum.-Mimosoid.* 29 (1959).

Tall unarmed trees with hard wood; leaves bipinnate, pinnae 1 pair, leaflets large, few-paired or smaller and with numerous pairs; petiolar gland elevated or obscure; stipules small, linear, deciduous; capitula globose, peduncles axillary, subfasciculate or racemose at the top of the branches; flowers 5-merous, sessile, mostly bisexual, small, pale green; calyx tubular-campanulate, dentate; petals slightly coherent at the base; stamens numerous, free, exserted; anthers ovate, glandular at the apex; pollen grains numerous; ovary sessile, many-ovuled; style filiform, stigma terminal, small; fruit sessile, broadly falcate, compressed, thick, woody, 2-valved, valves elastically recurved from the apex, septate within between the seeds; seeds transverse, obovate, compressed, funicle short, fleshy.

A valuable timber tree (*X. xylocarpa*) known as Ironwood.

38. **Delaportea** Thorel ex Gagnep., Lecomte Not. Syst. 2: 117 (1911). 1 sp., *D. armata* Thorel ex Gagnep., Indo-China. Gagnep., Fl. Indo-Ch. 2: 69, fig. 10.

Tree with spiny branches; leaves abruptly bipinnate; pinnae 3 pairs; leaflets 5–8 pairs, broadly oblong, nervose; heads globose, very small, pedunculate, arranged in panicles; peduncle involucrate in the middle; flowers polygamous, bracteolate, very minute, sessile; calyx campanulate, 5-toothed; corolla sympetalous, 5-lobed; stamens 30–15, free; anthers glandular at the apex; fruit many-seeded, continuous within, spirally twisted or falcate; seeds 14–10, compressed, ovate, funicle capillary, short.

39. **Neptunia** Lour., Fl. Cochinch. 653 (1790). *Hemidesmas* Rafin. (1838). *Hemidesma* Raf. (1838). 15 spp., trop. Asia and Australia, Africa, Madagascar, North and South America; type *N. oleracea* Lour., tropics. B.H. 1: 592; E.P. 3, 3: 118; Burkart, Legum. Argent. ed. 2: 125, fig. 18; Gilbert & Boutique, Fl. Congo Belge, 3: 198.

Diffuse undershrubs or perennial herbs, sometimes prostrate or floating; leaves bipinnate, leaflets small; stipules membranous, obliquely cordate; petiolar glands rare; flower-heads ovoid-globose; peduncles axillary, solitary; flowers 5-merous, some males and some neuter; calyx and corolla small; staminodes 10, linear, petaloid, and elongated; calyx campanulate, shortly dentate; petals coherent to the middle or free; stamens 10 or rarely 5, free; anthers crowned by a stipitate gland; ovary stipitate; ovules numerous; style filiform; stigma concave; fruit oblong, deflexed from the stipe, plano-compressed, 2-valved, subseptate between the seeds within or rarely 1-seeded; seeds transverse, ovate, compressed, funicle filiform.

40. **Piptadeniopsis** Burkart, Darwiniana, 6: 477, fig. 1 (1944). 1 sp., *P. lomentifera* Burkart, Paraguay.

Arborescent shrub; leaves bipinnate, pinnae 1 pair; leaflets obliquely oblong, about 3 pairs; stipules spinescent; inflorescence globose, axillary; flowers bisexual, uniform, sessile, calyx gamosepalous, 5-toothed; petals 5, free, valvate; stamens 10, free; anthers glandular at the apex; ovary several-ovuled, stipitate, stigma terminal; fruit linear, compressed, stipitate, indehiscent, transversely jointed, breaking up into 1-seeded segments; seeds compressed.

41. **Xerocladia** Harv., Harv. & Sond., Fl. Cap. 2: 278 (1861–2). 1 sp., *X. viridiramis* (Burch.) Taub. (*X. zeyheri* Harv.), S. Africa. B.H. 1: 591; E.P. 3, 3: 118; E. G. Bak., Legum. Trop. Afr. 3: 805.

Rigid undershrub, much branched, armed with recurved spinescent stipules; leaves few, bipinnate, pinnae 1–2 pairs, leaflets small, in few pairs; flowers 5-merous, sessile, small, in globose heads; calyx campanulate, shortly dentate; petals coherent below the middle; stamens 10, free; anthers crowned by a minute deciduous gland; ovary sessile, 1-ovuled; style filiform; fruit sessile, broadly falcate-ovate or semiorbicular, plano-compressed, laterally apiculate, not dehiscent, 1-seeded, wing-like on the lower suture; seed ovate, compressed.

Tribe 6. INGEAE

Leaves simply pinnate:
  Gynoecium composed of 2–6 free carpels with separate styles; flowers
    rather large, villous; leaves with glands on the petiole   42. **Affonsea**
  Gynoecium composed of 1 carpel; flowers various, spicate, racemose or
    capitate; leaf-rhachis often broadly winged between the leaflets
                                                                  43. **Inga**
Leaves bipinnate:
  Carpels 15–5, free; leaflets large, in few pairs; corolla tubular to above the
    middle; seeds transverse to the length of the fruit   44. **Archidendron**
  Carpel 1:
    Exocarp of the fruit not jointed between the seeds:
      Valves of the fruit not recurved elastically or fruit indehiscent:
        Fruits indehiscent or if dehiscent then straight or nearly so:
          Fruit septate between the seeds (but not jointed), thick, often fleshy:
            Fruit straight or at most falcate:
              Flowers in short terminal racemes   45. **Serianthes**
              Flowers pedicellate in globose heads   46. **Samanea**
            Fruit broadly circinate or kidney-shaped; flowers sessile in globose
              heads   47. **Enterolobium**
          Fruit not septate between the seeds, flat, thin, straight or slightly curved:
            Valves of the fruit not separating from the sutures:
              Heads or spikes borne on the leafy branches, often racemose or
                paniculate:
                Endocarp not articulated between the seeds:
                  Fruit indehiscent or dehiscing by both margins   48. **Albizia**
                  Fruit dehiscing by only one margin:

Pinnae 3–5 pairs; leaflets 4–6 pairs; central flower of umbel sterile
and larger   **49. Pseudosamanea**
Pinnae 2 pairs; leaflets 2–4 pairs; flowers all bisexual
                                                    50. Cedrelinga
Endocarp articulated between the seeds; petiolar glands absent;
jugal glands large   **51. Wallaceodendron**
Heads or spikes borne in fascicles on the older leafless part of the
branches or on the stem: pinnae 1 or rarely 2 pairs   52. **Zygia**
Valves of the fruit becoming detached as a whole on each side from the
persistent sutures; stipules mostly foliaceous; petiolar gland often
conspicuous; flowers in cylindric spikes or globose heads
                                                    53. **Lysiloma**
Fruit dehiscent, more or less contorted and sometimes torulose, the
endocarp often coloured within; petiolar and jugal glands usually
present; stipules sometimes indurated or spinescent; seeds arillate
                                                    54. Pithecellobium
Valves of the fruit separating elastically from each other from the apex
to the base and becoming recurved; stipules sometimes indurated or
spinescent; flowers in globose heads, the middle flower sometimes
different with an elongated tubular corolla   **55. Calliandra**
Exocarp of the fruit and sutures jointed between the seeds, the latter falling
away surrounded by the exocarp   **56. Cathormion**

42. **Affonsea** A. St. Hil., Voy. Diam. 1: 387 (1833). 7 spp., E. Brazil; type *A. juglandifolia* A. St. Hil. B.H. 1: 599; E.P. 3, 3: 100; Fl. Bras. 15, 2: 500.

Unarmed trees or shrubs; leaves once pinnate, petiole glandular and sometimes winged between the leaflets, leaflets rather large in few pairs; stipules persistent; spikes or racemes longer and loose at the base or interrupted; flowers large, villous; stamens very numerous; carpels villous, often 3, rarely 2, 5, or 6; flowers most bisexual; calyx amply tubular-campanulate, 5- or more-toothed; corolla tubular of 5 petals connate beyond the middle, valvate; filaments connate at the base into a tube; anthers small, verrucose, pollen clustered in each anther-loculus into 4 masses; ovules numerous; style filiform, stigma capitellate; fruit not seen.

43. **Inga** Scop., Introd. 298 (1777). *Amosa* Neck. (1790). *Torealia* Nor. (1790). *Ingaria* Raf. (1838). *Feuilleea* O. Ktze. (1891). 350 spp., trop. and subtrop. America; type *I. vera* (Linn.) Willd., W. Indies, trop. and subtrop. S. America. B.H. 1: 599; E.P. 3, 3: 100; Pittier, Contrib. U.S. Nat. Herb. 18: 173 (1916); Burkart, Legum. Argent. ed. 2, 104, fig. 9.

Unarmed trees or shrubs; leaves once pinnate, leaflets in few pairs, rather large, the petiole winged or not between the pairs of leaflets; stipules caducous and small, rarely larger and persistent; peduncles solitary or fasciculate, axillary or crowded into panicles; flowers rather large, often tomentose, in globose umbels, capitula, or in ovate, oblong, or rarely elongated spikes, 5–6-merous, mostly bisexual; calyx tubular or campanulate, dentate or shortly lobed; corolla tubular or funnel-shaped, the petals united to or above the middle; stamens numerous, long-exserted, connate at the base or higher into a tube; anthers small; ovary sessile, ovules numerous; style subulate; fruit linear, flat, 4-sided or subterete, coriaceous or subfleshy, scarcely opening, the sutures often thickened or dilated and sulcate; seeds covered with sweet pulp or rarely nude.

44. **Archidendron** F. Muell., Fragm. 5: 59 (1865). *Hansemannia* K. Schum. (1887). About 30 spp., Philippine Isls. and New Guinea to Solomon Isls. and

NE. Australia; type *A. vaillantii* F. Muell., Rockingham Bay, NE. Australia. B.H. 1: 1004; E.P. 3, 3: 102; de Wit, Conspectus of *Archidendron*, Bull. Bot. Gard. Buitenz. ser. 3, 17: 256 (1942), and Revision of *Archidendron*, Reinwardtia, 2: 69 (1952).

Trees; leaves bipinnate, pinnae in few pairs, leaflets large, in few pairs; flowers large, umbellate-capitate in the axils or cauliflorous; calyx large and tubular-campanulate, truncate; corolla tubular, the petals connate above the middle; stamens numerous, filaments connate at the base and shortly adnate to the corolla; anthers small; carpels 15–5, free, sessile, many-ovuled; styles filiform, stigmas terminal, capitellate; fruit hard and coriaceous, arcuate or variously twisted, sometimes moniliform, slowly opening, not pulpous; seeds transverse, funicle short.

45. **Serianthes** Benth., Hook. Lond. Journ. 3: 225 (1844). 10 spp., trop. Asia, Pacific Isls.; type *S. dilmyi* Fosberg (*S. grandiflora* (Wall.)). Benth., Malay Penins. and Archip. B.H. 1: 599; E.P. 3, 3: 103; Fosberg, Reinwardtia, 5: 293 (revision) (1960).

Unarmed trees; leaves large, bipinnate, pinnae and leaflets in many pairs; petiolar and jugal glands present; stipules obsolete; flowers 5-merous, mostly bisexual, large, tomentose, in short racemes at the apex of the shoots; calyx large and campanulate, shortly lobed or lobed to the middle; petals adnate at the base to the staminal tube; stamens very numerous, often about 500, connate at the base into a tube; anthers minute; ovary sessile, ovules numerous; style filiform; fruit ovate or oblong, straight or falcate, plano-compressed or undulate, woody, not dehiscent, transversely septate between the seeds; seeds transverse, compressed.

46. **Samanea** Merrill, Journ. Wash. Acad. Sci. 6: 46 (1916). 18 spp., *S. saman* (Jacq.) Merrill, N. South America, widely distributed in most tropical countries. Britton & Rose, N. Amer. Fl. 23: 34 (1928).

Large trees with expanded crown, unarmed; leaves bipinnate; pinnae 4–6 pairs, with glands between them; stipules lanceolate, deciduous; peduncles solitary or subfasciculate, elongated in the upper axils; flowers rose, pedicellate in globose heads, 5-merous, bisexual; calyx shortly lobed; petals connate to the middle; stamens numerous, connate at the base into a tube, long-exserted; anthers not glandular; ovary sessile; style filiform; ovules numerous; fruit straight or slightly curved, not dehiscent, thick and compressed, septate between the seeds, sutures thickened; seeds numerous, transverse, slightly compressed, shining, not arillate.

47. **Enterolobium** Mart., Flora, 20, 2: Beibl.: 117 (1837). 10 spp., West Indies and Cent. America to Argentina; type *E. timboüva* Mart., Brazil. B.H. 1: 598; E.P. 3, 3: 104; Burkart, Legum. Argent. ed. 2, 106, fig. 10.

Unarmed trees; leaves bipinnate, pinnae and leaflets in numerous pairs; stipules not conspicuous; peduncles solitary or subfasciculate, axillary or in a short raceme; flowers 5-merous, mostly bisexual, sessile in globose capitula; calyx shortly dentate; corolla rather funnel-shaped, the petals connate to the middle; stamens numerous, connate at the base into a tube; anthers small; ovary sessile, many-ovuled; style filiform; fruit broadly circinate or incurved-reniform, thick and compressed, hard, not dehiscent, mesocarp spongy, at length hardened, divided between the seeds by septa continuous with the endocarp; seeds transverse, compressed, funicle filiform.

48. **Albizia** Durazz., Mag. Tosc. 3: 11 (1772). *Sericandra* Raf. (1838). *Besenna* A. Rich. (1847). *Albizzia* auct. 145 spp., tropics and subtropics; type *A. julibrissin* Durazz., trop. Asia, widely cult. B.H. 1: 596; E.P. 3, 3: 106; E. G. Bak., Legum. Trop. Afr. 3: 855; Gilbert & Boutique, Fl. Congo Belge, 3: 170, with figs.; Burkart, Legum. Argent. ed. 2, 111, fig. 13; Hutch. & Dalz.,

Fl. W. Trop. Afr. ed. 2 (Keay), 1: 501; Brenan, Fl. Trop. E. Afr. *Legum.-Mimosoid.* 136, figs. 20–22 (1959).

Unarmed trees or shrubs; leaves bipinnate, leaflets small in numerous pairs or larger in few pairs; petiolar and jugal glands more or less conspicuous; stipules setaceous or obsolete, or rarely larger and membranous; peduncles axillary or paniculate; flowers in globose capitula or cylindric spikes; stamens elongated, often numerous, white, rose, or rarely purple; flowers often 5-merous, bisexual or rarely polygamous; calyx dentate or shortly lobed; corolla funnel-shaped, the petals often connate beyond the middle; stamens 10, connate at the base or higher into a tube, more or less long-exserted; anthers small; fruit broadly linear, straight, plano-compressed, thin, not dehiscent, or 2-valved, continuous inside, the valves neither elastic nor twisted; seeds ovate or orbicular, compressed, funicle filiform.

49. Pseudosamanea Harms, Notizbl. Bot. Gart. Berlin 11: 54 (1930). 1 sp., *P. guachapele* (H. B. & K.) Harms, Ecuador, Venezuela; (cult. Cameroons).

Unarmed tree; leaves bipinnate, pinnae 3–5 pairs, leaflets 4–6 pairs, obovate or oblong-subrhomboid; flowers umbellate, pedicels rather long; central flower in the middle of the umbel, sterile, much larger; calyx tubular-cup-shaped or narrowly campanulate, shortly lobulate; corolla exserted, tubular, 5–6-lobulate at the apex; stamens about 20–15, filaments united at the base into a short tube, long-exserted; ovary shortly stipitate; fruit broadly or narrowly linear, long-beaked at the apex, transversely striate-venose, the ventral margin slightly nervosely thickened, often more or less undulate, at length splitting open, the dorsal margin thicker and undivided, straight or nearly so, valves flat and thin; seeds 15–12, compressed, elliptic, with a very slender funicle.

50. Cedrelinga Duke, Arch. Jard. Bot. Rio de Janeiro, 3: 70, t. 6 (1922). 1 sp., *C. catenaeformis* (Ducke) Ducke, Brazil (Para Reg.).

Large tree (70 m.); leaves bipinnate; pinnae 2-pairs, opposite; leaflets opposite, 2–4 pairs, ovate-elliptic, closely reticulate; inflorescence terminal and in the upper axils; capitula few-flowered, paniculate; flowers sessile, bisexual; calyx 5-toothed; corolla deeply 5-lobed; stamens connate into a tube; fruit pendulous, much elongated, stipitate, very flat, slightly constricted between the joints, submembranous, reticulate, not dehiscent, joints several (up to 6), 1-seeded, breaking away when mature, thickened around the seeds but not hardened, sutures with elevated lines; seed in the middle of the joints, large, flat, sub-orbicular.

51. Wallaceodendron Koorders, Mededeel. van's Lands Plantentuin Buitenzorg, no. 19: 630 (1898). 1 sp., *W. celebicum* Koorders, Celebes, Philippine Isls. E.P. Nachtr. 2: 30.

A very tall unarmed tree; leaves bipinnate, pinnae in few pairs; petiolar glands absent; jugal glands large; racemes axillary, paired, erect, few-flowered; gland present below the racemes; flowers rather large; bracts very caducous; bracteoles absent; calyx minutely 5-toothed; petals 5–3, connate at the apex and callous, adnate at the base to the staminal tube; stamens numerous, included, connate at the base; anthers minute, versatile, not glandular; ovary sessile, many-ovuled; style filiform; fruit oblong, straight or slightly falcate, plano-compressed, thickly coriaceous, sutures thickened, persistent, continuous; exocarp continuous, 2-valved, endocarp breaking away and transversely jointed, joints 1-seeded, persistent around the seed; seeds without pulp, oblong, compressed, with a long filiform funicle.

52. Zygia Boehmer, Ludwig Defin. Gen. Pl. 72 (1760). *Pithecellobium* sect. *Caulanthon* Benth., partly. 15 spp., trop. America, Malaya, Australia; type *Z. latifolia* (Linn.) Fawc. & Rendle, West Indies to Brazil; Kostermans, Bull. Org. Sci. Res. Indones. 20: 24 (1954). Fawc. & Rendle, Fl. Jamaica, 4, 2: 149, fig. 46.

Unarmed trees; leaves bipinnate, pinnae 1-few pairs; rhachis very short; leaflets large, 1–5 pairs, glands present between the pinnae and between some of the leaflets; stipules sometimes present; flowers in heads or spikes at the nodes of the leafless branches; peduncles short, clustered; calyx campanulate; corolla tubular, toothed; stamens partly connate; fruits continuous within, flat-compressed, leathery, straight or curved, tardily dehiscent; seeds compressed.

53. Lysiloma Benth., Hook. Lond. Journ. 3: 82 (1844). *Lyriloma* Schlechtd. (1845). *Dugandia* Britton & Killip (1936). 50 spp., trop. America, West Indies; type[1] *L. schiedeana* Benth., Cent. America. B.H. 1: 596; E.P. 3, 3: 107.

Unarmed trees or shrubs; stipules mostly foliaceous; leaves bipinnate, leaflets small, in numerous pairs or rarely larger and few pairs; petiolar gland often conspicuous; peduncles axillary, solitary, fasciculate or shortly racemose; flowers 5-merous, in globose capitula or cylindric spikes; calyx shortly dentate; corolla funnel-shaped-campanulate; stamens numerous (30–12), exserted, connate at the base into a tube but free from the corolla; anthers minute; ovary sessile or shortly stipitate; ovules numerous; style subulate; fruit linear, often broad, straight or nearly so, plano-compressed, submembranous, valves breaking away from the persistent margins, continuous within; seeds transverse, ovate, compressed.

54. Pithecellobium[2] Mart., Hort. Reg. Monac. 188 (1829), and Flora, 20, 2, Beibl. 114 (1837) ('Pithecollobium') (conserved name). *Spiroloba* Raf. (1838). *Pithecolobium* Auct. About 100 spp., trop. and subtrop. America; type *P. unguis-cati* (Linn.) Benth., Florida to Venezuela. B.H. 1: 597, partly; E.P. 3, 3: 104; Merrill, Journ. Wash. Acad. Sci. 6: 43 (1916); Merrill, The system posit. of the Rain tree, Journ. Wash. Acad. Sci. 6: 42 (1916); Gilbert & Boutique, Fl. Congo Belge, 3: 190, with figs.; Burkart, Legum. Argent. ed. 2, 113, fig. 14; Kostermans, Asiatic, Malaysian, Australian, and Pacific species of *Mimosaceae* formerly included in *Pithecellobium* Mart. (1955) (see following notes).

Trees or shrubs, unarmed or the stipules spinescent or spines axillary; leaves bipinnate, leaflets small in many pairs or larger and in few pairs; petiolar and jugal glands rarely absent; stipules small or persistent, indurated or spinescent; peduncles solitary, subfasciculate or supraposed, axillary or racemose or fasciculate at the ends of the shoots; flowers in globose heads or rarely oblong or cylindric spikes, mostly white, 5–6-merous, bisexual or polygamous; calyx shortly toothed; petals united above the middle; stamens numerous to few, rather long-exserted, more or less united into a tube; anthers small; ovary sessile or stipitate, ovules numerous; style filiform; fruit compressed, circinate, variously twisted, falcate, or rarely nearly straight, 2-valved or rarely not opening or splitting into joints, valves often twisted but not elastically revolute; seeds ovate or orbicular, compressed, funicle filiform or expanded into a fleshy aril.

In 1955 Kostermans published an account of the Old World genera and species formerly included in *Pithecellobium* (*Pithecolobium*) Mart., recognizing in that region no fewer than 10 genera (**Pithecellobium**, *sensu stricto*, introduced). For those who prefer this splitting up of the genus here is his key in condensed form together with the type species of each. Pending a comprehensive revision of this group on a world basis, I have given above descriptions only of those genera generally accepted previous to Kostermans's work. The genus requires a monograph on a world basis.

[1] Not *L. bahamensis* Benth. as stated by Britton & Rose (Fl. N. Amer.) because the fruit of that species was unknown to Bentham, who says: 'The generic character lies in the combination of the pod of a *Mimosa* with the monadelphous stamens of the *Ingoid* genera.'

[2] Other synonyms of **Pithecellobium**: *Jupunba, Punjuba, Cojoba, Ebenopsis, Painteria, Chloroleucon, Havardia, Pseudalbizzia,* Britton & Rose (1926). *Siderocarpus* Small (1901), not Pierre (1888). *Abarema* Pittier (1927). *Macrosamanea, Klugiodendron, Arthrosamanea,* Britton & Rose (1936). *Marmaroxylon* Killip (1940). *Ortholobium* Gagnep. (1952).

Kostermans's key to Old World genera: **1.** Seeds arillate; stipular thorns present . . . **Pithecello-bium. 1a.** Seeds without arils; thorny or spineless trees: **2.** Rachilla bearing only 1 leaflet . . . **Morolobium** (1 sp., *M. monopterum* Kostermans); **2a.** Rachilla bearing one to several pairs of leaflets: **3.** Pod provided with pulp . . . **Parasamanea** (1 sp., *P. landakensis* Kostermans). **3a.** Pod without pulp: **4.** Pod not dehiscent: **5.** Pod straight or falcate, moniliform, breaking at the joints; trees with thorns . . . **Cathormion** (see descr. below); **5a.** Pod straight, not moniliform, strap-shaped, breaking irregularly; spineless trees . . . **Serialbizzia** (2 spp., type *S. acle* (Blanco) Koster-mans); **5b.** Pod circinate in one plane, breaking irregularly; spineless trees . . . **Parenterolobium** (1 sp., *P. rosulatum* Kostermans). **4b.** Pod dehiscent: **6.** Stipular spines present . . . **Painteria** Britt. & Rose; **6a.** Spineless trees: **7.** Seeds cylindrical, truncate; pod dehiscent along both sutures, valves hardly or not twisted after dehiscence . . . **Cylindrolelupha** (3 spp., type *C. bubalina* (Jack) Kostermans. **7a.** Seeds biconvex, compressed, not truncate; pod dehiscent along both or only along the ventral suture: **8.** Inflorescence on older branches (below the leaves) or on the trunk. . . . **Zygia** (see descr. above); **8a.** Inflorescence terminal or axillary: **9.** Pod straight or slightly falcate, dehiscent along both sutures; seeds large; valves not twisted after dehiscence . . . **Paralbizzia** (3 spp., type *P. turgida* (Merrill) Kostermans). **9a.** Pod twisted into a loose or flattened, often circular spiral, dehiscent along the ventral suture (only tardily and rarely also a little at one end of dorsal suture); valves twisted after dehiscence . . . **Abarema** Pittier.

55. Calliandra Benth., Hook. Journ. Bot. 2: 138 (1840) (conserved name). *Anneslia* Salisb. (1807). *Annesleya* G. Don (1832). *Celebia Casar.* (1845). *Codonandra* Karst. (1862). *Anneslea* Auth. 200 spp., trop. and subtrop. America, Madagascar, W. trop. Africa, India; type *C. inermis* (Linn.) Druce (*C. grandiflora* (L'Hérit.) Benth.), trop. America. B.H. 1: 596; E.P. 3, 3: 107; Burkart, Legum. Argent. ed. 2: 109, fig. 12.

Shrubs or small trees, usually unarmed; leaves bipinnate, leaflets thin or coriaceous and shining, small and numerous or larger and from few pairs to one, sometimes the single pair of pinnae 3-foliolate, 2–3-nerved or pinnately nerved; stipules often persistent, membranous, foliaceous or hardened, sometimes spinescent, rarely absent; flowers in globose capitula, these axillary or in terminal racemes; flowers 6–5-merous, polygamous, often with long stamens, red, white, and showy, the middle flowers sometimes polymorphic with an elong-ated tubular corolla; calyx dentate or rarely deeply divided; petals united to the middle; stamens numerous (up to 100), more or less united into a tube and long-exserted; anthers mostly glandular-hairy; ovary sessile, ovules numerous; style filiform; fruit linear, straight or nearly so, often narrowed to the base, plano-compressed, margins thickened, 2-valved, valves elastically opening from the apex to base, continuous inside; seeds obovate or orbicu-lar, compressed; funicle often short.

56. Cathormion Hassk., Retzia 1: 231 (1855). 10 spp., trop. America, trop. Africa, Malay Archip., N. Australia; type *C. moniliforme* (DC.) Merrill, Timor. Merrill, Journ. Wash. Acad. Sci. 6: 43 (1916); Kostermans, Bull. Org. Sci. Res. Indones. no. 20: 11 (1954); Hutch. & Dalz., Fl. W. Trop. Afr. ed. 2 (Keay), 1: 504; Brenan, Fl. Trop. E. Afr. *Legum.-Mimosoid.* 166, fig. 23 (1959).

Trees; leaves bipinnate; pinnae 2-pairs, opposite; leaflets several pairs; flower-heads axillary; calyx tubular, dentate; petals connate below; stamens numerous to 10, filaments connate at the base; ovary with several ovules, slightly stipitate; style slender; fruit com-pressed, linear-oblong, sometimes at length subcochleate, margins sinuate, much constricted between the seeds, at length breaking up into somewhat rounded joints; seeds rounded, much compressed.

29. FABACEAE

Lindl., Nat. Syst. ed. 2, 148 (1836) (*Papilionaceae* Giseke,
Praelect. Ord. Nat. Pl. 415 (1792))

Trees, shrubs, or herbs, sometimes climbing or decumbent, rarely branches transformed into cladodes with scale-like leaves. Leaves alternate or rarely opposite, rarely simple, mostly compound, impari- or paripinnate, trifoliolate, digitate, or unifoliolate, rarely reduced to scales; stipules mostly present, free or adnate to the petiole; stipels present or absent. Flowers solitary to race-mose, paniculate, or capitate, rarely spicate, zygomorphic (except tribe *Cadieae*), mostly bisexual, very rarely cleistogamous. Calyx tubular, regularly 5-toothed (rarely 4-) or lobed, bilabiate or spathaceous, lobes or teeth imbri-cate or valvate. Petals (very rarely absent) 5, imbricate, free or rarely partially connivent; adaxial petal (vexillum or standard) outermost, the two lateral (alae or wings) more or less parallel with each other, the lower two innermost and forming the keel (carina). Stamens inserted with the petals, often 10, monadelphous or diadelphous, rarely all quite free; often the adaxial (vexil-lary) filament free or partly united with the others; free part of filaments usually filiform, rarely swollen; anthers 2-locular, uniform or more rarely dimorphic and then alternately basifixed and dorsifixed, usually opening by a slit lengthwise. Disk rarely present. Ovary of 1 carpel, superior, 1-locular or sometimes transversely, very rarely longitudinally, septate; ovules numerous to one, inserted on the adaxial suture. Fruit dehiscent by one or both sutures, or indehiscent, sometimes winged, sometimes jointed and breaking up into 1-seeded segments; seeds without or with very scanty endosperm, sometimes stro-phiolate; radicle sometimes inflexed. Type genus *Vicia* Linn. (*Faba* P. Miller).

Genera 482; species about 12,000.

DISTRIBUTION. World-wide, the more primitive woody genera mostly in the southern hemisphere and in the tropics, the more advanced and herbaceous genera in temperate regions; very numerous in Mediterranean countries.

CLASSIFICATION. Benth. & Hook. f., Gen. Pl. 1: 465 (1865); Taubert, Engl. & Prantl, Nat. Pflanzenfam. 3, 3: 184 (1891) (both in *Leguminosae*); Rydberg, *Fabaceae*, N. Amer. Fl. 24: 1–462 (1919–29); Genera of N. Amer. *Fabaceae*, i–iv, Amer. Journ. Bot. 10: 485 (1923) et seq.; Gams in Hegi, Ill. Fl. Mitt.-Eur. 4, 3 (1923); E. G. Bak., Legum. Trop. Afr. (1926).

ANATOMY. Sol. 253; M.C. 1: 502. POLLEN. Erdt. 229.

ADDITIONAL LITERATURE. Benth., Synopsis of *Dalbergieae*, Journ. Linn. Soc. 4: Suppl. (1860); Mönch, Über Griffel und Narbe einiger *Papilionaceae*, Beih. Bot. Centralbl. 27, 1: 83 (1911); Moore, Vascular anatomy of flower in papilionaceous *Legum.*, Amer. Journ. Bot. 23: 279, 349 (1936); Burkart, Legum.-Hedisareas Repub. Argentina, Darwinia, 3: 117 (1939); Pittier, Legum. de Venezuela, 1: Papilionaceas (1944); Dormer, Veg. morph. as guide to classification of *Papilionatae*, New Phytol. 45: 145 (1946); Ducke, *Legum.* Amaz. Brasil., Bol. Técn. Inst. Agron. do Norte no. 18: 146 (1949); Burkart, *Legum.* Argent. ed. 2, 1–569, numerous figs. and plates of seeds (1952); J. Léonard, Mém. Acad. Roy. Belg. Cl. Sci. 30, 2 (1957); van Steenis (&c.), Preliminary revisions of some genera of Malaysian *Papilionaceae*, Rein-wardtia, 5: 419 (1961); loc. cit. 6: 85 (1961).

Characters occurring in relatively few Genera and Species. Aquatic or semi-aquatic habit in *Sesbania* spp.; **branches** flattened in *Templetonia sulcata*, and leaves reduced to scales in *Brachysema* and *Jacksonia*; densely spiny cushion-plants, *Erinacea*; shrubs with spiny branches in *Gourliea*, *Genista* spp., *Ulex*,

Ononis spp., *Nepa*; indumentum of T-shaped hairs in tribe *Indigofereae*, of stellate hairs in *Erythrina* spp.; **leaves** opposite or whorled in some Australian *Podalyrieae, Hebestigma, Eutaxia, Platymiscium, Platylobium* spp., *Dipteryx* spp.; digitate leaves characteristic of all genera of tribes *Lotononideae, Crotalarieae, Lupineae, Laburneae, Genisteae, Cytiseae,* and in some genera of *Trifolieae, Indigofereae, Astragaleae, Stylosantheae, Cajaneae,* and *Sophoreae*; simple or unifoliolate also occur in many of the tribes and very rarely in *Tephrosia*; reduced to leaf-like phyllodes in *Papilionopsis*; with strong 3–5 longitudinal parallel nerves in *Liparia,* and *Dolichos* spp.; **leaf-rhachis** ending in a bristle in tribes *Abreae, Ammodendron, Notodon, Bembicidium,* and *Halimodendron,* in a tendril or barren point in most of the tribe *Vicieae*; Holly-like (prickly) leaves in *Podolobium* spp., *Gastrolobium, Platylobium* spp., *Hovea* spp., *Chorizema* spp., *Mirbelia* spp.; perfoliate leaves in *Pericaulon perfoliatum* Raf.; peltate unifoliolate leaves in *Indigofera peltata* Gillett; leaflets often spinescent at the tip in *Pictetia*; glandular-punctate or gland-dotted leaves occur in tribes *Cajaneae, Psoraleae, Daleae,* in *Adenodolichos* in tribe *Phaseoleae,* in *Harpalyce* in tribe *Brongniartieae* and *Schefflerodendron* and *Terua* in tribe *Millettieae*; **stipules** spiny in *Belairia*; partially united and leaf-opposed in *Anagyris, Astrolobium,* and *Piptanthus*; large and foliaceous in *Brongniartia* spp.; united at the base with the leaf into a whorl or sheath in *Anarthrophyllum*; axis of the **inflorescence** with swollen tubercle-like nodes at the insertion of the pedicels in tribes *Diocleae, Galactieae,* and in many *Phaseoleae*; flowers in terminal clusters with very villous bracts in *Lathyriogyne* and *Liparia*; inflorescence cymose in *Dalbergia* and a few related genera; **bracts** enlarged and membranous and enclosing the flower and fruit in *Phylacium*; hooked in *Mecopus*; **bracteoles** large and enclosing the flower-bud in *Dalhousieae* (as in many *Caesalpiniaceae*); **flowers** dimorphic, some (often solitary or crowded in the leaf-axils) apetalous with the genitalia much reduced but fertile, others (often racemose or spicate) perfect but often sterile observed in *Ononis, Trifolium, Parochetus, Lespedeza, Vicia, Lathyrus, Clitoria, Cologania, Amphicarpa, Glycine, Galactia, Voandzeia*; cleistogamous flowers occur in *Neocracca, Lupiniphyllum,* and *Robinia* sp.; calyx remarkable in *Monopteryx,* 2-lobed, upper lobe large and enclosing the petals and genitalia, lower very small and pointed; enlarged and striate in fruit resembling a Dipterocarp in *Apoplanesia*; inflated in fruit in *Erinacea* and *Astragalus* spp., spathaceous in *Fissicalyx* and *Spartium*; upper two calyx-lobes large, lateral very small, lower medium-sized in *Amicia*; long-tubular in *Barbieria*; single petal (the vexillum) present in *Amorpha, Swartzia* spp.; claws of petals more or less adnate to the staminal tube in *Genisteae,* in *Phyllota* (tribe *Podalyrieae*), *Trifolium,* and *Dalea*; petals very unequal in size (length), either the vexillum or the keel-petals much longer than the wings in tribe *Erythrineae*; petals absent from *Paryella, Cordyla, Mildbraedodendron,* and *Swartzia* spp.; upper margin of wing-petals fringed with stipitate glands in *Petaladenium*; keel-petals spirally twisted in *Bolusia* and some genera of *Phaseoleae*; **stamens** numerous in many of tribe *Swartzieae*; reduced to 9 (adaxial missing) in *Abrus* and a few *Psoraleae*; reduced to 5 in *Petalostemon* and *Kuhnistera*; only 5 fertile in *Biserrula* and *Robynsiophyton*; free or nearly free stamens in tribes *Cadieae, Swartzieae, Sophoreae, Podalyrieae,* and *Adesmieae,* these probably representing the most primitive groups; monadelphous stamens united into a single closed tube (not a split sheath) characteristic of tribes *Genisteae, Laburneae, Lupineae, Cytiseae, Diocleae, Stylosantheae, Galegeae*, and of some genera of *Robinieae, Indigofereae* (*Cyamopsis* only), and *Desmodieae*; dimorphic anthers occur in all genera of the following tribes: *Borbonieae, Crotalarieae, Lupineae, Laburneae, Genisteae, Cytiseae, Stylosantheae*, and *Ononideae*; they also occur in some genera of *Podalyrieae, Liparieae, Bossieae, Lotononideae, Indigofereae, Brongniartieae, Glycineae, Erythrineae*, and *Phaseoleae*; in all other tribes the anthers are uniform in size and shape; anther-connective with a gland or mucro at the apex in tribes *Indigofereae, Galegeae*, and *Brongniartieae*, and in some *Daleae*; with a gland at the base of alternate anthers in *Haydonia*; free parts of the filaments swollen towards the apex in tribe *Loteae, Coronilleae, Ononideae*, and in some genera of *Trifolieae, Vicieae*, and *Desmodieae*; anthers opening by terminal pores in *Fissicalyx*; **ovary** and fruit divided longitudinally by a false septum in *Mirbelia* (*Podalyrieae*), and in part of tribe *Astragaleae*; a bearded **style**, probably a relatively advanced character concerned with pollen-presentation, occurs in all of tribe *Crotalarieae, Barbierieae, Coluteae*, many *Phaseoleae* (sometimes only around the stigma), and in some genera of *Psoraleae, Tephrosieae, Robinieae, Corynelleae, Sesbanieae, Carmichaelieae, Vicieae*, and *Glycineae*; style circinately coiled in bud in *Lennea*; **fruits** maturing below the soil in *Neocollettia, Arachis, Kerstingiella, Voandzeia*, and *Galactia canescens* Benth.; also those of cleistogamous flowers in *Lupiniphyllum*; transversely septate and breaking up into 1-seeded segments in tribes *Coronilleae, Hedysareae, Aeschynomeneae, Adesmieae, Stylosantheae*, and *Desmodieae*; old fruit persisting around the seedling in *Onobrychis caputgalli* Lamk.; a few tribes have exclusively indehiscent fruits; these are *Psoraleae, Daleae, Diphyseae, Stylosantheae, Dalbergieae, Pterocarpeae, Lonchocarpeae*, and *Geoffraeae*; fruits enclosed by the calyx in tribe *Daleae*; bladder-like in tribes *Coluteae* and *Diphyseae*; drupaceous in tribe *Geoffraeae*; divided into superposed disks in *Medicago, Discolobium*; very deeply indented in *Hippocrepis*; circinate-involute in *Scorpiurus*; densely glandular in *Adenocarpus*; 4-winged in *Psophocarpus*; winged in *Amphimas, Bowdichia, Sakomala, Myrocarpus, Ammodendron, Ateleia, Ferreira, Luetzelbergia, Myrospermum* and *Myroxylon* (below the seed), *Platylobium*; top of the fruit extended into a wing in *Nissolia*; along the upper suture in *Platylobium*; **seeds** quadrate and constricted in the middle in *Sphinctospermum*.

SPOTTING TRIBAL CHARACTERS

Certain tribes may be readily recognized by some outstanding character, common more or less to all or many of the genera contained in them and easily detected in the field or herbarium. The following notes may help towards their identification, but should not be entirely relied upon:

Indumentum mostly of medifixed (T-shaped hairs): *Indigofereae, Astragaleae*.
Leaves primitively simple (not unifoliolate): *Borbonieae, Liparieae, Bossieae, Crotalarieae* (part).
Leaves gland-dotted or glandular-punctate: *Daleae, Psoraleae, Cajaneae*,

Phaseoleae (part), *Brongniartieae* (part), *Pterocarpeae* (part), *Aeschyno-meneae*(*Poiretia*), *Indigofereae* (small part), *Millettieae* (small part), *Tephro-sieae* (*Tephrosia* spp.).

Leaves digitate (often trifoliolately so, very rarely 1-foliolate); *Podalyrieae*, *Lotononideae*, *Cytiseae*, *Genisteae*, *Laburneae*, *Lupineae*, and the following in part: *Crotalarieae*, *Psoraleae*, *Desmodieae*, *Trifolieae*, *Indigofereae*, *Cajaneae*, *Tephrosieae*, *Sophoreae* (*Camoensia*).

Leaves stipellate: *Glycineae*, *Galactieae*.

Leaves reduced to scales: *Carmichaelieae* (part), *Coluteae* (*Eremosparton*), *Pterocarpeae* (*Ramorinoa*).

Leaf-rhachis ending in a tendril or barren tip: *Vicieae*, *Abreae*.

Leaflets lobed: *Phaseoleae* (part).

Leaflets toothed: *Trifolieae*, *Indigofera* (small part).

Stipules mostly adnate to the petiole: *Trifolieae*; absent: *Borbonieae*, *Lipari-eae*, *Lotononideae* (part).

Inflorescence with swollen nodes at the insertion of the pedicels: *Galactieae*, *Erythrineae*, *Phaseoleae* (part), *Diocleae*.

Flowers actinomorphic: *Cadieae*.

Calyx entire and closed in bud and then split irregularly: *Swartzieae*.

Vexillum more or less hairy outside: *Tephrosieae* (mostly).

Stamens numerous: *Swartzieae*.

Stamens free except at the very base: *Cadieae*, *Sophoreae*, *Swartzieae*, *Adesmieae*, *Psoraleae* (*Paryella*).

Stamens monadelphous in a more or less *closed tube*; *Ononideae*, *Robinieae*, *Millettieae*, *Cytiseae*, *Genisteae*, *Lupineae*, *Diocleae*, *Lonchocarpeae* (part), *Borbonieae* (*Euchlora*), *Hedysareae* (*Onobrychis*), *Galegeae*, *Tephrosieae* (part), *Indigofereae* (*Cyamopsis*), *Astragaleae* (very rare).

Anthers gland-tipped: *Indigofereae* (part), *Daleae* (part).

Free part of all or alternate filaments dilated or expanded upwards: *Coronil-leae*, *Loteae* (part), *Tephrosieae* (*Mundulea*), *Trifolieae* (*Trifolium*).

Anthers dimorphic and all fertile: *Ononideae*, *Laburneae*, *Cytiseae*, *Lupineae*, *Genisteae*, *Crotalarieae*, *Borbonieae*, *Liparieae* (part), *Bossieae* (part), *Phaseoleae* (part), *Brongniartieae* (part), *Erythrineae* (*Mucuna* only), *Glyci-neae*(*Teramnus*), *Lotononideae* (part), *Stylosantheae*(part), *Aeschynomeneae* (part), *Millettieae* (*Poecilanthe*).

Ovary 1-ovuled and hence fruit 1-seeded: *Lespedezieae*, *Psoraleae* (mostly), *Sophoreae* (small part), *Hedysareae* (small part), *Desmodieae* (rare).

Fruits inflated and bladder-like or markedly turgid: *Coluteae*, *Crotalarieae*, *Diphyseae*, *Astragaleae* (part), *Pseudarthrieae* (*Pycnospora*).

Fruits longitudinally septate within by the intrusion of the seed-bearing suture: *Astragaleae* (part), *Podalyrieae* (*Mirbelia*).

Fruits transversely septate and breaking up when ripe into 1-seeded joints: *Hedysareae*, *Aeschynomeneae*, *Desmodieae*, *Adesmieae*.

Fruits indehiscent and orbicular to ovate or samara-like, winged or keeled, with 1 or 2 seeds in the middle: *Pterocarpeae*, *Dalbergieae*.

Radicle inflexed: *Swartzieae*, *Podalyrieae*; twice folded: *Carmichaelieae*.

Economic Properties. Very many valuable commodities, the most important being: Peas, *Pisum sativum* Linn.; Broad Bean, *Vicia faba* Linn.; Ground

Nut, *Arachis hypogaea* Linn.; Peanut, *Voandzeia subterranea*; Soy Bean, *Glycine max* Merr.; Lentils, *Lens culinaris* Medic.; Clover, *Trifolium pratense* Linn. and *T. repens* Linn.; Tagasaste, *Cytisus palmensis* Christ (Canary Isls.); Broom Tops, *Cytisus scoparius* Linn.; Calabar Bean, *Physostigma venenosum* Balf. (W. Africa); Tonka Bean, also known as Angostura and Para Bean, *Dipteryx odorata* Willd. (South America); Liquorice Root, *Glycyrrhiza glabra* Linn. (Europe and Asia); Indigo Dyes, *Indigofera tinctoria* Linn., &c.; Gum Tragacanth, *Astragalus gummifer* Lab., &c. (Orient); Tolu Balsam, *Myroxylon balsamum* (Linn.) Harms (South America); Balsam of Peru, *Myroxylon pereirae* (Royle) Klotzsch (Peru); Kino, *Pterocarpus marsupium* Roxb. (S. India, Ceylon); Derris Powder, Rotenone, *Derris* and *Lonchocarpus* spp. Many valuable timbers, including American Rosewood *Dalbergia* spp.; Indian Rosewood, *D. latifolia* Roxb.; Bastard Teak, *Pterocarpus marsupium* Roxb. (India); Camwood, *Baphia nitida* Lodd. (W. Africa); Moreton Bay Chestnut, *Castanospermum australe* A. Cunn. (Australia), and many others of less importance, references to which are given at the end of the generic descriptions.

Phylogeny and Morphology. Bentham said of the aggregate family *Leguminosae* in the *Genera Plantarum* (1: 435, translation):

> A vast family (Ordo), very natural, divided into three subfamilies (Subordines) by sufficiently well defined characters. Amongst so many species there are very few which are ambiguous between the *Papilionaceae* and *Caesalpiniaceae*, and between the latter and the *Mimosaceae*. However, *the boundaries between the tribes and subtribes are very uncertain.*
>
> The direction of the radicle, the character of the cotyledons during germination, the cohesion ('adhesio') of the filaments, and the arrangement of the leaflets are very constant in many genera, but variable in others. For this reason, characters which distinguish the divisions of the family are frequently liable to exceptions. We have sought for better ones in vain.

Though *Fabaceae* undoubtedly represent a climax group derived from the *Rosales*, their more primitive tribes are as equally near to *Rosaceae* as are the generally more primitive *Caesalpiniaceae* and *Mimosaceae*. The floral structure of some members of those tribes which have 10 stamens with free filaments comes very close to that of certain *Rosaceae*, such as tribe *Chrysobalaneae*.

Below is shown the tribal arrangement of subfamily *Papilionaceae* (here treated as a family, *Fabaceae*), as set out in Bentham & Hooker's *Genera Plantarum*, with a translation of the Latin text. It will be observed that *Podalyrieae*, *Sophoreae*, and *Swartzieae* are widely separated, though closely related and perhaps representing the most primitive tribes because of their *free stamens* and other associated characters. These tribes are therefore given priority of place in our phylogenetic arrangement. It may also be seen on comparing the descriptions that the differences between some of the tribes are sometimes rather trivial, and they have largely broken down owing to the discovery of so many new genera and the recognition of numerous segregates out of the broader concepts of Bentham & Hooker and other of the older botanists.

Bentham & Hooker's conspectus of tribes of suborder
Papilionaceae, neglecting exceptions (translation)

    I. **Podalyrieae.** Shrubs, rarely herbs. Leaves simple or digitately compound. Stamens 10, free.

II. **Genisteae.** Shrubs or herbs. Leaves simple or digitately compound; leaflets entire; racemes terminal or leaf-opposed, or flowers solitary or subfasciculate in the leaf-axils. Stamens 10, monadelphous, rarely diadelphous.

III. **Trifolieae.** Herbs, very rarely fruticose. Leaves pinnately, rarely digitately, 3-foliolate, the nerves of the leaflets often running out into teeth; flowers solitary or race-mose, peduncles axillary, rarely crowded in a terminal raceme. Stamens 10, diadelphous or monadelphous.

IV. **Loteae.** Herbs or shrublets. Leaves pinnately 3–more-foliolate, leaflets entire. Flowers capitate or umbellate, rarely solitary, peduncles axillary or crowded at the ends of the branches. Stamens 10, diadelphous or monadelphous; filaments alternately often dilated at the apex.

V. **Galegeae.** Herbs, not climbing, erect shrubs, rarely trees or tall climbing shrubs. Leaves pinnately 5–more rarely 3–1-foliolate, leaflets often entire; petiole not tendriliform. Flowers solitary, racemose, or paniculate. Stamens 10, diadelphous, or if monadelphous vexillary stamen often free at the base. Legume 2-valved, or if rarely indehiscent small 1–2-seeded or membranous-inflated.

VI. **Hedysareae.** Habit of *Loteae*, *Galegeae*, or *Phaseoleae*. Legume jointed.

VII. **Vicieae.** Herbs, leaves abruptly pinnate, petiole (rhachis) ending in a bristle or tendril; leaflets often denticulate at the apex. Stamens and legume as in *Phaseoleae*.

VIII. **Phaseoleae.** Climbing herbs or rarely erect or shrubby, very rarely trees. Leaves pin-nately, very rarely subdigitately, 3-foliolate, rarely 1–5–7-foliolate, leaflets entire or lobed, mostly stipellate; flowers racemose or fasciculate; peduncles often axillary. Stamens diadelphous or submonadelphous. Legume 2-valved.

IX. **Dalbergieae.** Trees or tall shrubs or high climbers. Leaves pinnately 5–more-foliolate, very rarely 3–1-foliolate. Inflorescence various, often paniculate or fasciculate. Stamens monadelphous or diadelphous. Legume exserted, indehiscent, mem-branous, coriaceous, woody or drupaceous.

X. **Sophoreae.** Trees or tall shrubs or tall climbers, very rarely small shrubs or sub-herbaceous. Leaves pinnately 5- or more-foliolate, or large and 1-foliolate, rarely 3-foliolate. Stamens 10, free.

XI. **Swartzieae.** Trees or tall shrubs. Leaves pinnately 5–more-, rarely 3–1-, foliolate. Calyx always (rarely in *Sophoreae*) entire before flowering, closed. Stamens numer-ous, rarely sub-10, free.

Since Bentham published the above conspectus in the year 1862, the num-ber of genera has nearly doubled and the number of 'ambiguous' characters correspondingly increased. In consequence I found it quite impossible to key out satisfactorily these comparatively few tribes as defined by Bentham and later by Taubert (Engler, *Nat. Pflanzenfamilien*). In the present work, there-fore, I have considered it better, in order to reduce the number of exceptions, to treat most of Bentham's *subtribes* as *tribes*. Even so it has not been found possible to confine all of these smaller concepts to a single entry in the key to tribes, for only 14 of the 50 occupy one place, 18 appear twice over, 12 three times, and 5 tribes as many as four times, because of exceptional combina-tions of characters.

It may be observed in the key to tribes on p. 304 that the two main types of compound leaves, *pinnate* and *digitate*, have been used frequently, and the form of the anthers, either *uniform* or *dimorphic*, has been stressed, being con-stant for some tribes and perhaps concerned with pollination; also whether the free parts of the filaments are *filiform* or *swollen*. The *dehiscence* or *inde-hiscence* of fruits is also of great importance, though liable in some cases to produce a measure of artificiality. Then some tribes or part of them are characterized among other features by having *gland-dotted* or *pellucid-glandular* leaves, and finally the presence or absence of *stipels* (used in Taubert's key especially, and occasionally by Bentham) has proved of considerable importance, though sometimes of not more than generic value.

The linear arrangement of the tribes follows approximately that of the key and perhaps results in a more phylogenetic scheme than hitherto published. The HEDYSAREAE (*sensu stricto*) and DESMODIEAE, with their transversely septate and jointed pods, occupy the highest place, other things combined these tribes seeming to represent the most highly evolved of the *Fabaceae*, and farthest removed phylogenetically from the more primitive groups shown at the beginning of the key.

KEY TO TRIBES

Filaments all free from one another from the base to apex, rarely shortly and more or less equally connate only at the base; anthers uniform in size and shape or very rarely dimorphic (to p. 305):
Corolla actinomorphic and not clearly papilionaceous, i.e. the petals (always present) equal in size and shape or nearly so; leaves sometimes glandular below; anthers uniform   1. CADIEAE
Corolla distinctly zygomorphic and papilionaceous, i.e. composed of vexillum, wings, and keel-petals, or sometimes petals absent or reduced to 1 adaxial:
Fruits when ripe neither jointed nor transversely septate, though sometimes partly filled between the seeds (to p. 305):
Leaves pinnately foliolate or if only 1 leaflet then with a distinct pulvinus at the apex of the petiolule; trees and shrubs, rarely subherbaceous:
Leaves not gland-dotted below; petals nearly always present, sometimes reduced to 1:
Calyx entire and closed in bud, at length more or less irregularly split; stamens usually numerous; radicle always inflexed; stipels absent
                                                                2. SWARTZIEAE
Calyx more or less open in bud, at length distinctly regularly toothed, lobed or truncate; stamens 10; radicle straight, incurved or inflexed; stipels rarely present   3. SOPHOREAE
Leaves gland-dotted or pellucid-punctate below; petals absent:
Flowers in racemes, produced with the young leaves from the older branches; stamens about 15; ovules 8–7; fruit ovoid; seeds 5–4
                                      2. SWARTZIEAE (*Mildbraediodendron*)
Flowers in terminal spikes; stamens 10; ovules 2; fruit obliquely obovate, coarsely glandular; seed 1   32. PSORALEAE (*Paryella*)
Leaves digitately foliolate or simple, very rarely pinnate or reduced to scales:
Shrubs or rarely herbs; stipels absent; embryo with inflexed radicle
                                                                4. PODALYRIEAE
Tall climbing shrubs; stipels present; embryo with straight radicle
                                                3. SOPHOREAE (*Camoensia*)

Fruits jointed, transversely septate within; flowers in terminal racemes; leaves pinnate; leaflets without stipels   45. ADESMIEAE

Filaments partly or almost wholly united to one another, either monadelphous in a closed tube, or diadelphous, in the latter case the vexillary (adaxial) filament often free or partly free from the remainder:

Anthers uniform in size and shape or nearly so, not alternately basifixed and dorsifixed (to p. 312):

Free upper part of filaments more or less filiform, not dilated upwards (to p. 311):

Fruits not breaking up into separate joints when mature, though sometimes filled between the seeds or divided by a longitudinal septum, sometimes 1-seeded (to p. 311):

Filaments monadelphous and partly connate into a single more or less *closed tube* (neither unilaterally nor bilaterally split or only partially so), sometimes the adaxial filament free at the base but connate higher up with the remainder (to p. 306):

Racemes or panicles not swollen at the nodes of the rhachis (at the insertion of the pedicels), or the infloresence fasciculate, capitate, or subumbellate:

Trees and shrubs (rarely climbers), rarely herbs; indumentum when present not composed of medifixed (-shaped) hairs; style glabrous or hairy; anthers neither tipped by a gland nor mucronate:

Fruits dehiscent:

Flowers in axillary racemes or fasciculate at the older leafless nodes:
Leaves pinnate   14. ROBINIEAE
Leaves digitately 3-foliolate   3. SOPHOREAE (*Camoensia*)

Flowers in terminal racemes or panicles and sometimes also in the upper axils, or flowers axillary:

Trees or shrubs, sometimes climbing; stipules not sagittate
                                                17. MILLETTIEAE (part)

Shrublets or herbs, rarely annuals, not climbing; stipules not sagittate or absent; vexillum often hairy outside
                                                23. TEPHROSIEAE (part)

Perennial herbs; stipules more or less sagittate   27. GALEGEAE

Fruits indehiscent:

Fruits not semi-orbicular or circinate; usually more than 2-seeded:

Calyx mostly cyathiform, truncate with small teeth; vexillum often silky outside; trees or tall scrambling shrubs
                                                18. LONCHOCARPEAE (part)

Calyx not cyathiform; shrublets or herbs; flowers mostly capitate or umbellate   43. LOTEAE (part)

Fruits semi-orbicular or circinate, 2-1-seeded; herbs or shrublets, rarely spiny   46. HEDYSAREAE (*Onobrychis*)

Herbs or shrublets with indumentum (usually present) composed mainly of medifixed (T-shaped) hairs; racemes or spikes axillary; anther-connective tipped by a gland or mucro; style glabrous
                                                25. INDIGOFEREAE (part)

Racemes with swollen (tumid) nodes at the insertion of the pedicels; bracts small or very caducous; style glabrous; calyx-lobes 4 (upper 2 connate), very rarely unequally 2-lipped   34. DIOCLEAE

Filaments diadelphous, mostly the adaxial (vexillary) filament free or partly adnate to the remainder, or if monadelphous then all more or less connate into a sheath split adaxially and more rarely also abaxially:

*Leaves *simple* (not unifoliolate),[1] neither reduced to scales nor phyllodes:

Shrubs or herbs with indumentum (when present) composed of simple (not medifixed) hairs; anthers not tipped by a gland or mucro:

Leaves without stipules; flowers mostly in heads or clusters; style glabrous; S. Africa   6. LIPARIEAE

Leaves mostly with stipules; flowers axillary:

Shrubs and shrublets; Australia and S. Africa   7. BOSSIAEEAE

Annual herbs   23. TEPHROSIEAE (*Sphinctospermum*)

Herbs mostly, with indumentum (when present) of medifixed (T-shaped) hairs; anthers tipped by a gland or mucro

     25. INDIGOFEREAE (part)

*Leaves *digitately foliolate* (sometimes sessile), sometimes unifoliolate by reduction, never reduced to scales or phyllodes (to p. 307):

Leaves neither gland-dotted nor pellucid-punctate below:

Fruits *not longitudinally septate*, i.e. without an intrusion of the seed-bearing suture:

Shrubs or herbs with indumentum (when present) composed of simple (not medifixed) hairs; anthers not tipped by a gland or mucro:

Leaflets not toothed; mostly shrubs or shrublets, rarely herbs:

Ovary with more than 1 ovule:

Stipels absent; mostly shrubs or shrublets; flowers in terminal (rarely leaf-opposed) spikes, racemes, or heads, rarely axillary   11. LOTONONIDEAE (part)

Stipels present; mostly herbs, often climbing; no cleistogamous flowers and no fruits buried in the soil:

Fruits jointed but dehiscing its full length

     48. DESMODIEAE (part)

Fruits not jointed, though sometimes filled between the seeds

     38. GLYCINEAE (part)

Stipels present; perennial herbs; lower flowers cleistogamous and fruits of these burrowing into the soil

     23. TEPHROSIEAE (part)

Ovary with more than 1 ovule; fruit 1-seeded

     50. LESPEDEZEAE (part)

Leaflets more or less toothed, the nerves continued to the margin; mostly herbs and often with trifoliolate leaves; stipules often adnate to the petiole; stipels absent   42. TRIFOLIEAE (part)

---

[1] Unifoliolate leaves may usually be recognized by a swelling (pulvinus) at the top of the petiolule.

Herbs or shrublets with indumentum (usually present) composed
of medifixed (T-shaped) hairs; racemes or spikes axillary;
anther-connective tipped by a gland or mucro; style glabrous
25. INDIGOFEREAE (part)

Fruits *longitudinally septate* or partly so by the intrusion of the seed-
bearing suture; stipels absent; inflorescence axillary or from the
rootstock or base, composed of spikes, racemes, or heads
30. ASTRAGALEAE (part)

Leaves glandular or pellucid-punctate below:

Fruits dehiscing by valves, 2- or more-seeded
33. CAJANEAE (part)

Fruits indehiscent, usually 1-seeded   32. PSORALEAE (part)

*Leaves *pinnately trifoliolate* or *pinnate*, never reduced to scales or phyllodes (to p. 309):

Leaves gland-dotted or pellucid-punctate below; ovules few (4–1):

Fruits not enclosed by the calyx; petals neither inserted on nor adnate
to the staminal sheath, sometimes absent:

Fruits dehiscent; seeds mostly 2 or more, rarely 1:

Bracteoles mostly present; leaves imparipinnate or 3- or 1-foliolate;
trees or erect shrubs:

Leaflets opposite; vexillary filament united with the others
22. BRONGNIARTIEAE (part)

Leaflets alternate or opposite; vexillary filament free or free at the
base   17. MILLETTIEAE (part)

Bracteoles absent; leaves 3-foliolate, rarely 1-foliolate; shrubs or
herbs, sometimes climbing or creeping, rarely with gland-
tipped bracts and calyx-lobes   33. CAJANEAE (part)

Fruits usually indehiscent and nearly always 1-seeded; shrubs and
herbs, rarely climbing; bracteoles absent or minute and caducous; anthers versatile:

Fruits not samaroid; shrubs and herbs   32. PSORALEAE (part)

Fruits large and samaroid; trees   19. PTEROCARPEAE (part)

Fruits enclosed by the persistent calyx; flowers in terminal or leaf-
opposed spikes or the spikes subcapitate and involucrate; petals
inserted on or adnate to the staminal sheath   13. DALEAE

Leaves neither gland-dotted nor pellucid-punctate; ovules usually
more than 4, rarely 2 or 1:

†Fruits dehiscent by a valve or valves (sometimes only at the apex)
(to p. 310):

Petals very unequal in length, either the vexillum or the keel petals
much longer than the others or each other; stipels usually
present, sometimes gland-like; seeds estrophiolate
36. ERYTHRINEAE

Petals more or less equal in length (or at any rate the keel-petals not
much longer than the others, though sometimes beaked or
spirally twisted):

Indumentum (when present) usually composed, at least in part, of
adpressed medifixed (T-shaped) hairs; anther-connective with

a gland or mucro at the apex; adaxial filament free from the base or rarely united with the others; stipels mostly absent
                        25. INDIGOFEREAE (part)
Indumentum not as above; anther-connective without a gland or mucro at the apex:
Rhachis of the inflorescence thickened (nodose) at the insertion of the pedicels; leaves mostly stipellate; vexillary filament usually quite free; radicle inflexed:
Style glabrous or penicellate only around the stigma; keel-petals not spirally twisted   35. GALACTIEAE (part)
Style bearded along the inner (adaxial) face; keel-petals often spirally twisted   37. PHASEOLEAE (part)
Rhachis of the inflorescence not thickened at the insertion of the pedicels, or the flowers fasciculate, capitate, or axillary:
Rhachis of the leaves transformed at the apex into a tendril or barren tip or bristle; stipels absent:
Stamens 10; flowers solitary or racemose in the leaf-axils; claw of the vexillum free from the staminal-sheath
                        40. VICIEAE
Stamens 9, the vexillary absent; flowers in terminal or subterminal racemes; claw of the vexillum more or less adnate to the staminal sheath   39. ABREAE
Rhachis of the leaves not ending in a tendril or barren tip:
Fruits *longitudinally septate* within by the intrusion of the seed-bearing suture, often inflated; anther-loculi mostly separate at the apex; style glabrous   30. ASTRAGALEAE (part)
Fruits *not longitudinally septate* as described above, sometimes transversely septate but not breaking up into separate joints:
Fruits inflated and bladder-like, sometimes dehiscent only at the apex:
Style bearded along the adaxial (vexillary) side or near the apex; plants not glandular   29. COLUTEAE (part)
Style glabrous; trees and shrubs, often glandular
                        28. DIPHYSEAE
Fruits not inflated, mostly compressed, though sometimes turgid around the seeds:
Radicle twice folded; erect shrubs or small trees or climbers; style hairy or glabrous; stipels absent; Australasian Islands genera   15. CARMICHAELIEAE (part)
Radicle straight or at most curved:
Stipules when present not adnate to the petiole or only slightly so; leaflets entire (to p. 309):
Ovary with more than 1 ovule (to p. 309):
Style glabrous; racemes axillary or at the older leafless nodes:

Hard-wooded trees and shrubs:
Seeds strophiolate; flowers paired in the leaf-axils or in terminal raceme or panicle
22. BRONGNIARTIEAE
Seeds estrophiolate; flowers in axillary racemes or these fasciculate at the older nodes
14. ROBINIEAE (part)
Herbs and herbaceous climbers or creepers, sometimes subshrubby:
Upright herbs, rarely tall and subshrubby; fruit mostly filled between the seeds
26. SESBANIEAE (part)
Climbing herbs, rarely shrubs or trees; fruits usually not filled between the seeds
38. GLYCINEAE (part)
Style glabrous; racemes or panicles terminal or leaf-opposed:
Hard-wooded trees or climbing shrubs
17. MILLETTIEAE (part)
Herbs or shrublets; leaves with stipels
24. PSEUDARTHRIEAE
Herbs sometimes climbing or shrublets; stipels absent
23. TEPHROSIEAE (part)
Style bearded:
Calyx long-tubular, the lobes shorter than the tube; shrubs; bracteoles paired at the base of the calyx; stipels long and setaceous   16. BARBIERIEAE
Calyx not as above, shortly dentate or lobed or 2-lipped; stipels rarely present:
Hard-wooded trees and shrubs, rarely climbing shrubs
14. ROBINIEAE (part)
Herbs, sometimes tall or subshrubby, or rigid under-shrubs:
Racemes axillary or rarely flowers single or few in the leaf-axils, not leafy at the base
26. SESBANIEAE (part)
Racemes terminal or leaf-opposed or in the upper leaf-axils, often leafy at the base
23. TEPHROSIEAE (part)
Ovary with 1 ovule and fruit therefore 1-seeded, the fruit often enclosed by the persistent calyx; leaves pinnately 3-foliolate or 1-foliolate
50. LESPEDEZEAE (part)
Stipules mostly adnate to the petiole; fruits not septate; leaflets often toothed; mostly herbs
42. TRIFOLIEAE (part)
*Leaves reduced to scales or leaf-like phyllodes (from pp. 306 and 307):
Leaves reduced to scales:

Radicle of the seeds twice folded; Australasian genera
>> 15. CARMICHAELIEAE (part)

Radicle of the seeds not folded:

Style longitudinally bearded in the upper part; flowers in elongated racemes >> 29. COLUTEAE (*Eremosparton*)

Style glabrous; flowers axillary, solitary >> 7. BOSSIEAE

Leaves reduced to leaf-like phyllodes:

Inflorescence terminal; phyllodes glandular on the margin near the apex; imperfectly known genus >> 23. TEPHROSIEAE (*Papilionopsis*)

Inflorescence axillary; phyllodes not glandular on the margin
>> 40. VICIEAE (*Lathyrus*)

†Fruits indehiscent, sometimes inflated and bladder-like (from p. 307):

Fruits inflated and bladder-like or inflated on each face; stipels absent:

Fruits not *longitudinally* septate (seed-bearing suture not intruded):

Style glabrous; trees and shrubs, often glandular; leaves pinnate
>> 28. DIPHYSEAE

Style bearded along the adaxial (vexillary) side or near the apex; shrubs and herbs; leaves pinnate or 1-foliolate
>> 29. COLUTEAE (part)

Fruits longitudinally septate or partly so by the intrusion of the seed-bearing suture; style glabrous >> 30. ASTRAGALEAE (part)

Fruits neither inflated nor bladder-like, sometimes winged:

Leaves reduced to scales; radicle twice folded
>> 15. CARMICHAELIEAE (part)

Leaves not reduced to scales; radicle straight or at most curved:

Leaflets (most of them) alternate; rarely only 1 leaflet:

Anthers small, didymous, not versatile, loculi erect, opening by a short terminal slit, or divergent at the base with a slit lengthwise >> 20. DALBERGIEAE

Anthers versatile, loculi parallel, opening by a slit or rarely by terminal pores:

Fruit drupaceous or turgid, woody; seed pendulous; filaments not in 2 lateral bundles >> 21. GEOFFRAEAE

Fruits not drupaceous, often flat; seed not pendulous; filaments sometimes in 2 lateral bundles >> 19. PTEROCARPEAE

Leaflets opposite or a few at the same time alternate, or leaflets 3:

Fruits not drupaceous, often compressed or winged, sometimes orbicular:

Leaves imparipinnate; vexillum often silky outside; ovary with 2 or more ovules:

Trees or tall scrambling shrubs; flowers in racemes or panicles
>> 18. LONCHOCARPEAE (part)

Shrublets or herbs; flowers capitate or umbellate
>> 43. LOTEAE (part)

Leaves pinnately 3-foliolate or 1-foliolate:

Ovary with numerous ovules and fruits with several seeds
>> 35. GALACTIEAE (*Mastersia*)

Ovary with 1 ovule and fruit 1-seeded; fruit often enclosed by
the calyx   50. LESPEDEZEAE
Fruits drupaceous, woody, sometimes winged; seeds 2–1, pendulous; leaves imparipinnate   21. GEOFFRAEAE (part)
Fruits jointed when ripe and transversely septate, usually breaking up into
1-seeded segments (from p. 305):
Leaves without stipels:
Keel-petals often obliquely truncate at the apex, wings short or very
small, rarely equalling the keel-petals; filaments connate into a
single sheath split adaxially, or vexillary filament free
46. HEDYSAREAE (part)
Keel-petals obtuse or beaked, incurved; wings often transversely
plicate; filaments sometimes connate into 2 lateral bundles
47. AESCHYNOMENEAE

Leaves with stipels:
Plants not dotted with glands; adaxial filament free or more or less
connate with the others into a closed tube   48. DESMODIEAE (part)
Plants dotted with glands; stamens all connate into a closed tube
47. AESCHYNOMENEAE (*Poiretia*)
Free upper part of all or half of the filaments dilated or expanded upwards;
lower pair of leaflets sometimes resembling stipules (from p. 305):
Fruits 2-valved or indehiscent, sometimes transversely septate but not
breaking up into separate joints (see below):
Leaf-rhachis not ending in a bristle or tendril:
Claw of the petals not adnate to the staminal sheath or tube:
Stamens united into an open sheath:
Stipules more or less free from the petiole; leaflets entire, nerves not
running into the margin; lowermost pair often resembling
stipules   43. LOTEAE (part)
Stipules mostly partly adnate to the petiole; nerves of the leaves ex-
tended to the usually toothed margin   42. TRIFOLIEAE (part)
Stamens united into a closed tube:
Subarborescent shrubs, silky pubescent, not glandular; leaves imparipinnate; stipules small, free; racemes terminal
23. TEPHROSIEAE (*Mundulea*)
Mostly perennial or annual herbs clothed with glandular hairs;
leaves pinnately trifoliolate, rarely 1-foliolate or 2–3 pairs;
stipules mostly herbaceous, adnate to the petiole 41. ONONIDEAE
Claws of some or all of the petals partly adnate to the staminal sheath;
flowers in heads or dense spikes; leaflets usually toothed, the lateral
nerves extended to the teeth or margin   42. TRIFOLIEAE (*Trifolium*)
Leaf-rhachis ending in a bristle or tendril; flowers solitary or racemose
in the leaf-axil   40. VICIEAE (part)
Fruits jointed and breaking up into separate segments, these indehiscent
or rarely dehiscing by 2 valves:
Stipels absent; flowers not precocious   44. CORONILLEAE
Stipels present; flowers mostly precocious
48. DESMODIEAE (*Droogmansia*)

Anthers dimorphic, alternately dorsifixed and basifixed, either all equal or alternately longer and shorter (from p. 305):

Upper part of filaments swollen or expanded; perennial or annual herbs or shrublets, often spiny and glandular   41. ONONIDEAE

Upper part of filaments neither swollen nor expanded:

Fruits not transversely septate or if so then not breaking up into separate joints (to p. 313):

Filaments *connate into a more or less closed tube*, but free at the top; stipels absent:

Leaves simple (not 1-foliolate) or reduced to scales; perennial herbs:

Calyx regularly lobed or toothed:

Stipules absent; seeds not strophiolate   5. BORBONIEAE (*Euchlora*)

Stipules mostly present, sometimes spiny; seeds strophiolate
7. BOSSIAEEAE (part)

Calyx 2- or 1-lipped   9. GENISTEAE (part)

Leaves digitately or pinnately foliolate or rarely 1-foliolate:

Claws of all the petals free from the staminal tube:

Ovary more than 1-ovuled; fruit more than 1-seeded:

Calyx-lobes or teeth much shorter than the tube, or calyx 2-lipped:

Trees and shrubs, rarely spiny; leaves 3-foliolate; calyx equally lobed or toothed or sometimes 2-lipped; seeds without a strophiole   10. LABURNEAE

Shrubs or low shrublets, sometimes very spiny; leaves 3- or 1-foliolate or reduced to a spiny tip or small scale; calyx often 2-lipped; seeds with a strophiole   8. CYTISEAE

Calyx-lobes or lips much longer than the tube; shrublets or herbs, sometimes annuals; leaves digitate; stipules often partly adnate to the petiole; seeds without a strophiole   12. LUPINEAE

Ovary 1-ovuled; fruit 1-seeded   49. STYLOSANTHEAE

Claws of the lower petals more or less adnate to the staminal tube; stipules minute or absent; seeds without a strophiole; shrubs or rarely small trees or shrublets   9. GENISTEAE (part)

Filaments *connate into a sheath split adaxially* or sometimes the adaxial (vexillary) filament free or partly so, rarely absent; leaves simple or 1- or more-foliolate:

Leaves simple (not 1-foliolate) or reduced to scales (to p. 313):

Style glabrous:

Flowers mostly in heads or clusters or scattered along the branches; leaves alternate; stipules absent; S. Africa:

Vexillary (adaxial) filament free from the others 6. LIPARIEAE (part)

Vexillary filament connate with the others into an open sheath or part tube   5. BORBONIEAE

Flowers mostly axillary; leaves alternate or opposite or reduced to scales; stipules usually present, sometimes spiny; Australia and S. Africa   7. BOSSIAEEAE (part)

Style bearded; flowers mostly in terminal or leaf-opposed racemes or spikes   13. CROTALARIEAE (part)

Leaves 3- or more-foliolate or 1-foliolate by reduction (detected by a distinct pulvinus at the top of the petiolule):

Leaves glandular below; stipels mostly present; style bearded lengthwise or pilose around the stigma:

Anthers alternately basifixed and dorsifixed; calyx 2-lipped; leaves usually with stipels 37. PHASEOLEAE (part)

Anthers subuniform, all versatile; calyx not 2-lipped; stipels mostly absent 32. PSORALEAE (part)

Leaves not glandular below:

Style glabrous:

Leaves pinnately foliolate; stipels mostly present; mostly climbers, the fruits sometimes with stinging hairs:

Vexillary filament free from the others or nearly so; petals very unequal in length 36. ERYTHRINEAE (*Mucuna*)

Vexillary filament connate with the others:

Trees or erect shrubs; leaves imparipinnate; stipules often very large; calyx 2-lipped 22. BRONGNIARTIEAE (part)

Climbing herbs; leaves 3-foliolate; stipules small; calyx scarcely 2-lipped 38. GLYCINEAE (*Teramnus*)

Leaves digitately 3- or rarely 1-foliolate, sometimes sessile; mostly erect shrubs or shrublets, the fruits without stinging hairs; stipels absent; inflorescence mostly terminal or leaf-opposed:

Calyx-lobes or teeth at most only slightly longer than the tube 11. LOTONONIDEAE (part)

Calyx-lobes or lips much longer than the tube 12. LUPINEAE (*Argyrolobium*)

Style bearded lengthwise or ciliate on the adaxial side; fruits usually turgid or inflated 13. CROTALARIEAE (part)

Style at most pubescent only towards the base; fruits not inflated 38. GLYCINEAE (part)

Fruits transversely septate and breaking up into 1-seeded joints (sometimes some fruits reduced to 1 joint) leaves few-foliolate (from p. 312):

Filaments all connate into a closed tube; flowers spicate, capitate, or rarely subracemose, terminal or axillary; fruits maturing above or below the ground 49. STYLOSANTHEAE (part)

Filaments all connate into a sheath split adaxially or into 2 lateral bundles, rarely the vexillary filament free; flowers in axillary racemes rarely in axillary fascicles or subcymose; fruits maturing above the ground 47. AESCHYNOMENEAE (part)

Tribe 1. CADIEAE

Baill., Hist. des Pl. 2: 156, 170 (1870)

Trees and shrubs; leaves imparipinnate or very rarely 1-foliolate, sometimes pellucid-punctate; leaflets alternate; stipules present, small; stipels usually absent; *flowers actinomorphic*, in racemes or panicles of racemes, rarely solitary and axillary; petals 5, free, *equal or nearly so*; stamens 10, *filaments free*; anthers uniform; ovary sessile to stipitate; style glabrous;

stigma terminal; ovules numerous to 1; fruit 2-valved or indehiscent, sometimes winged. Type genus *Cadia* Forssk.

Ovules numerous; leaves imparipinnate:
  Petals oblong-obovate or suborbicular; leaflets not punctate; flowers soli-
  tary or few in loose racemes   1. **Cadia**
  Petals linear; leaflets pellucid-punctate; fruits compressed, winged along
  each suture, pericarp filled with resinous cells; racemes catkin-like
                                                          2. **Myrocarpus**
Ovules few or 1:
  Leaves imparipinnate or rarely paripinnate:
    Fruits where known not winged or only slightly so at the apex; petals not
    lobed; stipels absent or minute:
      Fruits more or less straight:
        Branchlets not scarred; fruits oblong, lanceolate or broadly linear,
        flat; ovules 4–2   3. **Sweetia**
        Branchlets densely covered with circular scars; fruits not known;
        ovules 2 or 1   4. **Dicraeopetalum**
      Fruits semilunar, reticulate; seed 1; leaflets 2 pairs   5. **Riedeliella**
    Fruits winged on both margins, with a thin reticulate exocarp; seeds in-
    vested by a thin spongy aril; leaflets stipellate; petals deeply 2-lobed
                                                          6. **Amphimas**
  Leaves 1-foliolate; fruits not winged:
    Fruits oblong-lanceolate, flat, thin, transversely reticulate, stipitate; leaves
    ovate-subcordate, digitately nerved at the base   7. **Barklya**
  Fruits obovate, 2-valved but drupe-like; seed 1; leaves pinnately nerved
                                                          8. **Inocarpus**

1. **Cadia** Forssk., Fl. Aeg. Arab. 90 (1775). *Panciatica* Piccioli (1783). *Spaen-
doncea* Desf. (1796). *Mozambe* Raf. (1838). 5 spp., E. trop. Africa, Arabia,
Madagascar; type *C. purpurea* (Piccioli) Ait., Arabia, N. and E. trop. Africa.
B.H. 1: 560; E.P. 3, 3: 187.

   Shrubs; leaves imparipinnate, leaflets numerous and small or few and larger, exstipellate;
   stipules minute; flowers rather large, white, rose, or purple, solitary in the upper axils or few
   in racemes; bracts small; bracteoles absent; calyx broadly campanulate, lobes broad, subequal; petals all rather similar, free, erect-patent, oblong-obovate or suborbicular, very
   shortly clawed, the adaxial one outermost in bud; stamens 10, free, subequal; anthers uniform, ovate-sagittate, versatile; ovary subsessile or shortly stipitate; ovules numerous;
   style incurved, subulate, stigma small, terminal; fruit shortly stipitate, linear, acuminate,
   plano-compressed, coriaceous, 2-valved, continuous within; seeds numerous, compressed,
   ovate or orbicular, orange-red; radicle rather long, inflexed.

2. **Myrocarpus** Allem., Plant. Nov. Brasil (1846). 4 spp., Brazil, Paraguay,
Argentina; type *M. fastigiatus* Allem. B.H. 1: 559; E.P. 3, 3: 189; Burkart,
Legum. Argent. ed. 2: 200, fig. 43.

   Tall trees, with hard wood and resinous bark; leaves imparipinnate, leaflets pellucid-
   punctate; stipules small; stipels absent; flowers white, small, racemose, racemes in the upper
   leaf-axils or at the apex of leafless branches, almost catkin-like, with very conspicuous
   stamens; bracts small, scale-like; bracteoles absent; calyx-teeth short, subequal or the upper
   connate; petals 5, clawed, linear, slightly unequal; stamens free, exserted; anthers small,

uniform; ovary stipitate, ovules numerous; style short, inflexed, stigma small, terminal; fruit shortly stipitate, elongated, compressed, 2–1-seeded, not dehiscent, winged along each suture; pericarp above the seeds turgid and filled with resinous cells; seeds oblong, hilum near the apex; radicle straight.

3. **Sweetia** Spreng., Syst. 2: 171, 213 (1825) (conserved name). *Acosmium* Schott (1827). *Leptolobium* Vog. (1837). *Thalesia* Mart. ex Pfeiffer (1874). 14 spp., Cent. and South America; type *S. fruticosa* Spreng., Brazil. B.H. 1: 559; E.P. 3, 3: 189; Amshoff, Pulle Fl. Suriname, 2, 2: 104; Burkart, Legum. Argent. ed. 2, 199, fig. 42.

Trees; leaves pari- or imparipinnate, leaflets few pairs or rarely small and numerous pairs; stipules small, caducous or inconspicuous; stipels minute or absent; flowers rather small, racemose, racemes paniculate at the tops of the branches; bracts and bracteoles narrow or small, often caducous; calyx-teeth or lobes subequal, valvate or rarely very narrowly imbricate; petals all rather similar, free, erect-patent, upper outer and sometimes broader; stamens free, subequal, longer than the petals, filaments inflexed; anthers uniform, ovoid; ovary sessile or shortly stipitate, 4–2-ovuled: style filiform, stigma small or truncate, terminal; fruit oblong, lanceolate or broadly linear, plano-compressed, not dehiscent, not winged or only slightly so at the apex; seeds ovate or orbicular, flat.

Sweetia elegans Benth.; Perobinha, Lapachillo, S. Brazil; wood used for carpentry and manufacture of charcoal. *S. panamensis* Benth.; Billyweb Sweetia; Cent. America to N. Colombia, Venezuela; Bitter Bark, Cascara Amarga, used in scrofula; wood durable used for heavy construction.

4. **Dicraeopetalum** Harms, Engl., Bot. Jahrb. 33: 161 (1902). 1 sp., *D. stipulare* Harms, Somaliland.

Tree; branchlets marked with dense circular scars; leaves imparipinnate, borne on short densely stipulate branchlets; leaflets opposite, small; flowers racemose; calyx-tube cupular, teeth 5, lanceolate, almost equalling the tube; petals 5, inserted in the lower part of the tube, imbricate, almost equal, shortly clawed, obovate to oblong, shortly bilobed at the apex, or emarginate; stamens 10, exserted, filaments free, elongated, filiform, glabrous; anthers small, broadly ovate, attached towards the base; ovary shortly stipitate, linear, densely villous; style glabrous, stigma small, capitellate; ovules 2 or 1; fruit not known.

5. **Riedeliella** Harms, Engl. Bot. Jahrb 33; Beibl. 72: 25 (1903). *Sweetiopsis*. Chod. & Hassl. (1904). 2 spp., Brazil and Paraguay; type *R. graciliflora* Harms, Brazil. Burkart, Legum. Argent. ed. 2: 216.

Erect shrub; leaves imparipinnate, leaflets 2 pairs; flowers in panicles of racemes; bracts lanceolate, subpersistent; bracteoles 2, smaller; calyx-tube campanulate, teeth subequal, very short, deltoid; petals 5, almost equal among themselves, free, inserted at the base of the calyx-tube, lanceolate, clawed; stamens 10, filaments slender, shortly connate at the base; anthers broadly subquadrate-ovate, small; ovary very shortly stipitate, obliquely ovoid; style slender, filiform; ovules 2; fruits semilunar, reticulate; seed 1.

6. **Amphimas** Pierre ex Dalla Torre & Harms, Gen. Siphonog. 220 (1901), name only; Harms, Engl. & Prantl, Pflanzenfam. Nachtr. 3: 157 (1906). 4 spp., trop. Africa; type *A. ferrugineus* Pierre ex Pellegr., Gabon. Hutch. & Dalz., Fl. W. Trop. Afr. 1: 448; Wilczek, Fl. Congo Belge, 3: 546, t. 40.

Tall trees; leaves imparipinnate, leaflets alternate or opposite, 6–9 pairs, with subulate stipels; stipules subulate, soon falling off; flowers very small, in long or short racemes collected into a terminal panicle; bracts and bracteoles deciduous; calyx-tube campanulate, 10-ribbed; teeth 5, all alike, valvate, triangular, hairy on both sides; petals 5, imbricate, linear, deeply 2-lobed, somewhat fleshy; stamens 10, unequal in length, thickened towards the base, free but inserted on the disk; anthers ovoid or rounded; ovary stipitate; style with capitate stigma; ovules 2; fruit 2–1-seeded, 2-valved, shortly stipitate, more or less oblong-lanceolate, very compressed, broadly winged on both margins, with thin reticulate exocarp; seeds sessile, rather long and kidney-shaped, invested by a thin spongy aril.

Amphimas pterocarpoides Harms, trop. Africa; bark source of red sticky resin; decoction used in Liberia for dysentery.

7. **Barklya** F. Muell., Journ. Linn. Soc. Bot. 3: 158 (1859); Fragm. 1: 109 (1859). 1 sp., *B. syringifolia* F. Muell., Australia (Queensland and New South Wales). B.H. 1: 559; E.P. 3, 3: 188.

Tree, handsome and very floriferous; leaves 1-foliolate, leaflet long-petiolulate, ovate-subcordate, digitately nerved at the base; stipules small, rounded; petiolule swollen at the top; flowers densely racemose, orange-yellow; racemes collected in a terminal panicle or axillary; bracts minute; bracteoles absent; calyx campanulate, shortly toothed; petals all alike, clawed, free, adaxial outermost in bud; stamens free, subequal; anthers uniform, ovate-sagittate; ovary stipitate; ovules few; style short, stigma terminal; fruit stipitate, oblong-lanceolate, flat, thin, transversely reticulate; seeds 2–1, compressed, with thin endosperm; radicle inflexed.

8. **Inocarpus** Forst., Char. Gen. 65, t. 33 (1776) (conserved name). *Aniotum* Parkinson (1773). *Renia* Nor. (1790). *Etaballia* Benth. (1840). *Inodaphnis* Miq. (1860). *Gajanus* Rumph. ex O. Ktze. (1891). 2 spp., E. tropics; type *I. edulis* Forst., trop. Asia, Malaya, Polynesia. Benth., Journ. Linn. Soc. 6: 146 (1862); Fosberg, Journ. Wash. Acad. Sci. 31: 95 (1941); Kuhlman, Lilloa, 17: 57, with fig. (1949); Hook., Ic. Pl. t. 1837.

Tall trees; leaves alternate, 1-foliolate, large, entire, pinnately nerved; stipules small, soon deciduous; petiolule very short; flowers in axillary spikes resembling catkins when young; bracts and bracteoles small, deciduous; calyx tubular, closed in bud, subregularly 2–5-toothed; petals 5, free, subequal, linear, resembling those of *Hamamelis*, imbricate; stamens 10, filaments shortly connate at the base into a tube free or shortly adnate to the petals; anthers uniform, short, didymous, opening lengthwise; ovary subsessile, few–2-ovuled; style short, stigma oblique; fruit obovate, 2-valved but drupe-like; seed 1, cotyledons fleshy.

Tribe 2. SWARTZIEAE

DC., Prodr. 2: 422 (as Suborder) (1825); Benth. & Hook. f., Gen. Pl. 1: 457 (1865)

Trees or tall shrubs; leaves pinnately many-foliolate or 1-foliolate, very rarely gland-dotted; *stipels absent*; calyx closed before flowering, at length splitting more or less irregularly into *valvate* lobes or teeth; petals either 5 and *subequal* with the uppermost (adaxial) *outermost*, or petal 1 (adaxial), or petals absent; disk rarely present; stamens *numerous* (up to 100) to 9, *filaments free* or rarely shortly connate at the base; *anthers uniform*, attached near the base, rarely versatile, opening lengthwise; style glabrous; fruit 2-valved or indehiscent, not jointed; *radicle inflexed*. Type genus *Swartzia* Schreb.

Bentham remarked about the tribe *Swartzieae* in the *Genera Plantarum* (translation): 'A tribe formerly held to be a suborder, as much distinguished from the *Papilionaceae* as from the *Caesalpiniaceae*, or, neglecting the radicle, assigned by us to the *Caesalpiniaceae*; but among the better specimens more accurately examined in the genera with 5 petals, the uppermost seems to be most often *outside*, and the radicle, where noted, always *inflexed* as in the *Papilionaceae*. The calyx of *Swartzieae* is to be seen in *Fissicalyx*,[1] among the *Dalbergieae*,

---

[1] *Fissicalyx*, in this work, is included in the Tribe *Geoffraeae*.

and in *Baphia* and allies among the *Sophoreae*.' Bentham's inclusion of the tribe in *Papilionaceae* is therefore followed here.

Petals or petal present:
  Stamens numerous (14 or more):
    Petals 6–5; fruits 1-seeded:
      Leaves pinnate, or the upper ones 1-foliolate; flowers rather large;
        stamens more than 20; ovary and fruit stipitate   **9. Aldina**
      Leaves all 1-foliolate; flowers small, in very short axillary racemes;
        stamens 18–16; ovary and fruit sessile   **10. Baphiopsis**
    Petals 3, the 2 lateral small, or petal 1; seeds more than 1
                          11. Swartzia (part)
  Stamens few (up to 13):
    Calyx at length divided into lobes, acuminate in bud; fruits dehiscent:
      Leaves pinnate; stamens 10; calyx-tube short; racemes elongated; petal 1;
        ovules 2   **12. Cashalia**
      Leaves 1-foliolate, sometimes prickly; stamens 13–9; calyx-tube very
        short; petals 5; ovules numerous   **13. Zollernia**
    Calyx truncate and remaining entire or at most minutely toothed, obtuse
      in bud; stamens 12–9; fruits indehiscent:
      Leaves pinnate; leaflets numerous, dentate, with subparallel nerves;
        shrubs; fruit ovoid, turgid   **14. Holocalyx**
      Leaves 1-foliolate, with pinnate nerves; trees; fruit thick, compressed
                          15. Lecointea
Petals absent:
  Stamens numerous (30 or more); disk absent:
    Stamens free or very shortly connate at the base; calyx-tube very short or
      absent   **11. Swartzia** (part)
    Stamens shortly united within the bell-shaped calyx-tube and free or
      adnate to it, 1–2-seriate; ovary and fruit long-stipitate; calyx 4–5-lobed
                        16. Cordyla
    Stamens about 15, in a single series inserted on the margin of a flat disk not
      adnate to the very short broad calyx-tube; ovary and fruit long-
      stipitate; calyx dividing into 2–3-lobes; leaves pellucid-punctate
                    17. Mildbraedeodendron

9. Aldina Endl., Gen. 1322 (1841) (conserved name). *Allania* Benth. (1840).
10 spp., trop. South America; type *A. insignis* (Benth.) Endl., Guiana.
B.H. 1: 560; E.P. 3, 3: 183.

Trees; leaves imparipinnate or the upper 1-foliolate; leaflets opposite or subopposite,
often large; stipules small; stipels absent; flowers handsome, white, in axillary racemes or
terminal panicles; bracts, small, caducous; bracteoles absent; calyx-tube turbinate; limb
entire in bud, obovoid or globose, splitting valvately into 5–2 lobes; petals 6–5, unequal,
imbricate, the adaxial exterior, broad, remainder oblique; stamens numerous, perigynous,
filaments filiform; anthers uniform, large, linear, acuminate, versatile, loculi opening by
slits lengthwise; ovary stipitate, incurved; stigma small, terminal; fruit thick, ovoid, 1-seeded.

10. Baphiopsis Benth. ex Bak., Oliv., Fl. Trop. Afr. 2: 256 (1871). 2 spp., trop.
Africa; type *B. parviflora* Benth. ex Bak. Hutch. & Dalz., Fl. W. Trop. Afr. 1:
370; Gilbert & Boutique, Fl. Congo Belge, 3: 553.

Trees and shrubs; leaves 1-foliolate, oblong, entire; stipules absent (or deciduous), flowers small, in racemes or umbels from the leaf-axils or woody branches; bracts and bracteoles striate; calyx small, oblong, membranous, at first closed and entire, at length splitting irregularly; petals 6, oblong, nearly equal; stamens 18–14, almost hypogynous; anthers oblong, equal, filaments filiform, varying from as long as the anthers to twice as long; ovary sessile, 2-ovuled, narrowed into a much-hooked style; fruit semi-orbicular or broadly oblong, upper suture straight, apiculate, 1-seeded; seed very large, filling the fruit.

11. **Swartzia**[1] Schreb., Gen. 2: 518 (1791) (conserved name). About 150 spp., trop. America, trop. Africa, Madagascar; type *S. guianensis* (Aubl.) Urb. (*S. alata* Willd.), Guiana. B.H. 1: 561; E.P. 3, 3: 182; Hutch. & Dalz., Fl. W. Trop. Afr. 1: 368, fig. 141; Gilbert & Boutique, Fl. Congo Belge, 3: 550.

Unarmed trees; leaves imparipinnate or 1-foliolate; rhachis sometimes winged; stipules very small or rarely leaf-like; flowers racemose, racemes often short and fasciculate at the older nodes, or paniculate on leafless branchlets, rarely axillary or solitary; bracts very caducous, mostly small; bracteoles small, rarely persistent; calyx-tube short, limb entire, obovoid or globose in bud, variously split on opening; petal (vexillum) 1, broad, crumpled, remainder absent or the 2 lateral small, or petals absent; stamens numerous, free or nearly so, declinate; anthers uniform or some with filaments longer, attached near the base, loculi opening by slits lengthwise; ovary stipitate, often incurved, ovules numerous; style narrow, stigma terminal small or rarely capitate; fruit ovoid or elongated, turgid or subterete, leathery or fleshy, 2-valved or indehiscent; seeds kidney-shaped, ovoid or globose, with or without an aril; cotyledons fleshy; radicle inflexed.

Swartzia madagascariensis Desv., Madagascar, trop. Africa; wood heavy, hard, deep red; used for furniture, pianos, heavy construction.

12. **Cashalia** Standley, Journ. Wash. Acad. Sci. 13: 440 (1923). 1 sp. *C. cuscatlanica* Standley, Salvador.

Large unarmed tree; leaves imparipinnate, leaflets 11–13, alternate, oblong or lanceolate-oblong, acuminate; stipules minute, caducous; racemes long, many-flowered; bracts and bracteols ecaducous; calyx-tube campanulate, 5-lobed, lower lobes triangular-ovate, subequal, upper 2 similar, united for half their length; petal 1, rounded-obovate, broadly clawed; stamens 10, free; anthers oval, uniform, attached near the base, opening lengthwise; ovary shortly stipitate, 2-ovuled; style curved, stigma minute; fruit ovoid or cylindric, 1–2-seeded, turgid and subterete, coriaceous, 2-valved; seeds large, ovoid, not arillate, without endosperm; cotyledons thick.

13. **Zollernia** Nees, Nov. Act. Acad. Nat. Cur. 13: 2, praef. p. 13, t. C, D (1827). *Coquebertia* Brongn. (1833). *Acidandra* Mart. ex Endl. (1839). 12 spp., Cent. America, Brazil, and Guianas; type *Z. falcata* Maximil. & Nees, Brazil. B.H. 1: 560; E.P. 3, 3: 184; Britt. & Rose, N. Amer. Fl. 23: 349.

Trees or shrubs; leaves 1-foliolate, sometimes Holly-like, petiole very short; stipules rigid; flowers racemose, racemes paniculate at the apex of the branches; bracts small; bracteoles minute or absent; calyx-tube very short; limb closed, entire and acuminate in bud, split when in flower, reflexed or deciduous; petals 5, imbricate, the vexillum broader and exterior; stamens 13–9, subhypogynous, filaments very short; anthers uniform, linear, acuminate, attached near the base, loculi opening by slits lengthwise; ovary subsessile or stipitate, ovules numerous; style short, subulate, stigma small, obliquely terminal; fruit

[1] Synonyms of **Swartzia**: *Possira* Aubl. (1775). *Tounatea* Aubl. (1775). *Rittera* Schreb. (1789). *Hoelzelia* Neck. (1790). *Gynanthistrophe* Poit. ex DC. (1825). *Riveria* H. B. & K. (1825). *Dithyria* Benth. (1840). *Possiria* Steud. (1841). *Rossina* Steud. (1841). *Possura* Aubl. ex Steud. (1841). *Trischidium* Tul. (1843). *Tunatea* O. Ktze. (1891). *Fairchildia* Britt. & Rose (1930).

ovoid, thick, 2-valved; seeds solitary or few, ovate or orbicular, compressed; cotyledons broad.

Z. ilicifolia Vogel; Mocitahyba, Brazil; bark source of tannin; wood used for railroad ties, cabinet work and beams. *Z. paraensis* Huber; Muirapinima Preta, Brazil; wood highly prized for cabinet work and turnery; in U.S.A. for handles of cutlery, brush blades, and butts of billiard cues.

14. **Holocalyx** M. Micheli, Mem. Soc. Phys. Genève, 28; no. vii. 41, t. 15 (1883). 2 spp., Argentina, Paraguay, Brazil; type *H. balansae* M. Micheli, Paraguay to Brazil. E.P. 3, 3: 184; Burkart, Legum. Argent. ed. 2: 183, fig. 30.

Shrubs; leaves paripinnate; leaflets oblong, leathery, dentate, with subparallel nerves; stipules minute; flowers small, shortly racemose, racemes axillary; bracts and bracteoles small, persistent; calyx-tube obconic, entire; petals 5, linear or spathulate, soon falling off; stamens 12–10, free; anthers attached above the base; ovary stipitate, ovules 5–4, pendulous; style very short, stigma terminal, small; fruit-ovoid, turgid, thick and succulent, indehiscent; seeds 3–1, ovoid or globose.

Wood of *H. balansae* yellowish, durable; used for *de luxe* articles.

15. **Lecointea** Ducke, Arch. Jard. Bot. Rio de Janeiro, 3: 128 (1922). 3 spp., South America; type *L. amazonica* Ducke, Amazon.

Trees; leaves 1-foliolate; stipules caducous; flowers small, in axillary often one-sided racemes; bracts persistent; bracteoles subpersistent, small; calyx-tube rather long, almost campanulate or turbinate, limb membranous, subentire or obscurely 5-toothed, split unilaterally during flowering; petals 5, very deciduous, imbricate, erect, clawed, 4 slightly unequal, outer one twice as broad; stamens 10 or 9, slightly unequal, filaments free, anthers small, acuminate, attached near the base, opening by slits lengthwise; ovary stipitate, 6–4-ovulate; style straight or slightly curved at the top, stout, elongated, exserted in bud; stigma small, obliquely terminal; fruit indehiscent, thick; seeds 2 or 1, thick, compressed, orbicular or rarely rather kidney-shaped.

16. **Cordyla** Lour., Fl. Cochinch. 411 (1790). *Cordylia* Pers. (1807). *Calycandra* Lepr. ex A. Rich. (1832). 5 spp., trop. Africa, Madagascar; type *C. africana* Lour. Milne–Redh., Fedde Repert. 41: 232 (1937); Vig., Notul. Syst. 13: 355 (1949).

Tall, unarmed trees; leaves imparipinnate, leaflets alternate; stipules lanceolate, very caducous; flowers shortly racemose, racemes subfasciculate at the older nodes or rarely axillary; bracts and bracteoles minute, linear, very caducous; calyx-tube disk-bearing, campanulate; limb entire in bud, subglobose, valvately 4–5-lobed in flower; petals absent; stamens 100–30, free or adnate to the calyx-tube, filaments filiform; anthers small, ovate, opening by slits lengthwise; ovary long-stipitate, ovules numerous; style subulate, stigma small, terminal; fruit ovoid, pulpy inside; seeds few, ovoid-subterete; endosperm thin; cotyledons elongated, fleshy.

17. **Mildbraedeodendron** Harms, Wiss. Ergebn. Zentr. Afr. Exped. 2: 241. t. 27 (1911). 1 sp., *M. excelsum* Harms, trop. Africa. Gilbert & Boutique, Fl, Congo Belge, 3: 552.

High tree, with a tall trunk, and large crown; leaves imparipinnate; leaflets alternate or subopposite, in many pairs, pellucid-punctate; flowers racemose; racemes produced with the young leaves, arising from the branchlets below the leaves, sometimes shortly paniculate; bracts lanceolate; bracteoles subulate; calyx subglobose or depressed-globose in bud, at length split into 3 or 2 broad deltoid spreading or reflexed lobes; disk thick, fleshy; petals absent; stamens about 15, very shortly connate at the base; anthers small, attached at the back, ovoid; ovary stipitate; ovule 8–7; style subulate, acute, glabrous; fruit indehiscent, ovoid, leathery, fleshy inside, with 5–4 large transverse seeds.

Tribe 3. SOPHOREAE

Spreng., Anleit. 2, 2: 741 (1818)

Trees and shrubs, rarely spiny, very rarely subherbaceous or climbing; leaves pinnately 5–many-foliolate or 1-foliolate, rarely digitately 3-foliolate (*Camoensia*); stipels rarely present; inflorescence racemose or paniculate, mostly terminal; bracteoles usually small, rarely large and enclosing the bud (*Dalhousiea*) (as in many *Caesalpiniaceae*); calyx 5-toothed or lobed or rarely entire in bud and opening irregularly; corolla papilionaceous or subactinomorphic, adaxial petal outermost, lower petals rarely absent; stamens 10, *filaments free* or *connate only at the base* (and then sometimes the adaxial more free); *anthers uniform*, linear to rounded; ovary several- to 1-ovuled; *style glabrous*; stigma terminal or lateral; fruit not jointed, indehiscent or 2-valved, sometimes winged above or below the seed; radicle straight, incurved, or inflexed. Bazilevskaja, Crit. surv. of systematic div. of Tribe *Sophoreae*, Bull. Jard. Bot. Prin. URSS. 29: 339 (1930); Ducke, Key to South American genera, Bol. Técn. Inst. Agron. do Norte no. 18: 146 (1949). Type genus *Sophora* Linn.

Leaves with 2 or more leaflets (neither simple nor 1-foliolate) (to p. 323):
 Ovules 3 or more (to p. 322):
 Fruits not winged:
 Fruits dehiscent, 2-valved (to p. 321):
 Ovary sessile or subsessile within the calyx (to p. 321):
 Calyx-teeth or lobes imbricate, or calyx 2-lipped:
 Fruits not twisted when ripe:
 Stigma terminal:
 Calyx persistent in fruit; leaflets numerous and small; seeds sub-
 compressed, ovate; S. Africa   18. **Virgilia**
 Calyx deciduous; leaflets few to 3; seeds globose, hard, black or
 red except the white hilum; South America   19. **Ormosiopsis**
 Stigma lateral; seeds hard, shining, yellowish or scarlet   20. **Ormosia**
 Fruits twisted when ripe; flowers in terminal racemes; stigma terminal
         21. **Ammothamnus**
 Calyx-teeth valvate; stigma terminal:
 Stamens all free:
 Vexillum oblong, often with 2 lateral appendages; seeds 2–1, ovate
 or oblong; trop. America   22. **Diplotropis**
 Vexillum suborbicular, without lateral appendages; seeds few, large,
 compressed; trop. America   23. **Clathrotropis**
 Vexillum suborbicular, more or less auriculate; seeds 5–8, com-
 pressed; Madagascar   24. **Neoharmsia**
 Vexillary stamen free, others connate at the base; seeds 2–1, oblong,
 slightly compressed   25. **Vexillifera**
 Ovary stipitate within the calyx-tube:
 Fruits flat and compressed; seeds large and orbicular:
 Upper margin of wing-petals fringed with stipitate glands; leaves im-
 paripinnate   26. **Petaladenium**

Upper margin of wing-petals not glandular:
Leaves pinnately foliolate:
Petals not very unequal in size; fruits at length spirally twisted
27. **Alexa**
Flowers with one large petal and 4 smaller ones; fruits elastically dehiscent   28. **Uleanthus**
Leaves digitately 3-foliolate, stipellate; flowers very large
29. **Camoensia**
Fruits subturgid or moniliform:
Stamens free or rarely all connate at the base into a ring; flowers bisexual; seeds obovoid or globose, not arillate
40. **Sophora** (part)
Stamens 9, connate at the base, 1 subfree; flowers andro-monoecious; seeds large and ellipsoid, with a red aril   30. **Dussia**
Fruits turgid; seeds large and subglobose; stamens free; flowers bisexual   31. **Castanospermum**
Fruits stipitate; seeds oblong, red; stamens free; disk adnate to the calyx, 10-grooved; flowers bisexual   32. **Podopetalum**
Fruits indehiscent:
Buds of shoots embraced by the inflated base of the petiole; unarmed; inflorescence terminal, often pendulous, paniculate; fruit linear-lanceolate or oblong, winged or not   33. **Cladrastis**
Buds not as described above:
Shrubs with spiny branches; flowers in short often fasciculate racemes at the older nodes; fruit ovoid-globose, subdrupaceous, woody
34. **Gourliea**

Trees, shrubs, or rarely herbs without spines:
Vexillum only slightly broader than the other petals:
Racemes paniculate, terminal; fruit stipitate, drupe-like, ellipsoid; seeds reniform, nearly black   35. **Xanthocercis**
Racemes axillary, solitary; fruit not drupe-like, compressed, linear-oblong when few-seeded; seeds compressed, rounded
36. **Uribea**
Vexillum much broader than the other petals:
Fruit not moniliform:
Fruits not winged, reticulate:
Calyx 2-lipped, at length split to the base into 2 reflexed segments; ovary subsessile   37. **Spirotropis**
Calyx equally 5-lobed; ovary shortly stipitate   38. **Bolusanthus**
Fruits winged along the ventral suture, hairy; calyx inflated, 4-lobed, upper lobe larger   39. **Maackia**
Fruits moniliform, not winged; erect trees or shrubs; calyx 5-toothed:
Anthers versatile; seeds obovoid or globose   40. **Sophora** (part)
Anthers subbasifixed; seeds narrowly oblong, turgid
41. **Angylocalyx**

Fruits more or less winged or margined:
Fruits 1–2-winged, not moniliform:
Leaflets without stipels:
Fruits winged only along one suture:
Keel-petals coherent dorsally; radicle of seed inflexed   42. **Calpurnia**
Keel-petals free; radicle of seed slightly incurved   43. **Bowdichia**
Fruits winged more or less on both sutures:
Leaf-rhachis ending in a spine; leaflets 1–2 pairs; fruits compressed,
2–1-seeded; N. Asia   44. **Ammodendron**
Leaf-rhachis not ending in a spine:
Ovary many-ovuled; leaflets 5–6 pairs; calyx-teeth suborbicular;
Madagascar   45. **Sakoanala**
Ovary few-ovuled; calyx-lobes narrowly ovate; Indo-Malaya, Micro-
nesia   46. **Pericopsis**
Leaflets with stipels; calyx tomentose or densely pubescent outside;
trop. Africa   47. **Afrormosia**
Fruits 4-winged, moniliform; low shrub, creeping from a rhizome; seeds
globose, shining   48. **Echinosophora**
Ovules 2; petals 5 or only 1:
Fruits not winged, oblong:
Shrubs armed with spiny stipules; fruits stipitate; vexillum trapeziform;
petals 5   49. **Belairia**
Trees, unarmed:
Fruits terete; petals 5, more or less alike; seeds enclosed by a fleshy aril
50. **Arillaria**
Fruits flat, 1-seeded at the top; petal 1, rounded-cordate   51. **Amburana**
Fruits narrowly winged, semiorbicular; unarmed trees and shrubs; petal 1
52. **Ateleia**
Ovule 1 (very rarely 2); petals 5; fruit 1-seeded:
Fruits not winged, flat, obliquely elliptic, narrowed at both ends, silky-
pubescent; leaflets 2–3 pairs; pedicels long and slender
53. **Platycelyphium**
Fruits variously winged:
Fruits winged above the seed; anthers shorter than the filaments:
Leaflets numerous, small; calyx truncate; bracteoles very caducous
54. **Ferreirea**
Leaflets few, larger; calyx 5-toothed; bracteoles paired at the base of the
calyx   55. **Luetzelburgia**
Fruits winged below the seed:
Leaflets with scattered pellucid-glandular dots and lines:
Anthers shorter than the filaments; stamens persistent
56. **Myrospermum**
Anthers longer than the filaments; stamens deciduous   57. **Myroxylon**
Leaflets not glandular; fruit compressed, elastically dehiscent; calyx
2-lobed, upper lobe large and enclosing the petals and genitalia
58. **Monopteryx**

Leaves reduced to 1 leaflet (1-foliolate) (from p. 320):
Bracteoles small and often caducous, not enclosing the flower in bud:
Calyx turbinate, with short lobes, the upper 2 connate; fruit flat, acuminate,
neither winged nor nerved   59. **Panurea**
Calyx cyathiform and truncate or cup-shaped:
Calyx with very short lobes; fruits transversely nerved; fruit turgid, ovoid,
or subglobose; seeds brown or bright scarlet   60. **Bowringia**
Calyx cup-shaped, lobed to the middle; fruits not nerved; fruit obliquely
oblong or obovate; seed thick, oblong or narrowly elliptic
61. **Haplormosia**
Calyx 2-fid or spathaceous:
Anthers shorter than the filaments:
Fruits narrow, linear or falcate; keel-petals dorsally coherent; anthers
short   62. **Baphia**
Fruits broad and short; keel-petals free; anthers long and narrow
63. **Baphiastrum**
Anthers longer than the filaments; fruits long-stipitate, ovate-falcate,
turgid   64. **Leucomphalos**
Bracteoles large, persistent, enclosing the flower in bud; leaflet sometimes
shortly peltate at the base; fruits obliquely oblong, acute at each end
65. **Dalhousiea**

18. **Virgilia** Poir., Lam. Enc. 8: 677 (1808) (conserved name). *Andrastis*
Raf. ex Benth. (1838). 1 sp.,[1] *V. oroboides* (Berg.) Salter (*V. capensis* Lam.),
S. Africa. B.H. 1: 554; E.P. 3, 3: 198.

Tree; leaves pinnate; leaflets small, exstipellate; stipules narrow, very caducous;
flowers rose-purple, in short terminal racemes; bracts broad, very caducous; bracteoles
absent; calyx-lobes connate into 2 lips, upper lip 2-toothed, lower 3-toothed; petals long-
clawed; vexillum recurved, orbicular; wings ovate, falcate; keel shorter than the wings,
beaked, incurved, petals dorsally connate; stamens free; anthers linear, versatile; ovary
sessile, ovules few; style incurved, subulate, stigma small, terminal; fruit linear, plano-
compressed, coriaceous, 2-valved, tomentose, margins thickened; seeds ovate, subcompressed; radicle incurved.

19. **Ormosiopsis** Ducke, Arch. Jard. Bot. Rio de Janeiro, 5: 133 (1930). 3 spp.,
Brazil; type *O. triphylla* Ducke. Amshoff, Pulle Fl. Suriname, 2, 2: 115.

Trees; stipules inconspicuous or absent; leaves imparipinnate, 11–3-foliolate; leaflets
rather large; flowers in terminal panicles, yellow or lilac; bracts small, caducous; bracteoles
2; petals clawed; vexillum suborbicular, without appendages;
keel-petals free or nearly so; stamens 10, free, subequal; anthers small, ovate; ovary subsessile, ovules few; style filiform, stigma small, terminal; fruits 1-seeded or if more seeds
then constricted between the seeds; seeds globose, pendulous, testa black or red, hilum
white.

20. **Ormosia** Jack, Trans. Linn. Soc. 10: 360, t. 25 (1811) (conserved name).
Toulichiba Adans. (1763). *Macrotropis* DC. (1825). *Layia* Hook. & Arn. (1833).
Chaenolobium Miq. (1860). *Macroule* Pierce (1942). About 120 spp., Asia,
Madagascar, trop. America; type *O. coccinea* (Aubl.) Jacks, E. trop. South
America. B.H. 1: 556; E.P. 3, 3: 194; Merrill & Chen, Sargentia, 3: 77 (1943)

[1] A second species has been described but is doubtfully distinct.

(Indo-China and Chinese spp.); Amshoff, Pulle Fl. Suriname, 2, 2: 109; van Meeuwen, Reinwardtia, 6: 227 (Malaysian spp.)

Trees; leaves imparipinnate or subparipinnate; leaflets coriaceous; stipels rare; stipules small or inconspicuous; flowers white, lilac, or dark purple, in terminal panicles or rarely in panicles of racemes and axillary; bracts and bracteoles small; upper 2 calyx-lobes sub-connate; vexillum suborbicular; wings oblique, obovate-oblong; keel-petals similar to the wings and more incurved, free, often overlapping dorsally; stamens free, all perfect or 1–2 without anthers; anthers versatile; ovary subsessile, 2- or more-ovuled; style filiform, stigma lateral, introrse; fruit oblong or rarely elongated, compressed or turgid around the seeds, woody or fleshy, 2-valved, continuous within or septate between the seeds; seeds obovate or oblong, shining, with a flexuous cartilaginous funicle; testa scarlet or 2-coloured; cotyledons thick.

21. **Ammothamnus** Bunge, Enum. Pl. Lehm. 67, t. 12 (1847). 4 spp., E. Asia; type *A. lehmannii* Bunge, Asiatic Russia. B.H. 1: 555; E.P. 3, 3: 197.

Shrublets, thinly silky-pubescent; leaves imparipinnate; leaflets numerous, small; stipels absent; stipules small, subulate; flowers white, in terminal racemes; bracts setaceous; bracteoles inconspicuous; calyx-teeth short, broad, subequal; vexillum ovate; wings broadly oblong, subfalcate; keel-petals slightly incurved, obtuse, overlapping on the back; stamens free; anthers equal, versatile; ovary sessile, many-ovuled; style short, stigma small, terminal; fruit linear, contorted, 2-valved, continuous inside; seeds ovoid, estrophiolate; cotyledons thick; radicle very short, incurved.

22. **Diplotropis** Benth., Ann. Wien. Mus. 2: 88 (1838). *Dibrachion* Tul. (1843). 14 spp., trop. South America; type *D. martiusii* Benth., Brazil. B.H. 1: 557; E.P. 3, 3: 193; Amshoff, Pulle Fl. Suriname, 2, 2: 106.

Trees; leaves imparipinnate; leaflets large, coriaceous, not stipellate; stipules small or absent; flowers rose or white, in racemes in the upper axils or panicles at the tops of the branches; bracts and bracteoles minute; calyx-teeth valvate, upper 2 connate high up; vexillum oblong, ovate, or suborbicular, appendaged on each side above the claw or nude; wings obovate or oblong, oblique or falcate; keel-petals similar to the wings, free or coherent dorsally; stamens free, the alternate filaments often shorter; anthers ovate or oblong; ovary sessile or shortly stipitate, ovules numerous to few; style incurved, stigma terminal and small or oblique; fruit ovate or oblong, compressed, thick and coriaceous or rather woody, 2-valved; seeds 2–1, obovate or suborbicular, compressed, transverse; cotyledons rather thick; radicle short, straight.

Diplotropis brachypetalum Tul., Guiana; wood hard and takes a fine polish; used for furniture, boat-building, house frames; decoction of bark used by Indians to destroy vermin.

23. **Clathrotropis** Harms, Dalla Torre & Harms Gen. Siphon. 221 (1901). 8 spp., Trinidad, Brazil, and Guianas; type *C. nitida* (Benth.) Harms, Brazil. B.H. 1: 557 (as sect. of *Diplotropis*); E.P. 3, 3: 193; Ducke, Arch. Jard. Bot. Rio de Janeiro, 6: pl. 1 (1933) (fig. of fruits and seeds); Amshoff, Pulle Fl. Suriname, 2, 2: 108 (1939).

Trees; leaves imparipinnate; stipules small; flowers in terminal panicles; calyx unequally 5-toothed; petals equal in length, shortly clawed; standard suborbicular, more or less auriculate; keel-petals slightly coherent; stamens free or nearly so, unequal; ovary sessile, 5–1-ovuled; style filiform, stigma small, terminal; fruit compressed, dehiscent, sutures often thickened and dilated, valves woody or coriaceous; seeds few, large, compressed, testa fragile.

24. **Neoharmsia** R. Vig., Notul. Syst. 14: 186 (1952). 1 sp., *N. madagascarien-sis* R. Vig., Madagascar.

Tree; leaves imparipinnate; calyx zygomorphic, very oblique at the apex and with short teeth; corolla red, papilionaceous, longer than the calyx; petals unequal, clawed, keel free;

stamens free; anthers dorsifixed; ovary sessile, many-ovuled; style straight, slender, longer than the ovary; stigma minute, terminal; fruit elongated, flat, dehiscent, not winged, reticulate; seeds 5–8, flattened.

25. **Vexillifera** Ducke, Arch. Jard. Bot. Rio de Janeiro, 3: 139, with fig. (1922). 1 sp., *V. micranthera* Ducke, Tapajoz.

Tree 35–45 m. high; bark with red sap; stipules not seen; leaves imparipinnate; leaflets large, not stipellate; flowers in paniculate racemes, rose-lilac, numerous on the defoliate branches; bracts and bracteoles rather large, subpersistent; calyx very oblique, campanulate, teeth 5, valvate, short; corolla papilionaceous, petals all free; vexillum suborbicular, persistent after flowering and longitudinally plicate; remaining petals equal among themselves, obliquely oblong, very caducous; stamens 10, the vexillary one free, the others connate at the base, subequal, all fertile; anthers very small, ovoid-oblong; ovary subsessile, 4-ovuled, style filiform, stigma terminal, small; fruit 2–1-seeded, compressed-ovate, thickly fleshy-coriaceous, opening from the apex to the base by valves; seeds oblong, slightly compressed.

26. **Petaladenium** Ducke, Archiv. Inst. Biol. Neg. Rio de Janeiro, 4: 20 (1938). 1 sp., *P. urceoliferum* Ducke, Rio Negro, Brazil.

Leaves alternate, imparipinnate; leaflets large, not stipellate; flowers lilac, in lateral simple or slightly branched racemes; bracts not seen; bracteoles rather large, subpersistent; calyx campanulate, slightly oblique, subequally 5-toothed, teeth valvate; corolla papilionaceous, petals caducous after flowering, clawed at the base; vexillum suborbicular, broadly cordate at the base, inflexed at the apex and retuse in the middle; wings oblong, auriculate on each side at the base, narrowed at the apex and remarkably glandular on the margin, glands shortly stipitate; keel-petals triangular-oblong, auriculate on each side at the base, keeled on the back; stamens 10, vexillary one free, other 9 shortly connate at the base; anthers attached at the back, oblong-linear, connective mucronulate below the apex; ovary long-stipitate, 4–5-ovuled; style filiform, stigma terminal, very small; fruit linear-oblong, very compressed, long-stipitate, acuminate at the apex, bivalved.

27. **Alexa** Moq., DC. Prodr. 13, 2: 168 (1849). *Alexandra* Schomb. (1845). 9 spp., trop. South America; type *A. imperatricis* (Schomb.) Baker, Brit. Guiana. B.H. 1: 556; E.P. 3, 3: 195; Amshoff, Pulle Fl. Suriname, 2, 2: 116.

Tall trees; leaves imparipinnate; leaflets alternate or subopposite, large, coriaceous, exstipellate; stipules caducous; flowers large, orange-coloured or scarlet, in pendulous racemes; bracts very small, no bracteoles; calyx large, coriaceous-fleshy, closed in bud, at length very shortly sinuate-dentate; petals thick, subequal in length; vexillum obovate, reflexed above the middle, emarginate or 2-lobed; lower 4 petals erect, oblong; similar to each other, free; stamens free; anthers oblong-linear, dorsifixed, versatile; ovary rather long-stipitate, ovules several; style incurved, stigma minute, terminal; fruit elongated, compressed, woody, 2-valved continuous within, at length spirally twisted; seeds suborbicular, thick, compressed; cotyledons thick; radicle very short, straight.

28. **Uleanthus** Harms, Verh. Bot. Ver. Brand. 47: 150, fig. 2 (1905). 1 sp., *U. erythrinoides* Harms, Brazil.

Tree; leaves imparipinnate, leaflets 1–2 pairs, mostly opposite, oblong or elliptic, acuminate; racemes axillary or on the trunk or branches, lax-flowered; calyx tubular, thickened next the pedicel, 4–5-toothed, teeth valvate, upper 2 larger and broader; vexillum large, rounded, clawed; other petals very small, linear-lanceolate; keel-petals free; stamens 10, free; anthers small, oblong, versatile; ovary stipitate, 8–5-ovuled, style filiform, stigma minute; fruit flattened, elastically dehiscent.

29. **Camoensia** Welw. ex Benth. & Hook. f., Gen. Pl. 1: 557 (1865) (conserved name). *Giganthemum* Welw., Trans. Linn. Soc. 25: 301, t. 36 (1859). 2 spp.,

W. trop. Africa; type *C. maxima* Welw. ex Benth. E.P. 3, 3: 192; Hutch. & Dalz., Fl. W. Trop. Afr. ed. 2 (Keay), 1:510.

Tall climbing shrubs; leaves digitately 3-foliolate; leaflets large, coriaceous, petiolulate; stipels subulate; flowers showy, very large in one species, racemose, racemes in the upper axils; bracts and bracteoles short, caducous; calyx campanulate or very long, lobes imbricate; petals clawed, corrugated; vexillum broadly orbicular, 4 lower petals free; stamens united in the lower third, or lower still; anthers uniform, linear, versatile; ovary stipitate, ovules numerous; style filiform, involute in bud, stigma terminal, small or capitate; fruit broadly linear, compressed, thick and coriaceous, 2-valved; seeds transverse, obovate, compressed; radicle short, straight.

30. **Dussia** Krug & Urb., Duss, Légum. Martinique, 11 (1891), and Engl. & Prantl, Pflanzenfam. 3, 3: 193 (1892); Urb., Symb. Antill. 1: 318 (1899). About 10 spp., Cent. to N. trop. America, West Indies; type *D. martinicensis* Krug & Urb., West Indies and Venezuela. Rudd, Contrib. Un. St. Nat. Mus. 32: 247 (1963) (revision).

Trees; unarmed; leaves imparipinnate; leaflets large, exstipellate; stipules minute, caducous; inflorescence axillary, simple, or racemes in panicles; flowers andro-monoecious, pale lilac; bracts and bracteoles present or at length caducous; calyx-tube obliquely campanulate, lobes closely imbricate, upper 2 connate high up, lower lip 3-lobed; petals subequal in length; vexillum orbicular-reniform, persistent; wings straight; keel-petals similar to the wings, dorsally tomentose; 9 stamens connate at the base, 1 subfree, anterior a little longer; anthers versatile, ovate; ovary in male flowers rudimentary, style very short, in bisexual flowers shortly stipitate, about 4–2-ovuled; style incurved above, stigma apical, minute; fruit narrowly ovoid-ellipsoid to obovoid, acuminate, subterete, 2-valved; seeds 3–1, oval or half-oval, slightly compressed; cotyledons thick and fleshy, radicle very short, inflexed, with a red aril.

31. **Castanospermum** A. Cunn., Hook., Bot. Misc. 1: 241, t. 51 (1830). *Castanocarpus* Sweet (1830). *Vieillardia* Montr. (1860). *Viellardia* Benth. & Hook. f. (1865). 2 spp., subtrop. Australia, N. Caledonia; type *C. australe* A. Cunn., Australia; often cult. B.H. 1: 556; E.P. 3, 3: 195.

Tall trees; leaves imparipinnate; leaflets large, coriaceous, exstipellate; flowers rather large, yellow, in short racemes on the one-year-old branches; bracts minute; bracteoles absent; calyx large, coloured, thick, with very short broad teeth; vexillum obovate-orbicular, recurved; lower 4 petals shorter than the vexillum, erect, oblong, concave, subequal, free; stamens free; anthers linear, versatile; ovary long-stipitate, ovules numerous; style incurved, stigma terminal, obtuse; fruit elongated, subfalcate, turgid, coriaceous-woody, 2-valved, spongy inside between the seeds; seeds large, subglobose; cotyledons thick; radicle very short, straight.

C. australe A. Cunn., Moreton Bay Chestnut; fruits roasted or made into a coarse flour and eaten by aborigines.

32. **Podopetalum** F. Muell., Melbourne Chemist (1882); Census 42 (1882); see also Bot. Centralbl. 12: 125 (1892). 1 sp., *P. ormondii* F. Muell., Queensland. E.P. 3, 3: 193.

Small tree; leaves opposite or subopposite, imparipinnate; stipules deciduous; stipels absent; flowers rose, racemose-paniculate; bracts minute, persistent; bracteoles rudimentary; calyx shortly 5-toothed, slightly imbricate in bud; petals free, upper extended in the middle, gradually narrowed into a claw, the others longer, spathulate or orbicular, almost equalsided, narrowed into a claw; stamens 10, free; anthers oblong; disk adnate to the calyx, 10-grooved; style filiform, stigma terminal, very minute; ovary long-stipitate, narrow; ovules 7 or 6; fruit stipitate; seeds 4–1, oblong, red, hilum small.

33. **Cladrastis** Rafin., Neogenyton 1: (1825). *Platyosprion* Maxim. (1873). 12 spp., E. North America, E. Asia; type *C. lutea* (Michx.) C. Koch (*C. tinctoria* Rafin.), SE. North America. B.H. 1: 554; E.P. 3, 3: 197 (excl. *Maackia* Rupr.); Takeda, Notes Roy. Bot. Gard. Edinb. 8: 96 (1913).

Large trees; buds embraced by the inflated base of the petiole; leaves alternate, imparipinnate, leaflets alternate, stipellate or not; inflorescence terminal, often pendulous, paniculate; bracts caducous; flowers showy, lax, not bracteolate; calyx 5-lobed, lobes subequal; vexillum orbicular, recurved; wings obliquely oblong, 2-auricled; keel slightly incurved, the petals closely overlapping dorsally; stamens 10, free; anthers versatile; ovary stipitate, few-ovuled; style subulate; fruit linear-lanceolate or oblong, winged or not; seeds oblong, compressed, testa brown.

C. lutea, Yellow Ash, Yellow Wood; wood strong, close-grained, yellow, used for gunstocks; heartwood source of yellow dye.

34. **Gourliea** Gill. ex Hook., Bot. Misc. 3: 207, t. 206 (1833). *Lucuma* Molina (1782). 4 spp., Chile, Paraguay, Bolivia, Argentina; type *G. decorticans* Gill. ex Hook., Argentina. B.H. 1: 555; E.P. 3, 3: 196.

Shrubs with spinescent branchlets; leaves imparipinnate, leaflets numerous, small, not stipellate; flowers small, golden-yellow, in short often fasciculate racemes at the older nodes; bracts very small; bracteoles absent; upper 2 calyx-lobes truncate, subconnate, lower narrower; petals rather long-clawed; vexillum broadly orbicular, spreading; wings obliquely obovate, undulate; keel shorter than the wings, slightly incurved, obtuse, the petals subcoherent dorsally; stamens free or shortly connate at the base; anthers small; ovary sessile, ovules numerous; style incurved, subulate, stigma small, terminal; fruit ovoid-globose, not opening, subdrupaceous, endocarp woody, epicarp crustaceous-fleshy; seeds 2–1, reniform, thick, not strophiolate; cotyledons thick; radicle short, slightly incurved.

35. **Xanthocercis** Baill., Adansonia, 9: 293 (1870). *Pseudocadia* Harms (1902). 2 spp.; type *X. madagascariensis* Baill., Madagascar; *X. sambesiaca* (Baker) Doumaz le Grand, S. and S. trop. Africa. Doumaz le Grand, Bull. Soc. Bot. Fr. 99: 313 (1952).

Trees; leaves imparipinnate, leaflets alternate; racemes paniculate, terminal, often silky-villous; bracts and bracteoles small; calyx truncate or shortly denticulate, silky outside, thickened and disk-like at the base; petals 5, inserted with the stamens at the bottom of the calyx, equal to each other in length, the outermost (vexillum) broader than the others, clawed, broadly oblong, shortly auricled at the base, other petals lanceolate, narrowed into a claw; all with a silky line down the middle; stamens 10; vexillary stamen free, remainder partly coherent at the base; ovary long-stipitate, linear, 10–12-ovuled; style very short; stipe villous, fruit stipitate, drupe-like, ellipsoid, not dehiscent; seeds reniform, thick, nearly black.

36. **Uribea** Dugand & Romero, Mutisia, 27: 1, tt. 1–2 (1962). 1 sp., *U. tamarindoides* Dugand & Romero, Colombia, Costa Rica.

Tall tree; leaves deciduous, alternate, imparipinnate, stipulate and stipellate; leaflets alternate, lanceolate or elliptic, pinnately nerved; flowers in short axillary racemes; bracts minute; bracteoles 2, minute below the calyx; upper 2 calyx-lobes connate high up, remainder subequal, ovate; corolla papilionaceous, rose or violet; vexillum broadly obovate-elliptic with a broad claw with inflexed margins; wings and keel-petals subsimilar, clawed; stamens 10, filaments free or united only at the base, inserted on a thin perigynous disk, persistent; anthers small, subbasifixed, connective produced at the top, acute; ovary stipitate, few-ovuled, style subulate, glabrous, stigma minute; fruit indehiscent, more or less compressed, slightly turgid over the seeds, shortly stipitate, linear-oblong when few-seeded, more or less elliptic when 1-seeded by abortion; seeds compressed, rounded, radicle straight.

37. **Spirotropis** Tul., Arch. Mus. Par. 4: 113 (1844). 1 sp., *S. longifolia* (DC.) Baill., Guiana. Bull. Torr. Club, 75: 393 (1948).

Tree; leaves imparipinnate, leaflets large, few pairs, opposite or subalternate, coriaceous, velvety below; stipules spathulate-oblanceolate, closely nerved; flowers purple-red, racemose-paniculate, terminal; bracts and bracteoles minute; calyx tubular, 2-lipped, upper lip 2- lower 3-toothed, at length split to the base into 2 reflexed segments; petals very shortly clawed; vexillum elliptic; wings linear-oblong, straight, shorter than the vexillum; keel-petals equal to the wings, linear-oblong, at length convolute; stamens free, anthers small, attached near the base; ovary subsessile, few-ovuled; style filiform, stigma small, terminal; fruit obliquely oblong, narrowed at each end, not winged, reticulate, indehiscent; seeds few.

38. **Bolusanthus** Harms, Fedde Repert. Nov. Sp. 2: 14 (1906). 1 sp., *B. speciosus* (Bolus) Harms, S. trop. and S. Africa.

Tree; leaves imparipinnate, leaflets 3–6 pairs, opposite or alternate, lanceolate or oblong-lanceolate, unequal-sided at the base, densely silky when young; racemes terminal, produced with the leaves, lax-flowered; bracts and bracteoles small, deciduous; calyx campanulate-cupular, silky, 5-lobed below the middle, lobes subequal, upper 2 more connate, ovate, remainder lanceolate; vexillum clawed, very broad, suborbicular; wings clawed, oblong, appendaged on each side; keel-petals free or nearly so, like the wings; stamens 10, free; anthers oval, dorsifixed; ovary at the base of the calyx, shortly stipitate, silky; style curved, stigma capitellate; ovules 5–4; fruit linear-oblong, compressed, flat, shortly stipitate, reticulate, not winged, tardily dehiscent; seeds up to 4 or 5.

39. **Maackia** Rupr. & Maxim., Bull. Phys.-Math. Acad. Sci. St. Petersb. 15: 143 (1856). *Buergeria* Miq. (1867). 12 spp., E. Asia; type *M. amurensis* Rupr. & Maxim., Amurland, Japan, Korea. Takeda, Notes Roy. Bot. Gard. Edinb. 8: 99 (1913).

Trees; buds axillary, free from the petiole; leaves alternate, imparipinnate; leaflets mostly opposite, not stipellate; inflorescence racemose or branched at the base; bracts deciduous; flowers numerous and dense, bracteolate; calyx inflated, 4-lobed, upper lobe larger; vexillum recurved, thickened at the base; wings obliquely oblong, hastate; keel-petals semi-sagittate, subcoherent dorsally; stamens 10, very shortly connate at the base; anthers versatile, quadrate-elliptic; ovary subsessile, few-ovuled, densely hairy; style subulate, stigma minute, terminal; fruit subsessile, winged along the ventral suture, plano-compressed, scarcely opening, hirsute; seeds oblong, compressed, testa thin, strophiolate, brown.

M. amurensis, wood heavy, close-grained, dark brown, used in Japan for interior finish of houses, furniture, gun-stocks, and handles of implements.

40. **Sophora**[1] Linn., Sp. Pl. 373 (1753). About 80 spp., warm and temp. regions of both hemispheres; type *S. tomentosa* Linn., tropics. B.H. 1: 555; E.P. 3, 3: 195; van Steenis, Malay spp., Bull. Bot. Gard. Buitenz. ser. 3, 17: 421; Burkart, Legum. Argent. ed. 2, 206, fig. 48; Chock, Revis. of Hawaiian spp., Pacific Science, 10: 136 (1956).

Trees, shrubs, or rarely perennial herbs; leaves imparipinnate, leaflets numerous and small or few and larger; stipels setaceous or often absent; flowers white, yellow, or rarely

---

[1] Synonyms of **Sophora**: *Broussonetia* Orteg. (1798). *Edwardsia* Salisb. (1808). *Patrinia* Raf. (1819). *Pseudosophora* DC. (1825). *Radiusia* Reichb. (1828). *Edwarsia* Dumort. (1829). *Pseudosophora* Sweet (1830). *Styphnolobium* Schott. (1830). *Vibexia* Raf. (1832). *Calia* Teran & Berland (1832). *Agastianis* Raf. (1836). *Zanthyrsis* Raf. (1836). *Dermatophyllum* Scheele (1848). *Goebelia* Bunge ex Boiss. (1872). *Keyserlingia* Bunge ex Boiss. (1872). *Platyosprion* Maxim. (1877).

blue-violet, in terminal racemes or leafy panicles; bracts linear, minute or absent; bracteoles often absent; calyx-teeth short; vexillum broadly obovate or orbicular, erect or spreading, usually shorter (rarely longer) than the keel; wings oblong, oblique; keel oblong, almost straight, the petals overlapping or connate dorsally; stamens free, or rarely connate at the base into a ring; anthers versatile; ovary shortly stipitate, ovules numerous; style incurved, stigma minute, terminal; fruit moniliform, terete or slightly compressed, fleshy to woody, not opening or very tardily 2-valved; seeds obovoid or globose, not strophiolate; cotyledons thick.

S. japonica L., Japanese Pagoda-tree, N. China, Japan; extract from leaves and fruits used in China to adulterate opium; dye prepared from fruits used to colour clothes yellow, with indigo becoming green. *S. secundiflora* (Orteg.) Lag., Mescalbean Sophora, SW. United States and Mexico, fruits called Mescal Beans, used in necklaces and as intoxicant in Red Bean dance. *S. tetraptera* Ait., Fourwing Sophora, New Zealand, Chile, Juan Fernandez; wood of great strength, extremely durable; used for bearings of shafts and machines, cabinet-work, and ornamental turnery.

41. **Angylocalyx** Taub., Engl. Bot. Jahrb. 23: 172 (1896). 14 spp., trop. Africa; type *A. oligophyllus* (Bak.) Bak. f. (*A. ramiflorus Taub.*), W. trop. Africa. E.P.N. 199; Hutch. & Dalz., Fl. W. Trop. Afr. 1: 370, fig. 142, B.; ed. 2 (Keay), 1: 509, fig. 161, B.

Shrubs or trees; leaves imparipinnate, leaflets few, alternate or subopposite, petiolulate, more or less acuminate; flowers in racemes on the old wood or on new growths; pedicels jointed; bracts very small; calyx tubular, bent in the middle, shortly toothed or subtruncate; petals 5, unequal, vexillum narrowly suborbicular, wings obliquely oblong; keel-petals free, linear-oblong, as long as the wings; stamens 10; filaments free, compressed; anthers oblong, subbasifixed; ovary tomentose; fruits torulose, 7–2-seeded, beaked and stipitate; seeds narrowly oblong, turgid.

42. **Calpurnia** E. Mey., Comm. Pl. Afr. Austr. 2 (1835). About 16 spp., S. and trop. Africa, India; lectotype *C. intrusa* (R.Br.) E. Mey., S. Africa. B.H. 1: 554; E.P. 3, 3: 197.

Trees or shrubs; leaves imparipinnate, leaflets numerous, exstipellate; stipules small or inconspicuous; flowers yellow, in axillary racemes or paniculate at the apex of the branches; bracts very small; bracteoles absent; calyx-teeth or lobes short, broad, upper 2 subconnate; vexillum suborbicular, erect or subrecurved; wings falcate-oblong; keel incurved, obtuse, petals coherent dorsally; stamens free; anthers versatile, often small; ovary stipitate, ovules numerous; style incurved, subulate, stigma terminal, capitate; fruit stipitate, linear, plano-compressed, membranous, not dehiscent, narrowly winged along the upper suture; seeds compressed, oval-oblong, transverse; radicle inflexed.

43. **Bowdichia** H. B. & K., Nov. Gen. et Spec. 6: 376 (1823). *Sebipira* Mart. (1828). *Bodwichia* Walp. (1842). *Cebipira* Post & Kuntze (1903). 12 spp., S. trop. America; type *B. virgilioides* H. B. & K. B.H. 1: 557; E.P. 3, 3: 193.

Tall trees, with hard wood; leaves imparipinnate, leaflets numerous, exstipellate; flowers blue or white, in lax terminal panicles; bracts and bracteoles small; petals often with crispate margins; calyx-teeth valvate; vexillum broadly orbicular; wings obovate or broadly oblong, longer than the vexillum; keel-petals oblong, free, smaller than the wings; stamens free, slightly unequal, 1–2 often wanting; anthers versatile; ovary stipitate, ovules numerous; style filiform, inflexed at the apex, stigma capitate, terminal; fruit oblong-linear, plano-compressed, membranous, not dehiscent, narrowly winged along the upper suture; seeds oblong, compressed, transverse; radicle slightly incurved.

B. virgilioides H. B. & K.; wood very heavy, difficult to work, used in Brazil for hubs and felloes of cartwheels.

44. Ammodendron Fisch. ex DC., Prodr. 2: 523 (1825). 8 spp., N. Asia; type *A. argenteum* (Willd.) O. Ktze. (*A. karelinii* Fisch. & Mey.). B.H. 1: 554; E.P. 3, 3: 197.

Silvery-silky shrubs; leaves paripinnate, leaflets 1–2 pairs, the rhachis ending in a spine; stipules small, stipels absent; flowers in terminal racemes; bracts small, caduous, or absent; bracteoles none; calyx-lobes subequal, upper 2 connate; vexillum orbicular, recurved; wings obliquely oblong; keel incurved, obtuse; petals free; stamens free, anthers versatile; ovary sessile; ovules few; style incurved, subulate, stigma small, terminal; fruit linear or lanceolate, compressed, indehiscent, 2–1-seeded, winged on both sutures; seeds oblong, subterete, estrophiolate; cotyledons thick, radicle inflexed.

45. Sakoanala R. Vig., Not. Syst. 14: 186 (1952). 2 spp., Madagascar; type *S. madagascariensis* R. Vig.

Trees; leaves imparipinnate; leaflets 5–6 pairs, alternate or subopposite, rather large, rounded at the base; stipels absent; panicles terminal; bracteoles very small; calyx campanulate, with small semiorbicular teeth; corolla papilionaceous; vexillum orbicular, clawed, wings shorter than the vexillum, not auriculate; keel-petals oblong; stamens 10, free; anthers dorsifixed; ovary stipitate, many-ovuled; style glabrous; fruit very flat, papery, narrowly winged, several-seeded, rounded at each end, middle part densely reticulate; seeds transverse, small.

46. Pericopsis Thwaites, Enum. Pl. Zeyl. 413 (1864). 1 sp., *P. mooniana* Thwaites, Ceylon, Malay Archip. B.H. 1: 556; E.P. 3, 3: 194; Knaap van Meeuwen, Bull. Bot. Jard. Brux. 32: 213 (1962) (excl. *Afrormosia*).

Tree; leaves imparipinnate, leaflets large, coriaceous; stipels absent; flowers dark-purple, racemose in the upper leaf-axils or paniculate at the tops of the shoots; bracts and bracteoles minute, very caducous; calyx-lobes subequal or the upper 2 slightly smaller and subconnate; vexillum broadly orbicular, reflexed; wings falcate-obovate; keel incurved, obtuse, petals free; stamens free; anthers versatile, dorsifixed; ovary stipitate, ovules few; style subulate, involute at the apex, stigma introrse; fruit stipitate, broadly linear, plano-compressed, margined on each suture; seeds much compressed, broadly ovate or orbicular; cotyledons obliquely cordate at the base, radicle subincurved.

P. mooniana, wood brown with dark shades, valued for furniture in Ceylon.

47. Afrormosia Harms, Engl. & Prantl., Pflanzenfam. Nachtr. 3: 158 (1906); Notizbl. Bot. Gart. Berl. App. 21: 2, 64, with fig. (1911); Engl. Bot. Jahrb. 49: 430 (1913). 6 spp., trop. Africa; type *A. laxiflora* (Benth.) Harms. Louis, Bull. Jard. Bot. Brux. 17: 109 (1943) (Congo spp.); Hutch. & Dalz., Fl. W. Trop. Afr. 1: 371; ed. 2 (Keay), 1: 510.

Trees and shrubs; stipules soon falling off; leaves imparipinnate, leaflets alternate or subopposite, stipellate; flowers paniculate or racemose; bracts and bracteoles small and deciduous; calyx campanulate, the 2 upper teeth partly connate; vexillum suborbicular; wings oblique, obovate-oblong; stamens free, all fertile or one or two abortive; anthers elliptic, versatile; ovary shortly stipitate, 2- or more-ovuled; style slender, curled at the top, with small stigma; fruit elliptic when 1-seeded, broadly oblong-linear when more-seeded, narrowly margined on both sutures especially the ventral.

Included by van Meeuwen (above) in *Pericopsis*, but differs in its *stipellate* leaflets and separate distribution.

48. Echinosophora Nakai, Bot. Mag. Tokyo 37: 33 (1923). 1 sp., *E. koreensis* (Nakai) Nakai, Korea.

Low shrub, creeping from a rhizome; stipules rigid, persistent, spinescent; leaves imparipinnate; racemes terminal on the new shoots; calyx oblique, almost saccate at the base behind, 5-toothed; petals yellow; vexillum long-clawed, elongated, emarginate, straight, the margin touching the wings; wings constricted at the base, much shorter than the vexillum;

keel-petals shorter than the others, free; stamens 10, free, 5 shorter than the others; anthers rounded, versatile; ovary stipitate; style elongated, stigma point-like; fruit moniliform, 4-winged; seeds globose, shining.

49. Belairia A. Rich., Sagra Hist. Fis. Cuba, 10: 235, t. 40 (1845). 5 spp., Cuba; type *B. spinosa* A. Rich. B.H. 1: 558; E.P. 3, 3: 192; Urb., Symb. Antill. 2: 297.

Shrubs, armed with subulate stipular spines; leaves paripinnate, leaflets few pairs, or leaves trifoliolate, small, rigid; flowers solitary or subfasciculate at the older nodes; bracts caducous; bracteoles small, ovate, persistent for a time; calyx shortly 5-toothed; petals acute, erect; vexillum trapeziform; lower 4 petals subequal, free, linear-lanceolate; stamens free, exserted; anthers uniform, ovate; ovary stipitate, 2-ovulate; style subulate, incurved, stigma minute; fruit stipitate, small, oblong, plano-compressed; cotyledons fleshy in thin endosperm; radicle incurved, accumbent.

50. Arillaria S. Kurz, Journ. As. Soc. Bengal, 42, pt. 2: 70 (1873). 1 sp., *A. robusta* S. Kurz, Burma. E.P. 3, 3: 194.

Tree; leaves imparipinnate; leaflets opposite, stipellate; flowers white, in terminal panicles; calyx large, the upper 2 teeth slightly larger; vexillum suborbicular; wings and keel-petals more or less alike, falcate, all shortly clawed and free; stamens 10, free, unequal, all fertile; anthers versatile; ovary shortly and thickly stipitate, 2-ovuled; style filiform, revolute, stigma lateral; fruit oblong, terete, fleshy-coriaceous, dehiscent; seeds 2 or 1 by abortion, large, oblong, black, completely enclosed by a fleshy aril; cotyledons thick.

51. Amburana Schwacke & Taub., E.P. 3, 3: 387 (1894). *Torresea* Allem. (1862) not Ruiz & Pavon (1794) (*Torresia*). 2 spp., trop. South America; type *A. cearensis* (Allem.) A. C. Smith, Brazil, N. Argentina. Burkart, Legum. Argent. ed. 2: 204, fig. 46; A. C. Smith, Trop. Woods no. 62: 30 (1940).

Trees; leaves imparipinnate; leaflets 11–15, alternate; flowers yellowish-white, racemose, probably on the old wood; bracts early deciduous; calyx long-tubular, sharply expanded into a 5-toothed limb; petal 1, rounded-cordate, shortly clawed, with cordate base; stamens 10, free, almost equal; filaments slender; anthers short, rounded, dorsifixed; ovary hook-like, long-stipitate, stipe for the most part adnate to the calyx-tube; ovules 2; seeds 1–2; style very short, with small terminal stigma; fruit narrowly oblong, coriaceous, dry, dehiscent at the apex, 2-valved, 1-seeded at the top; seed ovoid.

A. acreana (Ducke) Smith, Cumaru, Imburana de Cheiro, Brazil, wood with scent and taste of *Vanilla*, coarse grained; general construction; seeds source of volatile oil used in perfumery. *A. cearensis*, resin of bark also source of volatile oil, used in medicine; wood for furniture and general construction.

52. Ateleia D. Dietr., Syn. Pl. 4: 1219 (1847). *Pterocarpus* sect. *Ateleia* Moç. & Sesse (1825); DC., Mém. Légum. 394, t. 57 (1925). *Atelia* Steud. (1840). *Atalea* A. Rich. (1845). *Cyathostegia* Schery (1950). About 17 spp., trop. and subtrop. South America and Cent. America, West Indies; type *A. pterocarpa* Moç. & Sesse ex (DC.) D. Dietr., Mexico. B.H. 1: 558; E.P. 3, 3: 191; Burkart, Legum. Argent. ed. 2: 206, fig. 47; Mohlenbrock, Webbia, 17: 153, figs. 5–19 (1962).

Unarmed trees and shrubs; leaves imparipinnate, leaflets subcoriaceous; stipules minute or inconspicuous; flowers small, white, racemose, racemes axillary, sometimes subpaniculate; bracts very small; bracteoles absent; calyx truncate or very shortly dentate, soon open in bud; petal 1 (the vexillum), clawed, hooded, remainder deficient; stamens free; anthers uniform, ovate-rounded; ovary shortly stipitate, 2-ovulate; stigma subsessile, ovate, inflexed; fruit stipitate, semiorbicular, plano-compressed, membranous, not dehiscent, narrowly winged on the upper straight suture; seeds ovate-reniform, compressed, hilum small.

53. **Platycelyphium** Harms, Engl. Bot. Jahrb. 38: 74, fig. 1 (1905). 1 sp., *P. cyananthum* Harms., trop. E. Africa.

Tree, young parts densely silky; leaves imparipinnate, leaflets 2–3 pairs, opposite or sub-opposite, broadly ovate, silky below; racemes lax, from the one-year-old shoots, pedicels long and slender; calyx campanulate, equally lobed nearly to the middle, lobes deltoid-ovate; petals inserted at the base of the calyx, vexillum very shortly clawed, suborbicular or trans-versely elliptic, wings and keel-petals oblong, shortly clawed; stamens 10, free, inserted at the base of the calyx; anthers oblong, dorsifixed; ovary very shortly stipitate, silky, 1-ovulate, narrowed into the incurved style; stigma truncate; fruit shortly stipitate, flat, obliquely elliptic, narrowed at both ends, not dehiscent, silky-pubescent, 1-seeded.

54. **Ferreirea** Allem., Trab. Soc. Vell. 26 (1852). 1 sp., *F. spectabilis* Allem., Bolivia, Brazil, Paraguay, Argentina. B.H. 1: 558; E.P. 3, 3: 191; Burkart, Legum. Argent. ed. 2; 203, fig. 45.

Tall tree; leaves imparipinnate, leaflets numerous, small, without stipels; flowers small, yellow, in slender racemes paniculate at the ends of the branches; bracts and bracteoles small, very caducous; calyx membranous, somewhat coloured, truncate; vexillum broadly suborbicular, reflexed; lower 4 petals subsimilar to each other, free, narrowly oblong; stamens free; anthers uniform, ovate; ovary shortly stipitate, 1-ovulate; style very short, incurved, stigma small, terminal; fruit stipitate, samaroid, 1-seeded at the base, not dehis-cent, produced at the apex into a unilateral membranous transversely veined wing; seed oblong, subreniform, compressed.

55. **Luetzelburgia** Harms, Ber. Deutsch. Bot. Ges. 40: 177, fig. 1 (1922). 3 spp., Brazil; type *L. pterocarpoides* Harms.

Shrub or small tree; leaves imparipinnate, leaflets few, alternate or subopposite, ovate or elliptic, pinnately nerved; stipules and stipels absent; flowers racemose-paniculate; bracteoles paired at the base of the calyx, very small; calyx obliquely cupular, villous, teeth 5, upper 2 slightly connate; corolla exserted; petals 5, almost equal in length, clawed, oblong, margin corrugated-plicate, appendaged on each side; vexillum silky outside; stamens 10 (or 9 with the vexillary one aborted), free; filaments glabrous; anthers small, dorsifixed; ovary stipi-tate, style glabrous or nearly so; ovule 1; fruit 1-seeded, body hard, obliquely elliptic, nar-rowly laterally winged and topped by a large unilateral oblong spreading wing.

56. **Myrospermum** Jacq., Enum. Pl. Carib. 4 (1760). *Calusia* Bert. ex DC. (1825). 1 sp., *M. frutescens* Jacq., NE. South America, Cent. America, West Indies, Trinidad. B.H. 1: 558; E.P. 3, 3: 191.

Tree; leaves imparipinnate, leaflets without stipels, with scattered pellucid-glandular dots and lines; flowers rather large, white, in axillary racemes; calyx turbinate, incurved, mem-branous at the apex, teeth short and broad; vexillum obovate; lower 4 petals subsimilar to each other, free, falcate-lanceolate, acute; stamens persistent, free, filaments elongated; anthers very small; ovary stipitate, 2- or more-ovuled; style subulate, stigma terminal; fruit stipitate, compressed, not dehiscent, hardened at the apex and 1-seeded, long-narrowed to the base and 2-winged, lower wing narrow, upper broader; seed 1, oblong.

57. **Myroxylon** Linn. f., Suppl. 34, 233 (1781) (conserved name). *Toluifera* Linn. (1753). *Myroxylum* Schreb. (1789). 15 spp., trop. South America, Argentina; type *M. peruiferum* Linn. f., trop. South America. B.H. 1: 558; E.P. 3, 3: 189; Harms, Notizbl. Bot. Gart. Berl. 5: 85 (1808); Burkart, Legum. Argent. ed. 2: 201, fig. 202; Amshoff, Pulle Fl. Suriname, 2, 2: 105.

Trees; leaves imparipinnate, leaflets without stipels, with scattered pellucid-glandular dots and lines; flowers whitish, in axillary racemes or fasciculate-paniculate at the apex of the branches; calyx subincurved, irregularly toothed; vexillum broadly orbicular; lower 4 petals subequal, free, narrow; stamens deciduous, free, or shortly united at the base; anthers uniform, oblong, apiculate; ovary long-stipitate, 2-ovulate near the apex; style short, in-curved, stigma terminal; fruit stipitate, compressed, not opening, hardened and 1-seeded at the apex, long-narrowed at the base and 2-winged, lower wing narrower, upper broader; seed subreniform.

M. balsamum (Linn.) Harms, Balsam of Tolu, Venezuela, Colombia, Peru; source of a balsam, collected in gourds, used for ointments and salves, bronchitis, coughs, and colds, and as fixative in perfumery. *M. pereira* (Royle) Klotzsch, also Balsam of Peru, cult.; wood valuable, like Mahogany; balsam derived from stems and used as for *M. balsamum.*

58. Monopteryx Spruce ex Benth., Fl. Brasil. 15, 1: 307, t. 122 (1862). 3 spp., Brazil, Venezuela; lectotype *M. angustifolia* Spruce ex Benth., Brazil. B.H. 1: 552; E.P. 3, 3: 199.

Tall trees; leaves alternate, imparipinnate, leaflets coriaceous, not stipellate; flowers racemose, racemes in a terminal panicle; bracts and bracteoles small, very caducous; calyx-tube very short, lobes united into 2 lips, the upper lip large and enclosing the corolla, lower short, acute, entire or obscurely 3-toothed; petals sessile; vexillum obovate-suborbicular, remainder rather shorter; wings subfalcate-oblong, free; keel-petals rather similar to the wings, dorsally connate from the base to apex; stamens subequal, free; anthers linear-oblong; ovary stipitate, 1-ovuled; style short, arcuate, stigma introrse, lateral; fruit com-pressed, elastically dehiscent.

59. Panurea Spruce ex Benth. & Hook. f., Gen. Pl. 1: 553 (1865). 1 sp., *P. longifolia* Spruce ex Benth., Brazil. B.H. 1: 553; E.P. 3, 3: 198.

Much-branched tree; leaves alternate, 1-foliolate, oblong-elliptic, large, coriaceous, pinnately nerved; petiolule very short; stipules small, subulate, caducous; flowers small, yellowish, shortly paniculate in the leaf-axils; bracts small, caducous; bracteoles very small; calyx-lobes short, broad, upper 2 connate in a 2-toothed lip; petals shortly clawed; vexillum suborbicular, bilobed; wings obliquely ovate; keel-petals free, shorter than but similar to the wings; stamens free; anthers small, subglobose; ovary sessile, few-ovuled; style very short, thick, hooked-inflexed, stigma terminal, truncate; fruit flat, acuminate, 2-valved, not winged or nerved; seeds oblique to the valves, compressed, testa black when dry.

60. Bowringia Champ. ex Benth., Hook. Kew Journ. 4: 75 (1852). 2 spp., trop. Africa, Asia; type *B. callicarpa* Champ. ex Benth., S. China, Indo-China, Borneo. *B. mildbraedii* Harms., W. trop. Africa. B.H. 1: 553; E.P. 3, 3: 198; Hutch. & Dalz., Fl. W. Trop. Afr. ed. 2 (Keay), 1: 511.

Scandent shrubs; leaves 1-foliolate, leaflet large, exstipellate; stipules minute; flowers white, in short axillary racemes; bracts minute, falling off; bracteoles small, persistent for a time; calyx membranous, mouth truncate, teeth minute; petals very shortly clawed; vexillum orbicular; wings falcate-oblong; keel-petals subsimilar to the wings or slightly larger, scarcely connate dorsally; stamens free or connate only at the base; anthers oblong; ovary stipitate, ovules numerous; style subulate, stigma terminal; fruit stipitate, turgid, ovoid or subglobose, thinly coriaceous, 2-valved; seeds oblong or subglobose, brown or bright scarlet, hilum lateral, strophiole large, cyathiform.

61. Haplormosia Harms, Engl., Pflanzenv. Afr. 3, 1: 533 (1915), and Fedde Repert. 15: 23 (1917). 2 spp., trop. Africa; type *H. monophylla* (Harms) Harms, W. trop. Africa. Hutch. & Dalz., Fl. W. Trop. Afr. 1: 371; ed. 2 (Keay), 1: 510.

Trees; leaves 1-foliolate, oblong or lanceolate; racemes few- or several-flowered; pedicels with 2 short bracteoles at the apex; calyx cupular, lobed below the middle, 2 upper lobes more connate; vexillum almost semiorbicular, wings very obliquely ovate, keel-petals obliquely lanceolate, slightly coherent in the upper part; stamens 10, free; ovary stipitate, style slender, with minute stigma; ovules 4–2; fruit shortly stipitate, obliquely oblong or obovate, compressed, opening by somewhat woody valves; seed 1, thick, oblong or narrowly elliptic.

62. **Baphia** Afzel. ex Lodd., Bot. Cab. 1: t. 367 (1825). *Delaria* Desv. (1826). *Carpolobia* G. Don (1831). *Bracteolaria* Hochst. (1841). About 100 spp., trop. and S. Africa, Madagascar, Borneo, Philippine Isls.; type *B. nitida* Lodd., trop. Africa. B.H. 1: 553; E.P. 3, 3: 198; Pellegr., Bull. Soc. Bot. Fr. 90: 161 (1944).

Trees and shrubs; leaves 1-foliolate, leaflet large, without or very rarely with minute stipels (*B. borneensis* Oliv.); stipules small; flowers white or yellow, axillary or in short axillary and terminal racemes; bracts small; bracteoles sometimes large but deciduous, sometimes shorter than the calyx or small and persistent for a time; calyx ovoid or globose, membranous, shortly dentate at the apex, 2-fid or split spathaceously; petals subsessile; vexillum orbicular; wings obliquely oblong or obovate; keel slightly incurved, obtuse, petals dorsally subcoherent; stamens 10, free; anthers shorter than the filaments; ovary subsessile, 4–2-ovulate; style incurved, stigma small, terminal; fruit linear, lanceolate or falcate, acuminate, plano-compressed, coriaceous, 2-valved, continuous within or slightly filled; seeds suborbicular.

B. nitida, African Sandalwood, Camwood; used for beams, pillars, walking sticks, pestles; source of red and brown dye used for colouring wood; *B. pubescens* Hook. f., wood fine-grained, heavier than water, odour of violets; source of a dye.

63. **Baphiastrum** Harms, Engl. Bot. Jahrb. 49: 435 (1913). 12 spp., trop. Africa; type *B. brachycarpum* Harms, Cameroons. Pellegr., Bull. Soc. Bot. Fr. 90: 161 (1944).

Trees or scandent shrubs; leaves 1-foliolate, elliptic; stipules deciduous; flowers in axillary and terminal racemes or raceme-like panicles; bracts ovate-lanceolate, small; bracteoles paired at the base of the calyx, ovate, velvety-tomentose; calyx closed in bud, at length split into 2 segments; vexillum rounded, emarginate; keel-petals free; stamens 10; filaments free, glabrous; anthers long and narrow, attached near the base; ovary subsessile, 2-ovuled; style curved; fruit short and broad, 2-valved, or narrow and constricted between the seeds, velvety; seeds blackish or red when dry, punctate.

64. **Leucomphalos** Benth., Hook. Ic. Pl., t. 784 (1848). *Leucomphalus* Benth. (1849). 1 sp., *L. capparideus* Benth., trop. Africa. B.H. 1: 553; E.P. 3, 3: 198; Hutch. & Dalz., Fl. W. Trop. Afr. 1: 371.

Shrub; leaves 1-foliolate, leaflet large, without stipels; stipules inconspicuous; flowers white, in terminal panicles; bracts and bracteoles small; calyx subglobose, membranous, split during flowering; petals subsessile; vexillum broadly obovate; wings linear-oblong; keel-petals broader than the wings, free; stamens free; anthers linear, longer than the filament; ovary long-stipitate, few-ovuled; style incurved, subulate, stigma small, terminal; fruit long-stipitate, ovate-falcate, turgid, coriaceous, 2-valved; seeds 2–1, transversely oblong, thick, hilum lateral, strophiole thick and like a fungus.

65. **Dalhousiea** R. Grah., Wall. Numer. List no. 5339 (1832). *Dalhousia* Lem. (1849). 3 spp., E. Himalayas, W. trop. Africa; type *D. bracteata* R. Grah., E. Himalayas. *D. africana* S. Moore, W. trop. Africa. B.H. 1: 552; E.P. 3, 3: 199.

Shrubs; leaves 1-foliolate, leaflet large, without stipels, sometimes shortly peltate at the base; stipules ovate-lanceolate; flowers white, in axillary and terminal sometimes branched racemes; bracts large and stipule-like, opposite, ovate, subcordate, persistent; bracteoles similar or larger, enclosing the flower in bud; calyx-teeth very short; vexillum orbicular, subsessile; wings obliquely oblong, free; keel broader than the wings, erect, oblique, the petals dorsally subcoherent, with very short claws; stamens free; anthers oblong-linear; ovary subsessile, few-ovuled; style slightly incurved, stigma terminal; fruit obliquely oblong, acute at each end, compressed, coriaceous, 2-valved; seeds 3–2, suborbicular, compressed.

Tribe 4. PODALYRIEAE

Benth., Enum. Pl. Hugel 27 (1839); Benth. & Hook. f., Gen. Pl. 1: 437 (1865)

Shrubs or rarely perennial herbs; stems rarely climbing; leaves simple or digitately 3- or rarely many-foliolate, very rarely pinnate or reduced to scales; stipules free or minute or absent, rarely connate and leaf-opposed; stipels absent; corolla papilionaceous; stamens 10, *filaments free* or equally connate only at the base; *anthers uniform*, very rarely dimorphic; style glabrous, or very rarely with a ring of hairs below the stigma; fruit dehiscent, 2-valved, rarely indehiscent, continuous within or filled or partly so between the seeds, but not jointed; seeds with or without a strophiole; *embryo with inflexed radicle*. Mainly Australia and S. Africa. Type genus *Podalyria* Lam.

Stipules free from each other and not leaf-opposed, or minute or absent:
  Leaves simple or 1-foliolate (not reduced to scales) (to pp. 336 and 337):
  Anthers uniform in size and shape (to p. 336):
    Bracteoles free, not united and not forming a cup below the calyx, or
      rarely bracteoles absent (to p. 336):
    Vexillum small or very narrow or minute, smaller than the wing-petals;
      keel mostly longer than the wings:
      Flowers separate from each other; leaves alternate or opposite; disk
        around the ovary cup-shaped or sheathing   66. **Brachysema**
      Flowers 4 together within an involucre of 4 bracts; leaves opposite;
        disk absent   67. **Jansonia**
    Vexillum relatively large, orbicular or kidney-shaped:
      Ovary and fruit 1-locular, not divided by a longitudinal septum, rarely
        transversely subseptate between the seeds:
        Upper lip of the calyx very large; flowers in terminal or lateral racemes
          or fasciculate along the branches; style winged in the upper part
          or with a ring of hairs below the stigma   68. **Sphaerolobium**
        Upper lip of the calyx not or only slightly larger than the lower; style
          neither winged nor with a ring of hairs below the stigma:
          Calyx-lobes much longer than the tube, imbricate; fruit oblong-
            linear or lanceolate, more or less turgid; ovules numerous with
            slender funicles   69. **Isotropis**
          Calyx-lobes not longer than the tube:
            Bracteoles persistent, close to or adnate to the calyx:
              Petals not adnate to the stamens; flowers axillary and solitary or
                crowded in terminal heads, often surrounded by scarious or
                leafy stipules or bracts   70. **Pultenaea**
              Petals adnate at the base to all or part of the stamens and forming
                with them a short tube; flowers axillary or terminal 71. **Phyllota**
            Bracteoles absent or small and separate from the calyx, or soon de-
              ciduous:
              Leaves hooked at the apex; ovary sessile, 2-ovuled 72. **Erichsenia**
              Leaves not hooked at the apex:
                Fruits triangular, compressed; ovules 2; leaves rigid, flat or terete
                  or spine-like   73. **Daviesia**

Fruits not triangular:
Ovules several, 4 or more:
Fruit linear, flat, subtorulose; branches spinous at the apex
                                                        89. **Pickeringia**
Fruit not torulose; branches not spinous:
Seeds strophiolate:
Leaves opposite or 3–4 in a whorl; fruits turgid; flowers in
    dense fascicles or corymbs, rarely racemose 74. **Nemcia**
Leaves alternate:
Fruits turgid; peduncles axillary, 1–2- or rarely 3–4-flowered;
    S. Africa   75. **Podalyria**
Fruits flat and linear-oblong; flowers in short racemes; NE.
    Asia   90. **Ammopiptanthus**
Seeds not strophiolate:
Keel about as long as the wings; leaves more or less opposite
    or verticillate   76. **Oxylobium**
Keel much shorter than the wings or beaked; leaves mostly
    alternate   77. **Chorizema**
Ovules 2:
Seeds not strophiolate; flowers axillary, often 3 together; leaves
    scattered or verticillate in 3's, margins recurved 78. **Aotus**
Seeds strophiolate:
Leaves alternate or scattered; linear or subterete:
Fruits flat and compressed, ovate or lanceolate 79. **Latrobea**
Fruits turgid, ovate or orbicular   80. **Dillwynia**
Leaves opposite or verticillate:
Flowers axillary, solitary or 2–4 together   81. **Eutaxia**
Flowers in axillary or terminal racemes or dense contracted
    fascicles   82. **Gastrolobium**
Ovary and fruit 2-locular, turgid and divided by a longitudinal septum;
    leaves opposite, verticillate, or alternate   83. **Mirbelia**
Bracteoles orbicular and united below, forming a large cup below the
    calyx; leaves linear or lanceolate, 1-nerved; flowers axillary, solitary
    or paired on slender pedicels   84. **Cupulanthus**
Anthers dimorphic, alternately longer and shorter; flowers axillary, solitary
    or paired; style setaceous, glabrous   85. **Euchilopsis**
Leaves reduced to scales or filiform-elongated or absent (see also p. 337):
Ovary and fruit 1-locular, not divided by a longitudinal septum:
Fruits more or less compressed and not inflated:
Fruits dehiscent:
Calyx-lobes imbricate:
Fruits triangular; branchlets not cladodiform; flowers in axillary or
    lateral racemes or rarely solitary   73. **Daviesia**
Fruits globose or compressed; flowers in terminal or lateral racemes or
    fasciculate   68. **Sphaerolobium**
Calyx-lobes valvate; fruits ovate or oblong; branchlets cladodiform,
    spiny or rod-like; flowers in terminal or lateral racemes or spikes
    or scattered on the branchlets   86. **Jacksonia**

Fruits indehiscent, ovoid-oblong, with a very thin pericarp; flowers in terminal racemes; leaves reduced to a filiform elongated petiole
87. Viminaria

Fruits inflated, ovate or ovoid:
Vexillum shorter and narrower than the wings; stems often winged
88. Leptosema

Vexillum orbicular or reniform, broader than the wings
68. Sphaerolobium

Ovary and fruit 2-locular, turgid and divided by a false septum
83. Mirbelia

Leaves digitately compound or very rarely pinnate:
Shrubs or shrublets:
Calyx-lobes or teeth shorter than the tube:
Shrub armed with spines; leaves 3-foliolate; flowers in short terminal racemes; fruit linear, flat, subtorulose, several seeded; California
89. Pickeringia

Shrubs or shrublets unarmed:
Ovary sessile; ovules 2; fruits indehiscent, not stipitate; Australia
87. Viminaria

Ovary stipitate; ovules several; fruits linear-oblong, dehiscent, stipitate; seeds flattened, rounded or reniform; NE. Asia
90. Ammopiptanthus

Calyx-lobes longer than the tube:
Calyx-lobes imbricate; leaves alternate, sessile; pedicels axillary, 1-flowered; fruits oblong, compressed   91. Cyclopia

Calyx-lobes valvate; fruits inflated; leaves digitate or pinnate:
Ovary with 4 or more ovules; style filiform or slightly thickened in the upper part; seeds few   92. Gompholobium

Ovary with 2 ovules; style more or less dilated at the base, seeds 1–2
93. Burtonia

Herbs from a rhizome; keel-petals connate; flowers in terminal or leaf-opposed racemes; ovules numerous; northern hemisphere:
Calyx shortly turbinate at the base; fruit linear or oblong, inflated
94. Thermopsis

Calyx obtuse at the base; fruit globose or ovoid, turgid or inflated
95. Baptisia

Stipules partially united and leaf-opposed; leaves digitately 3-foliolate; ovules numerous; northern hemisphere:
Vexillum shorter than the wings, the sides not reflexed; keel-petals free; fruit septate within   96. Anagyris

Vexillum subequal to the wings, the margins reflexed; keel-petals connate; fruits continuous within   97. Piptanthus

66. **Brachysema** R.Br., Ait., Hort. Kew. ed. 2, 2: 10 (1811). 16 spp., W. and N. Australia; type *B. latifolium* R.Br., W. Australia. B.H. 1: 467 (partly); E.P. 3, 3: 204 (partly); Benth., Fl. Austral. 2: 9 (partly).

Shrubs or undershrubs; leaves alternate or opposite, simple; stipules subulate or obsolete; flowers red or rarely yellow-green or almost black, solitary or few at the top of the branchlets or in the leaf-axils; bracteoles absent; calyx-lobes subequal, upper 2 often connate high up; vexillum shorter and narrower than the wings, sometimes quite small, limb often recurved; wings narrowly oblong; keel often longer and broader than the wings, incurved, the petals connate along the back; stamens 10, free; disk around the ovary cup-shaped or sheathing; ovary sessile or stipitate, ovules numerous; style filiform, stigma minute, terminal; fruit ovoid or elongated, valves often coriaceous; seeds strophiolate.

67. **Jansonia** Kipp., Proc. Linn. Soc. 1: 330 (1847) and Trans. Linn. Soc. 20: 384, t. 16 (1851). *Cryptosema* Meisn. (1847). 1 sp., *J. formosa* Kipp., W. Australia. B.H. 1: 467; E.P. 3, 3: 203; Benth., Fl. Austral. 2: 8.

Shrub; leaves opposite, simple; stipules subulate-acuminate; flowers in a nodding sessile terminal head; bracteoles absent; flowers at first 4 together within a 4-leaved involucre; calyx obliquely split at the back, upper 2 teeth small, lower 3 lobes elongated; vexillum minute, replicate; wings oblong; keel longer than the wings, the petals connate along the back; stamens free; ovary sessile; ovules numerous; styles filiform, stigma minute, terminal; fruit.

68. **Sphaerolobium** Smith, König & Sims, Ann. Bot. 1: 509 (1805). *Roea* Hueg. (1837). *Hugelroea* Steud. (1840). 12 spp., Australia; type *S. vimineum* Smith. B.H. 1: 469; E.P. 3, 3: 208; Benth., Fl. Austral. 2: 63.

Shrubs or undershrubs, glabrous, branches often reed-like; leaves absent or narrowly linear or short and thread-like, alternate, opposite or verticillate; stipules absent; flowers yellow or red, in terminal or lateral racemes, or fasciculate on the branchlets; calyx-lobes imbricate, upper 2 larger and connate; petals shortly clawed; vexillum orbicular or reniform; wings oblong; keel longer or shorter than the wings, straight or incurved; stamens free, anthers equal; ovary stipitate, 2-ovuled, funicle short; style incurved, subulate or dilated at the base, longitudinally winged in the upper part or with a ring of hairs below the stigma or rarely bare; fruit stipitate, short, oblique, globose or compressed; seeds 1 or 2, without a strophiole.

69. **Isotropis** Benth., Enum. Pl. Huegel. 28 (1837). 10 spp., Australia; type *I. striata* Benth. B.H. 1: 468; E.P. 3, 3: 206; Benth., Fl. Austral. 2: 38.

Herbs or undershrubs; stems diffuse or ascending; leaves alternate, simple or 1-foliate, herbaceous; stipules linear-falcate or minute; flowers axillary, solitary, long-pedicellate, or racemose at the apex of the branches; calyx-tube short, lobes much longer, imbricate, upper 2 connate high up; petals clawed; vexillum orbicular; wings obovate, subfalcate; keel incurved, subequal to the wings; stamens free; ovary sessile; ovules numerous, with slender funicles; style filiform, stigma minute, terminal; fruit oblong-linear or lanceolate, acute, more or less turgid; seeds without a strophiole.

70. **Pultenaea**[1] Smith, Bot. New Holland, 1: 35, t. 12 (1793). 80 spp., Australia; type *P. stipularis* Smith, New South Wales. B.H. 1: 470; E.P. 3, 3: 210; Benth., Fl. Austral. 2: 107.

Shrubs; leaves alternate or rarely ternately verticillate, simple; stipules linear-lanceolate or subulate, scarious, appressed to the branches or spreading, often more or less connate within the leaf; flowers axillary and solitary or crowded in terminal heads, often surrounded by leafy or scarious stipules or bracts; bracteoles persistent, mostly close to the calyx or adhering to it; upper 2 calyx-lobes often broader or more connate, sometimes large; petals clawed; vexillum suborbicular; wings oblong; keel incurved; stamens free; ovary sessile or rarely shortly stipitate, 2-ovuled, funicle short; style subulate, filiform or dilated towards the base, stigma small, terminal; fruit ovate, compressed or turgid, 2-valved; seeds 1–2, kidney-shaped, strophiolate.

---

[1] Synonyms of **Pultenaea**: *Euchilus* R.Br. (1811). *Euchylus* Poir. (1819). *Pulteneya* Hoffmsgg. (1824). *Euchilos* Spreng. (1830). *Pultnaea* R. Grah. (1836). *Spadostyles* Benth. (1838). *Bartlingia* Brongn. (1827). *Urodon* Turcz. (1849).

71. **Phyllota** Benth., Enum. Pl. Huegel. 33 (1837). 9 spp., Australia; type *P. barbata* Benth. B.H. 1: 470; E.P. 3, 3: 210; Benth., Fl. Austral. 2: 93.

Shrubs, often ericoid; leaves scattered, simple, linear, with revolute margins; stipules often absent; flowers axillary or terminal, pedicels short; bracteoles inserted close to the calyx, leafy or scale-like; upper 2 calyx-lobes broader and sometimes connate; petals clawed; vexillum suborbicular; wings oblong; keel very incurved; outer 5 stamens or all of them adnate to the base of the petals and forming with them a short tube; ovary sessile, 2-ovuled, funicle short; style dilated or thickened at the base, subulate above, stigma small, terminal; fruit ovate, turgid, 2-valved; seeds 1–2, kidney-shaped, without a strophiole.

72. **Erichsenia** Hemsl., Hook. Ic. Pl. t. 2777 (1905). 1 sp., *E. uncinata* Hemsl., W. Australia.

Shrublet; leaves alternate, simple, rigid, hooked at the apex; stipules bract-like; calyx sub-bilabiate, lobes slightly unequal, ovate-rounded, half as long as the tube upper lip inner-most; middle lobe of the lower lip outermost; petals all clawed; vexillum reniform; wings oblong; keel-petals connate; stamens free, alternately shorter; ovary sessile, 2-ovuled; ovules estrophiolate; fruit and seed not seen.

73. **Daviesia** Smith, Trans. Linn. Soc. 4: 220 (1798). 60 spp., Australia; lectotype *D. acicularis* Smith. B.H. 1: 469; E.P. 3, 3: 209; Benth., Fl. Austral. 2: 68.

Shrubs or undershrubs; leaves alternate, simple, entire, coriaceous or rigid, either flat and horizontal or vertical, or terete or spine-like, sometimes short, prickly, or minute or absent; stipules very minute or absent; flowers often small, yellow, orange, or red, in axillary or lateral racemes or rarely solitary; racemes lax or abbreviated and umbel-like or reduced to fascicles; bracts often scaly, rarely at length enlarged and covering the fruit; bracteoles absent; calyx-teeth short, equal, or upper 2 broader and connate; petals slenderly clawed; vexillum orbicular or kidney-shaped; wings falcate-oblong or obovate; keel not longer than the wings, incurved; stamens free, 5 filaments often broader or rarely all connate into a short tube; ovary shortly stipitate, 2-ovuled, funicle short; style subulate, stigma small, terminal; fruit compressed, triangular, acute, with a straight vexillary suture; keel curved almost into a right angle; seeds 1–2, strophiolate.

74. **Nemcia** Domin, Mém. Soc. Sc. Bohême, 1921–2, no. 2: (1923); Preslia, 2: 27 (1923). *Oxylobium* series *Gastroloboideae* Benth. About 10–12 spp., W. Australia; lectotype *N. atropurpurea* (Turcz.) Domin.

Rigid shrubs; leaves opposite or 3–4 in a whorl, simple, rigid, rather thick and leathery; stipules setaceous; flowers purple, yellow, or of mixed colour, in dense fascicles or corymbs, rarely racemose; upper 2 calyx-lobes connate high up, lower 3 longer and about equal to the tube; petals clawed; vexillum orbicular or transverse; wings oblong; keel slightly incurved, subequal to the wings; stamens free; ovary villous or very villous, stipitate, 6–4-ovulate; style filiform or dilated at the base; stigma small; fruit small, turgid, not septate; seed strophiolate.

75. **Podalyria** Lam., Ill. 2: 454, t. 327, figs. 3, 4 (1793) (conserved name). *Aphora* Neck. (1790). *Podaliria* Willd. (1809). 20 spp., S. Africa; type *P. retzii* (J. F. Gmel.) Rickett & Stafleu (*P. biflora* Lam.). B.H. 1: 466; E.P. 3, 3: 203; Phillips, Gen. S. Afr. Fl. ed. 2: 401.

Shrubs, often silky-pubescent or villous; leaves alternate, simple; stipules subulate, often deciduous; peduncles axillary, 1–2 -or rarely 3–4-flowered; bracteoles very small, calyx broadly campanulate, teeth or lobes subequal; vexillum suborbicular, emarginate, slightly longer than the wings, with a short subrecurved claw; wings obovate, oblique; keel shorter than the wings, broadly obovate, slightly incurved; stamens free or shortly connate at the base; ovary sessile, villous; ovules numerous; style filiform, stigma minute, terminal; fruit ovoid or oblong, turgid, valves coriaceous; seeds with a strophiole.

76. **Oxylobium** Andr., Bot. Repos. t. 492 (1809) (conserved name). *Callistachys* Vent. (1803). *Callystachya* Smith (1808). *Podolobium* R.Br. (1811). 20 spp., Australia; type *O. cordifolium* Andr., New South Wales. B.H. 1: 467; E.P. 3, 3: 205; Benth., Fl. Austral. 2: 14 (partly, excl. series *Gastroloboideae* Benth.).

Shrubs or rarely undershrubs; leaves simple, very shortly petiolate, often more or less opposite or verticillate, rarely all alternate; stipules small, setaceous, minute or absent; flowers yellow or red or mixed with purple, in terminal or axillary racemes or sometimes in fascicles or dense contracted corymbs; bracts and bracteoles soon falling off; calyx-lobes imbricate, upper 2 often broader and connate high up; petals clawed; vexillum orbicular or kidney-shaped; wings oblong; keel straight or slightly incurved, subequal to the wings; stamens free; ovary sessile or stipitate, with numerous to 4 ovules with slender funicles; style filiform or thickened at the base, stigma minute, terminal; fruit ovoid or oblong, turgid, continuous within or rarely subseptate between the seeds; seeds without a strophiole.

77. **Chorizema** Labill., Voy. 1: 403 t. 21 (1799). *Chorozema* Smith (1808). *Choryzemum* (1822). *Orthotropis* Benth. (1839). *Aciphyllum* Steud. (1840). *Chorosema* Brongn. (1843). 15 spp. W. Australia; type *C. ilicifolium* Labill. B.H. 1: 467; E.P. 3, 3: 205; Benth., Fl. Austral. 2: 26.

Shrubs or undershrubs, sometimes prostrate; leaves simple, all alternate or rarely opposite; stipules small, setaceous or absent; flowers often orange or red, in terminal or rarely axillary racemes; bracteoles small, often deciduous; calyx-lobes imbricate, upper 2 often broader and more connate; petals clawed; vexillum orbicular or kidney-shaped; wings oblong; keel much shorter than the wings, straight, obtuse or acuminate, or rarely incurved; stamens free; ovary sessile or stipitate, 8- or more-ovuled, with slender funicles; style usually short, incurved, with an oblique stigma; fruit ovoid, turgid or compressed, continuous within; seeds without a strophiole.

78. **Aotus** Smith, König & Sims, Ann. Bot. 1: 504 (1805). 11 spp., Australia; type *A. villosa* (Andr.) Smith. B.H. 1: 470; E.P. 3, 3: 210; Benth., Fl. Austral. 2: 89.

Shrubs, branches often virgate; leaves scattered or ternately verticillate, simple, with recurved or revolute margins; stipules often absent; flowers yellow or mixed with purple, axillary, often ternate, pedicels short; bracts small, very caducous; bracteoles absent; upper 2 calyx-lobes broader and more connate; petals with rather long claws; vexillum suborbicular; wings oblong; keel incurved; stamens free; ovary sessile or stipitate, 2-ovuled, with a short funicle; style filiform, stigma minute, terminal; fruit ovate, compressed or almost turgid, 2-valved; seeds 1–2, without a strophiole.

79. **Latrobea** Meisn., Lehmann, Pl. Preiss. 2: 219 (1847). *Leptocytisus* Meisn. (1847). *Acarpha* R.Br. (1864). 6 spp., W. Australia; lectotype *L. brunonis* Meisn. B.H. 1: 471; E.P. 3, 3: 213; Benth., Fl. Austral. 2: 140.

Ericoid shrubs, branches often virgate; leaves alternate or scattered, simple, linear, concave or channelled above; stipules absent; flowers yellow or purplish, terminal or subaxillary on short branchlets, solitary, corymbose or capitate; bracts and bracteoles absent or small and distant from the calyx; calyx-lobes ribbed or teeth subequal; petals shortly clawed or subsessile; vexillum suborbicular, obtuse or acuminate; wings narrow; keel straight or slightly incurved; stamens free; ovary sessile or stipitate, 2-ovuled, funicle short, style filiform or slightly thickened at the base; stigma minute, terminal; fruit flat and compressed, ovate or lanceolate, 2-valved; seeds 1–2, reniform, strophiolate.

80. **Dillwynia** Smith, König & Sims, Ann. Bot. 1: 510 (1805). *Dillwinia* Poir. (1819). *Dyllwinia* Nees (1826). *Xeropetalum* Reichb. (1828). 10 spp., Australia; type *D. ericifolia* Smith. B.H. 1: 471; E.P. 3, 3: 213; Benth., Fl. Austral. 2: 146.

Ericoid shrubs; leaves alternate or scattered, simple, narrowly linear or subterete, channelled above; stipules absent; flowers yellow or reddish-orange, in axillary or terminal racemes or corymbs, sometimes few or rarely solitary; bracts small, dusky, very caducous; bracteoles minute on the pedicels; calyx-lobes short or with an elongated tube, upper 2 lobes more or less connate; petals clawed; vexillum broader than long; wings narrow, shorter than the keel, straight or nearly so; stamens free; ovary shortly stipitate, 2-ovuled, funicle short; style erect, rather thick, hooked towards the apex, stigma truncate or thick; fruit subsessile, ovate or orbicular, turgid, 2-valved; seeds 1–2, reniform, strophiolate.

81. **Eutaxia** R.Br. ex Ait., Hort. Kew. ed. 2, 3: 16 (1811). *Sclerothamnus* R.Br. (1811). 8 spp., Australia; type *E. myrtifolia* (Smith) R.Br. ex Ait. B.H. 1: 471; E.P. 3, 3: 212; Benth., Fl. Austral. 2: 142.

Shrubs, often glabrous; leaves decussately opposite, small, simple, concave or with involute margins; stipules minute or absent; flowers axillary, solitary or 2–4 together, often crowded at the tops of the branches; bracteoles short, separate from the calyx, often small; upper 2 calyx-lobes often broader and more or less connate; petals rather long-clawed; vexillum suborbicular; wings oblong; keel rather straight, obtuse, shorter than the wings; stamens free; ovary narrowed to the base or stipitate, 2-ovulate, with slender or short funicle; style filiform, incurved or hooked at the apex; stigma small, terminal; fruit ovate, compressed or turgid, 2-valved; seeds 1–2, reniform, strophiolate.

82. **Gastrolobium** R.Br. ex Ait., Hort. Kew. ed. 2, 3: 16 (1811). 32 spp., W. Australia; type *G. bilobum* R.Br. ex Ait. B.H. 1: 470; E.P. 3, 3: 212; Benth., Fl. Austral. 2: 96.

Shrubs; leaves opposite, 3–4-verticillate or rarely scattered, simple, often rigid, flat, margins revolute or complicate-keeled; stipules setaceous or rarely absent; flowers yellow or mixed with reddish-purple, in axillary or terminal racemes or in dense contracted fascicles; bracts very caducous or short; bracteoles absent or very caducous; upper 2 calyx-lobes often broader and connate high up; petals clawed; vexillum orbicular or kidney-shaped; wings oblong; keel broader and often shorter than the wings; stamens free; ovary stipitate or rarely sessile, 1–2-ovulate, funicle slender or short; style filiform, incurved, stigma minute, terminal; fruit ovoid or subglobose, turgid, valves leathery; seeds 1–2, strophiolate.

83. **Mirbelia** Smith, König & Sims, Ann. Bot. 1: 511 (1805). *Dichosema* Benth. (1837). *Oxycladium* F. Muell. (1857). 16 spp., Australia; type *M. rubrifolia* (Andr.) G. Don (*M. reticulata* Sm.). B.H. 1: 468; E.P. 3, 3: 206; Benth. Fl. Austral. 2: 32.

Shrubs; leaves simple, opposite, verticillate or alternate, or leafless; stipules small, setaceous or absent; flowers yellow, reddish-purple, or blue, axillary or terminal, solitary, fasciculate or racemose; bracts and bracteoles small or absent; calyx-lobes imbricate, upper 2 often broader and more connate; petals clawed; vexillum orbicular or kidney-shaped; wings oblong; keel broader than the wings and shorter or rarely as long; stamens free; ovary sessile or stipitate, 2- or more-ovuled, with a slender funicle; style often short, incurved, stigma terminal, capitate; fruit ovoid or oblong, turgid, 2-locular lengthwise, with a spurious septum intruded from the lower suture; seeds without a strophiole.

84. **Cupulanthus**[1] Hutch., new gen. 1 sp., *C. bracteolosus* (F. Muell.) Hutch. (*Brachysema bracteolosum* F. Muell.), Australia.

[1] **Cupulanthus** Hutch., gen. nov.; affinis *Brachysemati* R.Br., sed bracteolis 2 orbicularibus infra connatis et cupuliformibus differt.

Shrublet; leaves alternate, simple, linear or lanceolate, 1-nerved, finely reticulate below, margins recurved; stipules linear-subulate; flowers red, axillary, solitary or paired on slender pedicels; bracts absent; bracteoles 2, shortly connate and forming a large cup below the calyx; calyx broadly campanulate, silky-villous outside, equally 5-lobed; vexillum shortly clawed, ovate, reflexed, a little longer than the calyx; wings shorter than the keel; keel falcate, about twice as long as the calyx; stamens 10, free; anthers basifixed, ovoid, equal; ovary about 6-ovuled; style glabrous; fruit not seen.

85. Euchilopsis F. Muell., Melbourne Chemist (1882); Census 37 (1882); Bot. Centralbl. 12: 126 (1882). *Euchiloides* Benth. (1864) ex Dalla Torre & Harms. 1 sp., *E. linearis* (Benth.) F. Muell., W. Australia. E.P. 3, 3: 213.

Undershrub; leaves scattered, linear, coriaceous, with revolute margins; flowers axillary, solitary or paired; bracts basal, stipule-like, minute; bracteoles small; upper calyx-limb large, the 2 lobes cuneate-orbicular, lower minute with 3 equal half-lanceolate segments; vexillum orbicular, ecallose; wings shortly clawed; stamens 10, free; filaments slightly dilated in the lower half, the anthers alternately longer and shorter, the long basifixed; style setaceous, glabrous, stigma minute, terminal; ovary shortly stipitate, 2-ovuled; fruit obliquely orbicular-ovate, subcompressed; seeds 2, funicle short; strophiole absent.

86. Jacksonia R.Br. ex Ait., Hort. Kew. ed. 2, 3: 12 (1811). *Piptomeris* Turcz. (1853). 37 spp., Australia; type *J. spinosa* R.Br. ex Ait. B.H. 1: 469; E.P. 3, 3: 207; Benth., Fl. Austral. 2: 52.

Shrubs or rigid undershrubs, leafless, branchlets either phyllode-like resembling flat leaves, or spiny and much branched, or angular and rod-like; leaf-scales at the nodes minute; flowers yellow or mixed with purple, in terminal or lateral racemes or spikes, or scattered on the branchlets; bracts small, scale-like; bracteoles small, deciduous or persistent; calyx-tube often very short; lobes much longer, valvate, upper 2 broader, rarely connate; petals subsessile, rarely exceeding the calyx; vexillum orbicular or kidney-shaped; wings oblong; keel broader than the wings, almost straight, obtuse; stamens free; ovary sessile or stipitate, 2- or rarely 4-6-ovuled, ovules with short funicle; style subulate, incurved, stigma minute, terminal; fruit ovate or oblong, compressed or turgid; seeds 1 or 2, without a strophiole.

87. Viminaria Smith, König & Sims, Ann. Bot. 1: 507 (1805). 1 sp. *V. juncea* (Willd.) Hoffmgg. (*V. denudata* Smith), Australia. B.H. 1: 469; E.P. 3, 3: 209.

Shrub, with whip-like branches; leaves alternate, reduced to a filiform elongated petiole, or rarely 1-3-foliolate; stipules small, triangular; flowers small, orange-yellow, in terminal racemes; calyx-teeth short, equal; petals rather long-clawed; vexillum suborbicular; wings oblong; keel incurved, subequal to the wings; stamens free; ovary sessile, 2-ovulate, with short funicles; style filiform, stigma small, terminal; fruit sessile, ovoid-oblong, indehiscent, with a thin pericarp; seed most often 1, surrounded by a cavity, with a small strophiole.

88. Leptosema Benth., Ann. Mus. Vindob. 2: 84 (1837). *Kaleniozenkia* Turcz. (1853). *Burgesia* Muell. (1860). 8 spp., Australia; type *L. bossiaeoides* Benth., N. Australia. *Brachysema* sect. *Leptosema* Benth., Fl. Austral. 2: 12 (1864).

Shrubs or undershrubs; stems often winged; leaves reduced to small scales; bracteoles absent; flowers solitary or clustered or crowded on short radical scapes; calyx-lobes subequal, the upper 2 connate to near the top; vexillum shorter and narrower than the wings; stamens 10, free, anthers uniform; disk absent; ovary sessile, with 4 or more ovules; style glabrous; fruit ovate or ovoid, inflated; seeds (where known) estrophiolate.

89. Pickeringia Nutt. ex Torrey & A. Gray, Fl. N. Amer. 1: 389 (1840) (conserved name). *Xylothermia* Greene (1891). 1 sp., *P. montana* Nutt. ex Torrey & A. Gray, Calif. B.H. 1: 466; E.P. 3, 3: 203; Jephson, Man. Fl. Pl. Calif. 515, fig. 517.

Shrub; branches spinose at the apex; leaves alternate, subsessile, digitately 3-foliolate or 1-foliolate, leaflets entire; stipules minute, caducous, or absent; flowers red, in short terminal racemes; pedicels solitary, very short, minutely 2-bracteolate; teeth of the campanulate long-attenuated calyx-tube subequal, very short; petals of subequal length; vexillum orbicular; wings broadly ovate; keel slightly narrower, petals free; stamens free; ovary shortly stipitate; ovules numerous; style rather incurved, stigma minute, terminal; fruit linear, flat, subtorulose, stipitate, several-seeded.

90. **Ammopiptanthus** Cheng f., Bot. Journ. URSS. 44: 1381, with 2 figs. (1959). 2 spp., NE. Asia; type *A. mongolicus* (Maxim.) Cheng f., Mongolia.

Shrubs; leaves evergreen, 3-foliolate or 1-foliolate, leaflets broadly oblanceolate or elliptic, entire, velvety-tomentose; stipules subulate, partly adnate to the petiole (not leaf-opposed); flowers in short racemes terminating short leafy branchlets, occurring singly on the axis; bracts small, deciduous; calyx campanulate, 4-toothed, teeth valvate; petals yellow; wings equal to the vexillum; stamens 10; filaments free; anthers rounded, equal, dorsifixed near the base; ovary stipitate, several-ovuled; style glabrous, stigma terminal, very small; fruits dehiscent, flat, linear-oblong, stipitate; seeds 2–5, flattened, rounded-reniform, strophiolate.

91. **Cyclopia** Vent., Dec. Gen. Nov. (1808). *Ibbetsonia* Sims (1810). *Ibbertsonia* Steud. (1840). 15 spp., S. Africa; type *C. genistoides* Vent. B.H. 1: 466; E.P. 3, 3: 203; Phillips, Gen. S. Afr. Fl. Pl. ed. 2: 401.

Shrubs, the young parts sometimes villous; leaves alternate, sessile, digitately 3-foliolate, rarely 1-foliolate; stipules absent; pedicels axillary, 1-flowered, 2-bracteolate at the base; flowers yellow; calyx-lobes subequal and slightly longer than the tube; petals subequal; vexillum suborbicular, folded at the base, with a short recurved claw; wings oblong, falcate with a transverse fold; keel incurved, obtusely beaked; stamens free or nearly so; ovary sessile or shortly stipitate; ovules numerous; style filiform, stigma minute, terminal; fruit oblong, plano-compressed, continuous inside, valves leathery; seeds with a strophiole.

Leaves of *C. genistoides* have been used as substitute for tea.

92. **Gompholobium** Smith, Trans. Linn. Soc. 4: 220 (1798). 24 spp., Australia; type *G. grandiflorum* Smith. B.H. 1: 468; E.P. 3, 3: 207; Benth., Fl. Austral. 2: 40.

Shrubs or rarely undershrubs; leaves alternate, simple or often digitately or pinnately compound, terminal leaflet always sessile; stipules small or absent; flowers yellow or red, terminal or rarely in the upper leaf-axils, solitary, 2–3 together or shortly racemose; bracts and bracteoles small or absent; calyx-tube very short, lobes much longer, valvate, all subsimilar; petals subsessile; vexillum orbicular or reniform; wings oblong, often falcate; keel broader than the wings, obtuse; stamens free; ovary shortly stipitate or subsessile, with many to 4 ovules with elongated funicles; style incurved, filiform or slightly thickened in the upper part; fruit broadly ovoid or subglobose, often oblique, inflated; seeds small, without a strophiole.

93. **Burtonia** R.Br. ex Ait., Hort. Kew. ed. 2, 3: 12 (1811). *Weihea* Reichb. (1828). 8 spp., Australia; type *B. scabra* R. Br. B.H. 1: 468; E.P. 3, 3: 207; Benth., Fl. Austral. 2: 49.

Shrubs or rarely undershrubs; leaves alternate, simple or often digitately or pinnately compound, terminal leaflet always sessile; stipules minute or absent; flowers yellow, orange, red, or purplish blue, solitary in the upper axils or racemose at the top of the shoots; bracts small; bracteoles in the middle of the pedicels, small; calyx-tube very short; lobes much longer, valvate, upper 2 rather broader; petals subsessile; vexillum orbicular or kidney-shaped; wings oblong or obovate, often falcate; keel broader than the wings, obtuse; stamens free: ovary sessile or shortly stipitate, 2-ovulate, ovules small, with curved or folded funicle; style incurved, more or less dilated at the base; fruit broadly ovoid or sub-globose, often oblique, inflated; seeds 1–2, small, without a strophiole.

94. **Thermopsis** R.Br. ex Ait., Hort. Kew ed. 2, 3: 3 (1811). *Thermia* Nutt. (1818). *Scolobus* Raf. (1819). *Drepilia* Raf. (1836). 15 spp., North America, Siberia, China, Japan, Himalayas; type *T. lanceolata* R.Br. ex Ait., NE. Asia. B.H. 1: 465; E.P. 3, 3: 201; Peter-Stibal, Act. Hort. Gotoburgensis, 13: 408 (1939) (key to Chinese spp.).

Herbs; rhizome often creeping, sheathing at the base, giving off annual erect stems; lower sheaths thin and scarious, somewhat 3-toothed, then leaf-like and 3-fid, passing into stipulate leaves; perfect leaves alternate, digitately 3-foliolate, with free leafy stipules; flowers rather large, yellow or rarely purple, in terminal or leaf-opposed racemes; bracts leafy, simple or connate with 1–2 lateral stipules; bracteoles absent; calyx narrowly campanulate, teeth or lobes subequal or the upper 2 connate into one; vexillum subequal to the wings, suborbicular, with reflexed sides; wings oblong; keel equal to the wings or scarcely longer, the petals subconnate on the back; stamens free; ovary subsessile or shortly stipitate; ovules numerous; style subincurved, stigma minute, terminal; fruit subsessile or shortly stipitate, linear, oblong, or ovate-inflated, straight or incurved, valves scarcely coriaceous; seeds with or without a small strophiole.

95. **Baptisia** Vent., Dec. Gen. Nov. 9 (1809). *Crotalopsis* Michx. (1825). *Eaplosia* Raf. (1836). *Lasinia* Raf. (1836). *Pericaulon* Raf. (1836). *Ripasia* Raf. (1836). About 50 spp., North America; type *B. alba* (Linn.) Vent., SE. United States. B.H. 1: 466; E.P. 3, 3: 201; Larisey, Monogr., Ann. Miss. Bot. Gard. 27: 119 (1940).

Perennial herbs with a rhizome; stem usually erect, annual, sheathing at the base; leaves alternate, digitately 3-foliolate or simple and sessile or perfoliate; stipules often small or absent, rarely large and leafy; flowers yellow, white, or blue, in terminal or leaf-opposed racemes; pedicels solitary; bracts simple; bracteoles absent or rarely 2; calyx campanulate, teeth or lobes subequal or the upper 2 connate into one; vexillum equal to the wings, orbicular, sides reflexed; wings oblong; keel slightly incurved, equal to the wings or scarcely longer, the petals subconnate on the back; stamens 10, free; ovary stipitate; ovules numerous; style subincurved, stigma minute, terminal; fruit stipitate, ovoid or subglobose, usually inflated, often coriaceous; seeds with or without a small strophiole.

B. leucantha Torr. & Gray, SE. United States; medicinal. *B. tinctoria* (L.) R.Br., Yellow Wild Indian, Rattleweed, used as a dye and fly brush; dried root used medicinally, emetic and cathartic.

96. **Anagyris** Linn., Sp. Pl. 374 (1753). 2 spp., Arabia, Mediterr. reg., Canary Isls.; type *A. foetida* Linn., Canary Isls., Mediterr. reg., Middle East. B.H. 1: 465; E.P. 3, 3: 201.

Shrubs; leaves alternate, petiolate, digitately 3-foliolate; stipules connate into one and leaf-opposed; flowers rather large, yellow, shortly racemose at the apex of the branches; pedicels 2–3 together; bracts stipule-like, sheathing, or small and deciduous; bracteoles absent; calyx-teeth or lobes subequal; vexillum shorter than the wings, rounded, folded, sides not reflexed; wings oblong; keel slightly longer than the wings, straight, obtuse, petals free; stamens free; ovary shortly stipitate; ovules numerous; style filiform, stigma minute, terminal; fruit stipitate, broadly linear, compressed, often torulose, septate inside with cellular intrusions between the seeds; seeds without a strophiole.

97. **Piptanthus** Sweet, Brit. Fl. Gard., t. 264 (1828). 9 spp., Himalayas to NE. Asia; type *P. nepalensis* Sweet. B.H. 1: 465; E.P. 3, 3: 201.

Shrubs; leaves alternate, petiolate, digitately 3-foliolate; stipules connate into one and leaf-opposed; flowers rather large, yellow, shortly racemose at the apex of the branches; pedicels 2–3 together in a whorl; bracts stipule-like, sheathing, deciduous; bracteoles absent;

calyx-lobes subequal; vexillum subequal to the wings, suborbicular, with reflexed sides; wings obovate-oblong; keel slightly longer than the wings, obtuse, slightly incurved, petals a little connate at the back; stamens free; ovary stipitate; ovules numerous; style filiform, stigma minute, terminal; fruit stipitate, broadly linear, plano-compressed, continuous within; seeds with a minute strophiole.

Tribe 5. Borbonieae

Lindl., Veg. Kingd. 553 (1847). Tribe *Genisteae* Subtribe *Crotalarieae*, in small part; Benth. & Hook. f., Gen. Pl. 1: 440 (1865)

Shrubs, shrublets, or perennial herbs; *leaves primitively simple*; *stipules and stipels absent*; flowers solitary to racemose or subcapitate, terminal or leaf-opposed; calyx-lobes subequal or not; corolla papilionaceous; stamens *all connate into a sheath or tube* split above (adaxially); *anthers dimorphic*, alternately basifixed and dorsifixed and versatile; style *glabrous*; fruit 2-valved, continuous inside; seeds estrophiolate. S. Africa. Type genus *Borbonia* Linn.

Calyx-lobes subequal; leaves 3–several-parallel-nerved; vexillum villous; fruit linear, compressed; shrubs or shrublets, glabrous or laxly villous
98. Borbonia

Calyx-lobes unequal, the lower smaller and narrower than the upper; leaves usually with 1 main nerve and several lateral nerves:
Fruit lanceolate or linear; shrubs or shrublets more or less glabrous and often glaucous; leaves from orbicular to linear, sessile or subsessile
99. Rafnia

Fruit ovate, turgid; perennial herb, very villous; stems prostrate from a large woody rootstock; leaves lanceolate **100. Euchlora**

98. **Borbonia** Linn., Sp. Pl. 707 (1753). *Bootia* Adans. (1763). 13 spp., S. Africa; type *B. cordata* Linn. B.H. 1: 475; E.P. 3, 3: 219; Phillips, Gen. S. Afr. Fl. Pl. ed. 2: 403.

Shrubs or shrublets; leaves simple, entire, rigid, many-nerved; stipules absent; flowers yellow, solitary, shortly racemose or subcapitate, terminal or leaf-opposed; bracts and bracteoles often setaceous; calyx-lobes subequal, acute or pungent; vexillum suborbicular, villous outside; wings oblique or obovate; keel incurved, obtuse, often with a fold on each side; stamens all connate into a sheath split above; anthers alternately short and versatile, alternately elongated and basifixed; ovary sessile, 2–many-ovuled; style subulate, stigma terminal; fruit linear or lanceolate, obliquely acute, compressed, often margined along the upper (adaxial) suture, 2-valved, continuous inside, valves coriaceous, rather convex; seeds estrophiolate.

99. **Rafnia** Thunb., Nov. Gen. Pl. 10: 144 (1800). *Oedmannia* Thunb. (1800) *Vascoa* DC. (1825). *Pelecynthis* E. Mey. (1835). *Hybotropis* E. Mey. (1840). *Aedmannia* Spach. (1841). 30 spp., S. Africa; type *R. amplexicaulis* (Linn.) Thunb. B.H. 1: 475; E.P. 3, 3; 220; Phillips, Gen. S. Afr. Fl. Pl. ed. 2: 403.

Shrubs or shrublets, sometimes glaucous; leaves simple, sometimes amplexicaul, entire, 1-nerved or reticulately venose; stipules absent; flowers yellow, solitary or shortly race-mose, terminal, or solitary in the axils of bracts similar to the leaves; bracteoles foliaceous or absent; lower lobe of the calyx smaller than the others; vexillum suborbicular, glabrous; wings falcate-oblong; keel incurved beaked or obliquely truncate the petals flat; stamens all connate into a sheath split above; anthers alternately short and versatile, alternately longer and basifixed; ovary 2–many-ovuled; style glabrous except sometimes around the stigma; fruit linear or lanceolate, obliquely acute, compressed, margined or narrowly winged on the upper (adaxial) suture, 2-valved, continuous inside, valves coriaceous; seeds estrophiolate.

100. **Euchlora** Eckl. & Zeyh., Enum. 171 (1836). *Microtropis* E. Mey. (1835) not Wall. (1831). *Microtropia* Reichb. (1841). 1 sp., *E. serpens* Eckl. & Zeyh., S. Africa. B.H. 1: 475; E.P. 3, 3: 220; Phillips, Gen. S. Afr. Fl. Pl. ed. 2: 404.

Perennial herb, prostrate, villous; leaves simple, entire; stipules absent; flowers purplish, small, in a dense subcapitate terminal raceme; upper 2 calyx-lobes broader than the lateral, lowermost narrower; vexillum suborbicular, long-clawed; wings obliquely obovate; keel incurved, obtuse, shorter than the wings; stamens all connate into a tube split above; anthers alternately ovate and versatile, alternately a little longer and basifixed; ovary sessile, many-ovuled; style incurved, stigma terminal, suboblique; fruit ovoid, turgid, 2-valved; seeds few, estrophiolate.

Tribe 6. LIPARIEAE

Benth., Lond. Journ. Bot. 2: 441 (1843). Tribe *Genisteae* Subtribe *Liparieae*
Benth. & Hook. f., Gen. Pl. 1: 439 (1865)

Shrubs; *leaves primitively simple*, entire (not toothed); *stipules and stipels absent*; flowers mostly in heads or clusters; corolla papilionaceous; *vexillary (adaxial) filament free from the others*, these connate into a sheath open on the upper (adaxial) side; anthers *subuniform* or more often *alternately basifixed and dorsifixed*; ovules many to 1; *style glabrous*; fruit compressed, *2-valved*, continuous inside; *seeds strophiolate*. S. Africa. Type genus *Liparia*.

Keel-petals not laterally appendaged; flowers mostly yellow; anthers more or less equal in length; flowers in terminal heads or clusters:
   Calyx-lobes subequal, not petaloid; leaves often nerveless, mostly silky-villous   101. **Priestleya**
   Calyx-lobes unequal, lowest petaloid and very large; leaves with strong longitudinally parallel nerves   102. **Liparia**
Keel-petals gibbous on one side or with a spur; flowers small; anthers dimorphic:
   Keel-petals beaked; flowers yellow, in terminal clusters subtended by very villous bracts; petals scarcely exceeding the calyx   103. **Lathriogyne**
   Keel-petals obtuse; flowers purple or purplish-white, often scattered along the branches   104. **Amphithalea**

101. **Priestleya** DC., Mem. Legum. 190 (1825), and Ann. Sci. Nat. 4: 90 (1825). *Achyronia* Wendl. (1798). *Xiphotheca* Eckl. & Zeyh. (1836). 8 spp., S. Africa; lectotype *P. myrtifolia* DC. B.H. 1: 472; E.P. 3, 3: 215; Phillips, Gen. S. Afr. Fl. Pl. ed. 2: 402.

Shrubs, often silky-villous; leaves simple, entire; stipules absent; flowers yellow, crowded in terminal heads or racemes, or rarely axillary; bracts ovate, lanceolate, or the inner seta-ceous; bracteoles setaceous, caducous; calyx-lobes subequal or the lowest a little longer; vexillum suborbicular; wings obovate-falcate; keel incurved, beaked or rather obtuse; vexillary stamen free from the base, remainder connate; anthers subuniform, attached above the base; ovary sessile, 2–many-ovuled; style subulate, apex entire or 2-toothed, stigma small, terminal; fruit oblong or broadly linear, oblique, compressed, 2-valved, continuous inside, valves coriaceous, flat or convex; seeds strophiolate.

102. **Liparia** Linn., Mant. 2: 156 (1771). 4 spp., S. Africa; type *L. sphaerica* Linn. B.H. 1: 472; E.P. 3, 3: 215; Phillips, Gen. S. Afr. Fl. Pl. ed. 2: 401.

Shrubs, becoming black when dry; leaves simple, entire, coriaceous; stipules absent; flowers yellow, in terminal heads; bracts large, imbricate, forming an involucre; 4 upper calyx-lobes lanceolate, lowest large, petaloid; vexillum oval-oblong; wings oblong; keel narrow, acute; vexillary stamen free from the base, remainder connate; anthers subuniform, attached near the base; ovary sessile, few-ovuled; style filiform, stigma small, terminal; fruit ovate or oblong, oblique, compressed, 2-valved, continuous inside, valves coriaceous, convex; seeds strophiolate.

103. **Lathriogyne** Eckl. & Zeyh., 170 (1836). *Heudusa* E. Mey. (1835). *Heydusa* Walp. (1849). 1 sp. *L. parvifolia* Eckl. & Zeyh., S. Africa. B.H. 1: 472; E.P. 3, 3: 215; Phillips, Gen. S. Afr. Fl. Pl. ed. 2; 402 (in *Amphithalea*).

Shrub, silky-villous, of ericoid habit; leaves simple, entire, flat; flowers in terminal heads, crowded amongst the leaves; calyx-lobes subequal, longer than the tube, upper 2 connate high up, all densely villous; petals shorter than the calyx; vexillum ovate; wings oblong, falcate; keel rostrate, gibbous on each side; vexillary stamen free from the base, remainder connate; alternate anthers smaller, versatile, others longer and basifixed; ovary sessile, 1-ovuled; style incurved, stigma terminal; fruit 2-valved, 1-seeded, densely villous.

104. **Amphithalea** Eckl. & Zeyh., Enum. 167 (1836). *Ingenhoussia* E. Mey. (1835). *Cryphiantha* Eckl. & Zeyh. (1836). *Epistemum* Walp. (1839). *Ingenhousia* Steud. (1840). About 15 spp., S. Africa; type *A. ericifolia* (Linn.) DC. B.H. 1: 472; E.P. 3, 3: 215; Phillips, Gen. S. Afr. Fl. Pl. ed. 2: 402 (excl. *Lathriogyne*)

Shrubs, silky-villous or rarely glabrous, often of ericoid habit; leaves simple, entire, flat or with recurved margins; flowers small, purple or rose, often 2 in the leaf-axils or crowded in a leafy spike; pedicels very short, 1-bracteate; calyx-teeth narrow, or the lobes subequal, upper 2 broader or connate higher up; vexillum ovate or orbicular; wings oblong, keel straight, obtuse, with a short spur or pouch on each side; vexillary stamen free from the base, remainder connate high up; alternate smaller anthers versatile, the others longer and basifixed; ovary sessile, 4–1-ovuled; style incurved, stigma terminal; fruit ovate or oblong, often acute, compressed, 2-valved, continuous inside, valves slightly convex; seeds 4–1 strophiolate.

Tribe 7. BOSSIAEAE[1]

Tribe *Genisteae* Subtribe *Bossiaeae* Benth. & Hook. f., Gen. Pl. 1: 440 (1865)

Shrubs or shrublets; leaves alternate or opposite, *simple* or reduced to scales, mostly *stipulate*; flowers axillary; corolla papilionaceous; *stamens all united into a sheath split above* (or very rarely the vexillary stamen free from near the base); *anthers uniform* and all versatile, or *dimorphic and alternately basifixed and dorsifixed*; *style glabrous*; fruit 2-valved, usually continuous within; *seeds strophiolate*. Australia and S. Africa. Type genus *Bossiaea* Vent.

[1] Tribus **Bossiaeae** (descr. ampl.). Frutices vel fruticuli; folia alterna vel opposita, simplicia, plerumque stipulata; flores axillares; corolla papilionacea; stamina in vaginam supra fissam connata (vel rarissime stamen vexillare e basi libero); antherae uniformes et omnes versatiles vel dimorphae et alternatim basifixae et dorsifixae; stylus glaber; fructus 2-valvis, saepe intra continuus; semina strophiolata.

Anthers more or less of equal size and shape, all versatile; leaves lanceolate to triangular or orbicular; Australia:
Fruits winged along the upper (adaxial) suture; leaves opposite or very rarely alternate 105. **Platylobium**
Fruits not winged:
Leaves and branchlets alternate; fruit sessile or shortly stipitate
106. **Bossiaea**
Leaves and branchlets opposite; fruit long-stipitate 107. **Scottia**
Anthers of two forms, alternately basifixed and dorsifixed and versatile:
Ovules 2 or more:
Claws of the petals free from the staminal sheath; Australia:
Stamens all connate into a sheath; leaves never prickly toothed:
Fruit twice as long as broad or more; leaves sometimes completely reduced; stipules sometimes spiny 108. **Templetonia**
Fruit not longer than broad; leaves various, linear to broad 109. **Hovea**
Vexillary stamen free almost to the base; leaves spiny-toothed
110. **Plagiolobium**
Claws of the petals adnate to the staminal sheath; fruit not known; S. Africa 111. **Walpersia**
Ovule 1; silky-villous, ericoid shrubs; flowers axillary or crowded into a leafy head; S. Africa 112. **Coelidium**

105. **Platylobium** Smith, Spec. Bot. New Holland, 1: 17 (1793); Trans. Linn. Soc. 2: 350 (1794). *Cheilococca* Salisb. ex Smith (1793). 6 spp., Australia; type *P. formosum* Smith. B.H. 1: 473; E.P. 3, 3: 216.

Shrubs with slender branches; leaves opposite or rarely alternate, simple, entire or with pungent angles; stipules small; flowers axillary, solitary, yellow; bracts rigid, dry, imbricate; bracteoles similar below the calyx; 2 upper calyx-lobes large, free or connate, 3 lower very small; vexillum orbicular or reniform; wings oblong or obovate, shorter; keel shorter than the wings, obtuse; stamens all connate into a sheath split above; anthers uniform, versatile; ovary sessile or stipitate, many-ovuled; style subulate, incurved, stigma terminal; fruit sessile or stipitate, compressed, winged along the adaxial suture, 2-valved, continuous within, valves flat, elastically revolute; seeds strophiolate.

106. **Bossiaea** Vent., Descn. Jard. Cels. 1: 7, t. 7 (1800). *Lalage* Lindl. (1834). *Bossieua* Pers. (1807). *Boissiaea* Lem. (1842). 40 spp., Australia; type *B. heterophylla* Vent. B.H. 1: 473 (excl. *Scottea*).

Shrubs or rarely shrublets, sometimes leafless; branches terete, compressed or 2-winged, rarely subangular; leaves alternate, simple, entire or dentate, or reduced to scales; stipules small or absent; flowers yellow, red or mixed with purple, axillary, solitary; bracts imbricate at the base of the pedicels, either dry and rigid or minute; bracteoles similar to the bracts; 2 upper calyx-lobes much shorter than the others, sometimes large, separate or connate into an upper lip, lower 3 small or minute; vexillum orbicular or reniform, often reflexed; wings oblong; keel-petals broader than the wings, shorter or longer than the vexillum, obtuse; stamens all connate into a sheath split above; anthers uniform, dorsifixed, versatile; ovary several- or rarely 3–2-ovuled; style subulate, incurved, stigma terminal; fruit sessile or shortly stipitate, compressed, sutures nerve-like, not winged, continuous or septate inside, valves flat, separating completely; seeds strophiolate.

107. **Scottia** R.Br. ex Ait., Hort. Kew. ed. 2, 4: 269 (1812). *Scottea* DC., Prodr. 2: 118 (1825). 6 spp., W. Australia; type *S. dentata* R.Br. ex DC. Benth., Fl. Austral. 2: 154 (*Bossiaea* ser. *Oppositifoliae*).

Shrubs; leaves opposite or rarely opposite and alternate on the same shoot, lanceolate to orbicular and then very small, sometimes triangular, entire or dentate; stipules very small; flowers axillary, solitary, pedicellate; calyx persistent, the upper 2 lobes broad and large, others small; vexillum 2–3 times as long as the calyx; stamens all connate into a sheath split above; anthers uniform, dorsifixed and versatile; ovary long-stipitate, with 8–2 ovules; fruits twice as long as broad, long-stipitate, valves coriaceous; seeds strophiolate.

108. **Templetonia** R.Br. ex Ait., Hort. Kew. ed. 2, 4: 269 (1812). *Nematophyllum* F. Muell. (1857). 7 spp., Australia; type *T. retusa* (Vent.) R.Br. ex Ait. B.H. 1: 474; E.P. 3, 3: 217.

Shrubs or rarely shrublets from a woody rootstock, sometimes leafless and with spiny stipules; branches angular or sulcate, sometimes compressed; leaves alternate, simple, entire or reduced to minute scales; flowers red, yellow, or mixed with purple; bracts imbricate at the base of the pedicels, either dry and rigid or very small; bracteoles similar to the bracts; 2 upper calyx-lobes or teeth connate into an upper lip or rarely separate, 2 lateral rather shorter, lowest a little longer; vexillum orbicular or ovate, often reflexed; wings narrow, often shorter; keel equal to the vexillum or shorter, obtuse; stamens all connate into a sheath split above; anthers slender, alternately smaller and versatile, alternately longer and basifixed; ovary sessile or stipitate, many- or rarely 3–2-ovuled; style subulate, incurved, stigma terminal; fruit compressed, oblong or linear, 2-valved, continuous inside, valves coriaceous, often convex; seeds strophiolate, funicle short.

109. **Hovea** R.Br. ex Ait., Hort. Kew. ed. 2, 4: 275 (1812). *Poiretia* Smith (1808). *Platychilum* Delaun. (1815). *Phusicarpos* Poir. (1816). *Physicarpos* DC. (1825). 10 spp., Australasia, Tasmania; type *H. linearis* (Smith) R.Br. ex Ait. B.H. 1: 474; E.P. 3, 3: 218.

Shrubs or shrublets, unarmed, or rarely spiny; leaves alternate, simple, entire, often tomentose below; stipules small or absent; flowers blue or purplish, axillary and fasciculate or rarely racemose or solitary; bracts and bracteoles small or minute; upper 2 calyx-lobes or teeth connate into a truncate or emarginate upper lip, lower 3 short, narrow; vexillum suborbicular; wings obliquely obovate; keel shorter than the vexillum, obtuse; stamens all connate into a sheath split above or rarely both above and below; anthers alternately shorter and versatile, alternately longer and basifixed; ovary 2 rarely many-ovuled; style incurved, stigma terminal; fruit sessile or stipitate, turgid, obliquely subglobose or rhomboid-ovoid, 2-valved, continuous inside, valves subcoriaceous; seeds strophiolate, funicle short.

110. **Plagiolobium** Sweet, Fl. Austral. t. 2 (1827). 1 sp., *P. chorizemifolia* (DC.) Sweet, W. Australia. Benth., Fl. Austral. 2: 174 (under *Hovea*).

Shrub or shrublet from a woody rootstock; leaves alternate, simple, ovate to lanceolate, pungent-pointed and prickly-toothed (very like the European *Ilex aquifolium* Linn.); stipules short, subulate, spine-like; flowers dark blue, 2–5 in the leaf-axils; bracteoles subulate, 2 at the base of the calyx; calyx 2-lipped, upper lip large and broad, obcordate, lower 3 lobes very small; vexillum obcordate, shortly clawed; wings spurred on one side; keel half as long as the wings; stamens 10, diadelphous, the vexillary one free to the base, remainder connate into an open sheath; filaments filiform; anthers uniform in size, alternately dorsifixed and basifixed; ovary 2-ovuled; style glabrous; fruit dehiscent, oblong, twice as long as broad, 2-seeded, seeds strophiolate.

111. **Walpersia** Harv., Harv. & Sond., Fl. Cap. 2: 26 (1861) (conserved name). 2 spp., S. Africa; type *W. burtonioides* Harv. & Sond. B.H. 1: 473; E.P. 3, 3: 216; Phillips, Gen. S. Afr. Fl. Pl. ed. 2: 403.

Shrub, much-branched, villous; leaves simple, entire, margins revolute; stipules absent; flowers yellow, in the upper axils; bracteoles below the calyx foliaceous; calyx-lobes subequal, upper 2 broader; claws of the petals adnate at the base to the staminal sheath;

vexillum ovate; wings oblong; keel subincurved, rather acute, with a pouch on each side; stamens all connate into a sheath split above; anthers alternately smaller and versatile, alternately longer and basifixed; ovary sessile, 2-ovulate, style filiform; fruit not known.

112. **Coelidium** Vog. ex Walp., Linnaea 13: 472 (1839). 15 spp., S. Africa; type *C. ciliare* Vog. ex Walp. B.H. 1: 473; E.P. 3, 3: 216; Phillips, Gen. S. Afr. Fl. Pl. ed. 2: 402.

Shrubs, silky-villous, ericoid; leaves simple, entire, concave or margins involute; stipules absent; flowers small, purple, rose, or yellow, often paired, axillary or crowded into a terminal leafy head; pedicels very short, 1-bracteolate; calyx-teeth or lobes subequal; vexillum ovate or orbicular; wings oblong, keel nearly straight, obtuse, gibbous on each side; stamens all connate into a sheath split above; anthers alternately smaller and versatile, alternately longer and basifixed; ovary sessile, 1-ovuled; style incurved, stigma terminal; fruit ovate, acute, 2-valved, valves convex; seed strophiolate.

Tribe 8. CYTISEAE[1]

Tribe *Genisteae* Subtribe *Cytiseae* Benth. & Hook. f., Gen. Pl. 1: 442 (1865)

Small trees or shrubs, sometimes spiny; *leaves digitately 3-foliolate or 1-foliolate*, or reduced to a spine-like tip or small scale; stipules present or absent; *stipels absent*; flowers in mostly terminal (rarely lateral) racemes, spikes, or panicles, sometimes solitary or fasciculate; corolla papilionaceous; calyx shortly lobed or 2-lipped and sometimes coloured; claws of lower petals free from staminal tube; *stamens monadelphous in a closed tube*; *anthers dimorphic, alternately basifixed and dorsifixed*; *style glabrous*; fruit 2-valved, continuous or rarely subseptate between the seeds; *seeds strophiolate*. Type genus *Cytisus* Linn.

Calyx-lobes short, subequal, triangular (not forming 2 lips); unarmed shrubs:
    Keel-petals shorter than the vexillum; fruits linear, not visibly nerved; leaflets obovate-cuneate, widely emarginate   113. **Hypocalyptus**
    Keel-petals longer than the vexillum; fruits obliquely oblong or lanceolate, transversely nerved; leaflets rounded-obovate   114. **Loddigesia**
Calyx 2-lipped, the 3 lower lobes connate; armed or unarmed shrubs or small trees:
    Calyx not coloured, divided to the middle, upper 2 teeth or lobes connate or free, lower connate into a lower lip   115. **Cytisus**
    Calyx divided to the base or nearly so:
        Branches alternate; calyx coloured; shrubs or small trees with spiny branchlets and petioles, otherwise leafless; flowers single in the axils of the phyllodes at the ends of the branches; vexillum glabrous outside   116. **Ulex**

[1] **Cytiseae**, trib. nov. (descr. ampl.). Arbores parvae vel frutices, interdum spinosi; folia digitatim 3-foliolata vel 1-foliolata vel ad apicem spiniformem vel squamam parvam reducta; stipulae interdum nullae; stipellae nullae; flores in racemis spicis vel paniculis terminalibus (rarius lateralibus) dispositi, interdum solitarii vel fasciculati; corolla papilionacea; calyx breviter lobatus vel bilabiatus, interdum coloratus; stamina in tubum clausum monadelpha; antherae dimorphae, alternatim basifixae et dorsifixae; stylus glaber; fructus 2-valvis, intra continuus vel rarius inter semina subseptatus; semina strophiolata.

Branches opposite or subopposite:
Leaves 3-foliolate on young shoots, otherwise branches clad only with the
  remains of the stipules and petioles; flowers in terminal heads; fruit
  oblong-ovoid, slightly exceeding the calyx   117. **Echinospartum**
Leaves reduced to phyllodes:
Glabrous or almost glabrous shrubs; flowers single in the axils of the
  phyllodes at the apex of the thorny branches; fruit short, ovoid-
  rhomboid, only a little longer than the calyx, 1–2-seeded
                                                                    118. **Nepa**
Silky-hairy shrubs; flowers in short thornless lateral racemes; fruit very
  long, linear, longer than the calyx; seeds 5 or more
                                                          119. **Stauracanthus**

113. **Hypocalyptus** Thunb., Prodr. Pl. Cap. 2: 124 (1800). *Duvalia* Bonpl.
(1813). 1 sp., *H. sophoroides* (Berg.) Druce (*H. obcordatus* (Linn.) Thunb.),
S. Africa. B.H. 1: 484; E.P. 3, 3: 240; Phillips, Gen. S. Afr. Fl. Pl. ed. 2: 409.

Shrub; leaves digitately 3-foliolate; stipules free; flowers purple, in terminal racemes
often paniculately branched; bracts and bracteoles setaceous; calyx broad and intrusive
at the base, teeth short, subequal; vexillum suborbicular, callose inside the very short claw;
keel incurved, obtuse, shorter than the vexillum; stamens all connate into a closed tube;
alternate anthers versatile, alternately a little longer and subbasifixed; ovary substipitate,
many-ovuled; style incurved, glabrous, stigma terminal; fruit linear, flat, slightly thickened
on the sutures, 2-valved, continuous inside; seeds strophiolate, funicle short.

114. **Loddigesia** Sims, Bot. Mag., t. 965 (1808). *Loddiggesia* Reichb. (1828).
1 sp., *L. oxalidifolia* Sims, S. Africa. B.H. 1: 485; E.P. 3, 3: 240.

Shrub; leaves digitately 3-foliolate, leaflets rounded-obovate; stipules free; flowers pale,
in terminal racemes, calyx broad and intrusive at the base, teeth short, subequal; vexillum
suborbicular, callose inside on the short claw; keel incurved, obtuse, longer than the vexillum; stamens all connate into a closed tube; alternate anthers versatile, alternately a little
longer and subbasifixed; ovary substipitate, many-ovuled; style incurved, glabrous, stigma
terminal; fruit obliquely oblong or lanceolate, transversely nerved, flat, sutures slightly
thickened, 2-valved, continuous inside; seeds strophiolate, funicles short.

115. **Cytisus**[1] Linn., Sp. Pl. 739 (1753). About 50 spp., Europe, W. Asia, N.
Africa, Makaronesia; type *C. sessilifolius* Linn., S. Europe. B.H. 1: 484; E.P.
3, 3: 239; Gams in Hegi, Ill. Fl. Mitt.-Eur. 4, 3: 1167, figs. 1318–24.

Shrubs or small trees, branches rarely spiny; leaves either digitately 3-foliolate, or
1-foliolate, or absent; stipules minute, setaceous or inconspicuous; flowers yellow, purple,
or white; racemes either terminal and elongated, or short and fascicle-like, terminal or

---

[1] Synonyms of **Cytisus**: *Chamaespartium* Adans. (1763). *Cytisogenista* Ort. (1772). *Teline*
Medik. (1787). *Cythisus* Schrank (1792). *Wiborgia* Moench (1794). *Tubocytisus* DC. (1825).
Corema Bercht. & Presl (1830–5). *Chamaecytisus* Link (1831). *Cyticus* Link (1831). *Saro-
thamnus* Wimmer (1832). *Meiemianthera* Raf. (1836). *Nubigena* Raf. (1836). *Verzinum* Raf.
(1836). *Oreosparton* Webb (1836–50). *Spartocytisus* Webb (1836–50). *Teline* Webb. (1836–
50). *Peyssonelia* Boiv. ex Webb. (1836–50). *Aulonix* Raf. (1838). *Diaxulon* Raf. (1838).
Cytisophyllum O. F. Lang (1843). *Trianthocytisus* Griseb. (1843). *Corothamnus* C. Presl
(1844). *Telinaria* C. Presl (1844). *Spartothamnus* Webb ex Walpers (1848). *Genistella* Vis.
(1850). *Chronanthus* K. Koch (1853). *Phyllocytisus* Fourr. (1868). *Tubocytisus* Fourr.
(1868). *Pterospartum* Spach (1845). *Sarothamnos* St.-Lag. (1880).

lateral or subaxillary; bracts and bracteoles small, very caducous, or rarely foliaceous and persistent for a time; calyx-teeth or lobes short, upper 2 connate into a lip, or free; vexillum suborbicular or ovate; wings obovate or oblong; keel straight or incurved, obtuse or scarcely acuminate, claws free; stamens all connate into a closed tube; alternate anthers shorter and versatile, alternately longer and basifixed; ovary sessile or rarely stipitate, many-ovuled; style incurved, glabrous, stigma terminal, capitate or oblique; fruit compressed, oblong or linear, 2-valved, continuous inside or rarely subseptate between the seeds; seeds strophiolate.

116. **Ulex** Linn., Sp. Pl. 741 (1753). About 20 spp., W. Europe, N. Africa; type *U. europaeus* Linn., Europe generally, introd. elsewhere. B.H. 1: 483; E.P. 3, 3: 238; Rothmaler, Engl. Bot. Jahrb. 72: 91 (1941).

Shrubs, branchlets sharply spiny; leaves reduced to a spine-like or small scale; stipules absent; flowers yellow, solitary or shortly racemose; bracts small; bracteoles small and broad below the calyx, minute or absent; calyx membranous, coloured, 2-partite, upper segment 2-toothed, lower 3-toothed; petals shortly clawed, subequal in length; vexillum ovate; wings and keel obtuse; stamens all connate into a closed tube; alternate anthers shorter and versatile, alternately longer, basifixed; ovary sessile, many-ovuled; style slightly incurved, glabrous, stigma terminal, capitate; fruit ovate, oblong or shortly linear, compressed or turgid, 2-valved, continuous inside; seeds strophiolate.

117. **Echinospartum** Rothmaler, Engl. Bot. Jahrb. 72: 79 (1941). *Echinosparton* Fourr. (1868), name only. *Cytisanthus* Gams in Hegi (1923), partly, not Lang. (1843). 4 spp., SW. Europe, type *E. horridum* (Vahl) Rothmaler.

Much-branched shrubs, branches and branchlets spiny, always opposite: leaves opposite, caducous, trifoliolate; leaflets linear, long-adnate to the persistent stipules; flowers crowded in the axils of bracts in head-like terminal spikes; calyx 2-lipped, lower lip long, curved, deeply 3-lobed, upper a little shorter, 2-lobed to the middle or more; petals mostly a little exserted, glabrous or pilose; anthers alternately basifixed and dorsifixed; fruit dehiscent, oblong-ovoid, 1- or 2-seeded.

118. **Nepa** Webb, Ann. Sci. Nat. sér. 3, 17: 286 (1852). *Leonhardia* Opiz & Weitenweber (1857). 1 sp., *N. boivinii* Webb, SW. Europe, NW. Africa. Rothmaler, Engl. Bot. Jahrb. 72: 89 (1941).

Low diffuse shrub; branches and branchlets spiny, angular; branchlets very short, subopposite; phyllodes short, triangular, scale-like, subspinescent and subopposite; flowers solitary in the axils of the phyllodes and crowded towards the ends of the branches; calyx bilabiate, upper lip longer, curved, 2-toothed, lower lip 3-toothed; petals twice as long as the calyx; vexillum reflexed, like the keel densely silky outside; anthers alternately basifixed and dorsifixed; fruit ovate, dehiscent, 1- or 2-seeded.

119. **Stauracanthus** Link, Schrad. Neues Journal 2, 2: 52 (1807). 1 sp., *S. genistoides* (Brot.) Samp., SW. Europe, NW. Africa. Rothmaler, Engl. Bot. Jahrb. 72: 84 (1941).

Rather tall diffusely branched shrub; branches and branchlets spiny, silky; branchlets often opposite or subopposite; phyllodes minute, scale-like, muticous, subopposite; flowers densely villous, in lateral or terminal racemes, not spiny; calyx bilabiate, lower lip long and curved, 3-toothed, upper a little shorter, 2-lobed to the middle; petals subincluded by the calyx; vexillum usually more or less silky outside; anthers alternately basifixed and dorsifixed; fruit dehiscent, linear-oblong, much longer than the calyx, 5- or 6-seeded.

Tribe 9. Genisteae[1]

Leguminosae sect. *Genisteae* Adans., Fam .2: 320 (1763); Tribe *Genisteae* Subtribe
Spartieae, partly, Benth. & Hook. f., Gen. Pl. 1: 441 (1865)

Shrubs or rarely small trees or shrublets, unarmed or armed; leaves simple
or absent, rarely digitately 3-foliolate or 1-foliolate; stipules minute or
absent; *stipels absent*; flowers racemose, fasciculate or capitate, *terminal*,
rarely lateral; calyx shortly tubular or rarely spathaceous, rarely inflated;
corolla papilionaceous; *claws of the lower petals more or less adnate to the
staminal tube*; *stamens all connate into a closed tube*; *anthers dimorphic*,
alternately basifixed and dorsifixed (versatile); *style glabrous*; fruit 2-valved
or indehiscent, usually continuous within; seeds estrophiolate.—Type genus
Genista Linn.

Calyx not inflated in fruit:
  Calyx 2-lipped; branches often spiny; stipules small or absent   **120. Genista**
  Calyx 1-lipped; branches not spiny, terete, often leafless; stipules absent;
    fruit glabrous   **121. Spartium**
  Calyx 2-lipped; branches not spiny; stipules intrapetiolar, triangular; fruit
    glabrous   **122. Petteria**
Calyx inflated in fruit; cushion-plant; branches all ending in a spiny tip;
  leaves rare; fruit glandular-villous   **123. Erinacea**

120. **Genista**[2] Linn., Sp. Pl. 709 (1753). About 80 spp., Europe, N. Africa,
W. Asia; type *C. tinctoria* Linn., Europe and W. Asia. B.H. 1: 482; E.P. 3,
3: 233; Gams in Hegi, Ill. Fl. Mitt.-Eur. 4, 3: 1340–50.

Shrubs or rarely shrublets or small trees, unarmed or spiny; leaves simple or absent,
rarely digitately 3-foliolate; stipules minute or absent: flowers yellow, rarely white, racemose, fasciculate or capitate at the ends of the shoots, rarely lateral, fasciculate or subsolitary; bracts and bracteoles either small and deciduous, or foliaceous and persistent for

[1] Trib. **Genisteae** (emend.) Frutices vel rare arbores parvae vel suffrutices, interdum
armati; folia simplicia vel nulla, rare digitate 3-foliolata vel 1-foliolata; stipulae minutae
vell nullae; stipellae nullae; flores racemosi, fasciculati vel capitati, terminales, rare laterales; calyx breviter tubulosus vel rare spathaceus, rare inflatus; corolla papilionacea;
petalorum inferiorum ungues plus minusve tubo stamineo adnati; stamina omnia in tubum
clausum connata; antherae dimorphae, alternatim basifixae, alternatim dorsifixae et versatiles; stylus glaber; fructus 2-valvis vel indehiscens, plerumque intra continuus, semina
estrophiolata.

[2] Synonyms of **Genista**: *Corniola* Adans. (1763). *Listera* Adans. (1763). *Lygos* Adans.
(1763). *Chamaespartium* Adans. (1763). *Genistella* Moench (1794). *Genistoides* Moench
(1794). *Scorpius* Moench (1794). *Saltzwedelia* Gaertn. (1800). *Voglera* Garetn.(1800).
Lotoides DC. (1825). *Chasmone* E. Mey. (1835). *Argyrolobium* Eckl. & Zeyh. (partly) (1836).
Avornella Raf. (1838). *Euteline* Raf. (1838). *Lugaion* Raf. (1838). *Lygoplis* Raf. (1838).
Asterocytisus Koch (1939). *Retama* Boiss. (1839). *Lissera* Steud. (1840). *Cytisanthus* Lang
(1843). *Eremolobium* Spach (1843). *Lembotropis* Griseb. (1843). *Spartium* Spach (1843). *Salz-
wedelia* Láng (1843). *Syspone* Griseb. (1843). *Cephalospartum* Spach (1844). *Corniola* C.
Presl (1844). *Drymospartum* C. Presl (1844). *Spartocaprus* Spach (1844). *Camptolobium*
Spach (1845). *Dendrospartum* Spach (1845). *Phyllobotrys* Spach (1845). *Stenocarpus* Spach
(1845). *Boelia* Webb (1853). *Pterospartum* K. Koch (1853). *Asterocytisus* Schur ex Fuss
(1866). *Argelasia* Fourr. (1868). *Chamaesparton* Fourr. (1868). *Echinosparton* Fourr. (1868).
Emeroides Ducommun (1869). *Enantiosparton* C. Koch (1869). *Phyllobotrys* Fourr. (1869).
Spartidium Pomel (1874). *Pterospartum* Willk. (1877).

             A a

some time; calyx-lobes short, upper 2 free or scarcely connate, lower 3 connate into a 3-toothed lip; vexillum ovate; wings oblong; keel oblong, often slightly incurved, obtuse, gibbous on each side, often deflexed during flowering, the claws of the lower petals adnate to the base of the staminal tube or rarely free; stamens all connate into a closed tube; alternate anthers shorter and versatile, alternately longer and basifixed; ovary sessile, 2–many-ovuled; style-apex incurved, inflexed, or rarely elongate-circinate, stigma terminal, capitate or often oblique or subdecurrent; fruit subglobose, ovate, oblong or linear, 2-valved or indehiscent, continuous within, valves convex or turgid, rarely flat; seeds estrophiolate.

121. **Spartium** Linn., Sp. Pl. 708 (1753). *Spartianthus* Link (1822). *Spartanthus* Link (1823). 1 sp., *S. junceum* Linn., Mediterr. reg., Canary Isls., introd. into South America and elsewhere. B.H. 1: 483; E.P. 3, 3: 232; Rehder, Trees and Shrubs, ed. 2: 491; Rothmaler, Engl. Bot. Jahrb. 74: 271 (1949) (revision).

Shrub, branches often leafless; leaves rare, 1-foliolate; stipules absent; flowers yellow, showy, in terminal racemes; bracts and bracteoles minute, very caducous; calyx subspathaceously split at the back, teeth short, upper 2 free, lower 3 connate into a lip; vexillum large; wings obovate; keel incurved, acuminate, longer than the wings, claw adnate to the staminal tube; stamens all connate into a closed tube; alternate anthers short and versatile, alternately longer and basifixed; ovary sessile, many-ovuled; style incurved, glabrous, stigma oblong, decurrent on the inside; fruit elongate-linear, glabrous, flat, 2-valved, subseptate inside between the seeds; seeds estrophiolate.

Ornamental flowering shrub much attacked by green fly.

122. **Petteria** C. Presl, Bot. Bemerk. 139 (1844) (conserved name). 1 sp., *P. ramentacea* (Sieber) C. Presl, Balkans. B.H. 1: 482; E.P. 3, 3: 235.

Shrub; leaves digitately 3-foliolate; stipules small, triangular, intrapetiolar; flowers yellow, in dense terminal racemes; bracts inserted on the pedicel, membranous, very caducous; bracteoles absent; 2 upper calyx-lobes broadly falcate, free, 3 lower connate into a 3-toothed lip; vexillum orbicular; wings and keel oblong, almost straight, claws adnate to the staminal tube; keel gibbous on each side; stamens all connate into a closed tube; alternate anthers short and versatile, alternately longer and basifixed; ovary sessile, many-ovuled; style scarcely incurved, glabrous, stigma terminal, slightly oblique; fruit broadly linear, subfalcate, compressed, 2-valved, continuous inside; seeds estrophiolate.

123. **Erinacea** Adans., Fam. 2: 321 (1763). 1 sp., *E. pungens* Boiss., S. France, Corsica, Spain, N. Africa. B.H. 1: 483; E.P. 3, 3: 235; Rehder, Trees and Shrubs, ed. 2: 491; Rothmaler, Engl. Bot. Jahrb. 74: 271 (1949) (revision).

Shrub, forming dense compact cushions; branches often leafless, rigid, ribbed, and very spiny; leaves rare, silky, 1-foliolate or digitately 3-foliolate; peduncles very short towards the end of the branches, 2–3-flowered; flowers pale violet; bracts and bracteoles small, foliaceous; calyx becoming membranous and inflated, teeth short, subequal in length, upper 2 broader; petals long-clawed, claws adnate to the staminal tube; vexillum ovate, subbiauriculate at the base; wings narrow; keel incurved, obtuse; stamens all connate into a closed tube; alternate anthers shorter and versatile, alternately longer and basifixed; ovary sessile, many-ovuled; style filiform, incurved; stigma terminal; fruit oblong, glandular-villous, 2-valved; seeds estrophiolate.

Tribe 10. LABURNEAE[1]

Tribe *Genisteae* Subtribe *Spartieae*, partly, Benth. & Hook. f., Gen. Pl. 1: 441 (1865)

Trees and shrubs, rarely spiny; *shoots sometimes long and short*; *stipels absent*; leaves *digitately 3-foliolate*; stipules very small or absent; flowers in racemes or rarely fasciculate on short branchlets; bracts sometimes foliaceous; calyx sometimes shortly bilabiate; corolla papilionaceous; claws of petals free; *stamens all connate into a closed tube*; *anthers dimorphic*, alternately basifixed, alternately dorsifixed and versatile; ovary sessile or stipitate; style glabrous; ovules several; fruit dehiscent and 2-valved, or tardily or not dehiscent, continuous within; seeds *estrophiolate*. Type genus *Laburnum* Medik.

Fruit neither glandular nor tuberculate:
  Fruit stipitate; shrubs or trees, not spinescent:
    Shoots of 2 kinds, long and short shoots; stipules small; racemes pendulous; fruit dehiscent, 2-valved   124. **Laburnum**
    Shoots of one kind, all long with the leaves scattered along the new growths; racemes erect; stipules absent:
      Leaves petiolate; fruit indehiscent   125. **Podocytisus**
      Leaves sessile; fruit tardily dehiscent   126. **Hesperolaburnum**
  Fruit not stipitate, 2-valved; shrubs, often spinescent; calyx truncate and obscurely denticulate   127. **Calycotome**
Fruit densely glandular or tuberculate, not stipitate, 2-valved   128. **Adenocarpus**

124. **Laburnum** Medic., Vorles. 2: 362 (1787). 4 spp., Europe, N. Africa, W. Asia; type *L. anagyroides* Medic. (*L. vulgare*, J. Presl), Europe. B.H. 1: 481; E.P. 3, 3: 236; Gams in Hegi, Ill. Fl. Mitt.-Eur. 4, 3: 1161, figs. 1314–16.

Trees; shoots of two kinds, long and very short; leaves digitately 3-foliolate; stipules small; flowers yellow, in terminal pendulous racemes; bracts and bracteoles very minute; calyx-teeth short, 2 forming an upper lip, 2 a lower lip; vexillum ovate or orbicular; wings obovate; keel incurved, rather obtuse, shorter than the wings, claws all free; stamens all connate into a closed tube; alternate anthers short and versatile, alternately longer and basifixed; ovary stipitate, many-ovuled; style glabrous, incurved, stigma terminal; fruit linear, compressed, each suture thickened, continuous within, 2-valved; seeds estrophiolate, kidney-shaped, funicle very short.

L. anagyroides, highly ornamental tree; wood very hard, used for turnery and instruments; seeds poisonous.

125. **Podocytisus** Boiss. & Heldr., Diagn. ser. 1, 9: 7 (1849). 1 sp., *P. caramanicus* Boiss., Greece, Asia Minor.

Shrub; shoots all of one kind; leaves scattered on the new shoots, trifoliolate, leaflets obovate, 1-nerved; stipules absent; flowers in terminal rather short erect racemes; pedicels

---

[1] **Laburneae**, trib. nov. Arbores vel frutices, rare spinosi; ramuli interdum longi et breves; stipellae nullae; folia digitate 3-foliolata; stipulae minores vel nullae; flores racemosi vel rare in ramulis brevibus fasciculati; bracteae interdum foliaceae; calyx interdum bilabiatus; corolla papilionacea; ungues petalorum liberi; stamina omnia in tubum clausum connata; antherae dimorphae, alternatim basifixae, alternatim dorsifixae et versatiles; ovarium sessile vel stipitatum; stylus glaber; ovula plura; fructus dehiscens et 2-valvis, vel tarde vel indehiscens, intra continuus; semina estrophiolata.

1–2-bracteolate at the apex; calyx campanulate, 2-lipped, upper lip ovate, very obtuse, shortly split, lower longer, minutely 3-toothed; vexillum orbicular, abruptly clawed; wings free, rather shorter than the keel, oblong, abruptly clawed; keel incurved, 2-toothed; stamens all united into a tube; anthers linear, glabrous, alternately shorter and versatile, longer and basifixed; ovary stipitate, 9–6-ovuled; style at a right angle to the ovary; stigma terminal, capitate-discoid, papillous, ciliate; fruit thin and flat, oblong-linear, stipitate, indehiscent, broadly winged on the adaxial suture; seeds not arillate, almost orbicular, on a long slender funicle.

126. **Hesperolaburnum** Maire, Bull. Soc. Hist. Nat. Afr. Nord. 39: 131 (1949). 1 sp., *H. platycarpum* Maire, Morocco.

Small unarmed tree; shoots all of one kind; leaves sessile, 3-foliolate; leaflets oblanceolate, entire; stipules absent; flowers yellow, in terminal erect racemes; bracts absent; bracteoles minute, very early deciduous; calyx campanulate, bilabiate, deciduous, upper lip 2-toothed, lower lip 3-toothed; claws of the wings and keel free; keel obtuse, equally the wings and vexillum, soon reflexed; stamens 10, all connate into a closed tube; alternate anthers basifixed and longer, others dorsifixed and shorter; ovary subsessile, linear; style as long as the ovary; stigma minute; fruit coriaceous, not stipitate, tardily dehiscent, few-seeded; seeds without an aril.

127. **Calycotome** Link, Schrader, Neu. Journ. 2: P. 2, 50 (1808). *Calicotome* Link (1808). *Calycotomum* Hoffmgg. (1824). 5 spp., Mediterr. reg., N. Africa; type *C. villosa* (Poir.) Link, Asia Minor, N. Africa. B.H. 1: 481; E.P. 3, 3: 236; Rothmaler, Engl. Bot. Jahrb. 74: 276; Rehder, Trees and Shrubs ed. 2: 495.

Shrubs with spinescent branchlets; leaves digitately 3-foliolate; stipules inconspicuous; flowers yellow, fasciculate on short branchlets among the clusters of leaves; bracteole broad and 3-toothed or 3-fid at the apex of the pedicels; calyx membranous, truncate, obscurely denticulate; vexillum ovate; wings obovate-oblong; keel incurved, obtuse, shorter than the vexillum, claws free; stamens all connate into a closed tube; alternate anthers shorter and versatile, alternately longer and basifixed; ovary sessile, many-ovuled; style incurved, glabrous, stigma capitate or oblique; fruit oblong-linear, compressed, 2-valved, continuous within, upper suture much thickened or sub-2-winged; seeds estrophiolate.

128. **Adenocarpus** DC., Lam. & DC., Fl. Franc. Suppl. 549 (1815). 10 spp., Mediterr. reg., Canary Isls., mountains of trop. Africa; lectotype *A. complicatus* (Brot.) Gay, Europe to Asia Minor. B.H. 1: 481; E.P. 3, 3: 236.

Shrubs, silky-pubescent or villous; leaves digitately 3-foliolate; stipules none or small and caducous; flowers yellow, in terminal racemes; bracts and bracteoles either small and caducous, or foliaceous and persistent for some time; upper 2 calyx-lobes free, lower 3 more or less connate; vexillum suborbicular; wings obovate or oblong; keel very incurved or shortly beaked, scarcely shorter than the vexillum, claws free; stamens all connate into a closed tube; alternate anthers shorter and versatile, alternately longer and basifixed; ovary sessile, many-ovuled; style incurved, glabrous, stigma terminal; fruit linear, compressed, glandular-tuberculate or muricate, 2-valved; seeds estrophiolate, with rather thick funicle.

Tribe 11. Lotononideae[1]

Tribe *Genisteae* Subtribe *Crotalarieae* Benth. & Hook. f., Gen. Pl. 1: 440 (partly) (1865)

Shrubs, shrublets, or rarely herbs; leaves *digitately* 3-foliolate or rarely 1-foliolate, sometimes sessile; stipules present or absent; *stipels absent*; flowers in *terminal* (rarely leaf-opposed) spikes, racemes, or heads, or rarely axillary; bracts and bracteoles small or sometimes foliaceous; calyx regularly 5-toothed or lobed, or the upper 2 lobes more or less united; corolla papilionaceous; *stamens all connate into a sheath* split above (adaxially) (except *Bolusia*); anthers *uniform*, or *dimorphic and alternately longer* (*basifixed*) *and shorter* (*dorsifixed*); ovules several to few; *style glabrous*; stigma terminal; fruit 2-valved or opening by one suture; seed estrophiolate. Type genus *Lotononis* Eckl. & Zeyh.

Stipules absent or very inconspicuous; anthers usually dimorphic:
  Calyx more or less regularly 5-toothed:
    Fruit linear:
      Leaves petiolate, 3-foliolate or simple and subulate or reduced to scales; plants sometimes spartioid; anthers dimorphic   129. **Lebeckia** (part)
      Leaves sessile, opposite; anthers uniform   130. **Sellocharis**
    Fruit semi-ovate or semi-lanceolate, obliquely acute or obliquely rhomboid; leaves in threes or fascicles, not petiolate:
      Seeds estrophiolate; anthers dimorphic; S. Africa   131. **Aspalathus**
      Seeds strophiolate; anthers subequal, but dimorphic; leaves sessile   132. **Plagiocarpus**
      Seeds estrophiolate; anthers uniform; leaves petiolate; Madagascar   133. **Edbakeria**
  Calyx with the upper 4 lobes more or less united in pairs, the lower lobe free; anthers dimorphic:
    Keel and style curved; mostly shrublets or shrubs   134. **Lotononis**
    Keel and style straight; mostly herbs   135. **Pearsonia**
  Calyx bilabiate; fruit subtorulose, linear, flat, not glandular; keel longer than the vexillum; anthers dimorphic   139. **Dichilus**
Stipules present and conspicuous:
  Stipules free from each other and from the leaf:
    Calyx equally 5-toothed or 5-lobed:
      Anthers uniform, sometimes half of them sterile:
        Leaves digitately 3-foliolate or only the upper 1-foliolate:
          All 10 filaments bearing anthers:
            Ovules numerous; calyx-lobes subequal   140. **Rothia**

---

[1] **Lotononideae**, trib. nov. Frutices, fruticuli, vel rare herbae; folia digitate 3-foliolata vel rare 1-foliolata; stipulae interdum nullae; stipellae nullae; flores in spicis, racemis, vel capitulis, vel rare axillares; bracteae et bracteolae parvae vel interdum foliaceae; calyx regulariter 5-dentatus vel lobatus, vel lobi superiores plus minusve connati; corolla papilionacea; stamina omnia in vaginam supra fissam connata; antherae uniformes vel dimorphae et alternatim longiores (basifixae) et breviores (dorsifixae); ovula plura ad pauca; stylus glaber; stigma terminale; fructus 2-valvis vel e suturo uno dehiscens; semina estrophiolata.

Ovules up to 9; calyx-lobes very unequal, the lowermost much longer
                                                141. **Muelleranthus**
Only 5 filaments bearing anthers, with 5 sterile between
                                                142. **Robynsiophyton**
Leaves all 1-foliolate; ovules 5–8   136. **Melliniella**
Anthers alternately longer (basifixed) and shorter (dorsifixed):
Fruits not winged:
  Stipules small; flowers in terminal often unilateral racemes; fruit
    linear   129. **Lebeckia** (part)
  Stipules conspicuous, sometimes foliaceous and toothed; peduncles
    leaf-opposed; keel and genitalia spirally coiled; vexillary filament
    free   137. **Bolusia**
  Stipules foliaceous; flowers crowded in terminal spikes or heads; fruit
    ovate   138. **Buchenroedera**
Fruits winged along the upper or both sutures, flat and indehiscent,
    ovate or oblong; stipules small or absent   143. **Wiborgia**
Calyx with the 4 upper teeth more or less united in pairs, the lower one
    free:
Keel-petals straight; bracts subulate; anthers almost alike
                                                144. **Phaenohoffmannia**
Keel-petals bent; bracts absent; anthers alternately dissimilar:
  Flowers solitary, racemose or umbellate; fruits straight or oblique
                                                134. **Lotononis**
  Flowers in terminal racemes; fruits flexuous-plicate within the persis-
    tent keel   145. **Listia**
Calyx bilabiate; anthers alternately dissimilar; fruits linear compressed,
    often torulose   146. **Melolobium**
Stipules united at the base with the leaf into a whorl or sheath:
  Style straight; ovary with several ovules; fruit linear; anthers all alike
                                                130. **Sellocharis**
  Style bent; ovary with few ovules; fruit obliquely ovate-cuspidate, oblong,
    rhomboid or broadly linear; anthers alternately dissimilar
                                                147. **Anarthrophyllum**

129. **Lebeckia** Thunb., Nov. Gen. et Spec. 10: 139 (1800). *Stiza* E. Mey.
(1835). *Sarcophyllum* E. Mey. (1835). *Acanthobotrya* Eckl. & Zeyh. (1836).
Calobota Eckl. & Zeyh. (1836). 45 spp., S. Africa, Madagascar; lectotype *L.*
sepiaria (Linn.) Thunb., S. Africa. B.H. 1: 477; E.P. 3, 3: 222; Phillips, Gen.
S. Afr. Fl. Pl. ed. 2: 406.

Shrubs or shrublets, either unarmed, with virgate branches, or much-branched and
spiny; leaves either linear-filiform, 1-foliolate, or simple with an obscure joint, or digitately
3–1-foliolate; stipules small or absent; flowers yellow, in terminal often unilateral racemes;
bracts and bracteoles small or inconspicuous; teeth or lobes of the oblique calyx short,
subequal; vexillum suborbicular or ovate; wings oblong or obovate; keel exceeding the
wings and often the vexillum, obtuse, acute or rather beaked; stamens all connate into a
sheath split above; anthers alternately shorter and versatile, alternately longer and basifixed;
ovary many-ovuled; style incurved, glabrous, stigma terminal; fruit linear, compressed or
terete, 2-valved, continuous inside or thinly septate between the seeds; seeds estrophiolate,
funicle very short.

130. **Sellocharis** Taub., Flora, 72: 421 (1889); Engl. & Prantl, Pflanzenfam. 3, 3: 226 (1888). 1 sp., *S. paradoxa*, Taub., S. Brazil.

Shrublet; leaves sessile, digitately 3-foliolate, leaflets sessile, appearing to be verticillate; stipels absent; flowers 1 or 2 in the axils of the 'whorls'; calyx with the upper 2 teeth triangular, acute, lower 3 a little longer, connate almost to the apex; vexillum orbicular, deeply emarginate, shortly clawed; wings equal to the vexillum, oblong, apex rounded, shortly clawed; keel petals longer than the vexillum, with a long filiform claw, obscurely 1-toothed above the claw; stamens connate into a sheath split above; anthers globose, all alike; ovary subsessile, linear, compressed, many-ovuled; style short, terete, subulate; stigma capitate, thick; fruit subsessile, linear, much compressed, upper suture thick, produced into the persistent style, 2-valved.

131. **Aspalathus**[1] Linn., Sp. Pl. 711 (1753). About 150 spp., S. Africa; type *A. chenopoda* Linn. B.H. 1: 478; E.P. 3, 3: 223; Phillips, Gen. S. Afr. Fl. Pl. ed. 2: 407; Dahlgren, Revis. of genus *Aspalathus*, Opera Bot. 4: 1 (1960).

Shrubs or shrublets, either ericoid or spinescent or rather fleshy; leaves simple, often in 3's (leaflets 3, digitate with obsolete petiole?), rarely solitary, inserted on a tubercle with others fasciculate from the axil, ericoid or rarely flat; stipules absent; flowers yellow, rarely purple-blue, red, or white, either crowded into a terminal spike or head, or solitary within the lateral fascicles; bracts and bracteoles often foliaceous; calyx-teeth or lobes of various lengths; vexillum oblong, ovate, or orbicular, claws often short; wings oblong or falcate; keel obtuse, incurved or somewhat beaked, shorter than the vexillum; stamens all connate into a sheath split above; anthers alternately shorter and versatile, alternately longer and basifixed; ovary 2–many-ovuled; style incurved, glabrous, stigma terminal; fruit semi-ovate or semi-lanceolate, oblique, acute, sometimes obliquely subrhomboid, compressed or turgid; seeds 1 or several, estrophiolate, funicle filiform.

132. **Plagiocarpus** Benth., Hook. Ic. Pl., t. 1162 (1873). 1 sp., *P. axillaris* Benth., trop. Australia.

Shrublet; leaves sessile, 3-foliolate; flowers axillary, solitary; calyx-lobes 5, equal, longer than the tube; petals shortly clawed, subequal in length; vexillum broadly ovate, broadly subcordate at the base; wings free, oblong, conspicuously auriculate at the base; keel-petals oblong, obtusely incurved at the apex, scarcely auriculate; stamens all connate into a sheath split above; anthers subequal, alternately basifixed and dorsifixed and versatile; ovary subsessile, 1(–2?)-ovuled; style filiform, glabrous, stigma minute, terminal; fruit obliquely ovate, turgid, valves coriaceous; seed 1, ovoid, strophiolate.

133. **Edbakeria** R. Vig., Not. Syst. 13: 364 (1949). 1 sp., *E. madagascariensis* R. Vig., Madagascar.

Shrub or shrublet; leaves digitately trifoliolate, densely villous; stipules absent; flowers axillary at the ends of the branches; calyx campanulate, teeth 5, lanceolate, longer than the tube; corolla yellow, slightly exceeding the calyx; keel straight; stamens monadelphous, sheath split above, anthers subglobose, uniform; ovary villous; style straight, glabrous, slender, shorter than the ovary; stigma capitate; fruits inflated, 1-seeded, tomentose; seed 1, estrophiolate.

---

[1] Synonyms of **Aspalathus**: *Scaligera* Adans. (1763). *Eriocylax* Neck. (1790). *Sarcophyllus* Thunb. (1799). *Sarcophyllum* Willd. (1800). *Aspalatus* J. St. Hil. (1804). *Acropodium* Desv. (1826). *Eriocalyx* Reichb. (1828). *Diallosperma* Raf. (1838). *Nefrakis* Raf. (1838). *Semetor* Raf. (1838). *Sarcocalyx* Walp. (1839). *Psilolepus* C. Presl (1844). *Cyphocalyx* C. Presl (1845). *Heterolathus* C. Presl (1845). *Lapasathus* C. Presl (1845). *Pachyraphea* C. Presl (1845). *Paraspalathus* C. Presl (1845). *Plagiostigma* C. Presl (1845). *Stroptosema* C. Presl (1845). *Trineruria* C. Presl (1845). *Achyronia* O. Ktze. (1891).

134. **Lotononis**[1] Eckl. & Zeyh., Enum. 176 (1836) (conserved name). About 110 spp., Africa, Cape Verdes, Mediterr. reg., Orient, Spain, E. India; lectotype *L. prostrata* (Linn.) Benth. (*L. vexillata* (E. Mey.) Eck. & Zeyh.), S. Africa. B.H. 1: 476; E.P. 3, 2: 220; Dümmer, Trans. Roy. Soc. S. Afr. 3: 275 (1913); Phillips, Gen. S. Afr. Fl. Pl. ed. 2: 405.

Shrubs, rarely shrublets, or herbs; leaves digitately 3-foliolate, rarely 5- or 1-foliolate; stipules solitary, unilateral or rarely absent, or 2 and free; flowers solitary, racemose or umbellate, terminal, leaf-opposed or very rarely subaxillary; 4 upper calyx-lobes more or less connate in pairs, very rarely free, the lowermost free, often narrower; vexillum orbicular to oblong; wings obliquely ovate or oblong; keel incurved, mostly obtuse; stamens all connate into a sheath split above; anthers alternately shorter and versatile, alternately longer and basifixed; ovary usually sessile, many-ovuled; style incurved, stigma terminal; fruit oblong to linear, compressed, rarely turgid, 2-valved, continuous inside, valves convex; seeds estrophiolate, funicle filiform.

135. **Pearsonia** Dümmer, Journ. Bot. 50: 353 (1912). 11–12 spp., S. trop. and S. Africa; type *P. sessilifolia* (Harv.) Dümmer, Transvaal. Phillips, Gen. S. Afr. Fl. Pl. ed. 2: 405.

Herbs with a woody base, rarely shrubby; leaves 3-foliolate, stipules absent; flowers in terminal racemes, rarely solitary; bracts and bracteoles present; calyx as in *Lotononis*; vexillum oblong or oblong-spathulate, wings straight; stamens all in a split sheath; alternate anthers basifixed and dorsifixed; ovary sessile, ovules several; style glabrous, stigma truncate; fruit much exceeding the calyx, oblong-lanceolate, straight, compressed, 2-valved; seeds estrophiolate, funicle thickened, short.

136. **Melliniella** Harms, Engl. Bot. Jahrb. 51: 359, fig. 1 (1914). 1 sp. *M. micrantha* Harms, W. trop. Africa. Hutch. & Dalz., Fl. W. Trop. Afr. 1: 386; ed. 2 (Keay), 1: 587.

Prostrate herb; leaves simple, small, broadly elliptic, obovate or suborbicular, subcordate at the base, entire, pinnately 3–4-nerved; stipules scarious, lanceolate, striate, acuminate; stipels absent; flowers very small, often paired in the axils of the bracts, in dense very short axillary clusters; calyx-tube short, lobes 5, subequal, narrow, densely pilose; corolla small, a little exserted; petals long-clawed; vexillum broadly spathulate-obovate, a little longer than the other petals; wings a little longer than the keel; keel-petals coherent at the back; stamens 10, all connate; anthers uniform; ovary subsessile, linear; ovules 8–5; style puberulous, sharply bent towards the apex, stigma capitate; fruit exserted, subsessile, oblong, compressed, straight, apiculate, slightly keeled, a little depressed between the seeds but not jointed, continuous inside, dehiscing by the ventral suture; seeds 8–5, very small, brown, shining, suborbicular, compressed.

137. **Bolusia** Benth., Hook. Ic. Pl. 12: 57, t. 1163 (1873). 4 spp., S. and trop. Africa; type *B. capensis* Benth., S. Africa. E.P. 3, 3: 273.

Many-stemmed undershrubs or perennial herbs, silky-pubescent; leaves digitately 3- rarely 1-foliolate; stipules obliquely cordate, sometimes foliaceous and coarsely toothed; peduncles leaf-opposed, 1–few-flowered; calyx deeply 5-lobed, lobes subequal in length, upper 2 broader and close together; vexillum very broad, emarginate; wings falcate-obovate, free; keel long and linear, with the stamens and style spirally coiled; vexillary stamen free, remainder shortly connate into a sheath split above; anthers alternately elongate-linear, basifixed with short filaments, alternately with much longer filaments, oblong-elliptic and

---

[1] Synonyms of **Lotononis**: *Amphinomia* DC. (1825). *Leobordea* Delile (1830). *Aulacinthus* E. Mey. (1835). *Capnitis* E. Mey. (1835). *Lipozygis* E. Mey. (1835). *Telina* E. Mey. (1835). *Krebsia* Eckl. & Zeyh. (1836). *Leptis* E. Mey. (1836). *Polylobium* Eckl. & Zeyh. (1836). *Leptidium* C. Presl (1844). *Leobardia* Pomel (1874).

dorsifixed; ovary sessile; style glabrous, stigma terminal, capitate; ovules numerous; fruit oblong, turgid, many-seeded; seeds horseshoe-shaped.

138. **Buchenroedera** Eckl. & Zeyh., Enum. 194 (1836). *Colobotus* E. Mey. (1835). *Colobatus* Walp. (1839). 20 spp., trop. and S. Africa; lectotype *B. alpina* Eckl. & Zeyh. B.H. 1: 478; E.P. 3, 3: 225; Phillips, Gen. S. Afr. Fl. Pl. ed. 2: 407.

Shrubs, silky-pubescent or villous; leaves digitately 3-foliolate; stipules foliaceous; flowers white or purplish, crowded in terminal spikes or heads; bracts foliaceous; bracteoles absent; calyx-teeth or lobes short, subequal; vexillum long-clawed, orbicular or ovate; wings oblong; keel obtuse, shorter than the vexillum; stamens all connate into a sheath split above, anthers alternately short and versatile, alternately longer and basifixed; ovary sessile, many-ovuled; style incurved, glabrous, stigma terminal; fruit ovate, obliquely acute, turgid, slightly exceeding the calyx; seeds 3-1, estrophiolate, funicle filiform.

139. **Dichilus** DC., Mém. Légum. 201, t. 35 (1825). *Dichilos* Spreng. (1827). *Calycotome* E. Mey. (1835). *Melinospermum* Walp. (1839). 5 spp., S. Africa; type *D. lebeckioides* DC. B.H. 1: 479; E.P. 3, 3: 225; Phillips, Gen. S. Afr. Fl. Pl. ed. 2: 408.

Slender shrublets, erect; leaves digitately 3-foliolate; stipules inconspicuous; flowers yellow, solitary to dichotomous at the ends of the branchlets; bracteoles minute; 2 upper calyx-lobes connate into a 2-toothed lip, 3 lower likewise and 3-dentate; vexillum suborbicular or ovate; wings obliquely oblong; keel obtuse, longer than the others, stamens all connate into a sheath split above; anthers alternately short and versatile, alternately longer and basifixed; ovary subsessile, many-ovuled; style incurved, glabrous, stigma terminal; fruit linear, compressed, subtorulose, eglandular, 2-valved, thinly septate between the seeds; seeds estrophiolate, funicle short.

140. **Rothia** Pers., Syn. 2: 638 (1807) (conserved name). *Dillwynia* Roth (1806). *Westonia* Spreng. (1826). *Goetzea* Reichb. (1828). *Xerocarpus* Guill. & Perr. (1832). *Harpelema* Jacq. (1844). 2 spp., India to Malaya, N. Australia, trop. and subtrop. S. Africa, Madagascar; type *R. trifoliata* (Roth) Pers. B.H. 1: 477; E.P. 3, 3: 222; Hutch. & Dalz., Fl. W. Trop. Afr. 1: 394; D. le Grand, Not. Syst. 14: 265.

Annual diffuse herbs; leaves digitately 3-foliolate; stipules free; flowers very small, solitary or 2-4 in a short raceme opposite the leaves; bracts and bracteoles setaceous; calyx-lobes 5, narrow, subequal, the upper 2 broader and falcate; vexillum ovate or oblong; wings narrow; keel-petals similar to the wings, scarcely coherent; stamens all connate into a sheath split above; anthers small, uniform; ovary sessile, many-ovuled; style straight, glabrous, stigma terminal; fruit linear or linear-lanceolate, acute, continuous inside, when mature gaping along the adaxial suture; seeds estrophiolate, funicle short, filiform.

141. **Muelleranthus**[1] Hutch., new genus; 1 sp., *M. trifoliolatus* (F. Muell.) Hutch. (*Ptychosema trifoliolatum* F. Muell.), Australia.

Annual herb with long wiry stems often pilose all over; leaves alternate, distant, digitately trifoliolate, fairly long-petiolate; leaflets subsessile, obovate, small, entire; stipules free, ovate, large, persistent; peduncles leaf-opposed, 1-flowered, rather long and persistent, with a linear bract at the base of the short pedicel; bracteole 1 just below the calyx, persistent; calyx almost 1-lipped, the upper 2 lobes short, the lowermost longest; vexillum purplish, obovate-orbicular, clawed, limb strongly obliquely nerved; keel-petals yellow; stamens 10, filaments connate into a sheath open on the adaxial side; anthers uniform; ovary shortly

---

[1] **Muelleranthus** Hutch., gen. nov.; herba annua, foliis trifoliolatis, stipulis magnis ovatis persistentibus, pedunculis oppositifoliis 1-floris, calyce fere unilabiato, distincta.

stipitate; style subulate, glabrous; ovules 8–9; fruit shortly stipitate, linear-oblong, 2-valved, faintly transversely reticulate; seeds with a short funicle, globose, brownish, estrophiolate.

142. **Robynsiophyton** Wilczek, Bull. Jard. Bot. Brux. 23: 126, t. 1 (1953). 1 sp., *R. vanderystii* Wilczek, trop. Africa.

Annual herb, prostrate or ascending; leaves digitately 3-foliolate, or the uppermost 1-foliolate; stipules 2, free, narrowly elliptic or lanceolate; stipels none; racemes axillary or terminal, subcapitate, 5–9-flowered, much shorter than the leaves; bracts linear-lanceolate, persistent; flowers subsessile; bracteoles none; calyx about as long as the corolla, silky-hairy, lobes subulate-lanceolate about as long as the tube; vexillum spathulate, clawed, not appendaged, a little longer than the wings and keel; wings narrow, oblanceolate; keel similar, not beaked, free; fertile filaments 5 with 4 sterile between; anthers suborbicular, subbasifixed; 3 anterior stamens contiguous; ovary sessile, 6–10-ovuled, silky-tomentose; style straight, glabrous, stigma terminal; fruit compressed, follicularly dehiscent, lanceolate, acute, style persistent, seeds subreniform, funicle short and filiform.

143. **Wiborgia** Thumb., Nov. Gen. et Spec. 10: 137 (1800) (conserved name). *Viborgia* Spreng. (1818). *Peltaria* [Burm. ex] DC. (1825). *Loethainia* Heynh. (1840). *Jacksonago* O. Ktze. (1891). About 10 spp., S. Africa; lectotype *W. obcordata* Thunb. B.H. 1: 477; E.P. 3, 3: 223; Phillips, Gen. S. Afr. Fl. Pl. ed. 2: 406.

Rigid shrubs, sometimes spinescent, glabrous or silky-pubescent; leaves digitately 3-foliolate; stipules small or absent; flowers yellow, in terminal often unilateral racemes; bracts and bracteoles small or inconspicuous; calyx-teeth subequal; vexillum ovate or orbicular; wings often shorter; keel incurved, obtuse or beaked, longer than the vexillum; stamens all connate into a sheath split above; anthers alternately shorter and versatile, alternately longer and basifixed; ovary stipitate, few ovuled; style incurved, glabrous, stigma terminal; fruit stipitate, ovate or rarely oblong, flat, indehiscent, winged along the upper (adaxial) or both sutures, surface rarely winged-crested; seeds estrophiolate, funicle filiform.

144. **Phaenohoffmannia** O. Ktze., Rev. Gen. Pl. 1: 940 (1891). *Pleiospora* Harv. (1859), not *Pleospora* Rabh. (1851). About 10 spp., SE. trop. and S. Africa; type *P. cajanifolia* (Harv.) O. Ktze., S. Africa. B.H. 1: 475; E.P. 3, 3: 220; N. 200; Dümmer, Trans. Roy. Soc. S. Afr. 3: 330 (1913); Phillips, Gen. S. Afr. Fl. Pl. ed. 2: 404.

Tall shrubs to prostrate herbs, densely leafy, rusty-silky; leaves digitately 3-foliolate; stipules free, linear to ovate; flowers spicate-capitate, spikes terminal, or flowering branch-lets short and subleafless; bracts and bracteoles subulate; lobes of the subinflated calyx sub-equal, upper 4 approximate in pairs, lower narrower; vexillum ovate; wings obliquely ovate; keel oblong, straight, obtuse; stamens all connate into a sheath split above; anthers almost alike; ovary sessile, many-ovuled; style nearly straight, glabrous, stigma terminal; fruit ovate-lanceolate, compressed, 2-valved, continuous within, valves convex; seeds estrophiolate, funicle short.

145. **Listia** E. Mey., Comm. Pl. Afr. Austr. 80 (1835). 1 sp., *L. heterophylla* E. Mey., trop. and S. Africa. B.H. 1: 476; E.P. 3, 3: 222; Phillips, Gen. S. Afr. Fl. Pl. ed. 2: 405.

Prostrate herb; leaves digitately 3-foliolate; flowers yellow, in a terminal raceme; bracts small; bracteoles absent; upper 4 calyx-lobes connate in pairs, lower free, narrower; vexillum ovate; wings falcate-oblong; keel incurved, obtuse, longer than the vexillum; stamens all connate into a sheath split above; anthers alternately shorter and versatile, alternately longer and basifixed; ovary sessile, many-ovuled; style incurved, glabrous, stigma terminal, oblique; fruit linear, compressed, flexuous-plicate within the marcescent keel; seeds estrophiolate, funicle filiform.

146. **Melolobium** Eckl. & Zeyh., Enum. 188 (1836). *Sphingium* E. Mey. (1835). *Mellolobium* Reichb. (1841). *Mellobium* A. Juss. (1849). 30 spp., S. Africa; lectotype *M. cernuum* (Linn.) Eckl. & Zeyh. B.H. 1: 478; E.P. 3, 3: 225; Phillips, Gen. S. Afr. Fl. Pl. ed. 2: 408.

Shrubs or shrublets, often spiny, glandular-villous or sticky; leaves digitately 3-foliolate; stipules often foliaceous; flowers small, yellow, in terminal spikes or racemes; bracts and bracteoles often foliaceous; 2 upper calyx-lobes free or connate, lower 3 connate into a 2-toothed lip; vexillum oblong to suborbicular; keel obtuse, shorter than the others; stamens all connate into a sheath split above; anthers alternately shorter and versatile, alternately longer and basifixed; ovary sessile, many-ovuled; style incurved, glabrous, stigma terminal; fruit linear, compressed, often torulose; seeds estrophiolate, funicle short.

147. **Anarthrophyllum** Benth., Benth. & Hook. f., Gen. Pl. 1: 478 (1865). 6 spp., temp. South America; type *A. desideratum* (DC.) Benth. B.H. 1: 478; E.P. 3, 3 : 226; Reiche, Fl. Chile, 2: 54 (1897); Burkart, Legum. Argent. ed. 2: 313, fig. 94.

Much-branched shrubs, rather silky; leaves small, entire or jointedly 3-lobed or trifoliolate, often spiny, united at the base with the stipules into a ring or amplexicaul sheath; flowers solitary, terminal; upper 2 calyx-lobes free, lower 3 united into a lower lip; vexillum obovate; wings oblong; keel slightly incurved, obtuse, with a fold on each side, clawed; stamens all connate into a sheath split above; alternate anthers shorter and versatile, alternately longer and basifixed; ovary subsessile, few-ovuled; style incurved, glabrous, stigma terminal, capitate; fruit obliquely ovate-cuspidate, oblong-rhomboid or broadly linear, compressed 2-valved, continuous inside, valves coriaceous, convex; seeds estrophiolate, funicle very short.

Tribe 12. LUPINEAE[1]

Tribe *Genisteae* Subtribe *Spartieae*, small part, Benth. & Hook. f., Gen. Pl. 1: 441 (1865)

Shrublets or herbs; leaves *digitately 5- or more-foliolate*, rarely 3- or 1-foliolate; stipules often adnate to the petiole; *stipels absent*; inflorescence racemose or subumbellate, *terminal or leaf-opposed*, rarely flowers solitary; calyx-lobes or lips *much longer than the tube*; corolla papilionaceous; claws of the petals free from one another and from the staminal tube; *filaments all connate into a closed tube* or rarely into a sheath split above (adaxially); *anthers dimorphic*, alternately basifixed and dorsifixed; *style glabrous*; ovules several to 2; fruit compressed, 2-valved, continuous within or septate between the seeds but not breaking into joints; *seeds estrophiolate*. Type genus *Lupinus* Linn.

Wing-petals mostly connate at the apex; keel-petals beaked; stipules adnate to the petiole; leaves simple, digitately several to many-foliolate, or 1-foliolate   148. **Lupinus**

[1] **Lupineae**, trib. nov. Fruticuli vel herbae; folia digitatim 5- vel plurifoliata, rare 3- vel 1-foliolata; stipulae ad petiolum saepe adnatae; stipellae nullae; inflorescentia racemosa vel subumbellata, terminalis vel oppositifolia, rare flores solitarii; calycis lobi vel labia quam tubus multo longiores; corolla papilionacea; petalorum ungues liberi; stamina omnia in tubum clausum vel rare in spatham supra fissam connata; antherae dimorphae, alternatim basifixae et dorsifixae; stylus glaber; ovula plura ad 2; fructus compressus, 2-valvis, intra continuus vel inter semina septatus sed non articulatus; semina estrophiolata.

Wing-petals free; keel-petals obtuse; stipules free from the petiole; leaves
3-foliolate   **149. Argyrolobium**

148. **Lupinus** Linn., Sp. Pl. 721 (1753). About 100 spp., North and South
America, Mediterr. reg., trop. Africa; type *L. albus* Linn., S. Europe. B.H.
1: 480; E.P. 3, 3: 231; Gams in Hegi, Ill. Fl. Mitt.-Eur. 4, 3: 1148, figs. 1305–
12; Burkart, Legum. Argent. ed. 2: 315, fig. 95.

Shrublets or herbs; leaves simple or digitately 5- or more-foliolate, very rarely digitately
3-foliolate or 1-foliolate; stipules adnate at the base to the petiole; flowers blue, violet, or
variegated, rarely yellow or white, scattered or whorled in terminal racemes; bracts often
caducous; bracteoles mostly persistent, usually adnate to the base of the calyx; calyx deeply
split, upper 2 lobes connate into an upper lip 2-toothed or 2-fid, lower 3 connate in an entire
or 3-toothed lip; vexillum orbicular or broadly ovate; wings falcate-oblong or obovate,
connate at the apex, enclosing the incurved, beaked, keel; stamens all connate into a
closed tube; alternate anthers short and versatile, alternately longer and basifixed; ovary
sessile, 2–many-ovuled; style incurved, glabrous, stigma terminal, often bearded; fruit more
or less compressed, usually silky-villous, 2-valved, transversely septate within between the
seeds, valves thick and coriaceous; seeds estrophiolate, funicle very short, hilum oblong or
linear. Popular garden plants.

149. **Argyrolobium**[1] Eckl. & Zeyh., Enum. 184 (1836) (conserved name).
About 130 spp., N., trop., and S. Africa, Madagascar, S. Europe, W. Asia,
India; lectotype *A. argenteum* (Jacq.) Eckl. & Zeyh. (*A. sericeum* (Spreng.) Eckl.
& Zeyh.), S. Africa. B.H. 1: 480; E.P. 3, 3: 232; Phillips, Gen. S. Afr. Fl. Pl.
ed. 2: 409.

Herbs or rarely small shrubs, often silky or villous; leaves digitately 3-foliolate; stipules
free, sometimes foliaceous; flowers yellow, solitary, racemose or subumbellate, terminal or
leaf-opposed; bracts and bracteoles often small; calyx deeply split, 2 upper lobes free or
connate, 3 lower connate into a 3-toothed or 3-fid lip; vexillum suborbicular; wings obovate;
keel slightly incurved, obtuse, shorter than the vexillum; stamens all connate into a closed
tube or rarely the latter split above; alternate anthers short and versatile, alternately longer
and basifixed; ovary sessile, many-ovuled; style glabrous, stigma terminal, often oblique;
fruit linear, compressed, silky-villous, eglandular, 2-valved, continuous inside or septate
between the seeds; seeds estrophiolate.

Tribe 13. CROTALARIEAE[2]

Genisteae div. *Crotalarieae* Lindl., Veg. Kingd. 554 (1847). Tribe *Genisteae* Subtribe
Crotalarieae Benth. & Hook. f., Gen. Pl. 1: 441 (in small part) (1865)

Leaves simple, *digitately* 3–many-foliolate or rarely 1-foliolate; stipels absent;
flowers solitary or subfasciculate and axillary, or mostly in terminal or *leaf-
opposed* racemes or spikes; corolla papilionaceous; *stamens all connate into a*

---

[1] Synonyms of **Argyrolobium**: *Tephrothamnus* Sweet (1830). *Lotophyllus* Link (1831).
Chasmone E. Mey. (1835). *Gamochilum* Walp. (1839). *Trichasma* Walp. (1839). *Diotolotus*
Tausch (1842). *Chamaecytisus* Vis. (1850). *Macrolotus* Harms (1897). *Calispepla* Vved.?
(1952).
[2] **Crotalarieae**, trib. nov. Folia simplicia, digitatim 3-plurifoliolata vel rare 1-foliolata;
stipellae nullae; flores solitarii vel subfasciculati et axillares, vel in racemis vel spicis terminalibus vel oppositifòliis dispositi; corolla papilionacea; stamina omnia in vaginam supra
fissam connata; antherae dimorphae, alternatim basifixae et dorsifixae; ovarium pluri- ad
2-ovulatum; stylus longitudinaliter barbatus vel superne minute ciliatus; fructus plerumque
turgidus vel inflatus, rare compressus, 2-valvis, intra continuus; semina estrophiolata.

single sheath split above (adaxially); anthers dimorphic, alternately basifixed and dorsifixed; ovary many–2-ovuled; style *bearded lengthwise* or minutely ciliate on the adaxial side; fruit usually *turgid or inflated,* rarely compressed, 2-valved, continuous within; seeds estrophiolate. Type genus *Crotalaria* Linn.

Fruit short and ovate, compressed; annual prostrate herb with simple leaves
    and axillary flowers   **150. Heylandia**
Fruit not as above, usually much longer than broad:
  Fruit turgid or inflated; racemes terminal or leaf-opposed; leaves simple,
    digitately foliolate or 1-foliolate   **151. Crotalaria**
  Fruit more or less compressed; leaves 3-foliolate; racemes terminal; shrubs;
    keel-petals beaked   **152. Priotropis**

150. **Heylandia** DC., Mém. Légum. 6: 198, t. 34 (1825). *Goniogyna* DC. (1825). *Goniogyne* Benth. & Hook. f. (1865). 1 sp., *H. latebrosa* (Linn.) DC. (*H. hebecarpa* DC.), Ceylon, India. B.H. 1: 479; E.P. 3, 3: 226.

Prostrate herb; leaves simple, entire; stipules absent; flowers small, axillary, solitary; 2 upper calyx-lobes shortly connate, lower 3 free; petals subequal in length; vexillum suborbicular, with 2 scales above the short claw; wings obovate-oblong; keel incurved, shortly beaked; stamens all connate into a sheath split above; alternate anthers short, versatile, alternate long and basifixed; ovary sessile, 2-ovuled; style abruptly inflexed above the ovary, bearded above lengthwise, stigma terminal; fruit ovate, compressed, 2-valved, continuous inside; seeds 1–2, estrophiolate, funicle filiform.

151. **Crotalaria**[1] Linn., Sp. Pl. 714 (1753). About 350 spp., trop. and subtrop. regions; type *C. laburnifolia* Linn., Trop. Asia. B.H. 1: 479; E.P. 3, 3: 226, Senn, North Amer. spp., Rhodora, 41: 317 (1939); Amshoff, Pulle Fl. Suriname, 2, 2: 169; Hutch. & Dalz., Fl. W. Trop. Afr. 1: 394, fig. 147; ed. 2 (Keay), 1: 544; Burkart, Legum. Argent. ed. 2: 326, fig. 97*b*; de Munk, Reinwardtia, 6: 195 (Malaysian spp.); Milne-Redhead, Fl. Trop. East Afr. (*ined.*).

Shrubs or herbs; leaves simple or digitately 3-foliolate, rarely 1–5- or 7-foliolate; stipules free from the petiole, sometimes decurrent, sometimes small or absent; flowers mostly yellow, racemose or rarely solitary, racemes terminal or leaf-opposed; bracts small or absent, rarely foliaceous; bracteoles small or rarely absent; calyx-lobes free or rarely the upper 2 forming a lip or the upper 4 subcoherent in pairs; vexillum orbicular or rarely ovate, often callose above the short claw; wings obovate or oblong, shorter than the vexillum; keel incurved, beaked; stamens all connate into a sheath split above; alternate anthers small and versatile, alternately long and basifixed; ovary usually sessile, 2–many-ovuled; style much incurved or inflexed, more or less longitudinally bearded above, or around the stigma; fruit globose or oblong, turgid or inflated, 2-valved, continuous inside; seeds estrophiolate, funicle filiform.

152. **Priotropis** Wight & Arn., Prodr. Fl. Pen. Ind. Or. 1: 180 (1834). 2 spp., Himalayas, China, Indo-China, trop. E. Africa, Socotra Isl.; type *P. cytisoides* Wight. & Arn., Himalayas to China and Indo-China. B.H. 1: 480; E.P. 3, 3: 230.

[1] Synonyms of **Crotalaria**: *Crotularia* Medik. (1789). *Atolaria* Neck. (1790). *Clavulium* Desv. (1826). *Chrysocalyx* Guill. et Perr. (1832). *Cyrtolobum* R.Br. (1832). *Clavulum* G. Don. (1832). *Crypsocalyx* Endl. (1834). *Anisanthera* Raf. (1836). *Jocaulon* Raf. (1836). *Maria-Antonia* Parl. (1844). *Quirosia* Blanco (1845). *Phyllocalyx* A. Rich. (1847). *Pentadynamis* R.Br. (1849).

Shrubs; leaves 3-foliolate; flowers yellow, racemose, racemes terminal and leaf-opposed; calyx-lobes subequal, free; vexillum suborbicular, shortly 2-callused above the claw; wings obovate, shorter than the vexillum; keel beaked; stamens all connate into a sheath split above; alternate anthers small, versatile, alternately long and basifixed; ovary stipitate, many-ovuled; style very incurved above the ovary, longitudinally bearded on the inside (adaxially), stigma terminal; fruit stipitate, oblong, compressed, 2-valved, continuous inside; seeds estrophiolate, funicle filiform.

Tribe 14. ROBINIEAE[1]

Tribe *Galegeae* Subtribe *Robinieae* Benth. & Hook. f., Gen. Pl. 1: 445, partly (1865)

Trees, erect, or rarely climbing shrubs; leaves pari- or imparipinnate; stipules present, sometimes setaceous or spinescent; stipels absent or present; *racemes all axillary or fasciculate at the older nodes*; bracts small; corolla papilionaceous; calyx shortly dentate or 2-lipped, upper 2 often more connate; *stamens diadelphous, the vexillary filament free or connate with the others higher up* into an open sheath or rarely closed tube; *anthers uniform* or nearly so; style often rigid, *glabrous*, rarely hairy along the adaxial side; stigma capitate, terminal; ovules numerous to several, rarely 2 or 1; *fruit 2-valved*, flat, or turgid only around the seeds, continuous within or rarely septate between the seeds; *seeds flat, without a strophiole*. Type genus *Robinia* Linn.

Fruits not septate between the seeds; style not coiled at the tip:
Vexillum with callosities inside above the claw:
Fruits clothed with glandular bristle-hairs; vexillum broad; style bearded above the middle; branches often armed with infra-stipular spines; ovules several   153. **Olneya**
Fruits without glandular hairs; branches without spines:
Vexillary stamen free only at the base and apex; ovary shortly stipitate; style shortly bearded in the upper part; ovules 2   154. **Afgekia**
Vexillary stamen at length completely free; ovary long-stipitate; style glabrous; ovules 8–6   155. **Hybosema**
Vexillum without callosities above the claw; fruits not glandular-hairy:
Style glabrous except sometimes just below the stigma:
Leaves imparipinnate:
Leaves alternate:
Fruits not winged:
Vexillary stamen free from the others or connate only at the base:
Ovules several (5 or more):
Leaves not stipellate:
Wings longer than the vexillum; valves of fruit not becoming coiled   156. **Poitaea**

[1] **Robinieae**, trib. nov. Arbores erectae, vel rare frutices scandentes; folia pari- vel imparipinnata, foliolis oppositis vel alternis; stipulae interdum setaceae vel spinescentes; stipellae saepe nullae; racemi omnes axillares vel ad nodos vetustos fasciculati; corolla papilionacea; calyx breviter dentatus vel bilabiatus, dentibus superioribus saepe plus connatis; stamen vexillare saepe liberum; antherae muticae, uniformes; stylus glaber, rare unilatere pubescens; stigma capitatum, terminale; ovula numerosa, pauca vel 1; fructus 2-valvis, planus nisi demum ad semina turgidus, intra continuus vel rare inter semina septatus; semina estrophiolata.

Wings equal to the vexillum; valves not coiled   157. **Salweenia**
Wings shorter than the vexillum; valves of fruit becoming spirally
   coiled   158. **Gliricidia**
Leaves stipellate; wings longer than the vexillum   159. **Sauvallella**
Ovules 4, 3, or 1:
   Vexillum subtriangular-ovate; ovules 4–3   160. **Margaritolobium**
   Vexillum obcordate; ovule 1   161. **Coroya**
Vexillary stamen connate with the others except at the base:
   Stipules obsolete; calyx truncate with small equal teeth; fruit linear-
      oblong   162. **Willardia**
   Stipules linear-lanceolate or linear; upper 2 calyx-lobes connate into
      a broad limb; fruit oblanceolate   163. **Apurimacia**
Fruits winged along the upper (adaxial) suture; vexillum broad; leaves
   imparipinnate, often stipellate   164. **Robinia**
Leaves opposite; stipules and stipels absent; racemes precocious; fruits
   usually 2-seeded   165. **Hebestigma**
Leaves paripinnate:
Leaf-rhachis winged, produced at the apex into a barren tip; leaflets not
   veined:
Petiole with a thickened pouch behind the base, the pouch expanded
   into a straight or recurved prickle-like tooth; stipules very decidu-
   ous; flowers fasciculate at the older leafless nodes   166. **Notodon**
Petiole without a thickened pouch as described above; stipules persis-
   tent; flowers solitary   167. **Bembicidium**
Leaf-rhachis not winged and not produced into a barren tip:
Stipules intrapetiolar, connate in the lower part; vexillum shortly ovate,
   not clawed   168. **Cajalbania**
Stipules not intrapetiolar, free:
Style thickened in the upper part, hooked and incurved at the apex;
   fruit lanceolate; stipules rigid, sometimes spinescent
                169. **Corynella**
Style filiform, not thickened; fruit linear; trees or shrubs with long and
   short shoots   170. **Sabinea**
Leaves trifoliolate; flowers glomerulate, glomerules mostly in elongated
   spike-like inflorescences   171. **Craspedolobium**
Style hairy along the upper (adaxial) side; leaves pari- or imparipinnate,
  with very small stipels; flowers in axillary racemes; stipules setaceous
              172. **Coursetia**
Fruits septate between the seeds; style circinately coiled towards the tip;
  stamens monadelphous in the middle; leaves imparipinnate 173. **Lennea**

153. **Olneya** A. Gray, Mem. Amer. Acad. N.S. 5: 328 (1855). *Tesota* C. Muell.
(1857). 1 sp., *O. tesota* A. Gray, New Mexico. B.H. 1: 500; E.P. 3, 3: 276.

Small tree, greyish with minute hairs, armed with infrastipular spines; leaves pari- or
imparipinnate, leaflets numerous, small, entire, without stipels; stipules obsolete; racemes
axillary; flowers white or purplish; bracts caducous; calyx-lobes subequal in length, upper
2 connate high up; vexillum clawed, broadly orbicular, emarginate, reflexed, appendaged at
the base with 2 broad inflexed auricles and with 2 callosities inside; wings obliquely oblong,
free; keel broad, incurved, obtuse; vexillary stamen free, remainder connate into a sheath

split above; anthers uniform; ovary sessile; ovules several; style inflexed, barbate all over above the middle, stigma thick, capitate; fruit compressed, 2-valved, setose-glandular, continuous within, valves thick, and coriaceous, at length very convex over the seeds; seeds 1–2, broadly ellipsoid, within a strophiole; funicle very short; hilum elliptic.

Seeds eaten by Indians and stored for the winter months.

154. **Afgekia** Craib, Kew Bull. 1927: 376. 1 sp., *A. sericea* Craib, Thailand.

Climbing shrub; leaves imparipinnate, leaflets opposite, very silky, oblong, stipellate; stipules conspicuous, persistent for a time, produced at the base; racemes axillary, elongated, with large imbricate tailed silky bracts in bud; axis of inflorescence at length much elongated and rough with the scars of fallen flowers; calyx 2-lipped, posterior lobe a little shorter, lower lobe longer than the tube; vexillum large, callous at the base in the middle and doubly so higher up; wings oblong, hastate at the base; keel incurved, obtuse; petals all clawed; vexillary stamen free at the base but connate with the others higher up; anthers uniform, pilose at apex and base; ovary stipitate, style inflexed, stigma small, terminal; ovules 2; fruit oblong-elliptic, dehiscent, valves woody; seeds 2, ellipsoid, shining, funicle elongated, hard and persistent, hilum extending half of the seed.

155. **Hybosema** Harms, Fedde Repert. 19: 66 (1923). 1 sp., *H. ehrenbergii* (Schlecht.) Harms, Mexico.

Shrub; leaves pinnate, leaflets small, 7–11-paired, oblong or elliptic; stipules rather long, linear-lanceolate, acuminate, deciduous; racemes axillary on short shoots, several-flowered, lax; pedicels single or paired, jointed a little below the calyx; calyx narrowly long-cupular or tubular-campanulate, abruptly narrowed to the joint at the base, shortly 2-lipped, upper lip broader, shortly 2-toothed, lower shortly 3-toothed; corolla long-exserted; vexillum shortly clawed, obovate, suddenly narrowed into the claw, with a thick bilobed callus at the base of the limb; wings clawed, narrow, lanceolate, obtuse, broadly appendaged at the base; keel-petals narrow, long-clawed, obtuse, slightly coherent at the back; vexillary stamen at length free; anthers small; ovary long-stipitate; style slightly curved, glabrous stigma capitellate; ovules 8–6; fruit linear-oblanceolate, dehiscent, continuous within, flat, valves rather woody, the ventral margin slightly thickened; seeds 5–3, suborbicular, flat, strophiolate.

156. **Poitaea** Vent., Choix, 36, t. 36 (1803). *Poitea* Vent. (1803). *Poitaea* DC. (1825). *Vilmorinia* DC. (1825). 5–6 spp., West Indies; type *P. galegoides* Vent. B.H. 1: 500; E.P. 3, 3: 275.

Shrubs; leaves imparipinnate, leaflets mostly numerous, membranous, entire, without stipels; stipules setaceous; racemes axillary; flowers rose or purple, pendulous, pedicels solitary; bracts small, bracteoles absent; calyx truncate with very short teeth; vexillum obovate, erect; wings oblong, longer than the vexillum; keel oblong, slightly falcate, acute, longer than the wings, all free at the apex; vexillary stamen free, the others connate into a sheath; anthers uniform; ovary stipitate, many-ovuled; style incurved, subulate, glabrous; stigma terminal; fruit linear, plano-compressed, not winged, 2-valved; seeds orbicular.

157. **Salweenia** Bak. f., Journ. Bot. 1935: 134, with fig. 1 sp., *S. wardii* Bak. f., S. Tibet.

Erect shrub; leaves imparipinnate, leaflets 4–5 pairs, opposite, entire, narrow and soon folded; stipules herbaceous, minute; stipels absent; flowers fasciculate at the ends of the shoots; bracts and bracteoles minute, the latter well below the calyx; calyx campanulate, teeth 5, very short, deltoid; disk adnate to the base of the calyx; vexillum obovate, emarginate, clawed; wings oblong, long-clawed; keel boat-shaped, clawed; stamens diadelphous, vexillary free; anthers dorsifixed, uniform; ovary stipitate, style glabrous; fruit linear-oblong, flattened, stipitate, 2-valved, valves thin; seeds 5–7, subcordate at the base on a fairly long funicle.

158. **Gliricidia** H. B. & K., Nov. Gen. et Spec. 6: 393 (1823). 6–9 spp., trop. America; type *G. sepium* (Jacq.) Steud. (*G. maculata* H. B. & K.), Cent.

America, cult. and naturalized elsewhere. B.H. 1: 499; E.P. 3, 3: 275; Amshoff, Pulle Fl. Suriname, 2, 2: 158.

Trees or shrubs; leaves imparipinnate, leaflets entire, reticulate-pinnately nerved, often spotted, without stipels; stipules small; racemes axillary or fasciculate on very short branch-lets at the older nodes; flowers rose; bracts and bracteoles small or absent; calyx-teeth short, broad, upper 2 subconnate; vexillum large, reflexed, without a callus, nude or appendaged with small inflexed auricles; wings falcate-oblong, free; keel incurved, obtuse; vexillary stamen free, remainder connate into a sheath; anthers uniform; ovary stipitate, many-ovuled; style inflexed, subulate, glabrous or with a few hairs below the small terminal stigma; fruit stipitate, broadly linear, plano-compressed, not winged, 2-valved, continuous within, valves coriaceous, becoming spirally coiled; seeds without a strophiole.

G. *sepium*, Madre de Cacao; Mexico, Cent. America, N. South America; shade tree in coffee plantations; seeds or powdered bark with rice used as a rat and mouse poison.

159. Sauvallella Rydb., Amer. Journ. Bot. 11: 480 (1924). 1 sp., *S. immarginata* (Wright) Rydb., Cuba.

Shrub; leaves imparipinnate; leaflets subopposite, several pairs; stipules subulate; stipels lanceolate, minute; flowers on short branchlets with a bunch of leaves at the top; bracts very small; pedicels slender; calyx campanulate, minutely toothed; vexillum shorter than the wings, suborbicular, shortly clawed; wings curved and shorter than the keel, auriculate at the base; keel-petals longer than the wings, pointed, united to the apex; stamens diadelphous, ovary many-ovuled; style glabrous, stigma terminal; fruit flat, undulate, several-seeded, obliquely striate.

160. Margaritolobium Harms, Fedde Repert. 19: 67 (1923). 1 sp., *M. luteum* (Johnston) Harms, Venezuela.

Shrub; leaves imparipinnate; leaflets 5; racemes precocious, several-flowered; pedicels in pairs; flowers small, yellow; calyx broadly cupular, subtruncate, very shortly broadly denticulate, upper teeth scarcely prominent, lateral very broad, obtuse, lower broad; corolla exserted; vexillum broadly clawed, lamina subtriangular-ovate, abruptly narrowed into the claw; wings with a long slender claw, lamina oblong-oblanceolate, obtuse at the apex, shortly and acutely auriculate at the side above the claw; keel petals long-clawed, lamina obliquely subrhomboid-ovate, very shortly acuminate or acute and there pubescent outside; vexillary stamen free, remainder connate; ovary shortly stipitate, like the stipe silky pubescent; style glabrous, stigma minute; ovules 4–3; fruit flat, thin, dehiscent (?).

161. Coroya Pierre, Fl. Cochinch., t. 392 c (1899). 1 sp., *C. dialoides* Pierre, Indo-China.

Small tree; leaves imparipinnate, leaflets few (3–6), alternate, terminal largest, ovate to elliptic; stipules caducous; panicles terminal; flowers very small in clusters on the panicle; bracts and bracteoles caducous; sepals hairy, the anterior larger than the others; vexillum obcordate, larger than the lateral and keel petals; stamens except the vexillary one connate, free at the top; anthers ellipsoid, dorsifixed; ovary stipitate; ovule 1; style very short; fruit not known.

162. Willardia Rose, Contrib. U.S. Nat. Herb. 1, 4: 97 (1891). 6 spp., Mexico, Cent. America; type *W. mexicana* (S. Wats.) Rose, Mexico. E.P. 3, 3: 275; Hermann, Journ. Wash. Acad. Sci. 37: 427 (1947).

Small trees; leaves imparipinnate; leaflets definite, entire, exstipellate; stipules obsolete; racemes axillary; flowers 'lilac', calyx truncate with small equal teeth; petals equal; vexillum orbicular, spreading; wings falcate-oblong; keel slightly incurved; vexillary stamen connate into a tube with the others except at base; anthers uniform; ovary subsessile with several ovules; style incurved, glabrous or with a few hairs at base; stigma capitate, minute; fruit linear-oblong, strongly compressed, continuous within; seeds reniform, strongly compressed.

163. **Apurimacia** Harms, Fedde Repert. 19: 10 (1923). 4 spp., trop. and subtrop. South America; type *A. michelii* (Rusby) Harms, Peru, Bolivia. Burkart, Physis, 20: 285 (1951); Legum. Argent. ed. 2: 257, fig. 69.

Shrubs; leaves imparipinnate; leaflets 5–9 pairs, small; stipules linear-lanceolate or linear, deciduous; panicles raceme-like, narrow, often elongated, many-flowered; flowers in pairs on the axis; bracteoles 2, small at base of calyx; calyx cupular, short, upper 2 lobes connate into a broad more or less bifid limb, lateral and lowermost deltoid or lanceolate; vexillum shortly clawed, suborbicular or obovate, ecallose, without auricles, more or less narrowed into a claw; wings obliquely oblong, clawed, obtuse, appendaged; keel-petals coherent dorsally, clawed, appendaged; stamens 10, filaments connate into a tube, vexillary free at base and apex; ovary shortly stipitate; ovules 6–4; style hooked, glabrous, stigma very minute; fruit compressed, rather woody, oblanceolate, 2-valved; seeds 5–3.

164. **Robinia** Linn., Sp. Pl. 722 (1753). *Pseudo-Acacia* Medik. (1787). (*Pseudacacia* Moench (1794). About 20 spp., North America to Cent. America; type *R. pseudoacacia* Linn., E. United States, naturalized and cult. in many temp. countries. B.H. 1: 499; E.P. 3, 3: 274; Tuzson, Über einen neuen Fall der Kleistogamie, Engl. Bot. Jahrb. 40: 1, tt. 1, 2 (1907); Burkart, Legum. Argent. ed. 2: 264, fig. 74; Rehder, Trees & Shrubs, ed. 2: 508.

Trees or shrubs, sometimes sticky or bristly with gland-tipped hairs; leaves imparipinnate; leaflets entire, reticulate-pinnately nerved, often stipellate; stipules setaceous or spinescent; racemes axillary; flowers white or rose-purple, sometimes some cleistogamous; bracts membranous, very caducous; bracteoles absent; calyx-teeth short, broad, upper 2 subconnate; vexillum large, reflexed, nude, inside; wings falcate-oblong, free; keel incurved, obtuse; vexillary stamen free at the base, connate in the middle with the others into a closed tube or at length free; anthers uniform, or alternately a little smaller; ovary stipitate, many-ovuled; style inflexed, subulate, hairy at the apex, stigma small, terminal; fruit linear, flat and compressed, narrowly winged along the upper suture, 2-valved, continuous inside, valves thin, sometimes densely bristly; seeds oblong or kidney-shaped, oblique, not strophiolate.

R. pseudoacacia, Locust, Black Locust, False Acacia; wood hard, heavy, very durable, used for ships, turnery, construction, fuel; poisonous properties; flowers source of honey; ornamental tree.

165. **Hebestigma** Urb., Symb. Antill. 2: 289 (1900). 1 sp., *H. cubense* Urb., Cuba.

Tree, leaves opposite, imparipinnate; leaflets entire, reticulate-penninerved; stipules and stipels absent; racemes precocious; flowers purplish or pale rose; bracts small; bracteoles none; calyx-teeth short, broad, 3 anticous and 2 posticous; vexillum orbicular, reflexed, not callous above the claw, margin not auriculate; wings oblong, nearly straight, free; keel curved on the bank, almost straight on the inside; obtuse, the petals shortly connate at the apex; vexillary stamen connate at the very base with the remainder; anthers uniform; ovary stipitate, 9–5-ovulate; style rectangular-inflexed, subulate; stigma small, terminal, villous; fruit sessile or subsessile, woody, broadly linear, plano-compressed, not winged, margin flat, 2-valved; seeds usually 2, separated by dissepiments, ovate, hilum orbicular; cotyledons cordate at the base.

166. **Notodon** Urb., Symb. Antill. 1: 324 (1899). 4 spp., West Indies; type *N. gracilis* Urb., Cuba.

Shrubs; stipules lanceolate, subulate-acuminate, very deciduous; petiole with a thickened pouch behind the base, pouch expanded into a straight or recurved prickle-like tooth; leaves alternate, paripinnate; rhachis winged, extended into a short apiculus; leaflets deciduous, without veins; stipels very minute; inflorescence not known; pedicels jointed at the apex; prophylls none; calyx membranous, shortly campanulate, teeth very short, 3 interior rather remote, 2 posticous contiguous, triangular, obtuse; vexillum suborbicular, reflexed, without a callus; wings oblong, straight; keel-petals connate in the upper half, subarcuate in the upper part at the back, nearly straight on the inside, rather obtuse, exceeding the wings and the vexillum; vexillary stamen free, remainder united in a tube but free at the apex, all subequal in length; anthers equal; ovary shortly stipitate, linear; ovules several; style linear-subulate, arcuate-curved, glabrous; stigma obsolete at the apex inside.

167. **Bembicidium** Rydb., Mem. Torr. Cl. 68 (1920). 1 sp., *B. cubense* Rydb., Cuba. Leon & Alain, Fl. Cuba, 2: 306 (1951).

Unarmed shrub; leaves paripinnate; stipules lanceolate, persistent; petiole and rhachis broadly winged, wings continuous, rhachis slightly produced above the uppermost leaflets; leaflets entire, nerveless; stipels obsolete; flowers axillary, solitary; calyx turbinate, with 2 broad subequal acute lips; corolla purplish, petals subequal; vexillum obovate, shortly clawed; blades of keel-petals united only at the middle; stamens diadelphous, adaxial filament free; anthers uniform; ovary slightly stipitate, many-ovuled; style glabrous, bent inward at the base and slightly arcuate, stigma minute, terminal fruit not known.

168. **Cajalbania** Urb., Symb. Antill. 9: 449 (1928). 1 sp., *C. immarginata* (Ch. Wright) Urb., Cuba.

Shrub; leaves alternate, paripinnate; rhachis not winged; stipules long-acuminate from a lanceolate base, connate in the lower part within the petioles; stipels minute; leaflets opposite or sulabternate, 9–17; flowers axillary or 1–few in clusters from the nodes of the older wood; pedicels jointed below the turbinate torus; petals bright purple; calyx-tube campanulate-cupular, limb subbilabiate; teeth short, the posterior much smaller; petals very unequal; vexillum shortly ovate, not clawed; wings intermediate in length, free from the keel, oblong-lanceolate, shortly clawed; keel-petals very long, oblong, rather acute, united in the upper part but free at the apex, shortly clawed; vexillary stamen free, remainder subunequal in length, the anterior a little longer; anthers ovate, equal; ovary linear, glabrous, stipitate; ovules numerous; style straight; stigma terminal, minute, flattened; fruit and seed not seen.

169. **Corynella** DC., Ann. Sci. Nat. 4: 93 (1825). *Corynitis* Spreng. (1827). *Corynelia* Reichb. (1841). *Toxotropis* Turcz. (1846). 6 spp., West Indies; lectotype *C. polyantha* (Sw.) DC. B.H. 1: 500; E.P. 3, 3: 276.

Shrubs; leaves paripinnate, leaflets scarcely stipellate; stipules rigid, sometimes spinescent; flowers purplish, fasciculate at the older nodes; bracts small; bracteoles absent; calyxteeth either very short or longer and subulate, upper 2 connate high up; vexillum clawed, suborbicular, reflexed; wings obliquely oblong, free; keel slightly incurved, longer than the wings and vexillum; vexillary stamen free, the remainder connate into a sheath split open above; anthers uniform; ovary stipitate; ovules numerous; style thickened in the upper part, somewhat hooked at the apex, incurved, stigmatose on the inside below the apex; fruit lanceolate, plano-compressed; seeds numerous.

170. **Sabinea** DC., Ann. Sci. Nat. 4: 92 (1825). 4 spp., West Indies; type *S. florida* (Vahl) DC. B.H. 1: 501; E.P. 3, 3: 276.

Trees or shrubs with long and short shoots; leaves paripinnate, leaflets deciduous, entire, without stipels; stipules short; flowers purplish, pedicels fasciculate at the older nodes on the short shoots; bracts small; bracteoles absent; calyx truncate, teeth very short; vexillum suborbicular, spreading or reflexed; wings falcate-oblong, free; keel incurved, obtuse, equal to or longer than the wings; vexillary stamen free, remainder connate into a sheath split open above; all equal or the lower 5 longer and more connate; anthers uniform; ovary stipitate, many-ovuled; style very incurved, filiform, glabrous, stigma minute, terminal; fruit stipitate, linear, plano-compressed, 2-valved, continuous within; seeds compressed, ovate, without a strophiole.

171. **Craspedolobium** Harms, Fedde Repert. 17: 135 (1921). 1 sp., *C. schochii* Harms, W. China.

Scandent shrub; leaves trifoliolate; flowers glomerulate, small, glomerules in mostly elongated spike-like inflorescences; calyx cupular, teeth subequal, lower lanceolate-ovate, lateral deltoid, acute, uppermost very broad and emarginate; vexillum shortly clawed, ovate or obovate-suborbicular, scarcely auriculate at the base; wings obliquely narrow-oblong, obtuse, very shortly denticulate at the base; keel almost straight, folded from the middle towards the base, very shortly denticulate at the base; vexillary stamen free, remainder connate; ovary slightly stipitate; style curved, glabrous or nearly so, stigma minutely capitate; ovules 8–5; fruit plano-compressed, lanceolate-linear or lanceolate, chartaceous, dehiscent, ventral side narrowly margined; seeds probably 5–3.

172. **Coursetia** DC., Ann. Sci. Nat. ser. 1, 4: 92 (1825). *Humboldtiella* Harms (1923). *Callistylon* Pittier (1928). About 25 spp., California to trop. South America; type *C. tomentosa* (Cav.) DC., Peru. Hermann, Journ. Wash. Acad. Sci. 38: 73 (1948); B.H. 1: 501; E.P. 3, 3: 277.

Trees and shrubs; leaves pari- or imparipinnate; stipels very small; stipules setaceous; racemes axillary or terminal; bracteoles none; calyx-teeth subequal, upper 2 connate high up; petals subequal; vexillum orbicular or reniform, sides reflexed; vexillary stamen free or slightly connate with the others in the middle; anthers uniform; ovary sessile, many-ovuled; style inflexed, barbate above, stigma capitate; fruit linear, compressed, 2-valved, continuous within; seeds suborbicular, estrophiolate.

173. **Lennea** Klotzsch, Link, Kl. & Otto, Ic. Pl. Rar. 2: 65, t. 26 (1842). *Calomorphe* Kunze ex Walp. (1842). 6 spp., Mexico, Cent. and South America; type *L. robinioides* Klotzsch, Mexico, Honduras. B.H. 1: 500; E.P. 3, 3: 275.

Trees or shrubs; leaves imparipinnate; leaflets membranous, entire, stipellate; stipules small; racemes axillary or fasciculate at the older nodes, short, slender, many-flowered; flowers rose or greenish; calyx-teeth short, upper 2 subconnate; vexillum suborbicular, reflexed, nude inside, claw short; wings obliquely oblong, free; keel slightly incurved, obtuse; vexillary stamen free at the base, bent, then connate with the others into a closed tube; anthers uniform; ovary subsessile, many-ovuled; style filiform, circinately coiled at the apex, slightly barbate at the back, stigma terminal; fruit linear, compressed, torulose, 2-valved, septate between the seeds.

Tribe 15. Carmichaelieae[1]

Tribe *Galegeae* Subtribe *Robinieae* Benth. & Hook. f., Gen. Pl. 1: 446 (small part) (1865)

Small trees or shrubs, rarely climbers, often leafless during flowering and with branches *Juncus-like* or *flattened*; leaves imparipinnate or reduced to scales; stipules small; *stipels absent*; flowers racemose or fasciculate, *often borne at the nodes*; calyx-teeth subequal; corolla papilionaceous; *vexillary filament free*, remainder connate into a sheath split adaxially; *anthers uniform*; style *glabrous* or *hairy on the adaxial side or only at the base*; ovules numerous to 2; fruit 2-valved or indehiscent, *continuous within*, valves often separating from

---

[1] **Carmichaelieae**, trib. nov. Arbores parvae vel frutices, rare scandentes, per anthesin saepius aphyllae, ramis junceis vel complanatis; folia imparipinnata vel squamiformia; stipulae parvae; stipellae nullae; flores racemosi vel fasciculati, saepe ad nodos laterales dispositi; stamen vexillare liberum, caetera in vaginam connata; antherae uniformes; stylus glaber, vel intus breviter barbatus vel solum ad basin; ovula numerosa ad 2; fructus 2-valvis vel indehiscens, intra continuus, valvis per dehiscentiam a margine persistenti secedentibus; semina estrophiolata; radicula biplicata.

the sutures; seeds *without a strophiole*; *radicle twice folded*. New Zealand, Lord Howe's and Norfolk Islands. Type genus *Carmichaelia* R.Br.

Style glabrous or hairy only at the base; fruits 2-valved:
  Leaves with 3–5 small leaflets or reduced to scales; not climbers:
    Flowers in racemes; ovules numerous; style glabrous at the base; fruit ovate or elliptic-oblong; seeds few   **174. Carmichaelia**
    Flowers in dense fascicles; ovules 4–2; style silky at the base; fruit deltoid; seeds 2–1; calyx woolly   **175. Corallospartium**
  Leaves with few rather large leaflets; tall climbing shrub; style glabrous; ovules numerous; fruit compressed, broadly oblong **176. Streblorrhiza**
Style with long hairs on the upper (adaxial) side; leaves reduced to scales; fruits indehiscent:
  Seeds more than 1 in each fruit, the latter narrowly linear   **177. Notospartium**
  Seed solitary in each fruit, the latter rhomboid-ovoid   **178. Chordospartium**

174. Carmichaelia R.Br., Bot. Reg. 11: t. 912 (1825). *Carmichaela* Reichb. (1841). *Huttonella* T. Kirk (1897). About 4 spp., New Zealand, Lord Howe's Island; type *C. australis* R.Br., New Zealand. B.H. 1: 502; E.P. 3, 3: 278; G. Simpson, Revision, Trans. Roy. Soc. New Zeal. 75: 231 (1945); Allan, Fl. New Zeal. 1: 373 (1961).

Small trees or shrubs, often leafless during flowering; branches *Juncus*-like or flattened, with minute scales at the nodes; leaves when present imparipinnate; leaflets 3 to numerous, small, obcordate; stipels absent; stipules small, membranous; flowers rose or white, shortly pedicellate, in racemes at the lateral nodes; bracts small, membranous; bracteoles small, inserted on the pedicel or adnate to the calyx; calyx-teeth subequal or the upper smaller; vexillum orbicular, contracted into a claw; wings oblong, often shorter than the vexillum, free; keel incurved or fornicate, obtuse, shorter or longer than the vexillum; vexillary stamen free, remainder connate into a sheath; anthers uniform; ovary shortly stipitate; style incurved, glabrous, stigma terminal; ovules numerous; fruit compressed, ovate or elliptic-oblong, apiculate by the style; sutures thickened, valves during dehiscence separating from the margin; seeds few, compressed, without a strophiole; radical elongated, twice folded.

175. Corallospartium J. B. Armstrong, Trans. New Zeal. Inst. 13: 333 (1881). 1 sp., *C. crassicaule* (Hook. f.) J. B. Armstrong, New Zealand. Cheeseman, Illustr. New Zeal. Fl. Pl. 31; Allan, Fl. New Zeal. 1: 371.

Shrub, leafless when mature; stems and branches thick, cylindric, ribbed and deeply sulcate; leaves very fugacious, small, linear-oblong or ovate-oblong; flowers densely fasciculate; calyx woolly, campanulate, 5-toothed, teeth subequal; vexillum large, broad, reflexed, shortly clawed; wings falcate, oblong, obtuse, auriculate towards the base, shorter than the keel; keel subequal in length to the vexillum, oblong, incurved, obtuse; vexillary stamen free, remainder connate; ovary densely villous; style silky at the base and near the apex; ovules 4–2; fruit 2-valved, deltoid, rounded and winged on the back, shortly beaked, villous; valves thin, slightly reticulate; seed 1 or rarely 2, reniform.

176. Streblorrhiza Endl., Prodr. Fl. Norf. 92 (1833). *Streblorhiza* Benth. & Hook. f. (1865). 1 sp., *S. speciosa* Endl., Norfolk Island. B.H. 1: 503; E.P. 3, 3: 279.

Tall climbing shrub; leaves imparipinnate, leaflets few, rather large, entire, without stipels; stipules small; flowers flesh-coloured, rather large, in axillary racemes; bracts small;

bracteoles minute; calyx rather broad, teeth short, upper 2 very short; vexillum ovate, erect-patent, subsessile, narrowed at the base; wings short, narrow; keel erect, incurved, rather acute, subequal to the vexillum; vexillary stamen free, remainder connate into an open sheath; anthers uniform; ovary stipitate; ovules numerous; style filiform, incurved, glabrous, stigma terminal; fruit compressed, broadly oblong, obliquely subfalcate, 2-valved, continuous within and pubescent; valves coriaceous, slightly convex; seeds reniform, without a strophiole, with a filiform funicle; radicle elongated, twice folded.

177. **Notospartium** Hook. f., Hook. Kew Journ. 9: 176, t. 3 (1857). *Nothospartium* Pritz. (1866). *Nothospermum* Hort. (1883). 3 spp., New Zealand; type *N. carmichaeliae* Hook. f. B.H. 1: 502; E.P. 3, 3: 279.

Small trees, leafless during flowering; branches *Juncus-* or whip-like, pendulous, leafless; leaves reduced to scales at the nodes, very minute; flowers in racemes at the nodes; bracts and bracteoles minute; calyx-teeth short, subequal; vexillum suborbicular, contracted into a short claw; wings oblong-falcate, free; keel incurved, obtuse; vexillary stamen free, remainder connate into a sheath; anthers subuniform; ovary sessile; style incurved, hooked-inflexed at the apex, shortly barbate inside; stigma terminal; ovules numerous; fruit linear, plano-compressed, membranous between the nerve-like sutures, indehiscent, septate between the seeds inside; seeds compressed, not strophiolate; radicle elongated, twice folded.

178. **Chordospartium** Cheeseman, Trans. New Zeal. Inst. 1910, 43: 175 (1911). 1 sp., *C. stevensonii* Cheeseman, New Zealand. Cheeseman, Illustr. New Zeal. Fl. Pl. 31A.

Small tree or shrub, leafless; branches *Juncus*-like, pendulous, with very small scales at the nodes; flowers purple, many in short dense racemes; bracts and bracteoles small; calyx-teeth short, subequal or the upper smaller; vexillum orbicular, reflexed, shortly clawed; wings strongly falcate, free, shorter than the vexillum; keel incurved, obtuse, subequal to the vexillum; vexillary stamen free, remainder connate into a sheath; anthers uniform; ovary sessile, silky, 6–3-ovuled; style incurved, inflexed at the apex, bearded longitudinally inside; stigma minute, terminal; fruit short, turgid, rhomboid-ovoid, incurved; indehiscent; seed solitary, without a strophiole.

Tribe 16. BARBIERIEAE[1]

Papilionaceae Subtribe *Barbierianae* Rydb., N. Amer. Fl. 24: 201 (1924)

Shrubs; leaves imparipinnate or pinnately trifoliolate; stipules and stipels narrow; leaflets net-veined; flowers in axillary and terminal racemes, solitary or paired, each subtended by a *pair of bracteoles*; calyx cylindric, 5-lobed; petals narrow, with long claws; stamens diadelphous, vexillary filament free, remainder connate in a split sheath; *anthers uniform*; *style with long hairs along the upper (adaxial) surface* or above the middle; fruit 2-valved, several-seeded; seeds estrophiolate. Mexico to South America. Type genus *Barbieria* DC.

Calyx long-tubular, lobes shorter than the tube; leaves imparipinnate; style
  bearded along the upper side   179. **Barbieria**
Calyx-lobes longer than the tube; leaves trifoliolate; style bearded all over
  above the middle   180. **Genistidium**

[1] **Barbierieae** trib. nov. Frutices; folia imparipinnata vel trifoliolata; foliola reticulata; stipulae et stipellae angustae; flores in racemis axillaribus et terminalibus dispositi, in rhachide solitarii vel geminati, bracteolis geminatis subtendentes; calyx cylindricus, 5-lobus; petala angusta, unguibus longis; stamina diadelpha, vexillari libero; antherae uniformes; stylus supra pilis longis instructus; fructus planus, 2-valvis; semina plura, estrophiolata.

179. **Barbieria** DC., Mém. Légum. 241, t. 39 (1825). *Barbiera* Spreng. (1831). 1 sp., *B. pinnata* (Pers.) Baill. (*B. polyphylla* DC.), Mexico to trop. South America, West Indies. B.H. 1: 495; E.P. 3, 3: 272; Rydb., Fl. N. Amer. 24: 201 (1919).

Shrub; leaves imparipinnate, leaflets numerous, entire, with long-subulate stipels; stipules subulate-acuminate; racemes terminal and from the upper axils; flowers 2–3 together on the rhachis, rather large, red; bracts and bracteoles subulate-acuminate; calyx long-tubular, subtended by 2 bracteoles, persistent, lobes long and setaceous; vexillum oblong, long-narrowed at the base into the claw, nude inside; lower petals long-clawed, the wings oblong, adherent to and shorter than the keel; keel obtuse, subequal to the vexillum; vexillary stamen free, remainder connate into a sheath; anthers uniform; ovary sessile; style long, bearded along the inside, stigma small, terminal; ovules numerous; fruit linear, straight, plano-compressed, 2-valved, septate inside between the seeds, transversely impressed outside; seeds transversely oblong, without a strophiole, funicle short.

180. **Genistidium** I. M. Johnston, Journ. Arn. Arb. 22: 113 (1941). 1 sp., *G. dumosum* I. M. Johnston, Mexico.

Erect shrub, much branched, strigose; leaves pinnately trifoliolate, leaflets entire, elongated, nerveless; stipules subulate, minute; flowers yellow, solitary or paired in the axils of the upper often 1-foliolate leaves; calyx-lobes elongated, longer than the tube, upper 2 connate high up; petals long-clawed; vexillum suborbicular; wings lunate-oblong, broadly auriculate; keel obtusely lunate, auriculate, partly connivent; vexillary stamen quite free, remainder connate into a sheath; anthers uniform; ovary subsessile, 6–4-ovuled; style inflexed, subterete, subulate, bearded all over above the middle, stigma capitate, minute, terminal; fruit linear, compressed, straight, 2-valved, valves coriaceous; seed suborbicular, compressed, estrophiolate.

Tribe 17. MILLETTIEAE

Miq. Fl. Ind. Bat. 1: 137 (1855); Benth. & Hook. f., Gen. Pl. 1: 445 (as part of Subtribe *Tephrosieae*)

Hard-wooded trees or woody climbers; leaves imparipinnate, rarely pinnately trifoliolate or 1-foliolate, rarely glandular below; *stipules usually present*; *stipels often present*; leaflets more or less reticulate; flowers in *terminal racemes or panicles* or also in the upper axils, rarely on the older branches or stem; bracts and bracteoles often very caducous; calyx 5-toothed or bilabiate; stamens monadelphous or diadelphous, with the vexillary filament quite free or free at the base; *anthers uniform*, very rarely dimorphic; *style glabrous*; fruit flat, 2-valved or tardily dehiscent; several- or few- or 1-seeded; seeds reniform or rounded, usually estrophiolate. Type genus *Millettia* Wight & Arnot.

Leaves neither glandular nor pellucid-punctate:
Upper two calyx-lobes united and forming a hood as long as and covering the vexillum in bud; leaves with stipels; vexillum long-acuminate; vexillary stamen free at the base then connate with the others into a closed tube; fruit beaked by the persistent style   181. **Platysepalum**
Upper two calyx-lobes not as above, though calyx sometimes bilabiate:
Calyx very distinctly bilabiate:
Trees; calyx-lips entire; flowers in axillary and terminal panicles; anthers glabrous; disk present   182. **Dewevrea**

Trees or shrubs; upper-calyx-lip of 2 large side-by-side petaloid lobes, lower lip very short and 3-toothed   183. **Taralea**

Erect shrubs; upper 2 calyx-teeth or lobes connate; flowers very showy, fasciculate at the often leafless nodes   184. **Chadsia**

Calyx not or only slightly bilabiate:

Anthers uniform or nearly so:

Leaves imparipinnate:

Stipules present:

Racemes not cauliflorous; buds not supra-axillary:

Disk present; leaflets opposite and mostly stipellate; fruits tardily dehiscent; Old World tropics and subtropics   185. **Millettia**

Disk absent; leaflets alternate, rarely stipellate; fruits soon dehiscent; trop. Africa   186. **Craibia**

Disk absent; leaflets often stipellate; tall scandent shrubs with terminal pendulous racemes; fruits soon dehiscent; temp. E. Asia and North America   187. **Wisteria**

Racemes mostly cauliflorous; buds supra-axillary, covered with numerous subulate spreading cataphylls; Malaya and China   188. **Fordia**

Stipules absent; ovules 3–2; fruit stipitate; Indo-China   189. **Antheroporum**

Leaves pinnately trifoliolate; disk present between the stamens and ovary; not climbing; ovules 3–2; fruits long-stipitate; Australia   190. **Goodia**

Leaves simple or unifoliolate; flowers numerous in axillary racemes   191. **Burkillia**

Anthers dimorphic, alternately oblong and shortly ovate; trees; stipels absent   192. **Poecilanthe**

Leaves more or less densely gland-dotted below or pellucid-punctate; stipels absent:

Vexillary stamen free; ovary stipitate; fruit curved, thick and woody; trop. Africa   193. **Schefflerodendron**

Vexillary stamen free at the base then united with the others; fruit straight, both sutures thickened, dehiscent along the adaxial suture; Cent. America   194. **Terua**

---

181. **Platysepalum** Welw. ex Baker, Oliv. Fl. Trop. Afr. 2: 131 (1871). 12 spp., trop. Afr.; type *P. violaceum* Welw. ex Baker, W. trop. Africa. Hauman, Fl. Congo Belge, 5: 63, t. 4; J. B. Gillett, Kew Bull. 14: 464 (key to spp.).

Small trees; leaves imparipinnate; leaflets 2 or more pairs, opposite, acuminate, stipellate; stipules very small and early caducous; stipels subulate; panicles axillary, rigid, many-flowered, branches raceme-like; bracteoles large, oblong, sometimes persistent; calyx-tube campanulate, upper 2 teeth connate, broad, emarginate, forming a hood as large as the standard, lower 3 linear-lanceolate; vexillum glabrous, obcordate, shortly clawed, subequal to the wings and keel; upper stamen free from the base; anthers oblong, versatile; ovary sessile, 7–5-ovulate, pubescent; style filiform, glabrous, incurved; stigma minute, terminal; fruit linear-lanceolate, compressed, woody, 2-valved, 5–3-seeded; seeds 3–5 discoid.

182. **Dewevrea** M. Micheli, Bull. Soc. Bot. Belg. 37, 1: 47 (1898); Ann. Mus. Congo, ser. 1, Bol. 1: 3, t. 2 (1898). 1–2 spp., type *D. bilabiata* M. Micheli, trop. Africa. Hauman, Fl. Congo Belge, 5: 61.

Trees; leaves large, imparipinnate; leaflets 3 pairs, ovate; stipules caducous, elliptic to obovate, acuminate; stipels absent; flowers yellow, in large axillary and terminal panicles; bracts and bracteoles very small, deciduous; calyx-tube short, broad, limb bilabiate, lips subequal, entire; vexillum reflexed in flower, shortly clawed, broadly ovate, emarginate, 2-calloused at the base; wings broadly ovate, free; keel-petals broad, obtuse, free; vexillary stamen free; ovary almost sessile, 4–3-ovulate, surrounded at the base by an elevated 10-lobed disk; style elongated, stigma small.

183. **Taralea** Aubl., Hist. Pl. Guian. Franç. 1: 745, t. 298 (1775). About 5 spp., trop. South America; type *T. oppositifolia* Aubl., Brazil, Guiana. B.H. 1: 551 (in *Dipteryx*); Ducke, Rev. Bot. Appliq. 14: 406 (1934); Ducke, Notizbl. Bot. Gart. Berlin, 14: 126 (1938); Amshoff, Pulle Fl. Suriname, 2, 2: 155.

Trees or shrubs; leaves alternate or opposite, imparipinnate, the rhachis not or only slightly flattened, but often produced beyond the last leaflet; leaflets alternate or opposite, coriaceous, pinnately nerved; stipels absent; stipules small, very soon deciduous; flowers in terminal panicles; bracts and bracteoles small, deciduous; calyx 2-lipped, the upper lip of 2 large side-by-side more or less petaloid lobes, the lower lip very short and 3-toothed; petals clawed; vexillum suborbicular, reflexed; wings emarginate, oblong; keel narrowly oblong, more or less straight; stamens 10, monadelphous in a sheath; anthers ovoid, versatile; ovary shortly stipitate, 1-ovuled; style filiform, glabrous; stigma small, terminal; fruit dehiscent, compressed, 2-valved; seed ovate, compressed.

184. **Chadsia** Boj., Ann. Sci. Nat. sér. 2, 20: 104 (1843). *Chaldia* Boj. (1843). 17 spp., Madagascar; type *C. flammea* Boj. B.H. 1: 497; E.P. 3, 3: 272.

Erect shrubs; leaves imparipinnate, leaflets entire, with close subparallel looped lateral nerves; stipules subulate; stipels absent; flowers showy, scarlet, fasciculate at the often leafless nodes; bracts minute; bracteoles absent; calyx broad, subgibbous at the back, upper 2 teeth or lobes connate, the lowermost rather longer than the others; vexillum lanceolate, long-acuminate; wings shorter than the vexillum, acuminate, coherent by the margins at the apex, adherent above the base to the keel; keel falcate, long-beaked, rather longer than the vexillum; vexillary stamen free at the base, then connate with the others into a closed tube; anthers uniform; ovary sessile; style filiform, glabrous, stigma small, terminal; ovules numerous; fruit elongated, beaked by the style, compressed, 2-valved; seeds oblong.

185. **Millettia**[1] Wight & Arn., Prodr. Fl. Pen. Ind. Or. 1: 263 (1834). About 150 spp., trop. and subtrop. regions of the Old World; type *M. rubiginosa* Wight & Arn., India. B.H. 1: 498; E.P. 3, 3: 270; Dunn, Revision of genus *Millettia*, Journ. Linn. Soc. Bot. 41: 123 (1912); Hutch. & Dalz., Fl. W. Trop. Afr. 1: 380; ed. 2 (Keay), 1: 524.

Hard-wooded trees or shrubs, sometimes tall woody climbers; leaves imparipinnate, leaflets often evergreen, pinnately nerved and reticulate-venose, mostly stipellate and opposite; stipules small; racemes terminal or paniculate at the ends of the branches; flowers purple, rose, or white, fasciculate or rarely scattered on the rhachis; bracts and bracteoles

---

[1] Synonyms of **Millettia**: *Milletia* Meisn. (1837). *Callerya* Endl. (1843). *Marquartia* Vog. (1843). *Berrebera* Hochst. (1844). *Fornasinia* Bertol. (1849). *Padbruggea* Miq. (1852). *Otosema* Benth. (1852). *Berebera* Bak. (1871). *Whitfordia* Elmer (1910), not Murr. (1908). *Whitfordiodendron* Elmer (1910). *Adinobotrys* Dunn (1911). *Neodunnia* Vig. (1950).

often deciduous before flowering; calyx-tube broad, truncate or with short teeth, upper 2 sometimes subconnate; vexillum large, spreading or reflexed, nude or callose above the claw, or rarely appendaged with inflexed auricles; wings falcate-oblong, free from the keel; keel incurved, obtuse; vexillary stamen free at the base, then more or less connate with the others or sometimes quite free; filaments filiform; anthers uniform; ovary sessile or rarely stipitate, often surrounded at the base by an annular disk or short sheath; style inflexed, terete, glabrous, stigma small, terminal; ovules numerous; fruit linear, lanceolate or oblong, compressed, flat or thick, rigidly coriaceous or woody, 2-valved or tardily dehiscent and drupe-like; seeds rarely reduced to 1, orbicular or reniform, without a strophiole.

186. **Craibia** Harms & Dunn, Journ. Bot. 49: 106 (1911). 10 spp., trop. Africa; lectotype *C. brevicaudata* (Vatke) Dunn. Hutch. & Dalz., Fl. W. Trop. Afr. 1: 383; ed. 2 (Keay), 1: 527; Gillett, Kew Bull. 14: 189 (1960); Fl. E. Trop. Afr. (*ined.*).

Trees or shrubs with nearly always golden-brown or black indumentum; leaves usually imparipinnate, rarely 1-foliolate, leaflets alternate or rarely subopposite, acuminate; stipels present or absent; inflorescence a terminal or rarely axillary raceme or panicle; bracts and bracteoles caducous; calyx-lobes broad, shorter than the tube, upper pairs united for at least half their length; corolla white, pink, or purplish, glabrous or nearly so; vexillum shortly clawed, lamina oblong, not appendaged; wing- and keel-petals auriculate; adaxial stamen free but sometimes adhering in the middle; anthers all alike; disk absent; ovary shortly stipitate; style glabrous, with small terminal stigma; ovules 6–2 in the upper part of the ovary; fruit shortly stipitate, flat, asymmetric, shortly beaked, dehiscing into thin woody twisted valves; seeds 3–1, ellipsoid, black or dark-brown; hilum short, near one end, surrounded by a short white cupular strophiole produced at one side into a curved strap-like process clasping the funicle.

187. **Wisteria**[1] Nutt., Gen. Amer. 2: 115 (1818) (conserved name). About 10 spp., China, Japan, Australia, NE. America; type *W. frutescens* (Linn.) Poir., North America. B.H. 1: 499; E.P. 3, 3: 271.

Tall climbing shrubs; leaves imparipinnate, leaflets entire, pinnately nerved and reticulate-venulose, often stipellate; stipules small; racemes terminal, pendulous; flowers blue or rarely white, scattered on the rhachis; bracts very caducous; bracteoles absent; upper 2 calyx-teeth short and subconnate, lower often longer; vexillum large, with 2 appendages above the claw; wings oblong-falcate, free from the keel, sometimes coherent at the apex; keel incurved, obtuse; vexillary stamen free or connate in the middle with the others; filaments not dilated; anthers uniform; ovary stipitate; style inflexed, terete, glabrous, stigma small, terminal; ovules numerous; fruit elongated, torulose, 2-valved, continuous inside, valves scarcely coriaceous, convex; seeds reniform, without a strophiole.

188. **Fordia** Hemsl., Journ. Linn. Soc. 23: 160, t. 4 (1886). 12 spp., Malaya, China; type *F. cauliflora* Hemsl., S. China. E.P. 3, 3: 271; Dunn, Kew Bull. 1911: 62.

Erect shrub; buds supra-axillary, covered with numerous striking subulate spreading cataphylls; leaves imparipinnate, leaflets opposite, up to 25, long- and acutely-acuminate, entire; stipels filiform, persistent; stipules subulate, persistent; racemes cauliflorous towards the base of the trunk; calyx truncate or obsoletely 5-toothed; petals with slender claws; vexillum large, not appendaged; wings oblong, almost straight; keel obtuse, slightly incurved; vexillary stamen free; filaments not dilated; anthers equal; ovary sessile, 2-ovuled; style inflexed, glabrous, stigma small, terminal; fruit clavate, compressed, coriaceous, dehiscent; seeds discoid, with a yellow strophiole.

---

[1] Synonyms of **Wisteria**: *Phaseoloides* Duhamel (1755). *Kraunhia* Raf. (1808). *Diplonyx* Raf. (1808). *Thyrsanthus* Ell. (1817). *Krauhnia* Steud. (1840). *Phaseolodes* O. Ktze. (1891). *Wistaria* Auct. and of Nutt.!

189. **Antheroporum** Gagnep., Lecomte Not. Syst. 3: 180 (1915). 2 spp., Cochinchina and Thailand; type *A. pierrei* Gagnep.

Trees; leaves imparipinnate, leaflets 3–9; stipules absent; racemes many-flowered, 2–5 in the upper axils or opposite the leaf at the top of the branchlets; nodes not tumid; bracts small, persistent; bracteoles 2, below the calyx; flowers rose or purple, calyx campanulate, teeth 4, upper truncate-emarginate, others triangular, all equal, shorter than the tube; petals subequal, all long-clawed; vexillum obcordate; wings oblong, narrow; keel ovate, adhering to the wings; stamens monadelphous; anther-loculi orbicular, separate at the base, dehiscing by a slit lengthwise;[1] ovary 2-ovuled, style subulate, short, glabrous, stigma terminal, point-like; fruit oblong, convex, 1-seeded, dehiscent, valves 2, woody, thick; seed rather large, compressed-spherical, strophiolate.

190. **Goodia** Salisb., Parad. Londin., t. 41 (1806). 2 spp., Australia; type *G. lotifolia* Salisb. B.H. 1: 474; E.P. 3, 3: 218; Benth., Fl. Austral. 2: 176.

Shrubs; leaves pinnately 3-foliolate; leaflets entire; flowers yellow mixed with purple, in terminal racemes; stipules, bracts and bracteoles membranous, very caducous; stipels absent; upper 2 calyx-lobes connate into a 2-toothed lip, lower 3 narrow, subequal; vexillum suborbicular; wings falcate-oblong; keel broad, incurved, obtuse; stamens all connate into a sheath split above; anthers dorsifixed, all equal and versatile; disk between the stamens and ovary cupular; ovary stipitate, 3–2-ovuled; style incurved or inflexed, glabrous, stigma terminal; fruit long-stipitate, oblong-falcate, compressed, 2-valved, sutures nerve-like, continuous inside; seeds strophiolate, with a very short funicle.

Bentham said of this genus, placed by him in *Genisteae*: 'genus anomalum, floribus et legumine *Bossiaeae* affine, inflorescentia *Crotalariae*, foliis pinnatim foliatis ab omnibus *Genisteis* discrepat.'

191. **Burkillia** Ridley, Fl. Mal. Penins. 5: 304 (1925). 1 sp., *B. alba* Ridley, Malay Peninsula.

Shrub; leaves simple, lanceolate or elliptic, large, alternate, petiolate; flowers small, numerous, in axillary racemes; calyx campanulate, unequally 5-toothed, 2 upper teeth very short, 3 lower ones longer, setaceous; standard round, broad, clawed, keel obcuneate, widely bilobed, lobes round; stamens 10, diadelphous, 5 lower ones longer than the upper ones; ovary cylindric, 2-ovuled; style long, stigma capitate; fruit long, flattened, narrowed to the base, dilated towards apex, 2-seeded, tip beaked.

192. **Poecilanthe** Benth., Journ. Linn. Soc. 4: Suppl. 80 (1860). 7 spp., trop. South America; type *P. falcata* (Vell.) Ducke (*P. grandiflora* Benth.); Brazil. B.H. 1: 547; E.P. 3, 3: 272; Burkart, Leg. Argent. ed. 2: 225, fig. 54.

Trees; leaves imparipinnate or unifoliolate; leaflets alternate, sometimes very large; stipels minute or absent; stipules very caducous or inconspicuous; flowers yellow or white, mixed with red or violet, in short axillary or lateral racemes or panicles, scattered on the rhachis; calyx turbinate at the base, upper 2 lobes connate into one sub-2-toothed lip; vexillum orbicular, not appendaged; wings falcate-oblong or obovate; keel incurved, subrostrate, the petals connate at the back; stamens all connate into a sheath split above; anthers alternately longer and basifixed and shorter and versatile; ovary subsessile or shortly stipitate; style filiform, glabrous, incurved, stigma small, terminal; ovules several; fruit hard, 2-valved; seeds obovate, hard and shining, compressed, with a basal hilum, estrophiolate.

193. **Schefflerodendron** Harms, Engl. Bot. Jahrb. 30: 87 (1901); Notizbl. Bot. Gart. Berl. 3: 147 (1901). 6 spp., trop. Africa; type *S. usambarense* Harms,

---

[1] Not by a terminal pore, as stated in the original description.

trop. Africa. Hauman, Fl. Congo Belge, 5: 58, fig. 8; J. Léonard & Letour, Bull. Soc. Bot. Belg. 82: 295 (1952).

Trees; leaves imparipinnate; leaflets alternate, gland-dotted below; stipels absent, flowers in axillary and terminal racemes; bracts deciduous; bracteoles minute; calyx campanulate, shortly dentate; petals longer than the calyx; vexillum longer than the others, suborbicular to obovate, clawed, wings narrow, sparingly glandular, keel rather obtuse, gland-dotted outside; vexillary stamen free; ovary stipitate, 3–4-ovuled; style short, subulate; fruit obliquely semi-obovate to semi-oblanceolate, curved, thick and woody, stipitate, beaked, dehiscent, tomentellous outside; seeds 2–1.

194. **Terua** Standley & Hermann, Journ. Wash. Acad. Sci. 39: 306 (1–49). 1 sp., *T. vallicola* Standley & Hermann, Cent. America.

Shrub or small tree; leaves alternate, imparipinnate, stipulate; leaflets opposite, entire, more or less punctate; stipels absent; panicles axillary; calyx cupular; wings of the corolla strongly adherent to the apical half of the keel; stamens monadelphous, the adaxial shortly free at the base; anthers versatile, lanceolate; style arcuate, stigma minute, terminal, glabrous; fruit compressed, stipitate, both sutures thickened, 1–4-seeded, elastically dehiscent along the adaxial suture; seeds subreniform, compressed, hilum surrounded by a membranous ridge.

Tribe 18. LONCHOCARPEAE

Tribe *Dalbergieae* Subtribe *Lonchocarpeae* Benth. & Hook. f., Gen. Pl. 1: 454 (1865)

Trees or tall scrambling shrubs; leaves alternate, very rarely opposite or verticillate, imparipinnate; *leaflets opposite*; stipels rarely present; flowers in racemes or rarely panicles; *pedicels usually fasciculate*; bracts and bracteoles small; calyx usually *cyathiform*, truncate with small teeth; vexillum often silky outside; wing-petals free from or adnate to the keel; keel-petals slightly coherent; vexillary filament free or partly connate with the others into a *split sheath or a closed tube* often open at the base; *anthers uniform*, versatile; *style glabrous*, stigma terminal; *fruit indehiscent*, linear or oblong, sometimes orbicular, one or both sutures sometimes narrowly winged, sometimes moniliform or torulose; seeds usually few or 1, compressed. Type genus *Lonchocarpus* H. B. & K.

Leaves alternate:
Wing-petals free from the keel:
  Normal leaves present:
  Keel-petals free from each other:
    Flowers in lax panicles on leafless branches; calyx obscurely sinuate-dentate; fruits with 2 nerves subparallel to the margin
                                               195. **Hymenolobium**
    Flowers in terminal panicles; fruits margined with a wing on each side
                                               196. **Ostryoderris**
    Flowers in axillary racemes; calyx 2-lipped to the middle; fruits reticulate, not winged   197. **Behaimia**
  Keel-petals coherent or connate; fruits not winged:
    Fruits strap-shaped   198. **Kunstleria**

Fruits orbicular   199. **Ostryocarpus**
Fruits oblong, anthers roundish, with dilated connective and projecting
    beyond the loculi   200. **Dalbergiella**
Normal leaves absent, reduced to scales; fruits narrowly winged all around
                                               201. **Ramorinoa**
Wing-petals adnate to the keel:
Fruits not winged:
Fruits torulose, moniliform, or subglobose, thick and coriaceous
                                               202. **Muellera**
  Fruits flat and compressed, membranous or coriaceous, upper suture
    with a nerve on each side, or thick and dilated   203. **Lonchocarpus**
  Fruits compressed, short, thick, smooth, with obtuse sutures:
    Flowers in axillary racemes; vexillum suborbicular, with inflexed auricles
      at the base   204. **Pongamia**
    Flowers in terminal or axillary panicles; vexillum oblong, not appen-
      daged   205. **Dahlstedtia**
  Fruits winged along the upper or both sutures:
    Fruits with a wing on one or both margins; calyx truncate or with very
      short or obsolete teeth; seeds reniform or orbicular   206. **Derris**
    Fruits longitudinally 4-winged, linear; seeds oval   207. **Piscidia**
Leaves opposite or verticillate; trees or shrubs; flowers in racemes at the
  nodes of the one-year-old branches; ovary long-stipitate, 1-ovuled
                                               208. **Platymiscium**

195. **Hymenolobium** Benth., Journ. Linn. Soc. 4: Suppl. 84 (1860). 8 spp.,
trop. South America; type *H. nitidum* Benth. B.H. 1: 548; E.P. 3, 3: 342;
Amshoff, Pulle Fl. Suriname, 2, 2: 139; Ducke, Archiv. Jard. Bot. Rio de
Janeiro, 3: 159 (1922) (key).

Trees; leaves alternate, imparipinnate, leaflets opposite, with or without stipels; stipules
linear or lanceolate, caducous; flowers rose, laxly paniculate on leafless branches; bracts
and bracteoles small, caducous; calyx truncate at the apex, but obscurely sinuate-dentate;
vexillum orbicular, reflexed, not appendaged; wings obliquely oblong; keel-petals a little
smaller than the wings, more falcate, free; stamens all connate into a sheath split above;
anthers versatile; ovary shortly stipitate, few-ovuled; style filiform, incurved, stigma small,
terminal; fruit oblong-linear, flat, membranous, indehiscent, nervose, 2 of the nerves subparallel near the margin towards the base, rarely fruit suborbicular; seed 1, transversely
oblong, compressed.

196. **Ostryoderris** Dunn, Kew Bull. 1911: 363. *Xeroderris* Roberty (1954).
About 6 spp., trop. and S. Africa; lectotype *G. impressa* Dunn, trop. Africa.
Hutch. & Dalz., Fl. W. Trop. Afr. 1: 379, fig. 144, E; ed. 2 (Keay), 1: 521, fig.
163, E; Hauman, Fl. Congo Belge, 6: 48.

Climbing or spreading shrubs; leaves alternate, imparipinnate: leaflets stipellate; panicles
terminal, thyrsoid; flowers mostly conspicuously bracteate; calyx campanulate, 5-toothed;
petals glabrous, vexillum shortly clawed, scarcely callused; wings not hooked at the base of
the limb; stamens diadelphous, the vexillary one separate; disk present, adnate to the
calyx; ovary few-ovuled; fruit indehiscent, compressed, margined with a wing on each side,
valves coherent between the seeds; seeds lenticular; embryo with a short spreading radicle
not appressed to the cotyledons.

197. Behaimia Griseb., Cat. Pl. Cub. 77 (1859). 1 sp., *B. cubensis* Griseb., Cuba. B.H. 1: 1002; E.P. 3, 3: 342.

Tree or shrub; leaves alternate, imparipinnate, leaflets opposite, 4–6 pairs, exstipellate; flowers in axillary racemes, minutely bibracteolate; calyx 2-lipped to the middle and 5-fid, acute at the base; vexillum orbicular, reflexed above the claw, not auricled; wings erect, spathulate-oblong; keel-petals distinct, obliquely semicordate, obtuse, with a slender claw; stamens diadelphous, vexillary separate, remainder connate or 7 connate and the others more or less free; anthers oblong-elliptic; ovary sessile, tomentose, few-ovuled; stigma minute, capitate; fruit sessile, membranous, not winged, flat, indehiscent, elliptic-oblong, acute at both ends, transversely reticulate; seeds mostly 1, flat, kidney-shaped.

198. Kunstleria Prain, Journ. Asiat. Soc. Bengal, 66, 2: 109 (1897). 9 spp. Malaya and Philippines; type *K. curtisii* Prain, Malay Penins.

Woody climbers; leaves unequally pinnate, 1–7-foliolate, exstipellate: stipules small, deciduous; flowers rather small in ample terminal thyrsoid panicles extending into the axils of the upper leaves; pedicels solitary, nodes not tumid; calyx campanulate, teeth lanceolate, the two upper connate; corolla distinctly exserted; vexillum ovate, entire; keel boat-shaped, the petals slightly cohering; stamens diadelphous, the upper one quite free from the other 9 and adnate at base to the claw of the vexillum; anthers versatile, uniform, on alternately short and long free filaments; ovary sessile, few-ovuled; style incurved, filiform, stigma capitate; pod thin, flat, strap-shaped, membranous or coriaceous, indehiscent, style terminal, sutures not winged; seeds 1–3, much compressed, oblong; radicle inflexed.

199. Ostryocarpus Hook. f., Hook. Niger Fl. 316 (1849). 4 spp., trop. Africa; type *O. riparius* Hook. f. B.H. 1: 548; E.P. 3, 3: 343; Dunn, Kew Bull. 1911: 362; Hutch. & Dalz., Fl. W. Trop. Afr. 1: 379; ed. 2 (Keay), 1: 519; Hauman, Fl. Congo Belge, 6: 13 (1954).

Tall sarmentose shrubs; leaves alternate, imparipinnate, leaflets opposite, exstipellate; stipules minute or inconspicuous; flowers whitish-yellow, clustered along the elongated peduncles on short axillary branchlets and forming a raceme-like panicle; bracts and bracteoles minute, deciduous; calyx truncate with minute teeth; vexillum broadly rhomboid, recurved, not appendaged; wings falcate-oblong, free; keel oblong, incurved, obtuse, the petals connate at the back; vexillary stamen free from the base, remainder connate; anthers versatile; ovary sessile, few-ovuled; style filiform, stigma small, terminal; fruit orbicular, flat and compressed, indehiscent, coriaceous, not winged, with a terminal style; seed 1, transverse, broadly oblong, compressed.

200. Dalbergiella Bak. f., Journ. Bot. 1928, Suppl. 1: 127; Legum. Trop. Afr. 535. 3 spp., trop. Africa; type *D. welwitschii* Bak. f., Angola. Hutch. & Dalz., Fl. W. Trop. Afr. ed. 2 (Keay), 1: 517.

Scandent shrubs; leaves imparipinnate, leaflets numerous opposite or subopposite; flowers numerous in panicles of racemes; calyx campanulate, 2-lipped, upper lip slightly longer than the lower, emarginate, lower lip deeply 3-toothed, teeth acuminate; vexillum orbicular, keeled on the back, claw long and slender; wings oblong, long-clawed; keel shorter than the wings, cohering at the apex; stamens 10, vexillary free, remainder united into a sheath split above; anthers dorsifixed, connective dilated at the apex, blackish; ovary sessile, 5–8-ovuled; fruit oblong, thin, reticulate, usually with only 1 reniform seed.

201. Ramorinoa Speg., Physis, 7: 262 (1924). 1 sp., *R. girolae* Speg., Argent. Burkart, Legum. Argent. ed. 2, 237, fig. 62.

Small tree, leafless but for very small scales; branches rigid, cylindric, ending in a spine; racemes lateral, simple or branched; rhachis finely nodose; bracts small, caducous; calyx campanulate, 5-lobed, lobes triangular, shorter than the tube, the upper a little united; corolla glabrous, papilionaceous; petals subequal in length; vexillum suborbicular; stamens

10, diadelphous, vexillary free, the others united to the middle; anthers uniform, dorsifixed, versatile, elliptic; filaments filiform; ovary sessile, 2–6-ovuled; style curved at a right angle, stigma terminal; fruit indehiscent, dry, venose, obovoid or elliptic, rather compressed, narrowly winged all around; seeds 1–4, transverse, oval, hilum subapical; cotyledons sagittate at the base.

202. **Muellera** Linn. f., Suppl. 53 (1781) (conserved name). *Coublandia* Aubl. (1775). *Mullera* Juss. (1789). *Cyanobotrys* Zucc. (1845). 2 spp., trop. America; type *M. frutescens* (Aubl.) Standl. (*M. moniliformis* Linn. f.), Cent. & trop. America. B.H. 1: 550; E.P. 3, 3: 344; Amshoff, Pulle Fl. Suriname, 2, 2: 147; Burkart, Legum. Argent. ed. 2, 234, fig. 59.

Trees; leaves alternate, imparipinnate, leaflets opposite, exstipellate; stipules minute; flowers violet or white, in axillary or lateral racemes; bracts and bracteoles very minute, caducous; calyx truncate, with very short or obsolete teeth; vexillum broadly ovate or suborbicular, without auricles; wings falcate-oblong, slightly adherent to the keel; keel incurved, obtuse, the petals coherent at the back; vexillary stamen free at the base, but connate from the middle with the others into a closed tube; anthers versatile; ovary subsessile, ovules numerous; style filiform, incurved, stigma small, terminal; fruit thick, fleshy, and hard, indehiscent, subterete, often constricted between the seeds and moniliform or by abortion 1-seeded and subglobose; seeds ovoid-subglobose, with a lateral hilum.

203. **Lonchocarpus**[1] H. B. & K., Nov. Gen. et Sp. 6: 383 (1823) (conserved name). About 100 spp., America, trop. Africa, Australia; lectotype *L. punctatus* H. B. & K., trop. America. B.H. 1: 548; E.P. 3, 3: 343; Burkart, Legum. Argent. ed. 2: 231, fig. 58; Amshoff, Pulle Fl. Suriname, 2, 2: 141; H. Pittier, Middle Amer. spp. of *Lonchocarpus*, Contrib. U.S. Nat. Herb. 20: 37 (1917); Hutch. & Dalz., Fl. W. Trop. Afr. 1: 379, fig. 145; ed. 2 (Keay), 1: 522, fig. 164; Hauman, Fl. Congo Belge, 6: 5.

Trees or tall scrambling shrubs; leaves alternate, imparipinnate, leaflets opposite, very rarely stipellate; flowers violet, purple, or white, in racemes or rarely panicles; pedicels fasciculate or paired or 2-flowered; bracts small, caducous; bracteoles caducous or subpersistent; calyx mostly cyathiform, truncate with very short or obsolete teeth; vexillum often silky, orbicular to rarely oblong, 2-appendaged at the base above the claw or nude; wings oblong or falcate; keel almost straight to arcuate, obtuse, petals slightly coherent at the back; vexillary stamen free at the base but from the middle connate into a closed tube; anthers versatile; ovary more or less stipitate, 2- or more-ovuled; style incurved, filiform, stigma small, terminal; fruit oblong or elongated, flat, membranous or coriaceous, indehiscent, with a terminal style, the sutures not winged, the upper sometimes laterally dilated; seeds 1–2, rarely numerous, compressed, reniform or suborbicular.

204. **Pongamia** Vent., Jard. Malm. 28, t. 28 (1803) (conserved name). *Pongam* Adams. (1763). *Galedupa* Lam. (1786). *Pungamia* Lam. (1794). *Malaparius* Miq. (1857). *Cajum* O. Ktze. (1891). 1 sp. *P. pinnata* (Linn.) Pierre, trop. Asia, Malaya, New Guinea, Polynesia, Australia, Mascarenes. B.H. 1: 549; E.P. 3, 3: 344.

Tree; leaves imparipinnate, leaflets opposite, exstipellate; flowers whitish, in axillary racemes; bracts very caducous; bracteoles minute or absent; calyx truncate, with obsolete

---

[1] Synonyms of **Lonchocarpus**: *Clompanus* Aubl. (1775). *Robina* Aubl. (1775). *Sphinctolobium* Vog. (1837). *Clomopanus* Steud. (1840). *Neuroscapha* Tul. (1843). *Philenoptera* Fenzl. (1844). *Capassa* Klotzsch (1861). *Icthyoctonum* Boiv. ex Baillon (1884).

teeth; vexillum thinly silky outside, suborbicular, with inflexed auricles at the base; wings obliquely oblong, slightly adherent to the keel; keel obtuse, the petals coherent at the apex; vexillary stamen free at the base, but connate from the middle into a closed tube; anthers versatile; ovary subsessile, 2-ovuled; style filiform, incurved, stigma small, terminal; fruit obliquely oblong, flat, thickly coriaceous sub-fleshy or almost woody, indehiscent, 1-seeded, beaked; seed reniform, rather thick, with a small hilum.

205. **Dahlstedtia** Malme, Arkiv. Bot. Stockh. 4, no. 9: 1 (1905). 1 sp., *D. pinnata* (Benth.) Malme, Brazil.

Shrub; leaves imparipinnate; leaflets opposite, about 3 pairs, elliptic, acuminate, exstipellate; inflorescence terminal or axillary, paniculate; flowers large and showy, red, pendulous; bracts and bracteoles very minute; calyx tubular, 4-toothed; petals 5, subequally long, all clawed, vexillum oblong, not appendaged, keel-petals connate at the apex and similar to the wing-petals; stamens 10, monadelphous, free from the middle; anthers dorsifixed near the base; style filiform, glabrous; fruit large, indehiscent, oblong, pericarp thin; seeds few, large, reniform, hilum orbicular.

206. **Derris**[1] Lour., Fl. Cochinch. 432 (1790) (conserved name). About 70 spp., trop. regions; type *D. trifoliata* Lour., Old World tropics. B.H. 1: 549; E.P. 3, 3: 345; Amshoff, Pulle Fl. Suriname, 2, 2: 145; Hauman, Fl. Congo Belge, 6, 32, t. 2 (as *Leptoderris*).

Tall climbing shrubs or rarely trees; leaves alternate, imparipinnate, leaflets opposite, exstipellate; flowers violet-purple or white, in racemes or panicles; bracts small, caducous; bracteoles ovate or orbicular, small, often caducous; calyx often cyathiform, truncate with very short or obsolete teeth; petals nearly always glabrous; vexillum obovate or orbicular, not appendaged; wings obliquely oblong, slightly adherent to the keel above the claw; keel slightly incurved, the petals slightly united at the back; vexillary stamen free at the base but connate from the middle with the others in a closed tube, rarely altogether free; anthers versatile; ovary sessile or shortly stipitate, 2- or more-ovuled; style filiform, incurved, stigma small, terminal; fruit obliquely orbicular, oblong or elongated, flat, indehiscent, style terminal, the upper suture or both sutures margined with a narrow wing; seed solitary or scattered, flat, reniform or orbicular.

207. **Piscidia** Linn., Syst. ed. 10: 1155 (1759) (conserved name). *Piscipula* Loefl. (1758). *Ichtyomethia* O. Ktze. (1891). *Canizaresia* Britton (1920). 8 spp., Florida, Cent. America, West Indies; type *P. piscipula* (Linn.) Sarg., Florida, Jamaica. B.H. 1: 550; E.P. 3, 3: 345; Blake, Journ. Wash. Acad. Sci. 9: 241 (1919) (*Ichthyomethia*).

Trees; leaves alternate, imparipinnate, leaflets opposite, exstipellate; flowers white mixed with blood-red, in short lateral panicles; bracts early caducous; bracteoles very small or absent; calyx-teeth broad, short, upper 2 subconnate; vexillum orbicular, not appendaged; wings falcate-oblong, adhering to the keel; keel obtuse, the petals connate at the back; vexillary stamen free at the base, connate from the middle with the others in a closed tube; anthers versatile; ovary sessile, ovules numerous; style filiform, incurved, stigma small, terminal; fruit stipitate, linear, plano-compressed, indehiscent, longitudinally and broadly 4-winged; seeds numerous, oval, compressed.

208. **Platymiscium** Vog., Linnaea 11: 198 (1837). *Hymenolobium* Benth. (1837). About 15 spp., trop. America; type *P. floribundum* Vog., trop. South America. B.H. 1: 548; E.P. 3, 3: 342; Amshoff, Pulle Fl. Suriname, 2, 2: 137.

---

[1] Synonyms of **Derris**: *Deguelia* Aubl. (1775). *Cylizoma* Neck. (1790). *Brachypterum* Benth. (1838). *Aganope* Miq. (1855). *Nothoderris* Blume ex Miq. (1855). *Pterocarpus* O. Ktze. (1891). *Leptoderris* Dunn (1910).

Trees or shrubs; leaves opposite or 3–4-verticillate, imparipinnate, leaflets opposite, exstipellate; stipules interpetiolar, rather thick, caducous; flowers yellow, arranged in racemes at the nodes of one-year-old branches; bracts and bracteoles small; calyx turbinate at the base or rarely obtuse, teeth short, subequal; vexillum orbicular or ovate, not appendaged; wings obliquely oblong; keel-petals straight or slightly incurved, obtuse, connate at the apex on the back; stamens all connate into a sheath split above or vexillary stamen rarely separate; anthers versatile, loculi often confluent at the apex; ovary long-stipitate, 1-ovulate; style filiform, incurved, stigma small, terminal; fruit stipitate, oblong, flat, thin, smooth, indehiscent, with thin or nerviform margins; seed 1, large, reniform, compressed.

Tribe 19. PTEROCARPEAE[1]

Tribe *Dalbergieae* Subtribe *Pterocarpeae* Benth. & Hook. f.,
Gen. Pl. 1: 454 (greater part) (1865)

Trees and shrubs, latter sometimes scandent; leaves *imparipinnate, leaflets mostly alternate*, rarely subopposite and rarely 1-foliolate, very rarely absent, *sometimes glandular below*; stipels very rarely present; flowers in axillary or terminal racemes or panicles; bracts and bracteoles mostly small and caducous, sometimes bracteoles orbicular and persistent; calyx shortly toothed, *upper lobes more or less connate higher up*; corolla papilionaceous, the keel-petals more or less connate on the lower margins; filaments all connate into a sheath split adaxially or equally split into 2 lateral bundles, or vexillary filament free; *anthers uniform, versatile; style glabrous; fruit compressed, indehiscent*, orbicular to ovate or samara-like, with 1 or 2 seeds in the middle, winged or keeled, sometimes membranous; seeds mostly compressed and reniform. Type genus *Pterocarpus* Linn.

Leaves pinnate:
  Fruit narrowed at the base or apex into a wing; seed not in the middle:
  Seed borne in the basal portion of the fruit, the wing terminal:
    Vexillum often silky-hairy outside; stipules often hard and spiny
                                                   209. **Machaerium**
    Vexillum glabrous outside:
      Ovary shortly stipitate or subsessile; stamens monadelphous or vexillary
        stamen free:
      Calyx narrowed or turbinate at the base; wing of fruit tipped by the persistent base of the style; stipules minute, caducous:
        Petals very unequal in length; vexillary filament free; ovules several
                                                   210. **Tipuana**

---

[1] **Pterocarpeae** trib. nov. Arbores et frutices, interdum scandentes; folia imparipinnata, rare 1-foliolata, foliolis plerumque alterna, rare subopposita, interdum infra glandulosa; stipellae plerumque nullae; flores in racemis vel paniculis axillaribus vel terminalibus dispositi; bracteae et bracteolae plerumque parvae et caducae, interdum bracteolae orbiculares et persistentes; calyx breviter dentatus, lobis superioribus superne connatis; corolla papilionacea, petalis carinae margine inferiore plus minusve connatis; stamina omnia in spatham supra fissam connata, vel vagina utrinque fissa aequaliter diadelpha, vel vexillare solutum; antherae aequales, versatiles; stylus glaber; fructus compressus, indehiscens, orbicularis ad ovatus vel samariformis, alatus vel carinatus, interdum membranaceus, seminibus in medio 1–2 compressis plerumque reinformibus.

C C

Petals subequal in length; vexillary filament united with the others into
a split sheath; ovule 1   211. **Vatairea**
Calyx broad and obtuse at the base; style at the base of the wing forming
a lateral spur; leaves glandular below; stipules large and caducous
212. **Centrolobium**
Calyx curved in bud, campanulate; fruit-wing with a cuspidate tip;
stipules subulate, caducous   213. **Vataireopsis**
Ovary very long-stipitate; vexillary stamen coherent with the others in the
middle; stipules lanceolate, acute, striate, deciduous
214. **Steinbachiella**
Seed borne in the upper portion of the fruit, the wing at the base; fruit
stipitate; 2 stamens free, remainder connate into 4-anthered bundles
215. **Platypodium**
Fruit reniform, circinate, orbicular or broadly oblong, not specially narrowed or winged at the base or apex:
Calyx-base obtuse; vexillum silky outside; stipules often hard and spiny;
flowers purple, violet, or white   216. **Drepanocarpus**
Calyx-base acute or turbinate; vexillum glabrous outside; stipules sometimes large and foliaceous; flowers mostly yellow   217. **Pterocarpus**
Leaves unifoliolate, with a pair of stipels; calyx obtuse at the base; fruit
orbicular or broadly falcate, upper suture narrowly winged
218. **Cyclolobium**

209. **Machaerium** Pers., Syn. 2: 276 (1807). *Paramachaerium* Ducke (1925).
About 100 spp., trop. America; type *M. ferrugineum* Pers., Guiana. B.H. 1:
545; E.P. 3, 3: 336; Amshoff, Pulle Fl. Suriname, 2, 2: 123; Burkart, Legum.
Argent. ed. 2, 226, fig. 56.

Erect trees or tall scandent shrubs; leaves imparipinnate, most of the leaflets alternate,
sometimes numerous and small; stipules often hard and spiny; stipels absent; flowers small
to medium-sized, purple, violet, or white, in short axillary secund racemes or crowded in
terminal panicles; bracts small, caducous; bracteoles usually orbicular below the calyx, persistent; calyx-teeth short; vexillum broadly ovate or orbicular, often silky outside; wings
oblong, often falcate; keel incurved, the petals connate at the back; stamens all connate
into a sheath split above, or the sheath also split below and forming 2 equal bundles; anthers
versatile; ovary usually stipitate, 2–1-ovulate; style filiform, incurved, stigma small, terminal; fruit compressed, samaroid, indehiscent, more or less thickened at the base and
1-seeded, the upper suture more or less intruded to the seed, narrowed at the apex into an
oblong reticulate wing; seed compressed, ovate, orbicular, or reniform.

210. **Tipuana** Benth., Journ. Linn. Soc. 4, Suppl.: 72 (partly) (1860); Ducke,
Arch. Jard. Bot. Rio de Jan. 5: 137 (1930). 1 sp., *M. tipu* (Benth.) O. Ktze.
(*T. speciosa* Benth.), trop. South America. Burkart, Legum. Argent. ed. 2: 228,
fig. 57.

Tree; leaves alternate, imparipinnate, leaflets alternate, 11–25; stipules very small; stipels
none; flowers in terminal panicles; bracts and bracteoles very caducous; calyx broadly
campanulate, stipitate at the base, apex broadly truncate or subbilabiate, teeth 5, short;
upper 2 connate higher up; petals clawed, very unequal in size; vexillum very broad, not
appendaged; wings a little longer than the vexillum; keel much smaller than the wings,
coherent on the back; vexillary filament free, remainder connate into a split sheath; anthers

uniform, versatile; ovary shortly stipitate, several-ovuled; style short; fruit indehiscent, winged at the top and style persistent; seeds 1–4, small, incurved-oblong.

211. **Vatairea** Aubl., Pl. Guian. 755, t. 302 (1775). 6–7 spp., trop. South America; type *V. guianensis* Aubl., Guianas.

Trees; leaves imparipinnate, leaflets several, alternate, pinnately nerved; stipules small, caducous; stipels absent; flowers in large terminal panicles; bracts and bracteoles very small and early caducous; calyx thick, turbinate-campanulate, narrowed at the base, broadly truncate but 5-toothed; petals subequal in length; vexillum orbicular or ovate, not appendaged at the base; wings and keel narrowly obovate, shortly connate dorsally; stamens all united into a split sheath; anthers versatile or subbasifixed; perfect ovule 1; style short; fruits indehiscent, winged at the top and with a persistent style, or rarely orbicular or elliptic with only a rudimentary wing; seed 1, large, oblong or suborbicular.

212. **Centrolobium** Mart. ex Benth., Ann. Wien. Mus. 2: 95 (1838). 3 spp., trop. America; type *C. robustum* Mart. ex Benth., Brazil. B.H. 1: 546; E.P. 3, 3: 339; Rudd, Journ. Wash. Acad. Sci. 44: 284 (1954).

Unarmed trees; leaves large, imparipinnate, leaflets irregularly opposite and alternate, rather densely covered with reddish glands below; stipules large and caducous; stipels absent; flowers medium sized, in large terminal panicles; bracts ovate or narrow; bracteoles narrow, caducous; calyx broad, obtuse at the base, upper 2 lobes connate but 2-dentate; vexillum broadly ovate or orbicular; wings obliquely obovate or oblong; keel-petals subsimilar to the wings, connate on the back; stamens all connate into a sheath split above; anthers versatile; ovary sessile or shortly stipitate, about 3-ovuled; style filiform, incurved, stigma small, terminal; fruit subsessile, large and samaroid, indehiscent, thick at the base and prickly, produced at the top into a falcate-oblong wing, style at the base of the wing forming a lateral spur; seeds 3–1, separated by transverse septa, oblong-subreniform.

213. **Vataireopsis** Ducke, Notizbl. Bot. Gart. Berl. 11: 473 (1932). 2 spp., E. trop. South America; type *V. speciosa* Ducke, Brazil. Amshoff, Pulle Fl. Suriname, 2, 2: 132.

Trees with yellow heart-wood; leaves imparipinnate, leaflets numerous, alternate, oblong, emarginate; stipules subulate, caducous; flowers numerous in terminal panicles; bracts and bracteoles small, caducous; calyx curved in bud, campanulate, shortly 5-toothed; petals subequally long, clawed; vexillum broadly orbicular, not appendaged at the base; wings and keel narrower, obovate, almost straight, free; stamens 10, monadelphous for one-quarter of their length at their base; anthers versatile, dehiscing lengthwise; ovary stipitate, ovules 1 or 2; style short; fruit indehiscent, compressed, with the seed at the base and with 2 lateral smaller wings, the upper part broadly winged, wing with a cuspidate tip; seed large, reniform-oblong, rather hard.

214. **Steinbachiella** Harms, Notizbl. Bot. Gart. Berlin, 10: 345 (1928). 1 sp., *S. leptoclada* Harms, Bolivia.

Small tree; leaves imparipinnate, leaflets 11–13, alternate, oblong-oblanceolate or obovate-oblanceolate or narrowly oblong; stipules lanceolate, acute, striate, deciduous; racemes short, 1–4-flowered, arising below the young leaves from slender branchlets; pedicels slender, jointed at the apex; bracteoles 2 at the base of the calyx, obovate-oblong, deciduous; calyx obliquely cupular-funnel-shaped; lobes 5, half as long as the tube, lowermost lanceolate, lateral broadly lanceolate, upper slightly connate, obliquely deltoid; corolla exserted, petals shortly clawed, almost equal in length; vexillum suborbicular; stamens 10, 9 filaments connate, the tenth (vexillary) coherent in the middle; anthers small, equal; ovary very long-stipitate, narrowed into a filiform style, stigma very minute; ovules 1–2 in the lower part of the ovary.

215. **Platypodium** Vog., Linnaea, 11: 420 (1837). *Callisemaea* Benth. (1838.) *Callisema* Steud. (1840). 2 spp., trop. South America; type *P. elegans* Vog., Brazil, Bolivia, Panama. B.H. 1: 546; E.P. 3, 3: 338.

Trees; leaves imparipinnate or paripinnate, leaflets alternate or irregularly opposite; stipules linear, deciduous; stipels absent; flowers showy, yellow, laxly racemose in the upper leaf-axils; bracts and bracteoles small, caducous; calyx turbinate at the base, upper 2 teeth or lobes broader, connate high up; vexillum large, not appendaged; wings obliquely obovate or oblong; keel-petals oblong or obovate, obtuse, connate at the back; 2 stamens (vexillary and lower) free, remainder connate into 4-anthered bundles; anthers versatile; ovary long-stipitate, ovules numerous; style filiform, stigma small, terminal; fruit stipitate, samaroid, indehiscent, woody at the apex, narrowed at the base into an obliquely oblong venose wing; seed 1, rarely 2, oblong-reniform.

216. **Drepanocarpus** G. F. W. Mey., Prim. Fl. Esseq. 236 (1818). *Nephrosis* Rich. ex DC. (1825). *Crucaria* Juss. ex DC. (1825). *Sommerfeldtia* Schum. & Thonn. (1827). About 12 spp., trop. America, W. trop. Africa; type *D. lunatus* (Willd.) G. F. W. Mey., South America, W. trop. Africa. B.H. 1: 546; E.P. 3, 3: 338; Hutch. & Dalz., Fl. W. Trop. Afr. 1: 376, fig. 144, D; ed. 2 (Keay), 1: 519, fig. 163, D.

Erect trees or tall scandent shrubs; leaves imparipinnate, leaflets mostly alternate; stipels absent; stipules often hard and spiny; flowers purple, violet, or white, in short secund racemes fasciculate in the leaf-axils or crowded into terminal panicles; bracts small, caducous; bracteoles mostly orbicular, persistent; calyx obtuse at the base, truncate, with short teeth; vexillum broadly ovate or orbicular, silky outside; wings oblong, often falcate; keel incurved, petals connate at the back; stamens all connate into a sheath split above or the vexillary stamen free, or the sheath also split below into 2 equal bundles; anthers versatile; ovary shortly stipitate, 2–1-ovulate; style incurved, filiform, stigma small and terminal; fruit broadly falcate or curved almost in a circle, flat and compressed, thick, indehiscent, 1-seeded, the upper suture intruded, lower very arcuate; seed large, compressed, kidney-shaped.

217. **Pterocarpus**[1] Linn., Sp. Pl. ed. 2, 1662 (1763). About 30 spp., tropics, few in America; type *P. draco* Linn., South America. B.H. 1: 547; E.P. 3, 3: 340; Amshoff, Pulle Fl. Suriname, 2, 2: 133; Burkart, Legum. Argent. ed. 2, 225, fig. 55; Hutch. & Dalz., Fl. W. Trop. Afr. 1: 375, fig. 143; ed. 2 (Keay), 1: 517, fig. 162; Hauman, Fl. Congo Belge, 6: 15, t. 1.

Trees; leaves alternate, imparipinnate, leaflets alternate or irregularly opposite; stipules sometimes large and foliaceous; stipels absent; flowers yellow, rarely whitish mixed with violet, usually showy, in simple racemes or lax axillary or terminal panicles; bracts and bracteoles small, caducous; calyx turbinate at the base, often incurved, upper 2 teeth or lobes more or less connate; vexillum orbicular or broadly ovate; wings obliquely obovate or oblong; keel-petals similar to or shorter than the wings; stamens all connate into a sheath split above, or the sheath equally split into 2 bundles, or vexillary stamen free; anthers versatile; ovary sessile or stipitate, 6–2-ovuled; style filiform, slightly incurved, stigma small, terminal; fruit compressed, indehiscent, orbicular or ovate, rarely oval-oblong, more or less oblique or falcate, with a lateral or rarely terminal style, with seed in the middle and

[1] Synonyms of **Pterocarpus**: *Lingoum* Adans. (1763). *Moutouchi* Aubl. (1775). *Griselinia* Scop. (1777). *Nephrea* Nor. (1790). *Mutuchi* J. F. Gmel. (1791). *Amphymenium* H. B. & K. (1823). *Clypeola* Burm. ex DC. (1825). *Weinreichia* Reichb. (1828). *Moutouchia* Benth. (1838). *Echinodiscus* Benth. (1838). *Phellocarpus* Benth. (1838). *Ancylocalyx* Tul. (1843). *Nephraea* Nor. ex Hassk. (1844). *Pterocarpos* St. Lag. (1880).

more or less thickened or hardened, winged or keeled, sometimes membranous; seeds 2–1, separated by hard septa.

Barwood, *P. erinaceus* Poir. and *P. soyauxii* Taub., trop. Africa, yield dyes for wool; a blood-red dye is obtained from *P. santalinus* Linn. f., an Indian sp.

218. **Cyclolobium** Benth., Ann. Wien. Mus. 2: 92 (1838). 4 spp., trop. South America; type *C. brasiliense* Benth., Brazil. B.H. 1: 545; E.P. 3, 3: 336.

Shrubs; leaves alternate, 1-foliolate, with 2 stipels; stipules small; flowers medium-sized, racemes axillary or lateral, solitary or fasciculate; bracts small, narrow; bracteoles minute, caducous; calyx-teeth subequal or upper 2 connate high up; vexillum suborbicular, spreading; wings oblong; keel-petals oblong, obtuse, overlapping at the back or slightly connate; vexillary stamen free, others connate; anthers versatile; ovary stipitate, ovules numerous; style filiform, slightly incurved, stigma truncate, terminal; fruit stipitate, orbicular or broadly falcate, membranous, indehiscent, upper suture narrowly winged, style terminal; seeds 3–2, oblong, transverse.

Tribe 20. DALBERGIEAE[1]

Brogn., Diss. Legum. 134 (1822); Benth. & Hook. f., Gen. Pl. 1: 454
(Subtribe *Pterocarpeae*, in small part) (1865)

Trees and shrubs, latter often climbing or straggling; leaves *imparipinnate* or rarely 1-foliolate, leaflets mostly alternate; *stipels absent*; flowers small in terminal or axillary racemes, spikes, or panicles; bracts and bracteoles usually very small; *upper 2 calyx-lobes broadest*; corolla papilionaceous; *keel-petals connate at the apex*; stamens all connate into a sheath split along the upper (adaxial) side, or vexillary filament free or absent, or sheath split also on the lower side forming 2 bundles; anthers small, *uniform, didymous, not versatile*; ovary stipitate; *style glabrous*, stigma terminal; ovules few to 1; fruit *samaroid, indehiscent*, few- to 1-seeded in the middle; seeds reniform, compressed; radicle inflexed. Type genus *Dalbergia*.

219. **Dalbergia**[2] Linn. f., Suppl. 52 (1781) (conserved name). More than 100 spp., tropics and subtropics generally, incl. SE. temp. Asia and N. Australia; lectotype *D. lanceolaria* Linn. f., India. B.H. 1: 544; E.P. 3, 3: 333; Prain, Ann. Bot. Gard. Calc. 10: pt. 1 (1904): Amshoff, Pulle Fl. Suriname, 2, 2:

---

[1] Tribe **Dalbergieae** Brogn. (descr. emend.). Arbores et frutices saepe scandentes; folia imparipinnata vel rare 1-foliolata, foliolis plerumque alternatis; stipellae nullae; flores parvi in racemis spicis vel paniculis terminalibus vel axillaribus dispositi; bracteae et bracteolae plerumque minimae; calycis lobi 2 superiores latiores; petala carinae apice connata; stamina omnia in vaginam latere superiore fissam connata, vel vexillare solutum vel deficiens, vel vagina etiam latere inferiore fissa in phalanges 2 disposita; antherae parvae, aequales, didymae, haud versatiles; ovarium stipitatum, stigmate terminali; ovula pauca ad 1; fructus samaroideus, indehiscens, planus, medio pauci- ad 1-spermus; semina reniformia, compressa, radicula inflexa.

[2] Synonyms of **Dalbergia**: *Ecastaphyllum* P.Br. (1756). *Amerimnon* P.Br. (1756). *Salken* Adans. (1763). *Solori* Adans. (1763). *Pterocarpus* Berg. (1769). *Acouroa* Aubl. (1775). *Drakenstenia* Neck. (1790). *Endespermum* Blume (1823). *Hecastophyllum* H. B. & K. (1823). *Amerimnum* DC. (1825). *Drakensteinia* DC. (1825). *Semeionotis* Schott (1829). *Miscolobium* Vog. (1837). *Triptolemea* Mart. (1837). *Leiolobium* Benth. (1838). *Trioptolemea* Mart. ex Benth. (1838). *Podiopetalum* Hochst. (1841). *Endospermum* Endl. (1841). *Salkea* Stend. (1841). *Triptolemaea* Walp. (1842).

117; Cronquist, Fl. Congo Belge, 6: 52, tt. 3–5; Burkart, Legum. Argent. ed. 2, 222, fig. 53; Bak. f., Legum. Trop. Afr. 2: 515; Cronquist, Fl. Congo Belge, 6: 52 tt. 3–5.

Trees or shrubs, often tall or climbing, sometimes spiny; leaves alternate, imparipinnate or rarely 1-foliolate; most of the leaflets alternate; stipels absent; flowers small, often numerous, purple, violet or white, in terminal or axillary cymes or panicles; bracts small, subpersistent; bracteoles usually minute; upper 2 calyx-teeth broader, lowest often longest; vexillum ovate or orbicular; wings oblong; keel-petals connate at the apex; stamens all connate into a sheath split on the upper side, or the vexillary stamen free or absent, or the sheath split also on the lower side making 2 bundles; anthers small, erect, didymous; ovary stipitate; style incurved, short, stigma small, terminal; ovules few to 1; fruit samaroid, indehiscent, oblong or linear, rarely falcate, flat, thin, 1-seeded in the middle, or rarely few-seeded, often harder and reticulate around the seed, not winged; seeds reniform, plano-compressed; radicle inflexed.

Tribe 21. GEOFFROEEAE[1]

Tribe *Dalbergieae* Suur̃ι̃be *Geoffraeeae* Benth. & Hook. f., Gen. Pl. 1: 455 (1865)

Erect trees or shrubs; leaves alternate or opposite, *imparipinnate*, leaflets alternate or opposite; stipels present or absent; flowers in *axillary* racemes, panicles, or subfasciculate; bracts and bracteoles small, often very caducous; calyx-teeth or lobes equal or upper 2 large and wing-like, sometimes calyx spathaceous; corolla papilionaceous; wings free; vexillary filament free or connate with the others into a sheath split above (adaxially); *anthers subuniform, versatile*, the alternate sometimes smaller or abortive, rarely opening by terminal pores; ovary few- to 1-ovulate; *style glabrous*, stigma terminal; *fruit drupaceous, woody, indehiscent*, sometimes winged; seeds 2–1, *pendulous*. Type genus *Geoffroea* Jacq.

Anthers opening by slits lengthwise:
  Calyx truncate or very slightly dentate, not winged; fruit not winged:
    Branches not flattened into cladodes:
      Flowers in leaf-opposed or terminal racemes; fruit very fragile, drupe-like
        220. **Euchresta**
      Flowers in panicles; fruit hard and woody   221. **Andira**
    Branches flattened into cladodes; leaves minute or rarely 1-foliolate; fruits turgid, narrowed at the base and apex   222. **Phylloxylon**

---

[1] **Geoffroeeae** trib. nov. Arbores et frutices; folia alterna vel opposita, imparipinnata, foliolis alternis vel oppositis, stipellae interdum nullae; flores in racemis vel paniculis dispositi vel subfasciculati; bracteae et bracteolae parvae, saepe caducissimae; calycis dentes vel lobi aequales vel 2 superiores magni et aliformes, interdum calyx spathaceus; corolla papilionacea; alae liberae; carinae petala libera vel rarius connata; stamen vexillare liberum vel cum ceteris in spatham supra fissam connatum; antherae versatiles, alternis interdum minoribus et abortivis, rarius apice 2-porosae; ovarium pauci- ad 1-ovulatum; stylus glaber, stigmate terminali; fructus drupaceus, lignosus, indehiscens, interdum alatus; semina 2–1, pendula.

Calyx distinctly lobed or deeply dentate, sometimes winged:
Calyx-lobes or teeth equal, not wing-like; fruits drupaceous, woody
223. **Geoffroea**
Calyx-lobes very unequal, the upper 2 large and wing-like:
Fruits thick and drupaceous, woody, not winged; bracts and bracteoles
small; leaf-rhachis flattened or winged 224. **Dipteryx**
Fruits compressed, narrowed all around into a woody wing, full of oil;
bracteoles membranous and resembling the calyx-wings, soon
falling off; leaf-rhachis not winged 225. **Pterodon**
Anthers opening by terminal pores; stamens all connate into a sheath split
along the upper (adaxial) side; calyx entire or shortly 2-toothed, 1-lipped;
fruit flat and broadly winged, indehiscent 226. **Fissicalyx**

220. **Euchresta** Benn., Pl. Jav. Rar. 148, t. 31 (1838). 4 spp., Himalayas to
Malaya and Japan; type *E. horsfieldii* Benn., Formosa, Malay Archip. B.H.
1: 550; E.P. 3, 3: 346.

Shrubs or shrublets with tuber-like rootstock; leaves alternate, imparipinnate, leaflets
3–7, opposite, exstipellate; flowers white, in leaf-opposed or terminal racemes; bracts small,
narrow; bracteoles inconspicuous; calyx gibbous at the back, dentate; vexillum oblong;
wings narrow, oblong, slightly falcate, free; keel-petals rather like the wings, coherent at the
apex; vexillary stamen free, remainder connate; anthers versatile; ovary long-stipitate, 2–1-
ovulate; style filiform, incurved, stigma small, terminal; fruit stipitate, ovoid or ellipsoid,
drupe-like, shining, fragile, indehiscent; seed 1, pendulous.

221. **Andira** Lam., Encycl. 1: 171 (1783) (conserved name). *Lumbricidia* Vell.
(1825). *Poltolobium* C. Presl (1844). About 25 spp., trop. America, trop.
Africa; type *A. racemosa* Lam. ex J. St.-Hil., Cent. America. B.H. 1: 550;
E.P. 3, 3: 346; Amshoff, Pulle Fl. Suriname, 2, 2: 149; Hutch. & Dalz., Fl.
W. Trop. Afr. 1: 378.

Trees; leaves alternate, imparipinnate, rarely trifoliolate, leaflets opposite or rarely
alternate; stipels setaceous or absent; flowers rose or violet, in terminal or subterminal
panicles, often crowded and subsessile; bracts and bracteoles small or rarely about equal to
the calyx; calyx truncate or with short obsolete teeth; vexillum suborbicular, exappendicu-
late; wings straight, oblong, free; keel-petals similar, overlapping at the back; vexillary
stamen free or rarely connate with the others; anthers versatile; ovary rarely subsessile,
4–2- or rarely 1-ovulate; style short, incurved, stigma small, terminal; fruit drupaceous, ovoid
or obovoid, indehiscent, woody; seed 1, pendulous.

Chrysarobinum or Araroba, substance found in cavities of trunks of *Andira araroba* Aguiar,
Brazil, used in various skin diseases.

222. **Phylloxylon** Baill., Adansonia, 2: 54 (1861). *Neobaronia* Bak. (1884).
5 spp., Mascarene Isls.; type *P. decipiens* Baill., Mauritius. E.P. 3, 3: 348; N. 2:
33; 3, 5: 117.

Trees or shrubs, usually without leaves, the branches (cladodes) flattened, dilated, crenate,
bearing minute scales; flowers small, borne in the crenations of the cladodes; pedicels
short; bracts minute, deltoid; calyx small, campanulate, teeth minute; petals of equal
length; vexillum obovate, obtuse, clawed; wings narrower; keel-petals straight, subacute;
stamens 10, diadelphous, upper free; anthers small, globose; ovary sessile, ovules few; style
short, abruptly incurved, stigma capitate; fruit coriaceous, indehiscent, turgid, 2–1-seeded,
narrowed at the base and apex,

223. **Geoffroea** Jacq., Enum. Pl. Carib. 7 (1760). *Geoffraea* Linn. (1763). *Umari* Adans. (1763). *Geoffroya* Murr. (1774). *Geoffrea* Spreng. (1818). 4 spp., trop. and temp., South America; type *G. spinosa* Linn., West Indies, Brazil. B.H. 1: 551; E.P. 3, 3: 347; Burkart, Darwiniana, 9: 9 (1949); Burkart, Legum. Argent. ed. 2: 219, figs. 51, 52.

Trees; leaves alternate, imparipinnate, leaflets alternate or opposite; stipels rarely conspicuous; flowers yellow, mostly with unpleasant smell, in simple axillary racemes or subfasciculate at the tops of the branchlets; bracts very caducous; bracteoles small or absent; calyx-teeth or lobes subequal; vexillum suborbicular; wings erect, obtuse, straight or incurved, free; keel-petals imbricate at the back; vexillary stamen free or connate with the others in a split sheath; anthers versatile; ovary sessile or shortly stalked, 4–3-ovulate; style incurved, stigma small, terminal; fruit drupaceous, ovoid or obovoid, indehiscent, woody; seed 1, pendulous.

224. **Dipteryx**[1] Schreb., Gen. 2: 485 (1791) (conserved name). 8 spp., trop. America; type *D. odorata* (Aubl.) Willd., Guianas and Brazil. B.H. 1: 551 (partly); E.P. 3, 3: 347 (partly); Amshoff, Pulle Fl. Suriname, 2, 2: 153; Ducke, Trop. Woods, no. 61: 1 (1940).

Trees; leaves opposite or alternate, subabruptly pinnate, leaflets opposite or alternate, sometimes glandular-punctate, exstipellate; leaf-rhachis flattened or winged, prolonged at the apex; flowers violet or rose, in terminal panicles; bracts and bracteoles small, or the latter absent; calyx often coloured and glandular-punctate; tube short, upper 2 lobes large and wing-like, lower 3 connate into a small entire or 3-toothed lip; vexillum emarginate; wings falcate or obliquely oblong, shortly 2-fid, free; keel-petals subentire, slightly coherent at the back, or free; stamens all connate into a sheath split above; anthers versatile, the alternate smaller or abortive; ovary stipitate, 1-ovulate; style straight or incurved; fruit indehiscent, thick and drupaceous, ovoid, woody; seed pendulous.

225. **Pterodon** Vog., Linnaea 11: 384 (1837). *Commilobium* Benth. (1838). 4 spp., Brazil, Bolivia; type *P. emarginatus* Vog., Brazil. B.H. 1: 551; E.P. 3, 3: 347.

Trees; leaves abruptly pinnate, leaflets opposite or alternate, the end one subterminal, glandular-punctate; stipels absent; flowers rose or white, in a terminal panicle leafy at the base; bracts very caducous; bracteoles membranous, similar to the calyx-wings, falling off long before flowering; calyx-tube very short, upper 2 lobes large and wing-like, petaloid, lower 3 connate into a 3-toothed lip; vexillum broadly ovate or orbicular, emarginate; wings obovate or oblong, falcate, shortly 2-fid, free; keel-petals slightly smaller than the wings, entire, slightly coherent at the back; stamens all connate into a split sheath; anthers versatile, uniform; ovary stipitate or subsessile, 1-ovulate; fruit flattened, indehiscent, oval or oblong, oblique, endocarp woody, 1-seeded, full of balsam oil; seed pendulous.

226. **Fissicalyx** Benth., Journ. Linn. Soc. 5: 79 (1861). 1 sp., *F. fendleri* Benth., Venezuela. B.H. 1: 552; E.P. 3, 3: 348.

Tree; leaves alternate, imparipinnate, leaflets subopposite, exstipellate; stipules deciduous; flowers orange, crowded in terminal panicles; bracts minute, bracteoles small, persistent; calyx-tube turbinate, 1-lipped, limb acuminate, entire or shortly 2-dentate, splitting in flower and spathaceous; petals inserted with the stamens at the top of the calyx-tube;

[1] Synonyms of **Dipteryx**: *Coumarouna* Aubl. (1775). *Heinzia* Scop. (1771). *Bolducia* Neck. (1790). *Cumaruna* J. F. Gmel. (1791). *Baryosma* Gaertn. (1791). *Dipterix* Willd. (1803). *Cumaruma* Steud. (1821). *Cumarouma* Steud. (1840). *Comarouna* Carr. (1873).

vexillum ovate; wings obliquely oblong, free; keel-petals subsimilar to the wings, free; stamens all connate into a sheath split above; anthers versatile, opening by 2 apical pores; ovary shortly stipitate, 2-ovuled; style filiform, stigma minute, terminal; fruit flat, ovate-elliptic including the broad wings, indehiscent; seed pendulous, hilum small.

Tribe 22. BRONGNIARTIEAE

Lindl., Veg. Kingd. 554 (1847). Tribe *Galegeae* Subtribe *Brongniartieae*
Benth. & Hook. f., Gen. Pl. 1: 444 (1865)

Trees or erect shrubs; leaves imparipinnate, rarely gland-dotted; leaflets numerous, 3 or 1; stipules (often very large) and sometimes stipels present; flowers paired in the leaf-axils or in a terminal raceme or panicle; calyx-tube short, more or less *2-lipped*, upper 2 calyx-lobes united high up or to the apex; *vexillary filament free* or united with the others into a *single sheath split above*; anthers uniform or dimorphic; *style glabrous*; stigma terminal; fruit dehiscent, 2-valved, sometimes filled with spongy tissue or septate between the seeds but not breaking into separate joints; *seeds strophiolate*, with the longer axis ar right angles to the fruit; embryo with straight radicle. Type genus *Brongniartia* H. B. & K.

Vexillary stamen free; stipules foliaceous or setaceous; bracteoles usually caducous but sometimes broad and persistent; calyx-lobes subequal in length, upper 2 connate high up   227. **Brongniartia**
Vexillary stamen united with the others into a single sheath split on the adaxial side; stipules minute:
Calyx deeply split, upper 2 lobes connate high up; keel incurved, obtuse; leaves not sessile   228. **Lamprolobium**
Calyx-tube very short, lobes elongated, connate into 2 entire lips; leaves not sessile, gland-dotted; keel long-linear, somewhat twisted
229. **Harpalyce**

227. **Brongniartia** H. B. & K., Nov. Gen. et Sp. 6: 465, t. 587 (1823). *Peraltea* H. B. & K. (1823). *Megastegia* G. Don (1832). *Brogniartia* Walp. (1843). About 55 sp., Mexico, Cent. America, S. American Andes; lectotype. *B. podalyrioides* H. B. & K., Mexico. B.H. 1: 495; E.P. 3, 3: 266; Standley, Contrib. U.S. Nat. Herb. 23: 466.

Shrubs, silky-villous or rarely glabrous; leaves imparipinnate, leaflets numerous, rarely few, opposite, entire, not stipellate; stipules herbaceous, sometimes large, persistent or deciduous; flowers violet or fleshy-coloured, pedicels 2–3 in the leaf-axils or rarely in a terminal raceme; bracts ovate-lanceolate or setaceous, often caducous; bracteoles sometimes persistent, large and broad; calyx-lobes subequal in length, upper 2 connate high up; petals subequal in length, clawed; vexillum ovate or orbicular, nude inside; wings oblong, falcate, free; keel incurved or boat-shaped, obtuse; vexillary stamen free, remainder connate into a sheath; anthers uniform or alternately shorter; ovary sessile or stipitate; style incurved, subulate, not barbate, stigma small, terminal; ovules numerous; fruit oblong or broadly linear, plano-compressed, 2-valved, often filled with cellulose, valves coriaceous; seeds ovate, strophiolate, funicle short.

228. **Lamprolobium** Benth., Fl. Austral. 2: 202 (1864). 2 spp., Australia, type *L. fruticosum* Benth. B.H. 1: 495; E.P. 3, 3: 266.

Shrubs; leaves imparipinnate, softly pubescent, without stipels; leaflets few pairs, opposite, or only 1 leaflet; stipules minute; flowers small, yellow, axillary, single or paired; bracts and bracteoles minute, very caducous; calyx deeply split, upper 2 lobes connate high up; petals scarcely exceeding the calyx; vexillum orbicular, not appendaged; wings oblique, oblong, free; keel incurved, obtuse; stamens all connate into a sheath split above; anthers uniform, dorsifixed; ovary shortly stipitate; style incurved, not barbate, filiform, stigma terminal; ovules numerous; fruit stipitate, oblong-linear, plano-compressed, 2-valved, septate between the seeds inside, valves coriaceous; seeds oblong, compressed, strophiolate.

229. **Harpalyce** Moc. & Sesse ex DC., Mém. Légum. 496 (1825). 25 spp., Brazil, Mexico, Cent. America, Cuba; type *H. formosa* DC., Mexico. B.H. 1: 494; E.P. 3, 3: 266; Standley, Contrib. U.S. Nat. Herb. 23: 465.

Erect shrubs, branches often herbaceous, tomentose; leaves imparipinnate, leaflets opposite, entire, gland-dotted, scarcely stipellate; stipules minute, caducous; racemes short, terminal, or in a terminal panicle; flowers scarlet or purple, rather large, pedicels solitary; bracts and bracteoles linear, deciduous; calyx-tube very short; lobes elongated, connate into 2 entire lips; vexillum large, nude inside, claw short; wings oblong falcate; keel long-linear, incurved, subtwisted, obtuse; stamens all connate into a sheath split above; anthers linear, alternately shorter; ovary sessile; style glabrous, stigma terminal; ovules numerous; fruit oblong or broadly linear, plano-compressed, 2-valved, septate between the seeds inside; seeds compressed, oblong or ovate, strophiolate, with a very short funicle.

Tribe 23. TEPHROSIEAE

Tribe *Galegeae* Subtribe *Tephrosieae* Benth. & Hook. f., Gen. Pl. 1: 444
(in small part, excl. *Millettia* and related genera)

Herbs, rarely annuals, shrublets or soft-wooded subarborescent shrubs, often very silky-pubescent; leaves imparipinnate, leaflets entire, rarely leaves simple, 1-foliolate or digitately foliolate, mostly with closely parallel lateral nerves very oblique to the midrib, in one genus (*Papilionopsis*) reduced to leaf-like phyllodes with parallel nerves; stipules various, rarely spinous-subulate, rarely absent; stipels rare; flowers in terminal or leaf-opposed, rarely axillary racemes, or 1–few and axillary; bracts small; bracteoles often absent; calyx shortly lobed, lobes equal or the upper 2 more connate; corolla papilionaceous, vexillum conspicuous and very often *pubescent to silky tomentose outside*; stamens 10, vexillary filament often free and bent at the base then connate with the others into a *tube or sheath*; alternate filaments rarely dilated at the apex; *anthers uniform*; ovary many–1-ovuled; style glabrous or *variously bearded along the adaxial side* or around the stigma; *fruit 2-valved*, continuous within or septate, rarely tardily dehiscent; seeds usually without a strophiole. Type genus *Tephrosia* Pers.

Alternate filaments slightly dilated at the apex; filaments united into a tube; subarborescent shrubs, silky pubescent; racemes terminal; fruits linear, compressed; stipels absent   230. **Mundulea**

Alternate filaments not dilated; mostly herbs or undershrubs:

Stipules spinous-subulate, persistent; rigid undershrubs with thick tuberous
    roots; style bearded around the stigma; peduncles elongated
                  231. Peteria

Stipules not as above or rarely absent:
  Leaves pinnately foliolate, 1-foliolate, or simple:
    Perennial herbs or shrublets:
      Leaves 1-foliolate, obcordate, pinnately nerved; flowers axillary, solitary
        or paired, subsessile; stamens monadelphous in a sheath split above;
        fruit 1-seeded   **232. Requienia**
      Leaves pinnate, rarely 1-foliolate, never obcordate, usually very closely
        parallel-nerved; flowers in terminal or leaf-opposed racemes, or in
        the upper axils; ovules and seeds usually several:
        Flowers terminal or leaf-opposed or in the upper axils; petals longer
          than the calyx; ovules usually several   **233. Tephrosia**
        Flowers fasciculate in the leaf-axils; petals shorter than the calyx;
          ovule 1   **234. Paratephrosia**
    Annual herbs; stipels absent:
      Leaves imparipinnate; leaflets with spreading parallel nerves; stamens all
        connate into a sheath split above   **235. Ptychosema**
      Leaves reduced to leaf-like phyllodes; stamens as in preceding genus
                  236. Papilionopsis
      Leaves simple, linear, with ascending lateral nerves; vexillary stamen
        free from the base   **237. Sphinctospermum**
  Leaves digitately foliolate:
    Stipels absent; no cleistogamous flowers:
      Flowers 2–3 in the leaf-axils; filaments united into a closed tube
                  238. Sylitra
      Flowers in a terminal raceme; filaments diadelphous   **239. Caulocarpus**
    Stipels present, a pair at the top of the petiole, subulate; flowers in
      racemes, the lowermost cleistogamous, their fruits more or less buried
      in the soil   **240. Lupiniphyllum**

230. **Mundulea** Benth., Miq. Pl. Jungh. 248 (1852). About 15 spp., Madagascar, East Indies, China, trop. Africa; lectotype *M. sericea* (Willd.) A. Chev.
(*M. suberosa* DC.), Old World tropics and subtropics. B.H. 1: 497; E.P. 3,
3: 270; Hutch. & Dalz., Fl. W. Trop. Afr. ed. 2 (Keay), 1: 527.

Subarborescent shrubs, silky-pubescent; leaves imparipinnate, leaflets entire, reticulate-
penninerved; stipules small; stipels absent; racemes terminal; flowers rose, pedicels fasciculate on the axis; bracts small; bracteoles absent; calyx-teeth short, upper 2 subconnate;
vexillum large, silky-pubescent, spreading, transversely callose above the short claw, wings
falcate-oblong, slightly adherent to the keel; keel incurved at the apex, obtuse; vexillary
stamen free at the base, bent, then connate with the others into a closed tube; alternate
filaments slightly dilated; anthers uniform; ovary many-ovuled; style incurved, hardened,
subterete, glabrous, inflexed at the apex, stigma capitate; fruit linear, plano-compressed,
sutures much thickened, tardily dehiscent; seeds reniform, without a strophiole.

231. **Peteria** A. Gray, Pl. Wright. 1: 50 (1852). 4 spp., North America; type *P. scoparia* A. Gray, New Mexico, S. United States. B.H. 1: 495; E.P. 3, 3: 273; Rydb., N. Amer. Fl. 24: 183; C. L. Porter, Rhodora, 58: 344 (1956).

Rigid undershrubs; root thick and tuberous, edible; leaves imparipinnate; leaflets numerous, small, entire, without stipels; stipules spinous-subulate; racemes terminal or leaf-opposed; flowers yellow; bracts small; bracteoles absent; calyx tubular, gibbous above the base, teeth or lobes subequal, upper 2 connate high up; vexillum ovate-oblong, spreading at the apex, with reflexed sides, long-narrowed into the claw, nude inside; wings obliquely oblong, free; keel slightly incurved, obtuse; vexillary stamen free, remainder connate into a sheath; anthers uniform; ovary stipitate; style inflexed, barbate around the stigmatic apex, stigma capitate, terminal; ovules numerous; fruit stipitate, linear, straight, plano-compressed, 2-valved, continuous inside, valves coriaceous with rather thick sutures; seeds transversely oblong or ovate, without a strophiole.

232. **Requienia** DC., Ann. Sci. Nat. sér. 1, 4: 91 (1825); Mém. Légum. 224, tt. 37, 38. 2 spp., trop. and S. Africa; type *R. obcordata* (Lam.) DC. Lamarck Ill. t. 327, fig. 5; Guill. & Perr., Fl. Seneg. 168; Harv. & Sond., Fl. Cap. 2: 231; Hutch. & Dalz., Fl. W. Trop. Afr. 1: 387; ed. 2 (Keay), 1: 527 (in *Tephrosia*).

Shrublets; leaves 1-foliolate, obcordate, pinnately nerved; stipules paired; flowers small, axillary, subsessile, solitary or paired; calyx acutely and subequally 5-lobed, persistent; petals free, keel obtuse; stamens monadelphous, sheath split above; style filiform; fruit ovate, compressed, hooked by the base of the style, 1-seeded; seeds orbicular.

233. **Tephrosia**[1] Pers., Syn. 2: 328 (1807) (conserved name). Over 400 spp., warm reg. of the world, especially Africa and trop. Australia; type *T. villosa* (Linn.) Persia. B.H. 1: 496; E.P. 3, 3: 269; Amshoff, Pulle Fl. Suriname, 2, 2: 163; Cronquist, Fl. Congo Belge, 5: 85; Wood, Amer. barbistyled spp. of Tephrosia, Contrib. Gray Herb. 170: 193 (1949), &c.; Hutch. & Dalz., Fl. W. trop. Afr. 1: 383; ed. 2 (Keay), 1: 527 (excl. *Requienia* DC.); Burkart, Legum. Argent. ed. 2: 253, fig. 67; Gillett, Fl. Trop. East Afr. *ined.*

Shrubs, shrublets, or herbs; leaves imparipinnate; leaflets several, rarely 3–1, usually with close parallel nerves oblique to the midrib and extended to the margin, often silky below; stipules various; stipels none; racemes terminal, leaf-opposed, or in the upper axils; bracts present; bracteoles absent; flowers red, purple, or white; calyx-teeth or lobes subequal or the upper 2 more connate; petals clawed; vexillum suborbicular, hairy outside; wings obliquely obovate or oblong, slightly adherent to the keel; keel incurved; vexillary stamen free at the base, more or less connate with the others from the middle upwards, at length often quite free; anthers uniform; ovary sessile, many-ovuled, rarely 1–few-ovuled; style incurved or inflexed, often flattened, glabrous or variously bearded, stigma terminal, penicillate or rarely nude; fruit linear, rarely ovate or oblong, compressed, 2-valved, continuous within or thinly septate between the seeds; seeds sometimes with a small strophiole.

---

[1] Synonyms of **Tephrosia**: *Cracca* Linn. (1753). *Colinil* Adans. (1763). *Needhamia* Scop. (1777). *Brissonia* Neck. (1790). *Reineria* Moench (1802). *Crafordia* Raf. (1814). *Kiesera* Reinw. (1828). *Xiphocarpus* C. Presl (1830). *Apodynomene* E. Mey. (1835). *Pogonostigma* Boiss. (1843). *Catacline* Edgew. (1847). *Macronyx* Dalz. (1850). *Balboa* Liebm. (1856). *Seemannantha* Alef. (1862). *Brittonia* O. Ktze. (1891). *Ptycholobium* Harms (1915). *Ophrestia* M. Forbes (1948).

234. Paratephrosia Domin, Fedde Repert. 11: 261 (1912). 1 sp., *P. lanata* Domin, Cent. Australia.

Shrublet, densely silky-tomentose all over; leaves dense on the branches, pinnately tri-foliolate; stipules and bracts linear-subulate; flowers fasciculate in the leaf-axils; calyx-tube very short, much shorter than the lobes, the latter much elongated, linear-subulate, free and subequal; petals shorter than the calyx, tomentose outside; vexillum transversely oblong-orbicular, entire, shortly clawed; keel slightly incurved, obtuse; wings free; vexillary stamen free at the base, connate with the others above the middle into a tube; anthers uniform; ovary 1-ovuled; style filiform, flattened, glabrous, stigma small, terminal; fruit sessile, longer than the calyx, obliquely semi-ovate, 1-seeded, tomentose; seed suborbicular, estrophiolate.

235. Ptychosema Benth., Lindl. Swan Riv. App. 16 (1839). 2 spp., Australia; type *P. pusillum* Benth., W. Australia. B.H. 1: 496; E.P. 3, 3: 269.

Annual herbs, diffuse; leaves imparipinnate; leaflets entire, with parallel nerves below; stipels absent; stipules small; peduncles terminal, 1-flowered; bracts 1–2 at the base of the pedicel; bracteoles 2 in the middle of the pedicel; flowers violet; calyx turbinate, lobes sub-equal in length, upper 2 connate into a truncate emarginate lip; petals rather long-clawed; vexillum suborbicular, emarginate; wings falcate-oblong, free; keel shorter than the wings, almost straight, obtuse; stamens all connate into a sheath split above; anthers uniform; ovary sessile, style glabrous, short, inflexed, stigma extrorsely oblique; ovules numerous.

236. Papilionopsis van Steen., Nova Guinea, 3: 17, fig. 3 (1960). 1 sp., *P. stylidioides* van Steen., New Guinea.

Small annual herb with glabrous sterile stems; leaves reduced to sessile leaf-like phyllodes, linear-lanceolate, with about 9 parallel longitudinal nerves, tips with marginal glands; stipules and stipels absent; flowering stem with 3 types of hairs, some minute and dense, some long-spreading 1-celled, and a few many-celled with glandular tips; flowers few in a unilateral cyme; pedicels filiform; calyx campanulate, equally 4-lobed to the middle, anterior lobe bifid; petals clawed, vexillum obliquely obovate-orbicular; stamens 10, filaments united into a tube split in the upper half on the adaxial side; anthers equal, orbicular; ovary linear; style glabrous; stigma terminal; ovules 4; fruit not known 'but probably a flattish linear 4-seeded beaked pod'.

237. Sphinctospermum Rose, Contrib. U.S. Nat. Herb. 10: 107 (1906). 1 sp., *S. constrictum* (S. Wats.) Rose, Lower California, Mexico.

Annual herb; leaves simple, linear, with ascending lateral nerves; stipules subulate; flowers axillary, single or very rarely paired, shortly pedicellate; calyx-teeth 5, acuminate, the upper 2 more united; petals nearly equal in length; vexillum nearly orbicular, emarginate, very shortly clawed; wings oblong; stamens 10, the vexillary one free to the base, remainder united half-way up; style slender, hairy near the top; ovary sessile, many-ovuled; fruits linear, 2-valved, septate between the seeds; seeds 10–6, compressed and quadrangular, constricted in the middle, brown.

238. Sylitra E. Mey., Comm. Pl. Afr. Austr. 114 (1835). 1 sp., *S. biflora* E. Mey, S. and S. trop. Africa. B.H. 1: 496; E.P. 3, 3: 269; Phillips, Gen. S. Afr. Fl. Pl. ed. 2: 412.

Slender undershrub, thinly canescent; leaves digitately 3–1-foliolate, very rarely 5-foliolate on the same specimen; petiole short, jointed at the apex, leaflets entire, obliquely ner-vose; hairs grey, adpressed; stipules small; flowers very small, paired in the leaf-axils, shortly pedicellate; bracts and bracteoles minute or absent; calyx narrow, lobes subequal, upper 2 close together; vexillum pubescent, nude inside, narrowed into the claw; wings falcate-oblong, adherent to the keel; keel obtuse, shorter than the wings; vexillary stamen free at the base, then connate with the others into a closed tube; anthers uniform; ovary sessile, many-ovuled; style inflexed, filiform, glabrous, stigma terminal, capitate; fruit oblong, broadly plano-compressed, undulate or twisted, membranous; seeds suborbicular, without a strophiole, funicle shortly filiform.

239. **Caulocarpus** Bak. f., Legum. Trop. Afr. 169 (1926). 1 sp., *C. gossweileri* Bak. f., trop. Africa (Angola).

Shrublet with a woody rootstock and numerous stems; leaves sessile, digitately 3–5-foliolate, leaflets cuneate-oblanceolate; stipels absent; flowers in a short terminal raceme; calyx-lobes subequal; vexillum spreading, densely tomentose outside, longer than the keel; wings oblong; vexillary stamen free, remainder connate in a sheath; anthers uniform; ovary stipitate, linear, many-ovuled; style subulate, slightly flattened, stigma small, terminal; fruit oblong, stipitate, about 7-seeded.

240. **Lupiniphyllum** Gillett, Kew Bull. 1964 (*ined.*), 1 sp., *L. lupinifolium* (DC.) Gillett (*Tephrosia lupinifolia* DC.), trop. and S. Africa.

Perennial herb with woody rootstock and prostrate radiating shoots rooting at the nodes; leaves alternate, digitately 3–7-foliolate, mostly 5-foliolate, long-petiolate, leaflets folding up during the heat of the day, narrowly oblanceolate, apiculate, with numerous ascending closely parallel nerves; stipules subulate-lanceolate, persistent; stipels 2, lateral to the lateral leaflets, filiform-subulate, persistent and recurved; racemes terminal, bearing normal pink-mauve flowers and fertile fruits, lower lateral racemes bearing some cleistogamous flowers; bracts small, linear; calyx campanulate, equally 5-lobed, lobes triangular, acute; vexillum broadly obovate, shortly clawed; wings clawed, oblong, auriculate; keel obliquely elliptic; stamens monadelphous; free part of filaments filiform; anthers equal, ellipsoid, basifixed; ovary subsessile, ovules several; style bent at a right angle, slightly hairy towards the base; normal fruits broadly linear, about 5-seeded, shortly beaked, with spongy septa between the seeds; seeds subreniform, faintly reticulate, the hilum near the middle; cleistogamous flowers with fruits 1–2-seeded, probably remaining buried in the soil.

Tribe 24. PSEUDARTHRIEAE[1]

Shrublets or herbs; leaves *pinnately 3-foliolate*; stipules and *stipels present*; *racemes or panicles terminal*; flowers paired or fasciculate on the rhachis; *bracteoles absent*; upper 2 calyx-lobes connate high up; corolla papilionaceous; vexillary filament free or connate high up with the others into a sheath split adaxially; *anthers uniform*; ovules numerous; *style glabrous*, inflexed, stigma terminal; fruit *dehiscent*, flat or turgid, 2-valved, continuous within; seeds subreniform, sometimes with a very small strophiole. Old World tropics and subtropics. Type genus *Pseudarthria* Wight & Arn.

[1] **Pseudarthrieae** trib. nov. Fruticuli vel herbae; folia pinnatim 3-foliolata, stipulata et stipellata; racemi vel paniculae terminales; flores geminati vel fasciculati; calycis lobi 2 superiores connati; filamentum vexillare liberum vel partim connatum vel demum liberum; antherae uniformes; ovula numerosa; stylus glaber, inflexus, stigmate terminali; fructus dehiscens, planus vel turgidus, 2-valvis, haud articulatus, intra continuus; semina subreniformia, interdum minute strophiolata.

Fruit flat; vexillary filament free   241. **Pseudarthria**

Fruit turgid; vexillary filament united high up with the others or at length
free   242. **Pycnospora**

241. **Pseudarthria** Wight & Arn., Prodr. Fl. Pen. Ind. Or. 1: 209 (1834).
Anarthrosyne E. Mey. (1835). 12 spp., trop. Asia, trop. and S. Africa,
Mauritius; type *P. viscida* (Linn.) Wight & Arn., Ceylon, India, Malaya.
B.H. 1: 521; E.P. 3, 3: 329; Schindler, Fedde Repert. Beih. 2: 1 (1914);
Hutch. & Dalz., Fl. W. Trop. Afr. 1: 386.

Shrublets or herbs, sometimes tomentose or viscid-pubescent; leaves pinnately 3-foliolate,
leaflets stipellate; stipules free, membranous or striate; flowers small, purple, paired or
fasciculate on the branches of the terminal raceme or panicle; bracts narrow; bracteoles
absent; upper 2 calyx-lobes connate high up; vexillum suborbicular; wings obliquely
oblong, free from the keel; keel oblong, obtuse, laterally not appendaged; vexillary stamen
free, remainder connate; anthers uniform; ovary subsessile; ovules several; style inflexed,
subulate, stigma small, terminal; fruit flat and compressed, sutures straight or slightly
sinuate between the seeds, 2-valved, continuous inside, valves thin, transversely venulose,
not articulated; seeds compressed, subreniform, estrophiolate.

242. **Pycnospora** R.Br. ex Wight & Arn., Prodr. Fl. Pen. Ind. Or. 1: 197
(1834): 1 sp., *P. lutescens* (Poir.) Schindler (*P. hedysaroides* R.Br.), trop.
Africa, trop. and subtrop. Asia, Malaya, New Guinea, NE. Australia. B.H.
1: 521; E.P. 3, 3: 329; Léonard, Fl. Congo Belge, 5: 238, fig. 16; van Meeuwen,
Reinwardtia, 5: 419 (1961).

Shrublets; leaves pinnately 3-foliolate, leaflets entire, stipellate; stipules free, membranous,
striate; flowers small, purplish, often paired on the rhachis of the terminal raceme or
panicle; bracts membranous, caducous; bracteoles absent; 2 upper calyx-lobes connate
high up; vexillum suborbicular; wings obliquely oblong, adherent to the keel; keel-petals
slightly incurved, obtuse, with a narrow lateral appendage on each side; vexillary stamen
connate high up with the remainder or at length free; anthers uniform; ovary sessile,
ovules several; style inflexed, subulate, stigma terminal; fruit oblong, turgid, 2-valved, continuous within, valves thin, transversely lined-venose, subreticulate, not articulated; seeds
small, subreniform, thinly strophiolate at the hilum.

Tribe 25. INDIGOFEREAE

Tribe *Galegeae* Subtribe *Indigofereae* Benth. & Hook. f., Gen. Pl. 1: 444 (1865)

Shrubs or herbs, rarely glandular-punctate, often grey or silvery with *medifixed* T-*shaped hairs*; leaves imparipinnate or pinnately or digitately 3-folio-
late, sometimes 1-foliolate or primitively simple; stipules usually small;
stipels mostly absent; flowers papilionaceous, *in axillary racemes or spikes*;
bracteoles absent; stamens mostly diadelphous, vexillary filament free from
the base or rarely united with the others into a sheath split above or closed
tube; *anthers uniform* or *dissimilar*, mostly *gland-tipped*; ovules numerous to
1; *style glabrous*; fruits 2-valved, *septate between the seeds but not jointed*;
seeds estrophiolate. Tropics and subtropics. Type genus *Indigofera* Linn.

Vexillary (adaxial) stamen free from the others or united with them only at the base:

Anthers tipped by a gland; leaves simple or more usually pinnate, rarely unifoliolate   243. **Indigofera**

Anthers bearded at each end; leaves simple   244. **Rhynchotropis**

Vexillary stamen completely united with the others into a closed tube; anther-connective apiculate; leaves imparipinnate   245. **Cyamopsis**

243. **Indigofera**[1] Linn., Sp. Pl. 751 (1753). About 800 spp., trop. and subtrop. regions; type *I. tinctoria* Linn., tropics. B.H. 1: 494; E.P. 3, 3: 259; Amshoff, Pulle Fl. Suriname, 2, 2: 167; Cronquist, Fl. Congo Belge, 5: 117, 1954; Gillett, Kew Bull. Addit. ser. 1: 1–166 (1958); in Hutch. & Dalz., Fl. W. Trop. Afr. ed. 2 (Keay), 1: 533, fig. 165, and Fl. Trop. E. Afr. *ined.*; Burkart, Legum. Argent. ed. 2, 245, fig. 63 (1952); Phillips, Gen. S. Afr. Fl. Pl. ed. 2: 412.

Shrubs or herbs, more or less clothed with adpressed medifixed hairs, sometimes mixed with other indumentum; leaves imparipinnate or pinnately or digitately 3-foliolate, sometimes 1-foliolate or quite simple; leaflets entire, sometimes stipellate; stipules often small and setaceous, very shortly adnate to the petiole; flowers often rose or purple, in axillary racemes or spikes, single in the axil of a caducous bract; no bracteoles; calyx-teeth or lobes subequal or the lowermost longer; vexillum often persisting for a time, sessile or clawed; wings slightly cohering with the keel; keel erect, obtuse or acuminate, gibbous on each side and often spurred; vexillary stamen free from the base, remainder connate; anthers uniform, tipped by a gland; ovary sessile or nearly so; ovules numerous to 1 or 2; style glabrous, stigma capitate, often penicillate; fruit linear to globose, straight, arcuate, or rarely circinate, terete, 4–3-sided, or plano-compressed, septate within between the seeds; seeds globose to cylindric and truncate, compressed or quadrate, estrophiolate.

244. **Rhynchotropis** Harms, Engl. Bot. Jahrb. 30: 86 (1901). 3–4 spp., trop. Africa; type *R. poggei* (Taub.) Harms, Congo, Angola, Rhodesia. Cronquist, Fl. Congo Belge, 5: 173, fig. 9.

Perennial erect herbs with often numerous slender angular stems from a fleshy or woody rootstock; leaves simple, sessile, linear or narrowly lanceolate, entire; hairs medifixed; stipules subulate, persistent; racemes axillary and paniculate, elongated; bracts subulate; no bracteoles; calyx campanulate, 5-lobed; vexillum suborbicular, shortly acuminate, wings shortly acuminate, keel-petals coherent, beaked; stamens diadelphous, vexillary coherent at the base with the others, alternately longer and shorter; anthers barbate at each end, longer so at the base; ovary linear; ovules 6–4; style flattened and twisted, stigma terminal, shortly hairy; fruits linear, shortly stipitate, beaked, slightly compressed, broadly keeled; seeds 4–2, separated by thin partitions.

245. **Cyamopsis** DC., Mém. Légum. 230 (1825). *Cordaea* Spreng. (1831). 3 spp., E. India, Afghanistan, Arabia, trop. and S. Africa; type *C. tetragonoloba* (L.) Taub., India (*C. psoraloides* DC.). B.H. 1: 493; E.P. 3, 3: 259;

---

[1] Synonyms of **Indigofera**: *Brissonia* Desv. (1814). *Sphaeridiophorum* Desv. (1814). *Hemispadon* Endl. (1832). *Oustropis* G. Don (1832). *Tricoilendus* Raf. (1836). *Eilemanthus* Hochst. (1846). *Amecarpus* Benth. (1847). *Elemanthus* Schlechtd. (1847). *Acanthonotus* Benth. (1849). *Indigastrum* Jaub. & Spach (1857). *Microcharis* Benth. (1865). *Anil* O. Ktze. (1891).

Hutch. & Dalz., Fl. W. Trop. Afr. 1: 394; ed. 2 (Keay), 1: 543; Phillips, Gen. S. Afr. Fl. Pl. ed. 2: 411.

Erect herbs, with adpressed medifixed hairs or woolly; leaves imparipinnate, leaflets 3 or more, opposite, dentate or entire, exstipellate; stipules small, setaceous; flowers small, purplish, in axillary racemes, single in the axil of caducous bracts; bracteoles absent; lower teeth of the oblique broad calyx longer; vexillum obovate, sessile; wings oblong, free from the keel, the latter erect, subincurved, obtuse, sides not appendaged; stamens all connate into a closed tube; anthers uniform, connective apiculate; ovary sessile; ovules numerous; style incurved at the apex, stigma capitate; fruit linear, subtetragonous-compressed, acuminate, 2-valved, septate within between the seeds; seeds estrophiolate, quadrate, compressed.

Tribe 26. SESBANIEAE[1]

Tribe *Galegeae* Subtribe *Robinieae*, partly, Benth. & Hook. f., Gen. Pl. 1: 445 (1865)

Herbs, rarely tall and shrubby; leaves pari- or imparipinnate or 1-foliolate; stipules present; stipels present or absent; flowers in *axillary racemes* or rarely single or few in the leaf-axils, bisexual or rarely cleistogamous; calyx truncate or 5-lobed or toothed; vexillum orbicular or ovate to reniform, spreading or reflexed, often with 2 appendages on the claw; vexillary filament free or rarely partly connate in the middle with the remainder all connate into an open sheath; *anthers uniform, muticous*; style glabrous or bearded lengthwise on the upper (adaxial) side or below the stigma; fruit mostly *transversely septate between the seeds* but not breaking up into joints, rarely 4-winged, 2-valved or subindehiscent; seeds without a strophiole; radicle at most incurved (not folded). Type genus *Sesbania* Scop.

Style glabrous or rarely pubescent all around:
  Fruits many-seeded, transversely septate between the seeds, endocarp remaining attached to the exocarp; stipels minute or absent
246. **Sesbania**
  Fruits 2–1-seeded, continuous within, with a thin membrano4s endocarp becoming detached with the seeds; stipels absent   247. **Glottidium**
Style longitudinally bearded along the upper (adaxial) side or below the stigma:
  Fruits not glandular; no cleistogamous flowers:
    Leaves imparipinnate; stipules setaceous; racemes axillary; stipels present
248. **Cracca**
    Leaves 1-foliolate; stipules linear subulate; flowers solitary, axillary, resupinate; stipels absent   249. **Poissonia**

[1] **Sesbanieae** trib. nov. Herbae, rarius frutices elati ramis subherbaceis; folia pari- vel imparipinnata vel 1-foliolata; stipulae saepius caducissimae; stipellae interdum adsunt; flores in racemis axillaribus dispositi vel rarius singuli vel pauci et axillares, bisexuales vel rarius cleistogami; calyx truncatus vel 5-lobatus vel dentatus; vexillum orbiculare, ovatum vel reniforme, patulum vel reflexum, saepe unguibus 2-appendiculatis; stamen vexillare liberum vel rare medio connatum; antherae uniformes; stylus glaber vel intus longitudinaliter vel infra stigma barbatus; fructus plerumque inter semina septatus sed non articulatus, rarius 4-alatus, 2-valvis vel subindehiscens; semina estrophiolata; radicula incurva, nec plicata.

D d

Fruits covered with stipitate glands; stipules elongate-linear; stemless herbs; leaves imparipinnate; stipels absent; flowers axillary, some cleistogamous **250. Neocracca**

246. **Sesbania**[1] Scop., Introd. 308 (1777) (conserved name). About 70 spp., warmer regions of the world; type *S. sesban* (Linn.) Merrill. B.H. 1: 502; E.P. 3, 3: 277; Phillips & Hutch., Bothalia, 1: 40 (1921); Hutch. & Dalz., Fl. W. Trop. Afr. 1: 386; ed. 2 (Keay), 1: 531; Hauman, Fl. Congo Belge, 5: 74; Burkart, *Legum.* Argent. ed. 2: 267, fig. 75; B. L. Turner, Chromosome nos., Rhodora, 57: 213 (1955); J. B. Gillett, *Sesbania* in trop. Afr., Kew Bull. 17: 91 (1963).

Small trees, shrubs, or herbs; leaves paripinnate, leaflets in many pairs, entire, often glaucous; stipels minute or absent; stipules often very caducous; racemes axillary, lax; flowers yellow, purplish, variegated or spotted, or white (sometimes very large, e.g. *S. grandiflora* Pers.); pedicels slender; bracts and bracteoles setaceous, caducous or rarely persistent; calyx-tube broad, truncate or equally lobed or toothed; vexillum orbicular or ovate, spreading or reflexed; wings falcate-oblong; keel incurved, obtuse or obtusely acuminate, with long claws; vexillary stamen free, bent at the base with the staminal sheath; anthers uniform or alternately a little longer; ovary often stipitate; ovules numerous; style incurved, glabrous or rarely pubescent all around, stigma small, capitate; fruit linear and subterete, or rarely oblong, compressed and subtorulose, 4-sided or rarely 4-winged, 2-valved or subindehiscent, transversely septate between the seeds inside; seeds transversely oblong or subquadrate, without a strophiole.

247. **Glottidium** Desv., Journ. de Bot. Desv. 2, 1: 119 (1813). 1 sp., *G. vesicarium* (Jacq.) Harper, S. United States. Rydb., N. Amer. Fl. 24: 208; Phillips & Hutch., Bothalia, 1: 40 (1921), in obs.

Annual herb with wiry rigid stems; leaves paripinnate; leaflets numerous, alternate or subopposite, narrowly oblong; stipules deciduous; stipels absent; flowers few in slender pedunculate racemes; calyx campanulate, oblique, 5-toothed; vexillum broad, reniform, reflexed, shortly clawed; wings auriculate at the base and shortly clawed; keel-petals long-clawed, with a sharp basal auricle; stamens diadelphous; style glabrous; fruits compressed, oblong-elliptic, long-stipitate and shortly beaked, 1-locular, 2-valved, continuous within, 2–1-seeded, valves at length separating into 2 distinct layers, the inner very thin and membranous and containing the broadly kidney-shaped seeds with a deep-set hilum extending about two-thirds the length of the seed.

248. **Cracca** Benth. ex Oersted, Kjöbenhavn Vid. Meddel. 8 (1853) (conserved name). *Benthamantha* Alef. (1862). *Brittonamra* O. Ktze. (1891). 10 spp., N. Cent. and trop. America, West Indies; lectotype *C. glandulifera* Benth., Ecuador. B.H. 1: 501; E.P. 3, 3: 277; Burkart, Legum. Argent. ed. 2: 262, fig. 72 (as *Benthamantha*).

Perennial herbs; leaves imparipinnate; leaflets with stipels; stipules setaceous; racemes axillary; flowers yellowish or whitish; pedicels solitary in the setaceous bracts; bracteoles absent; calyx-lobes subequal, setaceous-acuminate; petals subequal in length; vexillum orbicular or reniform, with reflexed sides; wings obovate-oblong, free; keel broad, incurved, acute or subrostrate; vexillary stamen free, remainder connate into a sheath;

[1] Synonyms of **Sesbania**: *Sesban* Adans. (1763). *Sesbana* R.Br. (1812). *Agati* Adans. (1813). *Darwinia* Raf. (1817). *Monoplectra* Raf. (1817). *Daubentonia* DC. (1825). *Resupinaria* Raf. (1838). *Moniligera* Taub. (1889). *Emerus* O. Ktze. (1891). *Daubentoniopsis* Rydb. (1923).

ovary sessile; ovules numerous; style rigid, incurved, barbate in the upper part inside; stigma capitate; fruit linear, compressed, 2-valved, transversely septate between the seeds, constricted with transverse lines outside; seed subquadrate, without a strophiole.

249. **Poissonia** Baill., Adansonia 9: 295 (1870). *Chiovendaea* Speg. (1916). 3 spp., Peru, Argentina; type *P. orbicularis* (Benth.) Haum. (*P. solanacea* Baill.), Peru. E.P. 3, 3: 273; Hauman, Kew Bull. 1925: 279; Burkart, Legum. Argent. ed. 2: 260, fig. 71.

Undershrubs, grey-tomentose all over; leaves alternate, petiolate, 1-foliolate; leaflet obovate or ovate, pinnately nerved, jointed at the base; stipules 2, linear-subulate; flowers axillary, solitary; pedicels reflexed after flowering; flowers resupinate; calyx obconic-turbinate, lined inside by a fleshy disk, deeply 5-lobed; lobes long-subulate, subequal, the posterior 2 connate high up, imbricate; petals clawed; vexillum suborbicular, wings obliquely obovate; keel incurved, rather obtuse; stamens 10, in 2 bundles (9 and 1); anthers uniform; ovary very shortly stipitate; ovules numerous; style incurved, clothed below the stigma with a dense mass of short pyriform hairs; stigma capitate; fruit shortly stipitate, with the persistent calyx at the base, compressed, depressed with oblique lines between the seeds, locellate within; seeds transversely obovate, compressed, funicle short.

250. **Neocracca** O. Ktze., Rev. Gen. Plant. 3, 2: 68 (1898). 1s p., *N. heterantha* (Griseb.) Speg., Bolivia, Argentina. Burkart, Legum. Argent. ed. 2, 260, fig. 71, N (1952).

Herb, stemless, with a thick tap-root, villous; leaves imparipinnate; leaflets 5–7, obovate to orbicular; stipules elongate-linear or filiform; stipels absent; peduncles elongate, white-villous and with stipitate glands, 3–4-flowered; flowers cleistogamous and normal, 1–3 axillary; calyx-tube short, cupular, teeth lanceolate-subulate, upper 2 connate high up; corolla blue; vexillum very shortly clawed, reniform-orbicular, wings obliquely clawed, auriculate on one side, keel-petals cohering in the upper part; vexillary stamen free, 9 remainder connate; ovary very shortly stipitate, linear, covered with glands, many-ovulate; style inflexed and curved, lower part glabrous, upper part pilose on adaxial side only, stigma capitellate; fruit linear, flattened, densely white-villous and covered with stipitate glands transversely septate; seeds several.

Tribe 27. GALEGEAE

Benth. & Hook. f., Gen. Pl. 1: 443 (1865) (as to Subtribe *Tephrosieae* (partly, p. 444))

Perennial herbs, erect; leaves imparipinnate, leaflets entire, venose; stipules sagittate or foliaceous; flowers white or blue, in axillary and terminal racemes; bracts narrow, often persistent; bracteoles absent; calyx-teeth subequal; vexillum obovate-oblong, narrowed into a short claw; wings oblong, slightly adherent to the keel; keel slightly incurved, obtuse; stamens all connate into a closed tube; anthers uniform or alternately slightly smaller; ovary sessile; style subulate, incurved, not barbate; stigma small, terminal; ovules numerous; fruit linear, subterete, tipped by the style, 2-valved, continuous within, valves slender, obliquely striate; seeds transversely oblong, without a strophiole. Type genus *Galega* Linn.

251. **Galega** Linn., Sp. Pl. 714 (1753). *Callotropis* G. Don (1832). *Accorombona* Endl. (1841). 8 spp., S. Europe, W. Asia, E. trop. Africa; type *G. officinalis* Linn., Europe, W. Asia. B.H. 1: 496; E.P. 3, 3: 268; Gams in Hegi, Ill. Fl. Mitt.-Eur. 4, 3: 1387, figs. 1446, 1607; J. B. Gillett, *Galega* in trop. Afr., Kew Bull. 17: 81. *Characters of the tribe.*

Tribe 28. DIPHYSEAE[1]

Subtribe *Diphysanae* Rydb., N. Amer. Fl. 24: 209 (1924).

Trees and shrubs, sometimes spiny; leaves imparipinnate; stipules caducous; *stipels absent*; flowers in *axillary* racemes or fascicles; pedicels jointed; bracteoles 2, caducous; calyx 5-lobed, lobes unequal, the upper 2 broader and united higher up; corolla papilionaceous; vexillary filament free, the remainder connate into a sheath split adaxially; *anthers uniform*; fruit stipitate, elongated, *pericarp separating into 2 layers*; endocarp chartaceous, forming a flattened loculus somewhat interrupted between the seeds; exocarp papery, reticulate, *inflated and forming 2 elongated bladders*, one on each side of the pod; seeds compressed. Type genus *Diphysa* Jacq.

252. **Diphysa** Jacq., Enum. Pl. Carib. 7 (1760). About 18 spp., Mexico, Cent. America, South America; type *D. carthagenensis* Jacq., Mexico to Colombia. B.H. 1: 500; E.P. 3, 3: 276.

Trees or shrubs, often glandular, sometimes spiny; leaves imparipinnate, leaflets entire, not glandular, without stipels; stipules small; racemes short, lax, axillary or fasciculate at the older nodes; flowers yellow; pedicels solitary, jointed below the calyx and with 2 caducous bracteoles; calyx turbinate at the base, upper 2 lobes broad, obtuse, lowest longer than the rest, acute; vexillum clawed, orbicular, reflexed, with 2 callosities inside; wings obovate or oblong, very incurved; keel arcuate, often beaked; vexillary stamen free, remainder connate into a sheath split above; anthers uniform; ovary stipitate; ovules numerous; style much incurved, subulate, glabrous, stigma small, terminal; fruit stipitate, elongated, endocarp nearly flat, exocarp inflated on each face into a membranous reticulate bladder, sutures keeled-subwinged or nude, valves closely cohering inside between the seeds; seeds transversely oblong or ovate, compressed.

Tribe 29. COLUTEAE

Tribe *Galegeae* Subtribe *Coluteae* Benth. & Hook. f., Gen. Pl. 1: 446 (1865); Rydb., Fl. N. Amer. 24: 249 (also as Subtribe)

Shrubs or herbs; leaves imparipinnate, rarely 1-foliolate, rarely reduced to scales; leaflets entire; *stipels absent; flowers in axillary sometimes pendulous racemes*; bracts and bracteoles small or absent; calyx-teeth subequal or upper 2 shorter; corolla papilionaceous, vexillum often sharply reflexed; *vexillary stamen free*, remainder connate into a split sheath; *anthers uniform*, muticous; ovules several, rarely few or 2; *style barbate along the inner (adaxial) side or near the apex, rarely glabrous*; fruit *inflated and membranous or turgid*, usually *indehiscent*, rarely 2-valved or only so at the apex; seeds reniform, with a filiform funicle but *no strophiole*. Old World. Type genus *Colutea* Linn.

[1] **Diphyseae** trib. nov. Arbores vel frutices, interdum spinosi; folia imparipinnata; stipulae caducae; stipellae nullae; flores in racemis axillaribus vel fasciculatis dispositi; pedicelli articulati; bracteolae 2, caducae; calyx 5-lobatus, lobis inaequalibus 2 superioribus latioribus et connatis; corolla papilionacea; stamen vexillare liberum; cetera in vaginam supra fissam connata; fructus stipitatus, elongatus, endocarpio subplano, exocarpio ad utramque faciem in membranam reticulatam vesiculosam vel compresso-carinatam inflato, suturis carinato-subalatis vel nudis; semina compressa.

Vexillum long-acuminate; flowers large and very showy, pendulous;
  leaves imparipinnate, leaflets numerous, entire   253. **Clianthus**
Vexillum not long-acuminate:
 Leaves pinnate or pinnately 3-foliolate:
  Style with a strongly hooked persistent tip, bearded along the upper
    (adaxial) face; fruit membranous, inflated, indehiscent or 2-valved only
    at the apex   254. **Colutea**
  Style not hooked at the tip:
   Style bearded with hairs on the upper (adaxial) face; fruit inflated:
    Seed-bearing suture not intruded into the oblong-ellipsoid fruit; S.
      Africa   255. **Sutherlandia**
    Seed-bearing suture slightly intruded into the fruit; fruit subglobose;
      Asia   256. **Sphaerophysa**
   Style bearded only around the stigma:
    Seed-bearing suture not intruded into the loculus; S. Africa and S. trop.
      Africa   257. **Lessertia**
    Seed-bearing suture sometimes intruded into the loculus; Australia
                                                            258. **Swainsona**
   Style glabrous; leaves imparipinnate, leaflets 3–5, opposite; ovary long-
     stipitate, 2-ovuled   259. **Neodielsia**
 Leaves 1-foliolate; fruit inflated   260. **Smirnowia**
 Leaves reduced to scales; style bearded lengthwise below the stigma; fruit
   thin, almost flat, not inflated, 2-valved   261. **Eremosparton**

253. **Clianthus** Banks & Solander ex G. Don, Gen. Hist. 2: 468 (1832) (conserved name). *Sarcodum* Lour. (1790). *Donia* G. Don (1832), not R.Br.
(1813). *Eremocharis* R.Br. (1849). 8 spp., New Zealand, Australia, Malaya,
Philippines, Indo-China; type *C. puniceus* (G. Don) Banks & Solander, New
Zealand. B.H. 1: 503; E.P. 3, 3: 279; Allan, Fl. New Zeal. 1: 368.

Ascending herbs or undershrubs or semiscandent, glabrous or villous; leaves imparipinnate, leaflets numerous, entire, without stipels; stipules herbaceous; flowers large, red or
white, pendulous in axillary short or umbel-like racemes; bracts and bracteoles subpersistent; calyx-lobes or teeth subequal or upper 2 broader at the base; vexillum acuminate,
sharply reflexed above the calyx; wings shorter than the vexillum, falcate-lanceolate; keel
erect, incurved, acute, subequal to the vexillum; vexillary stamen free, remainder connate
into a sheath; anthers uniform; ovary stipitate; style subulate, incurved, longitudinally
bearded inside the upper part, stigma terminal, minute; ovules numerous; fruit turgid,
oblong, acuminate, incurved, 2-valved; seeds reniform, without a strophiole.

254. **Colutea** Linn., Sp. Pl. 723 (1753). *Oreophysa* Bornm. (1905). About 25
spp., S. Europe to W. Himalayas and NE. Africa; type *C. arborescens* Linn.,
Europe, Orient. B.H. 1: 505; E.P. 3, 3: 281; Browicz, Kew Bull. 16: 493.

Shrubs or shrublets; leaves imparipinnate or rarely trifoliolate; leaflets entire, without
stipels; stipules small; flowers yellow or reddish, in axillary racemes; bracts and bracteoles
very small or absent; calyx-teeth subequal or upper 2 shorter; vexillum suborbicular,
spreading, with 2 folds or callosities above the claw; wings falcate-oblong, with short
claws; keel broad, much incurved, obtuse, with long connate claws; vexillary stamen free,
remainder connate into a sheath; anthers uniform; ovary stipitate; style incurved, barbate
along the inner side, inflexed at the apex or involute, the stigma thick and prominent
below the apex; fruit stipitate, inflated and membranous, indehiscent or 2-valved at the
apex; seeds reniform, estrophiolate, with a filiform funicle.

255. **Sutherlandia** R.Br., Ait. Hort. Kew. ed. 2, 4: 327 (1812) (conserved name). *Colutia* Medik. (1789). 1 sp., *S. frutescens* (Linn.) R.Br., S. Africa. B.H. 1: 503; E.P. 3, 3: 280.

Canescent shrub; leaves imparipinnate; leaflets numerous, entire, without stipels; stipules small, narrow; flowers showy, scarlet, few in short axillary racemes; bracts small; bracteoles minute; calyx-teeth subequal; vexillum erect, spreading at the apex, margins replicate, claw short; wings small, oblong; keel erect, incurved, longer than the vexillum; vexillary stamen free, remainder connate into a sheath; anthers uniform; ovary stipitate; style filiform, incurved, barbate along the inner (adaxial) side; stigma minute, terminal; ovules numerous; fruit oblong-ellipsoid, membranous, much inflated, subindehiscent; seeds reniform, without a strophiole, funicle filiform.

256. **Sphaerophysa** DC., Mém. Légum. 288 (1825); Prodr. 2: 270 (1825). 3 spp., SW. Asia to China; type *S. salsula* DC., N. Asia and China. B.H. 1: 504; E.P. 3, 3: 281 (in *Swainsona*).

Perennial herbs or shrublets; leaves imparipinnate, leaflets 3 to numerous, entire, exstipellate; stipules small; flowers in axillary racemes; calyx-tube subequal or upper 2 close together; vexillum orbicular, sides reflexed, nude inside; wings falcate-oblong; keel incurved at the apex, obtuse; vexillary stamen free, remainder connate into a sheath; anthers uniform; ovary stipitate, many-ovuled; style incurved, longitudinally bearded on the adaxial side; stigma terminal, capitate, oblique; fruit long-stipitate, inflated, membranous or coriaceous, subglobose, scarcely dehiscent, seed-bearing suture slightly intruded; seeds reniform, estrophiolate, funicle shortly filiform.

257. **Lessertia** DC., Astrag. 47 (1802); Prodr. 2: 271 (1825). *Sulitra* Medik. (1787). *Sutera* Hort. ex Steud. (1821). *Coluteastrum* O. Ktze. (1891). About 50 spp., S. and trop. Africa; lectotype *L. perennans* DC., S. Africa, Rhodesia. B.H. 1: 503; E.P. 3, 3: 280; L. Bolus, Ann. Bolus Herb. 1: 93 (1915); Phillips, Gen. S. Afr. Fl. Pl. ed. 2: 416.

Undershrubs or herbs, wooly-pubescent or rarely glabrous; leaves imparipinnate; leaflets entire, without stipels; stipules small; flowers rose or red, rarely white, in pedunculate axillary racemes; bracts small; bracteoles minute or absent; calyx-teeth or lobes subequal; vexillum suborbicular, spreading or reflexed, nude inside, claw short; wings oblong, keel straight or incurved, obtuse, often shorter than the vexillum, vexillary stamen free, remainder connate into a sheath; anthers uniform; ovary subsessile or stipitate; style incurved, subulate, barbate below the stigma at the back or all around, nude inside or rarely shortly barbate; ovules numerous; fruit ovate, oblong or broadly linear, thinly membranous, inflated or compressed, gaping at length at the apex or sub-2-valved; seeds reniform, without a strophiole, funicle filiform.

258. **Swainsona** Salisb., Parad. Londin., t. 28 (1806). *Loxidium* Vent. (1808). *Phyllolobium* Fisch. ex DC. (1825). *Cyclogyne* Benth. (1839). *Diplolobium* F. Muell. (1863). About 55 spp., Australia, New Zealand; type *S. galegifolia* (Andr.) R.Br. (*S. coronillifolia* Salisb.), Australia. B.H. 1: 504; E.P. 3, 3: 281; A. T. Lee, Contrib. New South Wales Herb. 1: 131 (1948) (revision); Allan, Fl. New Zeal. 1: 367.

Undershrubs or herbs, glabrous or with adpressed hairs; leaves imparipinnate; leaflets numerous, entire, without stipels; stipules often herbaceous, broad at the base, rarely setaceous; flowers blue-violet, purple, red, or rarely white or yellow, in axillary racemes; bracts membranous, often narrow or small; bracteoles small or absent, sometimes adpressed to the calyx-tube; calyx-teeth subequal or upper 2 shorter; vexillum orbicular or reniform, spreading or reflexed, with 2 short callosities above the claw inside, or nude; wings oblong, falcate or subtwisted, often shorter than the keel; keel broad, incurved, obtuse or produced into a twisted beak; vexillary stamen free, remainder connate into a sheath; anthers uniform; ovary sessile or stipitate; style incurved, subulate or inflexed at the apex or involute, barbate lengthwise inside the upper part or rarely on the back, stigma terminal; ovules numerous; fruit ovoid or oblong, turgid or inflated, coriaceous or membranous, 2-valved or subindehiscent, undivided inside or the seed-bearing suture more or less intrusive, longitudinally 2-locular; seeds subreniform, without a strophiole.

259. **Neodielsia** Harms, Engl. Bot. Jahrb. 36: Beibl. 82: 68 (1905). 1 sp., *N. polyantha* Harms, China.

Herb; leaves imparipinnate; leaflets 3–5, opposite; stipules lanceolate, membranous; racemes elongated, many-flowered, slender, axillary and crowded at the apex of the stem and branchlets; calyx tubular-cylindric, mouth obliquely truncate, minutely 5-denticulate; corolla exceeding the calyx, petals almost equal in length; vexillum obovate-oblong, clawed, slightly emarginate; wings and keel clawed; stamens 10, vexillary one only united with the others in the middle, otherwise free; disk very short, surrounding the stipe of the ovary, mouth obliquely truncate; ovary long-stipitate, 2-ovuled, sometimes constricted between the ovules; style with a scarcely distinct stigma; young fruit long-stipitate, compressed, flat, oblong or narrowly elliptic, 1–2-seeded.

260. **Smirnowia** Bunge, Act. Hort. Petrop. 4: 339 (1876). 1 sp., *S. turkestana* Bunge, Turkestan. E.P. 3, 3: 281.

Shrub with very long filiform sparsely leafy branches; leaves unifoliolate, exstipulate, jointed at the base, deciduous, leaflet rounded-obovate; racemes short, few-flowered; calyx bilabiate, 5-lobed, 2-bracteolate; vexillum with very resupinate limb, not callous at the base; keel obtuse; stamens diadelphous; ovary shortly stipitate, many-ovuled style inflexed, terete, densely bearded behind the apex; stigma terminal, subcapitate; fruit large and bladdery, deeply sulcate on each side, dorsal suture concave, ventral suture produced within into an incomplete dissepiment, several-seeded; seeds flattened, reniform, smooth.

261. **Eremosparton** Fisch. & Mey., Enum. Pl. Schrenk 1: 75 (1841). 4–5 spp., SW. Asia; type *E. aphyllum* Fisch. & Mey., Caspian Sea, Turkestan. B.H. 1: 504; E.P. 3, 3: 280.

Low shrubs, with leafless juncus-like branches, the leaves reduced to scales at the nodes; flowers small, violet, racemose; racemes elongated, pedunculate at the axils of the scales; bracts small; bracteoles minute towards the apex of the pedicels; calyx-teeth subequal; vexillum broadly orbicular, emarginate, subreflexed, nude inside, claw short; wings falcate-oblong; keel much incurved, rather obtuse; vexillary stamen free, remainder connate; anthers uniform; ovary sessile; style incurved, longitudinally bearded on the back in the upper part, stigma terminal; ovules numerous; fruit broadly falcate-ovate, membranous, planocompressed or at length turgid, 2-valved; seeds often 1 or 2, reniform, without a strophiole.

Tribe 30. ASTRAGALEAE

Adans., Fam. 2: 324 (1763). Tribe *Galegeae* Subtribe *Astragaleae*
Benth. & Hook. f., Gen. Pl. 1: 446 (1865)

Herbs, shrubs, or rarely trees; leaves pari- or imparipinnate, very rarely digitately 3–5-foliolate or 1-foliolate; stipules present; *stipels absent*; inflorescence or solitary flowers *always axillary*; corolla papilionaceous; vexillum erect, with reflexed sides; stamens *diadelphous, vexillary filament free,* remainder connate into a sheath split adaxially; *anthers uniform*, muticous, loculi separate at the apex or rarely confluent, very rarely only 5 perfect anthers; ovules several to numerous; *style glabrous*; *fruit inflated*, 2-valved or indehiscent, turgid, or rarely compressed, mostly *longitudinally septate* or partly so by the *intrusion of the seed-bearing suture*; seeds estrophiolate. Type genus *Astragalus* Linn.

Anther-loculi separated at the apex:
  Trees or shrubs with paripinnate leaves:
    Fruit obovoid or oblong, obtuse, very turgid; peduncles umbellately 2–3-flowered or flowers fasciculate at the older nodes; leaf-rhachis ending in a spine   262. **Halimodendron**
    Fruit linear, at length terete or turgid, often acute, peduncles usually 1-flowered; leaf-rhachis often ending in a spine   263. **Caragana**
  Herbs, undershrubs, or much-branched small shrubs with imparipinnate leaves, or the leaf-rhachis ending in a spine, rarely digitately 3-foliolate:
    Fruit not divided lengthwise into separate loculi, linear or oblong:
      Leaves pinnate or 1-foliolate (very rarely 3-foliolate); stipules free:
        Keel subequal to the wing-petals:
          Shrubs; stipules membranous; flowers in short racemes; ovary sessile, stipitate-glandular   264. **Calophaca**
          Herbs; stipules foliaceous; peduncles axillary, 1–3-flowered; ovary not glandular   265. **Chesneya**
        Keel less than half as long as the wing-petals; stipules adnate to the petiole or free; ovary sessile   266. **Gueldenstaedtia**
      Leaves ternate; keel- and wing-petals equally long; stipules adnate to the petiole; ovary stipitate   267. **Kostyczewa**
    Fruit divided inside lengthwise by septa or if undivided then often ovoid or globose or rarely elongated:
      Keel-petals obtuse:
        Keel of the fruit armed with 2-forked tipped spines   269. **Sewerzowia**
        Keel of the fruit not spiny, at most sinuate-dentate:
          Calyx-teeth subequal; fruit not didymous:
            Fruit dehiscent; stamens with 10 fertile anthers   268. **Astragalus**
            Fruit indehiscent; stamens with only 5 fertile anthers   271. **Biserrula**
          Calyx-teeth unequal, upper smaller; fruit didymous, on a filiform stipe   270. **Didymopelta**
      Keel-petals mucronate or acuminate or with a recurved apex   272. **Oxytropis**
Anther-loculi confluent at the apex:
  Perennial herbs, often glandular; anthers alternately unequal   273. **Glycyrrhiza**
  Tall tree; anthers equal; leaves and fruit glandular   274. **Cascaronia**

262. **Halimodendron** Fisch. ex DC., Mém. Légum. 283 (1825). *Halodendron* DC. (1825). 1 sp., *M. argenteum* Fisch. ex DC., Transcaucasia to Altai. B.H. 1: 505; E.P. 3, 3: 283.

Shrub with long and short shoots, the latter in the axils of the previous season's spinescent rhachis; leaves paripinnate, leaflets towards the apex of the spinescent rhachis; stipules subulate-spinescent from a broad base; flowers violet, rather large, on axillary peduncles or fasciculate at the older nodes; bracts small; bracteoles minute; calyx gibbous at the back, teeth short, upper 2 close together; vexillum suborbicular, sides replicate; wings falcate-oblong, free; keel incurved, obtuse; vexillary stamen free, remainder connate into a sheath; anthers uniform; ovary stipitate; style inflexed, not bearded; stigma small, terminal; ovules numerous; fruit stipitate-obovoid or oblong, very turgid, thickly coriaceous, seed-bearing suture slightly impressed, tardily dehiscent; seeds subreniform, shining, without a strophiole.

263. **Caragana** Lam., Encycl. 1: 615 (1783). *Aspalathus* O. Ktze. (1891). About 80 spp., E. Europe, Asia, and China; lectotype *C. arborescens* Lam., N. Asia. B.H. 1: 505; E.P. 3, 3: 283.

Trees or shrubs; leaves paripinnate, often fasciculate, rhachis terminated by a sharp point or spinescent; leaflets entire, without stipels; stipules subulate or spinescent or minute; flowers yellow or rarely whitish-red, peduncles 1-flowered or rarely umbellately 2–3-flowered, fasciculate at the older nodes or axillary at the base of the young shoots; bracts and bracteoles often subulate; calyx subgibbous at the back, teeth subequal or the upper 2 smaller; vexillum ovate or suborbicular, erect-patent, sides replicate, narrowed into a claw; wings obliquely oblong, free; keel nearly straight, obtuse; vexillary stamen free, remainder connate; anthers uniform; ovary subsessile; style straight or slightly incurved, not barbate, stigma small, terminal; fruit sessile, linear, at length terete or turgid, often acute, 2-valved, villous inside or nude; seeds transversely oblong or subglobose, without a strophiole.

264. **Calophaca** Fisch., Cat. Jard. Gorenki 67 (1812). 4 spp., S. Russia to N. Asia; type *C. wolgarica* Fisch., S. Russia, N. Asia. B.H. 1: 505; E.P. 3, 3: 284 (excl. Sect. *Chesneya*).

Shrubs; leaves imparipinnate, leaflets entire, without stipels; stipules large, membranous; flowers few, rather large, yellow or violet, shortly racemose; bracts and bracteoles rarely persistent; calyx tubular, lobes subequal or upper 2 connate high up; vexillum ovate or suborbicular, erect-patent, sides replicate; wings obovate-oblong, subfalcate, free; keel incurved, subequal to the wings; vexillary stamen free; remainder connate; anthers uniform, orbicular; ovary sessile; style filiform, glabrous, stigma small, terminal; ovules numerous; fruit stipitate-glandular when young, linear, at length terete or turgid, often acute, 2-valved, undivided within, thinly filled; seeds subreniform, without a strophiole.

265. **Chesneya** Lindl. ex Endl., Gen. 1275 (1839). 18 spp., Armenia to Mongolia, Himalayas; lectotype *C. rytidosperma* Jaub. & Spach. Jaub. & Spach, Ill. 1: 93, tt. 47, 48 (1942).

Herbs, woody at the base or cushion-shaped, stems diffuse; leaves imparipinnate, rarely pinnately trifoliolate, leaflets entire; stipels foliaceous; stipels absent; peduncles axillary, 1–3-flowered; calyx tubular, subbilabiate, upper lip 2-toothed, lower a little longer, trifid; corolla elongated; vexillum ovate, retuse, hairy, a little longer than the obtuse keel and wings; stamens diadelphous, vexillary free, remainder connate; anthers uniform; ovary sessile, several ovuled; style hairy below, stigma capitate, papillous; fruit not glandular, oblong-linear, subcompressed, undivided inside; seeds reniform.

266. **Gueldenstaedtia** Fisch., Mém. Soc. Nat. Moscow 6: 170 (1823). *Guldenstaedtia* Dumort. (1829). *Guldaenstedtia* A. Juss. (1849). *Amblyotropis* Kitagawa (1936). 20 spp., E. and Cent. Asia, Himalayas; type *G. asiatica* Fisch., Cent. Asia. B.H. 1: 506; E.P. 3, 3: 284.

Perennial herbs, decumbent or subacaulescent, with a thick sometimes tuber-like root-stock; leaves imparipinnate or 1-foliolate, leaflets entire, without stipels; stipules adnate to the petiole or free; flowers mostly violet, subumbellate on axillary peduncles or rarely solitary; upper 2 calyx-teeth broader; vexillum obovate or orbicular, erect-patent; wings obovate-oblong, free; keel more than half shorter than the vexillum and wings, obtuse; vexillary stamen free, remainder connate; anthers uniform; ovary sessile; style short, inflexed, subinvolute at the apex, not barbate, stigma broad, terminal; ovules numerous; fruit linear or rarely ovoid, terete or turgid, undivided inside, 2-valved; seeds subreniform, scrobiculate or smooth.

267. **Kostyczewa** Korshinsky, Mém. Acad. St. Petersb. 8, sér. 4, n. 4: 91, t. 2 (1896). 2 spp., W. Asia; type *K. ternata* Korshinsky, Turkestan. E.P. Nachtr. 3, 3: 166 (1906).

Perennial herbs, shrubby at the base, with woody rhizome; leaves ternate, long-petiolate, leaflets entire, without stipels; stipules triangular-lanceolate, united at the base to the petiole, persistent; flowers solitary, axillary; calyx tubular, teeth short, almost alike but the lower smaller; petals somewhat exceeding the calyx, vexillum small, obovate-oblanceolate, clawed; wings and keel very long-clawed, oblong, equally long; vexillary stamens free, the others united; anthers uniform; ovary stipitate; ovules numerous in 2 rows; style subulate, hairy; stigma small; fruit lanceolate or linear-lanceolate, stipitate, turgid, 2-valved, the valves spirally twisted when open, with thin transverse walls between the seeds; seeds 8–12, almost kidney-shaped; testa smooth, chestnut-brown.

268. **Astragalus**[1] Linn., Sp. Pl. 755 (1753). About 1,500 spp., northern parts of northern hemisphere, South America (mountains and extratropical), SE. Africa; type *A. christianus* Linn., E. Mediterr. B.H. 1: 506; E.P. 3, 3: 285. Bunge, Generis *Astragali* species gerontogeae, Mém. Acad. Sci. St. Petersb., sér. 7, 11: n. 16 (1868); Jones, Review of N. Amer. Species (1923); Peter-Stibal, Review of Chinese Species, Acta Horti Gotoburg. 12: 21 (1937–8); Wheeler, *Astragalus* versus *Oxytropis*, Leaflets Western Bot. 2: 209 (1939); Burkart, Legum. Argent. ed. 2: 272, fig. 80 (1952); Gams in Hegi, Ill. Fl. Mitt.-Eur. 4, 3: 1402, figs. 1459–96, t. 167 (col.).

Shrublets, undershrubs, or herbs, sometimes with indurated spinescent petioles; leaves imparipinnate, rarely digitately 3-foliolate or 1-foliolate, leaflets entire, without stipels;

[1] Synonyms of **Astragalus**: *Tragacantha* Tourn. ex Linn. (1735). *Phaca* Linn. (1753). *Astragaloides* Adans. (1763). *Hippomanica* Molina (1782). *Contortuplicata, Glandula, Glaux, Glottis, Hamosa, Onix, Stella, Tium, Triquetra, Glottes, Onyx,* all of Medik. (1787). *Aragallus* Neck. (1790). *Phyllobium* Fisch. ex Spreng. (1818). *Thium* Steud. (1821). *Alopecias, Ammodytes, Anaphragma, Caryolobium, Chondrocarpos, Craccina, Cymbicarpus, Cystium, Euprepia, Glycyphylla Macrosema, Myobroma, Philammos, Physondra, Picraena, Psorelias, Psychridium, Rysodium, Saccocalyx, Solenotus,* all of Stev. (1832). *Erophaca* Boiss. (1839). *Podolotus* Royle (1839). *Aragus* Steud. (1840). *Homolobus* Nutt. ex Torr. & Gray (1840). *Kentrophyta* Nutt. ex Torr. & Gray. *Orophaca* Torr. & Gray (1840). *Centrophyta* Reichb. (1841). *Aulosema* Walp. (1842). *Diplotheca* Hochst. (1846). *Ailuroschia* Stev. (1856). *Ankylobus* Stev. (1856). *Enilus* Stev. (1856). *Feidanthus* Stev. (1856). *Hedyphylla* Stev. (1856). *Pedina* Stev. (1856). *Xerophysa* Stev. (1856). *Kirchnera* Opiz (1858). *Medyphylla* Opiz (1858). *Diphtherophorus* Bunge (1868). *Hamaria* Fourr. (1868). *Hypoglottis* Fourr. (1868). *Onobrychium* Bunge (1868). *Podochrea* Fourr. (1868). *Xeiophilus* Bunge (1868). *Macrophyllum* Boiss. (1872). *Rhabdotus* Boiss. (1872). *Ctenophyllum* Rydb. (1903). *Geoprummon* Rydb. (1903). *Cnemidophacos* Rydb. (1905). *Diholcos* Rydb. (1905). *Hesperastragalus* A. Heller (1905). *Orophaca* Britton (1913). *Rydbergiella* Fedde & Sydow (1917). *Atelopragma, Batidophaca, Brachyphragma, Cnemidophragma, Gynophoraria, Hesperonix, Holcophacos, Jonesiella, Lonchophaca, Microphacos, Phacomene, Phacopsis, Pisophaca, Pterophacos, Xylophacos,* all of Rydb. (1929). *Acanthophaca, Astenolobium, Cryptorrhynchus, Hali, Lithoon, Mystirophora, Oedicephalus, Oxyglottis, Poecilocarpus,* all of Nevski (1937). *Kiapasia* Woronow (1939).

stipules free or adnate to the petiole, or connate into one opposite the leaf; flowers violet or purple to white or pale yellow, racemose, spicate or very rarely umbellate or solitary; peduncles axillary or arising from the rootstock; bracts often small, membranous; bracteoles very small or absent, rarely larger; calyx tubular, teeth subequal; petals often with long claws; vexillum erect, ovate, oblong or pandurate, wings oblong; keel equal to the wings or a little shorter, substraight, obtuse; vexillary stamen free, remainder connate; anthers uniform; ovary sessile or stipitate; style filiform, straight or incurved, not barbate, stigma small, terminal; fruit sessile or stipitate, 2-valved, sometimes imperfectly divided into 2 loculi by an intrusive membrane from the dorsal (lower) suture, or very turgid or membranous-inflated and imperfectly divided inside, or the seed-bearing suture intrusive and forming 2 loculi; seed often reniform, without a strophiole, funicle filiform.

269. Sewerzowia Regel & Schmalh., Act. Hort. Petrop. 5: 580 (1877). 1 sp., S. turkestanica Regel & Schmalh., Turkestan. E.P. 3, 3: 284.

Annual erect herb; leaves imparipinnate; stipules free, subulate; stipels absent; flowers small, in axillary racemes, few to several; calyx tubular, teeth subulate; petals rather long-clawed; vexillum erect, truncate at the apex; wings oblong; keel straight, obtuse, a little shorter than the wings; stamens 10, vexillary free, remainder connate; ovary sessile, many-ovuled; style short, stigma capitate, terminal; fruit elliptic, 3-angled, flat on the back, ventrally keeled, with a double septum intruded from the dorsal suture dividing the loculus into two; membrane of the septum at first closely connate, in the mature fruit breaking away from the dorsal suture; valves boat-shaped, keels spinous with 2-forked tipped spines; seeds compressed, reniform-ovate.

270. Didymopelta Regel & Schmalh., Act. Hort. Petrop. 5: 669 (1877). Dipelta Regel & Schmalh. (1877). 1 sp., D. turkestanica Regel & Schmalh., Turkestan. E.P. 3, 3: 284.

Tiny annual herb, hairs simple, adpressed; leaves imparipinnate; flowers racemose; calyx campanulate-tubular, teeth subulate, upper smaller; petals clawed; vexillum erect, bilobed, lobes rounded; wings oblong; keel straight, obtuse, a little longer than the wings; stamens 10, vexillary free, remainder connate; ovary stipitate, 4-ovuled; style filiform, stigma capitate; fruit didymous on a filiform stipe, flattened, with a narrow double septum intruded from the dorsal suture dividing the fruit into two 2-seeded loculi; valves boat-shaped, quadrate-ovate, compressed, equal or unequal, margin entire, often falling off from the mature fruit; seeds reniform, compressed; cotyledons flat.

271. Biserrula Linn., Sp. Pl. 762 (1753). Pelecinus Medik. (1787). 1 sp., B. pelecinus Linn., Madeira, Canary Isls., Mediterr. reg., NE. trop. Africa. B.H. 1: 507; E.P. 3, 3: 307; Gillett, Kew Bull. 1964: ined.

A spreading pubescent herb; leaves imparipinnate, leaflets numerous, emarginate, without stipels; stipules membranous; flowers small, bluish, in short axillary spikes; calyx-lobes subequal; petals shortly clawed; vexillum erect, oblong; wings falcate-oblong, free; keel subequal to the wings, obtuse; fertile stamens 5, vexillary free, remainder connate; anthers uniform; ovary sessile; style short, rather thick, incurved, stigma capitate, terminal; ovules numerous; fruit linear, indehiscent, flattened at the back, divided inside by a very narrow longitudinal septum connecting the sutures; 'valves' boat-shaped-compressed, keeled, sinuate-dentate; seeds orbicular-reniform, without a strophiole.

272. Oxytropis DC., Astrag. 24 and 26, tt. 2–6 and 8 (1802) (conserved name). Spiesia Neck. (1790). Calycophysa A. Gray (1866). Physocalyx Nutt. (1866). About 300 spp., Europe, Asia, North America, type O. montana (Linn.) DC., Europe. B.H. 1: 507; E.P. 3, 3: 304; Fernald, The genus Oxytropis in NE. Amer., Rhodora, 30: 137 (1928); Wheeler, Astragalus versus Oxytropis,

Leafl. West. Bot. 2: 209 (1939); Barneby, Proc. Calif. Acad. Sci. 27: 177 (1952) (revision of Amer. spp.).

Shrublets or herbs, sometimes the petioles hardened and spinescent; leaves imparipinnate, leaflets entire, without stipels; stipules adnate to the petiole or free; flowers violet, purple, white, or pale yellow, in axillary racemes or spikes or arising from the caudex; bracts often small, membranous; bracteoles minute or absent; calyx tubular, teeth subequal; petals often with rather long claws; vexillum erect, ovate or oblong; wings oblong; keel equal to the wings or shorter, erect, appendaged at the apex with an erect or recurved subdorsal acumen or mucro; vexillary stamen free, remainder connate; anthers uniform; ovary sessile or stipitate; style filiform, straight or incurved, not barbate, stigma minute, terminal; fruit sessile or stipitate, rather turgid, 2-valved, the seed-bearing suture often more or less intruded, otherwise undivided; seeds reniform, without a strophiole, funicle filiform.

273. **Glycyrrhiza** Linn., Sp. Pl. 741 (1753). *Liquiritia* Medik. (1787). *Glicirrhiza* Necca (1793). *Meristotropis* Fisch. & Mey. (1844). *Clidanthera* R.Br. (1849). *Glycyrrhizopsis* Boiss. (1856). About 30 spp., Mediterr. reg., temp. and subtrop. Asia, Australia, NW. and South America exclud. tropics; type *G. glabra* Linn., Mediterr. reg., Orient. B.H. 1: 508; E.P. 3, 3: Burkart, Legum. Argent. ed. 2: 270, fig. 78; Gams in Hegi, Ill. Fl. Mitt.-Eur. 4, 3: 1453, fig. 1497.

Perennial herbs, often glandular or lepidote, some with sweet roots; leaves imparipinnate, leaflets numerous, rarely 3, entire or glandular-denticulate, without stipels; stipules narrow, membranous, caducous; flowers blue, violet, white, or yellowish, in axillary racemes or spikes; bracts narrow, membranous, very caducous; bracteoles absent; calyx-lobes subequal, or upper 2 shorter or connate at the base; vexillum narrowly ovate or oblong, erect, shortly contracted at the base; wings obliquely oblong, rather acute, free; keel longer than the wings, acute or obtuse; petals scarcely connate; vexillary stamen free or connate with the rest into a sheath split above; anthers with the loculi confluent at the apex, sub-2-valved, alternately smaller with large unequal valves more deeply open; ovary sessile, 2- or more-ovuled; style filiform or rather thick, incurved at the apex, stigma terminal; fruit ovate, oblong or shortly linear, straight or arcuate, turgid or compressed, glandular, muricate, bristly or rarely smooth, indehiscent or tardily 2-valved, continuous within; seeds reniform or subglobose, without a strophiole.

274. **Cascaronia** Griseb., Goetting. Abh. 24: 100 (1879). 1 sp., *C. astragalina* Griseb., Argentina. E.P. 3, 3: 308; Burkart, Legum. Argent. ed. 2: 236, fig. 61.

Tall tree, sticky; leaves imparipinnate, leaflets alternate, glandular below, not stipellate; stipules caducous; racemes axillary, pedunculate; bracts minute, caducous; bracteoles absent; flowers yellow; calyx turbinate-campanulate, limb bilabiate-5-toothed, teeth deltoid, upper 2 longer; vexillum obovate; wings and keel-petals free, obliquely clawed; stamens diadelphous, vexillary free,[1] remainder connate into a split sheath, unequal; anthers oval-globose, all alike, loculi arcuate-convergent, contiguous and confluent at the apex; ovary stipitate, glandular, 3-2-ovuled, narrowed into a slender style, stigma terminal, minute; fruit shortly stipitate, plano-compressed, oblong-elliptic, indehiscent, with a narrow wing on the dorsal side, keeled on the suture, glandular; seeds 2-1, free, compressed.

---

[1] I have found the vexillary filament to be free and not united as described by Burkart, who included this genus in the *Dalbergieae*.

Tribe 31. DALEAE[1]

Tribe *Galegeae* Subtribe *Psoralieae* Benth. & Hook. f., Gen. Pl. 1: 441 (small part) (1865)

Shrubs or herbs, *glandular-punctate*; leaves imparipinnate, with or without stipels; stipules small; flowers in terminal or leaf-opposed spikes or the spikes capitate and involucrate; *petals inserted on or adnate to the staminal sheath*; stamens 10–5, more or less *connate into a sheath split above*; *anthers uniform*, sometimes *gland-tipped*; ovary 3–2-ovuled; *style glabrous*; *fruit enclosed by the calyx*, mostly indehiscent and 1-seeded; seeds without a strophiole. Type genus *Dalea* Juss.

Wing- and keel-petals distinctly clawed, inserted below the mouth of the staminal sheath; stamens 10 or 9   275. **Dalea**
Wing- and keel-petals not or only shortly clawed, inserted at the mouth of the staminal sheath:
  Stamens 10, rarely 9; calyx campanulate, 10-ribbed, 5-lobed   276. **Thornbera**
  Stamens 5:
    Vexillum much broader than the other petals; spikes not involucrate; calyx shortly lobed or toothed, not plumose   277. **Petalostemon**
    Vexillum similar to the other petals but long-clawed and inserted at the bottom of the calyx, the other petals inserted at the mouth of the staminal sheath; spikes involucrate by many empty scarious bracts (resembling a member of *Asteraceae*); calyx deeply divided into narrow silky-plumose lobes   278. **Kuhnistera**

275. **Dalea**[2] Juss., Gen. 355 (1789) (conserved name). About 150 spp., North temp. America, Cent. America, S. Chile, Galapagos Isls., Philippine Isls.; type *D. alopecuroides* Willd., United States, Mexico. B.H. 1: 493; E.P. 3, 3: 265; Rydb., N. Amer. Fl. 24: 48 (as *Parosela*); Wiggins, Taxonom. notes on *Dalea*, Contrib. Dudley Herb. 3: 41 (1940). See also Gentry, Madrono, 10: 225 (1950); Burkart, Legum. Argent. ed. 2: 251, fig. 66.

Shrubs or herbs, very often gland-dotted; leaves imparipinnate, leaflets small, entire, sometimes stipellate, or rarely digitately 3-foliolate; stipules often small, subulate; flowers purplish, blue, white, or rarely yellow, in terminal or leaf-opposed spikes; bracts membranous or setaceous; bracteoles absent; calyx-teeth or lobes subequal; vexillum cordate, clawed, sometimes appendaged with 2 inflexed auricles; wings and keel straight, often longer than the vexillum, claws adnate at the base to the staminal tube, at length jointed at the apex; stamens 10 or 9, all connate into a sheath split above and dilated into a cup at the base; anthers uniform, often tipped by a gland; ovary sessile or shortly stipitate, 2- rarely

---

[1] **Daleae** trib. nov. Frutices vel herbae, glanduloso-punctatae; folia imparipinnata, rare digitate 3-foliolata, stipellata vel exstipellata; stipulae parvae; spicae terminales vel oppositifoliae, vel capitatae et involucratae; petala unguibus tubo stamineo plus minusve adnatis; stamina 10–5, in vaginam supra fissam connata; antherae uniformes, glandula interdum apiculata; ovarium 3–2-ovulatum; stylus glaber; fructus calyce inclusus, indehiscens et 1-spermus; semina estrophiolata.

[2] Synonyms of **Dalea**: *Parosela* Cav. (1802). *Cylipogon* Raf. (1819). *Parosella* Cav. ex DC. (1825). *Jamesia* Raf. (1832). *Trichopodium* C. Presl (1844). *Carroa* C. Presl (1858). *Asagraea* Baill. (1870). *Errazurizia* Phil. (1872). *Dalia* St.-Lag. (1881). *Psorobatus* Rydb. (1919). *Psorothamnus* Rydb. (1919).

3-ovuled; style subulate, stigma small, terminal; fruit enclosed by the calyx, membranous, mostly indehiscent and 1-seeded; seed subreniform, without a strophiole.

276. **Thornbera** Rydb., Journ. N.Y. Bot. Gard. 20: 66 (1919). About 12 spp., S. States North America, Mexico; type *T. albiflora* (A. Gray) Rydb.

Perennial or annual herbs with gland-dotted branches and leaves pinnate; stipules and stipels present, the latter often gland-like; flowers in usually dense spikes; calyx campanulate, 10-ribbed, 5-lobed; vexillum cordate or ovate, long-clawed; wings and keel oblong or oblanceolate to obovate, subsessile, inserted at the mouth of the staminal tube; stamens 10 or 9, monadelphous; ovary sessile, 2-ovuled; style filiform, stigma minute; fruit membranous, enclosed by the calyx, mostly 1-seeded, obliquely obovate, somewhat compressed.

277. **Petalostemon**[1] L. C. Rich., Michx. Fl. Bot. Amer. 2: 48, t. 37 (1803) (conserved name). ('Petalostemum'.) About 40 spp., North America, Mexico; type *P. candidum* (Willd.) Michx., United States. B.H. 1: 493; E.P. 3, 3: 265; Rydb., N. Amer. Fl. 24: 121.

Herbs, often perennial, glandular-punctate; leaves imparipinnate, leaflets small, entire, without stipels; stipules minute, setaceous; flowers rose, purple-violet or white, in terminal or leaf-opposed spikes; bracts membranous or setaceous; bracteoles absent; calyx-teeth or lobes subequal; vexillum cordate with a slender free claw or oblong, concave or cupular; lower 4 petals subsimilar, obliquely-oblong, claws slender, adnate up to the apex of the staminal sheath; stamens 5, connate into a sheath split above and expanded at the base into a cup; filaments alternate at the apex with the petals; anthers sometimes glandular-apiculate; ovary sessile, 2-ovuled; style subulate, stigma small, terminal; fruit enclosed by the calyx, membranous, often indehiscent and 1-seeded; seeds subreniform, without a strophiole.

278. **Kuhnistera** Lam., Encycl. 3: 370 (1789). *Gatesia* Bertol. (1849). 2 spp., North America; type *K. pinnata* (Walt.) Kuntze, Carolina to Florida and Mississippi. Rydb., Fl. N. Amer. 24: 135.

Perennial herbs with long tap-roots; leaves pinnate, leaflets linear-filiform to obovate, glandular-punctate; stipules very small; stipels absent; flowers in corymbose head-like spikes subtended by 3–4 rows of broadly ovate persistent scarious empty bracts; calyx deeply divided; lobes subulate-filiform, about 3 times as long as the tube, silky-plumose; corolla nearly actinomorphic; petals nearly equal, oblong, the adaxial (vexillum) long-clawed and inserted at the bottom of the calyx, the other petals shortly clawed and inserted at the mouth of the staminal tube and alternate with the stamens; stamens 5, monadelphous, filaments united about half their length; ovary sessile; style filiform; stigma minute; ovules 2–1; fruit indehiscent, enclosed by the plumose calyx-lobes; seed 1. A very remarkable genus with heads of flowers resembling some *Asteraceae*.

Tribe 32. PSORALIEAE[2]

Tribe *Galegeae* Subtribe *Psoralieae* (greater part) Benth. & Hook. f., Gen. Pl. 1: 443 (1865)

Herbs and shrubs, *glandular-punctate*; leaves pinnate, usually imparipinnate, rarely 1-foliolate or digitate; leaflets usually numerous, often entire; stipules

---

[1] Synonyms of **Petalostemon**: *Dalea* Cram. (1803). *Cylipogon* Raf. (1819).

[2] **Psoralieae** trib. nov. Frutices et herbae, glanduloso-punctatae; folia saepe imparipinnata, rare 1-foliolata vel digitata, foliolis saepe numerosis plerumque integris; stipulae plerumque adsunt; stipellae saepe nullae; petala e tubo staminum libera, rare nulla; stamina 9 ad medium vel altius in spatham supra fissam connata, vexillari vel e basi libero vel cum ceteris medio connato rare nullo; filamenta ad apicem filiformia; antherae versatiles, plerumque uniformes, muticae; stylus glaber vel rare stigmate barbato; ovula 6–1; fructus plerumque indehiscens et 1-spermus; semina estrophiolata.

present or absent; stipels usually absent; corolla papilionaceous; petals free from the staminal tube, rarely absent or only the vexillum present; vexillary filament (rarely absent) free from the base or connate to the middle with the others into a sheath split adaxially, rarely into a closed tube, very rarely stamens free (*Paryella*): anthers *mostly uniform* or nearly so, *versatile*; *style glabrous* or rarely stigma bearded; ovules 6–1; fruits usually *indehiscent* and mostly *1-seeded*; seeds estrophiolate. Type genus *Psoralea* Linn.

Ovules 6–2:
  Stamens free or united only at the base; petals absent; leaves imparipinnate
    with many leaflets   279. **Parryella**
  Stamens diadelphous or monadelphous:
    Stamens diadelphous; vexillary filament free   280. **Eysenhardtia**
    Stamens monadelphous:
      Petals 5:
        Corolla scarcely papilionaceous, the petals all free and nearly clawless;
          stipules spinescent; leaves pinnate, leaflets orbicular; stamens 9
                                                          281. **Psorobatus**
        Corolla papilionaceous; petals clawed, and those of the keel usually
          adnate or coherent; leaves pinnate or simple:
          Flowers pedicellate; fruit exserted from the calyx   282. **Psorodendron**
          Flowers sessile; fruit not exserted from the calyx   283. **Psorothamnus**
      Only 1 petal (vexillum) present; fruits more or less compressed, often
        densely glandular-warted   284. **Amorpha**
Ovule solitary; fruit 1-seeded:
  Calyx-lobes much enlarged and spreading stellately in fruit, reticulate;
    corolla scarcely papilionaceous; shrubs with imparipinnate leaves;
    leaflets alternate, oblong   285. **Apoplanesia**
  Calyx-lobes not as described above, remaining erect; corolla distinctly
    papilionaceous:
    Fruit dehiscent, circumscissile or bursting irregularly, with a long flat
      sword-shaped deciduous beak as long as or longer than the body, free
      from the seed; perennials with deep-seated round or fusiform erect
      tuber-like rootstock   286. **Pediomelum**
    Fruit indehiscent:
      Pericarp free from the ripe seed:
        Leaves pinnately 3-foliolate, rarely 1- or 5-foliolate:
          Fruit coriaceous or bony, exserted from the calyx, very strongly trans-
            versely wrinkled or ribbed; leaves pinnately 3- rarely 1- or 5-
            foliolate   287. **Orbexilum**
          Fruit membranous or coriaceous, hidden by the persistent calyx, not
            transversely ribbed; leaves pinnately 3-foliolate; stigma bearded
                                                          288. **Hoita**

        Leaves digitately 3- or more-foliolate:
          Fruit crescent-shaped, flat, obliquely cross-ribbed; claw of vexillum
            twice bent   289. **Rhytidomene**
          Fruit orbicular to oblong, slightly compressed, gland-dotted but not
            cross-ribbed; claw of vexillum straight:

Shrubs or shrublets   290. **Psoralea**
Perennial herbs with rootstocks   291. **Psoralidium**
Pericarp adherent to the ripe seed:
    Leaflets numerous, small, entire, minutely stipellate; fruits enclosed by
        the persistent calyx; slender annual herbs   292. **Marina**
    Leaves trifoliolate or 1-foliolate:
        Flowers solitary, axillary; fruit ovoid, enclosed by the calyx
                                                          293. **Hallia**
        Flowers in slender racemes; perennial or annual herbs; fruit shortly
            beaked   294. **Cullen**
        Flowers capitate or shortly spicate-capitate on long slender peduncles;
            calyx-lobes spine-tipped; fruits with a sword-like beak; perennial
            herbs   295. **Asphalthium**
        Flowers in dense axillary clusters; calyx bilabiate, upper lip 4-lobed,
            lower longest and entire; shrubs   296. **Meladenia**

279. **Parryella** Torr. & Gray ex Gray, Proc. Amer. Acad. 7: 397 (1868).
2 spp., North America; type *P. filifolia* Torr. & Gray, New Mexico and
Arizona. E.P. 3, 3: 264; Rydb., N. Amer. Fl. 24: 25.

Small shrubs, much branched; branches slender, whip-like, like the leaves gland-dotted; leaves imparipinnate; leaflets several pairs, filiform; stipules and stipels absent or reduced to small glands; flowers in terminal spikes; calyx obconic, 5-toothed, teeth short, equal; petals absent; stamens 10; filaments inserted at the base of the calyx, free; anthers uniform; ovary 2-ovuled; style rather thick, slightly exserted from the calyx, hooked at the apex; stigma gland-like; fruit indehiscent, obliquely obovate, coarsely glandular-warted, narrowed at the base; seed solitary, oval; cotyledons oblong, foliaceous; radicle inflexed.

280. **Eysenhardtia** H. B. & K., Nov. Gen. et Spec. 6: 489, t. 592 (1823) (conserved name). *Viborquia* Ortega (1798). *Varennea* DC. (1825). *Essenhardtia* Sweet (1839). *Wiborgia* O. Ktze. (1891). 15 spp., S. United States, Mexico, Cent. America; type *E. polystachya* (Ortega) Sarg. (*E. amorphoides* H. B. & K.), S. United States, Cent. America. B.H. 1: 492; E.P. 3, 3: 265; Rydb., N. Amer. Fl. 24: 34.

Small trees or shrubs, glandular-punctate; leaves imparipinnate, leaflets numerous, small, minutely stipellate; stipules subulate, small; flowers small, white, densely spicate-racemose, racemes terminal or in a leafy terminal panicle; bracts and bracteoles narrow, very caducous; calyx-teeth subequal; petals erect, all free, subequal in length, narrowed into a claw; vexillum obovate, concave; wings and keel-petals oblong, obtuse, subsimilar; vexillary stamen free, remainder connate into a sheath split above; anthers uniform; ovary subsessile, 2-3- rarely 4-ovuled; style rather thick, hooked at the apex, stigma introrsely oblique; fruit small, oblong or linear-falcate, compressed; seeds solitary or rarely 2, oblong-reniform.

281. **Psorobatus** Rydb., N. Amer. Fl. 24: 40 (1919). 2 spp., North America; type *P. benthamii* (Brand.) Rydb., islands off west coast of California.

Low shrubs with spinescent stipules; leaves pinnate, leaflets orbicular; flowers spicate; bracts narrow, gland-tipped; calyx deeply campanulate, lobes oblong; petals yellow, inserted at the base of the staminal tube, not distinctly clawed, the adaxial (vexillum) broader than the rest; stamens 9, monadelphous, alternately longer and shorter; ovary 2-ovuled; stigma capitate; fruit ovoid or ellipsoid, turgid, without prominent sutures, exserted, 2-1-seeded, with a slender beak.

282. **Psorodendron** Rydb., N. Amer. Fl. 24: 41 (1919). 12 spp., North America; type *P. johnsonii* (S. Wats.) Rydb., S. Utah to S. California.

Trees or shrubs; leaves pinnate or simple, gland-dotted; branches often spinescent; glands, especially on the peduncles, often subulate or conical; flowers racemose; rhachis often more or less spinescent; calyx-tube turbinate; corolla papilionaceous; petals subequal or the keel rarely longer, inserted at the base of the staminal tube; vexillum usually deeply notched at the apex, usually with 2 small lobes at the base of the blade; keel-petals slightly united along the lower edge; stamens 10 or 9, monadelphous; ovary mostly 2- rarely 4–6-ovuled; fruit longer than the calyx, long-beaked, oblique, usually with prominent sutures, conspicuously gland-dotted.

283. **Psorothamnus** Rydb., N. Amer. Fl. 24: 45 (1919). 8 spp., North America; type *P. emoryi* (A. Gray) Rydb.

Intricately branched shrubs; leaves pinnate or simple; flowers in dense, short, often subglobose spikes; bracts lanceolate, caducous; bracteoles absent or represented by glands; calyx-tube turbinate, strongly 10-ribbed, with a row of glands in each furrow; corolla dark blue or dark purple, papilionaceous; petals inserted at the base of the staminal tube, nearly equal in length, often with a gland near the apex except the keel-petals; vexillum suborbicular or rounded-cordate, slightly retuse; stamens 10 or 9, monadelphous, united high up into a tube; fruit obliquely obovoid, turgid, sutures not prominent.

284. **Amorpha** Linn., Sp. Pl. 713 (1753). *Bonafidia* Neck. (1790). *Monosemeion* Raf. (1840). About 25 spp., North America, Mexico; type *A. fruticosa* Linn., North America. B.H. 1: 492; E.P. 3, 3: 264; Palmer, Journ. Arn. Arb. 12: 157 (1931) (conspectus); Burkart, Legum. Argent. ed. 2: 251.

Shrubs or shrublets, glandular-punctate; leaves imparipinnate, leaflets numerous, small, sometimes minutely stipellate; stipules small or absent; flowers small, blue-violet or white, densely spicate-racemose, racemes terminal or in a leafy terminal panicle; bracts and bracteoles narrow, very caducous; calyx-teeth or lobes subequal, lower longer; vexillum obovate, erect, clawed, embracing the stamens and pistil; wings and keel absent; stamens all connate into a sheath split above, upper often longer; anthers uniform; ovary sessile, 2-ovuled; style recurved, glabrous or villous, stigma terminal; fruit short, oblong, falcate or lunulate, indehiscent, often densely glandular-warted; seeds 2–1, oblong or subreniform.

285. **Apoplanesia** C. Presl, Symb. Bot. 1: 63, t. 41 (1831). *Apolanesia* Reichb. (1841). *Microlobium* Liebm. (1853). 1 sp., *A. paniculata* Presl, Mexico, Yucatan. B.H. 1: 492; E.P. 3, 3: 264; Rydb., N. Amer. Fl. 24: 24 (1919).

Erect shrub, glandular-punctate; leaves imparipinnate, leaflets numerous, entire, petiolulate, without stipels; stipules absent; panicles axillary and terminal, diffuse, many-flowered; flowers small, white; bracts minute; calyx membranous, lobes obtuse, subequal, after flowering much-enlarged, 3-nerved and reticulate-venose; petals subequal in length, clawed; vexillum obovate-oblong, reflexed; wings obliquely linear, undulate; keel-petals free, spathulate, obtuse, undulate; stamens 10, all connate into short sheath split above; anthers uniform; ovary sessile, 1-ovuled; style filiform, glabrous, stigma oblique, capitate; fruit semi-orbicular, compressed, half enclosed by the enlarged calyx, the whole resembling a small *Dipterocarp*, coriaceous, glandular, rugose, boat-shaped, apiculate.

286. **Pediomelum** Rydb., N. Amer. Fl. 24: 17 (1919). 22 spp., North America; type *P. esculentum* (Pursh) Rydb.

Perennial herbs with deep-seated round tuberous farinaceous and edible rootstock; leaves alternate, digitately 3–7-foliolate, or with the terminal leaflet borne on an elongated rhachis, more or less glandular-punctate; flowers in axillary pedunculate dense spikes or racemes; calyx 5-lobed, deeply campanulate, the lowest lobe usually the longest; corolla blue or purple; vexillum broadly oblanceolate or obovate, tapered into the claw; wings with a basal lobe; keel-petals broader and shorter, united at the rounded apex and each adnate to that of the adjacent wing at the base; vexillary stamens free except at the base or united higher up with the others; anthers equal; ovary 1-ovuled; style abruptly bent above; stigma capitate; fruit oval, compressed, and with a long flat sword-shaped beak as long or longer; pericarp thin, free from the seed, dehiscing by a transverse circular slit or irregularly, the upper part deciduous.

287. **Orbexilum** Raf., Atl. Journ. 145 (1832). *Psoralea* sect. *Poikadenia* Ell. (1822). 8 spp., North America; type *O. onobrychis* (Nutt.) Rydb. Rydb., N. Amer. Fl. 24: 4 (1929).

Perennial herbs with rootstocks or fusiform roots, rarely shrubby below; leaves alternate, usually gland-dotted, pinnately 3–1-foliolate rarely 5-foliolate; flowers in long-pedunculate axillary spikes or racemes; calyx campanulate, mostly glandular, 5-lobed, lowest lobe often longest; corolla blue or purple; vexillum broadly obovate or suborbicular, claw narrow, often with small basal lobes at the base of the limb; wings as long as the vexillum, with a small basal lobe; keel-petals shorter, united at the tip; vexillary stamen free except at the base, or united to the tube high up, or absent; anthers alternately often smaller; ovary 1-ovuled; style curved, stigma capitate; fruit ovate to orbicular, not enclosed by the calyx, indehiscent, with an incurved short beak; pericarp wrinkled, free from the seed; seed suborbicular to reniform.

288. **Hoita** Rydb., N. Amer. Fl. 24: 7 (1919). 11 spp., North America; type *H. macrostachya* (DC.) Rydb.

Perennial herbs with rootstocks, rarely shrubby below; leaves pinnately 3-foliolate, leaflets entire, glandular-punctate; flowers in long-pedunculate axillary spikes or racemes; calyx campanulate, gland-dotted, 5-lobed, lowest lobe longest; corolla purple or yellowish, the keel with a darker purple tip; vexillum broadly obovate, with basal lobes and a short claw; wings and keel clawed; vexillary stamen free except at the base, or united with the others in the upper part; anthers alternately slightly shorter; ovary 1-ovuled; style usually abruptly bent above; stigma globose, bearded; fruit obliquely oval or ovate, with a short slender beak, included in the calyx; pericarp thin, free from the seed; seed oval-reniform, shining.

289. **Rhytidomene** Rydb., N. Amer. Fl. 24: 12 (1919). 1 sp., *R. lupinellus* (Michx.) Rydb., N. Carolina to Florida.

Perennial herb with creeping rootstock; stem erect; leaves alternate, digitately 5–7-foliolate, leaflets linear-filiform, gland-dotted; stipules small; flowers in long-pedunculate axillary lax racemes; bracts minute, cuspidate; calyx campanulate, enlarged in fruit, tube short, 5-lobed, lowest lobe longest, subulate; corolla blue; vexillum orbicular, claw short, doubly bent; wings narrowly obliquely obovate, apex rounded, basal lobe small, claws free; keel-petals shorter, united at the rounded apex, each adnate to the adjacent wing at the base; stamens, 10, vexillary stamen free or united to the others high up; anthers subuniform; ovary 1-ovuled; style curved upwards; fruit crescent-shaped, exserted from the calyx, flat, obliquely cross-ribbed, glandular; seeds kidney-shaped, brown.

290. **Psoralea**[1] Linn. Sp. Pl. 762 (1753). About 130 spp., S. Africa, Australia, temp. and trop. regions of Old World; type *P. pinnata* Linn., S. Africa. B.H. 1: 491; E.P. 3, 3: 263; Burkart, Legum. Argent. ed. 2: 249, fig. 65; Forbes, Bothalia, 3: 116 (1930).

Shrubs or shrublets, with black glands or pellucid-punctate; leaves digitately 3- or more-foliolate or rarely with a few additional pairs and pinnate, leaflets entire, or pinnately 3-foliolate or 1-foliolate with entire or dentate leaflets; stipules embracing the stem by the

---

[1] Synonyms of **Psoralea**: *Rutenia* Medik. (1787). *Munbya* Pomel (1860). *Lamottea* Pomel (1870). *Lotodes* O. Kuntze (1891).

broad base; flowers purple, blue, rose, or white, capitate, spicate, subracemose or fasciculate, rarely solitary; bracts membranous, each often embracing 2–3 flowers; bracteoles absent; calyx-lobes subequal or the lower larger, upper 2 often connate; petals subequal in length or shorter than the keel; vexillum ovate or orbicular, contracted into a claw, or appendaged above the claw with small inflexed auricles; wings oblong, subfalcate; keel incurved, obtuse, the petals subcoherent in the middle; vexillary stamen free or more or less connate with the others; anthers small, uniform or alternately attached higher up; ovary sessile or shortly stipitate, 1-ovuled; style filiform or dilated at the base, incurved in the upper part, stigma terminal; fruit ovate, indehiscent, pericarp free from the seed; seed without a strophiole, with a very short funicle.

291. **Psoralidium** Rydb., N. Amer. Fl. 24: 12 (1919). 14 spp., North America; type *P. tenuiflorum* (Pursh) Rydb., N. Dakota and Montana to Texas and Arizona.

Perennial herbs with rootstocks; leaves digitately 3–5-foliolate, gland-dotted; flowers in long-pedunculate interrupted spikes or racemes, bearing 1–4 flowers at each node; calyx campanulate, 5-lobed, lowest lobe longest; corolla blue; vexillum orbicular, claw short, doubly bent; wings rounded at the apex, with a small basal lobe, claws free; keel-petals shorter, united at the rounded apex, each adnate to the adjacent wing; vexillary stamen usually free, remainder united into a sheath; style curved upwards; fruit crescent-shaped, exserted from the calyx, shortly beaked, pericarp coriaceous, obliquely cross-ribbed; seed kidney-shaped, brown.

292. **Marina** Liebm., Kjoebenhavn Vid. Meddel. 103 (1853). 1 sp., *M. gracilis* Liebm., Mexico. B.H. 1: 492; E.P. 3, 3: 264.

Slender herb, annual, diffuse, glandular-punctate; leaves imparipinnate, leaflets numerous, very small, entire, minutely stipellate; stipules broad, scarious, dentate; racemes extra-axillary or leaf-opposed, peduncle filiform; flowers few, small, violet; bracts minute, scarious; calyx-lobes subequal, dentate-ciliate; vexillum long-clawed, obovate-rounded; wings falcate-obovate; keel hooded, shorter than the wings and vexillum; stamens 10, all connate into a sheath split above; anthers uniform; ovary sessile, 1-ovuled; style filiform, glabrous, stigma undivided; fruit enclosed by the calyx, membranous, indehiscent; seed subreniform.

293. **Hallia** Thunb., Schrad. Journ. 1: 318 (1799). 9 spp., S. Africa; lectotype *H. alata* Thunb. B.H. 1: 523; E.P. 3, 3: 332.

Low shrublets or herbs, spreading or prostrate; leaves 1-foliolate, exstipellate; stipules striate, adnate at the base to the petiole; peduncles axillary, 1-flowered, jointed above the middle and bearing a small 3-lobed bract; bracteoles absent; calyx-lobes subequal, tube narrowed at the base; vexillum clawed, obovate or orbicular; wings obliquely oblong, slightly adherent to the keel or free; keel incurved at the apex, obtuse, subequal to or shorter than the wings; stamens all connate into a sheath or the vexillary rarely free; anthers uniform; ovary sessile, 1-ovulate; style inflexed above, dilated at the bent part, subulate at the apex, stigma capitate, terminal; fruit ovoid, enclosed by the calyx, pericarp membranous, reticulate; seed 1, shaped like the fruit, hilum lateral, estrophiolate.

294. **Cullen** Medik., Vorles. Churpf. Phys.-Oek. Ges. 2: 380 (1787). *Dorychnium* Moench, partly (1794). *Bipontinia* Alef. (1866). 2 spp., Arabia through India and Ceylon to Burma; type *C. corylifolia* (Linn.) Medik., Arabia to Burma. Rydb., N. Amer. Fl. 24: 3 (1919).

Perennial or annual herbs, shrubby at the base; leaves digitately 3–1-foliolate, conspicuously gland-dotted; leaflets coarsely dentate; flowers in axillary pedunculate spikes; calyx strongly glandular-punctate, tube campanulate, 5-lobed, lowest lobe longest, upper 2 often more or less united; corolla scarcely longer than the calyx-lobes; vexillum obovate, claw short, straight wings as long as the vexillum, oblong, basal lobe prominent, claws free; keel-petals shorter than the wings, broadly obliquely lunate, united at the rounded apex; vexillary stamen free except at the base, remainder united in a split tube; ovary 1-ovuled; style curved upwards, stigma capitate; fruit conspicuously glandular-warted, beak short, erect; pericarp thin, adherent to the seed; seed obliquely reniform.

295. **Asphalthium** Medik., Vorles. Churpf. Phys.-Oek. Ges. 2: 380 (1787). *Rhynchodium* Presl partly (1844). 2 spp., *A. bituminosum* (Linn.) O. Kuntze, S. Europe, N. Africa, Orient; elsewhere escape from cult. *A. acaulis* (Stev.) (*Psoralea acaulis* Stev.), Asia Minor to Caucasus. Rydb., N. Amer. Fl. 24: 4 (1919).

Herbaceous gland-dotted perennials; leaves pinnately or subdigitately trifoliolate, leaflets entire or denticulate; flowers capitate or shortly spicate on elongated axillary peduncles; stipules lanceolate, bracts ovate, subulate-pointed, calyx 5-lobed, tube campanulate, lobes unequal, lanceolate, sharply subulate-tipped, lowest much longer than the rest; vexillum narrow, oblanceolate, sagittate, claw broad, basal lobes small; wings shorter, semisagittate, clawed; keel-petals shorter, rounded and adnate to each other at the apex; stamens monadelphous at the base, vexillary stamen free above, remainder alternately longer and shorter; fruit indehiscent, with a long sword-shaped beak which at length breaks off; pericarp adnate to the seed.

296. **Meladenia**[1] Turcz., Bull. Soc. Nat. Mosc. 21, 1: 576 (1848). 3 spp., Philippine Isls., New Guinea, Australia; type *M. badocana* (Blanco) (*Liparia badocana* Blanco; *Meladenia densiflora* Turcz.), Philippine Isls.

Glandular shrubs; leaves alternate, unifoliolate, petiolate, lanceolate, undulate to repand-denticulate, densely black-glandular on both surfaces, pinnately nerved; petiole jointed near the top and with 2 minute stipels or a rim; stipules linear-subulate, persistent; flowers in dense axillary shortly pedunculate or subsessile clusters or short racemes; bracts and calyx black-glandular; bracts ovate; bracteoles absent; calyx bilabiate, deeply partite, upper lip 4-lobed, lower entire; corolla papilionaceous; vexillum narrowly obovate, not clawed; wing-petals oblong, obtuse; keel-petals broader, with a rectangular top; stamens diadelphous, vexillary filament free; remainder connate into a sheath split adaxially; anthers equal, subbasifixed; ovary elliptic, 1-ovuled, style very slender, glabrous; stigma terminal, minute; fruit enclosed by the persistent calyx, indehiscent; seed 1, closely adherent to the endocarp; seed estrophiolate; radicle incurved.

Tribe 33. CAJANEAE

Benth., Ann. Wien. Mus. 2: 213 (1838). Tribe *Phaseoleae* Subtribe *Cajaneae* Benth. & Hook. f., Gen. Pl. 1: 453 (1865)

Shrubs or herbs, sometimes climbing or creeping; leaves pinnately 3-foliolate or rarely digitate or 1-foliolate, *glandular-punctate* below; stipules present; stipels usually absent; racemes not swollen at the nodes, or flowers solitary; bracts often membranous and very caducous; *bracteoles none*; upper two calyx-lobes usually more or less connate into one; petals subequal in length; stamens diadelphous, *vexillary filament free*, the remainder partly connate into a sheath split above; *anthers uniform*; ovules several to 2; *style glabrous*; stigma terminal; fruits compressed, *2-valved*, sometimes septate between the seeds but not jointed; seeds strophiolate or not. Type genus *Cajanus* DC.

[1] Other spp. of this genus: *M. archeri* (F. Muell.), *M. balsamica* (F. Muell.), both in N. Australia.

Ovules 4 or more:
  Fruits more or less compressed:
    Fruits depressed between the seeds:
      Seeds not strophiolate; fruits acuminate, marked between the seeds with
        oblique depressed lines   297. **Cajanus**
      Seeds strophiolate; fruits obtuse, transversely depressed or lined
                                                   298. **Atylosia**
    Fruits not depressed between the seeds, often falcate, acuminate; seeds
      substrophiolate   299. **Dunbaria**
    Fruits turgid; seeds strophiolate; upper 2 calyx-lobes subdistinct
                                                   300. **Fagelia**

Ovules 2, vary rarely 3:
  Calyx-lobes not enlarged after flowering:
    Bracts and calyx-lobes not tipped by a gland:
      Fruits turgid:
        Leaves digitately 3-foliolate or 1-foliolate; flowers spicate-racemose or
          paniculate   301. **Moghania**
        Leaves pinnately 3-foliolate; flowers umbellate   303. **Chrysoscias**
      Fruits compressed:
        Flowers solitary in the leaf-axils   302. **Carissoa**
        Flowers several in racemes or rarely axillary:
          Stems twining or trailing, rarely erect; funicle of the seed attached in
            the middle of the hilum   304. **Rhynchosia**
          Stems usually stiff and erect; funicle of the seed attached at the end of
            the linear hilum   305. **Eriosema**
    Bracts and calyx-lobes tipped by a gland; flowers precocious; shrubs
                                                   306. **Eminia**
  Calyx-lobes enlarged and membranous or scarious after flowering, the
    lowermost largest; fruits falcate-ovate, enclosed by the calyx; seeds
    estrophiolate   307. **Cylista**

297. **Cajanus** DC., Catal. Hort. Bot. Monspel. 85 (1813) (conserved name).
Cajan Adans. (1763). *Cajanum* Raf. (1838). 2 spp., Africa, naturalized in
tropical regions of both hemispheres; type *C. cajan* (Linn.) Millsp. B.H. 1:
541; E.P. 3, 3: 372; Hutch. & Dalz., Fl. W. Trop. Afr. 1: 559; Amshoff, Pulle
Fl. Suriname, 2, 2: 213; Burkart, Legum. Argent. ed. 2: 397, fig. 118.

Erect shrublets, often tomentose; leaves pinnately 3-foliolate, exstipellate, leaflets resinous-
glandular below; stipules caducous; flowers yellow or lined with purple, in axillary pedunculate racemes; bracts very caducous; bracteoles absent; calyx-lobes acuminate or acute,
upper 2 connate into one 2-toothed; vexillum orbicular, reflexed, with basal inflexed appendages; wings obliquely obovate; keel incurved at the apex, obtuse; vexillary stamen free,
remainder connate; anthers uniform; ovary subsessile; ovules numerous; style thickened
above the middle, not barbate, slightly dilated below the oblique terminal stigma; fruit
linear, obliquely acute, compressed, 2-valved, obliquely depressed between the seeds with
transverse lines, scarcely septate within; seeds with a lateral oblong hilum, estrophiolate.

298. **Atylosia** Wight & Arn., Prodr. Pen. Ind. Or. 1: 257 (1834). *Cantharo-
spermum* Wight & Arn. (1834). About 35 spp., Old World tropics; lectotype
A. candollei Wight & Arn., India. B.H. 1: 542; E.P. 3, 3: 372.

Shrubs or herbs, erect or climbing; leaves pinnately, rarely subdigitately, 3-foliolate, without stipels; leaflets with scattered resinous dots below; flowers yellow, axillary and fasciculate or irregularly racemose at the apex of an axillary peduncle, or upper flowers paniculate; bracts often broad, membranous, deciduous long before flowering; bracteoles absent; calyx-lobes acuminate, upper 2 connate or 2-toothed; corolla persistent; vexillum orbicular, with inflexed auricles at the base; wings obliquely obovate or oblong; keel slightly incurved, obtuse; vexillary stamen free, remainder connate; anthers uniform; ovary sessile, 3–more-ovuled; style inflexed in the middle, filiform or slightly thickened, stigma small, terminal; fruit oblong or linear, often obtuse, compressed, 2-valved, septate between the seeds, with transverse or oblique lines; seeds ovate or suborbicular, strophiolate.

299. Dunbaria Wight & Arn., Prodr. Fl. Pen. Ind. Or. 1: 258 (1834). 15 spp., Asia, Malaya, New Guinea, trop. Australia; lectotype *D. heynei* Wight & Arn., India. B.H. 1: 541; E.P. 3, 3: 372.

Prostrate or climbing herbs, often tomentose; leaves pinnately 3-foliolate, exstipellate, leaflets with resinous dots below; flowers often yellow, in axillary pedunculate racemes; rhachis scarcely nodose, rarely flowers axillary and solitary; bracts often membranous, deciduous long before flowering; bracteoles absent; calyx-lobes acuminate, upper 2 connate into 1 entire or 2-toothed; vexillum orbicular, erect or spreading, with auriculate inflexed appendages at the base; wings obliquely obovate or oblong; keel a little shorter than the wings, incurved, obtuse; vexillary stamen free, remainder connate into a sheath split above; anthers uniform; ovary sessile, many-ovuled; style inflexed from the middle, glabrous; fruit linear, straight or falcate, acuminate, compressed, 2-valved, subseptate within; seeds suborbicular, the funicle expanded into a thick membrane.

300. Fagelia Neck., Elem. 3: 41 (1790). *Bolusafra* O. Ktze. (1891). 1 sp., *F. bituminosa* (Linn.) Meisn., S. Africa. B.H. 1: 541; E.P. 3, 3: 372.

Climbing herb, rather woody at the base, sticky, odorous; leaves pinnately 3-foliolate, exstipellate; stipules striate; flowers yellow, scattered on the rhachis of long-pedunculate axillary racemes; bracts ovate, very caducous; bracteoles absent; calyx-lobes acuminate, 2 upper shortly connate; vexillum suborbicular, reflexed, with 2 inflexed auricles at the base; wings narrow, shorter than the keel; keel incurved, obtuse; vexillary stamen free, remainder connate; anthers uniform; ovary sessile; ovules numerous; style inflexed in the middle, filiform or slightly thickened, stigma small, terminal; fruit oblong-falcate, acute, turgid, 2-valved, continuous inside, subdepressed outside between the seeds; seeds ovoid, hilum short, lateral, strophiolate.

301. Moghania[1] St. Hil., Journ. Bot. Paris, 1: 61 (1813). *Flemingia* Roxb. ex Ait. (1812), not Roxb. (1803). About 30 spp., trop. regions of the Old World; lectotype *M. macrophylla* (Willd.) O. Ktze. (*M. congesta* (Roxb.)), trop. Africa and in Asia. B.H. 1: 544; E.P. 3, 3: 375; Amshoff, Pulle Fl. Suriname, 2, 2: 219 (*Flemingia*); Hui-Lin Li, Amer. Journ. Bot. 31: 224 (1944); Hauman, Fl. Congo Belge, 6: 257; Nooteboom, Reinwardtia, 5: 433 (1961) (Malaysian spp.).

Shrubs or herbs, erect, prostrate, or rarely climbing; leaves digitately 3-foliolate or 1-foliolate, exstipellate, gland-dotted below, nerves often prominent below; stipules striate, often caducous; flowers red or purple and yellow mixed, either densely spicate-racemose or paniculate, bracts broad, foliaceous, concave, persistent, overtopping the flowers, or dry, striate, narrow, persistent or caducous; bracteoles absent; calyx-lobes subequal or the lowest longer, free, often falcate; vexillum oval, obovate or orbicular, with inflexed basal auricles; wings obliquely obovate or oblong, often adherent to the keel; keel straight or

---

[1] Synonyms of **Moghania**: *Lourea* J. St.-Hil. (1812). *Ostryodium* Desv. (1813). *Millingtonia* Roxb. ex Wight & Arn. (1834). *Maghania* Steud. (1841). *Moghamia* Steud. (1841). *Flemmingia* Walp. (1842). *Lepidocoma* Jungh. (1845).

incurved, obtuse or acute; vexillary stamen free, remainder connate, anthers uniform; ovary subsessile, short, 2-ovuled; style filiform or slightly thickened in the upper part, stigma small, terminal; fruits short, oblique, turgid, 2-valved, continuous within; seeds rather thick, hilum short, estrophiolate.

302. **Carissoa** E. G. Bak., Bol. Soc. Brot. sér. ii. 8: 108 (1933). 1 sp., *C. angolensis* E. G. Bak., trop. Africa (Angola).

Low shrublet with thick elongated woody rootstock; stems several; leaves 1-foliolate, linear-lanceolate, pinnately nerved, closely glandular below; stipules linear-lanceolate; stipels absent; flowers axillary, solitary, shortly pedicellate; calyx-tube short, 2-lipped, upper shorter, lower longer, linear; vexillum clawed; wings oblong or elliptic-oblong; keel rounded on the back; fruit elliptic-oblong, dehiscent, often 2-seeded; style pubescent, stigma terminal.

303. **Chrysoscias** E. Mey., Comment. Pl. Afr. Austr. 139 (1835). 6 spp., S. Africa; lectotype *C. erecta* (Thunb.) C. A. Smith (*C. grandiflora* E. Mey.). C. A. Smith, Burtt Davy Fl. Transvaal, 2: 405.

Woody climbers, silky and glandular all over; leaves pinnately 3-foliolate, leaflets linear to lanceolate, gland-dotted; stipules ovate, subpersistent; stipels absent; flowers yellow, few in axillary pedunculate umbels; bracts small and deciduous; bracteoles absent; calyx deeply 5-lobed, lobes subequal, lanceolate, vexillum large, clawed; wings semicordate at the base; keel with scale-like appendages; stamens diadelphous, vexillary filament free; anthers uniform; fruits turgid, dehiscent, 2-seeded; seeds reniform, black, strophiolate.

304. **Rhynchosia** Lour., Fl. Cochinch. 400 (1790) (conserved name). About 150 spp., warm regions; type *R. volubilis* Lour., China, Japan. B.H. 1: 542; E.P. 3, 3: 373; Amshoff, Pulle Fl. Suriname, 2, 2: 214; Hauman, Fl. Congo Belge, 6: 149, tt. 12–16; Burkart, Legum. Argent. ed. 2: 394, fig. 117.

Shrublets or herbs, climbing, prostrate, or rarely erect; leaves pinnately, very rarely subdigitately 3-foliolate, exstipellate or minutely stipellate, leaflets with scattered resinous dots below; stipules ovate or lanceolate; flowers yellow, the vexillum often lined, rarely purple, in axillary racemes, rarely axillary and solitary; bracts caducous; bracteoles absent; upper 2 calyx-lobes more or less connate; vexillum obovate or orbicular, spreading or reflexed, auriculate at the base; wings narrow; keel incurved at the apex; anthers uniform; ovary subsessile, 2- or very rarely 1-ovuled; style incurved above, filiform or thickened, stigma small, terminal; fruit compressed, obliquely orbicular, oblong or falcate, 2-valved, continuous within or rarely septate; seeds 2, rarely 1, compressed-globose or subreniform, hilum lateral, funicle central or scarcely oblique, strophiole thick, small, or absent.

305. **Eriosema** DC. ex Desv., Ann. Sc. Nat. 9: 421 (1826). *Euriosma* Desv. (1826). *Pyrrhotrichia* Wight & Arn. (1834). *Euryosma* Walp. (1842). *Muxiria* Welw. (1858). About 100 spp., trop. and S. Africa and America, trop. Asia and Australia; lectotype *E. sessiliflorum* (Poir.) Desv., Peru. B.H. 1: 543; E.P. 3, 3: 375; Amshoff, Pulle Fl. Suriname, 2, 2: 216; Hauman, Fl. Congo Belge, 6: 193, tt. 17–22; Burkart, Legum. Argent. ed. 2: 396, fig. 118.

Herbs, shrublets, erect or prostrate, or rarely climbing; leaves pinnately 3-foliolate, often exstipellate, leaflets resinous-dotted below; stipules lanceolate, free or connate into one and

---

[1] Synonyms of **Rhynchosia**: *Dolicholus* Medik. (1787). *Arcyphyllum* Ell. (1818). *Austerium* Poit. ex DC. (1825). *Polytropia* C. Presl (1831). *Cyanospermum* Wight & Arn. (1834). *Nomismia* Wight & Arn. (1834). *Pitcheria* Nutt. (1834). *Copisma* E. Mey. (1835). *Hidrosia* E. Mey. (1835). *Orthodanum* E. Mey. (1835). *Rynchosia* Macfadyen (1837). *Chrysonias* Benth. (1838). *Phyllomatia* Benth. (1838). *Ptychocentrum* Benth. (1838). *Sigmodostyles* Meisn. (1843). *Walpersia* Meisn. ex Krauss (1844). *Rhinchosia* Zoll. & Mor. (1846). *Stipellaria* Klotzsch (1848). *Hydrosia* A. Juss. (1849). *Rhyncosia* Webb (1850). *Dolichoides* Bak. (1871).

leaf-opposed; flowers yellow, the vexillum often silky-villous, in axillary racemes, rarely solitary and axillary; calyx-lobes all separate or the upper 2 shortly connate; vexillum obovate or oblong, with inflexed auricles at the base; wings narrow; keel slightly incurved at the apex, obtuse; vexillary stamen free, remainder connate; anthers uniform; ovary sessile, 2-ovuled; style filiform or slightly thickened upwards, stigma small, terminal; fruit compressed, obliquely orbicular, rhomboid, or broadly oblong, 2-valved, continuous within, 2- rarely 1-seeded; seeds compressed, obliquely transverse, funicle attached at the end of the linear hilum, estrophiolate.

306. **Eminia** Taub., Ber. Deutsch. Bot. Ges. 9: 30, t. 2 (1891). 3 spp., trop. Africa; type *E. eminens* Taub. E.P. 3, 3: 359; Hauman, Fl. Congo Belge, 6: 253, t. 23.

Shrubs; leaves pinnately trifoliolate, stipellate, leaflets entire or lobulate; stipules striate, persistent; flowers precocious, 1–3 at the nodes of fallen leaves; bracts stipule-like, produced at the apex into a clavate gland; calyx 5-lobed, tube subcampanulate, lobes long, subulate, produced at the apex into a gland, upper 2 connate for one-third their length, 3 lower subequal; vexillum obovate, inflexed-appendaged at the base, clawed; wings obliquely and narrowly oblong, upper margin inflexed in the middle, lower twice folded towards the apex, 1-toothed near the base, clawed, keel-petals falcate-oblong, lower margin coherent, about as long as the wings; stamens 10, exserted; vexillary stamen free, persistent after flowering, remainder connate; anthers subglobose, dorsifixed; ovary shortly stipitate, surrounded by a cupular disk; ovules 2; style elongated, filiform, horizontally compressed-dilated above the middle, upper part filiform, glabrous, rectangularly reflexed; stigma terminal, minute; fruit rectangular-oblong, compressed, 2–1-seeded, sutures slightly thickened, dehiscent, continuous within, surrounded by the persistent calyx and disk; seeds orbicular, compressed, funicle short, estrophiolate.

307. **Cylista** Ait., Hort. Kew. ed. 1, 3: 512 (1789). 3 spp., E. India, Indo-China, trop. and S. Africa, Socotra; type *C. villosa* Ait., S. Africa. B.H. 1: 542; E.P. 3, 3: 373.

Climbing herbs, tomentose; leaves pinnately 3-foliolate, exstipellate, leaflets with scattered resinous dots below; flowers in axillary racemes; bracts membranous, hyaline, caducous; bracteoles none; calyx-lobes obtuse, scarious, at length much enlarged, upper 2 connate into 1 emarginate, lateral shorter, lowermost largest, concave; vexillum suborbicular, with inflexed basal auricles; wings narrow; keel incurved, obtuse; vexillary stamen free, remainder connate; anthers uniform; ovary subsessile, 1-ovuled; style filiform, stigma terminal; fruit falcate-ovate, enclosed by the calyx, 2-valved; seed estrophiolate.

Tribe 34. Diocleae

Tribe *Phaseoleae* Subtribe *Diocleae* Benth., Ann. Wien. Mus. 2: 113 (1838); Benth. & Hook. f., Gen. Pl. 1: 452 (1865)

Shrubs or shrublets, climbing or suberect, or climbing or prostrate herbs; leaves *pinnately* 3-foliolate, rarely 5–7- or 1-foliolate; stipules sometimes produced below the point of insertion; *stipels present*; inflorescence racemose, with *swollen nodes*; bracts and bracteoles small or very caducous; calyx mostly 4-lobed (upper 2 lobes united into 1), rarely unequally 2-lipped; corolla papilionaceous; vexillary filament *free at the base*, then *connate with the others into a closed tube*; *anthers uniform*; ovary stipitate or subsessile; *style glabrous*; ovules numerous or rarely few; stigma terminal; fruit dehiscent, 2-valved, *filled inside between the seeds*; seeds estrophiolate. Type genus *Dioclea* H. B. & K.

Calyx with 4 more or less similar lobes, not 2-lipped:
  Wing-petals mostly longer than (rarely as short as) the keel-petals:
    Ovary stipitate; flowers large and showy; sutures of the fruit scarcely thickened:
      Vexillum long or ovate, auriculate; stigma small; South America
        308. **Camptosema**
      Vexillum orbicular, not auriculate; stigma capitate; South America
        309. **Cratylia**
      Vexillum obovate; New Guinea   310. **Macropsychanthus**
    Ovary subsessile; flowers medium-sized or small; fruits mostly with the upper suture thickened or 2-winged:
      Fruit broad, the upper suture thickened or with two wings 311. **Dioclea**
      Fruit mostly narrow, compressed, the upper suture neither thickened nor winged; stipules sometimes produced below the point of attachment
        312. **Pueraria**
  Wing-petals small, much shorter than the keel; flowers very small; upper suture neither winged nor thickened   313. **Cleobulia**
Calyx 2-lipped, the upper lip relatively very large, entire or 2-lobed, the lower very small; fruit ribbed or winged:
  Flowers fasciculate-racemose on elongated peduncles; fruits with a single wing or rib close to the upper suture   314. **Canavalia**
  Flowers numerous in raceme-like thyrses; fruits with 3–4 longitudinal ribs on each valve (i.e. including the marginal ribs)   315. **Wenderothia**

308. **Camptosema** Hook. & Arn., Hook. Bot. Misc. 3: 200 (1833). *Bionia* Mart. ex Benth. (1838). 15 spp., South America, especially Brazil; type *C. rubicundum* Hook. & Arn. B.H. 1: 536; E.P. 3, 3: 369; Burkart, Legum. Argent. ed. 2: 400, fig. 119.

Shrubs or shrublets, climbing or suberect; leaves pinnately 3-foliolate, rarely 1- or 5–7-foliolate, stipellate; stipules deciduous; flowers showy, scarlet, axillary, fasciculate-racemose; rhachis nodose; bracts deciduous; bracteoles small, often deciduous; calyx tubular, 2 upper lobes connate into 1, lateral shorter, lowermost longer; vexillum ovate or oblong, appendaged at the base with inflexed auricles; wings oblong, free or scarcely adherent to the keel; keel oblong, almost straight, subequal to the wings; vexillary stamen free at the base, often connate with the others in the middle; anthers uniform; ovary stipitate, many-ovuled; style subulate, stigma small, terminal; fruit stipitate, linear, compressed, coriaceous, 2-valved, filled inside between the seeds; seeds compressed, hilum shortly oblong, estrophiolate.

309. **Cratylia** Mart. ex Benth., Ann. Wien. Mus. 2: 131 (1838). 5–6 spp., South America; lectotype *C. hypargyrea* Mart. ex Benth., Brazil. B.H. 1: 536; E.P. 3, 3: 369; Burkart, Legum. Argent. ed. 2: 402, fig. 120.

Tall climbing shrubs; leaves pinnately 3-foliolate, stipellate; stipules small; flowers white or rose-violet, racemose-fasciculate, axillary; rhachis nodose; bracts very caducous; bracteoles broad, small, caducous; calyx often silky outside; upper 2 calyx-lobes connate into 1 entire or emarginate; vexillum orbicular, not appendaged; wings obovate, free; keel scarcely shorter than the wings, broadly oblong, incurved, obtuse; vexillary stamen free at the base, connate with the others in the middle; anthers uniform; ovary stipitate, many-ovuled; style incurved, beardless, stigma terminal, capitate; fruit oblong-linear, compressed, sutures scarcely thickened, 2-valved, thinly filled inside between the seeds; seeds compressed, hilum small, oblong, estrophiolate.

310. **Macropsychanthus** Harms, K. Schum. & Lauterbach, Deutsch. Sudsee 366, t. 10 (1900). 3 spp., Philippines, New Guinea; type *M. lauterbachii* Harms, New Guinea.

Tall climbing shrubs; leaves trifoliolate; leaflets broad and rounded, entire; stipules and stipels deciduous, panicles terminal, raceme-like; pedicels very short; buds obtuse, densely silky; flowers large and showy; calyx-tube broadly campanulate-cylindric, lobes 5–4, small; petals subequal in length; vexillum broadly clawed, obovate, deeply emarginate; wings clawed, narrowly falcate-oblong, rounded at apex, with a rounded auricle on one side at the base of the limb; keel-petals coherent in the upper part, falcate-oblong, long-clawed; stamens 10, vexillary free in the lower part but united in the middle with the other connate filaments; anthers oblong-ellipsoid, dorsifixed; ovary stipitate, villous; style with a minute truncate stigma.

311. **Dioclea**[1] H. B. & K., Nov. Gen. et Sp. 6: 437 (1823). About 30 spp., trop. and subtrop. America, and tropics of the Old World; lectotype *D. sericea* H. B. & K., Colombia, Guiana. B.H. 1: 536; E.P. 3, 3: 369; Hutch. & Dalz., Fl. W. trop. Afr. 1: 412; Amshoff, Pulle Fl. Suriname, 2, 2: 200; Robyns, Fl. Congo Belge, 6: 141, t. 11; Burkart, Legum. Argent. ed. 2: 402, fig. 121.

Shrubs or shrublets, or tall and climbing; leaves pinnately 3-foliolate, stipellate; stipules present; flowers blue, violet, or white, fasciculate-racemose on a thick or elongated peduncle, sometimes cauliflorous; bracts very caducous; bracteoles membranous, caducous; upper 2 calyx-lobes connate into 1, lateral smaller, lowermost longer; vexillum orbicular or ovate, reflexed, appendaged with basal inflexed auricles; wings obovate or oblong, free, rather longer than the keel; keel incurved, beaked or obtuse; vexillary stamen free at the base, connate with the others in the middle; anthers uniform, or the alternate smaller and empty; ovary subsessile, 2–many-ovuled; style incurved, beardless, thickened or dilated towards the apex, stigma terminal, truncate; fruit linear-oblong to semiorbicular, compressed or rather turgid, coriaceous or woody, upper suture dilated or both sutures winged, 2-valved, filled inside between the seeds; seeds compressed, estrophiolate, hilum short or long and linear.

312. **Pueraria** DC., Ann. Sci. Nat. 9: 97 (1825). *Neustanthus* Benth. (1851–5). *Zeydosa* Lour. ex Gomes (1868). 15 spp., trop. Asia, China, Japan, New Guinea, Polynesia; type *P. tuberosa* (Roxb.) DC., India. B.H. 1: 537; E.P. 3, 3: 370; Amshoff, Pulle Fl. Suriname, 2, 2: 209; Burkart, Legum. Argent. ed. 2: 405, fig. 122.

Stems tall and climbing; roots sometimes bearing tubers; leaves pinnately 3-foliolate, leaflets large, ovate or rhomboid, entire or sinuately lobed, stipellate; stipules herbaceous, in some species produced below the point of insertion; flowers blue or purplish, in axillary racemes or panicles, these sometimes very long; rhachis often nodose; bracts usually small or narrow, very caducous; bracteoles small, subpersistent or minute and caducous; 2 upper calyx-lobes or teeth connate into 1 entire or 2-toothed; vexillum appendaged with 2 inflexed auricles; wings narrowly oblong or obovate-falcate, often adherent to the middle of the keel; keel sometimes beaked, subequal to the wings; vexillary stamen free at the base, connate in the middle with the others, rarely quite free; anthers uniform; ovary subsessile, many-ovuled; style filiform, inflexed above, beardless, stigma small, capitellate; fruit elongated, 2-valved, continuous within or filled or septate between the seeds; seeds compressed, suborbicular or transversely oblong.

P. thunbergiana Benth.; Thunberg Kudzu vine; perennial woody climber, China and Japan, cult. in other mild countries; grown as hay and green feeding for livestock; also for soiling; tubers eaten cooked in some regions.

---

[1] Synonyms of **Dioclea**: *Hymenospron* Spreng. (1827). *Crepidotropis* Walp. (1840). *Lepidamphora* Zoll. ex Miq. (1855). *Crepidoteris* Benth. (1859). *Taurophthalmum* Duchassaing ex Griseb. (1866). *Trichodoum* P. Beauv. ex Taubert (1894).

313. **Cleobulia** Mart. ex Benth., Ann. Wien. Mus. 2: 131 (1838). 3 spp., Brazil; type *C. multiflora* Mart. ex Benth. B.H. 1: 537; E.P. 3, 3: 370.

Shrubs or shrublets, tall and climbing; leaves pinnately 3-foliolate, stipellate; stipules not produced at the base; flowers small, densely fasciculate-racemose on elongated axillary peduncles; rhachis nodose; bracts very caducous; bracteoles small, caducous; upper 2 calyx-lobes connate into 1 entire, lateral smaller; vexillum suborbicular, appendaged with inflexed auricles at the base; wings very small; scarcely exceeding the calyx, free; keel incurved, obtuse; vexillary stamen free at the base, connate with the others in the middle; anthers uniform; ovary subsessile, many-ovuled; style dilated-truncate at the apex, beardless, stigma subdorsal; fruit broadly linear, compressed, 2-valved, filled inside between the seeds; seeds with a short oblong hilum, estrophiolate.

314. **Canavalia**[1] DC., Mém. Légum. 375 (1825) (conserved name); DC. Prodr. 2: 403 (1825). About 40 spp., warm regions of both hemispheres; type *C. ensiformis* (Linn.) DC. B.H. 1: 537; E.P. 3, 3: 371; Piper & Dunn, Revision of *Canavalia*, Kew Bull. 1922: 129; Piper, Contrib. U.S. Nat. Herb. 20: 559 (1925); Amshoff, Pulle Fl. Suriname, 2, 2: 210; Burkart, Legum. Argent. ed. 2: 407, fig. 123.

Climbing or prostrate herbs; leaves pinnately 3-foliolate, stipellate; stipules small, either wart-like or inconspicuous; flowers purple-violet, rose, or whitish, fasciculate-racemose on elongated peduncles, rhachis nodose; bracts minute; bracteoles small, caducous; calyx-lobes connate into 2 lips, upper large, truncate or 2-lobed, lower much smaller or minute, entire or 3-fid; vexillum large, suborbicular, reflexed; wings narrow, falcate or subtwisted, free; keel broader than the wings, incurved, obtuse or beaked, beak inflexed or spirally twisted; vexillary stamen free at the base, connate with the others in the middle; anthers uniform; ovary many-ovuled; style incurved or folded in the keel, beardless, stigma small, terminal; fruit oblong or broadly linear, compressed or turgid, with a wing or rib near the upper suture, 2-valved, often thinly filled within between the seeds; seeds ovate-rounded, compressed, hilum linear.

C. ensiformis (Linn.) DC., Jack Bean, Chickasaw Lima Bean; probably native of West Indies; cult. in tropics; food for livestock; roasted seeds used as substitute for coffee, when fresh and unripe considered poisonous; also *C. obtusifolia* DC., fruits of white vars. eaten preserved in salt, of black vars. eaten fresh or boiled.

315. **Wenderothia** Schlechtd., Linnaea, 12: 330 (1838). 12 spp., trop. America; type *W. discolor* Schlechtd., Mexico. Piper, Contrib. U.S. Nat. Herb. 20: 576 (1925).

Shrubs or herbs, mostly twining; leaves pinnately 3-foliolate; stipules caducous, not striate; peduncles axillary; flowers numerous in raceme-like thyrses, the axis nodose; bracts minute, caducous; bracteoles mostly orbicular, caducous; calyx tubular-campanulate, bilabiate, upper lip large, entire, lower small, 3-lobed; vexillum large, reflexed, without basal auricles, with 2 callosities towards the base; wings free, narrow, auriculate; keel falcate, mostly beaked, sometimes spirally coiled at the tip, partly connate; stamens diadelphous, the vexillary more or less free; anthers all alike; style glabrous; stigma capitate; fruit stipitate, oblong or linear, beaked, straight or curved, compressed, valves with 3 or 4 longitudinal ribs; seeds several to many, ellipsoid and compressed or lenticular, hilum linear.

Tribe 35. GALACTIEAE

Tribe *Phaseoleae* Subtribe *Galactieae* Benth. & Hook. f., Gen. Pl. 1: 452 (1865)

Shrubs and herbs, often climbing, rarely creeping; leaves pinnately 5- or 3-foliolate, very rarely 1-foliolate, *stipellate*; stipules present; inflorescence

[1] Synonyms of **Canavalia**: *Canavali* Adans. (1763). *Clementea* Cav. (1804). *Malocchia* Savi (1824). *Cavanalia* Griseb. (1866). *Cryptophaseolus* O. Ktze. (1891).

nodose-racemose or rarely paniculate; bracts small or very caducous; calyx often 4-lobed, the upper 2 lobes more or less united; petals subequal in length, very rarely absent in lower flowers; vexillum often with *inflexed basal auricles*; keel-petals usually straight, vexillary filament usually free, rarely united half-way with the others, connate in a split sheath; *anthers uniform*; ovules mostly numerous; style *glabrous or penicillate only around the stigma*; fruit usually 2-valved throughout or rarely indehiscent, those of apetalous flowers (rare) maturing below the surface of the soil. Type genus *Galactia* P.Br.

Upper calyx-lip 2-toothed or 2-fid:
    Fruit empty and not dehiscent in the lower part, 1-seeded and tardily 2-valved at the top; flowers small, in large panicles; ovules 2   316. **Spatholobus**
    Fruit not as described above, 2-valved throughout, filled or septate between the seeds; flowers in racemes or fascicles:
        Leaflets 5; stipules setaceous; ovules numerous; style penicillate around the stigma   317. **Cruddasia**
        Leaflets 3; style glabrous around the stigma:
            Fruit linear, straight, septate; leaflets sometimes lobulate; vexillum appendaged at the base with 2 inflexed auricles   318. **Calopogonium**
            Fruit not known; leaflets entire, vexillum not auricled at the base   319. **Leycephyllum**
            Fruit oblong-falcate; leaflets not lobed; vexillum with basal inflexed auricles   320. **Cymbosema**
            Leaflet 1; fruit linear, filled between the seeds; vexillum with minute basal auricles   321. **Nogra**
Upper calyx-lip entire:
    Fruit dehiscent, 2-valved:
        Stipules elongated-linear-lanceolate; ovary stipitate; ovules often 5   322. **Hesperothamnus**
        Stipules small or deciduous; ovary subsessile; ovules numerous:
            Vexillary filament free from the others; twiners or rarely suberect   323. **Galactia**
            Vexillary filament united half-way up with the others; mostly erect shrubs   324. **Collaea**
    Fruits indehiscent, very thin and flat; anthers linear, versatile   325. **Mastersia**

316. **Spatholobus** Hassk., Flora 25: P. 2, Beibl. 52 (1842). *Drebbelia* Zoll. (1846). 15 spp., S. China, trop. Asia, Malaya, Philippines; type *S. littoralis* Hassk., Malay Archip. B.H. 1: 534; E.P. 3, 3: 367.

Tall climbing shrubs, often tomentose; leaves pinnately 3-foliolate, stipellate; stipules small; flowers small, rose, purple, or white, numerous, paniculate; bracts and bracteoles small, narrow; 2 upper calyx-teeth or -lobes connate into 1 entire or emarginate; vexillum ovate or suborbicular, obtuse, not appendaged; wings obliquely oblong, free; keel almost straight, obtuse, shorter than the wings; vexillary stamen free, remainder connate; anthers uniform; ovary sessile or stipitate; ovules 2; style subulate or compressed, incurved, not barbate, stigma small, terminal; fruit subsessile or stipitate, broadly linear, often falcate, base long, flat, indehiscent and empty, thicker at the top and 1-seeded, tardily 2-valved; seed flat, obovate, estrophiolate.

317. **Cruddasia** Prain, Journ. As. Soc. Beng. 67: 287 (1899). 1 sp., *C. insignis* Prain, Burma, Thailand.

Stem climbing; leaves pinnately 5-foliolate, leaflets elliptic-lanceolate, stipellate; stipules setaceous, caducous, basifixed; flowers white and purple, in axillary racemes of fascicles, the axis nodose; bracts and bracteoles caducous; calyx-lobes acute, upper 2 connate into one 2-toothed at the apex, remainder equally broad, triangular; vexillum suborbicular, not inflexed at the base; wings oblong-ovate, adherent to the base of the keel; keel boat-shaped, not beaked, as long as the wings; vexillary stamen closely connate with the others; anthers uniform; ovary sessile; ovules numerous; style filiform, incurved, penicillate around the terminal stigma; fruit elongate, flat, 2-valved, thinly filled inside between the seeds; seeds compressed, suborbicular, hilum ovate, estrophiolate.

318. **Calopogonium** Desv., Ann. Sci. Nat. 9: 423 (1826). *Stenolobium* Benth. (1838). *Cyanostremma* Benth. ex Hook. & Arn. (1841). 4 spp., North trop. and subtrop. America; type *C. mucunoides* Desv., Guiana. B.H. 1: 534; E.P. 3, 3: 367; Amshoff, Pulle Fl. Suriname, 2, 2: 196; Burkart, Legum. Argent. ed. 2: 413, fig. 125.

Tall climbing herbs; leaves pinnately 3-foliolate, leaflets sometimes lobulate, stipellate; flowers medium-sized or small, narrow, blue or violet, fasciculate-racemose on axillary elongated or abbreviated peduncles, fascicles nodose; bracts and bracteoles small, caducous; upper 2 calyx-lobes separate or connate into 1 2-toothed; vexillum obovate, appendaged at the base with 2 inflexed auricles; wings narrow, adherent to the keel; keel shorter than the wings, obtuse; vexillary stamen free, remainder connate; anthers uniform; ovary sessile; ovules numerous; style filiform, not barbate, stigma terminal, capitate; fruit linear, plano-compressed or at length convex on both sides, 2-valved, septate inside between the seeds; seeds orbicular, compressed, estrophiolate.

319. **Leycephyllum** Piper, Journ. Wash. Acad. Sci. 14: 363 (1924). 1 sp., *L. micranthum* Piper, Costa Rica.

Climbing shrub; leaves trifoliolate, leaflets entire; stipules striate; flowers small, yellowish, numerous, in racemes from the axils of the upper leaves; calyx campanulate, the upper lip short, bidentate, the lower lip 3-toothed, the median one as long as the calyx-tube, the lateral ones short; standard obovate, stipitate, the upper margin incurved or hooded, the base without callosities or auricles, but the basal margins thickened; wing oblong, stipitate, the auricle somewhat hook-like; keel oblong-obovate, clawed, not auricled; vexillary stamen free, its filament enlarged at base, the other stamens united below, free above the middle; anthers oval; style curved, glabrous; stigma terminal, very oblique, minute; ovary pubescent.

320. **Cymbosema** Benth., Hook. Journ. Bot. 2: 61 (1840). 1 sp., *C. roseum* Benth., Brazil. B.H. 1: 534; E.P. 3, 3: 367.

Tall climbing herb; leaves pinnately 3-foliolate, stipellate; flowers showy, purplish or rose, fasciculate-racemose towards the apex of axillary peduncles, rhachis nodose; bracts and bracteoles minute; upper 2 calyx-lobes connate into one 2-toothed; vexillum oblong-ovate, with basal inflexed auricles; wings narrow; keel oblong, slightly incurved, subacuminate, scarcely shorter than the wings; vexillary stamen free, remainder connate; anthers uniform; ovary subsessile; ovules numerous; style incurved, not barbate, stigma terminal, truncate; fruit oblong-falcate, compressed, apiculate, 2-valved, thinly filled inside; seeds transversely oblong or reniform, half surrounded by a linear hilum, estrophiolate.

321. **Nogra** Merrill, Trans. Amer. Phil. Soc. N.S. 24, 2: 201 (1935). *Grona* Benth. (1865), not Lour. (1790).[1] 3 spp., trop. Asia; type *G. grahamii* (Wall.) Merrill, India to Thailand.

---

[1] *Grona repens* Lour. = *Desmodium heterocarpum* (Linn.) DC.

Prostrate or climbing herbs; leaves 1-foliolate, stipellate; stipules very caducous; racemes axillary or subterminal, flowers sometimes contracted into fascicles, rhachis nodose; bracts narrow, deciduous; bracteoles small, tardily persistent; calyx-lobes longer than the tube, upper 2 connate at the base or beyond the middle; vexillum obovate or suborbicular, with minute inflexed basal auricles; wings falcate, slightly adherent to the keel; keel narrowly incurved, obtusely beaked; vexillary stamen free, remainder connate; anthers uniform; ovary subsessile; ovules numerous; style filiform, incurved, not barbate, stigma capitate; fruit linear, compressed, 2-valved, filled within between the seeds; seeds orbicular, with a thick strophiole at the small hilum.

322. Hesperothamnus T. S. Brandegee, Univ. Calif. Publ. Bot. 6: 499 (1919). *Selerothamnus* Harms (1921). 3 spp., Mexico; type *H. littoralis* Brandegee.

Shrubs; leaves imparipinnate, leaflets 5, in 2 pairs, oblong or obovate or lanceolate, silky when young; stipules elongated-linear-lanceolate, deciduous; stipels linear; flowers fasciculate in elongated raceme-like inflorescences; bracts and bracteoles linear; calyx obliquely cupular, 4-toothed, teeth nearly as long as the tube or half as long, lower 3 lanceolate or ovate, upper often entire or bifid, lanceolate-acuminate or broadly ovate, obtuse or acute; corolla exserted, petals clawed; vexillum obovate or suborbicular-obovate, clawed; vexillary stamen connate with the others except at the base; anthers small; ovary stipitate; ovules often 5; style glabrous, curved, stigma minute, capitellate; fruit oblong, planocompressed, 2-valved, valves coriaceous; seeds orbicular, estrophiolate, funicle broad, cotyledons foliaceous.

323. Galactia[1] P.Br., Hist. Jamaica 298 (1756); Adans., Fam. 2: 322 (1763). About 50 spp., warmer regions of both hemispheres especially America; type *G. pendula* Pers., West Indies. B.H. 1: 535 (excl. *Collaea* DC.); E.P. 3, 3: 368 (partly); Amshoff, Pulle Fl. Suriname, 2, 2: 199; Burkart, Legum. Argent. ed. 2: 410, fig. 124, *a–d*, G.

Prostrate or climbing or suberect herbs; leaves pinnately 3-foliolate, rarely 1–5- or 7-foliolate, stipellate; stipules small or deciduous; flowers in axillary racemes, remotely paired or fasciculate, or the lower ones subsolitary in axils of the small setaceous bracts, rarely lower flowers apetalous; bracteoles very small; calyx-lobes acuminate, upper 2 connate, lateral smaller, lower often longer; vexillum ovate or orbicular, margins slightly inflexed at the base or subappendaged; wings narrow or obovate, adherent to the keel; keel subequal to or longer than the wings, not beaked; vexillary stamen free; anthers uniform; ovary subsessile; ovules numerous; styles filiform, not barbate, stigma small, terminal; fruit linear, straight or incurved, plano-compressed or rarely convex, 2-valved, thinly filled or subseptate between the seeds; seeds estrophiolate, rarely fruits of lower apetalous flowers penetrating the soil and rounded, 1-seeded.

324. Collaea DC., Mém. Lég. 6: 244 (1825); and Ann. Sci. Nat. sér. 1, 4: 96, tt. 40, 41 (1825); Prodr. 2: 240. *Betencourtia* St. Hil. (1833). About 20 spp., trop. America, Argentina; type *C. speciosa* DC., Brazil, Peru, Bolivia, Paraguay. Benth., Mart. Fl. Bras. 15: 144, tt. 39, 40; B.H. 1: 535 (in *Galactia*); Burkart, Legum. Argent. ed. 2: 411, fig. 124, C, *f*.

Erect shrubs or shrublets from a woody rhizome, rarely twining; leaves usually trifoliolate or unifoliolate, stipulate; flowers in axillary racemes or subumbellate; calyx campanulate, 4-lobed, upper broader, lower longest; vexillum ovate or orbicular, narrowed or rounded at the base, margins inflexed at the base; wings obovate or oblong; keel oblong, subequal to the wings; vexillary filament connate with the others to the middle; anthers equal, short, dorsifixed; disk shortly sheathing; ovary subsessile, several-ovuled; style linear, incurved, stigma small; fruit sessile, linear, compressed, coriaceous, filled between the seeds; seeds oblong, hilum short to rather long.

---

[1] Synonyms of **Galactia**: *Odonia* Bertol. (1822). *Sweetia* DC. (1825). *Galactea* Wight (1841). *Heterocarpaea* Scheele (1848). *Leucodictyon* Dalz. (1850). *Galaction* St. Lag. (1880).

325. **Mastersia** Benth., Trans. Linn. Soc. 25: 300, t. 34 (1865). 2 spp., Indo-Malaya; type *M. assamica* Bak., E. Himalayan region. B.H. 1: 535; E.P. 3, 3: 368.

Stem tall, climbing; leaves pinnately 3-foliolate, leaflets large, stipellate; stipules very caducous; flowers fasciculate-racemose on elongated axillary peduncles, joints of rhachis nodose; bracts ovate, paired, very caducous; bracteoles suborbicular, persistent for some time; calyx-lobes longer than the tube, upper 2 connate into a broad entire one; vexillum suborbicular, very shortly clawed, not auricled; wings obliquely oblong; keel broad, slightly incurved, obtuse, subequal to the wings; vexillary stamen free, remainder connate; anthers linear, versatile; ovary sessile; ovules numerous; style shortly filiform, incurved, not barbate, stigma terminal, capitate; fruit oblong-linear, plano-compressed, indehiscent, upper suture narrowly margined; seeds numerous, transversely oblong, hilum lateral, small, estrophiolate, funicle filiform.

Tribe 36. ERYTHRINEAE[1]

Tribe *Phaseoleae* Subtribe *Erythrineae* Benth., Ann. Wien. Mus. 2: 113 (1838); Benth. & Hook. f., Gen. Pl. 1: 452 (1865)

Erect trees or shrubs, or climbers; leaves *pinnately 3-foliolate*, rarely 1- or 5-7-foliolate; leaflets entire or lobed, *mostly stipellate*; flowers in axillary racemes with *swollen nodes*, often showy; *petals very unequal in length*; vexillum large, with smaller wings or keel, or shorter than the wings and keel; vexillary filament free or connate with the others only at the base, the remainder united in a sheath split above (adaxially); *anthers uniform* (except *Mucuna*); *style glabrous*; fruit 2-valved or follicularly dehiscent by the upper suture; *seeds estrophiolate*. Type genus *Erythrina* Linn.

*Vexillum the largest petal; anthers uniform:
Keel-petals much shorter than the vexillum:
  Erect trees or shrubs with handsome flowers; calyx-mouth truncate or spathaceous or rarely equally 5-toothed; leaves 3-foliolate
          326. **Erythrina**
  Climbers; calyx-lobes 4, lateral shorter; leaves 1-foliolate   327. **Rhodopsis**
Keel-petals subequal to the vexillum, beaked; climbers; leaves 3-foliolate; seeds orbicular, hilum linear, half encircling the seed   328. **Strongylodon**
*Keel-petals the largest or longest of all:
Anthers uniform:
  Vexillum longer than the wing-petals, orbicular; fruit linear, subfalcate, 2-valved; several-seeded   329. **Apios**
  Vexillum shorter than the wing-petals; climbing herb, becoming black when dry; fruit linear, incurved, 2-valved, several-seeded
          330. **Cochlianthus**
  Vexillum as long as the keel-petals; trees or tall climbing shrubs; fruit 2-valved and 1-seeded at the top, empty below   331. **Butea**

[1] **Erythrineae**, trib. nov. Arbores vel frutices erecti vel scandentes; folia pinnatim 3-folio-lata, rare 1- vel 5–7-foliolata; foliola integra vel lobata, plerumque stipellata; flores in race-mis nodosis dispositi, speciosi; petala inaequilonga; vexillum magnum et alis vel carina minore, vel alis et carina brevius; stamen vexillare liberum vel basi cum ceteris connatum; antherae nisi *Mucunae* uniformes; stylus glaber; fructus 2-valvis vel secus suturam superio-rem folliculatim dehiscens; semina estrophiolata.

Anthers of two forms, alternately dorsifixed and basifixed, the shorter often bearded; fruits often clothed with stinging hairs, 2-valved, septate or filled between the seeds; mostly climbers, rarely short and erect

332. Mucuna

326. **Erythrina**[1] Linn., Sp. Pl. 706 (1753). About 200 spp., trop. and subtrop. regions of both hemispheres; type *E. corallodendron* Linn., trop. America. B.H. 1: 531; E.P. 3, 3: 363; Standley, Mexican and Cent. Amer. spp., Contrib. U.S. Nat. Herb. 20: 175 (1919); Hutch. & Dalz., Fl. W. trop. Afr. 1: 406; ed. 2 (Keay), 1: 562; Amshoff, Pulle Fl. Suriname, 2, 2: 188; Krukoff, Brittonia, 3: 205 (Amer. spp.) (1939); Majot-Rochez, Fl. Congo Belge, 6: 113, t. 10; Burkart, Legum. Argent. ed. 2: 387, fig. 115.

Trees or shrubs, rarely subherbaceous; branchlets often prickly; leaves pinnately 3-foliolate; indumentum sometimes stellate; stipules small; stipels gland-like; racemes axillary and leafless or terminal and leafy at base; flowers very showy, mostly scarlet, paired or clustered on the rhachis; bracts and bracteoles small or absent; calyx truncate, split or more or less 5-toothed; vexillum large or elongated, erect or spreading, subsessile or long-clawed, not appendaged; wings short, sometimes very small or absent; keel much smaller than the vexillum, longer or shorter than the wings; vexillary stamen free or connate only at the base, the remainder connate to the middle; anthers uniform; ovary stipitate; ovules numerous; style incurved, not barbate, stigma small, terminal; fruit stipitate, linear, falcate, constricted or sinuate between the seeds, 2-valved or follicularly dehiscent by the upper suture, rarely scarcely dehiscent; seeds ovoid, hilum lateral, oblong, estrophiolate.

327. **Rhodopsis** Urb., Symb. Antill. 2: 304 (1900). *Rudolphia* Willd. (1801), not Medik. (1787). *Neorudolphia* Britton (1924). 2 spp., West Indies; type *R. planisiliqua* (Linn.) Urb. B.H. 1: 532; E.P. 3, 3: 364.

Climbing shrubs; stipules small, subulate; leaves unifoliolate; petiole jointed at the base and apex, stipellate; inflorescence long-pedunculate, elongated, many-flowered, flowers fasciculate; bracts subulate; upper 2 calyx-lobes united into 1 ovate lobe, lateral smaller, lower lanceolate, as long as the upper; vexillum oblong, erect, clawed, auriculate at the base; wings linear-oblong, auriculate, long-clawed; keel-petals connate at the back, auriculate, much longer than the wings, claws of the wings and keel adnate to the base of the staminal tube; vexillary stamen free at the base, then shortly connate with the others; anthers linear-oblong, uniform; ovary surrounded at the base by short conical-tubular disk, shortly stipitate, many-ovuled; style beardless, stigma terminal, minute; fruit shortly stipitate, linear-compressed, nearly straight, shortly beaked, 2-valved, valves rather woody, dorsal margin not thickened; seeds numerous, separated by a narrow space, horizontal, funicle short, obovate, hilum short, oblong, estrophiolate; testa smooth.

328. **Strongylodon** Vog., Linnaea, 10: 585 (1836). About 20 spp., Polynesia, Indo-Malayan Archip., Ceylon, Madagascar; type *S. ruber* Vog., Hawaii Isls. B.H. 1: 532; E.P. 3, 3: 365; M. L. Steiner, The Philippine Jadevine, National Hort. Mag. 38: 43, with photos. (1959).

Shrubs or shrublets, climbing; leaves pinnately 3-foliolate, stipellate; stipules small; flowers red, showy, fasciculate-racemose on elongated axillary often pendulous peduncles, rhachis node-like; bracts minute or small; bracteoles orbicular, small, very caducous; calyx-teeth broad, obtuse, upper 2 scarcely connate; vexillum ovate-oblong, acute, recurved, at length reflexed, with 2 appendages above the claw; wings much shorter than the vexillum,

---

[1] Synonyms of **Erythrina**: *Tetradapa* Osbeck (1757). *Mouricou* Adans. (1763). *Xyphanthus* Raf. (1817). *Chirocalyx* Meisn. (1843). *Duchassaingia* Walp. (1850). *Micropteryx* Walp. (1850). *Macrocymbium* Walp. (1853). *Stenotropis* Hassk. (1855). *Hypaphorus* Hassk. (1858). *Corallodendron*, O. Ktze. (1891).

adhering to the keel; keel much incurved, beaked, equal to the vexillum, petals connate; vexillary stamen free, filiform from the base, remainder connate; anthers uniform; ovary stipitate, few- to 1-ovuled; style filiform, not barbate, stigma small, terminal; fruit stipitate, obliquely ovate-oblong, 2-valved; seeds thick, orbicular, hilum linear, half-circular on the seed, estrophiolate.

329. **Apios** Moench, Method. 165 (1794) (conserved name). *Bradlea* Adans. (1763). *Cyrotropis* Wall. (1830). 10 spp., North America, China, Indo-China, India; type *A. americana* Medik. (*A. tuberosa* Moench), North America. B.H. 1: 532; E.P. 3, 3: 365.

Climbing herbs; leaves pinnately 3–7-foliolate, stipellate; stipules small; flowers dull purple or scarlet, on axillary peduncles or terminal panicles, rhachis nodose; bracts and bracteoles small, narrow, very caducous; upper 2 calyx-teeth very broad, connate, lateral very short, lowest longer and acute; vexillum reflexed, ovate or orbicular, appendaged with inflexed auricles at the base; wings obliquely obovate, shorter than the vexillum, adherent to the keel; keel elongated, very incurved above, involute or spirally twisted; vexillary stamen free, remainder connate; anthers uniform; ovary subsessile; ovules numerous; style inflexed in the upper part, often thickened, not barbate, stigma terminal; fruit linear, subfalcate, flat, 2-valved; seeds estrophiolate.

330. **Cochlianthus** Benth., Miquel Pl. Jungh. 1: 234 (1851–5). 2 spp., Himalayas; type *C. gracilis* Benth. B.H. 1: 533; E.P. 3, 3: 365.

Climbing herb, blackish when dry; leaves pinnately 3-foliolate, stipellate; flowers racemose-fasciculate on slender axillary peduncles, rhachis nodose; bracts and bracteoles minute, caducous, or absent; upper 2 calyx-teeth connate into 1, lateral smaller, lowest longer; vexillum broadly ovate, appendaged with inflexed auricles; wings oblong, shortly exceeding the vexillum; keel linear, cochleate-contorted, not longer than the wings; vexillary stamen free, remainder connate; anthers uniform; ovary shortly stipitate; ovules numerous; style filiform, not barbate, peltate-dilated; fruit linear, incurved, 2-valved, obscurely septate; seeds quadrate, hilum short, estrophiolate.

331. **Butea** Konig ex Roxb., Pl. Corom. 1: 22, t. 21 (1795) (conserved name). *Plaso* Adans. (1763). *Meizotropis* Voight (1845). *Megalotropis* Griff. (1854). 3 spp., N. India; type *B. monosperma* (Lam.) Taubert, India, Burma. B.H. 1: 533; E.P. 3, 3: 365.

Trees, or tall and climbing shrubs, tomentose; leaves pinnately 3-foliolate, stipellate; stipules small, caducous; flowers showy, orange or flame-coloured, densely fasciculate, fascicles racemose or paniculate; bracts and bracteoles narrow, caducous; teeth or lobes of the large calyx short, upper 2 connate into a broad entire or emarginate lip; vexillum ovate, acute, recurved, not appendaged; wings falcate, adherent to the keel; keel much incurved, acute, equal to the vexillum; vexillary stamen free, remainder connate; anthers uniform; ovary sessile or shortly stipitate; ovules 2; style elongated, incurved, not barbate, stigma terminal, very small or truncate; fruit oblong or broadly linear, long and flat at the base and empty, 2-valved and 1-seeded at the top; seed plano-compressed, obovate, hilum small, estrophiolate.

332. **Mucuna**[1] Adans., Fam. 2: 325 (1763) (conserved name). About 160 spp., warm regions of both hemispheres; type *M. urens* (Linn.) Medik., South America and tropics generally. B.H. 1: 533; E.P. 3, 3: 365; Hutch. & Dalz.,

---

[1] Synonyms of **Mucuna**: *Stizolobium* [P.Br. (1756)]. *Zoophthalmum* P.Br. (1756). *Macuna* [Marcgr. ex] Scop. (1777). *Cacuvallum* Medik. (1787). *Citta* Lour. (1790). *Hornera* Neck. (1790). *Macranthus* Lour. (1790). *Negretia* Ruiz & Pav. (1794). *Labradia* Swediaur (1801). *Lavradia* Swediaur (1801). *Macranthus* Poir. (1813). *Carpopogon* Roxb. (1814). *Macroceratides* Raddi (1820). *Micranthus* Loud. (1830). *Pillera* Endl. (1833).

Fl. W. Trop. Afr. 1: 405, ed. 2 (Keay), 1: 561; Amshoff, Pulle Fl. Suriname, 2, 2: 192; Hauman, Fl. Congo Belge, 6: 126, figs. 2–4.

Tall climbing shrubs or herbs or rarely short and erect; leaves pinnately 3-foliolate, often stipellate; stipules deciduous; flowers showy, purple, red, or greenish-yellow, fasciculate-racemose on axillary peduncles, or subcymose; bracts small or caducous; upper 2 calyx-teeth quite connate, lower longer than the others; vexillum complicate, shorter than the wings, appendaged with inflexed auricles at the base; wings oblong or ovate, incurved, often adherent to the keel; keel equal to the wings or longer, apex incurved, acute, or beaked; vexillary stamen free, remainder connate; alternate anthers longer and subbasifixed, others shorter, often barbate, versatile; ovary sessile, villous; ovules few; style filiform, not barbate, stigma small, terminal; fruit thick, ovate, oblong or linear, often clothed with stinging hairs, 2-valved, septate between the seeds or filled, valves coriaceous, variously ribbed or nude; seeds rounded or oblong, hilum short or linear, estrophiolate.

Tribe 37. PHASEOLEAE[1]

Brongn., Diss. Legum. 133 (as Subtribe (1822). *Phaseoleae* Subtribe) *Euphaseoleae*
Benth. & Hook. f., Gen. Pl. 1: 453 (1865)

Herbs, erect, creeping or climbing, sometimes woody at the base; leaves pinnately 3-foliolate, rarely 1- or 5–7-foliolate, leaflets entire or lobed, very rarely gland-dotted; *stipels mostly present*; inflorescence often with *swollen nodes*; bracts small or very caducous, rarely densely imbricate; corolla papilionaceous; petals normal or the *keel long-beaked or spirally twisted*; vexillary filament usually free, sometimes partly connate with the others *into a sheath split adaxially*; *anthers usually uniform*; ovules numerous to few; *style bearded lengthwise* on the inner (adaxial) side, or *pilose only around the stigma*; fruit 2-valved, partitioned or not between the seeds, but not jointed; seeds strophiolate or not; *radicle inflexed*. Type genus *Phaseolus* Lamarck (*emend*. DC.), not Linn. For key to American *Phaseoleae* see Piper, Contrib. U.S. Nat. Herb. 22: 664 (1926).

Keel-petals spirally twisted:
    Style hooded at the apex above the stigma; ovules 3–2; seeds with a linear hilum half around the circumference   **333. Physostigma**
    Style not hooded at the apex:
      Ovules numerous; vexillary (adaxial) filament free from the others:
        Upper or all the calyx-lobes shorter than the tube:
          Bracteoles present   **334. Phaseolus**
          Bracteoles absent   **335. Alepidocalyx**
        All the calyx-lobes as long as or longer than the tube:
          Leaves pinnately 3-foliolate; peduncles 1-flowered; rootstock tuberous
              336. Minkelersia

[1] Tribe **Phaseoleae** (ampl. et emend.). Herbae, erectae, prostratae vel volubiles, interdum basi lignosae; folia pinnatim 3-foliolata, rare 1- vel 5–7-foliolata, foliolis integris vel lobatis plerumque stipellatis; inflorescentia saepe nodosa; bracteae parvae vel caducissimae, rare dense imbricatae; corolla papilionacea; petala interdum spiraliter torta; stamen vexillare liberum, interdum cum ceteris medio connatum; antherae plerumque uniformes; ovula numerosa ad pauca; stylus superne longitudinaliter barbatus, rare circa stigma pilosus; fructus 2-valvis, intus inter semina farctus vel continuus; semina strophiolata vel estrophiolata, radicula inflexa.

Leaves pinnately 3-foliolate or rarely 1-foliolate; peduncles more than
1-flowered   337. **Macroptilium**
Ovules few (4–3); calyx 5-lobed to about the middle; vexillary stamen con-
nate with the others in the middle; flowers crowded in thickened fas-
cicles on slender elongated racemes   338. **Peckelia**
Keel-petals not spirally twisted but sometimes curved:
Fruits ripening above the ground:
Stigma lateral:
Stigma very oblique, not globose; style filiform or thickened or dilated
only in the upper part:
Stamens without a gland at the base of the anthers:
Keel-petals beaked   339. **Oxyrhynchus**
Keel-petals not beaked:
Style with a globose enlargement near the middle   340. **Condylostylis**
Style not enlarged in the middle   341. **Vigna**
Stamens with a gland at the base of each of 5 anthers; keel-petals shortly
beaked   342. **Haydonia**
Stigma globose; style compressed; fruits septate between the seeds
343. **Pachyrrhizus**
Stigma cupular; style dilated in the lower half, bearded above; fruits
septate between the seeds   344. **Dolichopsis**
Stigma terminal:
Stigma bilabiate; stamens monadelphous   345. **Otoptera**
Stigma not bilabiate; adaxial (vexillary) stamen usually free:
Style flattened adaxially and abaxially:
Style ending in a flattened spathulate tip, pubescent on the margin
346. **Sphenostylis**
Style winged laterally, glabrous on the margin   347. **Alistylus**
Style flattened laterally, pubescent in the upper part on the adaxial face
348. **Lablab**
Style more or less terete, not flattened:
Leaves gland-dotted, pinnately 3–5-foliolate, rarely 2-foliolate
349. **Adenodolichos**
Leaves not gland-dotted:
Racemes swollen at the insertion of the pedicels:
Stipules not prolonged below the point of insertion; fruits not winged:
Style glabrous:
Stigma glabrous   350. **Neorautanenia**
Stigma with a ring of hairs below   351. **Dolichos**
Style bearded lengthwise:
Pedicels with a prominent gland at the base of each; Cent. America
352. **Monoplegma**
Pedicels without a gland at the base; trop. Africa 353. **Spathionema**
Stipules produced below the point of insertion; fruits 4-winged
354. **Psophocarpos**
Racemes not swollen at the point of insertion of the pedicels:
Racemes densely flowered, at first covered by large densely imbricate
striate bracts; calyx-teeth about equal   355. **Ramirezella**

Racemes or panicles lax, not covered by bracts as above, these soon deciduous:

Calyx-teeth subequal, small   356. **Endomallus**

Lowermost calyx-lobe long and pointed, longer than the tube   357. **Baukea**

Lowermost calyx-lobe longer than the rest but shorter than the tube   358. **Dysolobium**

Fruits ripening below the ground, transversely oblong, 2-valved, 2–1-seeded; creeping herb; leaves pinnately 3-foliolate, stipellate; flowers bisexual and female   359. **Voandzeia**

333. **Physostigma** Balf. f., Trans. Roy. Soc. Edinb. 22: 310, t. 16 (1861). *Decorsea* R. Vig. (1952). 3–4 spp., trop. Africa, Madagascar; type *P. venenosum* Balf. f. B.H. 1: 538; E.P. 3, 3: 377; Hutch. & Dalz., Fl. W. Trop. Afr. 1: 404; Wilczek, Fl. Congo Belge, 6: 339, fig. 17.

Herbs, woody at the base, or tall climbers; leaves pinnately 3-foliolate, stipellate, leaflets large, sometimes lobulate; stipules very small; flowers fasciculate-racemose on elongated axillary peduncles; rhachis thick and node-like; bracts small, caducous; calyx-teeth very short, broad, upper 2 subconnate; vexillum ovate-orbicular, recurved, appendaged at the base with inflexed auricles; wings obovate-oblong, incurved, free; keel obovate, produced into a subspirally twisted beak; vexillary stamen free, appendaged above the base; anthers uniform; ovary stipitate, 3–2-ovulate; style thickened within the beak of the keel and twisted like it, longitudinally barbate on the inner side, fruit broadly linear, compressed, convex on each side, 2-valved, thinly filled inside with wool-like matter between the seeds; seeds oblong, thick, hilum long, linear, half around the seed, estrophiolate.

334. **Phaseolus**[1] Linn., Sp. Pl. 723 (1753). About 150 spp., warm regions of both hemispheres; type *P. vulgaris* Linn., widely cult. B.H. 1: 538; E.P. 3, 3: 379; Amshoff, Pulle Fl. Suriname, 2, 2: 220; Hassler, Revision of S. Amer. spp., Candollea, 1: 417 (1923); Wilczek, Fl. Congo Belge, 6: 334, t. 27; Burkart, Legum. Argent. ed. 2: 426, fig. 130; Gams in Hegi, Ill. Fl. Mitt.-Eur. 4, 3: 1626, figs. 1599–1604.

Herbs, rarely woody at the base, climbing, prostrate or short and erect; leaves pinnately 3-foliolate, stipellate, very rarely 1-foliolate; stipules persistent, striate; flowers white, yellow, red, violet, or purple, fasciculate-racemose above the middle of axillary peduncles; rhachis node-like; bracts often caducous, stipule-like or very small; bracteoles often broader, sometimes persistent for a time; upper 2 calyx-lobes or teeth connate or free; vexillum orbicular, recurved-spreading or subtwisted, somewhat appendaged at the base by the inflexed margins; wings obovate or rarely oblong, equally or exceeding the vexillum, above the claw adherent to the keel, often twisted; keel linear or obovate, beak long, obtuse, spirally twisted; vexillary stamen free, often thickened above the base or appendaged, remainder connate; anthers uniform; ovary subsessile; ovules numerous; style thickened within the beak of the keel and twisted with it, mostly barbate lengthwise in the upper part, stigma

---

[1] Synonyms of **Phaseolus**: *Candelium* Medik. (1787). *Phasellus* Medik. (1787). *Cadelium* Medik. (1789). *Phasiolus* Moench (1794). *Strophostyles* DC. (1822).* *Caracalla* Tod. (1861). *Lipusa* Alef. (1866). *Phaseolos* St. Lag. (1880). *Rudua* Maekawa (1955).

* Regarded as a separate genus by some botanists; the stipules are sometimes more or less produced at the base, a character of very doubtful generic value.

oblique or introrse; fruit linear or falcate, subterete or compressed, 2-valved, filled inside between the seeds; seeds with a small hilum or shortly linear, estrophiolate.

335. **Alepidocalyx** Piper, Contrib. U.S. Nat. Herb. 22: 672 (1926). 3 spp., S. United States to Mexico; type *A. parvulus* (Greene) Piper.

Perennials with a globose tuber; stems erect or twining above, leaves pinnately trifoliolate, stipellate; bracteoles absent; petals long-clawed, the vexillum with a transverse callosity; characters otherwise as in *Phaseolus*.

336. **Minkelersia** Mart. & Gal., Bull. Acad. Brux. 10, 2: 200 (1843). 4 spp., Mexico; type *M. galactoides* Mart. & Gal. B.H. 1: 539; E.P. 3, 3: 380; Piper, Contrib. U.S. Nat. Herb. 22: 671 (1926).

Creeping or climbing herbs with tuberous rootstock; leaves pinnately 3-foliolate, stipellate; stipules membranous-foliaceous, not produced at the base; peduncles axillary, 1– several-flowered, jointed below the apex, and with 2–3 stipule-like persistent bracts; calyx-lobes oblong, subequal, longer than the tube; vexillum obovate-oblong, erect, folded, not appendaged at the base; wings shorter than the vexillum, obovate-oblong, slightly adherent to the keel; keel linear, spirally twisted at the apex; vexillary stamen free, remainder connate; anthers uniform; ovary sessile; ovules numerous; style elongated, thickened within the beak of the keel and twisted with it, bearded lengthwise in the upper part on the inside; stigma large, oblique or introrsely lateral; fruit elongated-linear, flat, 2-valved; seeds rounded.

337. **Macroptilium** Urb., Symb. Antill. 9: 457 (1928). 8 spp., trop. Amer.; lectotype *M. lathyroides* (Linn.) Urb., West Indies, Trop. America.

Erect or climbing herbs; leaves pinnately 3- very rarely 1-foliolate; stipules not produced below the base, strongly nervose; stipels similar but smaller; peduncles elongated; flowers purplish, violet, or white, wings often more deeply coloured; calyx-tube narrowly campanulate or subtubular, lobes all free, acute, posterior sometimes much reduced; vexillum reflexed above, obovate or orbicular, with 2 small reflexed auricles at the base of the limb; wings much longer than the vexillum, very broad, obovate or suborbicular, erect, 2-auricled below the base of the limb, long-clawed, claw partly adnate to the staminal-tube; keel-petals with 4 broadly linear and boat-shaped, twisted, apex subhooded, claws partly adnate to the staminal tube; vexillary stamen free, sometimes dilated above the base, remainder connate; anthers uniform; ovary subsessile, few- or many-ovuled; style involute and thickened in the upper part, bearded inside below the apex; stigma capitate a little towards the inside; fruit reflexed, linear, subterete or compressed, straight or falcate, 2-valved; seeds numerous or few, hilum short.

338. **Peckelia** Harms, Notizbl. Bot. Gart. Berlin 7: 370 (1920). 1 sp., *P. papuana* (Pulle) Harms, New Guinea.

Herb or shrublet, climbing; leaves trifoliolate; flowers small, crowded in thickened fascicles on slender elongated racemes; calyx 5-lobed to about the middle, upper lobes connate to the middle or higher, oblong, lateral lobes obliquely lanceolate; vexillum shortly clawed, subreniform, rounded, cordate at the base, with a callous fold and auricle above the claw; wings rather long-clawed, obliquely obovate-rounded, subequal, undulate; keel shortly clawed, curved almost at a rectangle, acute and beaked, upper part laterally twisted; stamens 10; vexillary stamen connate with the others in the middle, appendaged above the base; ovary linear, shortly stipitate; ovules 4–3; style slightly laterally twisted and bearded in the upper part, apex obliquely truncate, stigma small; disk tubular, obliquely truncate, encircling the base of the ovary; fruit oblong to suboval, dehiscent, valves chartaceous; seeds 3–2, subglobose, shining, dull dark-brown, with an impressed linear umbilicus, extending for half or two-thirds the circumference.

339. **Oxyrhynchus** T. S. Brandegee, Univ. Calif. Publ. Bot. 4: 270 (1912).
3 spp., S. United States, Mexico, West Indies; type *O. volubilis* Brandeg.,
Mexico. E. V. Piper, Journ. Wash. Acad. Sci. 14: 46, with good fig. (1924)
(new descr.).

Twining perennial herbs; leaves trifoliolate, stipellate; stipules striate; bracteoles ovate; calyx bilabiate, campanulate, lobes rounded, subequal; standard reniform, broader than long, emarginate, with 2 reflexed auricles at the base; wings free, as long as the keel; keel-petals falcate, beaked, partly united; stamens diadelphous, filaments slightly enlarged at the base; ovary with 2–3 ovules; style glabrous except near the apex where bearded on each side with long hairs and at the tip around the lateral stigma; fruits shortly stipitate, straight, cylindric, beaked, terete or compressed, 2–3-seeded; seeds subglobose, hilum extending half the circumference and covered with a white caruncle.

340. **Condylostylis** Piper, Contrib. U.S. Nat. Herb. 22: 667, pl. 64 (1926).
2 spp., Cent. and trop. South America; type *C. venusta* Piper, Costa Rica.

Twining herbs; leaves pinnately trifoliolate; leaflets 3-nerved from the base; stipules and stipels striately nerved; rhachis with glands; bracteoles striately nerved; calyx campanulate, teeth broad, obtuse, short; vexillum orbicular, auriculate, very shortly clawed; wings long-clawed, oblong, constricted below the middle; keel long-clawed; stamens diadelphous, vexillary filament free, anthers equal, oblong; style with an ovoid enlargment in the middle and a spathulate appendage at the tip, bearded below the stigma lower down; stigma lateral; fruit dehiscent, linear, shortly beaked; seeds cylindric, the hilum more than half as long as the seed.

341. **Vigna**[1] Savi, Osserv. Phas. 3: 7 (1824); Nuovo Giorn. Pisa, 8: 113
(1824); Linnaea, 1: 331 (1826). About 150 spp., tropical regions of both
hemispheres; type *V. luteola* (Jacq.) Benth. (*V. repens* (Linn.) O. Ktze.), tropical
and subtropical America. B.H. 1: 539; E.P. 3, 3: 381; Hutch. & Dalz., Fl. W.
Trop. Afr. 1: 407; ed. 2 (Keay), 1: 565. Amshoff, Pulle Fl. Suriname, 2, 2:
230; Wilczek, Fl. Congo Belge, 6: 343, tt. 28–31; Burkart, Legum. Argent.
ed. 2: 417, fig. 127.

Climbing or prostrate herbs, rarely short and erect; leaves pinnately 3-foliolate, stipellate; stipules rarely produced below the base; flowers yellow or rarely purplish, shortly fasciculate-racemose at the top of axillary peduncles, fascicles node-like; bracts and bracteoles small, caducous; 2 upper calyx-teeth or lobes connate or separate; vexillum orbicular, with basal inflexed appendages; wings rather shorter than the vexillum; keel subequal to the wings, incurved, not beaked or produced into an incurved somewhat spiral beak; vexillary stamen free, remainder connate; anthers uniform; ovary sessile; ovules numerous; style filiform or thickened or dilated above, bearded lengthwise in the upper part inside, stigma very oblique or introrsely lateral; fruit linear, straight or scarcely incurved, subterete, 2-valved, filled within between the seeds; seeds reniform or subquadrate, hilum lateral, short, estrophiolate.

342. **Haydonia** Wilczek, Bull. Jard. Bot. Brux. 24: 405 (1954). 2 spp., trop.
Africa; type *H. monophylla* (Taub.) Wilczek. Wilczek, Fl. Congo Belge, 6:
261, t. 24; Hutch. & Dalz., Fl. W. Trop. Afr. ed. 2 (Keay), 1: 565.

Erect or prostrate herbs with woody tuber-like rootstock; stems more or less winged or ribbed; leaves simple and subsessile, or pinnately trifoliolate and petiolate; stipules persistent, not produced at the base, strongly nerved; stipels present or absent; racemes axillary,

---

[1] Synonyms of **Vigna**: *Plectrotropis* Schum. & Thonn. (1827). *Callicysthus* Endl. (1833).
Scytalis E. Mey. (1835). *Strophostyles* E. Mey. (1835). *Liebrechtsia* de Willd. (1902).
Valovaea Chiov.? (1951). *Azukia* Takahashi (1953).

few-flowered, peduncles elongated, ribbed or winged; rhachis glandular; bracts lanceolate, more or less persistent; bracteoles 2, adnate to the calyx-tube; calyx campanulate, 2-lipped, lobes 5, imbricate, subequal, upper 2 lobes connate and 2-toothed; petals shortly clawed, vexillum auriculate at the base and with 2 callosities above the claw; wings spurred at the base; keel shortly beaked; stamens 10, diadelphous, vexillary free, 5 with a gland at the base of each anther, 5 without a gland; ovary several-ovuled; style curved, bearded above in the upper part, stigma oblique; fruit cylindric, linear, straight, 2-valved, valves convex, subterete; seeds separated by a septum, estrophiolate.

343. **Pachyrrhizus** Rich. ex DC., Mém. Légum. 379 (1825) (conserved name). *Cacara* Rumph. ex Thou. (1805). *Taeniocarpum* Desv. (1826). *Pachyrrhizos* Spreng. (1827). *Robynsia* Mart. & Gal. (1843). 2 spp., trop. America, Asia, Australia; type *P. erosus* (Linn.) Urb. B.H. 1: 540; E.P. 3, 3: 383; Burkart, Legum. Argent. ed. 2: 413, fig. 126.

Tall climbing herbs; leaves pinnately 3-foliolate, stipellate, leaflets often angular or sinuately lobed; flowers fasciculate-racemose on long axillary peduncles, fascicles node-like or expanding into a branchlet; bracts and bracteoles small, setaceous, caducous; 2 upper calyx-lobes connate into one 2-toothed lip; vexillum broadly obovate, appendaged at the base with 2 inflexed auricles; wings oblong, falcate; keel incurved, obtuse, equal to the wings; vexillary stamen free, remainder connate; anthers uniform; ovary subsessile; ovules numerous; style subinvolute at the apex, flattened, introrsely pilose, stigma globose, lateral to the inferior side; fruit linear, plano-compressed, transversely depressed outside between the seeds, filled inside; seeds ovate or orbicular-compressed, hilum small, estrophiolate.

344. **Dolichopsis** Hassler, Bull. Herb. Boiss. Ser. 2, 7: 161 (1907). 1 sp., *D. paraguariensis* Hassler, Paraguay, Argentina. Burkart, Legum. Argent. ed. 2: 424, fig. 129.

Climbing or subprostrate herb; stipules not produced at the base; leaves pinnately trifoliolate, stipellate; inflorescence axillary, racemose, very long-pedunculate, nodes thick, 1–2-flowered; calyx campanulate, upper 2 lobes rounded, connate up to five-sixths, lower 3 to one-third, triangular-dentate; vexillum orbicular, appendaged with inflexed basal auricles; wings falcate-obovate; keel incurved, beaked at the apex; vexillary stamen free, filament thickened at the base, remainder connate; anthers linear; ovary subsessile, 10–8-ovuled, villous; style dilated up to the middle, compressed-nodiform and jointed, filiform above, bearded lengthwise; stigma lateral, cupular, bearded with short hairs; fruit reflexed, oblong, slightly falcate, compressed, subseptate between the seeds; funicle spreading; seeds oblong, attached in the middle, parallel with the funicle, aril elongated.

345. **Otoptera** DC., Mem. Leg. 249, t. 42 (1825). 2 spp., S. trop. and S. Africa, Madagascar; type *O. burchellii* DC., S. Africa and S. trop. Africa. Burtt Davy, Fl. Transv. 1, 2: 421 (in *Vigna*, but with footnote).

Shrubs with long trailing branches; leaves glaucous, pinnately 3-foliolate, leaflets lanceolate, apiculate, pinnately nerved, nerves branched within the margin; stipules lanceolate, striate, produced downwards at the base; stipels paired, linear-subulate, persistent; flowers blue, paired at the top of axillary peduncles; bracts subulate-lanceolate; bracteoles 2, closely subtending the calyx, closely nerved; calyx widely campanulate, 4-lobed (upper 2 lobes completely connate); corolla papilionaceous; vexillum oblong-orbicular, clawed, with 2 close callosities at the base of the limb; wings and keel nearly as long as the vexillum, auriculate at the base of the limb; stamens 10; vexillary filament adnate for about one-third to the remainder, these united into a sheath split adaxially; anthers uniform, dorsifixed near the base, versatile; calyx deciduous in the ripe fruit; fruit linear, turgid, dehiscent, valves curling when ripe, filled between the seeds with spongy tissue; seeds several, oblong-kidney-shaped, blackish, with a very small hilum in the middle, estrophiolate.

346. **Sphenostylis** E. Mey., Comm. Pl. Afr. Austr. 148 (1835). 18 spp., trop. and S. Africa; type *S. marginata* E. Mey., S. Africa. Wilczek, Fl. Congo Belge, 6: 273, t. 25; Bak. f., Legum. Trop. Afr. 2: 418; Hutch. & Dalz., Fl. W. Trop. Afr. 1: 407; ed. 2 (Keay), 1: 564.

Prostrate or climbing herbs or erect shrubs, often with underground tubers; leaves alternate, pinnately 3-foliolate; stipules not produced at the point of insertion, more or less persistent; stipels persistent; racemes axillary, few- or several-flowered; rhachis swollen at the insertion of the pedicels; bracts striate; bracteoles 2 at the base of the calyx; calyx-tube cupular, longer than the limb; limb 2-lipped; corolla papilionaceous; vexillum without appendages on the inner face; wings longer than the keel; keel obtuse; stamens 10, vexillary free; 5 anthers dorsifixed, 5 subbasifixed; ovary subsessile, many-ovuled; disk annular; style twisted, enlarged and flattened upwards into a spathulate top pubescent on the inner face and margins; stigma terminal; fruit linear, straight, flattened, dehiscent, more or less spongy between the seeds, becoming spirally twisted after dehiscence; style more or less persistent; seeds 5 or more, cylindric or ellipsoid.

347. **Alistylus** N. E. Br., Kew Bull. 1921: 294. 1 sp., *A. bechuanicus* N. E. Br., Bechuanaland and N. Transvaal.

Procumbent or prostrate perennial herbs; stems terete; leaves pinnately trifoliolate, stipellate; leaflets rhomboid, more or less 3-lobed, 3-nerved at the base; stipules ovate, closely nerved lengthwise, persistent; racemes axillary, few-flowered on very long peduncles which in fruit increase in length; bracts small, deciduous; bracteoles absent; calyx campanulate, shortly 5-toothed; vexillum orbicular, with 2 callosities at the base; wings gibbous near the base; keel incurved, very blunt; stamens monadelphous in the middle, diadelphous at the base and apex; anthers uniform, ovoid, dorsifixed near the base; ovary 5-ovuled; style abruptly inflexed at a right angle, flat, indurated and narrowly winged on each side, glabrous; stigma terminal, truncate, glabrous; fruit (young) arcuate, flat, about 5-seeded, style persistent for some time.

348. **Lablab** Savi, Mém. Phaséol. 2: 19; DC. Prodr. 2: 401. *Lablavia* D. Don (1834). 2 spp., type *L. niger* Medik., tropics generally (*Dolichos lablab* Linn.). Wilczek, Fl. Congo Belge, 6: 279, fig. 9 (1954); Hepper in Hutch. & Dalz., Fl. W. Trop. Afr. ed. 2 (Keay), 1: 571 (1958).

Erect or climbing herb; leaves pinnately 3-foliolate; stipules reflexed, persistent; stipels lanceolate; flowers in axillary racemes longer than the leaves; rhachis swollen at the insertion of the pedicels; bracts soon caducous; calyx-tube campanulate, longer than the lobes, bilabiate, upper lip entire or emarginate, lower 3-lobed; vexillum orbicular, reflexed, auriculate at the base, with 2 callosities on the inner face; wings longer than the keel; keel beaked, incurved at a right angle; stamens 10, vexillary filament free, remainder connate into a sheath; anthers uniform; disk lobed; ovules several, style incurved at a right angle, flattened laterally, barbate with soft hairs towards the top on the adaxial face; stigma terminal, glabrous; fruits obliquely oblong-falcate, beaked by the style; seeds slightly compressed, dark brown, with a white aril exceeding more than half the length.

349. **Adenodolichos** Harms, Engl. Bot. Jahrb. 26: 319 (1899); ic. 33: 179 (1902). About 15 spp., trop. Africa; lectotype *A. rhomboideus* (O. Hoffm.) Harms. Wilczek, Fl. Congo Belge, 6: 392, t. 32; Bak. f., Legum. Trop. Afr. 2: 454; Hutch. & Dalz., Fl. W. Trop. Afr. 1: 410.

Herbs, shrublets, or shrubs, erect or straggling, glandular; leaves alternate, opposite or subverticillate, pinnately 3- (5-) foliolate, sometimes 2-foliolate by abortion; stipules not prolonged at the base, more or less persistent; stipels rarely absent; leaflets glandular below;

inflorescence racemose or paniculate; rhachis swollen at the insertion of the pedicels; bracts present; bracteoles 2; calyx-tube shorter than the lobes, 2-lipped, upper lip 2-lobed, rarely entire, lower lip 3-lobed; petals clawed; vexillum longer than the others, obovate to orbicular, with 2 callosities at the base; wing longer than the keel, latter truncate at the apex; stamens 10, vexillary free, remainder partly connate; 5 anthers dorsifixed, 5 basifixed; ovary shortly stipitate, 2-ovuled; style curved, laterally flattened, villous on the inner face towards the top; stigma terminal; fruit obliquely oblong, wider upwards, more or less glandular, dehiscent; seeds 2, subglobose.

350. **Neorautanenia** Schinz, Bull. Herb. Boiss. 7: 35 (1899). *Bisrautanenia* O. Ktze. (1903). 8 spp., trop. and S. Africa; type *N. amboensis* Schinz, S. Africa. Hutch. & Dalz., Fl. W. Trop. Afr. ed. 2 (Keay), 1: 563.

Prostrate or climbing herbs, sometimes with a large turnip-like rootstock; leaves pinnately trifoliolate, petiolate; stipules 2, persistent; stipels present; racemes axillary, more or less densely flowered rhachis swollen at the nodes; bracts caducous; bracteoles absent; calyx 2-lipped, upper lip 2-toothed, lower 3-lobed to the middle; petals clawed; vexillum suborbicular, auricled at the base, without appendages; wings spurred at the base; keel incurved, obtuse; stamens 10, vexillary free or more or less coherent; anthers equal, dorsifixed; ovary sessile, 8–3-ovuled; disk present; style thicker towards the base, glabrous; stigma capitate, terminal, glabrous; fruit oblong-linear, dehiscent, partitioned; seeds 8–3, subglobose, with a large short funicle.

351. **Dolichos**[1] Lam. emend. DC., Mém. Lég. 381 partly (1826), not of Linn. (2). About 100 spp., tropics and subtropics; lectotype *D. uniflorus* Lam. (*D. biflorus* auct. not Linn. acc. to Brenan, Nyasaland Pl. Mem. N. York. Bot. Gard. 8: 411 (1954)); India, trop. Africa. Wilczek, Fl. Congo Belge, 6: 290 (1954); Hutch. & Dalz., Fl. W. Trop. Afr. ed. 2 (Keay), 1: 569.

Herbs or undershrubs, stems often climbing, prostrate or erect; sometimes with large carrot-like rootstock; leaves pinnately 3-foliolate, sometimes the rhachis short and then subdigitate and with longitudinal nerves; stipules not prolonged at the base, rarely large and foliaceous; stipels more or less persistent, filiform to orbicular; racemes axillary or terminal, sometimes subumbellate, or flowers axillary or solitary; calyx bilabiate, upper lip entire, 2-toothed or 2-lobed, lower lip 3-lobed; petals clawed; vexillum orbicular, often with inflexed auricles at the base; wings more or less adherent to the keel; keel incurved, often beaked but not spirally twisted; vexillary stamen free, remainder connate into an open sheath; anthers uniform; ovary 2- or more-ovulate; disk present; style swollen and more or less twisted towards the base or narrowed from the base to the tip, glabrous or shortly pubescent all over, sometimes only with a ring of hairs around the terminal capitate stigma; fruit straight or arcuate, flattened, not septate; seeds more or less flattened, arillate or strophiolate, hilum short, usually central.

352. **Monoplegma** Piper, Journ. Wash. Acad. Sci. 10: 432 (1920). 1 sp., *M. trinervium* (Donn. Smith) Piper, Cent. America. Piper, Contrib. U.S. Nat. Herb. 22: 664 (1926).

Herb; leaves pinnately trifoliolate; leaflets entire, 3-nerved from the base, the two lateral nerves nearly as large as the midrib; stipules and stipels nervose; flowers in racemes, each pedicel with prominent glands at the base; calyx campanulate, 2-lipped, the upper lip broad, emarginate, as long as the tube, the lower lip with 3 broad ovate lobes nearly as long as the upper lip, the median lobe smallest; standard orbicular, emarginate, biauriculate at base,

---

[1] Synonyms of **Dolichos**: *Macrotyloma* Wight & Arn. (1834). *Dolichus* E. Mey. (1835), *Dipogon* Liebm. (1854). *Dolichovigna* Hayata (1920).

shortly unguiculate, with a narrow thick gland near the middle of the petal; wings spathulate, unguiculate, obtuse and hooded at apex, without a median auricle; keel geniculate, unguiculate, blunt at apex, as long as but broader than the wings; stamens diadelphous, the vexillary one free; anthers small; style hairy on the inner side; stigma lanceoloid, terminal; pod large, woody, 1- or 2-seeded, a small longitudinal ridge on each valve very near the ventral suture, the inner layer of the pod not separating at maturity; seed globose, the narrow linear hilum covered with spongy tissue and extending for three-fifths of the circumference.

353. **Spathionema** Taub., Engl. Pflanzenw. Ostafr. C. 224 (1895). 1 sp. *S. kilimandscharicum* Taub., E. trop. Africa. E.P.N. 203.

Climbing shrublet, with slender whip-like branches; leaves developed after the flowers; stipules and stipels present; racemes lateral, few-flowered, the rhachis much swollen at the nodes; flowers showy; calyx campanulate, upper 2 lobes connate, villous inside; vexillum dull green outside, blue-violet inside like the wings, keel whitish-blue; 2 upper calyx-teeth connate into 1 emarginate, 2 lateral broad, obtuse, lower triangular-acute; vexillum suborbicular, shortly clawed, 2-auricled; wings obliquely obovate-oblong, 1-toothed, transversely callose, slightly longer than the vexillum; keel-petals a little shorter, coherent with the wings, clawed, connate on the back and above to the middle; vexillary stamen connate only at the base with the other united longer 9 and towards the apex dilated into a spathulate lamina and shortly cuspidate at the tip; anthers dorsifixed, oval; ovary very shortly stipitate; style much elongated, thickened in the middle, bearded inside in the upper part, stigma saucer-like; ovules 2; fruit shortly oblong, 2-valved; seeds kidney-shaped, flattened, dark brown and shining, with hilum near the middle.

354. **Psophocarpos** Neck., Elem. 3: 45 (1790) (conserved name). *Botor* Adans. (1763). *Diesingia* Endl. (1832). *Psilocarpus* Pritz. (1866). *Vigneopsis* De Wild (1902). 5 spp., trop Asia and Africa, Madagascar, 1 naturalized in trop. America; type *P. tetragonolobus* (Linn.) DC., Mauritius. Wilczek, Fl. Congo Belge, 6: 80, figs. 10, 11; Hutch. & Dalz., Fl. W. Trop. Afr. 1: 411; ed. 2 (Keay), 1: 572.

Tall climbing herbs; leaves pinnately 3-foliolate, stipellate; stipules membranous, produced below the base; flowers lilac or violet, fasciculate-racemose at the top of often long axillary peduncles, nodes swollen; bracts small, very caducous; bracteoles larger, membranous, persistent for a time; 2 upper calyx-lobes connate into 1 emarginate or 2-lobed; vexillum suborbicular, appendaged with basal auricles; wings obliquely obovate; keel incurved at the apex, obtuse; vexillary stamen free at the base, connate in the middle with the others; anthers uniform; ovary shortly stipitate; ovules numerous; style thickened above the ovary, subulate, incurved, bearded lengthwise, stigma globose, terminal or introverted, very densely penicillate-villous; fruit 4-sided, 4-winged lengthwise, 2-valved, filled between the seeds; seeds transversely oblong, hilum lateral, oblong, estrophiolate.

355. **Ramirezella** Rose, Contrib. U.S. Nat. Herb. 8: 44 (1903). About 8 spp., Cent. America; type *R. strobilophora* (Robinson) Rose, Mexico. Piper, Contrib. U.S. Nat. Herb. 22: 669 (1927). Morton, Contrib. U.S. Nat. Herb. 29: 84 (in *Phaseolus*) (1944).

Tall twining woody plants; leaves pinnately 3-foliolate; leaflets ovate, acuminate; stipules and stipels present; inflorescence a dense axillary raceme, at first covered by large densely imbricate striate bracts; bracteoles at base of calyx small, ovate; calyx campanulate; teeth 5, about equal; corolla large and showy, purple and white; standard orbicular, with scale-like appendages at the base; wings auriculate on the upper side; keel elongated, straight at the base but bent in the middle nearly at a right angle and at the tip curved inwards; stamens 10, diadelphous; style bearded near the end; stigma oblique; fruit straight, oblong, turgid, dehiscent; seeds orbicular, embedded in a white spongy mass.

356. **Endomallus** Gagnep., Lecomte Not. Syst. 3: 184 (1915). 2 spp., Indo-China; lectotype *E. pellitus* Gagnep.

Climbing shrubs; leaves pinnately trifoliolate; stipules ovate-acuminate, persistent; stipels subulate; racemes or panicles terminal; bracts and bracteoles minute or absent; nodes not tumid; flowers showy; calyx campanulate, teeth small, as long as the tube, upper 2 connate to the middle; petals subequal; vexillum a little longer than the wings, with 2 scales above the base; wings auriculate; keel obtriangular, beak oblique, short; stamens diadelphous, the vexillary free; anthers equal; ovary densely silky, sessile, many-ovuled; style longer than the ovary, filiform, curved and hardened above, glabrous; stigma globose, terminal capitate.

357. **Baukea** Vatke, Linnaea, 43: 104 (1880–2). 1 sp., *B. maxima* (Boj.) Baill. (*B. insignis* Vatke), Madagascar. E.P. 3, 3: 361.

Arborescent climbing shrub; leaves pinnately trifoliolate, stipellate; leaflets entire, lateral oblique; stipules sessile, narrower from a broader base, aristate; flowers showy, yellowish, in axillary racemes; bracts and bracteoles caducous; upper 2 calyx-lobes connate into a 2-toothed lobe, ciliate, lower much longer and pointed; vexillum broadly obovate-oblong, with inflexed auricles at the base; wings oblong, adherent to the keel; keel oblong, obtuse, longer than the wings, not beaked; vexillary stamen free, remainder connate; anthers basifixed, uniform; ovary stipitate, villous; ovules 3; style subulate, barbate lengthwise; stigma globose, terminal, glabrous; fruit 2-valved.

358. **Dysolobium** Prain, Journ. Asiat. Soc. Bengal, 66: 425 (1897). 4 spp., E. India to China and Malaya; type *D. dolichoides* (Roxb.) Prain, India, Thailand, Java.

Twiners, usually woody, with 3-foliolate, stipellate leaves; flowers in copious axillary racemes, bracteoles inconspicuous, deciduous; calyx campanulate, the lower tooth lanceolate longer than the rest, but shorter than the tube, the two uppermost connate; corolla much exserted, keel beaked and sometimes distinctly curved and laterally deflexed; stamens diadelphous; anthers uniform; ovary sessile, many-ovuled, style filiform, bearded below the oblique stigma; pod thick, woody, subterete, oblong, villous, very markedly septate, with double septa between the velvety seeds.

359. **Voandzeia** Thou., Gen. Nov. Madag. 23 (1806). *Cryptolobus* Spreng. (1826). *Geolobus* Raf. (1836). 1 sp. *V. subterranea* Thou., trop. Africa; widely cult. B.H. 1: 539; E.P. 3, 3: 380; Hutch. & Dalz., Fl. W. Trop. Afr. 1: 411.

Creeping herb; leaves long-petiolate, pinnately 3-foliolate, stipellate; peduncles short, axillary, few-flowered, recurved after flowering; bisexual flowers small, pale yellow, fertile flowers apetalous, female; bracts and bracteoles small, striate; upper 2 calyx-teeth or lobes connate into one emarginate, lower longer; vexillum orbicular, appendaged with small, inflexed, auricle; wings oblong-obovate; keel equal to the wings, slightly incurved, obtuse; vexillary stamen free, remainder connate; anthers uniform; ovary subsessile, few-ovuled; style incurved, bearded in the upper part, stigma introrsely lateral, oblong; fruit maturing below the soil, transversely oblong, 2-valved, nude inside, 1–2-seeded; seeds subglobose, hilum shortly oblong.

Tribe 38. GLYCINEAE

Benth., Ann. Wien. Mus. 2: 112 (1838). Tribe *Phaseoleae* Subtribe *Glycineae*
Benth. & Hook. f., Gen. Pl. 1: 451 (1865)

Shrubs (rarely trees) or herbs, often climbing; leaves pinnately 3- or more-foliolate, rarely some 1-foliolate, very rarely digitate; *stipules and stipels always present*; flowers fasciculate or racemose in the leaf-axils, solitary or paired on the rhachis, now and then a few flowers apetalous; bracteoles often rather large and closely striate, mostly adpressed to the calyx; vexillum sometimes large and reversed by the *resupination of the flowers*; vexillary stamen free or connate with the others from the base upwards into an open sheath; *anthers uniform* or very rarely dimorphic or some aborted; *style glabrous* or rarely bearded; fruit dehiscent, 2-valved, filled or empty between the seeds; seeds carunculate or strophiolate. Type genus *Glycine* Linn.

Anthers more or less uniform in size and shape, all fertile:
Style bearded along the adaxial surface; flowers resupinate, the vexillum very large and flag-like; bracteoles large, opposite; fruits compressed, sometimes with a longitudinal rib along the middle of the valves; trees, shrubs, or herbs   360. **Clitoria**
Style glabrous except rarely only around the stigma:
Vexillum spurred or gibbous on the back of the short claw, large and broadly orbicular; bracteoles large and adpressed to the calyx; leaves pinnately 3- rarely 5–7-foliolate, 1-foliolate, rarely digitate; shrubs or herbs, prostrate or climbing   361. **Centrosema**
Vexillum neither spurred nor gibbous:
Upper suture of the fruit winged; stem woody; racemes in terminal panicles; leaves pinnately 3–11-foliolate, leaflets large; bracteoles minute, very caducous; disk crenulate   362. **Platycyamus**
Upper suture of fruit not winged:
Mouth of the cylindric calyx-tube obliquely truncate, with obsolete teeth; style filiform but dilated above the middle; fruit torulose between the blue or black seeds   363. **Dumasia**
Mouth of the rather shortly tubular calyx more or less regularly lobed or 2-lipped; style not dilated:
*Bracteoles present; bracts more or less persistent:
Bracteoles larger than the bracts and adpressed to the calyx, usually closely nervose-striate, sometimes at first hiding the flower:
Leaves pinnately 3-foliolate or the lower 1-foliolate; peduncles 1-flowered, often much elongated, axillary or irregularly racemose at the ends of the branches; trop. America   364. **Periandra**
Leaves always pinnately 3-foliolate, leaflets large and ovate; racemes axillary and terminal, crowded into panicles; Indo-China
365. **Diphyllarium**
Bracteoles smaller than the bracts:
Erect herbs or subshrubs:
Seeds with a scale-like papery caruncle; bracts and bracteoles more or less membranous and caducous   374. **Glycine**

Seeds with a conspicuous cartilaginous arilloid strophiole around the hilum; bracts and bracteoles accrescent, stiff, persistent, linear-setaceous; inflorescence subcapitate

366. **Pseudoeriosema**

Climbing shrubs or climbing or procumbent herbs:

Ovary stipitate; lower calyx-lobes the longest; vexillary stamen free; fruits linear, compressed, straight or incurved, subseptate between the seeds; trop. and subtrop. America   367. **Cologania**

Ovary sessile or subsessile; other characters above not associated:

Calyx-lobes or teeth more or less equal, the upper 2 not more connate than the others:

Creeping herbs rooting at the nodes; ovules 4–2; fruits septate; leaves subdigitately 3-foliolate; West Indies   368. **Herpyza**

Twining or climbing herbs, not rooting at the nodes:

Seeds with a scale-like papery caruncle; leaflets 5–7, rarely 3; calyx-lobes with wide petaloid margins; style persistent, indurated in fruit   369. **Pseudoglycine**

Seeds with a conspicuous arilloid strophiole; leaflets 1–7; calyx-lobes not petaloid; style not as above   370. **Paraglycine**

Calyx-lobes or teeth more or less unequal owing to the upper 2 being connate higher up or to the apex:

Upper 2 calyx-teeth completely united giving a 4-toothed calyx:

Fruits septate between the seeds; vexillum suberect

371. **Shuteria**

Fruits continuous within; vexillum erect   372. **Amphicappa**

Upper 2 calyx-teeth free at least at the apex giving a 5-toothed calyx:

Calyx truncate or inflexed at the base, the teeth silky inside; pedicels conspicuously nodose and jointed at the base

373. **Teyleria**

Calyx tapered at the base, lobes or teeth glabrous inside; pedicels scarcely nodose or jointed   374. **Glycine**

*Bracteoles absent; bracts deciduous, usually very small:

Vexillum appendaged with often small auricles; leaflets mostly broad and obovate or rounded; fruit septate between the seeds; Australia   375. **Kennedya**

Vexillum not appendaged:

Keel-petals shorter than the wings   376. **Hardenbergia**

Keel-petals nearly equal to the wings   377. **Vandasia**

Anthers dimorphic or half of them sterile:

Anthers alternately dorsifixed and basifixed, the latter on longer filaments, all fertile; erect shrublet; leaves pinnately 3-foliolate, the pair of leaflets near the base of the rhachis; vexillary filament free

378. **Clitoriopsis**

Anthers alternately small and sterile; climbing herbs; leaves pinnately 3-foliolate; vexillary filament connate with the others into a sheath; fruits uncinate   379. **Teramnus**

360. **Clitoria**[1] Linn., Sp. Pl. 753 (1753). About 30 spp., warm reg. of both hemispheres; type *C. ternatea* Linn., cosmopol. tropics. B.H. 1: 528; E.P. 3, 3: 357; Amshoff, Pulle Fl. Suriname, 2, 2: 176; Wilczek, Fl. Congo Belge, 6: 264, fig. 7; Burkart, Legum. Argent. ed. 2, 379, fig. 112; Hutch. & Dalz., Fl. W. Trop. Afr. 1: 405.

Shrubs or herbs, rarely trees, sometimes climbing; leaves pinnately 3–more-foliolate, rarely unifoliolate, stipellate; stipules persistent, striate; flowers showy, purplish, blue, white, or red, racemose or 1–2 axillary or on old wood; pedicels often paired; bracts persistent, stipule-like, paired, lower opposite, upper connate into one; bracteoles usually large, striate, persistent; upper 2 lobes of the tubular calyx subconnate, lowermost narrower; vexillum large and flag-like, erect, emarginate, not appendaged; wings falcate-oblong, spreading, adherent in the middle to the keel; keel shorter than the wings, incurved, acute; vexillary stamen free or more or less connate with the others; anthers uniform; ovary stipitate, many-ovuled; style elongated, incurved, bearded lengthwise above; fruit stipitate, linear, compressed, slightly thickened on the upper or both sutures, flat or convex, nude or with a longitudinal rib, 2-valved, filled or continuous inside; seeds subglobose or compressed.

361. **Centrosema**[2] Benth., Ann. Wien. Mus. 2: 117 (1838) (conserved name). About 50 spp., America, introd. elsewhere; type *C. brasilianum* (Linn.) Benth., trop. America. B.H. 1: 527; E.P. 3, 3: 358; Amshoff, Pulle Fl. Suriname, 2, 2: 182; Wilczek, Fl. Congo Belge, 6: 271, fig. 8; Burkart, Legum. Argent. ed. 2, 377, fig. 111.

Shrubs or herbs, prostrate or climbing; leaves pinnately 3- rarely 5–7-foliolate, 1-foliolate, or digitately 3–5-foliolate, leaflets entire, stipellate; stipules persistent, striate; flowers showy, white, violet, rose, or bluish; peduncles axillary, single or paired, 1- or more-flowered; lower bracts stipule-like, paired, upper united into 1 and striate; pedicels 1–2 to each bract; bracteoles adpressed to the calyx, striate, sometimes much larger than the bracts; lobes or teeth of the shortly campanulate calyx subequal or the upper 2 connate; vexillum broadly orbicular, shortly spurred or rarely slightly gibbous at the back near the base, claw short, incurved, folded; wings falcate-obovate; keel broad, incurved, scarcely shorter than the wings; vexillary stamen free or more or less connate with the others; anthers uniform; ovary subsessile, many-ovuled; style incurved, bearded around the terminal stigma; fruit subsessile, linear, flat, 2-valved, subseptate between the seeds, each suture thickened, valves with a rather prominent nerve near each margin or winged next the lower suture, sometimes with a sword-like point; seeds transversely oblong or subglobose, thick or compressed, shortly arillate, hilum small.

Used as a cover-crop.

362. **Platycyamus** Benth., Fl. Brasil. 15, 1: 323 (1862). 2 spp., trop. South America; type *P. regnellii* Benth., Brazil. B.H. 1: 531; E.P. 3, 3: 363.

Stem woody; leaves pinnately 3–11-foliolate, stipellate, leaflets large; stipules deciduous; flowers in terminal panicles of racemes, solitary in each bract; bracts small, deciduous; bracteoles minute, very caducous; calyx-lobes short, upper 2 connate into 1 emarginate; vexillum suborbicular, narrowed at the base, not appendaged; wings subfalcate-oblong; keel subequal to the wings, petals free; vexillary stamen free, remainder connate; anthers uniform; disk crenulate; ovary sessile, many-ovuled; style filiform, incurved, beardless,

---

[1] Synonyms of **Clitoria**: *Neurocarpum* Desv. (1813). *Vexillaria* Raf. (1818). *Martia* Leandr. Sacr. (1821). *Martiusia* Schult. (1822). *Ternatea* H. B. & K. (1823). *Nauchea* Descourt. (1825). *Rhombifolium* Rich. ex DC. (1825). ?*Glycinopsis* DC. (1825). *Clytoria* J. S. Presl (1835). *Neurocarpus* Hassk. (1844). *Macrotrullion* Klotzsch (1848). *Rhombolobium* Rich. ex Pfeiffer (1874).

[2] Synonyms of **Centrosema**: *Bradburya* Raf. (1817). *Bradburia* Spreng. (1826). *Vexillaria* Hoffmgg. (1824). *Centrosema* DC. (1825). *Cruminium* Desv. (1826). *Steganotropis* Lehm. (1826). *Platysema* Hoffmgg. ex Benth. (1838). *Pilanthus* Poit. ex Endl. (1841).

stigma small, terminal; fruit large, broadly linear, compressed, 2-valved, upper suture winged; seeds broadly reniform, compressed, estrophiolate.

363. **Dumasia** DC., Ann. Sci. Nat. 4: 96 (1825). About 10 spp., Asia, Madagascar, Africa; type *D. villosa* DC., India, China, Malaya, New Guinea, trop. Africa, S. Africa, Madagascar. B.H. 1: 529; E.P. 3, 3: 359.

Climbing herbs; leaves pinnately 3-foliolate, stipellate; stipules setaceous or striate; flowers yellow, in axillary racemes, solitary or paired on the rhachis; bracts small, narrow; bracteoles minute, subulate or lanceolate; calyx-tube cylindric, gibbous dorsally at the base, mouth obliquely truncate, teeth obsolete; vexillum obovate, erect, margins above the claw auriculate and slightly inflexed; wings falcate-obovate, adherent to the keel; keel rather shorter than the wings, slightly incurved, obtuse; vexillary stamen free, remainder connate; anthers uniform; ovary substipitate, many-ovuled; style filiform, dilated above the middle, inflexed in the upper part and subulate, beardless, stigma terminal; fruit subsessile, narrow, compressed, torulose by the seeds, 2-valved, continuous within; seeds subglobose, estrophiolate, blue or black.

364. **Periandra** Mart. ex Benth., Ann. Wien. Mus. 2: 120 (1838). *Glycinopsis* O. Ktze. (1891). 6 spp., Cent. America, Brazil; type *P. mediterranea* (Vell.) Taub. (*P. dulcis* Mart. ex Benth.). B.H. 1: 528; E.P. 3, 3: 358.

Shrubs or herbs, erect or climbing; leaves pinnately 3-foliolate or the lower 1-foliolate, stipellate; stipules striate; peduncles 1-flowered, often much elongated, axillary or irregularly racemose at the ends of the branches; bracts paired, like the stipules, upper united; bracteoles large and adpressed to the calyx, striate; flowers blue or scarlet; teeth of the shortly campanulate calyx short, upper 2 subconnate, lower longer; vexillum broadly obovate or orbicular, nude at the back, claw short, incurved, folded; wings obliquely obovate or oblong; keel broad, incurved, scarcely shorter than the wings; vexillary stamen free or more or less connate with the others, filaments filiform; anthers uniform; ovary subsessile, many-ovuled; style incurved, slightly clavate at the apex, stigma terminal, beardless; fruit subsessile, linear, acuminate, flat, thickened along each suture, 2-valved; seeds compressed, estrophiolate.

365. **Diphyllarium** Gagnep., Lecomte Not. Syst. 3: 183 (1915). 1 sp., *D. mekongense* Gagnep., Indo-China.

Climbing shrublet; leaves pinnately 3-foliolate, leaflets large, ovate; stipules and stipels persistent; racemes axillary and terminal, crowded into panicles; nodes not tumid; bracts stipule-like, persistent; bracteoles 2, larger than the bracts, at first hiding the flowers; flowers 2–3 together at the nodes, rose; calyx shortly tubular-campanulate, upper and lower teeth longer, lateral 2 scarcely equalling the tube; petals equal, all shortly clawed; vexillum orbicular, not appendaged; wings and keel similar, almost straight; stamens diadelphous; anthers equal; ovary sessile, many-ovuled; style almost straight, subglabrous, subulate, stigma terminal, point-like; fruit flat, linear, entire, sessile, 2-valved; seeds arranged lengthwise, orbicular-reniform, hilum subbasal, ovate.

366. **Pseudoeriosema** Hauman, Bull. Jard. Bot. Brux. 25: 96 (1955); Fl. Congo Belge, 6: 107, t. 9. 6 spp., trop. Africa; type *P. andongense* (Welw.) Hauman.

Erect herbs, or more or less sarmentose, or shrublets, covered with long white hairs; leaves 1–3-foliolate, rather large, prominently reticulate below; inflorescence racemose, axillary or terminal and more or less capitate-paniculate; bracts linear, more or less persistent; flowers small, bibracteolate; calyx 5-toothed; corolla scarcely exceeding the calyx, whitish, villous outside; stamens 10, diadelphous; ovary 2-ovuled, style short, stigma capitate, glabrous; fruit ovate-oblong, 2-seeded, long-villous; seeds small, oblong, with a short median hilum, funicle dilated at the apex.

367. **Cologania** Kunth, Mimos. 204, tt. 57, 58 (1823). About 15 spp., trop. America, Argentina; type *C. procumbens* Kunth. B.H. 1: 529; Burkart, Legum. Argent. ed. 2, 385, fig. 114.

Climbing or procumbent herbs; rootstock sometimes tuber-like; leaves pinnately 3-foliolate, very rarely 1- or 5-foliolate, stipellate; stipules small or striate; flowers violet or red, axillary, solitary, fasciculate or in short racemes; bracts and bracteoles persistent, either lanceolate and striate or linear or setaceous; upper 2 teeth or lobes of the tubular calyx connate high up or to the apex, lower longer; vexillum obovate, narrowed into a broad claw, erect, sides reflexed; wings obliquely oblong, slightly adherent to the keel; keel shorter than the wings, slightly incurved, obtuse; vexillary stamen free, remainder connate; anthers uniform, or alternately a little smaller; ovary stipitate, many-ovuled; style incurved, shortly subulate, beardless, stigma terminal, capitate; fruit linear, compressed, straight or incurved, 2-valved, subseptate between the seeds; seeds compressed, orbicular or subquadrate, estrophiolate, hilum oblong.

368. **Herpyza** Ch. Wright, Sauvalle Fl. Cubana, Anal. Acad. Cienc. Med. 5: 335 (1869); Urb. Symb. Antill. 5: 368, with fig. (1908). 1 sp., *H. grandiflora* (Griseb.) Ch. Wright, Cuba.

Creeping herb rooting at the nodes; leaves petiolate, 3-foliolate; stipules free, ovate, striate; stipels linear; leaflets obovate, entire, pinnately nerved, not glandular; racemes axillary, 1–3-flowered; peduncle slender, elongated; bracts subulate; bracteoles at the base of the calyx, persistent; calyx campanulate; lobes 5, subequal, subulate-lanceolate, ciliate; vexillum obovate, auriculate, shortly clawed; wings equal to the vexillum, oblong-spathulate; keel-petals connate except the apex and the claws; stamens 10, vexillary filament free, remainder half connate; anthers all fertile, rounded; ovary sessile, 4–2-ovuled; style glabrous except at base, slender, stigma terminal; fruit sessile, oblong and 2–3-seeded, or 1-seeded and ovate, compressed, septate within, beaked; seeds 4–1, reniform, estrophiolate.

369. **Pseudoglycine** F. J. Hermann, United States Depart. Agric. Tech. Bull. no. 1268: 74, fig. 22 (1962). 1 sp., *P. lyallii* (Benth.) F. J. Hermann, Madagascar.

Twining or climbing herb with rusty hairs; stems slender; leaves mostly 5–7- rarely 3-foliolate, leaflets elliptic, pointed, flowers small, in axillary racemes, fasciculate on the rhachis; bracteoles 2 at the base of the calyx, the latter regularly 5-lobed, lobes except the lowest petaloid, obtuse; corolla whitish-yellow, about twice as long as the calyx, silky outside towards the apex; wings and keel oblong, subequal, as long as the vexillum; stamens 10, diadelphous; ovary 6–8-ovuled; style persistent, hardened and accrescent; fruit linear-oblong, cuspidate; seeds 4–6, transversely oblong, with a membranous scale-like and annular caruncle.

370. **Paraglycine** F. J. Hermann, United States Depart. Agric. Tech. Bull. no. 1268: 52, figs. 13–21 (1962). 10 spp., trop. Africa, Madagascar, trop. and subtrop. Asia; type *P. hedysaroides* (Willd.) F. J. Hermann, trop. Africa.

Climbing or rarely suberect herbs; leaves 1–7-foliolate; inflorescence simple, axillary, more or less nodose; flowers small, bibracteolate, fasciculate on the rhachis; calyx 5-toothed; corolla scarcely twice the length of the calyx; vexillum silky or strigose; stamens 10, diadelphous; ovary 2–8-ovuled; style not persistent; fruit oblong or linear-oblong, compressed, slightly margined; seeds 2–8, oblong, hilum in the middle, short, with a short cartilaginous strophiole and scale-like caruncle.

371. **Shuteria** Wight & Arn., Prodr. Fl. Pen. Or. 1: 207 (1834) (conserved name). 5 spp., trop. and subtrop. Asia; type *S. vestita* Wight & Arn., India,

China, Philippines, Malaya, New Guinea. B.H. 1: 529; E.P. 3, 3: 360; van Steenis, Bull. Bot. Gard. Buitenz. ser. 3, 17: 459 (1948) (as to name).

Slender climbing herbs; leaves pinnately 3-foliolate, stipellate; stipules striate; flowers small, white, rose, or violet, in axillary racemes, paired or fasciculate on the axis; bracts persistent, striate, sometimes foliaceous; bracteoles small, calyx-lobes or teeth short, upper 2 connate to the apex; vexillum obovate, suberect, narrowed into the claw, not appendaged; wings narrow, oblique, adherent to the keel; keel shorter than the wings, almost straight, obtuse; vexillary stamen free, remainder connate; anthers uniform; ovary subsessile; style incurved, filiform, beardless, stigma capitate, terminal; fruit linear, 2-valved, septate; seeds suborbicular or transversely oblong, estrophiolate, hilum small.

372. **Amphicarpa**[1] Elliot, Journ. Acad. Philad. 1: 372 (1818) (conserved name). *Amphicarpaea* Auth. About 10 spp., N. and trop. America, trop. Africa, Himalayas, Cent. and N. Asia; type *A. bracteata* (Linn.) Fernald, North America, Mexico. B.H. 1: 529; E.P. 3, 3: 359; Hauman, Fl. Congo Belge, 6: 89, t. 7; Hutch. & Dalz., Fl. W. Trop. Afr. ed. 2 (Keay), 1: 560.

Climbing herbs; leaves pinnately 3-foliolate, stipellate; stipules striate; flowers violet, blue, or white, in axillary racemes or the lower axillary and solitary, now and then apetalous; bracts striate, 1–2-flowered, persistent; bracteoles setaceous or absent; upper teeth of the tubular calyx connate; vexillum obovate, erect, slightly inflexed-auriculate above the claw; wings falcate-obovate, adherent to the keel; keel rather shorter than the wings, slightly incurved, vexillary stamen free, remainder connate; anthers uniform; ovary subsessile or stipitate, many-ovuled; style inflexed, filiform, beardless, stigma small, terminal; fruit linear or falcate, compressed, 2-valved, continuous within; seeds rather compressed or subglobose, estrophiolate.

373. **Teyleria** Backer, Bull. Jard. Bot. Buitenz. ser. 3, 16: 107 (1939). 1 sp., *T. koordersii* (Backer) Backer, Malay Archip., Hainan. F. J. Hermann, United States Depart. Agric. Tech. Bull. no. 1268: 77, fig. 23 (1962).

Perennial herb, climbing; stems with retrorse hairs; leaves pinnately 3-foliolate; leaflets broadly ovate; stipules small, basifixed; stipels filiform-subulate, small, inflorescence racemose, simple or slightly branched; bracts small, persistent; flowers 3 together at the nodes of the rhachis, small; bracteoles 2 at the base of the calyx, erect, narrow, persistent; calyx-tube campanulate, segments 5, longer than the tube, upper 2 connate high up into a bifid lip; vexillum not auricled; wings long-clawed, adhering to the keel, obtuse, with a retrorse auricle towards the base; keel shorter than the wings, long-clawed, obtuse, partly coherent; vexillary stamen coherent with the others but easily separated; anthers dorsifixed, oval, small; ovary sessile, 8–6-ovuled; style short, curved, glabrous above the base, stigma capitate, small; fruit sessile, linear, shortly beaked, much compressed, slightly compressed and septate between the seeds, 2-valved; seeds 7–4, transversely oval, with a short ligule-like scarious caruncle.

374. **Glycine**[2] Linn., Sp. Pl. 753 (1753). 10 spp., tropical and warm temperate regions of the Old World; type *G. javanica* Linn., trop. Asia and trop. Africa. F. J. Hermann, Revision of the genus *Glycine* and its immediate allies, United States Depart. Agric. Tech. Bull. no. 1268, figs. 1–12 (1962).

Perennial, twining, climbing or procumbent, very rarely erect annual herbs; leaves pinnately trifoliolate, rarely digitate; stipules small; stipels present; flowers very small, in

---

[1] Synonyms of **Amphicarpa**: *Falcata* J. F. Gmel. (1791). *Savia* Raf. (1808). *Xypherus* Raf. (1819). *Amphicarpaea* DC. (1825). *Cryptolobus* Spreng. (1826). *Lobomon* Raf. and *Tetrodea* Raf. (1836).

[2] Synonyms of **Glycine**: *Soja* Moench (1794). *Johnia* Wight & Arn. (1834). *Notonia* Wight & Arn. (1834). *Bujacia* E. Mey. (1835). *Leptolobium* Benth. (1838). *Soya* Benth. (1838). *Leptocyamus* Benth. (1839). *Kennedynella* Steud. (1840). *Chrystolia* Montr. (1901).

axillary solitary racemes, rarely in terminal panicles or in a sessile fascicle in the lower axils; bracts and bracteoles present, small, not accrescent; calyx 5-toothed, subbilabiate, upper pair more connate; petals long-clawed, vexillum suborbicular to obovate or rhomboid; wings narrow, more or less adherent to the keel; keel shorter than the wings, obtuse; stamens 10, monadelphous, or the adaxial filament at length free; ovary subsessile, several-ovuled; style glabrous; stigma terminal, capitate; fruit linear or oblong, straight or falcate, more or less septate between the seeds, 2-valved; seeds ovoid or oblong to subspherical, with a short lateral hilum and a small scale-like thin caruncle.

375. **Kennedya**[1] Vent., Jard. Malm. 2: 104, t. 104 (1804) (conserved name). 15 spp., Australia; type *K. rubicunda* (Schneev.) Vent. B.H. 1: 531; E.P. 3, 3: 361.

Perennial climbing or prostrate herbs; leaves pinnately 3-foliolate, rarely 1- or 5-foliolate, stipellate; stipules broad, striate, sometimes connate; flowers red or blackish, showy, racemose, subumbellate or solitary in the leaf-axils; bracts either similar to the stipules and persistent, or small and very caducous; bracteoles none; calyx-lobes subequal to the tube or a little shorter, upper 2 connate into an upper entire cr emarginate lip; vexillum obovate or orbicular, narrowed into the claw, appendaged with often minute auricles; wings obliquely oblong, adherent to the keel; keel incurved, acute or obtuse; vexillary stamen free, remainder connate; anthers uniform; ovary subsessile or shortly stipitate, many-ovuled; style filiform, inflexed upwards, rarely with a tooth at the apex, beardless, stigma terminal; fruit linear, compressed, terete or turgid, 2-valved, septate between the seeds within, rarely empty, glabrous or villous; seeds ovoid or oblong, hilum lateral, strophiolate.

376. **Hardenbergia** Benth., Hueg. Enum. 40 (1837). 3 spp., Australia, New Guinea; lectotype *H. monophylla* (Vent.) Benth. B.H. 1: 530; E.P. 3, 3: 361.

Climbing shrublets or herbs with long carrot-like root; leaves 1- or 3-foliolate, stipellate; stipules striate, often small; flowers small, violet, in elongated axillary racemes or terminal panicles, paired or fasciculate on the axis; bracts small, deciduous or the lower persistent; bracteoles none; calyx-teeth short, upper 2 connate; vexillum broadly orbicular, not appendaged; wings falcate-obovate, adherent to the keel; keel incurved, obtuse, often much shorter than the wings; vexillary stamen free, remainder connate; anthers uniform; ovary sessile, many-ovuled; style short, thick, incurved, beardless, stigma terminal, capitate; fruit linear, compressed or cylindric, 2-valved, full or vacant between the seeds; seeds ovoid or oblong, hilum short, lateral, strophiolate.

377. **Vandasia** Domin, Biblioth. Bot. 22: 774 (1926). 1 sp., *V. retusa* (Benth.) Domin, New Guinea, Queensland.

Handsome climbing shrub; leaves large, trifoliolate, leaflets broadly obcordate or obovate-truncate and emarginate, all pinnately nerved, transversely veined and finely reticulate, stipellate; stipules ovate and ovate-lanceolate, subauriculate; flowers showy, violet and spotted with yellow, fasciculate and the fascicles racemose, racemes in terminal panicles; calyx toothed, upper 2 teeth connate; vexillum broadly orbicular, emarginate, not appendaged; wings adherent to the keel and slightly longer; keel much incurved, obtuse; vexillary stamen free, remainder connate; anthers uniform; ovary subsessile, 10–8-ovuled; style incurved, slender, stigma small, terminal; fruit broadly linear, flattened but turgid, 2-valved, empty inside except for the large oblong seeds with a short lateral hilum and large strophiole.

378. **Clitoriopsis** Wilczek, Fl. Congo Belge, 6: 269, fig. 8 (1954). 1 sp., *C. mollis* Wilczek, trop. Africa (Congo).

Erect shrublet; leaves pinnately 3-foliolate; leaflets broadly obovate, lower pair near the base of the rhachis, entire; stipules persistent, not prolonged at the base; stipels persistent;

---

[1] Synonyms of **Kennedya**: *Caulinia* Moench (1802) not Willd. (1801). *Amphodus* Lindl. (1829). *Physolobium* Huegel (1837). *Zichya* Huegel (1837). *Physalobium* Steud. (1841). *Zichia* Steud. (1841).

racemes axillary, dense, many-flowered; bracts and bracteoles persistent; flowers large; calyx tubular, limb bilabiate, upper lip 2-toothed; standard a little longer than the other petals, broadly clawed, without callosities; wings and keel clawed; stamens 10, vexillary free, others connate; anthers dimorphic, apiculate, 5 dorsifixed, the others basifixed on longer filaments; ovary stipitate; disk lobed; style long, pubescent towards the base, glabrous upwards; stigma terminal, puberulous; fruit stipitate, narrowed at both ends, style persistent; seeds not seen.

379. **Teramnus** [P.Br., Hist. Jamaica 290 (1756)] Swartz, Prodr. Veg. Ind. Occ. 105 (1788). 6 spp., trop. and subtrop. reg. of both hemispheres; type *T. volubilis* Swartz, trop. America. B.H. 1: 530; E.P. 3, 3: 361; Hauman, Fl. Congo Belge, 6: 101; Burkart, Legum. Argent. ed. 2: 386, fig. 114.

Climbing herbs, slender; leaves pinnately 3-foliolate, stipellate; stipules small; flowers small, few in the axils or in axillary racemes, paired or fasciculate on the axis; bracts small; bracteoles linear or lanceolate and striate; upper 2 calyx-lobes connate or distinct; vexillum obovate, narrowed at the base, not appendaged; wings narrow, adherent to the keel; keel shorter than the wings, almost straight, obtuse; stamens all connate into a sheath; alternate anthers small and sterile, empty; ovary sessile, many-ovuled; style short, thick, beardless, stigma capitate; fruit linear, 2-valved, septate between the seeds, style hooked.

Tribe 39. ABREAE

Wight & Arn., Prodr., 1: 236 ('*Abrineae*') (1834). Benth. & Hook. f., Gen. Pl. 1: 527 (in tribe *Vicieae*)

Shrubs or shrublets, often climbing; *leaves paripinnate*, leaflets many-pairs; *rhachis terminated by a bristle*; *stipels absent*; racemes terminal or sub-terminal, flowers fasciculate on the rhachis; calyx truncate with short teeth; corolla papilionaceous; claw of vexillum more or less *adnate to the staminal sheath*; *stamens 9*, filaments connate into a sheath split above (adaxially); no vexillary stamen; *anthers uniform*; ovules numerous; *style glabrous*; fruit compressed, 2-valved, subseptate but not breaking up into separate joints; seeds subglobose or ellipsoid, shining, sometimes *brightly coloured*. Type genus *Abrus* Adans.

380. **Abrus** Adans., Fam. 2: 327 (1763). *Zaga* Raf. (1836). *Hulthemia* Blume ex Miq. (1855). *Hoepfneria* Vatke (1879). 6 spp., almost all trop. and subtrop. regions; type *A. precatorius* Linn., trop. and subtrop. B.H. 1: 527; E.P. 3, 3: 355; Amshoff, Pulle Fl. Suriname, 2, 2: 234; Hutch. & Dalz., Fl. W. Trop. Afr. 1: 412; Boutique, Fl. Congo Belge, 6: 82, fig. 1.

Shrubs or shrublets, branches often elongated and climbing; leaves abruptly pinnate, leaflets many-paired, exstipellate; petiole terminated by a bristle; racemes terminal or on shortened leafless branchlets; flowers fasciculate at the nodes, small, rose or white; calyx truncate, teeth very short, upper 2 subconnate; vexillum ovate, claw short, broad, more or less adherent to the staminal tube; wings narrowly falcate-oblong; keel longer and broader than the wings, arcuate; stamens 9, connate into a sheath split above, vexillary stamen absent; anthers uniform; ovary subsessile; ovules numerous; style short, incurved, not bearded, stigma capitate; fruit oblong or linear, plano-compressed, 2-valved, subseptate within between the seeds; seeds subglobose or ellipsoid, shining, sometimes red and black.

Seeds used as ornaments in various countries; they are poisonous.

Tribe 40. Vicieae

Adans., Fam. 2: 329 (1763). Benth. & Hook. f., Gen. Pl. 1: 450 (excl. *Abrus*) (1865)

Low or climbing herbs; leaves often paripinnate, *the rhachis ('petiole') ending in a tendril or bristle*, very rarely imparipinnate or reduced to a phyllode; stipules often foliaceous, oblique or semi-sagittate; *stipels absent*; flowers solitary or racemose in the leaf-axils; corolla papilionaceous; vexillary filament free or more or less connate with the others into an adaxially split sheath; free part of filaments filiform or dilated upwards; *anthers uniform, versatile*; ovules 2 or more; style hairy or glabrous; *fruit 2-valved*; seeds often with the *funicle expanded above the hilum*. Type genus *Vicia* Linn.

Style glabrous; fruits turgid; wing-petals free from the keel; filaments dilated
    upwards   381. **Cicer**
Style hairy (rarely glabrous); fruit more or less compressed:
    Staminal tube with an oblique top; wing-petals adherent to the keel; filaments filiform:
        Ovules and seeds usually more than 2   382. **Vicia**
        Ovules and seeds 2, or the latter solitary   383. **Lens**
    Staminal tube not oblique at the top; wing-petals slightly adherent to or free from the keel:
        Style dilated in the upper part, the inner face longitudinally bearded; filaments filiform or dilated upwards   384. **Lathyrus**
        Style dilated in the upper part with reflexed margins forming a laterally compressed body; filaments slightly dilated upwards   385. **Pisum**

381. **Cicer** Linn., Sp. Pl. 738 (1753). *Nochotta* S. G. Gmel. (1774). *Spiroceras* Jaub. & Spach (1842). 14 spp., Europe, W. Asia; type *C. arietinum* Linn., Madeira and S. Europe to Persia. B.H. 1: 524; E.P. 3, 3: 350; Gams in Hegi, Ill. Fl. Mitt.-Eur. 4, 3: 1498, fig. 1528.

Perennial or annual herbs, often glandular-pubescent, sometimes almost leafless; leaves pinnate, petiole ending in a small tendril or spine or terminated by a leaflet or rarely leaves trifoliolate; leaflets dentate or incised, exstipellate; stipules foliaceous, oblique, often dentate or incised; flowers white, blue, or violet, solitary or few on axillary peduncles; bracts small; bracteoles absent; calyx-tube oblique or gibbous at the back, lobes subequal or the upper 2 rather shorter, connivent; vexillum narrowed into a broad claw; wings obliquely obovate, free; keel rather broad, incurved, obtuse or rather acute; vexillary stamen free, remainder connate; filaments dilated upwards; anthers uniform; ovary sessile, ovules 2 or more; style filiform, incurved or inflexed, not bearded, stigma terminal; fruit ovoid or oblong, turgid, 2-valved; seeds subglobose or irregularly obovoid, funicle not dilated, hilum small.

382. **Vicia**[1] Linn., Sp. Pl. 734 (1753). About 120 spp., N. temp. hemisphere, S. and W. America; type *V. sativa* Linn., Europe and cult. B.H. 1: 524: E.P. 3,

---

[1] Synonyms of **Vicia**: *Ervum* Linn. (1753). *Faba* Adans. (1763). *Arachus* Medik. (1787). *Bona* Medik. (1787). *Cracca* [Riv.] Medik. (1787). *Vicioides* Moench (1794). *Wiggersia* Gaertn. (1801). *Ervilia* Link (1822). *Orobella* C. Presl (1837). *Coppoleria* Todaro (1845). *Endiusa* Alef. (1859). *Parallosa* Alef. (1859). *Sellunia* Alef. (1859). *Swantia* Alef. (1859). *Hypechusa* Alef. (1860). *Abacosa* Alef. (1861). *Atossa* Alef. (1861). *Cujunia* Alef. (1861). *Tuamina* Alef. (1861). *Endusia* Benth. & Hook f. (1865). *Vicilla* Schur (1866). *Rhynchium* Dulac (1867).

3: 350. Burkart, Legum. Argent. ed. 2: 353, fig. 106, 107; Gams in Hegi, Ill. Fl. Mitt.-Eur. 4, 3: 1506, figs. 1530–59.

Herbs, usually climbing by means of tendrils or rarely low or suberect; leaves pinnate, petiole of the upper leaves or of all ending in a simple or branched tendril or a recurved bristle; leaflets numerous, rarely only 1–3 pairs, entire or dentate at the apex, exstipellate; stipules semisagittate; flowers often blue, violet, or yellowish, either 1 or few in the leaf axils or racemose; bracts very caducous, mostly minute; bracteoles absent; calyx-tube often oblique at the base, obtuse; teeth or lobes subequal or the upper 2 shorter and the lower longer; vexillum narrowed into a broad claw; wings obliquely oblong, adherent to the middle of the keel; keel shorter than the wings; vexillary stamen free or more or less connate with the remainder, sheath with an oblique mouth; filaments filiform; anthers uniform; ovary subsessile or stipitate; ovules numerous or rarely only 2; style compressed dorsally, with a bunch of hairs at the apex or pubescent or pilose all around, rarely glabrous, stigma terminal; fruit compressed, 2-valved, continuous within; seeds globose or rarely compressed, funicle dilated into a thin aril.

383. **Lens** Moench, Meth. 131 (1794) (conserved name); Gren. & Godr. Fl. France, 1: 476 (1848). About 6 spp., Mediterr. reg., W. Asia; type *L. esculenta* Moench, Mediterr. reg., widely cult. B.H. 1: 525; E.P. 3, 3: 352; Burkart, Legum. Argent. ed. 2: 359, fig. 108; Gams in Hegi, Ill. Fl. Mitt.-Eur. 4, 3: 1501, fig. 1529.

Low, erect or subscandent herbs; leaves pinnate, petiole ending in a bristle or tendril, or terminated by a leaflet, leaflets 2 or more pairs, entire, exstipellate; stipules semisagittate; flowers small, few on axillary peduncles, racemose or solitary; bracts and bracteoles often absent; calyx-lobes elongated, subequal; vexillum narrowed into a short broad claw; wings obliquely obovate, adherent in the middle of the keel; keel shorter than the wings, rather acute or a little beaked; vexillary stamen free, remainder connate, sheath with an oblique mouth; ovary subsessile; ovules 2; style inflexed, slightly flattened dorsally, bearded lengthwise with minute hairs on the inside; fruit compressed, 2-valved, continuous within, 2–1-seeded; seeds compressed, funicle dilated into a thin aril.

384. **Lathyrus**[1] Linn., Sp. Pl. 729 (1753). About 130 spp., N. hemisphere, Africa, trop. S. America; type *L. sylvestris* Linn., Europe, N. Africa. B.H. 1: 526; E.P. 3, 3: 353; Boutique, Fl. Congo Belge, 6: 76, t. 6; Burkart, Legum. Argent. ed. 2: 362, fig. 109; Gams in Hegi, Ill. Fl. Mitt.-Eur. 4, 3: 1562, figs. 1561–91.

Herbs, sometimes climbing by means of tendrils; leaves pinnate, petiole either terminating in a tendril or bristle or rarely a leaflet, sometimes dilated and phyllode-like, leaflets 2–few rarely numerous pairs, entire, or rarely absent; stipules foliaceous, semisagittate, subequally sagittate or rarely entire at the base; flowers solitary or racemose on axillary peduncles; bracts very caducous, usually minute; bracteoles absent; calyx-tube often oblique at the base or gibbous at the back; teeth subequal or upper shorter; vexillum with a short broad claw; wings falcate-obovate or oblong, slightly adherent in the middle to the keel or almost free; keel shorter than the wings, incurved, obtuse; vexillary stamen free or more or less connate with the others; filaments filiform or dilated upwards; anthers uniform; ovary subsessile or stipitate, ovules numerous or rarely few; style inflexed, dorsally flattened and often indurated in the upper part, bearded lengthwise on the inner side, otherwise glabrous, stigma terminal; fruit 2-valved, continuous within; seeds mostly numerous, globose, angular or rarely compressed, funicle expanded into a thin aril.

---

[1] Synonyms of **Lathyrus**: *Orobus* Linn. (1753). *Aphaca* Adans. (1763). *Clymenum* Tourn. ex Adans. (1763). *Nissolia* Tourn. ex Adans. (1763). *Ochrus* [Tourn. ex] Adans. (1763). *Lathirus* Neck. (1768). *Cicercula* Medik. (1787). *Athyrus* Neck. (1790). *Nissolia* [Tourn.] Moench (1794). *Oxypogon* Raf. (1819). *Cicerella* DC. (1825). *Platystylis* Sweat (1828). *Spatulima* Raf. (1836). *Anurus* C. Presl (1837). *Astrophia* Nutt. ex Torrey & Gray (1838). *Graphiosa* Alef. (1861). *Lastila* Alef. (1861). *Navidura* Alef. (1861). *Lathyros* St. Lag. (1880).

385. **Pisum** Linn., Sp. Pl. 727 (1753). 6 spp., Mediterr. reg., W. Asia; type *P. sativum* Linn., cult. B.H. 1: 527; E.P. 3, 3: 354; Gams in Hegi, Ill. Fl. Mitt.-Eur. 4, 3: 1610, figs. 1592–6.

Spreading herbs or climbing by tendrils; leaves pinnate, common petiole ending in a bristle or tendril, leaflets 3–1 pairs; stipules foliaceous, semicordate or semisagittate; flowers showy, purple, rose, or white, solitary or few and racemose on elongated axillary peduncles; bracts very caducous, minute; bracteoles absent; calyx-tube oblique at the base or gibbous at the back, lobes subequal or upper 2 broader; vexillum broad, with short broad claw; wings falcate-oblong, adherent in the middle to the keel; keel shorter than the wings, incurved, obtuse; vexillary stamen free or connate in the middle with the remainder, sheath subequal at the apex; filaments slightly dilated upwards; anthers uniform; ovary subsessile; ovules numerous; style inflexed, hardened, dilated, margins retroflexed and united above to the compressed style, inner face bearded lengthwise, stigma subterminal; fruit compressed, obliquely acute, 2-valved; seeds subglobose, funicle dilated into a thin aril covering the oblong hilum.

Tribe 41. ONONIDEAE[1]

Tribe *Trifolieae*, small part, Benth. & Hook. f., Gen. Pl. 1: 442 (1865)

Perennial or annual herbs, rarely shrubs or small trees, often spiny and glandular; leaves pinnately 3- or rarely more- or 1-foliolate, the lateral nerves ending in a tooth; *stipules adnate to the petiole*; stipels absent; flowers solitary or 2–3 on axillary peduncles; corolla papilionaceous; claws of petals free from staminal tube; *stamens monadelphous in a closed tube*, or very rarely vexillary filament free; *alternate or all free parts of the filaments dilated at the apex*; *anthers dimorphic*, alternately versatile, alternately basifixed, or very rarely all small and uniform; *style glabrous*; fruit 2-valved, rarely torulose and septate between the estrophiolate seeds but not separating into joints when ripe. Type genus *Ononis* Linn.

Fruits 2-valved, continuous inside, not torulose   386. **Ononis**
Fruits torulose and septate between the seeds   387. **Passaea**

386. **Ononis** Linn., Sp. Pl. 716 (1753); Gen. Pl. ed. 5: 772 (1754). *Anonis* (Tourn. ex) Adans. (1763). *Bonaga* Medik. (1787). *Natrix* Moench (1794). *Bugranopsis* Pomel (1874). About 70–80 spp., N. and Cent. Europe, Mediterr. reg., Canaries, W. Asia, Ethiopia; type *O. spinosa* Linn., Europe to W. Asia, N. Africa. B.H. 1: 485; E.P. 3, 3: 241; Sirjaev, Generis *Ononis* Linn. revisio critica, Beihefte Bot. Centralbl. 49: 381 (1932); Gams in Hegi, Ill. Fl. Mitt.-Eur. 4, 3: 1215, figs. 1352–9.

Mostly perennial or annual herbs, rarely shrubs, very rarely small trees, sometimes spiny, usually clothed with glandular and simple hairs; leaves often pinnately trifoliolate, rarely 1-foliolate, or very rarely with 2–5 pairs of leaflets; stipules mostly herbaceous, adnate to the

---

[1] **Ononideae**, trib. nov. Herbae perennes vel annuae, rare frutices vel arbores parvae, plerumque spinosae et glandulosae; folia pinnatim 3- vel rare plurifoliata; stipulae ad petiolum adnatae; stipellae nullae; flores solitarii vel 2–3 in pedunculis axillaribus; corolla papilionacea; stamina in tubum clausum connata vel rare vexillare libero; partes liberae filamentorum alternae vel omnes apice dilatatae; antherae dimorphae; stylus glaber; fructus 2-valvis, rare torulosus et inter semina estrophiolata septatus.

petiole, rarely united at the base into a ring, bifid; stipels absent; leaflets toothed, very rarely subentire, terminal largest; flowers solitary or 2–3 on short axillary peduncles, peduncles often bristle-like; sometimes the floral leaves reduced to bracts with the flowers crowded into a terminal spike; real bracts and bracteoles minute or absent; calyx-tube short, lobes subequal; petals rose, yellow, purple, or white; vexillum suborbicular or obovate, claw short; wings obovate-oblong; keel incurved, beaked; stamens connate into a closed tube or rarely vexillary free, alternate free parts of filaments or all dilated at the apex, alternate anthers versatile, remainder basifixed; ovary shortly stipitate, 2–more-ovuled; style inflexed, glabrous; stigma terminal, oblique or subcapitate; fruit linear, oblong, ovate or ovate-rhomboid, stipitate or not, 2-valved, turgid or terete, continuous inside; seed reniform, estrophiolate, punctate to smooth or rugose.

387. **Passaea** Adans., Fam. 2: 509 (1763). 1 sp., *P. ornithopodioides* Scop., Mediterr. region.

Glandular annual herb, simple or branched, clothed with simple and glandular hairs; stipules small, adnate to the petiole, subentire, glandular; leaves all 3-foliolate, sparsely glandular-pilose, denticulate; peduncles filiform, glandular, 1–2-flowered; calyx exceeding the petals, tube very short, segments narrowly linear, almost filiform, glandular, 4–6 times as long as the tube; petals yellow, glabrous; vexillum rounded, apiculate, equal to the keel; wings oblong, obtuse, with a basal reflexed auricle; keel straight, scarcely beaked, longer than the wings; stamens monadelphous, anthers very small, alternately ovate and dorsifixed, alternately oblong and basifixed; fruit linear-compressed, torulose, septate between the 5–10 seeds, glandular-pilose; seeds ovoid, acutely tuberculate.

Tribe 42. Trifolieae

Bronn., Diss. Legum. 132 (1822); Benth. & Hook. f., Gen. Pl. 1: 442 (excl. *Ononis*) (1865)

Herbs or very rarely shrubs; leaves pinnately or digitately 3-foliolate, very rarely 5–7- or 1-foliolate; nerves of the leaflets mostly *extended to the teeth on the margin*; *stipules mostly adnate to the petiole*; inflorescence various, often *capitate or spicate*; corolla papilionaceous; claws of petals free from or adnate to the staminal sheath; *vexillary filament free*, the others united into a sheath split above (adaxially); *free part of filaments filiform or often dilated upwards*; *anthers uniform*; ovules numerous to 2; *style glabrous*; fruit 2-valved or small and indehiscent; *seeds estrophiolate*. Type genus *Trifolium* Linn.

Petals falling after flowering; filaments not dilated upwards:
  Keel-petals acute; prostrate herb rooting at the nodes; leaves digitately tri-
    foliolate; flowers solitary or 2–3 in an umbel; ovules numerous; fruit
    2-valved   388. **Parochetus**
  Keel-petals obtuse; leaves pinnately trifoliolate:
    Flowers in slender racemes; ovules few; fruit indehiscent or tardily 2-
      valved   389. **Melilotus**
    Flowers in heads or short racemes or rarely solitary:
      Fruit straight or curved, mostly linear:
        Fruits not geocarpic, dehiscent or indehiscent; ovules numerous
                                                            390. **Trigonella**
        Fruits geocarpic, indehiscent; ovules 2   391. **Factorovskya**
      Fruits mostly spirally coiled, scarcely dehiscent, mostly very prickly;
        ovules numerous, rarely 1.   392. **Medicago**

Petals becoming dry and persistent after flowering, claws of some or all partly adnate to the staminal sheath; leaves usually digitately 3- rarely 5-7-foliolate; fruit indehiscent; filaments mostly dilated upwards; ovules few   **393. Trifolium**

388. **Parochetus** Buch.-Ham. ex D. Don, Prodr. Fl. Nepal. 240 (1825). *Cosmiusa* Alef. (1866). 1 sp., *P. communis* Buch.-Ham. ex D. Don, trop. Asia, trop. Africa. B.H. 1: 485; E.P. 3, 3: 243.

Prostrate herb rooting at the nodes; leaves digitately 3-foliolate, leaflets obcordate, sometimes denticulate; stipules free or shortly adnate to the petiole; flowers blue-purple, solitary or 2-3 in umbels at the apex of axillary peduncles; bracts stipule-like at the base of the pedicels; bracteoles absent; calyx-lobes subequal, upper 2 connate high up; petals free from the staminal tube; vexillum obovate, contracted at the base into a short claw; wings falcate-oblong; keel shorter than the wings, abruptly inflexed, rather acute; vexillary stamen free, remainder connate, filaments not dilated; anthers almost uniform; ovary sessile; ovules numerous; style inflexed above, glabrous, stigma small, terminal; fruit linear, at length turgid, obliquely acute, 2-valved, continuous within; seed estrophiolate with a filiform funicle.

389. **Melilotus** Adans., Fam. 2: 322 (1763). *Sertula* O. Ktze. (1891). *Melilota* Medik. (1787). *Melilothus* Hornem. (1819). *Meliotus* Steud. (1841). *Brachylobus* Dulac (1867). About 20 spp., Cent. Asia, Europe, N. Africa; lectotype *M. officinalis* Willd., Europe. B.H. 1: 487; E.P. 3, 3: 247; Gams in Hegi, Ill. Fl. Mitt.-Eur. 4, 3: 1236, figs. 1362-8.

Annual or biennial herbs; leaves pinnately 3-foliolate, nerves often ending in teeth; stipules adnate to the petiole; flowers small, yellow, or white, in slender axillary racemes; bracts minute or absent; bracteoles absent; calyx-teeth short, subequal; petals free from the staminal tube, deciduous; vexillum obovate or oblong, contracted at the base, subsessile; wings oblong; keel shorter than the wings, obtuse; vexillary stamen free or connate to the middle with the others; filaments not dilated: anthers uniform; ovary sessile or stipitate; ovules few; style filiform, incurved above, stigma terminal; fruit subglobose or ovoid, as long as the calyx, straight, thick, indehiscent or tardily 2-valved; seeds solitary or few, estrophiolate.

390. **Trigonella**[1] Linn., Sp. Pl. 776 (1753). About 70 spp., E. Mediterr., Cent. Europe, N. and S. Africa, W. Asia, Australia; type *T. foenum-graecum* Linn., S. Europe to E. Asia, south to Ethiopia. B.H. 1: 486; E.P. 3, 3: 243; Gams in Hegi, Ill. Fl. Mitt.-Eur. 4, 3: 1228, figs. 1360-1.

Herbs; leaves pinnately 3-foliolate, nerves of the leaflets often running out into teeth; stipules adnate to the petiole; flowers yellow, blue, or white, solitary, capitate, subumbellate, or shortly and densely racemose; bracts minute or inconspicuous; bracteoles absent; calyx-teeth or lobes subequal; petals free from the staminal tube; vexillum obovate or oblong, sessile or contracted into a broad claw; wings oblong; keel shorter than the wings, obtuse; vexillary stamen free or connate in the middle with the others; filaments not dilated; anthers uniform; ovary sessile or shortly stipitate; ovules numerous; style filiform or rather thick, glabrous, stigma terminal; fruit thick and long-beaked or linear, compressed or terete, sometimes flat and broad, straight, falcate or arcuate, indehiscent or gaping along the seed-bearing suture, rarely 2-valved, continuous inside; seeds estrophiolate.

---

[1] Synonyms of **Trigonella**: *Kentia* Adans. (1763). *Fenu-graecum* Adans. (1763). *Buceras* Hall. ex Allioni (1785). *Melissitus* Medik. (1787). *Trifoliastrum* Moench (1794). *Pocockia* Ser. (1825). *Botryolotus* Jaub. & Spach (1842). *Nephomedia* Kostel (1844). *Grammocarpus* Schur (1853). *Aporanthus* Bromf. (1856). *Folliculligera* Pasq. (1867). *Falcatula* Fourr. (1868).

391. **Factorovskya** Eig, Zionist Org. Inst. Agric. and Nat. Hist. Bull. 6: 11, t. 1 (1927). 1 sp., *F. aschersoniana* (Urb.) Eig, E. Mediterr.

Annual prostrate herb; leaves trifoliolate, leaflets obovate, dentate; peduncles axillary, solitary, 1-flowered; calyx-lobes 5, triangular-lanceolate; petals yellow; vexillum suborbicular, keel obtuse; stamens diadelphous, filaments not dilated at the apex; ovary 2-ovuled, on a short gynophore; peduncle, pedicel, and gynophore growing out after flowering and penetrating the soil; fruit long-ovate, deeply partite, upper part mostly abortive, each part containing one seed lenticular in shape.

392. **Medicago**[1] Linn., Sp. Pl. 778 (1753). About 50 spp., W. and S. Europe, especially the Mediterr. reg., Cent. and W. Asia, N. and S. Africa, everywhere in trop. reg.; type *M. sativa* Linn., Europe, Asia, N. Africa. B.H. 1: 487; E.P. 3, 3: 245; Gams in Hegi, Ill. Fl. Mitt.-Eur. 4, 3: 1369–81.

Herbs or rarely shrubs; leaves pinnately 3-foliolate, nerves often running out into teeth; stipules adnate to the petiole; flowers often small, yellow or violet, in axillary racemes or heads, or subsolitary; bracts small or absent; bracteoles absent; calyx-teeth or lobes subequal; petals free from the staminal tube; vexillum obovate or oblong, contracted at the base, subsessile; wings oblong; keel shorter than the wings, obtuse; vexillary stamen free, remainder connate; filaments not dilated; anthers uniform; ovary sessile or shortly stipitate; ovules numerous, very rarely 1; style subulate, glabrous, stigma subcapitate, oblique; fruit spirally falcate or often shell-like, arcuate-reticulate, unarmed or prickly, scarcely dehiscent; seeds estrophiolate.

393. **Trifolium**[2] Linn., Sp. Pl. 764 (1753). About 300 spp., trop. and subtrop. reg. Old World, North and South America, trop. Africa; type *T. pratense* Linn., N. hemisphere and much cult. B.H. 1: 487; E.P. 3, 3: 249; Gams in Hegi, Ill. Fl. Mitt.-Eur. 4, 3: 1275, figs. 1382–1424.

Herbs; leaves digitately 3- rarely 5–7-foliolate, rarely pinnately 3–5-foliolate, leaflets mostly denticulate; stipules adnate to the petiole; flowers mostly purple, red, or white, rarely yellow, spicate, capitate, umbellate or rarely solitary; bracts small or absent, sometimes membranous, persistent or deciduous, sometimes the outer connate into a dentate or lobed involucre; bracteoles absent; calyx-teeth or lobes subequal or the lower longer, upper 2 sometimes more or less connate; petals marcescent, claws all, or the lower 4, more or less adnate to the staminal sheath; vexillum oblong or ovate; wings narrow; keel shorter than the wings, obtuse; vexillary stamen free or rarely connate in the middle with the others; alternate filaments or all of them dilated at the apex, or scarcely dilated; anthers uniform; ovary with few ovules, style filiform, incurved above, stigma capitate or hooked; fruit oblong and subterete or obovate-compressed, enclosed by the marcescent calyx and petals, mostly membranous, indehiscent; seeds 1–2 or rarely 2–3, estrophiolate.

---

[1] Synonyms of **Medicago**: *Medica* Adans. (1763). *Medicula* Medik. (1787). *Trifillium* Medik. (1787). *Radiata* Medik. (1789). *Triphyllum* Medik. (1789). *Cochleata* Medik. (1789). *Diploprion* Viv. (1824). *Lupulina* Noulet (1837). *Lupularia* Opiz (1852). *Spirocarpus* Opiz (1852).

[2] Synonyms of **Trifolium**: *Lupinaster* Adans. (1763). *Vesicaria* Crantz (1769). *Triphylloides* [Ponted. ex] Moench (1794). *Lagopus* Bernh. (1800). *Pentaphyllon* Pers. (1807). *Falcatula* Brot. (1816). *Dactyphyllon* Raf. (1818). *Dactiphyllum* Raf. (1819). *Vesicastrum* Ser. (1825). *Chrysaspis* Desv. (1827). *Lotophyllum* Reichb. (1827). *Amarenus* C. Presl (1830). *Amoria* C. Presl (1830). *Calycomorphum* C. Presl (1830). *Galearia* C. Presl (1830). *Micrantheum* C. Presl (1830). *Mistyllus* C. Presl (1830). *Mystyllus* C. Presl (1830). *Paramesus* C. Presl (1830). *Fragifera* Koch (1837). *Trichocephalum* Koch (1837). *Dactyphyllon* Endl. (1840). *Amooria* Walp. (1842). *Loxospermum* Hochst. (1846). *Glycirrhizum* Bertol. (1850). *Melilotea* Bertol. (1850). *Oliganthema* Bertol. (1850). *Microphyton* Fourr. (1868). *Platystylium* Willk. (1877). *Fissicalyx* Lojac. (1883). *Eleuterosemium* Gib. & Belli (1889). *Trigantheum* Gib. & Belli (1892). *Carpohypogaea* Gib. & Belli (1893). *Medusea* Gib. & Belli (1893).

Tribe 43. LOTEAE

Benth., Benth. & Hook. f., Gen. Pl. 1: 442 (1865)

Shrublets or mostly herbs, sometimes annuals; leaves pinnately 5–many-foliolate, rarely 4–1-foliolate; leaflets entire, the lowermost *often resembling stipules*, or leaves owing to the absence of a petiole *seeming to be digitate*; stipules present or absent; flowers capitate or umbellate, rarely racemose or solitary; peduncles axillary or crowded at the ends of the branchlets; *vexillary filament free* or connate with the others into a *closed tube*; alternate or all the filaments *often dilated upwards*; *anthers uniform*; ovary 2–many-ovuled, style glabrous; fruit 2-valved or indehiscent, sometimes transversely septate but not breaking into joints; *seeds estrophiolate*. Mostly temperate regions, especially Mediterranean. Type genus *Lotus* Linn.

Fruit dehiscent, 2-valved; leaflets often stipule-like:
  Vexillary (adaxial) stamen free from the others from the beginning:
    Calyx long-tubular (1·5 cm.); fruit straight, exserted, subterete; leaflets all
      sessile, without a rhachis, silky-hairy; stipules absent; peduncles
      axillary, broadly 2-bracteolate in the middle   394. **Cytisopsis**
    Calyx shortly tubular; leaflets not all sessile, or if so then on a rhachis:
      Keel-petals obtuse:
        Calyx-lobes longer than the tube; lower leaflets stipule-like:
          Flowers capitate or subumbellate, axillary or subterminal
                                                                395. **Dorycnium**
          Flowers racemose, racemes terminal and leaf-opposed; leaves imparipin-
            nate; bracteoles linear   396. **Gamwellia**
        Calyx-teeth shorter than the tube; lower leaflets not stipule-like; flowers
          in axillary umbels or rarely solitary   397. **Hosackia**
      Keel-petals beaked or acute:
        Calyx-lobes mostly longer than the tube; lower leaflets stipule-like
                                                                398. **Lotus**
        Calyx-lobes shorter than the tube; leaves sessile   399. **Lyauteya**
  Vexillary stamen united with the others:
    Free parts of filaments not dilated   400. **Pseudolotus**
    Free parts of filaments flattened-dilated   401. **Kerstania**
Fruit not dehiscent or very tardily so:
  Vexillary (adaxial) stamen already free in the young flowers and remaining
    free; fruit elongated:
    Calyx deeply 5-lobed; fruit exserted from the calyx, compressed, circinate,
      indehiscent; lower leaflets not stipule-like   402. **Hymenocarpos**
    Calyx 5-lobed to the middle; fruit exserted, straight but very closely torulose;
      lower leaflets stipule-like   403. **Benedictella**
    Calyx short; fruit long-linear, hooked at the apex, margins thickened;
      lower leaflets not stipule-like   404. **Securigera**
  Vexillary stamen more or less united with the others in the young flowers,
    sometimes at length free:
    Stamens remaining monadelphous:
      Calyx tubular or inflated in fruit, enclosing the fruit 405. **Anthyllis**

Calyx short; fruit linear, subtetragonous, circinately incurved nearly to the base, grub-like **406. Helminthocarpum**

Stamens at length diadelphous:

Perennial herb with numerous slender whip-like branches; leaf-rhachis not winged; flower-heads numerous on long peduncles, not subtended by leafy bract; fruit very small, straight, enclosed by the calyx **407. Dorycnopsis**

Annual herb with spreading or prostrate branches; leaf-rhachis winged; flowers several in a sessile cluster; calyx at length ovoid and bladder-like enclosing the fruit; fruit constricted and septate between the seeds **408. Physanthyllis**

Annual herb; flowers in axillary pedunculate heads subtended by a modified leaf; calyx long-tubular, not inflated in fruit; fruit strongly curved and long-beaked, several-seeded, indehiscent and transversely septate **409. Cornicina**

394. **Cytisopsis** Jaub. & Spach, Illustr. 1: 154, t. 84 (1842). 1 sp., *C. dorycnii-folia* Jaub. & Spach, Syria, Cilicia, Asia Minor. B.H. 1: 489; E.P. 3, 3: 256.

Spreading shrublet, silky-hairy; leaves sessile, 7–5-foliolate; stipules absent; pedicels 1–2, axillary, broadly 2-bracteolate in the middle; flowers yellow; upper 2 lobes of the tubular calyx dilated at the base, connate into an upper lip, lower 2 shorter and narrow; petals with very long claws, lower ones adnate to the staminal tube; vexillum ovate; wings and keel slightly incurved, obtuse; vexillary stamen free, remainder connate, filaments dilated at the apex; anthers uniform; ovary sessile; ovules numerous; style slightly incurved, thickened above, stigma truncate; fruit linear, straight, subterete, exceeding the calyx, 2-valved, thinly septate between the seeds; seeds subglobose, estrophiolate, funicle very short.

395. **Dorycnium** Vill., Hist. Pl. Dauph. 3: 416 (1789). *Bonjeanea* Reichb. (1832). *Bonjeania* Reichb. (1832). *Dorychnium* Brongn. (1843). *Ortholotus* Fourr. (1868). About 12 spp., Mediterr. reg., Canary Isls., type *D. suffruticosum* Vill., S. Europe. B.H. 1: 490; E.P. 3, 3: 257; Rikli, Engl. Bot. Jahrb. 31: 314 (1901); Gams in Hegi, Ill. Fl. Mitt.-Eur. 4, 3: 1376, figs. 1437–40.

Herbs or shrublets; leaves 5–4-foliolate, leaflets entire, 3 at the apex of the petiole, 1–2 near the stem and resembling stipules; stipules very minute or absent; flowers capitate or subumbellate; sometimes the bracts below the heads 3–1-foliolate; bracteoles absent; lobes of the subcampanulate calyx subequal or the lower longer; petals free from the staminal tube; vexillum ovate-oblong, clawed, wings obovate-oblong; keel smaller, incurved, rather obtuse, subgibbous on each side; vexillary stamen free, remainder connate, alternate filaments or all of them dilated at the apex; anthers uniform; ovary sessile; ovules numerous; style incurved, glabrous, stigma terminal; fruit oblong or linear, terete or turgid, 2-valved, continuous inside or often transversely septate between the seeds; seeds globose or compressed, estrophiolate.

396. **Gamwellia** Bak. f., Journ. Bot. 73: 160, with fig. (1935). 1 sp., *G. flava* Bak. f., trop. Africa (N. Rhodesia, S. Tanganyika).

Perennial diffuse herb, woody at the base, pilose all over; leaves sessile, imparipinnate, leaflets 2 pairs, opposite, the basal pair in place of the stipules, linear-oblanceolate, acute; stipules absent; flowers few in short leaf-opposed and terminal racemes; pedicels short; bracteoles linear; calyx campanulate, deeply 5-lobed, lobes subequal, linear-lanceolate, longer than the tube; petals longer than the calyx; vexillum obovate, shortly clawed; wings oblong-oblanceolate, claw slender, not appendaged; keel-petals oblong, clawed; vexillary stamen free, remainder united; filaments of unequal length; anthers equal, dorsifixed near the base; ovary several-ovuled; style filiform, glabrous, stigma obliquely terminal; fruit dehiscent, straight, linear, densely pilose, continuous inside, beaked by the persistent style; seeds compressed, kidney-shaped, smooth.

397. **Hosackia**[1] Dougl. ex Benth., Bot. Reg., t. 1257 (1829). About 30 spp., North and South America, Mexico, type *H. bicolor* Dougl. ex Benth., W. North America. B.H. 1: 491; E.P. 3, 3: 256; Burkart, Legum. Argent. ed. 2: 283.

Mostly perennial herbs or shrublets; leaves pinnately 2- or more-foliolate, rarely 3-foliolate; stipules membranous, foliaceous or minute and gland-like; flowers yellow or reddish, in pedunculate or sessile axillary umbels, rarely solitary, subtended by a 1- or more-foliolate bract; bracteoles often absent; calyx-teeth subequal, often shorter than the tube; claws of the petals free from the staminal tube; vexillum ovate or suborbicular, base obtuse, claw slender; wings obovate or oblong; keel incurved, obtuse, subequal to the wings; vexillary stamen free, remainder connate; alternate filaments or all of them slightly dilated upwards; anthers uniform; ovary sessile; ovules numerous; style incurved or inflexed, glabrous, stigma terminal; fruit linear, compressed or subterete, straight or arcuate, 2-valved, septate between the seeds; seeds estrophiolate.

398. **Lotus**[2] Linn., Sp. Pl. 773 (1753). 60 spp., Europe and temp. Asia, especially Mediterr. reg., N. and E. Africa, Australia; type *L. corniculatus* Linn., temp. N. hemisphere, N. and E. Africa, Australia. B.H. 1: 490; E.P. 3, 3: 257, Gams in Hegi, Ill. Fl. Mitt.-Eur. 4, 3: 1364, figs. 1431–5.

Herbs or shrublets; leaves 5–4-foliolate, leaflets entire, 3 crowded at the apex of the petiole, 1–2 near the stem, resembling stipules, rarely all scattered; stipules minute, tubercle-like or absent; flowers yellow, red, rose, or white, umbellate on axillary peduncles, or rarely solitary, often with a 3-foliolate bract; bracteoles mostly absent; calyx-lobes subequal or the lower longer, rarely more or less connate into 2 lips; petals free from the staminal tube; vexillum obovate, suborbicular or ovate-acuminate, contracted into a claw; wings obovate; keel incurved or inflexed, beaked, gibbous on each side; vexillary stamen free, remainder connate, alternate filaments dilated at the apex; anthers uniform; ovary sessile, ovules numerous; style inflexed above the ovary, glabrous, nude or variously appendaged, stigma terminal or lateral; fruit oblong or linear, straight or arcuate, terete, turgid or rarely plano-compressed, 2-valved, septate or rarely continuous between the seeds; seeds subglobose or lenticular, estrophiolate.

399. **Lyauteya** Maire, Bull. Soc. Hist. Nat. Afr. Nord. 10: 22 (1919). 1 sp., *L. ahmedii* (Batt. & Pit.) Maire, Morocco.

Shrub; leaves sessile on a pulvinus, mostly 3- rarely 4- or 1–2-foliolate, leaflets subequal, entire; stipules and stipels absent; flowers axillary, paired or rarely 3 on a peduncle, rarely only 1; bracteoles very minute; calyx subequally 5-lobed, not bilabiate, lobes shorter than the tube; claws of the petals free; keel acute, curved, ascending; vexillum recurved; stamens diadelphous, the adaxial free; anthers equal, subbasifixed, filaments dilated below the anther into a spathulate lamina; ovary sessile, style curved, filiform; stigma capitate; fruit linear, longer than the persistent calyx, subcompressed; seeds not strophiolate.

It is not stated whether the fruits are dehiscent or indehiscent, but I feel sure it does not belong to tribe *Cytiseae*, where it was originally included, because of the dilated filaments, so characteristic of most of tribe *Loteae*.

---

[1] Synonyms of **Hosackia**: *Acmispon* Raf. (1832). *Flundula* Raf. (1836). *Syrmatium* Vog. (1836). *Rafinesquia* Raf. (1836). *Anisolotus* Bernh. (1837). *Drepanolobus* Nutt. ex Torr. & A. Gray (1840). *Hosakia* Steud. (1840).

[2] Synonyms of **Lotus**: *Tetragonolobus* Scop. (1772). *Lotea* Medik. (1787). *Krokeria* Moench (1794). *Lotulus* Raf. (1818). *Andaca* Raf. (1836). *Pedrosia* Lowe (1856). *Heinekenia* Webb ex Benth. & Hook. f. (1865). *Lotos* St.-Lag. (1880).

400. **Pseudolotus** Rechinger f., Symbol. Afghan. 3: 20, fig. 10 (1957). 1 sp.,
P. makranicus Rechinger f., Baluchistan.

Perennial herb with a slender rhizome; stems simple, densely leafy; leaves digitately
3–5-foliolate, very shortly petiolate; leaflets obovate, villous, small, entire; petioles persistent and becoming hardened; stipules very minute, glandular; flowers axillary, 1–2 together;
bracts large, foliaceous, similar to the upper leaves; calyx shortly campanulate, equally
5-lobed, lobes subulate, a little longer than the tube; petals shortly clawed, vexillum orbicular, keel not beaked, shorter than the vexillum; wings about as long as the keel; stamens all
connate into a tube, the tube unequally split adaxially; free parts of the filaments not
thickened; anthers equal, ellipsoid; ovary linear; ovules about 3; style glabrous; fruit
sessile, compressed, membranous, 3-seeded, constricted between the seeds.

401. **Kerstania** Rechinger f., Symbol. Afghan. 3: 19, figs. 8, 9 (1957). 1 sp.,
K. nuristanica Rechinger f., Nuristan.

Perennial herb with a slender rhizome; leaves imparipinnate, leaflets opposite, several
pairs, elliptic, entire; stipules minute, membranous; peduncles axillary, half as long as the
leaves, bearing 1–3 subumbellate flowers; calyx shortly campanulate, subtruncate; petals
clawed, all much curved, glabrous; vexillum suborbicular; stamens 10; filaments connate
into a tube, the adaxial (vexillary) more free in the upper part, free parts flattened-dilated;
anthers equal, minute, ellipsoid; fruit long-stipitate, oblong-linear, compressed, 1-locular,
subconstricted between the 3–5 seeds.

402. **Hymenocarpos** Savi, Fl. Pisana 2: 205 (1798) (conserved name). *Cir-
cinnus* Medik. (1787). *Circinus* Medik. (1789). *Hymenocarpus* Reichb. (1828).
1 sp., *H. circinatus* (Linn.) Savi, Mediterr. reg., as far east as Persia. B.H. 1:
489; E.P. 3, 3: 255.

Annual prostrate herb; leaves imparipinnate or the lower 2-foliolate, leaflets entire;
stipules of the lower leaves adnate to the petiole, of the upper leaves obsolete; flowers small,
yellow, 2–4 on axillary peduncles; lower bract foliaceous, others small and setaceous;
bracteoles absent; calyx deeply divided, lobes subequal; petals free from the staminal tube;
vexillum suborbicular, shortly clawed; wings obovate; keel abruptly inflexed, beaked;
vexillary stamen free from the base; remainder connate; filaments dilated at the apex;
anthers uniform; ovary sessile; ovules 2; style abruptly inflexed, stigma terminal; fruit
broadly flattened, circinate, outer margin membranous, entire or dentate, indehiscent; seeds
reniform, estrophiolate.

403. **Benedictella** Maire, Bull. Soc. Hist. Nat. Afr. Nord. 15: 383 (1924).
1 sp., *B. benoistii* Maire, Morocco.

Annual herb, glaucous; stems numerous, prostrate; leaves sessile or subsessile, imparipinnate, 9–6-foliolate, leaflets 4–3-pairs, lowest 2 near the stem and stipule-like, all entire;
flowers 2–4 in axillary umbels, bearing a mostly 5-foliolate small leaf; calyx equally 5-lobed
almost to the middle, lobes long-ciliate; corolla glabrous, much exserted from the calyx;
vexillum pale purple; wings white, with a descending auricle; keel longer than the others,
dark purple at the apex, much curved above the claw, ending in an oblique straight obtuse
beak; stamens diadelphous, vexillary free, remainder connate up to two-thirds, alternate
filaments thickened below the anthers; ovary glabrous, abruptly contracted into the oblique
style, stigma truncate; fruit worm-like, long-exserted from the split marcescent calyx, at
first smooth and terete, at length dorsiventrally more or less compressed, indehiscent, very
torulose but not breaking into joints, septate, with one seed in each segment; septa thinly
membranous; seeds 2-seriate, much compressed, speckled with black.

404. **Securigera** DC., Lam. & DC., Fl. Fr. ed. 3, 4: 609 (1805) (conserved
name). *Bonaveria* Scop. (1777). *Securina* Medik. (1787). *Securilla* Gaertn. ex
Steud. (1821). 1 sp., *S. securidaca* (Linn.) Dalla Torre & Sarntheim (*Bonaveria securidaca* (Linn.) Scop.), Mediterr. reg. B.H. 1: 489; E.P. 3, 3: 256.

Glabrous herb, diffuse; leaves imparipinnate, leaflets entire; stipules small, membranous; flowers yellow, umbellate at the apex of axillary or terminal peduncles, nodding; bracts small; bracteoles absent; calyx-lobes subequal, upper 2 broader and connate high up; petals free from the staminal tube; vexillum suborbicular; wings obliquely oblong; keel incurved, somewhat beaked; vexillary stamen free, remainder connate; alternate filaments slightly dilated upwards; anthers uniform; ovary sessile; ovules numerous; style incurved, glabrous, stigma capitate; fruit linear, acuminate, plano-compressed, indehiscent or tardily 2-valved, margins broad and thickened and sulcate in the sutures, hooked by the persistent style; seeds flat, quadrate.

405. **Anthyllis**[1] Linn., Sp. Pl. 719 (1753); Gen. Pl. ed. 5: 355 (1754). About 30 spp., Europe, N. Africa, W. Asia; type *A. vulneraria* Linn. Europe, Asia, N. Africa, Ethiopia. B.H. 1: 488; E.P. 3, 3: 254; Gams in Hegi, Ill. Fl. Mitt.-Eur. 4, 3: 1352, figs. 1426–30.

Shrubs or herbs; leaves pinnate or rarely reduced to 1 terminal leaflet; stipules small or absent; flowers capitate or rarely subsolitary; bracts and bracteoles small, setaceous or absent; teeth or lobes of the often at length inflated calyx-tube subequal, or the upper 2 larger and more or less connate; petals long-clawed, 4 lower claws often adnate to the base of the staminal tube; vexillum ovate, abrupt or 2-auricled at the base; wings ovate, obtuse; keel smaller than the wings, incurved, obtuse or rather acute, gibbous on each side; all the stamens connate into a closed tube; alternate or all the filaments dilated at the apex: anthers uniform; ovary stipitate or rarely subsessile; ovules 2 or more; style glabrous, stigma terminal; fruit ovoid or shortly linear, straight, falcate or arcuate, more or less enclosed by the calyx, turgid, indehiscent or tardily 2-valved, 1- or more-seeded, continuous within or transversely septate; seeds estrophiolate.

406. **Helminthocarpum** A. Rich., Tent. Fl. Abyss. 1: 200, t. 36 (1847). 1 sp., *H. abyssinicum* A. Rich., Yemen, Ethiopia, Sudan. B.H. 1, 489; E.P. 3, 3: 255.

Slender herb, prostrate, minutely silky; leaves imparipinnate, leaflets entire; stipules minute or inconspicuous; flowers small, yellow, umbellate on axillary peduncles; bracts obsolete; bracteoles absent; upper 2 calyx-teeth broader; petals free from the staminal tube, long-clawed; vexillum suborbicular; wings obovate-oblong, slightly adherent to the keel; keel slightly incurved, rather obtuse; stamens all connate into a tube, or the vexillary at length almost free; alternate filaments dilated upwards; anthers uniform; ovary sessile; ovules 2; style inflexed, stigma terminal; fruit linear, subtetragonous, circinate-incurved and rather grub-like, coriaceous, indehiscent, not jointed, transversely veined, subseptate between the seeds.

407. **Dorycnopsis** Boiss., Voy. Bot. Espagne, 2: 163 (1840). 1 sp. *D. gerardii* (Linn.) Boiss., S. Europe and islands of W. Mediterranean.

Perennial herb with numerous slender whip-like branches; leaves alternate, imparipinnate, with 2–4 pairs of opposite or alternate entire leaflets; stipules small, subulate, deciduous; no stipels; flower-heads numerous on long peduncles, not subtended by a leafy bract; bracts minute; calyx campanulate, equally 5-toothed, not enlarged in fruit; petals rose; vexillum longer than the wings and keel, limb truncate and abruptly narrowed into the claw; stamens diadelphous, the adaxial (vexillary) free; free part of filaments not dilated; anthers uniform; ovary sessile; style glabrous; fruit very small, straight, 1- rarely 2-seeded, indehiscent, enclosed by the calyx.

408. **Physanthyllis** Boiss., Voy. Bot. Espagne, 162, t. 162 (1840). 1 sp., *P. tetraphylla* (Linn.) Boiss., E. Mediterr. reg., N. Africa (Morocco to Libya). Boiss., Fl. Or. 2: 159 (1872).

[1] Synonyms of **Anthyllis**: *Barba-Jovis* (Tourn.) ex Adans. (1753). *Triopodion* Medik. (1787). *Zenopogon* Link (1831). *Pogonitis* Reichb. (1837). *Fakeloba* Raf. (1838). *Aspalathoides* K. Koch (1853). *Acanthyllis* Pomel (1874).

Annual herb with spreading or prostrate branches; leaves alternate, sessile, imparipinnate, leaflets 2–3 pairs, terminal largest, obovate-elliptic, entire; rhachis winged; stipules absent; no stipels; flowers several in a sessile axillary cluster; bracts and bracteoles absent; calyx ovoid, at length inflated and bladder-like, narrowed to the 5-toothed mouth, finely pilose; petals long-clawed; vexillum the longest and gradually narrowed into the claw; stamens diadelphous, the adaxial (vexillary) free; free part of all filaments dilated at the apex; anthers uniform, suborbicular; ovary long-stipitate, 2-ovuled; style glabrous, stigma terminal; fruit indehiscent, enclosed by the bladder-like calyx, stipitate, constricted and septate between the 2 estrophiolate seeds.

409. Cornicina Boiss., Voy. Bot. Espagne, 2: 162 (1840). 1 sp., *C. hamosa* (Desf.) Boiss., Portugal and Spain, NW. Africa (Morocco to Tunis).

Annual herb; leaves sessile, pinnate, leaflets up to 4 pairs, basal pair in the place of absent stipules; flowers capitate, axillary, pedunculate, subtended by a modified leaf; calyx long-tubular, not inflated in fruit, with 5 subulate lobes; vexillum-limb truncate, emarginate at the base, abruptly narrowed into the claw; stamens diadelphous; adaxial (vexillary) filament free; free parts of filaments dilated at the apex; style glabrous; fruit strongly curved, long-beaked, several-seeded, indehiscent and transversely septate, pericarp hard.

Tribe 44. Coronilleae

Adans., Fam. 2: 327 (1763). Tribe *Hedysareae* Subtribe *Coronilleae*
Benth. & Hook. f., Gen. Pl. 1: 447 (1865)

Herbs, shrublets, or rarely shrubs; leaves imparipinnate or rarely simple; *stipels absent*; *peduncles axillary*, umbellately many-flowered or rarely 1-flowered; corolla papilionaceous; vexillary filament free, remainder connate into a sheath split above, alternate or all the *filaments dilated upwards*; *anthers uniform*, versatile or rarely subbasifixed; *style glabrous*; *fruits jointed*, segments indehiscent or rarely dehiscing by 2 valves; *seeds without a strophiole*. Type genus *Coronilla* Linn.

Leaves pinnate:
  Stipules lateral to the petiole and free from each other, sometimes foliaceous:
    Keel-petals obtuse:
      Ovary sessile; ovules numerous; joints of fruit indehiscent 410. **Ornithopus**
      Ovary stipitate; ovules few; joints of fruit dehiscing by valves
                                                          411. **Antopetitia**
    Keel-petals acute or beaked:
      Flower clusters not subtended by a leaf:
        Fruit terete, 4-sided or slightly compressed, joints oblong or linear; seeds
            transversely oblong; umbels leafless   412. **Coronilla**
        Fruits compressed, upper margin excavated to the seed; joints arcuate or
            horseshoe-shaped; peduncle 1–more-flowered   413. **Hippocrepis**
      Flower-clusters closely subtended by a trifoliolate leaf; fruits terete or
          compressed   414. **Hammatolobium**
  Stipules leaf-opposed and wholly or partly united   415. **Artrolobium**
Leaves simple; stipules partly adnate to the petiole; keel-petals beaked;
    fruit terete, circinate-involute, sulcate lengthwise; peduncle few- to 1-
    flowered, leafless   416. **Scorpiurus**

410. Ornithopus Linn., Sp. Pl. 743 (1753). *Ornithopodium* Adans. (1763). *Arthrolobium* Reichb. (1828). *Hormolotus* Oliv. (1886). 15 spp., Europe, Canary Isls., Mediterr. reg., W. Asia, trop. Africa, S. Brazil; type *O. perpusillus* Linn., Europe. B.H. 1: 509; E.P. 3, 3: 311; Gams in Hegi, Ill. Fl. Mitt.-Eur. 4, 3: 1475, figs. 1511–13.

Slender herbs; leaves imparipinnate, leaflets numerous, small, exstipellate; stipules lateral, small or membranous; flowers very small, in heads or umbels on long axillary peduncles, subtended or not by a floral leaf; bracts and bracteoles small; calyx-lobes subequal or the upper 2 connate high up; vexillum obovate or suborbicular, wings oblong; keel almost straight, obtuse, shorter than the wings or very short; vexillary stamen free, remainder connate, alternate filaments dilated above, anthers uniform; ovary sessile; ovules numerous; style inflexed, stigma capitate; fruit linear, compressed or subterete, arcuate or rarely straight, joints oblong or ovate, indehiscent, veiny or smooth; seeds transversely oblong, ovate, or subglobose.

411. Antopetitia A. Rich., Ann. Sci. Nat. sér. 2, 14: 262, t. 15, fig. 2 (1840); J. Léonard, Fl. Congo Belge, 5: 178, fig. 10. 1 sp., *A. abyssinica* A. Rich., trop. Africa.

Annual herb with long slender stems; leaves imparipinnate, leaflets few, small, entire; stipules minute, gland-like; stipels absent; flowers in long-pedunculate axillary umbels; bracts filiform; calyx 5-lobed; lobes filiform; vexillum suborbicular, clawed; wings oblong; keel obtuse, as long as the wings; stamens 10, vexillary free, remainder connate; anthers uniform; ovary stipitate; ovules few; style slender, stigma terminal; fruit falcate, composed of 4–5 distinct globose 1-seeded segments each dehiscing by 2 valves; dorsal suture persistent; seeds globose, rugulose.

412. Coronilla Linn., Sp. Pl. 742 (1753). *Emerus* Tourn. ex Mill. (1752). *Scorpius* Medik. (1787). *Aviunculus* Fourr. (1868). *Callistephana* Fourr. (1868). About 55 spp., N. and Cent. Europe, Canary Isls., Mediterr. reg., N. Asia, China, Somaliland; type *C. varia* Linn., Europe. B.H. 1: 509; E.P. 3, 3: 311; Uhrová, Revision der Gattung, Beihefte Bot. Centralbl. 53: 1 (1935) (20 spp.); Gams in Hegi, Ill. Fl. Mitt.-Eur. 4, 3: 1465, figs. 1504–10.

Shrubs or herbs; leaves imparipinnate, leaflets entire, often numerous, rarely 3, glaucous, small or rarely the end three largest; stipules lateral, either small and membranous or large and foliaceous; flowers yellow, rarely purple and variegated with white, in long-pedunculate axillary peduncles, pendulous; bracts small; bracteoles absent; calyx-teeth short, subequal, upper 2 connate high up; petals long-clawed; vexillum suborbicular; wings obliquely obovate or oblong; keel incurved, beaked; vexillary stamen free, remainder connate, alternate filaments or all of them dilated in the upper part; anthers uniform; ovary sessile; ovules numerous; style inflexed, subulate, glabrous, stigma small, terminal; fruit terete, tetragonous or slightly compressed, straight or arcuate, joints sometimes reduced to one, oblong or elongated, almost veinless; seeds transversely oblong, estrophiolate.

413. Hippocrepis Linn., Sp. Pl. 744 (1753). *Hipocrepis* Neck. (1768). *Ferrumequinum* (Tourn. ex) Medik. (1787). *Hippocris* Raf. (1814). 12 spp., Europe, Mediterr. reg., Canary Isls., Cape Verdes, N. Africa; type *H. unisiliquosa* Linn. B.H. 1: 510; E.P. 3, 3: 311; Gams in Hegi, Ill. Fl. Mitt-Eur. 4, 3: 1481, figs. 1515–17.

Shrubs or herbs; leaves imparipinnate, leaflets numerous, entire, exstipellate; stipules small, broad and membranous or inconspicuous; flowers yellow, nodding, in axillary pedunculate umbels or 1–2 in the axils; bracts small; bracteoles absent; 2 upper calyx-teeth more or less connate; petals long-clawed; vexillum suborbicular; wings falcate-obovate or oblong, keel incurved, beaked; vexillary stamen free, remainder connate, alternate filaments slightly dilated at the apex; anthers uniform; ovary sessile; ovules numerous; style inflexed, subulate at the apex, stigma small, terminal; fruit plano-compressed or rarely subterete, often arcuate, upper margin deeply excavated at each seed, joints horseshoe-shaped; seeds arcuate, hilum ventral, estrophiolate.

414. Hammatolobium Fenzl, Ill. Pl. Syr., t. 1 (1843). *Hamatolobium* Fenzl (1842). *Ludovicia* Coss. (1856). 3 spp., SE. Europe, Syria, Cilicia, N. Africa; type *H. lotoides* Fenzl, SE. Europe, Syria. B.H. 1: 509; E.P. 3, 3: 310.

Perennial herbs with woody rootstock, silky-villous; leaves often 5-foliolate, 2 lower leaflets resembling stipules, or all subdigitate because of the short petiole; stipules minute; flowers yellow, often paired on axillary peduncles; bracts 3-foliolate; calyx-lobes subequal, 2 upper scarcely connate at the base; petals long-clawed; vexillum suborbicular; wings obliquely obovate-oblong; keel incurved, rather acute, shorter than the wings; vexillary stamen free, remainder connate, filaments dilated upwards; anthers uniform; ovary sessile; ovules numerous; style inflexed, glabrous, subspathulate-dilated at the apex, stigma terminal; fruit linear, joints plano-compfessed or convex; seeds arcuate, estrophiolate.

415. Artrolobium Desv., Journ. Bot. 1: 121, t. 4 (1813) (partly). *Astrolobium* DC., Prodr. 2: 311 (1825) (excl. *A. ebracteatum*). 5 spp.,[1] Europe to Caucasus, N. Africa; lectotype *A. scorpioides* (Linn.) Desv. (*Ornithopus scorpioides* Linn.) Mediterr. reg., N. Africa. Sibth., Fl. Graec., t. 715; Boiss., Fl. Orient. 2: 183 (as sect. of *Coronilla*).

Annual herbs; leaves alternate, 3-foliolate or up to 9-foliolate, when 3-foliolate end leaflet obovate and much larger than the lateral; stipules partly or wholly united and leaf-opposed, membranous; flowers small, in heads on axillary and terminal peduncles; bracts deciduous; bracteoles absent; calyx campanulate, equally and shortly 5-toothed or truncate; corolla papilionaceous; petals clawed, vexillum obovate-orbicular, wings large and obovate; keel short, abruptly incurved at a right angle; stamens 10; vexillary filament free, remainder connate in a sheath split above; all free parts of filaments slightly dilated; ovary sessile; style inflexed at a right angle, glabrous; ovules several; fruits jointed, not stipitate, straight or circinately curved, joints more or less ridged; seeds estrophiolate.

416. Scorpiurus Linn., Sp. Pl. 744 (1753). *Scorpioides* Tourn. ex Adans. (1763). *Scorpius* Lois. (1806). 7 spp., Europe, Mediterr. reg., Canary Isls., NE. trop. Africa; type *S. sulcatus* Linn. B.H. 1: 508; E.P. 3, 3: 309; Gams in Hegi, Ill. Fl. Mitt.-Eur. 1463, fig. 1503.

More or less acaulescent or decumbent herbs; leaves simple, entire, continuous with the petiole; stipules partly adnate to the petiole; flowers yellow, often small, solitary or umbellate on axillary peduncles; bracts minute; bracteoles absent; 2 upper calyx-lobes connate high up; petals long-clawed; vexillum suborbicular; wings obliquely obovate or oblong; keel incurved, rostrate-acuminate; vexillary stamen free, remainder connate, alternate filaments dilated upwards; anthers uniform; ovary sessile; ovules numerous; style inflexed, rather dilated in the middle, stigma terminal, capitate; fruits subterete, circinately infolded, deeply sulcate-ribbed, ribs often tuberculate or muricate, indehiscent, jointed or the joints scarcely separating and subcontinuous; seeds ovoid-globose, hilum lateral or transversely oblong, estrophiolate; cotyledons elongated, twisted and folded.

---

[1] Other species of this genus are: *A. durum* Desv., *A. repandum* Desv., *A. minimum* (Linn.) (*Coronilla minima* Linn.), and *A. vaginalis* (Lam.) (*Coronilla vaginalis* Lam.).

H h

Tribe 45. ADESMIEAE[1]

Tribe *Hedysareae* Subtribe *Adesmieae* Benth. & Hook. f., Gen. Pl. 1: 449 (1865).
Subtribe *Patagoniinae* Taubert

Shrubs, shrublets, or herbs, sometimes armed with spinescent petioles; leaves pari- or imparipinnate, leaflets usually numerous, rarely few; *stipels absent*; stipules not produced below the base; flowers in *terminal racemes*, mostly red, often striate; pedicels *single on the rhachis*; corolla papilionaceous; *stamens free to the base*, 2 filaments rarely dilated at the base and adnate to the claw of the vexillum; *anthers uniform*, short; ovary 2–more-ovuled; style glabrous, stigma terminal; *fruit jointed*, often straight along the upper suture and the lower suture deeply sinuate, segments breaking away separately or from the upper suture, indehiscent or 2-valved; *seeds not strophiolate*. S. America. Type genus *Adesmia* DC.

417. **Adesmia** DC., Ann. Sci. Nat. 4: 94 (1825) (conserved name). *Patagonium* Schrank (1808). *Heteroloma* Desv. ex Reichenb. (1828). *Loudonia* Bert. ex Hook. (1833). *Streptodesmia* A. Gray (1853). About 250 spp., South subtrop. and temp. America; lectotype *A. muricata* (Jacq.) DC., Patagonia, Chile. B.H. 1: 517; E.P. 3, 3: 322; Burkart, Darwiniana, 10: 465 (1954).

Undershrubs or herbs, or small shrubs sometimes very spiny; leaves pari- or imparipinnate, leaflets numerous or rarely 3, entire or dentate; stipels absent; stipules not produced beyond the insertion; flowers yellow, often red-striate, in terminal racemes; pedicels single; bracts small; bracteoles absent; calyx-lobes subequal or the lowest a little longer; vexillum orbicular, wings obliquely oblong; keel obtuse, acute or beaked, slightly shorter than the vexillum; stamens free among themselves, 2 of the filaments rarely dilated at the base and adnate to the claw of the vexillum; anthers uniform; ovary sessile, 2- or more-ovulate; style filiform, stigma small, terminal; fruit often straight along the upper suture; lower suture deeply sinuate, segments flat or convex, breaking away entirely or from the upper margin, indehiscent or 2-valved, often covered with plumose soft bristles; seeds orbicular or subglobose, not strophiolate.

Tribe 46. HEDYSAREAE[2]

DC., Prodr. 2: 307 (1825). Subtribe *Euhedysareae* Benth. & Hook. f.,
Gen. Pl. 1: 447 (1865)

Shrubs, shrublets, and herbs; leaves imparipinnate or rarely 1-foliolate; stipules often scarious; *stipels absent*; racemes or spikes *axillary*; petals

---

[1] **Adesmieae**, trib. nov. Frutices, suffrutices vel herbae, interdum petiolis spinescentibus armatae; folia pari- vel imparipinnata, foliolis numerosis rare paucis; stipellae nullae; flores plerumque rubri, saepe striati, in racemis terminalibus dispositi; pedicelli singuli; corolla papilionacea; stamina inter se libera; antherae uniformes, breves; ovarium 2–multiovulatum; stylus glaber, stigmate terminali; fructus articulatus, sutura superiore saepe recta, sutura inferiore profunde sinuata, articulis omnino vel a margine superiore secedentibus, indehiscentibus vel 2-valvibus; semina estrophiolata.

[2] Tribe **Hedysareae** DC. (*sensu strictissimo*). Frutices, fruticuli vel herbae; folia pinnata vel rare 1-foliolata; stipulae saepe scariosae; stipellae nullae; racemi vel spicae axillares; petala interdum marcescentia et persistentia; stamen vexillare liberum vel in medio cum ceteris connatum; partes liberae filamentorum filiformes; antherae uniformes; stylus glaber, saepe abrupte inflexus; fructus (*Onobrychide* excepta) articulatus, articulis 1-spermis indehiscentibus vel rare sutura abaxiali dehiscentibus.

sometimes *marcescent and persistent*; vexillary filament free or connate in the middle with the others into a single sheath split adaxially; free part of filaments filiform; *anthers uniform*; *style glabrous*, often (like the stamens) abruptly inflexed; *fruits jointed* (except *Onobrychis*), joints 1-seeded, indehiscent, or rarely dehiscing by the lower (abaxial) suture, rarely only 1 joint by abortion of the ovules, or fruits 1-seeded from the beginning; seeds usually *estrophiolate*. Type genus *Hedysarum* Linn.

Fruits more or less compressed:
  Fruits exserted from the calyx:
    Fruits not stipitate; ovules 4 or more:
      Fruits jointed:
        Fruits prickly on the sutures   418. **Stracheya**
        Fruits not prickly:
          Replum persistent on the segments of the fruits   419. **Eversmannia**
          Replum not persistent on the segments of the fruit   420. **Hedysarum**
      Fruits not jointed, mostly prickly or crested; 2–1-seeded; ovules 2–1
                                        421. **Onobrychis**

    Fruits stipitate:
      Stipules scarious; petals scarious, persistent around the fruit; ovules 2, rarely 1; leaves 3- or 1-foliolate   422. **Taverniera**
      Stipules not scarious, small; petals not scarious; leaves 3-foliolate
                                  423. **Arthroclianthus**

  Fruits enclosed by the calyx, membranous, 2–1-seeded, not stipitate; calyx-lobes plumose   424. **Ebenus**
Fruits subterete, often moniliform, smooth:
  Lower leaves pinnate, the upper leafless petiole spinescent
                              425. **Corethrodendron**
  Leaves all simple; spines axillary   426. **Alhagi**
  Imperfectly known genus probably related here   427. **Baueropsis**

418. **Stracheya** Benth., Hook. Kew Journ. 5: 306 (1853). 1 sp., *S. tibetica* Benth., Himalayas, Tibet. B.H. 1: 510; E.P. 3, 3: 312.

Shrublet, subacaulescent; leaves imparipinnate, leaflets entire, without stipels; stipules scarious, villous; flowers 1–4 on axillary peduncles; bracts lanceolate, like the narrow bracteoles persistent; upper 2 calyx-lobes longer and partly united at the base; vexillum long-narrowed to the base; wings shorter, falcate-oblong; keel equal to the vexillum, obliquely truncate at the apex, obtuse; vexillary stamen free at the base, coherent in the middle with the others or free, remainder connate; anthers uniform; ovary subsessile; ovules few; style filiform, abruptly inflexed in the upper part together with the stamens, stigma small, terminal; fruit linear, straight, plano-compressed, rigid, indehiscent, sutures continuous, echinate-dentate, joints within the margin scarcely separating, transversely elevated-venose and muricate in the middle; seeds reniform, estrophiolate.

419. **Eversmannia** Bunge, Goebel, Reise, 2: 267, t. 6 (1838). 1 sp., *E. hedysaroides* Bunge, Volga to Persia and Songaria. B.H. 1: 510; E.P. 3, 3: 313.

Diffuse shrublet, with axillary solitary or paired spines; leaves imparipinnate, leaflets small, rigid, not stipellate; stipules scarious; flowers purple, in axillary racemes; bracts and bracteoles small, persistent; calyx more split above, upper teeth shorter; vexillum obovate, scarcely clawed; wings very short, acute; keel incurved, obtuse, subequal to the vexillum; vexillary stamen free or connate in the middle with the others; anthers uniform; ovary subsessile, many-ovuled; style filiform, inflexed, stigma small, terminal; fruit linear, compressed, smooth, indehiscent, with persistent nerve-like sutures, joints at length breaking up and leaving the nude replum; seeds orbicular-reniform, estrophiolate.

420. **Hedysarum** Linn., Sp. Pl. 745 (1753). *Hedisarum* Neck. (1768). *Sulla* Medik. (1787). *Echinolobium* Desv. (1813). About 100 spp., temp. Europe, N. Africa, Asia, North America; type *H. coronarium* Linn., Mediterr. reg. and cult. B.H. 1: 510; E.P. 3, 3: 313; Fedtschenko, Act. Hort. Petrop. 19: 183 (1902); Rollins, Studies in the genus *Hedysarum*, Rhodora, 42: 217 (1940); Gams in Hegi, Ill. Fl. Mitt.-Eur. 4, 3: 1484, figs. 1518–20.

Perennial herbs, shrublets or rarely shrubs; leaves imparipinnate, leaflets entire, often pellucid-punctate, exstipellate; stipules scarious; flowers purple, white, or rarely yellow, in axillary racemes or heads; bracts scarious or setaceous; bracteoles below the calyx setaceous; calyx-teeth or lobes subequal; vexillum obovate or obcordate, scarcely clawed; wings oblong, shorter than the vexillum; keel often exceeding the wings, apex oblique, truncate or rarely subarcuate, obtuse; vexillary stamen free, remainder connate; anthers uniform; ovary subsessile, many- or 4–5-ovuled; style filiform, abruptly inflexed above with the stamens, stigma small, terminal; fruit compressed, joints suborbicular or quadrate, indehiscent, smooth or muricate; seeds compressed, reniform, estrophiolate.

421. **Onobrychis** Adans., Fam. 2: 327 (1763). *Onobruchus* Medik. (1787). *Eubrychis* DC. (1825). *Dendrobrychis* DC. (1825). *Eriocarpaea* Bertol. (1843). *Sartoria* Boiss. (1849). About 130 spp., Europe, N. Africa, NE. trop. Africa, NW. India to N. Asia; lectotype *O. viciifolia* Scop. (*O. sativa* Lam.). B.H. 1: 511; E.P. 3, 3: 314; Sirjaev, *Onobrychis* generis revisio critica, Publ. Fac. Sci. de l'Univ. Masaryk, no. 56 (1925), 76 (1926); Gams in Hegi, Ill. Fl. Mitt.-Eur. 4, 3: 1487, figs. 1521–6.

Shrublets, sometimes armed, or herbs; seedlings of some herbs germinating within the fruit, the latter persistent around the seedling; leaves imparipinnate, leaflets entire, exstipellate; stipules scarious; flowers in axillary pedunculate racemes or spikes; bracts scarious; bracteoles below the calyx small, setaceous, or absent; calyx-lobes subulate, subequal or the lower smaller, usually shorter than the tube; vexillum obovate or obcordate, scarcely clawed; wings short; keel obliquely truncate at the apex, obtuse, equal to or longer than the vexillum; vexillary stamen free at the base, connate in the middle with the others into a closed tube; anthers uniform; ovary sessile, 2–1-ovuled; style filiform, inflexed, stigma small, terminal; fruit compressed, semi-orbicular or orbicular-circinate, not jointed, indehiscent, prickly, created or smooth, lacunate-rugose or reticulate; seeds 2–1, broadly reniform or transversely oblong, estrophiolate.

422. **Taverniera** DC., Mém. Légum. 339, t. 52 (1826). *Bremontiera* DC. (1825).[1] *Tavernaria* Reichb. (1828). 7 spp., Egypt, NE. trop. Africa, Socotra, Mauritius, Baluchistan, India; type *T. nummularia* DC., Orient to India. B.H. 1: 511; E.P. 3, 3: 314.

Shrublets; leaves few, 1-foliolate or pinnately 3-foliolate, leaflets often obovate or orbicular; stipels absent; stipules scarious; flowers rose or white, few in axillary racemes; calyx-teeth subequal or the upper 2 more remote; bracts minute or caducous; bracteoles small; petals scariose-persistent; vexillum broadly obovate, scarcely clawed; wings small; keel subequal to the vexillum, apex oblique, truncate; vexillary stamen free at the base, connate in the middle with the others or at length free, remainder connate; anthers uniform; ovary stipitate, 2- rarely 1-ovuled; style filiform, inflexed, stigma small, terminal; fruit compressed, indehiscent, joints 1-seeded, breaking up; seeds reniform, estrophiolate.

[1] Excluding var. which is an *Indigofera*.

423. **Arthroclianthus** Baill., Adansonia 9: 296 (1870). About 7 spp., New Caledonia; type *A. sanguineus* Baill. Hochr., Conserv. Jard. Bot. Genève, 13: 30 (1909) (monogr.).

Shrubs; leaves 3-foliolate; stipules 2, small; stipels absent; flowers in axillary racemes; bracts short, mostly distichous; bracteoles 2, small, below the calyx, persistent; 2 upper calyx-lobes connate, the calyx appearing 4-lobed, lower 3 lobes smaller; vexillum shorter than the wings and keel, often erect or reflexed and sometimes bent sharply back; wings mostly falcate, often adherent to the keel; keel beaked, mostly much produced, all petals clawed; stamens 10, diadelphous, the vexillary free, unequal in length, 5 longer and 5 a little shorter; anthers oblong, subdorsally attached; ovary stipitate, elongated; ovules many; style slender, stigma slightly thickened; fruit often stipitate, with persistent calyx, much elongated, compressed, many-jointed, joints oblong, 1-seeded, the top joint long-apiculate with the persistent style.

424. **Ebenus** Linn., Sp. Pl. 764 (1753). *Ebenidium* Jaub. & Spach (1843). 20 spp., Mediterr. reg.; type *E. cretica* Linn. B.H. 1: 512; E.P. 3, 3: 315.

Armed shrublets or unarmed herbs, silky-pubescent or villous; leaves imparipinnate or the lower subdigitately 3-foliolate, leaflets entire, exstipellate; stipules connate into one opposite the leaves; flowers crowded in long-pedunculate axillary spikes; bracts lanceolate or linear; bracteoles inconspicuous; calyx softly villous, lobes subequal, subulate, plumose, often as long as the petals and longer than the tube; vexillum obovate or obcordate, scarcely clawed; wings short; keel obliquely truncate at the apex, obtuse, equal to the vexillum; vexillary stamen free at the base, connate in the middle with the others in a closed sheath; anthers uniform; ovary sessile, very obtuse, 1-ovuled or rarely oblong and 3–2-ovuled; style filiform, inflexed, stigma small, terminal; fruit compressed, obovate or oblong, enclosed by the calyx-tube, membranous, indehiscent, 1- rarely 2-seeded.

425. **Corethrodendron** Fisch. & Basiner, Bull. Acad. St. Petersb. 4: 315 and Mém. Sav. Étrang. St. Petersb. 6: 90 (1851). 1 sp., *C. scroparium* Fisch. & Basiner, Songaria. B.H. 1: 512; E.P. 3, 3: 315.

Shrub; lower leaves imparipinnate, leaflets entire, exstipellate, the upper leafless and the petioles spiny; stipules united into one opposite the leaves, deciduous; flowers in long-pedunculate axillary racemes; bracts small, caducous; bracteoles very small; calyx-teeth subequal, upper 2 connivent; vexillum broadly obovate, shortly clawed; wings short; keel incurved, obtuse, a little shorter than the vexillum; vexillary stamen free, remainder connate; anthers uniform; ovary stipitate, many-ovuled; style filiform, incurved, stigma small, terminal; fruit linear, subterete, joints subovoid, breaking away and indehiscent; seeds reniform, estrophiolate.

426. **Alhagi** Tourn. ex Adans., Fam. 2: 328 and 514 (1763). *Manna* D. Don (1825). *Alhagia* Reichb. (1841). 3 spp., E. Mediterr., Orient, W. Cent. Asia, N. Africa; type *A. maurorum* Medic.

Rigid much-branched shrubs armed with axillary spines; leaves simple, entire, often small; stipules small; flowers red, often few in axillary racemes; rhachis rigid, spinescent at the apex; bracts very small; bracteoles none; calyx-teeth short, subequal; vexillum obovate, shortly clawed; wings falcate-oblong, free; keel incurved, obtuse, subequal to the wings and vexillum; vexillary stamen free, remainder connate; anthers uniform; ovary subsessile, many-ovuled; style filiform, incurved, glabrous, stigma small, terminal; fruit linear, thick or subterete, smooth, indehiscent, often contracted between the seeds and divided inside by subdouble septa, joints not separating; seeds reniform, estrophiolate; embryo covered by a fleshy membrane.

427. **Baueropsis** Hutch., new name. *Bauerella* Schindler, Fedde Repert. 22: 284 (1926), not Borzi (1897). 1 sp. *B. tomentosa* (Schindler) Hutch., Australia.

Shrub or shrublet with virgate branches; leaves 1-foliolate, stipulate but exstipellate; inflorescence axillary, capitate; flowers mostly 3 in the axil of each bract; bracteoles absent; calyx narrowly tubular, 5-partite; vexillum oblong, clawed, not auriculate and without callosities; wings spurred, slightly adherent to the keel; keel-petals long-clawed, half-obovate, obtuse, lower margins coherent; stamens diadelphous; vexillary stamen free, remainder connate for nine-tenths their length, free parts filiform; anthers uniform, narrowly ovoid, dorsifixed near the base; disk none; ovary shortly stipitate, 1-ovuled; style long, incurved at the top and thickened, stigma small, terminal; fruit not known.

Tribe 47. AESCHYNOMENEAE

Tribe *Hedysareae* Subtribe *Aeschynomeneae* Benth. & Hook. f., Gen. Pl. 1: 448 (1865)

Shrubs, shrublets, and herbs, *sometimes gland-dotted*; leaves usually imparipinnate, leaflets numerous, or rarely 3–1; stipels very rarely present; flowers racemose, *racemes axillary*, often few-flowered, or rarely flowers in *axillary fascicles or subcymose*; wing-petals often *transversely plicate*; stamens all connate into a sheath split above, or in 2 lateral bundles, the vexillary filament rarely free; *anthers uniform* or nearly so, versatile, rarely dimorphic; style filiform, *glabrous*; *fruits jointed*, joints often separating but indehiscent, rarely dehiscent, rarely only 1 joint; seeds with or without a strophiole. Type genus *Aeschynomene* Linn.

Staminal sheath split only on the upper (adaxial) side, or vexillary stamen free, or sheath not at all split:
  Upper segment of the fruit not winged (sometimes ribbed lengthwise):
    Leaves imparipinnate:
      Segments of the fruit ribbed or striate lengthwise   428. **Chaetocalyx**
      Segments of the fruit not as above:
        Small trees, shrubs, or shrublets:
          Vexillary filament free; ovules numerous:
            Ovary stipitate; leaflets mucronate or pungent-pointed   429. **Pictetia**
            Ovary sessile; leaflets not mucronate   430. **Bergeronia**
          Vexillary filament connate with the others:
            Ovules 2; shrubs or small trees; leaflets not glandular   431. **Brya**
            Ovules several; shrublets with a tuber-like rhizome; leaflets glandular-
              punctate   432. **Weberbauerella**
        Herb; stamens diadelphous; ovules 4–3   433. **Fibrigiella**
    Leaves paripinnate:
      Calyx-lobes short, subequal; joints of the fruit flat, quadrate or oblong, reticulate; leaflets 4, rarely 3; plants dotted with glands
              434. **Poiretia**
      Upper calyx-lobes much larger than the others, the lateral small, lower narrow; joints of the fruit subquadrate; leaflets mostly 2 pairs; plants sometimes glandular   435. **Amicia**
  Upper segment of the fruit winged and samaroid   436. **Nissolia**
Staminal sheath usually split both on the lower and along the upper side:
  Fruit-segments not expanded into superposed disk-like segments:
    Erect shrubs or herbs, not climbers:

Segments of the fruit rather long (longer than broad); shrubs
437. **Ormocarpum**
Segments of the fruit more or less square or semiorbicular; shrubs or
herbs:
Bracts mostly small and deciduous:
Fruit exserted from the calyx:
Fruit not compressed-circinate:
Vexillum not scarious after flowering:
Anthers uniform; style not bearded 438. **Aeschynomene**
Anthers dimorphic; style bearded 439. **Balisaea**
Anthers dimorphic; style glabrous 440. **Bakerophyton**
Vexillum scarious and persistent after flowering
441. **Soemmeringia**
Fruit compressed-circinate 442. **Cyclocarpa**
Fruit enclosed by the calyx:
Stipules not spurred at the base 443. **Kotschya**
Stipules spurred at the base, the spur 2-pronged, one side linear and
longer than the other 444. **Smithia**
Bracts large, obliquely reniform, imbricate, subtending the flowers:
Inflorescence more or less compressed in one plane:
Stipules basifixed, not prolonged below the base 445. **Bryaspis**
Stipules medifixed, i.e. prolonged below the point of attachment
446. **Geissaspis**
Inflorescence not compressed, zigzag, or more or less cylindric; bracts
present and persistent 447. **Humularia**
Climbers; segments of the fruit reticulate-nervose lengthwise:
Ovules numerous, 10 or more; flowers few 448. **Isodesmia**
Ovules 8–6; inflorescences many-flowered 449. **Raimondianthus**
Fruit-segments expanded into 3 horizontal superposed disk-like segments
450. **Discolobium**

428. **Chaetocalyx** DC., Mém. Légum. 262 (1825). *Boenninghausia* Spreng.
(1826). *Planarium* Desv. (1826). *Rhadinocarpus* Vog. (1838) *Nissoloides*
M. E. Jones? (1933). About 28 spp., trop. and subtrop. America; type *C.
scandens* (Linn.) Urb. (*C. vincentina* (Ker.) DC.), Isl. of St. Vincent. B.H. 1:
513; E.P. 3, 3: 317; Amshoff, Pulle Fl. Suriname 2, 2: 235; Rudd, Contrib.
U.S. Nat. Herb. 32: 207, figs. 1–13 (1958); Burkart, Legum. Argent. ed. 2: 291,
fig. 85.

Climbing herbs; leaves imparipinnate, leaflets mostly few, exstipellate; stipules lanceolate
or linear; inflorescence axillary, pedicels ebracteolate, 2–3 together in the axil of stipule-
like bracts, arranged in short racemes or on a common peduncle; flowers yellow; hairs
rigid from a tubercular base, scattered on the calyx and sometimes on the peduncles and
branchlets; calyx-teeth or lobes subequal or the upper 2 approximate; vexillum obovate, or
suborbicular, emarginate; wings oblong, free, scarcely shorter than the obtuse almost
straight keel; stamens all connate into a sheath split above or the vexillary stamen free;
anthers uniform; ovary shortly stipitate; ovules numerous; style filiform, incurved, stigma
small, terminal; fruit linear, subterete or compressed, scarcely constricted between the
seeds, joints linear, oblong, or quadrate, ribbed or striate lengthwise; seeds transversely
oblong or orbicular-reniform, estrophiolate.

429. **Pictetia** DC., Bibl. Univ. Genève 29: 40 (1825); Ann. Sci. Nat. 9: 93 (1825). 8 spp., West Indies, Mexico; lectotype *P. aculeata* (Nahl) Urb. (*P. aristata* (Jacq.) DC.), West Indies. B.H. 1: 514; E.P. 3, 3: 317.

Shrubs; leaves imparipinnate, leaflets 3 or more, mucronate or pungent-pointed, entire, exstipellate; stipules often spinescent; flowers yellow, in axillary racemes or rarely solitary; bracts and bracteoles very caducous; 2 upper calyx-lobes short, obtuse, lower 3 acuminate; vexillum suborbicular; keel obtuse, slightly shorter than the wings; vexillary stamen free, remainder connate; anthers uniform; ovary stipitate; ovules numerous; style filiform, glabrous, stigma small, terminal; fruit oblong or broadly linear, stipitate, compressed, indehiscent, either not jointed or breaking into only a few oblong joints; seeds oval, compressed, estrophiolate.

430. **Bergeronia** M. Micheli, Mém. Soc. Phys. Genève, 28: n. 7, 38, pl. 14 (1883). 1 sp., *B. sericea* Micheli, Paraguay, Argentina. E.P. 3, 3: 343; Burkart, Legum. Argent. ed. 2, 235, fig. 60.

Tree; leaves imparipinnate, 9–13-foliolate; leaflets opposite; stipules short, deciduous; stipels absent; racemes axillary; bracts small, caducous; bracteoles setaceous, falling before flowering; calyx tubular-campanulate, 5-dentate, upper teeth shorter, lower a little longer, all acute; petals yellow, densely silky outside; vexillum broad, almost orbicular, shortly clawed, not appendaged; wings free, slightly exceeding the keel, clawed; keel straight, obtuse, the petals connate at the back; stamens diadelphous, vexillary free from the base; anthers oblong, uniform, versatile; ovary sessile, several-ovuled, ovules 1-seriate; style incurved, glabrous, stigma terminal, small; fruit indehiscent, falcate, plano-compressed, several-seeded, jointed, the seeds in separate compartments, the segments indehiscent; seeds oblong-reniform, with a small orbicular hilum.

431. **Brya** P.Br., Hist. Jam. 299, t. 31 (1756). *Aldina* Adans. (1763). *Nefrakis* Raf. (1838). 8 spp., West Indies; type *B. ebenus* DC. B.H. 1: 514; E.P. 3, 3: 317.

Shrubs or small trees; leaves imparipinnate, either 1–3-foliolate and with scarcely a common petiole, or with numerous small leaflets, exstipellate; stipules rather spinescent and persistent, or very small and deciduous; flowers in axillary or subterminal cymes or fascicles; bracts and bracteoles small, persistent; calyx-lobes subequal or the lower longer, vexillum clawed, suborbicular; wings falcate-oblong; keel much incurved, obtuse; stamens all connate into a sheath split above; anthers uniform; ovary subsessile or stipitate; ovules 2; style filiform, incurved, stigma minute, terminal; fruit sessile or stipitate, joints 1–2, broad, flat, membranous, indehiscent, lower suture arcuate; seeds complanate-reniform, estrophiolate.

432. **Weberbauerella** Ulbrich, Engl. Bot. Jahrb. 37: 551, fig. 1 (1906). 1 sp. *W. brongniartioides* Ulbrich, Peru.

Shrublet with a tuber-like rhizome; branches glandular; leaves imparipinnate, leaflets not stipellate, about 12 pairs, opposite, small, elliptic, the terminal obovate and widely emarginate, all glandular-punctate; racemes axillary, shorter than the leaves; bracts lanceolate; calyx obliquely campanulate, 2-lipped, upper lip 2-lobed, lower 3-lobed; petals glandular-punctate, vexillum shortly clawed, ovate-orbicular, emarginate; keel-petals connate in the lower third; filaments all connate; anthers equal, ellipsoid; ovary stipitate, several-ovuled, transversely septate, style very slender, stigma punctiform.

433. **Fibrigiella** Harms, Engl. Bot. Jahrb. 42: 95 (1908). 1 sp., *F. gracilis* Harms, Bolivia.

Herb; leaves imparipinnate, leaflets 2–3 pairs, rarely 1 pair; stipules lanceolate; racemes axillary, several-flowered; calyx cup-like, lobed to the middle or beyond, lower tooth slightly exceeding the others, upper connate and bifid; corolla glabrous; vexillum clawed, lamina suborbicular; wings and keel-petals clawed, keel slightly shorter than the other petals; stamens 10, diadelphous; ovary shortly stipitate, 4–3-ovulate; style glabrous, stigma minute; fruit very shortly stipitate, oblong-linear, straight or slightly curved, compressed, jointed, joints mostly 3, oblong-rectangular or obliquely obovoid, or almost semilunar, acute on the back; seeds oblong-ovoid, slightly compressed laterally.

434. **Poiretia** Vent., Choix t. 42 (1803) (conserved name). *Turpinia* Pers. (1807). 11 spp., trop. America; type *P. scandens* Vent. B.H. 1: 513; E.P. 3, 3: 318; Burkart, Legum. Argent. ed. 2: 302, fig. 90.

Shrublets or herbs, climbing or rarely suberect, dotted with glands; leaves pinnate, leaflets 4 or rarely 3, often minutely stipellate; stipules sessile or shortly decurrent at the base; flowers yellow, in axillary racemes or terminal panicles; bracts lanceolate or subulate; bracteoles small; calyx-teeth short; vexillum broadly orbicular, reflexed; wings falcate-oblong; keel much incurved, subbeaked or rarely oblong and obtuse; stamens all connate into a closed tube; anthers subreniform or alternate ones a little longer; ovary sessile; ovules numerous; style incurved, stigma terminal; fruit linear, joints flat, oblong or quadrate, membranous or subcoriaceous, reticulate or verrucose.

435. **Amicia** H. B. & K., Nov. Gen. et Spec. 6: 511, t. 600 (1823). *Zygomeris* Moc. & Sessé ex DC. (1825). 8 spp., Bolivia as far as Mexican Andes, Brazil, Argentina; type *A. glandulosa* H. B. & K., Colombia, Ecuador, Peru. B.H. 1: 514; E.P. 3, 3: 318; Burkart, Legum. Argent. ed. 2: 293, fig. 86.

Shrubs, glabrous or glandular-dotted, branches flexuous and subscandent; leaves paripinnate, leaflets mostly 2 pairs, obovate or obcordate, exstipellate; stipules often large, deciduous; flowers fairly large, yellow, in short axillary racemes; bracts and bracteoles broad, herbaceous; 2 upper calyx-lobes large, obovate, lateral very small, lower oblong, shorter than the upper; vexillum clawed, suborbicular or obovate-oblong, emarginate; wings obliquely obovate or narrow or short; keel incurved, obtuse, subequal to the vexillum; stamens all connate into a sheath split above; anthers uniform; ovary sessile; ovules numerous; style filiform, stigma small, terminal; fruit linear, arcuate, joints quadrate.

436. **Nissolia** Jacq., Enum. Pl. Carib. 7 (1760) (conserved name). *Nissolius* Medik. (1787). *Pseudomachaerum* Hassler (1907). 25 spp., trop. America, N. Mexico; type *N. fruticosa* Jacq., South America. B.H. 1: 513; E.P. 3, 3: 317; Rudd, Contrib. U.S. Nat. Herb. 32: 173 (1956).

Shrublets or herbs, climbing; leaves imparipinnate, leaflets few, exstipellate; stipules setaceous; flowers yellow, in axillary racemes or terminal panicles; bracts subulate; bracteoles absent; teeth of the truncate calyx setaceous, subequal; vexillum ovate-orbicular, reflexed, claw short; wings falcate-oblong; keel incurved, obtuse; vexillary stamen free at the base, connate in the middle with the others into a closed tube; anthers subreniform; ovary subsessile; ovules few; style filiform, stigma terminal; fruit linear, indehiscent joints flat or convex, oblong or quadrate, the end one expanded into a straight or an oblique obovate wing; seeds orbicular-reniform, estrophiolate.

437. **Ormocarpum**[1] Beauv., Fl. d'Oware 1: 95, t. 58 (1804) (conserved name). About 30 spp., Old World, trop. reg., Arabia; type *O. verrucosum* Beauv., trop. Africa. B.H. 1: 515; E.P. 3, 3: 318; Hutch. & Dalz., Fl. W. Trop. Afr. 1: 413; ed. 2 (Keay), 1: 576.

Tall shrubs, often sticky; leaves either imparipinnate with numerous small exstipellate leaflets, or 1-foliolate with a large acute leaflet; stipules striate; flowers yellow, white, or purple-striate, few in short axillary racemes; bracts and bracteoles persistent, striate; 2 upper

---

[1] Synonyms of **Ormocarpum**: *Diphaca* Lour. (1790). *Rathkea* Schumach. & Thonn. (1827). *Hormocarpus* Spreng. (1831). *Russellia* Koenig ex Roxb. (1832). *Acrotaphros* Hochst. ex A. Rich. (1847). *Saldania* T. R. Sim (1909).

calyx-lobes broader, close together or subconnate, lowest a little longer; vexillum orbicular, clawed; wings obliquely obovate, keel broad, incurved, rather acute or obtuse, subequal to the wings; stamens all connate in a sheath split above or at length on both sides; anthers uniform; ovary sessile; ovules numerous; style much inflexed, filiform, stigma minute, terminal; fruit linear, compressed, sulcate-striate lengthwise and often glandular-muricate, joints oblong, narrow and hard on each side; seeds narrowly oblong, hilum lateral, near the apex; cotyledons narrow, semicordate.

438. **Aeschynomene**[1] Linn., Sp. Pl. 713 (1753). About 250 described spp., trop. and subtrop. reg. of almost the whole world, espec. Africa and South American Andes; type *A. aspera* Linn., Old World tropics. B.H. 1: 515; E.P. 3, 3: 319; Amshoff, Pulle Fl. Suriname, 2, 2: 236; C. V. Morton, Contrib. U.S. Nat. Herb. 29: 82 (1944) (Mexican herb. spp.); Hutch. & Dalz., Fl. W. Trop. Afr. 1: 415; ed. 2 (Keay), 1: 577; J. Léonard, Fl. Congo Belge, 5: 249, with figs. (excl. subgen. *Bakerophyton*); Jard. Bot. Brux. 24: 63 (1954); Burkart, Legum. Argent. ed. 2, 289, fig. 84; Rudd, Contrib. U.S. Nat. Herb. 32: 1 (1955) (Amer. spp.).

Shrubs or herbs; leaves subimparipinnate, leaflets numerous, small, entire, exstipellate; stipules setaceous or lanceolate; flowers yellow, often lined with purple, in simple or branched axillary racemes, rarely terminal; bracts often stipule-like; bracteoles adpressed to the calyx; calyx-lobes either subequal, or 2 connate into lips, upper entire or 2-fid, lower entire or 3-fid; vexillum orbicular, shortly clawed; wings obliquely obovate or oblong, subequal to the vexillum; keel either obovate and slightly incurved, or often narrow, much incurved or subbeaked, petals sometimes scarcely coherent; stamens connate into a sheath split towards the keel or on both sides, one very rarely separate from the others; anthers uniform; ovary stipitate, 2–more-ovuled; style incurved, not bearded, stigma terminal; fruit stipitate, joints 2 or more, flat or convex in the middle, smooth or muricate, indehiscent or rarely dehiscent by the lower suture, rarely spirally twisted.

439. **Balisaea** Taub., Engl. Bot. Jahrb. 21: 436 (1895). 1 sp., *B. genistoides* Taub., Brazil. E.P.N. 201.

Perennial herb; stipules small, persistent; leaves imparipinnate; leaflets rarely opposite, setaceous, exstipellate; flowers few, pale yellow, racemose, racemes leaf-opposed, elongated, lax; bracts minutely stipule-like; bracteoles 2 at the apex of the pedicels, persistent; calyx subcampanulate, 5-partite, segments subequal, lanceolate; petals subequal in length; vexillum suborbicular, slightly cordate at the base, shortly clawed; wings oblique, broadly obovate, apex obtuse, 1-toothed above the claw; keel almost rectangular-incurved, subrostrate at the apex, the petals connate from the apex to the middle, 1-toothed above the claw; stamens all connate into a sheath at length split along the keel or on both sides; anthers dimorphic, 5 alternately longer and basifixed, 5 shorter and dorsifixed; ovary stipitate, 2–1-ovuled; style slightly incurved, barbellate along the inside, stigma minute, terminal; fruit linear, compressed, slightly constricted between the seeds.

440. **Bakerophyton**, new gen.[2] *Aeschynomene* subgen. *Bakerophyton* J. Léonard, Fl. Congo Belge, 5: 251, 299, pl. 23 (1954). 1 sp. *B. lateritium* (Harms) Hutch., trop. Africa.

---

[1] Synonyms of **Aeschynomene**: *Gajati* (Rumph.) ex Adans. (1763). *Mantodda* Adans. (1763). *Rochea* Scop. (1777). *Aeschinomene* Nocca (1793). *Oeschinomene* Poir. (1797). *Herminiera* Guill. & Perr. (1832). *Patagonium* E. Mey. (1835). *Macromiscus* Turcz. (1846). *Rueppelia* A. Rich. (1847). *Ctenodon* Baill. (1870). *Ruppelia* Bak. (1871). *Climacorachis* Hemsl. & Rose (1903). *Secula* Small (1913). *Pongamiopsis* R. Vig. (1950). *Ormocarpopsis* R. Vig. (1952)?

[2] **Bakerophyton** Hutch., gen. nov., affine *Aeschynomeneae* Linn., sed antheris dimorphis differt.

Annual herb, stems prostrate or straggling, yet slender; leaves imparipinnate, leaflets several pairs, oblong-linear, with a median nerve and lateral nerves spreading at a right-angle, denticulate in the upper part; stipules ovate-lanceolate, not appendaged, serrulate, persistent; racemes axillary, axis very zigzag, several-flowered; bracts trilobed, persistent; pedicels filiform; bracteoles lanceolate, serrulate-ciliate, persistent; calyx 2-lipped, upper lip 2-toothed, lower 3-toothed; wing-petals free; keel-petals partly united; stamens 10, united in a sheath open above; anthers dimorphic half of them larger and basifixed, half much smaller and dorsifixed; ovary 2-ovuled; style very short, glabrous, persistent; fruit of 1 or 2 joints, these suborbicular, densely and finely verrucose, enclosed in the bracteoles and persistent calyx, indehiscent.

441. **Soemmeringia** Mart., Diss. Soemmer. 27 (1828). 1 sp., *S. semperflorens* Mart., Brazil. B.H. 1: 516; E.P. 3, 3: 320.

Annual herb; leaves imparipinnate, leaflets about 4 pairs, narrowly obovate-oblanceolate, with a median nerve and a few ascending lateral nerves; rhachis ending in a sharp point; stipules lanceolate, produced below the base; flowers 1–2, bracts small, subulate; bracteoles lanceolate, striate, persistent; calyx 2-lipped, upper lip 2-toothed, lower 3-fid; petals scarious and persistent, reticulate-venose; vexillum subsessile; stamens in 2 lateral bundles; anthers uniform; ovary stipitate, several-ovuled; style incurved; fruit stipitate, joints plano-convex, reticulate.

442. **Cyclocarpa** Afz. ex Bak., Oliv. Fl. Trop. Afr. 2: 151 (1871); Urban, Jahrb. Bot. Gart. Berl. 3: 247 (1884). 1 sp., *C. stellaris* Afz. ex Bak., trop. Africa., Malaya, N. Australia, Queensland. E.P. 3, 3: 320; Hutch. & Dalz., Fl. West Trop. Afr. 1: 416; J. Léonard, Fl. Congo Belge, 5: 240; van Steenis, Reinwardtia, 5: 430 (1961).

Erect herb; leaves paripinnate, sensitive; leaflets small, 2–5 pairs; stipules ovate-lanceolate, thin; no stipels; flowers few, in axillary umbel-like racemes; bracts acuminate, persistent; bracteoles small, membranous; calyx caducous, bilabiate, upper lip entire or bifid, lower trifid; vexillum obovate, emarginate, shortly clawed; wings oblong, obtuse, keel finely denticulate on the upper part; stamens 10, united into 2 bundles; anthers equal; ovary falcate, subsessile; ovules numerous; stigma small, terminal; fruit linear, compressed and disk-like, circinate; segments 8–9, subdeltoid, dehiscent; sutures persistent after the fall of the segments; seeds small.

443. **Kotschya** Endl., Nov. Stirp. Mus. Dec. no. 6 (1838). *Sarcobotrya* Vig. (1952). About 30 spp., Africa; type *K. africana* Endl. B.H. 1: 516 (in *Smithia*); E.P. 3, 3: 321 (in *Smithia*); De Wit & Duvign., Bull. Soc. Bot. Belg. 86: 207, figs. 1–3 (1954); Fl. Congo Belge, 5: 331; Hutch. & Dalz., Fl. W. Trop. Afr. ed. 2 (Keay), 1: 580.

Herbs, shrubs, or trees; leaves pinnate; leaflets 4 or more, alternate, asymmetric at the base, with several nerves from the base, the main nerve usually submarginal; stipules not spurred at the base, persistent or not; rhachis terminated by a short point; stipels absent; racemes distichous, more or less scorpioid, strobiliform, flowers reflexed; bracts entire, smaller than the flowers, scarious, striate, persistent; bracteoles free or united, persistent below the fruit remote from the calyx; calyx 2-lipped, the lips subfree, the upper bifid or bi-lobed, the lower 3-lobed; vexillum orbicular to obovate; keel-petals united dorsally, free at the apex; stamens 10, united for two-thirds into a tube split above and below; anthers uniform; ovary stipitate; disk very short; ovules 2–9; style inflexed, glabrous, stigma terminal; fruit stipitate, enclosed by the calyx; joints 1–9, indehiscent, semiorbicular, smooth; seeds reniform, smooth.

444. **Smithia**[1] Ait., Hort. Kew. ed. 1, 3: 496, t. 13 (1789) (conserved name). About 30 spp., Old World tropics, especially Asia and Malaya; type *S. sensitiva*

---

[1] Synonyms of **Smithia**: *Damapana* Adans. (1763). *Petagnana* J. F. Gmel. (1791). *Patagnana* Steud. (1841).

Ait. B.H. 1: 516 (excl. sect. *Kotschya*); E.P. 3, 3: 321 (excl. sect. *Kotschya*); De Wit & Duvigneaud, Fl. Congo Belge, 5: 344, fig. 23; Hutch. & Dalz., Fl. W. Trop. Afr. 1: 416 (partly); ed. 2 (Keay), 1: 582.

Herbs or shrublets; leaves pinnate, leaflets 6–12 pairs, opposite, asymmetric at the base, with the principal nerve in the middle; stipules appendaged at the base, appendix 2-auricled, one 'ear' rounded and short, the other linear and longer, persistent; stipels absent; inflorescence axillary, usually dense, a short umbel-like scorpioid cyme; bracts smaller than the flowers, scarious, striate, caducous; bracteoles below the calyx, scarious, persistent below the fruit and applied to the calyx; calyx scarious, 2-lipped, lips subentire; standard and other petals and stamens as in *Kotschya*; ovary shortly stipitate; disk short; ovules 2–9; style inflexed, glabrous, stigma terminal; fruit stipitate, enclosed by the persistent and accrescent calyx; joints indehiscent, semiorbicular, smooth or tuberculate; seeds reniform, smooth.

445. Bryaspis Duvign., Bull. Soc. Roy. Bot. Belg. 86: 151, sub fig. 13 (1954). 1 sp., *B. lupulina* (Planch. ex Benth.) Duvign., trop. Africa. Hutch. & Dalz., Fl. W. Trop. Afr. ed. 2 (Keay), 1: 582 (1958).

Herb; leaves very few, imparipinnate; leaflets about 3 pairs, small, unequal-sided at the base, glabrous, main nerve in the middle; stipules large, persistent, broadly ovate, several-nerved from the base; flowers in dense oblong pedunculate caterpillar-like racemes hidden by large imbricate finely reticulate orbicular-reniform bracts about 1·5 cm. diam.; calyx bilabiate, divided to the base, upper lip bifid, lower trifid; petals bright yellow, twice as long as the calyx; vexillum orbicular, bifid, long-clawed; stamens 10, in 2 lateral separate bundles; anthers equal, rounded; ovary 2-ovuled; style incurved; fruit with 2 rounded reticulate joints.

446. Geissaspis Wight & Arn., Prod. Fl. Pen. Ind. Or. 1: 217 (1834). *Geissapsis* Bak. (1876). 3 spp., trop. and subtrop. Asia; type *G. cristata* Wight & Arn., India. B.H. 1: 516 (partly); E.P. 3, 3: 321 (partly); Duvigneaud, Bull. Soc. Bot. Belg. 86: 145 (1954).

Herbs; leaves paripinnate, leaflets in few pairs, obovate, exstipellate; stipules membranous, produced below the insertion; flowers small, yellow or purplish, in long-pedunculate axillary racemes; bracts large, obliquely reniform, venose, imbricate, often covering the flowers and fruit, either ciliate or entire; bracteoles absent; calyx deeply split into 2 lobes, upper entire, lower 3-toothed; vexillum broadly suborbicular, claw short; wings obliquely obovate or oblong; keel incurved, obtuse, a little shorter than the vexillum; stamens all connate, sheath split above or at length also below; anthers uniform; ovary rather stipitate; ovules 2; style incurved, subulate or compressed, stigma small, terminal; fruit with the upper suture nearly straight, lower sinuate, joints flat, reticulate, indehiscent; seeds orbicular-reniform, estrophiolate.

447. Humularia Duvign., Bull. Soc. Roy. Bot. Belg. 86: 145, figs. 1–9 (1954). About 40 spp., trop. Africa; lectotype *H. drepanocepala* (Bak.) Duvign., Fl. Congo Belge, 5: 300, with figs., and Bull. Soc. Bot. Belg. 86: 154 (1954).

Shrublets, rarely shrubs, with glandular-based hairs; leaves paripinnate; leaflets 2–12, opposite or subalternate, asymmetric at the base, with the principal nerve submedian to marginal; inflorescence axillary or terminal, in dense scorpioid racemes, rarely loose and zigzag; bracts distichous, 2-lobed, persistent, large, densely imbricate and more or less hiding the flowers and fruit; bracteoles persistent, ciliate, nervose; calyx bilabiate, membranous, lips almost free, upper more or less 2-fid, lower 3-fid; vexillum subpandurate, clawed; wings spathulate, united by their basal appendages; keel obovate, partly united by their dorsal margin; stamens 10, united into 2 bundles of 5; ovary stipitate; ovules 2; style glabrous, fruit woody, of 2 or one segment; segments semi-orbicular, indehiscent; seeds reniform-suborbicular, glabrous and glossy.

448. Isodesmia Gardn., Hook. Lond. Journ. Bot. 2: 339 (1843). 2 spp., Brazil; type *I. tomentosa* Gardn. B.H. 1: 514; E.P. 3, 3: 318.

Scandent shrublets; leaves imparipinnate, leaflets numerous, exstipellate; stipules persistent, not produced at the base; flowers yellow, few in axillary racemes; bracts stipule-like and bracteoles persistent; calyx-teeth or lobes subequal or upper 2 subconnate; vexillum orbicular, emarginate; wings oblong, obtuse; keel obtuse, subequal to the wings; stamens connate in a sheath split towards the keel or on both sides; anthers uniform; ovary sessile; ovules numerous; style filiform, stigma small, terminal; fruit sessile, linear, straight, flattened, joints quadrate, coriaceous, reticulate-venose lengthwise.

449. Raimondianthus Harms, Notizbl. Bot. Gart. Berlin, 10: 387 (1928). 1 sp., *R. platycarpus* Harms, Peru.

Stem climbing, villous; leaves imparipinnate; leaves opposite, 2–3 pairs, densely pilose below; stipules lanceolate; panicles axillary and terminal, several-flowered, divaricate; bracts small, deltoid; pedicels slender; bracteoles paired below the base of the calyx, deciduous; calyx-teeth very short, upper pair a little connate; corolla long-exserted; vexillum broadly clawed, broadly obovate, almost truncate towards the claw; wings oblanceolate-oblong, obtusely appendaged at the base towards the claw, keel-petals narrowly clawed, obliquely oblong-oblanceolate, obtuse; stamens 10; tube of connate filaments sometimes split on each side, vexillary stamen free at the base and apex, connate with the others in the middle; anthers small; ovary sessile, style slender, pubescent below, stigma minute; ovules 8–6; fruit sessile, lanceolate, straight or nearly so, compressed, flat, chartaceous, probably indehiscent, with numerous oblique veins lengthwise converging on a median line; seeds 6, 1-seriate.

450. Discolobium Benth., Ann. Wien. Mus. 2: 105 (1838). 8 spp., Brazil, Paraguay, Argentina; type *D. pulchellum* Benth., Brazil. B.H. 1: 516; E.P. 3, 3: 321; Burkart, Legum. Argent. ed. 2, 294, fig. 87.

Shrublets; leaves imparipinnate, leaflets numerous, rarely only 1–3, exstipellate; stipules small; flowers in axillary racemes, peduncle elongated and rigid; pedicels solitary; bracts and bracteoles small, persistent; calyx-lobes subequal or upper 2 united; vexillum suborbicular, claw short; wings obovate, subequal to the vexillum; keel almost straight, obtuse, shorter than the wings; stamens all connate into a sheath at length split on both sides, vexillary and lowermost almost free from the base; anthers uniform; ovary shortly stipitate; ovules 3 or 2; style incurved, not barbate, stigma small, terminal, oblique; fruit short, upper suture almost straight, expanded towards the lower suture, divided into joints or 2 horizontal disks, the middle one the largest, reniform, reticulate, indehiscent, 1-seeded, the lowest and uppermost much smaller and sterile; seed lunate-reniform, strophiolate.

Tribe 48. DESMODIEAE[1]

Tribe *Hedysareae* Subtribe *Desmodieae* Benth. & Hook. f., Gen. Pl. 1: 449 (partly) (1865)

Herbs, rarely climbing, or shrublets, rarely shrubs, and very rarely trees; leaves pinnately 3-foliolate or 1-foliolate by reduction, *terminal leaflet with*

---

[1] **Desmodieae** trib. nov. Herbae rarius volubiles vel suffrutices, rarius frutices, rarissime arbores; folia pinnatim 3-foliolata vel 1-foliolata et rhachide alata, foliolo terminali 2-stipellato, lateralibus oppositis 1-stipellatis, rarissime 5–7-foliolata; stipulae plerumque striatae; flores in racemis terminalibus et interdum simulque axillaribus dispositi, secus rhachin racemi gemini, rarius fasciculati vel solitarii, rarius umbellati; corolla papilionacea; alae carinam aequantes vel superantes, et ei prope basin saepe adhaerentes; stamen vexillare liberum vel cum ceteris a basi in tubum clausum connatum; discus intra stamina interdum adest; stylus glaber; ovula plura vel pauca; fructus articulatus, articulis dehiscentibus vel indehiscentibus, rarius ad suturam inferiorem 2-valvatim dehiscens.

2 stipels, lateral each with 1 stipel, very rarely 5–7-foliolate; stipules mostly striate; flowers in *terminal* and at the same time sometimes axillary racemes, paired or rarely fasciculate or solitary along the rhachis, rarely subumbellate; bracts rarely foliaceous and composed of reduced leaves; wing-petals equal to or exceeding the keel and often adherent to it near the base; adaxial filament free or connate with the remainder into a *closed tube*, or only partially connate; *anthers uniform*; disk sometimes present within the stamens; style glabrous; ovules several to few or rarely 1; *fruits jointed*, joints dehiscent or indehiscent, very rarely the whole fruit though jointed dehiscing its full length by one suture (vary rarely fruits only 1-seeded); seeds with or without a strophiole. Type genus *Desmodium* Desv.

Bracts foliaceous, composed of reduced 3-foliolate leaves, the lateral 'leaflets' suborbicular, the terminal 'leaflet' reduced to a subulate point; flowers subumbellate-capitate in long raceme-like inflorescences 451. **Phyllodium**
Bracts not as described above, simple, often striate:
 Fruits dehiscing their full length by a continuous slit along one suture, the joints remaining attached to the other suture; leaves 3–1-foliolate, the terminal leaflet largest, the lateral very small or almost completely reduced   452. **Codariocalyx**
 Fruits breaking up into dehiscent or indehiscent joints (very rarely only 1 joint); leaflets not greatly different in size:
 Leaf-rhachis not winged:
  Inflorescence a raceme or panicle; fruits not geocarpic:
   Vexillary stamen free except sometimes at the very base (stamens diadelphous):
    Fruits covered with short hooked hairs; staminal sheath persistent in fruit:
    Ovary several-ovuled; fruits several-jointed   453. **Catenaria**
    Ovary 1-ovuled; fruit 1-seeded, obliquely lanceolate or scimitar-shaped
     454. **Monarthrocarpus**
    Fruits without hooked hairs:
    Racemes densely fasciculate at the older nodes of the branchlets; pedicels filiform   455. **Ougeinia**
    Racemes terminal or axillary:
     Fruit-segments flat or nearly so:
     Bracts not hooked at the apex:
      Disk present around the base of the ovary:
       Leaves pinnately trifoliolate; calyx 4-partite   456. **Nephrodesmus**
       Leaves 1-foliolate; calyx shortly 4-fid   457. **Hanslia**
      Disk absent:
       Fruits not enclosed by the calyx   458. **Desmodium**
       Fruits enclosed by the calyx:
        Calyx-lobes short and broad, enlarged in fruit   459. **Christia**
        Calyx-lobes subulate or setaceous, not enlarged in fruit
     460. **Uraria**
     Bracts hooked at the apex; pedicels hooked-inflexed at the apex and inverting the flowers; leaves 1-foliolate   461. **Mecopus**

Fruit-segments terete or subterete; calyx deeply divided and gluma-
ceous; leaves mostly 1-foliolate 462. **Alysicarpus**
Vexillary stamen connate up to one-third or to the middle with the others
(stamens partly monadelphous):
Calyx without bracteoles at the base:
Calyx 4-lobed; ovules 3–2; fruits of several orbicular joints
463. **Nephromeria**
Calyx 5-lobed beyond the middle; ovules 3–5; fruits of 1–5 joints
464. **Hegnera**
Calyx with 2 bracteoles at the base; ovules 2; fruits of 2 orbicular
joints 465. **Dicerma**
Inflorescence composed of 2 or more axillary flowers; fruits geocarpic
466. **Kerstingiella**
Inflorescence a short axillary shortly pedunculate umbel; stamens mona-
delphous up to or beyond the middle; fruits not geocarpic
467. **Dendrolobium**
Leaf-rhachis (petiole) mostly more or less broadly winged; leaves 1-folio-
late:
Free part of filaments not expanded; tropical Asia 468. **Pteroloma**
Free part of alternate filaments widely expanded; tropical Africa and
E. India 469. **Droogmansia**

451. **Phyllodium** Desv., Journ. de Bot. 1: 123, t. 5 (1813). 6 spp., trop. Asia;
type *P. elegans* Desv. Benth., Miq. Pl. Jungh. 1: 217, 218 (1851–5); Schindler,
Fedde Repert. 20: 269 (1924).

Shrubs or herbs; leaves trifoliolate; stipules striate; stipels present; flowers subumbellate-
capitate, arranged in long raceme-like inflorescences with very conspicuous leafy bracts,
these 3-foliolate, the lateral 2 leafy, the terminal reduced to a sharp point; these bracts provided with prominent stipules; calyx narrowly campanulate, 4-lobed, the upper lobe entire
or minutely 2-toothed, 2-bracteolate at the base; vexillum obovate, narrowed at the base,
nude; wings spurred above the claw; disk present, thin; ovary few-ovuled; stamens deciduous with the petals, monadelphous, the vexillary free above the middle, the others united for
two-thirds their length; style not thickened in the upper part; fruits jointed, joints 2–4,
orbicular-truncate, flat.

452. **Codariocalyx** Hassk., Flora 25: Beibl. 2: 48 (1842) partly. 2 spp., W.
China, Indo-Malaya, Philippine Isls., New Guinea; type *C. gyrans* (Linn. f.)
Hassk. Schindler, Fedde Repert. 20: 280 (1924).

Erect shrubs or shrublets; leaves 3–1-foliolate, terminal leaflet large, the lateral very small
or almost completely reduced; stipules and stipels present; inflorescence terminal and axillary, racemose or paniculate, in bud cone-like with overlapping striate bracts; bracts large
and caducous, 2-flowered; bracteoles none; calyx minute, campanulate, subbilabiate,
5-toothed; corolla much longer than the calyx; vexillum rounded, not auricled, wings
shortly clawed; keel-petals obtuse, long-clawed, lower margin incurved at a right angle;
stamens diadelphous, vexillary connate only at the base; free parts of the filaments alternately longer; anthers ovoid, dorsifixed; disk absent; style inflexed at a right angle, dilated
above, glabrous; stigma terminal, capitate; fruit subsessile, linear, compressed, jointed,
joints subquadrate, not breaking up but dehiscing by a continuous line along one suture the
full length; seeds arillate, aril bipartite.

453. Catenaria Benth., Miq. Pl. Jungh. 1: 220 (1841–5). 1 sp., *C. caudata* (Thunb.) Schindler (*C. laburnifolia* Benth.), China, Japan, Formosa, and India. Schindler, Fedde Repert. 20: 275 (1924).

Shrublet; leaves pinnately trifoliolate, lateral leaflets only a little smaller than the terminal; stipules and stipels subulate; flowers in terminal and axillary racemes; bracts subulate, persistent; calyx narrowly turbinate-campanulate, 4-lobed, upper lobe 2-toothed; disk rather thick; vexillum erect elliptic-oblong, obtuse or subcordate at the base, shortly clawed; vexillary stamen free except at the very base; ovary sessile, several-ovuled; style glabrous, stigma capitate; fruit sessile, linear, jointed, flat, joints about 5, oblong, truncate, covered with short hooked hairs; staminal sheath persistent in fruit.

454. Monarthrocarpus Merrill, Philipp. Journ. Sci. 5: 88 (1910). *Desmofischera* Holth. (1942). 2 spp., Indo-Malaya, Philippine Isls.; type *M. securiformis* (Benth.) Merrill, Philippine Isls. and Moluccas. Kostermans, Reinwardtia, 1: 456 (1952).

Undershrubs, suberect; leaves pinnately trifoliolate, leaflets lanceolate or ovate-lanceolate, entire, reticulate below; stipules ovate-lanceolate, longitudinally nerved; stipels subulate; flowers small, in long slender terminal racemes or subpanicles, fasciculate on the rhachis; bracts subulate-lanceolate, caducous; bracteoles none; calyx shortly toothed; vexillum orbicular, shortly clawed; vexillary filament free, remainder connate in a split sheath; anthers small, equal; ovary stipitate, 1-ovuled; fruit stipitate, 1-seeded, compressed, narrowly and obliquely lanceolate or scimitar-shaped, strongly reticulate and sprinkled with short hooked hairs; seed 1, estrophiolate, narrowly oblong.

455. Ougeinia Benth., Pl. Jungh. 216 (1851–5). 2 spp., India; type *O. oojeinensis* (Roxb.) Hochr. (*O. dalbergioides* Benth.). B.H. 1: 518; E.P. 3, 3: 326.

Trees; leaves pinnately 3-foliolate, leaflets large, stipellate; stipules free, deciduous; flowers white or pink, in densely fasciculate short racemes at the older nodes; pedicels filiform, often fasciculate; bracts small, scale-like; bracteoles minute below the calyx and persistent; 2 upper calyx-lobes connate into a broad emarginate lip, lower lobe larger than the lateral; petal-bearing disk fleshy at the bottom of the calyx-tube; vexillum suborbicular, shortly clawed, not appendaged; wings obliquely oblong, slightly adherent to the keel; keel slightly incurved, obtuse, subequal to the wings; vexillary stamen free, remainder connate; anthers uniform; ovary sessile; ovules numerous; style incurved, subulate, stigma capitate, terminal; fruit elongated, flat, with numerous joints, or by abortion these 1–2, long-oblong, thinly reticulate, scarcely dehiscent; seeds compressed, reniform, estrophiolate.

456. Nephrodesmus Schindler, Engl. Bot. Jahrb. 54: 66 (1916). 7 spp., New Caledonia; type *N. sericeus* (Hochreut.) Schindler. Schindler, Fedde Repert. 20: 277 (1924).

Trees or shrubs; leaves pinnately trifoliolate; stipules and stipels present; inflorescence racemose or subpaniculate, elongated; bracts very small; bracteoles 2 below the calyx; calyx campanulate, 4-partite; petals longer than the calyx, clawed, almost equal in length; vexillum suborbicular, not auricled; wings auricled, oblong, obtuse, adherent to the keel; keel abruptly narrowed into the claw, oblong, obtuse; stamens diadelphous, vexillary free, free parts of other filaments alternately longer and shorter; anthers shortly oval; ovary inserted within the tubular disk, shortly stipitate; ovules several; style arcuately incurved, filiform, glabrous; stigma point-like, terminal; fruit jointed, flat, almost linear, constricted at the joints, these 1-seeded, indehiscent.

457. Hanslia Schindler, Fedde Repert. 20: 276 (1924). 1 sp., *H. adhaerens* (Poir.) Schindler, SW. Malaya, New Guinea, Polynesia.

Scandent shrub or shrublet; leaves stipulate, petiolate, 1-foliolate, 2-stipellate; racemes terminal, pendulous; flowers fasciculate in the axils of setaceous bracts; calyx 2-bracteolate, campanulate, shortly 4-fid, lobes triangular, posterior very broad, emarginate; vexillum suborbicular, clawed; wings spurred, obtuse, straight; keel rather obtuse; stamens diadelphous; vexillary filament free, remainder partly connate; anthers ovoid, dorsifixed; ovary shortly stipitate, surrounded by a tubular disk; style arcuate, spirally twisted; stigma lateral, short; ovules many; fruit stipitate, linear, compressed-turgid, jointed, constricted on the lower suture a little more than the upper, joints unequal-sided, 4–5 times longer than broad, indehiscent; seeds linear-oblong, subterete, estrophiolate.

458. **Desmodium**[1] Desv., Journ. de Bot. sér. 2, 1: 122, t. 5 (1813) (conserved name). About 350 spp., trop. and subtrop. reg.; lectotype *D. scopiurus* (Swartz) Desv., West Indies. B.H. 1: 519 (partly); E.P. 3, 3: 327 (partly); Schubert, Prelim. Studies in *Desmodium*, Rhodora, 52: 135 (1950), and Fl. Congo Belge, 5: 180; Rose & Standley, Contrib. U.S. Nat. Herb. 16: 211 (*Meibomia*) (1913); Burkart, Legum. Argent. ed. 2, 296, figs. 88, 89; van Meeuwen, Reinwardtia, 6: 239 (Malaysian spp.); Hutch. & Dalz., Fl. W. Trop. Afr. 1: 417; ed. 2 (Keay), 1: 582.

Shrubs or shrublets, sometimes arborescent or subclimbing, or herbs; leaves pinnately 3- or very rarely 5-foliolate, or 1-foliolate, leaflets stipellate, often large; stipules often striate, dry, free or united into one and leaf-opposed; flowers in terminal or axillary racemes; bracts striate or subulate and persistent, or membranous and deciduous long before flowering; calyx-tube short, upper 2 lobes or teeth more or less connate, lower 3 acute or subulate-acuminate; vexillum oblong to orbicular, mostly narrowed to the base, not appendaged; wings more or less adherent to the keel; keel almost straight, incurved or rarely somewhat beaked, obtuse; vexillary stamen connate into a closed tube with the others or free below the middle or from the base; anthers uniform; ovary sessile or stipitate; ovules numerous to 2; style inflexed or incurved, not bearded, stigma terminal, capitate or minute; fruit exserted from the calyx, sessile or stipitate, compressed, jointed, joints membranous or coriaceous, flat or rarely rather turgid, mostly indehiscent and separating from each other or rarely dehiscent by 2 valves; seeds compressed, orbicular-reniform, estrophiolate.

459. **Christia** Moench, Meth. Suppl. 39 (1802). *Ploca* Lour. ex Gomes (1868). *Lourea* Neck. (1790), not St. Hilaire (1812). 10–12 spp., trop. and subtrop. Asia, trop. Australia, introd. into America; lectotype *C. vespertilionis* (Linn.) Bakh. f. B.H. 1: 522; E.P. 3, 3: 330 (*Lourea*); Bakh. f., Reinwardtia, 6: 89 (1961).

Herbs; leaves 1–3-foliolate, leaflets stipellate, often much broader than long; stipules free, subulate or striate; flowers purplish or white, in lax terminal racemes or panicles; pedicels often paired; bracts acuminate, very caducous; bracteoles absent; calyx broadly campanulate, enlarged after flowering, lobes equal; vexillum obovate or obcordate, narrowed into a claw; wings obliquely oblong, adherent to the keel; keel slightly incurved, obtuse; vexillary stamen free, remainder connate; anthers uniform; ovary 2- or more-ovuled; style subulate, inflexed above, stigma broadly capitate, terminal; fruit subsessile or stipitate, constricted between the seeds; joints ovate, compressed-turgid, plicately retrofracted, nestling within the calyx; seeds orbicular or subglobose, hilum lateral, estrophiolate.

460. **Uraria** Desv., Journ. de Bot. 1: 122, t. 5, f. 19 (1813). *Doodia* Roxb. (1814). *Urania* DC. (1825). *Urariopsis* Schindler (1916). 35 spp., trop. Africa,

---

[1] Synonyms of **Desmodium**: *Meibomia* Adans. (1763). *Edusaron* Medik. (1787). *Pleurolobus* (1812). *Nicolsonia* DC. (1825). *Perrottetia* DC. (1825). *Heteroloma* Desv. (1828). *Tetranema* Sweet (1830). *Nicholsonia* Span. (1835). *Tropitoma* Raf. (1836). *Ototropis* Nees (1838). *Oxydium* Bennett (1838). *Edusarum* Steud. (1840). *Dollinera* Endl. (1841). *Cyclomorium* Walp. (1843). *Sagotia* Walp. (1850). *Lagotia* C. Muell. (1857). *Murtonia* Craib (1912). *Aphyllodium* Gagnep. (1916). *Holtzea* Schindl. (1926). *Nissoloides* M. E. Jones (1933–5).

Asia, Australia, type *U. picta* (Jacq.) Desv. ex DC., Old World trop. B.H. 1: 521; E.P. 3, 3: 330; Hutch. & Dalz., Fl. W. Trop. Afr. 1: 419.

Shrubs or herbs; leaves pinnately 3- rarely 5–7-foliolate or rarely all 1-foliolate; leaflets often large, reticulate-venose, stipellate; stipules free, acuminate, striate at the base; flowers purplish or yellowish, in terminal elongated or spike-like racemes or rarely panicles; pedicels paired, hooked-inflexed at the apex; bracts ovate or lanceolate, acuminate, persistent or deciduous; bracteoles absent; calyx-lobes subulate-acuminate, spreading, 2 upper (becoming the lower by resupination) shorter; vexillum orbicular or obovate, narrowed into a claw; wings falcate-oblong, adhering to the keel; keel slightly incurved, obtuse; vexillary stamen free, remainder connate; anthers uniform; ovary sessile or shortly stipitate, 2- or more-ovuled; style filiform, inflexed above, stigma capitate, terminal; fruit subsessile, constricted between the seeds, joints ovate, compressed-turgid, plicate-retrofracted; seeds orbicular or subglobose, hilum lateral, estrophiolate.

461. Mecopus Benn., Pl. Jav. Rar. 154, t. 32 (1838). 1 sp., *M. nidulans* Benn., E. India, Hainan, Indo-China, Malay Archip. B.H. 1: 521; E.P. 3, 3: 327.

Slender annual herb with long whip-like branches and fox-tail-like inflorescences; leaves 1-foliolate, leaflet reniform, 2-stipellate; stipules free, lanceolate-setaceous; flowers very small, crowded in dense oblong terminal racemes; bracts subulate, hooked at the apex; pedicels paired, hooked-inflexed at the apex and inverting the flowers; calyx-lobes short, upper 2 connate; vexillum obovatum, narrowed at the base; wings falcate, adhering to the keel; keel much incurved, obtuse; vexillary stamen at length free, remainder connate; anthers uniform; ovary shortly stipitate; ovules 2; style inflexed, stigma small, terminal; fruit long-stipitate, long-exserted from the inverted calyx, nestling within the bracts against the axis of the racemes, joints 2 or 1, compressed, reticulate, indehiscent; seeds orbicular-reniform, estrophiolate.

462. Alysicarpus Neck., Elem. 3: 15 (1790) (conserved name); Desv., Journ. de Bot. 1: 120, t. 4 (1813). *Fabricia* Scop. (1777). *Hallia* J. St. Hil. (1812). *Hegetschweilera* Heer & Regel (1842). *Mysicarpus* Webb (1849). About 30 spp., Africa, Asia, Australia, Polynesia, and trop. America; type *A. bupleurifolius* (Linn.) DC., trop. Asia. B.H. 1: 522; E.P. 3, 3: 329; J. Léonard, Fl. Congo Belge, 5: 223.

Herbs; leaves 1-foliolate, 2-stipellate, very rarely 3-foliolate; stipules scarious, acuminate, free or connate; flowers small, in terminal or rarely axillary racemes; pedicels often paired and short; bracts scarious and mostly deciduous; calyx deeply divided, 2 upper lobes often connate almost to the apex; vexillum obovatum or orbicular, narrowed into the claw; wings obliquely oblong, adhering to the keel; keel slightly incurved, obtuse, often appendaged on each side with a membrane; vexillary stamen free, remainder connate; ovary sessile or shortly stipitate; ovules numerous; style filiform, incurved at the apex, stigma broadly capitate, terminal; fruit subterete or rather compressed, constricted between the seeds or equal, joints ovate, globose, or truncate at each end, convex or turgid, indehiscent; seeds suborbicular or globose, estrophiolate.

463. Nephromeria Schindler, Fedde Repert. 20: 281 (1924). *Desmodium* sect. *Nephromeria* Benth. (1851). 8 spp., trop. America; type *N. barclayi* (Benth.) Schindler, Mexico, Cent. America.

Shrubs or shrublets, climbing or creeping herbs rooting at the nodes; leaves stipulate, pinnately 3-foliolate; stipels present; inflorescence terminal and axillary, racemose or paniculate; bracts broad, caducous; flowers paired; bracteoles none; calyx broadly campanulate, 4-lobed, posterior lobe shortly bifid or entire; corolla much longer than the calyx, petals shortly clawed; vexillum neither auriculate nor callous, ovate or obovate; wings auriculate, very broad, straight, obtuse; keel not auriculate, lower margin curved almost at a right angle; petals united at the base; stamens monadelphous, vexillary free from the middle, free parts of filaments alternately of unequal length, filiform; anthers ovoid; disk none; ovary shortly stipitate, 3–2-ovuled; style inflexed at a right angle, glabrous; stigma terminal, capitate; fruit stipitate, very much compressed, jointed, lower suture deeply constricted, joints suborbicular; seed not arillate, compressed; staminal sheath persistent.

464. Hegnera Schindler, Fedde Repert. 20: 284 (1924). 1 sp., *H. obcordata* (Miq.) Schindler, Tenasserim.

Scandent shrub; leaves stipulate, petiolate, 3-foliolate, leaflets stipellate, terminal often very broadly retuse, obreniform or half-orbicular; flowers racemose or paniculate, fasciculate in the axils of narrow persistent bracts; bracteoles absent; calyx campanulate, 5-lobed beyond the middle, lobes narrow, acute, posterior scarcely fid; petals shortly clawed; vexillum not auricled, obovate; wings auriculate above the base, obtuse; keel not auriculate; stamens monadelphous, vexillary connate with the others for one-third; disk none; ovary shortly stipitate; ovules 3–5; style inflexed at a right angle; stigma terminal; fruit stipitate, compressed, constricted almost to the upper margin, 1–5-jointed, joints membranous, dilated, imbricate, 1-seeded, indehiscent, at length breaking away; seeds not filling the joints, compressed, not arillate; staminal column persistent.

465. Dicerma DC., Mém. Légum. 326 (1825); Prodr. 2: 339 (1825). 3 spp., Burma to New Guinea and subtrop. Australia; type *D. biarticulatum* (L.) DC., throughout the region. Schindler, Fedde Repert. 20: 267 (1924).

Herbs woody at the base, or shrublets; leaves pinnately trifoliolate, leaflets small; stipules united, striate, acuminate; stipels minute; inflorescence racemose, 2–3 flowers to each stipule-like bract; calyx with 2 bracteoles at the base, 2-lipped, lower of 3 acute lobes, upper of 2 lobes united nearly to the apex; disk tubular, thin around the base of the ovary; vexillum oblong-obovate, erect, nude at the base; wings oblong, keel straight, obtuse, nude; vexillary stamen free only in its upper third; ovary sessile, 2-ovuled; style glabrous, stigma capitate; fruit exserted, straight, flat, of 2 joints, these orbicular, narrowly truncate.

466. Kerstingiella Harms, Ber. Deutsch. Bot. Ges. 26: 230, t. 3 (1908). 1 sp., *K. geocarpa* Harms, trop. W. Africa. Hutch. & Dalz., Fl. W. Trop. Afr. 1: 411.

Prostrate herb, with habit of *Voandzeia*, rooting at the nodes; leaves pinnately trifoliolate; leaflets oval to obovate; stipules striate; stipels linear-setaceous; flowers small, 2 or more in the leaf-axils, subsessile; prophylls 2, lanceolate, at the base of the calyx; calyx cupular, partite to beyond the middle, segments narrow, subequal, upper more or less connate into one; petals a little exserted, subequal; vexillum shortly clawed; wings narrow, appendaged above the claw on one side; keel-petals coherent in the middle, similar to the wings; vexillary stamen free, remainder connate; anthers broadly oval; disk posticous, short; ovary shortly stipitate, style slightly curved, glabrous, stigma terminal, capitate; ovules mostly 2, rarely 1 or 3; stipe of the ovary after fertilization growing out into an elongated carpopodium bearing the fruit at the top and sparingly clothed with retrorse hairs; fruit geocarpic, mostly composed of 2 joints, pericarp thin, slightly rugose, not dehiscent; seeds ovoid, or oblong-ovoid, hilum small, linear-oblong, white, radicle lateral, conical.

467. Dendrolobium Benth., Miq. Pl. Jungh. 1: 215 (1851–5). About 12 spp., trop. Asia; type *D. umbellatum* (L.) Benth. Schindler, Fedde Repert. 20: 278 (1924).

Trees or shrubs; leaves pinnately trifoliolate; stipules striate, very caducous; stipels present; flowers in axillary shortly pedunculate umbels; bracts narrow, stipule-like; calyx narrowly turbinate-campanulate, 4-lobed, upper lobe entire or 2-toothed; disk thin; vexillum obovate, narrowed at the base, nude; wings oblong, keel rather straight, obtuse, not auricled; stamens monadelphous to the middle or beyond, sheath entire; ovary sessile, several-ovuled; style glabrous, stigma capitate; fruit subfalcate, jointed, joints several, at length thickened, indehiscent, quadrate or orbicular-truncate.

468. Pteroloma DC., Prodr. 2: 326 (1825); Benth., Miq. Pl. Jungh. 1: 217, 219 (1851–5). 5 spp., trop. Asia, India, China, Indo-China, Malaya, Philippines, New Guinea; type *P. triquetrum* (DC.) Benth. Schindler, Fedde Repert. 20: 271 (1924).

Shrublets or herbs; leaves 1-foliolate, petiole winged; stipules broadly lanceolate, striate, free; stipels present; flowers racemose; bracts stipule-like, 2–3-flowered; calyx turbinate-campanulate, 4-lobed, upper lobe minutely 2-toothed; disk thin; vexillum orbicular, abruptly reflexed into a slender claw, a callus above the claw; wings oblong; keel arcuate-substrate; vexillary stamen free or scarcely connate at the base with the others; ovary sessile, several-ovuled; style glabrous above, stigma capitate; fruit exserted, straight, flat, jointed joints quadrate.

469. Droogmansia De Wild., Ann. Mus. Congo Sér. 4: 53 (1902) t. 23. *Vaughania* S. Moore (1920). About 30 spp., trop. Africa; lectotype *D. pteropus* (Baker) De Wild. Schubert, Fl. Congo Belge, 5: 206, tt. 16, 17 (1954); Hutch. & Dalz., Fl. W. Trop. Afr. 1: 418; ed. 2 (Keay), 1: 586.

Shrubs or shrublets; leaves 1-foliolate, often developed after the flowers; stipules striate and ciliate; rhachis with a foliaceous wing (rarely without a wing); stipels 2; racemes or panicles terminal or terminal and axillary; bracts and bracteoles present; calyx bilabiate, upper lip more or less bifid, lower 3-toothed, the middle tooth longer; petals white to purple; vexillum suborbicular, clawed; keel-petals larger than the wings; stamens diadelphous, vexillary free at the base, then united for one-third to half its length, free at the top, or alternate filaments widely expanded; others in 2 bundles; anthers uniform; ovary stipitate, many-ovuled; stipe surrounded by a short disk; style glabrous; stigma terminal; fruit usually long-stipitate, jointed, mostly flat, joints more or less pubescent.

Tribe 49. STYLOSANTHEAE

Tribe *Hedysareae* Subtribe *Stylosantheae* Benth. & Hook. f., Gen. Pl. 1: 449 (1865)

Erect or prostrate *herbs*, very rarely shrubs; leaves imparipinnate or digitate, few–3-foliolate; stipules present, often adnate to the petiole; *stipels absent*; flowers spicate, capitate, or rarely subracemose, spikes terminal or axillary; bracts various, often *stipule-like*; calyx-tube short or elongated or filiform; corolla papilionaceous; petals inserted at the base or apex of the calyx-tube; *stamens all connate into a closed tube*; *anthers dimorphic*, oblong, basifixed and dorsifixed and versatile; *style glabrous*; ovules numerous to few or 1; fruit indehiscent, more or *less jointed or torulose*, maturing above or below the ground; seeds *estrophiolate*. Warmer regions of the world. Type genus *Stylosanthes* Swartz.

Calyx-tube not elongated at the base; ovules several; petals inserted towards the base of the calyx; fruit compressed, upper suture almost straight, lower deeply sinuate, segments smooth or echinate   470. **Zornia**
Calyx-tube elongated or filiform at the base:
  Fruits not maturing below the soil:
    Leaves imparipinnate; leaflets few; ovules several or few:
      Joints of the fruits linear, striate lengthwise and glandular-muricate
                             471. **Chapmannia**
      Joints of the fruit quadrate, pilose   472. **Pachecoa**
    Leaves pinnately 3-foliolate; petals and stamens inserted at the apex of the calyx-tube; ovules 3–2; fruit hooked at the apex, reticulate or muricate
                             473. **Stylosanthes**

Fruits maturing below the soil, reticulate; leaves pinnate or 3-foliolate; spikes axillary, sessile; petals and stamens inserted at the apex of the calyx-tube; ovules 3–2   **474. Arachis**

470. **Zornia** J. F. Gmel., Syst. 2: 1076 and 1096 (1791). *Zonaria* Steud. (1840). *Myriadenus* Desv. (1813). About 40 spp., warm reg. of both hemispheres; type *Z. bracteata* J. F. Gmel. B.H. 1: 518; E.P. 3, 3: 324; Amshoff, Pulle Fl. Suriname, 2, 2: 246; Milne-Redhead, Bol. Soc. Brot. ser. 2, 28: 79 (1954); Burkart, Legum. Argent. ed. 2, 303, fig. 91; Hutch. & Dalz., Fl. W. Trop. Afr. ed. 2 (Keay), 1: 575.

Herbs; leaves digitately 2–4-foliolate, leaflets often pellucid-punctate, exstipellate; stipules subfoliaceous, often punctate and produced below the base (peltate); flowers interruptedly spicate or solitary, peduncles terminal or axillary; bracts paired, lateral, enclosing the sessile flowers; stipules similar but larger and broader, striate; bracteoles absent; calyx often subhyaline, ciliate, 2 upper lobes connate high up, 2 lateral much smaller, lowest oblong or lanceolate, subequal to the upper lip; vexillum suborbicular, clawed; wings obliquely obovate or oblong; keel incurved, subrostrate; stamens all connate into a closed tube which splits transversely at the top and persists; anthers alternately longer, subbasifixed, alternately short and versatile; ovary sessile; ovules numerous; style filiform, stigma small, terminal; fruit compressed, upper suture almost straight, lower deeply sinuate, segments smooth or echinate, indehiscent; seeds orbicular-subreniform, estrophiolate.

471. **Chapmannia** Torr. & Gray, Fl. N. Amer. 1: 355 (1840). 1 sp., *C. florida* Torr. & Gray, Florida. B.H. 1: 517; E.P. 3, 3: 322.

Erect herb; leaves imparipinnate, leaflets few, entire, exstipellate; stipules subulate; flowers yellow in long-pedunculate short terminal racemes; bracts small, 2-stipulate; calyxtube narrowed at the base, membranous, shortly stipe-like; upper 4 lobes connate, lower narrow, distinct; vexillum suborbicular; wings obliquely obovate; keel incurved, obtuse, subequal to the vexillum; stamens all connate into a closed tube; anthers all oblong, alternately subbasifixed, alternately versatile; ovary sessile; ovules numerous; style elongated, filiform, stigma minute, terminal; fruit linear, subterete, upper suture almost straight, lower sinuate; joints ovoid, striate lengthwise and glandular-muricate; seeds subreniform, estrophiolate.

472. **Pachecoa** Standl. & Steyerm., Publ. Field Mus. Nat. Hist. Chicago Bot. Ser. 23: 12 (1943); Contrib. Gray Herb. no. 161: 24, pl. ii (1946). 3 spp., trop. America; type *P. prismatica* (Sesse & Macino) Standl. & Steyerm. (*P. guatemalensis* Standl. & Steyerm.), Cent. America. Burkart, Darwiniana, 11: 261 (1957).

Erect shrubs; leaves imparipinnate, leaflets few, entire; stipules linear-subulate, nervose; stipels absent; flowers yellow, axillary, peduncles 2-flowered; bracts small, rigid; bracteoles subulate or almost filiform; calyx deeply 5-lobed, lobes lanceolate, 4 subequal, lowermost a little longer and narrower; vexillum suborbicular, pilose outside, clawed; wings obliquely obovate, keel incurved, obtuse; stamens connate in a closed tube; anthers oval; ovary sessile, ovules few; style elongated, stigma minute, terminal; fruit linear-oblong, jointed, subtetragonous, sutures straight, joints quadrate, pilose.

473. **Stylosanthes** Swartz, Prodr. Veg. Ind. Occ. 108 (1788), & Fl. Ind. Occ. 3: 1280, t. 25 (1806). *Stylosma* Bak. (1871). *Astyposanthes* Herter (1943). About 50 spp., Asia, trop. Africa, trop. and subtrop. America; lectotype *S. procumbens* Swartz, West Indies. B.H. 1: 517; E.P. 3, 3: 323; Amshoff, Pulle Fl. Suriname, 2, 2: 241; R. H. Mohlenbroch, Ann. Missouri Bot. Gard. 44: 299 (1957); Burkart, Legum. Argent. ed. 2, 305, fig. 92.

Hard herbs, often sticky; leaves pinnately 3-foliolate, exstipellate; stipules adnate to the base or lower part of the petiole; flowers yellow, in dense spikes or heads, calyx-tube filiform; lobes membranous, upper 4 connate, lower narrow and distinct; petals and stamens inserted at the apex of the tube; vexillum orbicular; wings oblong, free; keel incurved, rather beaked; stamens all connate into a closed tube; alternate anthers longer and subbasifixed, others short and versatile; ovary 2–3-ovuled; style long and filiform, stigma minute, terminal, after flowering cut off near the base or towards the middle, lower part persistent, recurved or revolute, callous-dilated at the apex and resembling a stigma; fruit sessile, compressed, hooked at the apex by the persistent style-base, joints 1–2, reticulate or muricate; seed compressed, ovate or lenticular, strophiolate.

474. **Arachis** Linn., Sp. Pl. 741 (1753). *Mundubi* Adans. (1763). *Arachidna* Moench (1794). 19 spp., tropics; type *A. hypogaea* Linn., tropics. B.H. 1: 518; E.P. 3, 3: 324; Amshoff, Pulle Fl. Suriname, 2, 2: 245; Burkart, Legum. Argent. ed. 2, 308, fig. 93.

Low often prostrate herbs; leaves pinnate, leaflets 2-pairs or rarely 3-foliolate, exstipellate; stipules partly adnate to the petiole; flowers in a dense axillary sessile spike; bracteoles below the calyx linear; calyx-tube filiform; lobes membranous, upper 4 connate, lower slender and distinct; petals and stamens inserted at the apex of the calyx-tube; vexillum suborbicular; wings oblong, free; keel incurved, beaked; stamens all connate into a closed tube, one now and then deficient; alternate anthers elongate and subbasifixed, others short and versatile; ovary 3–2-ovuled; after flowering the torus soon elongates and is reflexed and rigid acute at the apex; fruit maturing under the ground, oblong, thick, reticulate, indehiscent, subtorulose but not jointed, continuous inside; seeds 3–1, irregularly ovoid; cotyledons thick, fleshy.

Tribe 50. LESPEDEZEAE[1]

Shrubs, shrublets, or perennial climbing or creeping, rarely annual herbs; leaves pinnately 3-foliolate or 1-foliolate; stipules and often stipels present; flowers in *axillary* fascicles, racemes or terminal racemes or panicles or capitate; calyx lobed, the upper 2 often connate higher up; corolla papilionaceous; *vexillary filament free* or rarely partly coherent with the others into a split sheath; *anthers uniform*; ovary sessile or stipitate, *1-ovuled*; *style glabrous*, inflexed or incurved; fruit *indehiscent* or rarely 2-valved, often enclosed by the calyx, the ripe fruit sometimes buried in the soil (*Neocollettia*); *seed 1, estrophiolate*. Type genus *Lespedeza* Mich.

Shrubs or herbs, never climbing, the latter sometimes diffuse:
  Ovary sessile or subsessile:
    Racemes subcapitate or spike-like, terminal; calyx deeply divided; fruit
      2-valved; leaves pinnately 3-foliolate or 1-foliolate, stipellate
                                                        475. **Leptodesmia**
    Racemes or panicles lax, terminal and axillary:

[1] **Lespedezeae** trib. nov. Frutices, fruticuli, vel herbae perennes volubiles vel prostratae, rare herbae annuae; folia pinnatim 3-foliolata vel 1-foliolata, stipulata et saepe stipellata; flores axillares, fasciculati vel racemosi vel paniculati et terminales; calycis lobi 2 superiores saepe connati; stamen vexillare liberum vel rare ceteris partim coherens; antherae uniformes; ovarium sessile vel stipitatum, 1-ovulatum; stylus glaber, inflexus vel incurvus; fructus indehiscens vel rare 2-valvis, saepe calyce inclusus, rare geocarpus; semen 1, estrophiolatum.

Calyx membranous, truncate, with very short teeth; fruit indehiscent;
leaves 3- or 1-foliolate, leaflets reniform or orbicular, stipellate
476. Eleiotis

Calyx lobed; fruit indehiscent; leaves 3- or rarely 1-foliolate:
Stipels absent:
Keel straight, obtuse or truncate; bracts 2-flowered, bracteoles persis-
tent; flowers in racemes or spike-like racemes or axillary fascicles
477. Lespedeza
Keel inflexed-acuminate; bracts 1-flowered, bracteoles soon deciduous;
shrubs with ample racemes   **478. Campylotropis**
Stipels present, subulate   **479. Cranocarpus**
Ovary stipitate; leaves 3- or 1-foliolate, leaflets large, 3-nerved at the base
454. Monarthrocarpus (see Tribe *Desmodieae*)
Climbing or creeping herbs; fruits indehiscent:
Upper two calyx-lobes connate; inflorescence subcymose-racemose; climbing
herbs; stipules narrow, caducous; some bracts enlarged and petaloid
480. Phylacium

Calyx subequally 5-toothed; flowers 1–3 on axillary peduncles; slender
creeping herbs rooting at the nodes:
Pedicels with 1 stipitate bracteole embracing the calyx; fruit turgid, the
pedicel recurving and penetrating the soil   **481. Neocollettia**
Pedicels with 4 bracteoles below the calyx; fruiting pedicel not penetrating
the soil   **482. Kummerowia**

475. Leptodesmia Benth., Benth. & Hook f., Gen. Pl. 1: 522 (1865). 5 spp.,
India, Mascarenes; type *L. congesta* Benth. ex Baker, India. B.H. 1: 522; E.P.
3, 3: 330.

Shrublets or perennial herbs; leaves pinnately 3-foliolate or 1-foliolate, leaflets small,
stipellate; stipules free; flowers small, in terminal short dense subcapitate or spike-like
racemes; bracts broad, imbricate before flowering, deciduous; lobes of the deeply divided
calyx narrow, subequal; vexillum suborbicular, clawed; wings obliquely oblong, free; keel
narrower, obtuse; vexillary stamen free or scarcely coherent at the base with the connate
ones; anthers uniform; ovary sessile, 1-ovuled; style filiform, stigma terminal, capitate;
fruit ovoid, 2-valved, 1-seeded, enclosed by the calyx; seed estrophiolate.

476. Eleiotis DC., Mém. Légum. 7: 348 (1825). 2 spp., India, Ceylon; type *E.
monophylla* (Burn. f.) DC. (*E. sororia* DC.). B.H. 1: 523; E.P. 3, 3: 331.

Herbs; leaves 1- or 3-foliolate, leaflets reniform or orbicular, 2-stipellate, sometimes with
2 small lateral leaflets; stipules short, striate; flowers very small, in terminal and axillary
racemes; pedicels often paired; bracts broad, striate, deciduous; teeth of the membranous
truncate calyx very short; vexillum suborbicular, emarginate, narrowed into a claw; wings
oblong, adhering to the obtuse keel; vexillary stamen at length free, remainder connate;
anthers uniform; ovary subsessile, 1-ovulate; style inflexed above, stigma capitate, terminal;
fruit compressed, boat-shaped, acute, membranous, reticulate, indehiscent, upper suture
straight, slightly dilated, 2-nerved, lower curved and thin; seed transversely oblong, subreniform, estrophiolate.

477. Lespedeza[1] Mich., Fl. Bor. Amer. 2: 70, t. 29 (1803). About 40 spp.,
temp. North America, E. and trop. Asia, trop. Australia; type *L. virginica*

---

[1] Synonyms of **Lespedeza**: *Lespedezia* Spreng. (1826). *Despeleza* Nieuwland (1914).

(Linn.) Britton (*L. sessiliflora* Mich.), E. North America. B.H. 1: 524 (partly); E.P. 3, 3: 332 (partly).

Shrubs or shrublets, often with soft or silky indumentum; leaves pinnately 3-foliolate, rarely 1-foliolate, leaflets entire; stipels absent; stipules free, often very small or caducous; flowers in axillary fascicles or racemes or rarely terminal panicles; bracts small, persistent; pedicels solitary, 2-bracteolate at the apex; calyx-lobes or teeth subequal or the upper 2 shortly connate; vexillum clawed; wings falcate-oblong, free or scarcely adherent to the keel; keel obtuse or beaked, not laterally appendaged; vexillary stamen free or rarely coherent with the others, these connate; anthers uniform; ovary 1-ovulate; style filiform, incurved, stigma small, terminal; fruit ovate or orbicular, plano-compressed, reticulate, indehiscent; seed compressed, suborbicular, estrophiolate.

478. Campylotropis Bunge, Descr. Nov. Gen. et Sp. Chin. et Mongol. 7, Mém. Univ. Kasan. 4 (1835). *Oxyramphis* Wall., name only (1831). *Phlebosporium* Jungh. (1845). *Lespedeza* sect. *Campylotropis* Maxim., Taub. E.P. 3, 3: 332. About 66 spp., E. Asia; type *C. chinensis* Bunge, China. Schindler, Fedde Repert. 11: 338 (1912); Ricker, Journ. Wash. Acad. Sci. 36: 37 (1946).

Shrubs or shrublets; leaves trifoliolate; stipules 2, persistent; stipels sometimes present; inflorescence mostly racemose, rarely paniculate, axillary, 1–3 together, and terminal; bracts small, persistent or caducous, 1-flowered; bracteoles 2, soon deciduous; pedicels single, jointed; calyx campanulate, 5-partite, upper 2 segments more or less connate; vexillum ovate or suborbicular, mostly acute; wings obtuse, semiorbicular or subfalcate, slightly adhering to the keel by a large basal auricle; keel very acute, curved mostly at a right-angle; stamens diadelphous, vexillary free or nearly so; filaments filiform; ovary shortly stipitate; ovule 1; style filiform, mostly pilose towards the base; stigma terminal, small; fruit lenticular, compressed, 1-seeded, indehiscent, mostly mucronate.

479. Cranocarpus Benth., Mart. Fl. Brasil. 15, 1: 106, t. 28 (1859). 2 spp., Brazil; type *C. martii* Benth. B.H. 1: 523; E.P. 3, 3: 331; Schindler, Fedde Repert. 20: 285 (1924).

Shrubs; leaves 1-foliolate, leaflet large, pinnately nerved, 2-stipellate, rarely with 2 small lateral leaflets; stipules free, setaceous-acuminate; stipels subulate; racemes axillary; bracts small; pedicels solitary, 2-bracteolate; flowers yellow or white; teeth or lobes of the oblique calyx subequal in length, upper 2 broader; vexillum obovate, narrowed into a longish claw; wings obliquely oblong, free; keel incurved, subcucullate; stamens all connate into a sheath open above; anthers uniform; ovary subsessile, 1-ovuled; style incurved, filiform, stigma small, terminal; fruit stipitate, much compressed, somewhat hooded, indehiscent, upper suture impressed in the middle, lower very arcuate, sides convex, bristly-hairy; seed subreniform, estrophiolate.

480. Phylacium Benn., Fl. Jav. Rar. 159, t. 31 (1838). *Heleiotis* Hassk. (1844). 3 spp., India, Malay Archip., Philippines, New Guinea; type *P. bracteosum* Benn., Malaya, Philippines, New Guinea. B.H. 1: 523; E.P. 3, 3: 331.

Climbing herbs; leaves pinnately 3-foliolate, leaflets entire, rather large, stipellate; stipules narrow, caducous; peduncles fasciculate in the axils, very short or elongated, irregularly subcymose-racemose at the apex; flowers small; some bracts much enlarged after flowering, membranous-foliaceous, folded, others small; pedicels short, 2-bracteolate at the apex; 2 upper calyx-lobes quite connate; petals long-clawed; vexillum suborbicular, callous inside at the base and appendaged with inflexed auricles; wings narrow, falcate, free, spurred at the base; keel incurved, obtuse, shorter than the wings; vexillary stamen free or at the very base, otherwise connate with the others into a sheath; anthers uniform; ovary subsessile, surrounded by an annular disk, 1-ovulate; style thickened above, incurved, subulate at the apex, stigma capitate; fruit plano-compressed, ovate, acuminate with the style, membranous, reticulate, indehiscent; seed compressed, orbicular, estrophiolate.

481. **Neocollettia** Hemsl., Journ. Linn. Soc. 28: 44, t. 6 (1890). 1 sp., *N. wallichii* (Kurz) Schindler (*N. gracilis* Hemsl.), Burma, Java. E.P. 3, 3: 384; Prain, Journ. Asiat. Soc. Bengal, 66: 386; Schindler, Fedde Repert. 21: 16 (1925); van Steenis, Reinwardtia, 5: 436 (1961).

Slender creeping herb rooting at the nodes; leaves pinnately trifoliolate; stipules rigid, striate, persistent; stipels small; flowers very small, axillary, solitary or 2–3 together on long slender pedicels, pedicels with a stipitate bracteole embracing the calyx; calyx tubular, 15-nerved, subequally 5-lobed, lobes very short, rounded; vexillum suborbicular, unappendaged; wings free, oblong, spurred; keel straight, very obtuse; vexillary stamen free, remainder connate into a sheath split above; anthers uniform; ovary sessile, 1-ovuled; style inflexed; fruit sessile, turgid, 1-seeded, the pedicel recurving and penetrating the soil; 'between the calyx and ovary two strong opposite roots develop on the short gynophore which in all probability feed the growing ovary and may be instrumental in pulling the pod deeper into the earth'—van Steenis, loc. cit.

482. **Kummerowia** Schindler, Fedde Repert. 10: 403 (1912). *Microlespedeza* Tanaka, partly (1914). 1 sp., *K. striata* (Thunb.) Schindler, NE. Asia, NE. India, United States.

Annual herb resembling some spp. of *Trifolium*, creeping and much-branched; leaves trifoliolate, closely parallel-nerved, rigidly long-ciliate; stipules 2, large; inflorescence axillary, short, either 1–2-flowered or many-flowered; flowers often reduced and without petals; bracts and bracteoles persistent, scarious; ovary with 1 ovule; bracteoles 4, below the calyx; fruit indehiscent, thick, subcompressed, 1-seeded.

ADDITION

p. 473. Add after **Ormocarpum**, genus no. 437 of **Fabaceae**:

437a. **Arthrocarpum** Balf. f., Proc. Roy. Soc. Edinb. 11: 510 (1882), and Bot. of Socotra (Trans. Roy. Soc. Edinb., vol. 31) 80, t. 21 (1888); Gillett, Kew Bull. 1964, *ined.*; 2 spp., Somaliland and Socotra; type *A. gracile* Balf. f., Socotra.

Differs from *Ormocarpum*, with which it has been confused, in a reticulate pattern of tannin cells on the under surface of the leaflet, the spicate inflorescence, the tubular receptacle enclosing the sessile ovary which is many times shorter than the style, the standard larger than the keel, and the claws of the wings and keel-petals adhering to the staminal sheath. Most closely related to *Chapmannia*, no. 471, p. 485, from which it differs in the unbranched inflorescence and the staminal tube being slit dorsally.—J. B. GILLETT.

INDEX TO ECONOMIC PROPERTIES

INDEX TO ORDERS, FAMILIES, TRIBES AND GENERA

Synonyms in italics